FIRE PROTECTION GUIDE TO

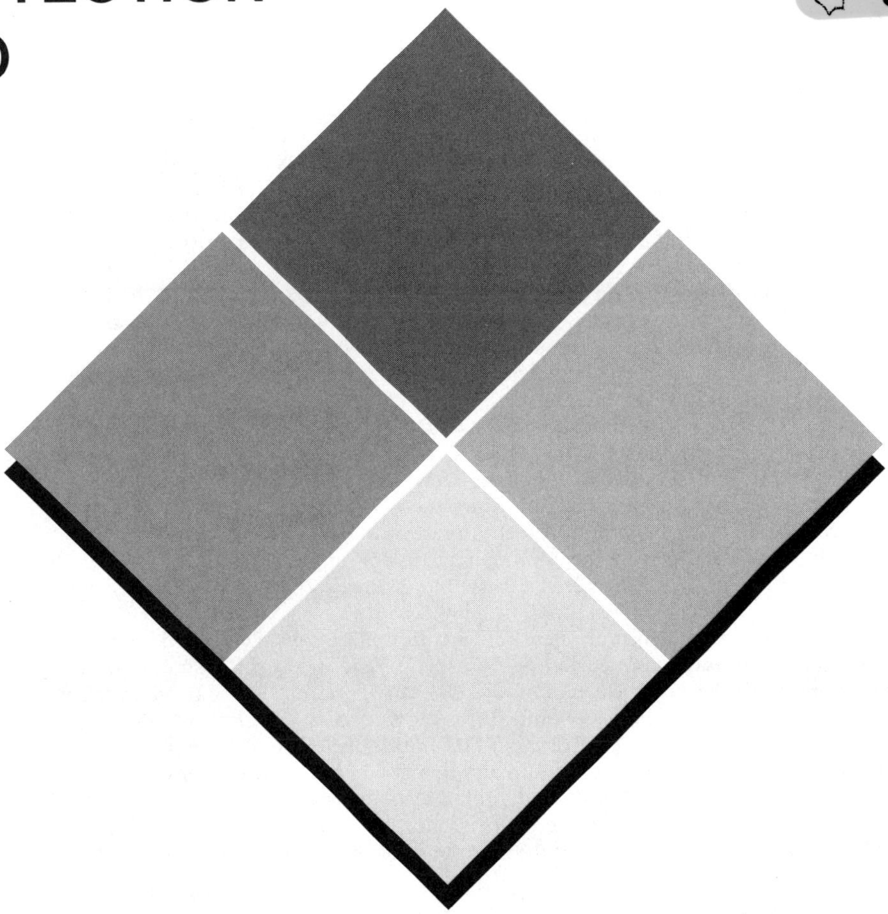

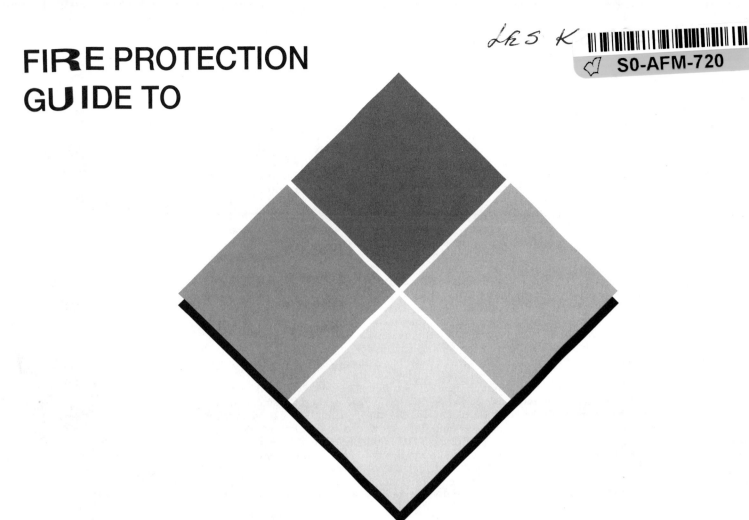

HAZARDOUS MATERIALS

13TH EDITION

Edited by

Amy Beasley Spencer
Senior Chemical Engineer, NFPA

Guy R. Colonna
Assisistant Vice President, NFPA

NFPA® INTERNATIONAL

National Fire Protection Association
One Batterymarch Park, Quincy, MA 02269

Foreword

Information on the hazardous properties of chemicals is essential for those using the chemicals and for those confronted with chemical emergencies such as fires, accidental spills, and transportation accidents. The six NFPA documents that make up this *Guide* can be used to identify the hazardous properties of most of the chemicals in commercial use today, as well as many that are available only in laboratory sample quantities.

With the date and recommendations in this *Guide*, one can take the proper steps to prevent fires and other emergencies during the use, storage, and transportation of chemicals and can make informed decisions on the procedures to follow in an emergency involving chemicals. The *Guide* will be particularly useful to fire and police department personnel and to others with responsibility for protection of life and property.

Preplanning is a well-proven means of increasing the effectiveness of fire-fighting operations; it will be useful in minimizing the effects of fire and other emergencies involving chemicals. The *Guide* provides essential information for preplanning activities. However, the exact plan of attack to be used at a chemical emergency cannot be decided until the emergency occurs and the properties of the chemicals involved have been identified. With the urgency of prompt identification in mind, the *Guide* has been arranged so that the user can get to the necessary information with a minimum of delay.

The Topic Finder, page v, is an alphabetical listing of the key topics to refer to in an emergency. These topics are printed in large type for easy reading under poor light conditions.

The three chemical matrixes are new to this 13th edition. Matrix 1 lists the major chemical entries and references the appropriate NFPA data document. Matrix 2 lists common synonyms and references official chemical names and the appropriate NFPA data document. Matrix 3 is a numerically ordered list of Chemical Abstracts Service (CAS) numbers and references the chemical name and the appropriate NFPA data document.

While every effort has been made to make this *Guide* useful and complete, there are sure to be additional entries that should be included. Anyone wishing to recommend an addition or a correction, or wishing to comment, is encouraged to do so. Additional chemical entries to NFPA 49 may be suggested using the sample data sheet included in Appendix B of that document.

Acknowledgments

The editors would like to thank those individuals who put in extra effort to ensure the quality of this revision of the *Guide*. First and foremost, we note the members of the Technical Committee on Classification and Properties of Hazardous Chemical Data. In particular, Dr. Larry Britton, Richard Gowland, Dr. Ron Kirsch, Dr. Arthur Krawetz, Owen Kubias, Dr. Robert Michaels, Jennifer Nelson, Curtis Payne, Gary Robinson, Bill Satterfield, and Ira Wainless, without whom this revision of the *Guide* would be nonexistent.

We also wish to acknowledge the computer expertise provided by Jeff Thompson, which was particularly invaluable for development of various algorithms to check data and tables. Administrative assistance was provided by Maureen Caron, Patti Mucci and Maureen Tobin; technical editing assistance was provided by engineering interns Alison Scoble, Fang Li, Joe Watson and Jeremy Mason; editorial expertise was provided by Misty Woodbury and David March; and the overall project management by Ann Coughlin.

Lastly, the editors would like to thank their families, John, Carly and Natalie Spencer and Laura, Rob, Steven and Suzanne Colonna for their support during the marathon editing sessions.

NFPA No. HAZ-01
Library of Congress Catalog Card Number 90-63780
ISBN 0-87765-473-5

5 4 3 05

Contents

Each of the sections contains important explanatory information in the front. This front matter should be studied before the text is utilized. The following summary statements identify the contents of the sections that make up this *Guide*.

Matrixes

For quick and easy reference, all chemicals contained in the *Guide* are listed in 3 cross-reference matrixes, listing the document(s) where the chemical can be found by chemical name, synonym, and Chemical Abstracts Service (CAS) number.

Full Document Texts

49 *Hazardous Chemicals Data,* 1994 edition, amended 2001.

Lists data on the fire hazard properties in MSDS format for approximately 325 chemicals. Includes recommendations on storage and fire fighting and NFPA 704 "diamond" hazard ratings. This new edition also includes NFPA 30/OSHA flammable and combustible liquids classifications.

325 *Guide to Fire Hazard Properties of Flammable Liquids, Gases, and Volatile Solids,* 1994 edition, amended 2001.

Lists data on the fire hazard properties in table format of more than 1,300 flammable substances including, but not limited to, flashpoint, boiling point, flammable limits, and the NFPA 704 "diamond" hazard ratings. This new edition also includes NFPA 30/OSHA flammable and combustible liquids classifications as well as CAS numbers.

432 *Code for the Storage of Organic Peroxide Formulations,* 1997 edition.

Provides requirements for the safe storage of commercially available formulations containing organic peroxides. Organic peroxide classification and NFPA 704 "diamond" ratings for approximately 160 organic peroxides included.

491 *Guide to Hazardous Chemical Reactions,* 1997 edition.

Includes 3,600 mixtures of two or more chemicals reported to be potentially dangerous in that they may cause fires, explosions, or detonations at ordinary or moderately elevated temperatures. Arranged alphabetically by chemical name. Reactions referenced.

497 *Recommended Practice for the Classification of Flammable Liquids, Gases, or Vapors and of Hazardous (Classified) Locations for Electrical Installations in Chemical Process Areas,* 1997 edition.

Includes parameters to determine degree and extent of hazardous locations for liquids, gases, and vapors including NEC groups for approximately 264 chemicals. Also provides data on the properties of chemicals enabling proper selection of electrical equipment for use in these atmospheres.

704 *Standard System for the Identification of the Hazards of Materials for Emergency Response,* 2001 edition.

Provides criteria for determining the degree of health, flammability, and instability hazard of materials that make up the "diamond" hazard ratings, as well as identification of special hazards (usually water reactivity and oxidizers). Provides guidance on how to apply the system.

Data Annexes

Each of the annexes contains extracted data from existing current NFPA codes, standards, or recommended practices. This data should be used in conjunction with the associated document to fully understand the applicable requirements. The following summary statements identify the contents of the annexes that make up this *Guide.* Annexes include tables extracted from the following documents:

77 Data from *Recommended Practice on Static Electricity,* 2000 edition.

Data provided for numerous commercially significant materials relevant to static electricity, including combustibility parameters for approximately 75 gases and vapors, and static electric characteristics for approximately 155 conductive liquids, 21 semiconductive liquids, and 33 nonconductive liquids.

430 Data from *Code for the Storage of Liquid and Solid Oxidizers,* 2000 edition.

Data for classification of 90 typical liquid and solid oxidizers provided to assist with safe handling, fire prevention, and storage provisions.

499 Data from *Recommended Practice for the Classification of Combustible Dusts and of Hazardous (Classified) Locations for Electrical Installations in Chemical Process Areas,* 1997 edition.

The parameters to determine the degree and extent of hazardous locations for dusts, including CAS number, NEC group, and layer or cloud ignition temperature are provided for approximately 220 combustible materials.

Topic Finder

Matrixes

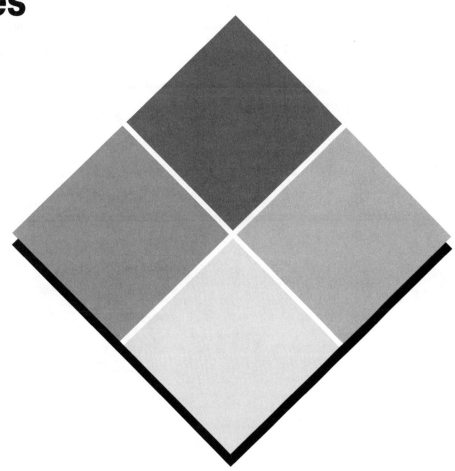

Chemical Matrix

CHEMICAL	NFPA Doc. No.
abalyn	325
acetal	325
acetal, linear	499
acetaldehyde	49, 77, 325, 491, 497
acetaldehyde (15°C)	77
acetaldehydediethylacetal	325
acetaldol	325
acetamide	77
acetanilide	49, 325
acetic acid	491, 497
acetic acid (0°C)	77
acetic acid (25°C)	77
acetic acid, glacial	49, 325
acetic acid, isopropyl ester	325
acetic acid, methyl ester	325
acetic acid, n-propyl ester	325
acetic acid, water solutions	325
acetic acid-tert-butyl ester	497
acetic aldehyde	325
acetic anhydride	49, 325, 491, 497
acetic anhydride (25°C)	77
acetic ester	325
acetic ether	325
o-acetoacet anisidide	325
m-acetoacet xylidide	325
acetoacet-ortho-toluidide	325
acetoacet-p-phenetidide	325, 499
acetoacetanilide	325, 499
acetoacetic acid, ethyl ester	325
acetoethylamide	325
acetone	77, 325, 491, 497
acetone cyanohydrin	49, 325, 491, 497
acetonitrile	49, 77, 325, 491, 497
acetonyl acetone	325
acetophenone	77, 325
p-acetotoluidide	325
acetyl acetone	325
acetyl bromide	77, 491
acetyl chloride	49, 77, 325, 491
n-acetyl ethanolamine	325
n-acetyl morpholine	325
acetyl oxide	325
acetyl peroxide	325, 491
acetylamino-t-nitrothiazole	499
acetylene	77, 325, 491, 497
acetylene dichloride-cis	325
acetylene dichloride-trans	325
acetylene, dissolved	49
acetylene in oxygen	77
acetylphenol	325
acrolein	77, 325, 491
acrolein dimer	325
acrolein, inhibited	49, 497
acrylamide	49, 491
acrylamide polymer	499
acrylic acid	491, 497
acrylic acid, glacial	325
acrylic acid, inhibited	49
acrylic aldehyde	325
acrylonitrile	77, 325, 491, 497
acrylonitrile, inhibited	49
acrylonitrile polymer	499
acrylonitrile-vinyl chloride-vinylidenechloride copolymer (70-20-10)	499
acrylonitrile-vinyl pyridine copolymer	499
adipic acid	325, 499
adipic ketone	325
adiponitrile	49, 325, 497
adipoyl chloride	325
alcohol	325
aldol	325
alfalfa meal	499
alkyl ketone dimer sizing compound	499
all inorganic nitrites	430
allene	491
allyl acetate	325
allyl alcohol	49, 77, 325, 491, 497
allyl alcohol derivative (CR-39)	499
allyl bromide	49, 325
allyl caproate	325
allyl chloride	49, 77, 325, 491, 497
allyl chlorocarbonate	325
allyl chloroformate	49, 325
allyl diglycol carbonate	325
allyl ether	325
allyl glycidyl ether	497
allyl isothiocyanate	325
allyl trichloride	325
allyl trichlorosilane	325
allyl vinyl ether	325
allylamine	49, 325
allylene	325
allylidene diacetate	325
allylpropenyl	325
almond shell	499
alpha methyl pyridine	325
alpha-methyl styrene	497
aluminum, A422 flake	499
aluminum alkyls	49
aluminum, atomized collector fines	499
aluminum carbide	491
aluminum chloride	491
aluminum chloride, anhydrous	49
aluminum fluoride	491

CHEMICAL	NFPA Doc. No.
aluminum hydride	491
aluminum hydroxide	491
aluminum oxide	491
aluminum phosphide	49, 491
aluminum powder, uncoated	49
aluminum–cobalt alloy (60–40)	499
aluminum–copper alloy (50–50)	499
aluminum–lithium alloy (15% Li)	499
aluminum–magnesium alloy (dowmetal)	499
aluminum–nickel alloy (58–42)	499
aluminum–silicon alloy (12% Si)	499
amino ethane	325
2-amino-1-butanol	325
2-amino-2-methyl-1-propanol	325
1-amino-2-propanol	325
1-amino-4-ethoxybenzene	325
2-amino-4-methylpentane	325
amino-5-nitrothiazole	499
aminobenzene	325
2-aminobiphenyl	325
1-aminobutane	325
aminocyclohexane	325
1-aminodecane	325
2-aminoethanol	325, 491
β-aminoethyl alcohol	325
4-(2-aminoethyl)morpholine	325
1-(2-aminoethyl)piperazine	325
n-aminoethyl piperazine	77
aminoethyl-ethanolamine	77
2-aminoethylethanolamine	325
aminoguanidine nitrate	491
1-aminoheptane	325
α-aminoisopropyl alcohol	325
1-aminooctane	325
2-aminopentane	325
p-aminophenetole	325
(m-aminophenyl) methyl carbinol	325
3-aminopropanol	325
n-(3-aminopropyl) cyclohexylamine	325
n-(3-aminopropyl) morpholine	325
2-aminothiazole	491
ammonia	77, 497
ammonia, anhydrous	49, 325, 491
ammonium acetate	491
ammonium carbonate	491
ammonium azide	491
ammonium bromide	491
ammonium dichromate	49, 430, 491
ammonium chloride	491
ammonium fluoride	49
ammonium hydroxide	491
ammonium iodide	491
ammonium nitrate	49, 491
ammonium oxalate	491

CHEMICAL	NFPA Doc. No.
ammonium perchlorate	49, 430, 491
ammonium permanganate	49, 430, 491
ammonium persulfate	430, 491
ammonium phosphate, monoammonium phosphate	491
ammonium picrate	491
ammonium sulfate	491
ammonium thiocyanate	491
ammonium thiosulfate	491
amoxybenzene	325
amyl acetate	77, 325
sec-amyl acetate	325, 497
n-amyl acetate	497
amyl alcohol	325, 491
sec-amyl alcohol	325
amyl bromide	325
amyl butyrate	325
amyl carbinol	325
amyl chloride	325
tert-amyl chloride	325
amyl chlorides (mixed)	325
amyl ether	325
amyl formate	325
t-amyl hydroperoxide	432
amyl lactate	325
amyl maleate	325
n-amyl mercaptan	325
amyl mercaptans	49, 325
amyl naphthalene	325
amyl nitrate	49, 325
amyl oleate	325
amyl oxalate	325
t-amyl peroxy-2-ethylhexanoate	432
t-amyl peroxyacetate	432
t-amyl peroxybenzoate	432
t-amyl peroxyneodecanoate	432
t-amyl peroxypivalate	432
o-amyl phenol	325
p-tert-amyl phenol	325
amyl phenyl ether	325
amyl phthalate	325
amyl propionate	325
amyl salicylate	325
amyl stearate	325
amyl sulfides (mixed)	325
amyl toluene	325
amyl trichlorosilane	325
amyl xylyl ether	325
amylamine	325
sec-amylamine	325
amylamines	49
p-tert-amylaniline	325
amylbenzene	325
amylcyclohexane	325
amylene	325

CHEMICAL	NFPA Doc. No.
amylene chloride	325
β-amylene-cis	325
β-amylene-trans	325
p-sec-amylphenol	325
2-(p-tert-amylphenoxy)ethanol	325
2-(p-tert-amylphenoxy) ethyl laurate	325
p-tert-amylphenyl acetate	325
p-tert-amylphenyl butyl ether	325
p-tert-amylphenyl methyl ether	325
aniline	49, 77, 325, 491, 497
aniline hydrochloride	325
2-anilinoethanol	325
β-anilinoethanol ethoxyaniline	325
o-anisaldehyde	325
o-anisidine	325
anisole	77, 325
anisoyl chloride	491
anol	325
anthracene	77, 325, 491
anthranilic acid	499
anthraquinone	325
antimony	491
antimony pentachloride, liquid	49
antimony pentafluoride	49, 491
antimony sulfide	49, 491
antimony tribromide	491
antimony trichloride	491
antimony triiodide	491
antimony trisulfide	491
antimonyl chloride	491
apricot pit	499
armeen	77
arsenic	491
arsenic disulfide	491
arsenic oxide	491
arsenic pentafluoride	49
arsenic pentoxide	49
arsenic sulfide, arsenic trisulfide	491
arsenic tribromide (25°C)	77
arsenic trichloride	49, 491
arsenic trichloride (25°C)	77
arsenic triiodide	491
arsenic trioxide	49, 491
arsenic trisulfide	49
arsine	49, 491
artificial almond oil	325
aryl-nitrosomethylamide	499
asphalt	491, 499
asphalt (cutback)	325
asphalt, liquid-medium curing grades MC-30 and MC-70; grades MC-250; MC-800; and MC-3000	325
asphalt, liquid-rapid curing grades RC-250; RC-800; and RC-3000	325
asphalt, liquid-slow curing (grade SC-250)	325
asphalt, liquid-slow curing (grade SC-3000)	325
asphalt, liquid-slow curing (grade SC-70)	325
asphalt, liquid-slow curing (grade SC-800)	325
asphalt (typical)	325
aspirin [acetol (2)]	499
azelaic acid	499
aziridine	325
azo-bis-butyronitrile	499
azobisisobutyronitrile	325
α, α′-azodiisobutyronitrile	491
azole	325
banana oil	325
barium bromate	430
barium chlorate	49, 430, 491
barium chloride	491
barium hydride	491
barium hypochlorite	430
barium nitrate	491
barium oxide	491
barium perchlorate	430, 491
barium permanganate	430
barium peroxide	430, 491
barium sulfate	491
barium sulfide	491
benzaldehyde	49, 77, 325, 491
benzedrine	325
benzene	49, 77, 325, 491, 497
benzene carbonyl chloride	325
benzene carbonal	325
benzenesulfonyl chloride	491
benzethonium chloride	499
benzine	325
benzocyclobutene	325
benzoic acid	325, 499
benzoic acid (125°C)	77
benzol	325
benzol diluent	325
benzonitrile (25°C)	77
p-benzoquinone	325
benzotriazole	499
benzotrichloride	49, 325
benzotrifluoride	49, 325
benzoyl chloride	49, 325, 491
benzoyl peroxide	491
benzyl acetate	325
benzyl alcohol	325, 491
benzyl alcohol (25°C)	77
benzyl benzoate	77, 325
benzyl butyl phthalate	325
benzyl carbinol	325

CHEMICAL	NFPA Doc. No.
benzyl chloride	49, 325, 497
benzyl cyanide	77, 325
benzyl ether	325
benzyl mercaptan	325
benzyl salicilate	325
benzylamine (25°C)	77
n-benzyldiethylamine	325
beryllium	491
beryllium oxide	491
beryllium, powder (often from machining operations)	49
bicyclohexyl	325
biphenyl	77, 325
2-biphenylamine	325
bis(p-tert-butylphenyl)phenyl phosphate	325
bis[2-(2-chloroethoxy)ethyl] ether	325
bis(2-chloroethyl) ether	325
bis(2-chloroethyl) formal	325
bis(β-chloroisopropyl) ether	325
bis-diethylene glycol ethyl ether phthalate	325
bis(2,4-dimethylbutyl) maleate	325
n,n-1-bis-(1,4-dimethylpentyl) p-phenylenediamine	325
1,3-bis(ethylamino) butane	325
bis(2-ethylhexyl) amine	325
bis(2-ethylhexyl) ethanolamine	325
bis(2-ethylhexyl) maleate	325
bis(2-ethylhexyl) phosphoric acid	325
bis(2-ethylhexyl) succinate	325
bis(2-hydroxy-5-chlorophenyl) methane	499
bis(2-methoxyethyl) ether	491
n,n-bis(1-methylheptyl) ethylenediamine	325
bis(β-methylpropyl) amine	325
bis(2,2,4-trimethylpentanediolisobutyrate) diglycolate	325
bismuth trichloride	491
bismuth trioxide	491
bisphenol-A	499
blast-furnace gas	325
boric acid	491
Borneo camphor	325
borneol	325
boron	491
boron, commercial amorphous (85% B)	499
boron nitride	491
boron tribromide	49, 491
boron trichloride	491
boron trifluoride	49, 491
boron trifluoride etherate	325, 491
brandy	325

CHEMICAL	NFPA Doc. No.
brazil wax	325
bromine	491
bromine (17.2°C)	77
bromine azide	491
bromine or bromine solutions	49
bromine pentafluoride	49, 491
bromine trifluoride	49, 491
3-bromo-1-propyne	491
1-bromo-3-chloro-5,5-dimethylhydantoin	430
bromobenzene	77, 325
1-bromobutane	325
4-bromodiphenyl	325
bromoethane	325
bromoform	77, 491
bromomethane	325
1-bromonaphthalene	77
1-bromopentane	325
3-bromopropene	325
3-bromopropyne	49, 325
bromopropyne	497
o-bromotoluene	325
p-bromotoluene	325
butadiene	77, 325, 491, 497
butadiene monoxide	325
butadienes, inhibited	49
butanal	325
butanal oxime	325
butane	77, 325
n-butane	491, 497
1,3-butanediamine	325
1,2-butanediol	325
1,3-butanediol	325
1,4-butanediol	325
2,3-butanediol	325
1,3-butanediol	325
2,3-butanedione	325
1-butanethiol	325
2-butanethiol	325, 491
1-butanol	325
2-butanol	325, 497
2-butanone	325
2-butenal	325
1-butene	325
2-butene nitrile	325
2-butene-1,4-diol	325
2-butene-cis	325
2-butene-trans	325
butenediol	325
butoxybenzene	325
1-butoxybutane	325
1-(butoxyethoxy)-2-propanol	325
2,β-butoxyethoxyethyl chloride	325
butoxyethyl diglycol carbonate	325
β-butoxyethyl salicylate	325

CHEMICAL	NFPA Doc. No.
butoxyl	325
n-butyl 4,4-di(t-butylperoxy)valerate	432
n-butyl acetamide	325
butyl acetate	325
sec-butyl acetate	325, 491
n-butyl acetate	497
butyl acetate (i- or n-)	77
butyl acetoacetate	325
butyl acetyl ricinoleate	325
butyl acrylate	77, 325
n-butyl acrylate (inhibited)	497
tert-butyl acetate	497
butyl alcohol	325, 491
sec-butyl alcohol	77
t-butyl alcohol	77
tert-butyl alcohol	325
butyl benzoate	325
butyl benzyl phthalate	325
butyl bromide	325
butyl butyrate	325
tert-butyl carbinol	325
butyl carbitol	325
4-tert-butyl catechol	325
butyl chloride	325
n-butyl chloride	77
sec-butyl chloride	77
tert-butyl chloride	325
t-butyl cumyl peroxide	432
butyl diglycol carbonate	325
butyl ethanedioate	325
n-butyl ethanolamine	325
butyl ether	325
butyl ethyl ether	325
butyl ethylene	325
n-butyl formal	497
butyl formate	325
n-butyl glycidyl ether	497
butyl glycolate	325
t-butyl hydroperoxide	432
tert-butyl hydroperoxide	325
n-butyl isocyanate	325
butyl isovalerate	325
butyl lactate	325
butyl mercaptan	325, 497
tert-butyl mercaptan	325
butyl methacrylate	325
butyl methanoate	325
butyl naphthalene	325
butyl nitrate	325
butyl oleate	325
butyl oxalate	325
tert-butyl peracetate	325
tert-butyl perbenzoate	325
t-butyl peroxy-2-ethylhexanoate	432
t-butyl peroxyacetate	432, 491
t-butyl peroxybenzoate	432, 491
t-butyl peroxyisobutyrate	432
t-butyl peroxymaleate	432
t-butyl peroxyneodecanoate	432
t-butyl peroxypivalate	432
tert-butyl peroxypivalate	325
β-(p-tert-butyl phenoxy) ethanol	325
butyl phenyl ether	325
butyl phosphate	325
butyl phthalyl butyl glycolate	325
butyl propionate	325
butyl ricinoleate	325
butyl sebacate	325
butyl stearate	77, 325
tert-butyl tetralin	325
para-tert-butyl toluene	497
butyl trichlorosilane	325
butyl vinyl ether	325
butyl-2-propenoate	497
p-tert-butyl-o-cresol	325
n-butylacetanilide	325
butylacrylate	49
n-butylamine	49
butylamine	325
sec-butylamine	325
tert-butylamine	325
butylamine	497
butylamine oleate	325
tert-butylaminoethyl methacrylate	325
n-butylaniline	325
butylbenzene	325
sec-butylbenzene	325
tert-butylbenzene	325
2-butylbiphenyl	325
butylcarbamic acid, ethyl ester	325
tert-butyl-m-cresol	325
butylcyclohexane	325
sec-butylcyclohexane	325
tert-butylcyclohexane	325
n-butylcyclohexylamine	325
butylcyclopentane	325
4-tert-butyl-2-chlorophenol	325
butyldecalin	325
tert-butyldecalin	325
n-butyldiethanolamine	325
tert-butyldiethanolamine	325
α-butylene	325
β-butylene	325
γ-butylene	325
butylene	497
α-butylene glycol	325
2,3-butylene oxide	325
1,2-butylene oxide	49, 325
butylethylacetaldehyde	325
2,2-(butylimino)diethanol	325

CHEMICAL	NFPA Doc. No.
butyllithium	49, 491
2-butyloctanol	325
t-butylperoxy 2-ethylhexyl carbonate	432
t-butylperoxy isopropyl carbonate	432
β-(p-tert-butylphenoxy) ethyl acetate	325
4-tert-butyl-2-phenylphenol	325
tert-butylstyrene	325
n-butylurethane	325
2-butyne	325
butyraldehyde	49, 325
n-butyraldehyde	491, 497
butyraldol	325
butyraldoxime	325
butyric acid	49, 325, 491
n-butyric acid	497
butyric acid, ethyl ester	325
butyric aldehyde	325
butyric anhydride	325
butyric ester	325
butyrolactone	325
butyrone	325
butyronitrile	49, 325
cadmium	491
cadmium bromide	491
cadmium chloride	491
cadmium fluoride	491
cadmium iodide	491
cadmium oxide	491
cadmium sulfide	491
calcium	49, 491
calcium carbide	49, 491
calcium carbonate	491
calcium chlorate	430, 491
calcium chloride	491
calcium chlorite	430, 491
calcium cyanide	49
calcium hydride	491
calcium hydroxide	491
calcium hypochlorite	49, 430, 491
calcium hypophosphite	491
calcium nitride	491
calcium oxide	49, 491
calcium perchlorate	430
calcium permanganate	430
calcium peroxide	430, 491
calcium phosphide	491
calcium silicide	491, 499
calcium sulfide	491
camphor	325, 491
camphor oil	325
caproaldehyde	325
caproic acid	325
capronitrile (25°C)	77
caprylaldehyde	325
caprylic acid	77
caprylic aldehyde	325
caprylyl chloride	325
carbitol	325
carbolic acid	325
carbon	491
carbon bisulfide	325
carbon black (more than 8% total entrapped volatiles)	499
carbon disulfide	49, 77, 325, 491, 497
carbon disulfide (1°C)	77
carbon monoxide	49, 325, 491, 497
carbon oxysulfide	325
carbon tetrabromide	491
carbon tetrachloride	49, 77, 491
carbon tetraiodide	491
carbonate 100 lb (45 kg) V	432
carbonyl sulfide	325
carboxymethyl cellulose	499
carboxypolymethylene	499
carnauba wax	325
cashew oil, phenolic, hard	499
castor oil	325
castor oil (hydrogenated)	325
cellulose	491, 499
cellulose acetate	499
cellulose acetate butyrate	499
cellulose nitrate wet with alcohol	325
cellulose triacetate	499
cerium	491
cesium	491
cesium chloride	491
cetane	325
charcoal	499
cherry pit	499
china wood oil	325
chlorex	325
chloric acid	430, 491
chlorinated phenol	499
chlorinated polyether alcohol	499
chlorine	49, 77, 491
chlorine dioxide	491
chlorine monofluoride	491
chlorine monoxide	325, 491
chlorine trifluoride	49, 491
2-chloro-α,α,α-trifluoro-5-nitrotoluene	325
o-chloro-α,α,α-trifluorotoluene	325
1-chloro-1-nitroethane	325
1-chloro-1-nitropropane	325, 497
2-chloro-1-propanol	325
1-chloro-1-propene	325
2-chloro-1,3-butadiene	325
1-chloro-2, 4-dinitrobenzene	491
1-chloro-2-methyl propane	325
4-chloro-2-nitroaniline	491

CHEMICAL	NFPA Doc. No.
2-chloro-2-nitropropane	325
1-chloro-2-propanol	325
chloro-4-ethylbenzene	325
2-chloro-4-phenylphenol	325
chloro-4-tert-amylphenol	325
2-chloro-4-tert-amylphenyl methyl ether	325
2-chloro-4,6-di-tert-amylphenol	325
2-chloro-5-nitrobenzotrifluoride	325
chloroacetaldehyde	497
chloroacetic acid	325
chloroacetic acid, solid	49
chloroacetoacetanilide	499
chloroacetone	491
chloroacetonitrile	49
chloroacetophenone	325
chloroacetyl chloride	49
m-chloroaniline (25°C)	77
p-chlorobenzaldehyde	325
chlorobenzene	49, 77, 325, 491, 497
chlorobenzol	325
chlorobenzotrifluoride	325
o-chlorobenzotrifluoride	325
chlorobutadiene	325
1-chlorobutane	325
2-chlorobutene-2	325
chlorodiethyl silane	49
chlorodiethylaluminum	325, 491
chlorodinitrobenzenes	49, 325
chloroethane	325
2-chloroethanol	325, 491
chloroethyl acetate	325
2-chloroethyl acetate	325
2-chloroethyl alcohol	325
2-chloroethyl vinyl ether	325
2-chloroethyl-2-xenyl ether	325
chloroethylene	325
chloroform	49, 77, 491
1-chlorohexane	325
chlorohydrin (25°C)	77
chloroisopropyl alcohol	325
chloromethane	325
1-chloronaphthalene	325
chloronitrobenzenes	49
1-chloropentane	325
β-chlorophenetole	325
o-chlorophenol	325
p-chlorophenol	325
chlorophenols, liquid	49
chlorophenols, solid	49
chloropicrin	49, 491
chloroprene	325, 497
1-chloropropane	325
2-chloropropane	325
3-chloropropene	325
α-chloropropionic acid	325
3-chloropropionitrile	325
2-chloropropionyl chloride	325
β-chloropropyl alcohol	325
1-chloropropylene	325
2-chloropropylene	325
3-chloropropylene oxide	325
γ-chloropropylene oxide	325
chlorosilanes, n.o.s.	49
chlorosulfonic acid	49
chlorosulfuric acid	491
chlorotoluene	325
α-chlorotoluene	325
chlorotrifluoroethylene	325
chlorotrifluoromethane	491
chromic acid, solid	49
chromic anhydride	491
chromic chloride	49
chromium	491
chromium (97%) electrolytic, milled	499
chromium oxychloride	49
chromium trioxide (chromic acid)	430
chromyl chloride	491
cimene	325
cinnamene	325
cinnamon	499
citral	325
citronellel	325
citronellol	325
citrus peel	499
cleaning solvent	325
coal gas	325
coal, Kentucky bituminous	499
coal oil	325
coal, Pittsburgh experimental	499
coal tar light oil	325
coal tar pitch	325
coal, Wyoming	499
cobalt	491
cobalt naphtha	325
cobalt naphthenate	325
cocoa bean shell	499
cocoa, natural, 19% fat	499
cocoanut oil	325
coconut shell	499
cod liver oil	325
coke	491
coke (more than 8% total entrapped volatiles)	499
collodion	325
Cologne spirits	325
Columbian spirits	325
colza oil	325
copper	491
copper chlorate	430

CHEMICAL	NFPA Doc. No.
cork	499
corn	499
corn dextrine	499
corn oil	325
corncob grit	499
cornstarch, commercial	499
cornstarch, modified	499
cottonseed meal	499
cottonseed oil	325
coumarone-indene, hard	499
crag no. 974	499
creosote oil	325
cresol	491, 497
cresols (o-, m-, p-)	49, 77, 325
m-cresol	77
o-cresol	77, 325
p-cresol	77
o-cresol	325
m- or p-cresol	325
p-cresyl acetate	325
cresyl diphenyl phosphate	325
crotonaldehyde	325, 491, 497
crotonaldehyde, stabilized	49
crotonic acid	49, 325
crotonic aldehyde	325
crotononitrile	325
crotonyl alcohol	325
1-crotyl bromide	325
1-crotyl chloride	325
cube root, South America	499
cumene	49, 325, 491, 497
cumene hydroperoxide	325, 491
cumol	325, 432
cumyl hydroperoxide 88 cumene	432
cumyl peroxyneodecanoate	432
cumyl peroxyneoheptanoate	432
cupric bromide	491
cupric chloride	491
cupric nitrate	491
cupric oxide	491
cupric sulfate	491
cupric sulfide	491
cuprous bromide	491
cuprous chloride	491
cuprous cyanide	491
cyanamide	325
cyanoacetic acid	49, 491
2-cyanoethanol, 3-hydroxypropionitrile	491
2-cyanoethyl acrylate	325
n-(2-cyanoethyl) cyclohexylamine	325
cyanogen	77, 325, 491
cyanogen bromide	49
cyanogen iodide	491
cyanogen, liquefied	49

CHEMICAL	NFPA Doc. No.
cyanuric chloride	491
cyclamen aldehyde	325
cyclobutane	325
1,5,9-cyclododecatriene	325
cycloheptane	325
cyclohexane	77, 325, 491, 497
1,4-cyclohexane dimethanol	325
cyclohexanethiol	325
cyclohexanol	325, 491, 497
cyclohexanone	77, 325, 491, 497
cyclohexene	325, 497
3-cyclohexene-1-carboxaldehyde	325
cyclohexenone	325
cyclohexyl acetate	325
cyclohexyl chloride	325
cyclohexyl formate	325
cyclohexylamine	49, 325
cyclohexylbenzene	325
cyclohexylcyclohexanol	325
cyclohexylmethane	325
o-cyclohexylphenol	325
cyclohexyltrichlorosilane	325
1,5-cyclooctadiene	325
cyclopentadiene	77
cyclopentane	77, 325
cyclopentanol	325
cyclopentanone	325
cyclopentene	325
cyclopropane	77, 325, 497
p-cymene	325, 497
cymene (25°C)	77
decaborane	49, 325, 491
decahydronaphthalene	325
decahydronaphthalene-trans	325
n-decaldehyde	497
decalin	77, 325
decane	325
decanol	325
n-decanol	497
1-decene	325
decene	497
decyl acrylate	325
decyl alcohol	325, 497
decyl nitrate	325
decylamine	325
decylbenzene	325
tert-decylmercaptan	325
decylnaphthalene	325
dehydroacetic acid	325
denatured alcohol	325
denatured alcohol government formula (CD-10)	325
denatured alcohol government formula (CD-5)	325

CHEMICAL	NFPA Doc. No.
dichloroanilines, solid or liquid	49
dichlorobenzene	77, 325, 491
o-dichlorobenzene	49, 497
p-dichlorobenzene	325
o-dichlorobenzol	325
2,4-dichlorobenzoyl peroxide	432
2,3-dichlorobutadiene-1,3	325
1,2-dichlorobutane	325
1,4-dichlorobutane	49, 325
2,3-dichlorobutane	325
3,4-dichlorobutene-1	325
2,2-dichlorodiethyl ether	49
dichlorodifluoromethane	491
dichlorodimethyl ether, symmetrical	49
dichlorodimethylsilane	325
1,1-dichloroethane	325
1,2-dichloroethane	325, 497
dichloroethanoyl chloride	325
2,2-dichloroethyl ether	325
2,2-dichloroethyl formal	325
dichloroethylene	49
cis-dichloroethylene	77
1,1-dichloroethylene	325
1,2-dichloroethylene	325, 491, 497
dichlorohydrin (25°C)	77
dichloroisopropyl ether	325
dichloromethane	49, 325, 491
1,5-dichloropentane	325
dichloropentanes (mixed)	325
2,4-dichlorophenol	325
1,2-dichloropropane	325, 491
dichloropropene	49
1,3-dichloropropene	325
2,3-dichloropropene	325, 497
dichlorosilane	49, 77, 325, 491
2,6-dichlorostyrene	325
dichlorvos	325
dicumyl peroxide	432
dicyclohexyl	325
dicyclohexylamine	49, 325
dicyclopentadiene	325, 497
dicyclopentadiene dioxide	432, 499
didecanoyl peroxide	432
didecyl ether	325
dieldrin (20%)	499
diesel fuel oil no. 1-D	325
diesel fuel oil no. 2-D	325
diesel fuel oil no. 4-D	325
diesel oil (purified)	77
diethanolamine	325
1,2-diethoxyethane	325
diethyl acetoacetate	325
diethyl benzene	497
diethyl carbamyl chloride	325
diethyl carbinol	325

CHEMICAL	NFPA Doc. No.
diethyl carbonate	325
diethyl carbonate (25°C)	77
diethyl ether	49, 77, 325, 491, 497
diethyl ether in oxygen	77
diethyl fumarate	325
diethyl glycol	325
diethyl ketone	325
diethyl maleate	325
diethyl malonate	325
diethyl oxalate (25°C)	77
diethyl oxide	325
diethyl peroxide	325
diethyl phthalate	325
p-diethyl phthalate	325
diethyl selenide	325
diethyl succinate	325
diethyl sulfate	49, 325, 491
diethyl sulfate (25°C)	77
diethyl tartrate	325
diethyl telluride	49
diethyl terephthalate	325
n,n-diethyl-1,3-butanediamine	325
1,3-diethyl-1,3-diphenyl urea	325
di-2-ethylhexyl adipate	325
di(2-ethylhexyl) maleate	325
di(2-ethylhexyl) peroxydicarbonate	432
di(2-ethylhexyl) phosphoric acid	325
di(2-ethylhexyl) succinate	325
n,n-diethyl-1,3-propanediamine	325
2,2-diethyl-1,3-propanediol	325
3,9-diethyl-6-tridecanol	325
diethylacetaldehyde	325
diethylacetic acid	325
n,n-diethylacetoacetamide	325
diethylaluminum chloride	49, 325
diethylaluminum hydride	325
diethylamine	49, 77, 325, 491, 497
2-(diethylamino)ethyl acrylate	325
3-(diethylamino)propylamine	325
2-diethylaminoethanol	325
diethylaminoethanol	497
n,n-diethylaniline	325
diethylarsine	491
o-diethylbenzene	325
m-diethylbenzene	325
p-diethylbenzene	325
di-2-ethylbutyl phthalate	325
diethylcyclohexane	325
diethylene diamine	325
diethylene dioxide	325
diethylene glycol	77, 325
diethylene glycol bis(2-butyoxyethyl carbonate)	325
diethylene glycol bis(allylcarbonate)	325

CHEMICAL	NFPA Doc. No.
diethylene glycol bis(butyl carbonate)	325
diethylene glycol bis(phenylcarbonate)	325
diethylene glycol butyl ether acetate	325
diethylene glycol diacetate	325
diethylene glycol dibenzoate	325
diethylene glycol dibutyl ether	325
diethylene glycol diethyl ether	325
diethylene glycol diethyl levulinate	325
diethylene glycol dimethyl ether	325
diethylene glycol dipropionate	325
diethylene glycol ethyl ether	325
diethylene glycol ethyl ether phthalate	325
diethylene glycol methyl ether	325
diethylene glycol methyl ether acetate	325
diethylene glycol methyl ether formal	325
diethylene glycol monobutyl ether	325, 497
diethylene glycol monobutyl ether acetate	325
diethylene glycol monoethyl ether	325
diethylene glycol monoethyl ether acetate	325
diethylene glycol monoisobutyl ether	325
diethylene glycol monomethyl ether	325, 497
diethylene glycol n-butyl ether	325
diethylene glycol phthalate	325
diethylene oxide	325
diethylenetriamine	49, 77, 325
diethylethanolamine	49
n,n-diethylethanolamine	325
n,n-diethylethylenediamine	325
diethylhexylamine	325
diethylhexylethanolamine	325
n,n-diethyllauramide	325
diethylmagnesium	491
3,3-diethylpentane	325
n,n-diethylstearamide	325
diethylzinc	49, 325, 491
difluoro-1-chloroethane	325
digermane	491
diglycol chlorformate	325
diglycol chlorohydrin	325
diglycol diacetate	325
diglycol dilevulinate	325
diglycol laurate	325
dihexyl	325
dihexyl ether	325
dihexylamine	325
dihydroacetic acid	499
dihydropyran	325
o-dihydroxybenzene	325
p-dihydroxybenzene	325
1,2-dihydroxybutane	325
2,2-dihydroxyethyl ether	325
2,5-dihydroxyhexane	325
diisobutyl carbinol	325
diisobutyl ketone	325, 497
diisobutyl phthalate	325
diisobutylaluminum hydride	325
diisobutylamine	325
diisobutylene	77, 325, 491, 497
diisodecyl adipate	325
diisodecyl phthalate	325
diisooctyl phthalate	325
diisopropanolamine	325
diisopropyl	325
diisopropyl ether	49, 77, 325, 491
diisopropyl maleate	325, 432
diisopropyl peroxydicarbonate	325, 432, 491
diisopropylamine	49, 325, 497
diisopropylbenzene	325
n,n-diisopropylethanolamine	325
diisopropylmethanol	325
diketene	325, 491
diketene, inhibited	49
dilauroyl peroxide	432
dilauroyol peroxide	432
dimethoxy tetraglycol	325
2,5-dimethoxyaniline	325
2,5-dimethoxychlorobenzene	325
1,2-dimethoxyethane	325
dimethoxyethyl phthalate	325
dimethoxymethane	77, 325
2-dimethoxypropane	491
dimethyl acetamide	77
n-n-dimethyl aniline	497
dimethyl anthranilate	325
dimethyl carbinol	325
dimethyl carbonate	325
dimethyl chloracetal	325
dimethyl decalin	325
dimethyl ether	77, 325, 491
dimethyl ethyl carbinol	325
dimethyl formamide	77, 497
dimethyl glycol phthalate	325
dimethyl hexynol	325
dimethyl isophthalate	499
dimethyl ketone	325
dimethyl maleate	325
dimethyl phthalate	325
2,2-dimethyl propane	77
dimethyl sebacate	325
dimethyl sulfate	49, 77, 325, 491, 497
dimethyl sulfoxide	77, 325, 491
dimethyl terephthalate	325, 499
2,3-dimethyl-1-butene	325
2,2-dimethyl-1-propanol	325

CHEMICAL	NFPA Doc. No.
1,3-dimethyl-1,3-diphenylcyclobutane	325
2,3-dimethyl-2-butene	325
2,5-dimethyl-2,5-di(2-ethylhexanoylperoxy) hexane	432
2,5-dimethyl-2,5-di(benzoylperoxy)hexane	432
2,5-dimethyl-2,5-di(t-butylperoxy)hexane	432
2,5-dimethyl-2,5-dihydroperoxyhexane	432
2,4-dimethyl-3-ethylpentane	325
2,4-dimethyl-3-pentanol	325
2,6-dimethyl-4-heptanone	325
dimethylacetamide	325
dimethylamine	49, 325, 497
2-(dimethylamino)ethanol	325
2-(dimethylamino)ethyl methacrylate	325
3-(dimethylamino)propionitrile	325
3-(dimethylamino)propylamine	325
di(methylamyl) maleate	325
n,n-dimethylaniline	325
o-dimethylaniline	325
1,2-dimethylbenzene	325
1,3-dimethylbenzene	325
1,4-dimethylbenzene	325
dimethylbenzylcarbinyl acetate	325
2,2-dimethylbutane	77, 325
2,3-dimethylbutane	325, 497
1,3-dimethylbutanol	325
1,3-dimethylbutyl acetate	325
1,3-dimethylbutylamine	325
dimethylcarbonate	49
dimethylcyanamide	325
1,2-dimethylcyclohexane	325
1,3-dimethylcyclohexane	325
1,4-dimethylcyclohexane	325
1,4-dimethylcyclohexane-cis	325
1,4-dimethylcyclohexane-trans	325
dimethyldichlorosilane	49, 325, 491
dimethyldioxane	325
dimethylene oxide	325
n,n-dimethylethanolamine	325
n,n-dimethylformamide	325
2,5-dimethylfuran	325
3,3-dimethylheptane	325, 497
2,3-dimethylhexane	325
2,4-dimethylhexane	325, 497
1,1-dimethylhydrazine	325
uns-dimethylhydrazine	49, 325, 491, 497
dimethylisophthalate	325
n,n-dimethylisopropanolamine	325
dimethylmagnesium	491
2,6-dimethylmorpholine	325
2,3-dimethyloctane	325

CHEMICAL	NFPA Doc. No.
3,4-dimethyloctane	325
2,3-dimethylpentaldehyde	325
2,3-dimethylpentane	325, 497
2,4-dimethylpentane	325
dimethylpiperazine-cis	325
2,2-dimethylpropane	325
2,5-dimethylpyrazine	325
n,n-dimethylthio-formamide	499
dinitro-o-toluamide	499
2,4-dinitroaniline	325
dinitroanilines	49
o-dinitrobenzene	325
dinitrobenzenes	49
dinitrobenzoic acid	499
dinitrochlorobenzene	325
2,4-dinitrotoluene	325
dinitrotoluenes, molten	49
dioctyl adipate	325
dioctyl azelate	325
dioctyl ether	325
dioctyl phthalate	325
dioctylamine	325
dioxane	49
1,4-dioxane	77
p-dioxane	325, 491, 497
dioxolane	325
dipentene	325, 497
diphenyl	325, 499
diphenyl ether	325
diphenyl (o-xenyl) phosphate	325
diphenyl oxide	77, 325
diphenyl phthalate	325
1,3-diphenyl-2-buten-1-one	325
diphenylamine	325, 491
1,1-diphenylbutane	325
diphenyldichlorosilane	325
diphenyldodecyl phosphite	325
1,2-diphenylethane (sym)	325
1,1-diphenylethane (uns)	325
diphenylmethane	325
1,1-diphenylpentane	325
1,1-diphenylpropane	325
dipropyl ether	325
dipropyl ketone	325
dipropylaluminum hydride	325
dipropylamine	325
dipropylene glycol	325
dipropylene glycol methyl ether	325, 497
di-n-propyl peroxydicarbonate	432
di-n-propylamine	497
disilane (silicoethane)	491
ditane	325
ditertiary-butyl-paracresol	499
dithane m-45	499
ditridecyl phthalate	325

CHEMICAL	NFPA Doc. No.
divinyl acetylene	325
divinyl ether	325, 491
divinylbenzene	49, 325
dodecane	325
1-dodecanethiol	325
1-dodecanol	325
dodecene	497
dodecyl benzene	325
dodecyl bromide	325
dodecyl mercaptan	325
tert-dodecyl mercaptan	325
dodecyl phenol	325
α-dodecylene	325
4-dodecyloxy-2-hydroxy-benzophenone	325
dypnone	325
eicosane	325
endrin	491
epichlorohydrin	49, 325, 491, 497
epichlorohydrin (25°C)	77
epoxy	499
epoxy-bisphenol A	499
1,2-epoxyethane	325
erbium	491
erythrene	325
ethanal	325
ethane	77, 325, 491, 497
ethane in oxygen	77
1,2-ethanediol	325
1,2-ethanediol diformate	325
ethanethiol	325
ethanoic acid	325
ethanoic anhydride	325
ethanol	325, 497
ethanolamine	77, 325
ethanolamine or ethanolamine solutions	49
ethanoyl chloride	325
ethene	325
ethenyl ethanoate	325
ethenyloxyethene	325
ether	325
ethine	325
2-ethoxy ethanol	325
2-ethoxy-3,4-dihydro-2-pyran	325
ethoxyacetylene	325
ethoxybenzene	325
2-ethoxyethyl acetate	325
3-ethoxypropanal	325
1-ethoxypropane	325
3-ethoxypropionaldehyde	325
3-ethoxypropionic acid	325
ethoxytriglycol	325
ethyl 3-oxobutanoate	325
ethyl 3,3-di(t-amylperoxy)butyrate	432

CHEMICAL	NFPA Doc. No.
ethyl abietate	325
n-ethyl acetanilide	325
ethyl acetate	77, 325, 491, 497
ethyl acetoacetate	325, 491
ethyl acetoacetate (25°C)	77
ethyl acetyl glycolate	325
ethyl acrylate	77, 325, 491
ethyl acrylate, inhibited	49, 497
ethyl alcohol	77, 325, 491, 497
ethyl alcohol and water	325
ethyl benzene	77, 497
ethyl benzoate	77, 325
ethyl benzoylacetate	325
ethyl borate	325
ethyl bromide	77, 325
ethyl bromoacetate	325
ethyl butanoate	325
ethyl butanol	497
ethyl butyl carbonate	325
ethyl butyl ether	325
2-ethyl butyl glycol	325
ethyl butyl ketone	325, 497
ethyl butylcarbamate	325
ethyl butyrate	325
ethyl caproate	325
ethyl caprylate	325
ethyl carbonate	325
ethyl cellulose	499
ethyl chloride	77, 325, 497
ethyl chloroacetate	325
ethyl chlorocarbonate	325
ethyl chloroformate	49, 325
ethyl chloromethanoate	325
ethyl crotonate	325
ethyl cyanoacetate	77, 325
ethyl decanoate	325
ethyl dichlorosilane	325
ethyl dimethyl methane	325
ethyl ethanoate	325
ethyl ether	325, 497
ethyl fluoride	325
ethyl formate	77, 325
o-ethyl formate	325, 497
ethyl glycol acetate	325
ethyl hydroxyethyl cellulose	499
ethyl isobutyrate	325
ethyl isothiocyanate (25°C)	77
ethyl lactate	77, 325
ethyl malonate	325
ethyl mercaptan	325, 497
ethyl methacrylate	325
ethyl methanoate	325
ethyl methyl acrylate	325
ethyl methyl ether	49, 325, 491
ethyl methyl ketone	325, 491

CHEMICAL	NFPA Doc. No.
n-ethyl morpholine	497
ethyl nitrate	77, 325
ethyl nitrite	49, 325, 491
ethyl orthosilicate	325
ethyl oxalate	77, 325
ethyl oxide	325
ethyl p-toluene sulfonamide	325
ethyl p-toluene sulfonate	325
ethyl phenyl ether	325
ethyl phenyl ketone	325
ethyl phenylacetate	325
ethyl phosphate	325
ethyl phthalyl ethyl glycolate	325
ethyl propenyl ether	325
ethyl propionate	77, 325
ethyl propyl ether	325
ethyl sec-amyl ketone	497
ethyl silicate	325, 497
ethyl sulfate	325
ethyl sulfhydrate	325
ethyl thiocyanate (25°C)	77
ethyl vinyl ether	325
2-ethyl-1-butanol	325
2-ethyl-1-butene	325
2-ethyl-1,3-hexanediol	325
2-ethyl-2-butyl-1,3-propanediol	325
7-ethyl-2-methyl-4-hendecanol	325
5-ethyl-2-methylpyridine	491
2-ethyl-3-propyl acrolein	497
2-ethyl-3-propylacrolein	325
2-ethyl-3-propylacrylic acid	325
n-ethylacetamide	325
ethylacetate (25°C)	77
ethylaluminum dichloride	325
ethylaluminum sesquichloride	325
ethylamine	49, 77, 325, 497
ethylaminoethanol	325
n-ethylaniline	49
o-ethylaniline	325
ethylbenzene	49, 325
ethylbenzol	325
ethylbenzylaniline	325
2-ethylbutanal	325
3-(2-ethylbutoxy) propionic acid	325
2-ethylbutyl acetate	325
2-ethylbutyl alcohol	325
ethylbutylamine	325
2-ethylbutyraldehyde	325
2-ethylbutyric acid	325
2-ethylcaproaldehyde	325
ethylcyclobutane	325
ethylcyclohexane	325
n-ethylcyclohexylamine	325
ethylcyclopentane	325
n-ethyldiethanolamine	325

CHEMICAL	NFPA Doc. No.
ethylene	77, 325, 491, 497
ethylene acetate	325
ethylene carbonate	77, 325
ethylene chlorohydrin	49, 325, 497
ethylene, compressed	49
ethylene cyanohydrin	49, 325
ethylene dibromide	49, 77
ethylene dichloride	49, 77, 325, 491, 497
ethylene dicyanide	325
ethylene formate	325
ethylene glycol	77, 325, 491
ethylene glycol acetate	325
ethylene glycol diacetate	325
ethylene glycol dibutyl ether	325
ethylene glycol diethyl ether	325
ethylene glycol diformate	325
ethylene glycol dimethyl ether	325
ethylene glycol ethyl ether	325
ethylene glycol ethylbutyl ether	325
ethylene glycol ethylhexyl ether	325
ethylene glycol isopropyl ether	325
ethylene glycol methyl ether	325
ethylene glycol methyl ether acetal	325
ethylene glycol methyl ether acetate	325
ethylene glycol methyl ether formal	325
ethylene glycol monoacrylate	325
ethylene glycol monobenzyl ether	325
ethylene glycol monobutyl ether	77, 325, 497
ethylene glycol monobutyl ether acetate	325, 497
ethylene glycol monoethyl ether	77, 497
ethylene glycol monoethyl ether acetate	325, 497
ethylene glycol monoisobutyl ether	325
ethylene glycol monomethyl ether	77, 497
ethylene glycol n-butyl ether	325
ethylene glycol phenyl ether	325
ethylene in oxygen	77
ethylene oxide	49, 77, 325, 491, 497
ethylene oxide polymer	499
ethylene-maleic anhydride copolymer	499
ethylenediamine	49, 77, 325, 491, 497
2,2-ethylenedioxydiethanol	325
ethyleneimene	77
ethyleneimine	77, 325, 491, 497
ethylenimine, inhibited	49
n-ethylethanolamine	325
ethylethylene glycol	325
2-ethylhexaldehyde	325, 497
2-ethylhexanal	325
2-ethylhexanoic acid	325
2-ethylhexanol	325, 497
2-ethylhexenyl	325
2-ethylhexoic acid	325

CHEMICAL	NFPA Doc. No.
2-ethylhexyl acetate	325
2-ethylhexyl acrylate	49, 77, 325, 497
n-2-(ethylhexyl) aniline	325
2-ethylhexyl chloride	325
n-(2-ethylhexyl)-cyclohexylamine	325
2-ethylhexyl ether	325
2-ethylhexyl vinyl ether	325
2-ethylhexylamine	325
ethylidene chloride	77
1,1-ethylidene dichloride	325
1,2-ethylidene dichloride	325
2-ethylisohexanol	325
4-ethylmorpholine	325
1-ethylnaphthalene	325
3-ethyloctane	325
4-ethyloctane	325
p-ethylphenol	325
m-ethyltoluene	325
o-ethyltoluene	325
p-ethyltoluene	325
ethyltrichlorosilane	49, 325
ethyne	325
eugenol (25°C)	77
europium	491
ferbam T	499
ferric ferrocyanide	491
ferromanganese, medium carbon	499
ferrosilicon (88% Si, 9% Fe)	499
ferrotitanium (19% Ti, 74.1% Fe, 0.06% C)	499
ferrous chloride	491
ferrous sulfide	491
fish oil (bisulfated mix)	325
flax shive	499
fluoboric acid	49, 491
fluorine	491
fluorine, compressed	49
fluorobenzene	325
formal	325
formaldehyde	49, 325, 491, 497
formalin	325
formamide	77, 325
formic acid	49, 325, 491, 497
formic acid (25°C)	77
formic acid, butyl ester	325
formic acid, ethyl ester	325
formic acid, methyl ester	325
fuel oil no. 1	325, 497
fuel oil no. 2	325
fuel oil no. 4	325
fuel oil no. 5	325
fuel oil no. 6	325
fumaric acid	499
2-furaldehyde	325
furan	77, 325

CHEMICAL	NFPA Doc. No.
furfural	49, 77, 325, 497
furfuraldehyde	325
furfuran	325
furfuryl acetate	325
furfuryl alcohol	325, 497
furfurylamine	325
furfyryl alcohol	491
furol	325
fusel oil	325
gadolinium	491
gallic acid	491
gallium arsenide	49
gallium phosphide	49
gallium trichloride	49
garlic, dehydrated	499
gas, blast furnace	325
gas, coal gas	325
gas, coke-oven	325
gas, natural	325
gas oil	325
gas, oil gas	325
gas, producer	325
gas, water	325
gas, water (carbureted)	325
gasoline	325, 497
gasoline, casinghead	325
gasoline (leaded)	77
gasoline (straight run)	77
gasoline (unleaded)	77
geraniol	325
geranyl acetate	325
geranyl butyrate	325
geranyl formate	325
geranyl propionate	325
germane	49
germane (germanium hydride)	491
germanium	491
germanium tetrachloride	491
gilsonite	499
gin	325
glucose pentapropionate	325
glycerine	325
glycerol	77, 325
glyceryl triacetate	325
glyceryl tributyrate	325
glyceryl trichlorohydrin	325
glyceryl trinitrate	325
glyceryl tripropionate	325
glycidyl acrylate	325
glycol	325
glycol benzyl ether	325
glycol diacetate	325
glycol dichloride	325
glycol diformate	325
glycol dimercaptoacetate	325

CHEMICAL	NFPA Doc. No.
glycol monoacetate	325
glyoxal	491
gold	491
gold cyanide	491
grain alcohol	325
graphite	491
green base Harmon dye	499
guaiacol (25°C)	77
guanidine nitrate	430
guanidine nitrate (self-reactive)	491
guar seed	499
gulasonic acid, diacetone	499
gum, arabic	499
gum, karaya	499
gum, manila	499
gum, tragacanth	499
halane (1,3-dichloro-5,5-dimethylhydantoin)	430
heavy hydrogen	325
hemp hurd	499
hendecane	325
heptadecanol	325
heptane	77, 325, 491
n-heptane	497
heptane (pure)	77
2-heptanol	325
3-heptanol	325
3-heptanone	325
4-heptanone	325
1-heptene	325
n-heptene	497
3-heptene (mixed cis and trans)	325
heptylamine	325
heptylene	325
heptylene-2-trans	325
hexachlorobenzene	491
hexachlorobutadiene	325
hexachlorodiphenyl oxide	325
hexadecane	325
tert-hexadecanethiol	325
1-hexadecene	325
hexadecyl-tert-mercaptan	325
hexadecyltrichlorosilane	325
2,4-hexadienal	325
1,4-hexadiene	325
hexahydroaniline	325
hexahydrobenzene	325
hexahydropyridine	325
hexahydrotoluene	325
hexahydroxylol	325
hexaldehyde	325
hexalin	325
hexalin acetate	325
hexamethyldisilazane	49, 77
hexamethylene	325
hexamethylene diisocyanate	491
hexamethylene tetramine	499
hexanal	325
hexane	77, 325
n-hexane	497
hexane (pure)	77
1,2-hexanediol	325
2,5-hexanediol	325
2,5-hexanedione	325
1,2,6-hexanetriol	325
hexanoic acid	325
1-hexanol	325
hexanol	497
2-hexanone	325
3-hexanone	325
2-hexanone	497
1-hexene	325
2-hexene	325
hexene	497
2-hexene-cis	325
3-hexenol-cis	325
hexone	325
hexyl acetate	325
sec-hexyl acetate	497
hexyl alcohol	325
sec-hexyl alcohol	325
hexyl chloride	325
hexyl cinnamic aldehyde	325
hexyl ether	325
hexyl hydride	325
hexyl methacrylate	325
hexyl methyl ketone	325
hexylamine	325
hexylene glycol	325
holmium	491
hydracrylonitrile	325
hydralin	325
hydrazine	491, 497
hydrazine, anhydrous	49, 325
hydrazine hydrate	491
hydriodic acid, hydrogen iodide	491
hydriodic acid, solution	49
hydrobromic acid solution	49
hydrochloric acid, hydrogen chloride	491
hydrochloric ether	325
hydrocyanic acid, 96%	325
hydrofluoric acid, hydrogen fluoride	491
hydrogen	77, 325, 491, 497
hydrogen bromide	77, 491
hydrogen chloride (96°C)	77
hydrogen chloride, anhydrous	49
hydrogen chloride, refrigerated liquid	49
hydrogen cyanide	325, 491, 497
hydrogen cyanide (0°C)	77

CHEMICAL	NFPA Doc. No.
hydrogen fluoride, anhydrous	49
hydrogen cyanide, anhydrous, stabilized, hydrogen cyanide, anhydrous, stabilized absorbed in a porous inert material	49
hydrogen in oxygen	77
hydrogen iodide (at boiling point)	77
hydrogen peroxide	491
hydrogen peroxide, aqueous solutions	49, 430
hydrogen, refrigerated liquid	49
hydrogen selenide	491, 497
hydrogen sulfide	77, 325, 491, 497
hydrogen sulfide (at boiling point)	77
hydrogen sulfide, liquefied	49
hydroquinone	325, 491
hydroquinone di-(β-hydroxyethyl) ether	325
hydroquinone monomethyl ether	325
2-hydroxy-2-methyl-propionitrile	325
4-hydroxy-4-methyl-2-pentanone	325
o-hydroxybenzaldehyde	325
3-hydroxybutanal	325
β-hydroxybutyraldehyde	325
hydroxycitronellal	325
n-(2-hydroxyethyl)-acetamide	325
2-hydroxyethyl acrylate	325
hydroxyethyl cellulose	499
n-(2-hydroxyethyl) cyclohexylamine	325
4-(2-hydroxyethyl) morpholine	325
1-(2-hydroxyethyl) piperazine	325
n-(2-hydroxyethyl) propylenediamine	325
(2-hydroxyethyl)-ethylenediamine	325
β-hydroxyethylaniline	325
hydroxylamine	49, 325, 491
hydroxypropyl acrylate	325
o-hydroxytoluene	325
indan	325
indium	491
iodine	77, 491
iodine monobromide	491
iodine pentafluoride	491
iodine pentoxide	491
iodoform	491
α-ionone	325
β-ionone	325
iridium	491
iron	491, 499
iron carbonyl	325
iron oxide	491
iron pentacarbonyl	491
isano oil	325
iso-nonane	325
isoamyl acetate	325, 497
isoamyl alcohol	77, 325, 497
tert-isoamyl alcohol	325

CHEMICAL	NFPA Doc. No.
isoamyl butyrate	325
isoamyl chloride	325
isoamyl nitrite	325, 491
isobornyl acetate	325
isobutane	325, 497
isobutyl acetate	325, 497
isobutyl acrylate	325, 497
isobutyl alcohol	77, 325, 497
isobutyl butyrate	325
isobutyl carbinol	325
isobutyl chloride	77, 325
isobutyl formate	325
isobutyl heptyl ketone	325
isobutyl isobutyrate	325
isobutyl phenylacetate	325
isobutyl phosphate	325
isobutyl vinyl ether	325
isobutylamine	325
isobutylbenzene	325
isobutylcyclohexane	325
isobutylene	325
isobutyraldehyde	325, 497
isobutyric acid	325
isobutyric anhydride	325
isobutyronitrile	325
isodecaldehyde	325, 497
isodecanes, mixed	325
isodecanoic acid	325
isodecanol	325
isoeugenol	325
isoheptane	325
isoheptane, mixed isomers	325
isohexane	497
isohexane (mixture of hexane isomers)	325
tert-isohexyl alcohol	325
isooctane	77, 325
isooctanoic acid	325
isooctenes	325
isooctyl alcohol	325
isooctyl aldehyde	497
isooctyl nitrate	325
isooctyl vinyl ether	325
isopentaldehyde	325
isopentane	77, 325, 497
isopentanoic acid	325
isophorone	49, 325, 497
isophorone diisocyanate	49
isophthaloyl chloride	325
isoprene	325, 491, 497
isoprene, inhibited	49
isopropanol	325
isopropanolamine	325
isopropenyl acetate	325
isopropenyl acetylene	325

CHEMICAL	NFPA Doc. No.
2-isopropoxypropane	325
3-isopropoxypropionitrile	325
isopropyl acetate	325, 497
isopropyl alcohol	77, 325, 491
isopropyl benzoate	325
isopropyl bicyclohexyl	325
isopropyl carbinol	325
isopropyl chloride	77, 325
isopropyl chloroformate	491
isopropyl ether	325, 497
isopropyl formate	49, 325
isopropyl glycidyl ether	497
isopropyl lactate	325
isopropyl mercaptan	77
isopropyl methanoate	325
isopropyl vinyl ether	325
4-isopropyl-1-methyl benzene	325
isopropyl-2-hydroxypropanoate	325
isopropylamine	49, 77, 325, 497
isopropylbenzene	325
2-isopropylbiphenyl	325
isopropylcyclohexane	325
isopropylcyclohexylamine	325
isopropylethylene	325
4-isopropylheptane	325
isotoic anhydride	499
isovaleric acid	77
isovalerone	325
jet fuel	77, 325
Katchung oil	325
kerosene	77, 325, 497
kerosene, deodorized	325
lactic acid	491
lactonitrile	325
lanolin	325
lanthanum	491
lanthanum oxide	491
lard oil (commercial or animal)	325
lard oil (pure) no. 2, mineral	325
lauryl alcohol	325
lauryl bromide	325
lauryl mercaptan	325
lead	491
lead acetate	491
lead azide	491
lead carbonate	491
lead chromate	491
lead cyanide	491
lead dioxide	430, 491
lead fluoride	491
lead nitrate	491
lead oxide	491
lead perchlorate	430, 491
lead styphnate	491
lead sulfate	491

CHEMICAL	NFPA Doc. No.
lead sulfide	491
lignin, hydrolized, wood-type, fine	499
lignite, California	499
limestone (crushed)	491
limonene	491
linalool, synthetic	325
linseed oil	491
linseed oil, raw	325
liquid camphor	325
liquified petroleum gas	497
lithium	49, 491
lithium aluminum hydride	49, 491
lithium amide	491
lithium azide	491
lithium carbonate	491
lithium chlorate	430
lithium chloride	491
lithium hydride	49, 491
lithium hypochlorite (39 percent or less available chlorine)	430
lithium hypochlorite (more than 39 percent available chlorine)	430
lithium perchlorate	430
lithium peroxide	430
lithium tetrahydroborate	491
lubricating oil, mineral (C20-C50)	325
lubricating oil, spindle	325
lubricating oil, turbine	325
Lucite, methyl methacrylate polymer	491
lutetium	491
lycopodium	499
lynalyl acetate, synthetic	325
magnesium	491
magnesium bromate	430, 491
magnesium chlorate	430, 491
magnesium chloride	491
magnesium, grade B, milled	499
magnesium hydride	491
magnesium hydroxide	491
magnesium nitrate	491
magnesium or magnesium alloys with more than 50 percent magnesium in pellets, turnings, or ribbons	49
magnesium oxide	491
magnesium perchlorate	430, 491
magnesium peroxide	430
magnesium phosphide	491
maleic anhydride	49, 325, 491
malt barley	499
manganese	491, 499
manganese dioxide	430, 491
manganese vancide	499
manganous chloride	491
manganous iodide	491
manganous oxide	491

CHEMICAL	NFPA Doc. No.
mannitol	499
marsh gas	325
menhaden oil	325
p-menthyl hydroperoxide	432
2-mercaptoethanol	325
mercuric bromide	491
mercuric chloride	491
mercuric cyanide	491
mercuric cyanide oxide	491
mercuric iodide	491
mercuric nitrate	491
mercuric oxide	491
mercuric sulfide	491
mercurous azide	491
mercurous chlorate	430
mercurous chloride	491
mercurous nitrate	491
mercurous oxide	491
mercury	77, 491
mercury cyanide	49
mesityl oxide	49, 325, 491, 497
mesitylene	325, 491
metaldehyde	325
α-methacrolein	325
methacrylic acid	325
methacrylic acid, inhibited	49
methacrylic acid polymer	499
methacrylonitrile	325
methallyl alcohol	325
methallyl chloride	325
methane	77, 325, 491, 497
methane in oxygen	77
methanethiol	325
methanol	77, 325, 491, 497
methionine (l-methionine)	499
methox	325
methoxy triglycol	77, 325
o-methoxybenzaldehyde	325
methoxybenzene	325
p-methoxybenzyl formate	491
3-methoxybutanol	325
3-methoxybutyl acetate	325
3-methoxybutyraldehyde	325
2-methoxyethanol	325, 491
2(2-methoxyethoxy) ethanol	491
2-methoxyethyl acrylate	325
methoxyethyl phthalate	325
3-methoxypropionitrile	325
3-methoxypropylamine	325
methoxytriglycol acetate	325
2-methycyclohexanone	497
methyl abietate	325
methyl acetamide	77
methyl acetate	77, 325, 497
methyl acetic ester	325

CHEMICAL	NFPA Doc. No.
methyl acetoacetate	325
p-methyl acetophenone	325
methyl acrylate	49, 325, 497
methyl alcohol	77, 325, 497
methyl amyl alcohol	497
methyl amyl ketone	325
methyl anthranilate	325
methyl benzoate	325
methyl borate	325
methyl bromide	49, 325, 491
methyl butane	77
2-methyl butyl ethanoate	325
methyl butyl ketone	325
3-methyl butynol	325
2-methyl butyraldehyde	49
methyl butyrate	325
methyl carbonate	325
methyl cellosolve acetate	325
methyl cellulose	499
methyl chloride	325, 491, 497
methyl chloroethanoate	325
methyl chloroform	491
methyl cyanide	325
methyl cyanoacetate	77
methyl cyclohexane	77
methyl cyclopentadiene	325
methyl cyclopentane	49
methyl dihydroabietate	325
methyl ether	325, 497
methyl ethyl carbinol	325
methyl ethyl ether	325
methyl ethyl ketone	77, 325, 497
methyl ethyl ketone peroxide	432
methyl ethyl ketone peroxide and cyclohexanone peroxide mixture	432
methyl ethyl ketoxime	325
methyl ethylene glycol	325
methyl eugenol	325
methyl formal	497
methyl formamide	77, 491
methyl formate	49, 77, 325, 497
methyl heptadecyl ketone	325
methyl heptine carbonate	325
methyl heptyl ketone	325
methyl hexyl ketone	325
methyl iodide (25°C)	77
methyl ionone	325
methyl isoamyl ketone	49, 77, 325
methyl isobutyl ketone	497
methyl isocyanate	49, 325, 497
methyl isoeugenol	325
methyl isopropenyl ketone	325
methyl lactate	325
methyl lithium	491
methyl mercaptan	49, 325, 497

CHEMICAL	NFPA Doc. No.
β-methyl mercaptopropionaldehyde	325
methyl methacrylate	325, 491, 497
methyl methacrylate monomer, inhibited	49
methyl methacrylate polymer	499
methyl methacrylate-ethyl acrylate	499
methyl methacrylate-styrene-butadiene	499
methyl methanoate	325
methyl n-amyl ketone	497
methyl n-propyl ether	325
methyl nitrate (25°C)	77
methyl nonyl ketone	325
methyl oxide	325
methyl p-cresol	325
methyl parathion	491
methyl pentadecyl ketone	325
methyl pentanal	325
o-methyl phenol	325
methyl phenyl carbinyl acetate	325
methyl phenyl ether	325
methyl phenylacetate	325
methyl phthalyl ethyl glycolate	325
1-methyl piperazine	325
2-methyl propanol-1	325
methyl propionate	325
methyl propyl acetylene	325
methyl propyl ketone	325
2-methyl pyridine	325
methyl salicylate	325
methyl stearate	325
methyl sulfate	325
methyl tertiary butyl ether	497
methyl thiocyanate (25°C)	77
methyl toluene sulfonate	325
methyl undecyl ketone	325
methyl vinyl ether	325
methyl vinyl ketone	49, 325
2-methyl-1-butanol	325
3-methyl-1-butanol	325
3-methyl-1-butanol acetate	325
3-methyl-1-butene	325
2-methyl-1-butene (technical grade)	325
2-methyl-1-pentanol	325
2-methyl-1-pentene	325
4-methyl-1-pentene	325
3-methyl-1-pentynol	325
methyl-1-propanol	497
2-methyl-1-propanol	497
2-methyl-1,3-butadiene	325
2-methyl-1,3-pentadiene	325
4-methyl-1,3-pentadiene	325
2-methyl-1,3-pentanediol	325
3-methyl-2-butanethiol	325
2-methyl-2-butanol	325

CHEMICAL	NFPA Doc. No.
2-methyl-2-butene	325
2-methyl-2-ethyl-1,3-dioxolane	325
4-methyl-2-pentanol	325
4-methyl-2-pentanol acetate	325
4-methyl-2-pentanone	325
2-methyl-2-pentene	325
4-methyl-2-pentene	325
2-methyl-2-propanethiol	325
2-methyl-2-propanol	325
methyl-2-propanol	497
2-methyl-2-propanol	497
n-methyl-2-pyrolidone	77
1-methyl-2-pyrrolidinone	325
2-methyl-2,4-pentanediol	325
2-methyl-3-ethylpentane	325
methyl-3-hydroxybutyrate	325
1-methyl-3,5-diethylbenzene	325
2-methyl-4-ethylhexane	325
3-methyl-4-ethylhexane	325
2-methyl-5-ethyl pyridine	497
2-methyl-5-ethylpiperidine	325
2-methyl-5-ethylpyridine	49, 325
n-methyl-n-nitroso urea	491
methylacetylene	77, 325, 497
methylacetylene-propadiene	497
α-methylacrolein	325
methylal	325, 497
methylaluminum sesquibromide	325
methylaluminum sesquichloride	325
methylamine	325, 497
methylamine, anhydrous methylamine, aqueous solution	49
2-(methylamino) ethanol	325
methylamyl acetate	325
methylamyl alcohol	325
2-methylaniline	325
4-methylaniline	325
methylbenzene	325
α-methylbenzyl alcohol	325
α-methylbenzyl dimethyl amine	325
α-methylbenzyl ether	325
α-methylbenzylamine	325
2-methylbiphenyl	325
2-methylbutane	325, 497
o-methylbutylamine	325
2-methylbutyraldehyde	325
methylchloroacetate	325
methylchloromethyl ether	49
methylcyclohexane	325, 497
2-methylcyclohexanol	325
3-methylcyclohexanol	325
4-methylcyclohexanol	325
methylcyclohexanol	497
methylcyclohexanone	325
4-methylcyclohexanone	491

CHEMICAL	NFPA Doc. No.
4-methylcyclohexene	325
methylcyclohexyl acetate	325
methylcyclopentane	325
2-methyldecane	325
methyldichlorosilane	49, 325
n-methyldiethanolamine	325
methylene chloride	77, 325
methylene iodide	491
methylene oxide	325
methylenedianiline	325
n-methylethanolamine	325
2-methylfuran	325
2-methylheptane	497
methylheptenone	325
2-methylhexane	325
3-methylhexane	325, 497
methylhydrazine	49, 325, 491
methylisobutylcarbinol acetate	325
4-methylmorpholine	325
1-methylnaphthalene	325
2-methyloctane	497
2-methyloctane	497
3-methyloctane	497
4-methyloctane	497
methylpentaldehyde	325
2-methylpentane	325
3-methylpentane	325, 497
2-methylpentanoic acid	325
methylphenyl carbinol	325
2-methylpropanal	325
2-methylpropane	325, 497
2-methylpropenal	325
2-methylpropene	325
methylpropylcarbinol	325
methylpropylcarbinylamine	325
2-methylpyrazine	325
methylpyrrole	325
methylpyrrolidine	325
α-methylstyrene	325
methylstyrene	325
2-methyltetrahydrofuran	325
methyltrichlorosilane	49, 325
2-methylvaleraldehyde	325
1-methylvinyl acetate	325
milk, skimmed	499
mineral oil	325
mineral seal oil	325
mineral spirits	325
mineral wax	325
molybdenum	491
molybdenum trioxide	491
mono-(trichloro) tetra-(monopotassium dichloro)-penta-s-triazinetrione, dry	49
mono-(trichloro)-tetra-(monopotassium dichloro)-penta-s-triazinetrione	430
monochloro-s-triazinetrione acid	49
monochlorobenzene	325
monoethanolamine	497
monoisopropanolamine	497
monomethyl aniline	497
monomethyl hydrazine	497
morpholine	49, 325, 497
muriatic ether	325
mustard oil	325
naphtha 49° be-coal tar type	325
naphtha (coal tar)	497
naphtha, petroleum	325, 497
naphtha, safety solvent	325
naphtha V.M. & P., 50° flash	325
naphtha V.M. & P., high flash	325
naphtha V.M. & P., regular	325
naphthalene	325, 491
naphthalene (82°C)	77
naphthalene, crude or refined	49
beta-naphthalene-axo-dimethylaniline	499
β-naphthol	325
1-naphthylamine	325
natural gas	325
natural gas, liquefied	49
neatsfoot oil	325
neodymium	491
neohexane	325
neopentane	325, 497
neopentyl glycol	325
neoprene	491
nickel	491
nickel bromide	491
nickel carbonyl	49, 325, 491
nickel catalyst	49
nickel chloride	491
nickel cyanide	491
nickel fluoride	491
nickel monoxide	491
nicotine	325
niobe oil	325
niobium (columbium)	491
nitric acid	49, 430, 491
nitric ether	325
nitric oxide	491
1,1′,1′-nitrilotri-2-propanol	325
2,2′,2″-nitrilotriethanol	325
2-nitro-p-toluidine	325
p-nitroaniline	325
nitroanilines (o-, m-, p-)	49
nitroanisole	491
nitrobenzene	49, 325, 491, 497
nitrobenzene (0°C)	77

CHEMICAL	NFPA Doc. No.
nitrobenzol	325
1,3-nitrobenzotrifluoride	325
4-nitrobenzoyl chloride	491
nitrobiphenyl	325
nitrocellulose	325
m-nitrochlorobenzene	325
p-nitrochlorobenzene	325
nitrocyclohexane	325
nitroethane	49, 77, 325, 491, 497
nitroform, trinitromethane	491
nitrogen	491
nitrogen dioxide	491
nitrogen iodide, nitrogen triiodide	491
nitrogen peroxide, nitrogen tetroxide	491
nitrogen, refrigerated liquid	49
nitrogen tetroxide	430
nitrogen trichloride	491
nitrogen trifluoride	491
nitrogen trioxide	491
nitroglycerin	491
nitroglycerine	325
nitromethane	49, 77, 325, 491, 497
1-nitronaphthalene	325
p-nitrophenol	49
o-nitrophenol	491
o-nitrophenylacetic acid	491
1-nitropropane	77
2-nitropropane	77, 325
sec-nitropropane	325, 491
nitropropane	491, 497
nitropropanes	49
nitropyridone	499
nitrosamine	499
nitrosophenol	491
nitrosyl chloride	491
nitrosylsulfuric acid	491
m-nitrotoluene	77, 325
o-nitrotoluene	77, 325
p-nitrotoluene	325, 491
nitrotoluenes, liquid o-, m-, p- nitrotoluenes, solid o-, m-, p-	49
nitrous ether	325
nitrous oxide	491
nonadecane	325
nonane	325
n-nonane	497
nonene	325, 497
nonyl acetate	325
nonyl alcohol	325, 497
nonylbenzene	325
tert-nonyl mercaptan	325
nonylnaphthalene	325
nonylphenol	325
2,5-norbornadiene	325
nylon polymer	499
octadecane	325
octadecyl vinyl ether	325
α-octadecylene	325
octadecyltrichlorosilane	325
octanal	325
n-octane	325, 497
1-octanethiol	325
1-octanol	325
2-octanol	325
1-octene	325
octene	497
2-octene (mixed cis and trans isomers)	325
octyl acetate	325
octyl alcohol	77, 325
n-octyl alcohol	497
octyl chloride	325
octylamine	325
tert-octylamine	325
octylene glycol	325
tert-octyl mercaptan	325
p-octylphenyl salicylate	325
oil of mirbane	325
oil of wintergreen	325
oleic acid	325
oleo oil	325
olive oil	325
osmium	491
oxalic acid	491
oxalic acid (as dihydrate)	49
oxalic ether	325
oxalyl bromide	491
oxalyl chloride	491
oxammonium	325
oxirane	325
oxygen	491
oxygen (liquid)	491
oxygen, refrigerated liquid	49
para-oxy-benzaldehyde	499
ozone	491
palladium	491
palm butter	325
palm kernel oil	325
palm nut oil	325
palm oil	325
paraffin oil, mineral	325
paraffin wax	325
paraformaldehyde	49, 325, 491
paraldehyde	49, 325
paraphenylene diamine	499
paratertiary butyl benzoic acid	499
parathion	491
pea flour	499
peach pit shell	499

CHEMICAL	NFPA Doc. No.
peanut hull	499
peanut oil (cooking)	325
peat, sphagnum	499
pecan nut shell	499
pectin	499
pent-acetate	325
pentaborane	49, 325, 491
pentachlorethane	491
pentachlorodiphenyl	77
pentachloroethane	77
pentachlorophenol	49
1,3-pentadiene (mixture of cis and trans isomers)	325
pentaerythritol	499
1,2,3,4,5-pentamethylbenzene, 95%	325
pentamethylene dichloride	325
pentamethylene glycol	325
pentamethylene oxide	325
pentanal	325
n-pentane	77
2-pentane	77
pentane	325, 497
1,5-pentanediol	325
2,4-pentanedione	325
2,4-pentanedione peroxide	432
pentanoic acid	325
1-pentanol	325
2-pentanol	325
3-pentanol	325, 497
1-pentanol acetate	325
2-pentanol acetate	325
2-pentanone	325
3-pentanone	325, 497
pentaphen	325
pentapropionyl glucose	325
1-pentene	325, 497
2-pentene	497
1-pentene-cis	325
2-pentene-trans	325
2-pentyl acetate	497
pentyl propionate	325
pentylamine	325
pentyloxypentane	325
1-pentyne	325
peracetic acid (less than 40%)	49, 325
perchloric acid	49, 430, 491
perchloroethylene	325
perchloryl fluoride	491
perhydrophenanthrene	325
perilla oil	325
periodic acid	491
permonosulfuric acid (Caro's acid)	491
peroxyacetic acid	432, 491
petrin acrylate monomer	499
petroleum coke (more than 8% total entrapped volatiles)	499
petroleum, crude, sour	325
petroleum, crude, sweet	325
petroleum ether	325
petroleum pitch	325
petroleum resin	499
petroleum sulfonate	325
β-phellandrene	325
phenanthrene	325
phenethyl alcohol	325
o-phenetidine	325
p-phenetidine	325
phenetole	77, 325
phenol	77, 325, 491
phenol formaldehyde	499
phenol furfural	499
phenol, solid phenol, molten phenol solutions	49
phenol-formaldehyde resin	491
phenoxy ethyl alcohol	325
2-phenoxyethanol	325
n-(2-phenoxyethyl) aniline	325
β-phenoxyethyl chloride	325
phenyl acetate	325
phenyl bromide	325
phenyl carbinol	325
phenyl chloride	325
phenyl di-o-xenyl phosphate	325
phenyl didecyl phosphite	325
phenyl diglycol carbonate	325
phenyl isocyanate	491
phenyl isothiocyanate (25°C)	77
phenyl lithium	491
phenyl methyl ketone	325
phenyl trichloro silane	325
1-phenyl-2-butene	325
n-phenyl-n-ethylethanolamine	325
phenylacetaldehyde	325
phenylacetic acid	325
phenylamine	325
n-phenylaniline	325
phenylbenzene	325
phenylbetanaphthylamine	499
phenylcyclohexane	325
n-phenyldiethanolamine	325
phenyldiethylamine	325
o-phenylenediamine	325
phenylethane	325
n-phenylethanolamine	325
β-phenylethyl acetate	325
phenylethyl alcohol	325
phenylethylene	325
phenylhydrazine	325, 491, 497
phenylmercuric acetate	49

CHEMICAL	NFPA Doc. No.
phenylmethane	325
phenylmethylethanolamine	325
4-phenylmorpholine	325
phenylpentane	325
o-phenylphenol	325
phenylpropane	325
2-phenylpropane	325
phenylpropyl alcohol	325
phenylpropyl aldehyde	325
o-phenyltoluene	325
phorone	325
phosgene	49, 77, 491
phosphine	49, 325, 491
phosphoric acid	49
phosphorus	77, 491
phosphorus, amorphous	49
phosphorus oxychloride	49
phosphorus oxychloride (25°C)	77
phosphorus pentachloride	49, 491
phosphorus pentasulfide	49, 491
phosphorus pentoxide	491
phosphorus tribromide	49, 491
phosphorus trichloride	49, 491
phosphorus trifluoride	491
phosphorus, white, molten	49
phosphoryl chloride	491
phthalic acid	325, 491
phthalic anhydride	49, 325, 491, 499
phthalimide	499
m-phthalyl dichloride	325
2-picoline	325
4-picoline	325
picric acid	491
picric acid, wet, with not less than 10% water	49
pimelic ketone	325
pinane	325
pine oil	325
pine pitch	325
pine tar	325
pine tar oil	325
α-pinene	325
pinene (23°C)	77
piperazine	325, 49
piperidine	77, 325, 491
pitch, coal tar	499
pitch, petroleum	499
platinum	491
plutonium	491
pogy oil	325
polyamyl naphthalene	325
polycarbonate	499
polychlorinated biphenyl	49, 491
polydimethylsiloxane	491
polyethylene	491
polyethylene glycols	325
polyethylene, high pressure process	499
polyethylene, low pressure process	499
polyethylene terephthalate	499
polyethylene wax	499
polyisobutylene	491
polyoxyethylene lauryl ether	325
polypropylene	491
polypropylene glycols	325
polypropylene (no antioxidant)	499
polystyrene latex	499
polystyrene molding compound	499
polytetrafluoroethylene, Teflon (polytetrafluoroethylene)	491
polyurethane foam, fire retardant	499
polyurethane foam, no fire retardant	499
polyvinyl acetate	499
polyvinyl acetate/alcohol	499
polyvinyl alcohol	325
polyvinyl butyral	499
polyvinyl chloride-dioctyl phthalate	499
poppy seed oil	325
potassium	49, 491
potassium amide	491
potassium azide	491
potassium bicarbonate	491
potassium bromate	430, 491
potassium bromide	491
potassium tert-butoxide	491
potassium carbonate	491
potassium chlorate	430, 491
potassium chloride	491
potassium cyanide	49, 491
potassium dichloro-s-triazinetrione	49
potassium dichloro-s-triazinetrione (potassium dichloroiso-cyanurate)	430
potassium dichromate	430, 491
potassium ferricyanide	491
potassium ferrocyanide	491
potassium fluoride	491
potassium hydroxide	491
potassium hydroxide, solid potassium hydroxide, solution	49
potassium iodate	491
potassium iodide	491
potassium nitrate	491
potassium nitrite	491
potassium oxide	491
potassium percarbonate	430
potassium perchlorate	430, 491
potassium permanganate	430, 491
potassium peroxide	49, 430, 491
potassium persulfate	430, 491
potassium sulfate	491
potassium sulfide, anhydrous	49

CHEMICAL	NFPA Doc. No.
potassium superoxide	430, 491
potassium tetrahydroborate	491
potassium tetroxide	491
potassium xanthate	325
potassium-sodium alloys	49
potato starch, dextrinated	499
praseodymium	491
process gas 30% H2	497
propanal	325
propane	77, 325, 491, 497
propane in oxygen	77
1,3-propanediamine	325
1,2-propanediol	325
1,3-propanediol	325
1-propanethiol	491
1-propanol	325
2-propanol	325, 497
2-propanone	325
propanoyl chloride	325
propargyl alcohol	49, 325
propene	325
propenyl ethyl ether	325
2-propenylamine	325
β-propiolactone	325
propiolactone	491, 497
propionaldehyde	49, 77, 325, 497
propionic acid	49, 77, 325, 497
propionic anhydride	49, 325, 497
propionic nitrile	325
propionitrile	77
propionyl chloride	325
2-propybiphenyl	325
propyl acetate	325
n-propyl acetate	497
propyl acetate (i- or n-)	77
propyl alcohol	325, 491
n-propyl alcohol (25°C)	77
n-propyl bromide	325
n-propyl butyrate	325
propyl carbinol	325
n-propyl chloride	77
propyl chloride	325
propyl chlorothiolformate	325
n-propyl ether	325, 497
propyl formate	77, 325, 491
propyl formates (class 3, un 1281)	49
propyl methanol	325
n-propyl nitrate	49
propyl nitrate	325, 497
propyl propionate	325
propylamine	49, 325
propylbenzene	325
propylcyclohexane	325
propylcyclopentane	325
propylene	77, 325, 491, 497

CHEMICAL	NFPA Doc. No.
propylene aldehyde	325
propylene carbonate	325
propylene chlorohydrin	325
sec-propylene chlorohydrin	325
propylene dichloride	49, 325, 497
propylene glycol	325
propylene glycol acrylate	325
propylene glycol isopropyl ether	325
propylene glycol methyl ether	325
propylene glycol methyl ether acetate	325
propylene oxide	49, 77, 325, 491, 497
propylenediamine	325
propyltrichlorosilane	49, 325
2-propyn-1-ol	491
propyne	325, 491
prussic acid	325
pseudocumene	325
pyrethrum	499
pyridine	49, 77, 325, 491, 497
pyroxylin solution	325
pyrrole	325
pyrrolidine	325
2-pyrrolidone	325
quenching oil	325
quinoline	325, 491
quinoline (25°C)	77
range oil	325
rapeseed oil	325
rayon (viscose) flock	499
red dye intermediate	499
red oil	325
resorcinol	325
rhenium	491
rhodinol	325
rhodium	491
rice	499
rice bran	499
rice hull	499
ricinus oil	325
rosin, DK	499
rosin oil	325
rubber	491
rubber, crude, hard	499
rubber, synthetic, hard (33% S)	499
rubidium	491
rubidium chloride	491
rum	325
ruthenium	491
safflower meal	499
safrole	325
salicylaldehyde	325
salicylaldehyde (25°C)	77
salicylanilide	499
salicylic acid	325
samarium	491

CHEMICAL	NFPA Doc. No.
santalol	325
selenium	491
selenium oxychloride	491
sesame oil	325
sevin	499
shale, oil	499
shellac	499
signal oil	325
silane	49, 325, 491
silane, (4-aminobutyl)-diethoxymethyl	49
silica (silica dioxide)	491
silicon	491
silicon monoxide	491
silicon nitride	491
silicon tetrachloride	49, 77, 491
silicon tetrafluoride	49
silver	491
silver chloride	491
silver cyanide	491
silver fluoride	491
silver iodide	491
silver nitrate	491
silver oxide	491
silver perchlorate	491
silver peroxide	430
sodium	49
sodium acetate	491
sodium amide	491
sodium azide	491
sodium bicarbonate	491
sodium bisulfide	491
sodium bromate	430, 491
sodium bromide	491
sodium carbonate	491
sodium carbonate peroxide	430
sodium chlorate	430, 491
sodium chloride	49, 430, 491
sodium chlorite	491
sodium cyanide	49, 491
sodium dichloro-s-triazinetrione dihydrate	430
sodium dichloro-s-triazinetrione (sodium dichloroisocya-nurate)	430
sodium dichromate	430, 491
sodium fluoride	49
sodium hydride	49, 491
sodium hydrosulfite	49, 491
sodium hydroxide	491
sodium hydroxide, solid sodium hydroxide solution	49
sodium hypochlorite	491
sodium hypophosphite	491
sodium iodate	491
sodium iodide	491
sodium methoxide	491
sodium monoxide, sodium oxide	491
sodium nitrate	491
sodium perborate (anhydrous)	430
sodium perborate monohydrate	430
sodium perborate tetrahydrate	430
sodium percarbonate	430
sodium perchlorate	430, 491
sodium perchlorate monohydrate	430
sodium permanganate	430
sodium peroxide	49, 430
sodium peroxide, sodium superoxide	491
sodium persulfate	430
sodium phosphide	491
sodium polysulfide	491
sodium resinate	499
sodium silicate	491
sodium sulfate	491
sodium sulfide, anhydrous	49
sodium tetrahydroaluminate	491
sodium tetrahydroborate	491
sodium thiosulfate	491
sodium-potassium alloy	491
sorbic acid (copper sorbate or potash)	499
l-sorbose	499
soy bean oil	325
soy flour	499
soy protein	499
sperm oil no. 1	325
sperm oil no. 2	325
spindle oil	325
stannic bromide	491
stannic chloride	491
stannic chloride, anhydrous	49
stannic iodide	491
stannic oxide	491
stannous chloride	491
stannous oxide	491
stearic acid	325
stearic acid (80°C)	77
stearic acid, aluminum salt	499
stearic acid, zinc salt	499
stearyl alcohol	325
stibine	49, 491
stoddard solvent	325
straw oil	325
strontium chlorate	430, 491
strontium chloride	491
strontium iodide	491
strontium perchlorate	430
strontium peroxide	430
strontium phosphide	491
styrene	325, 497
styrene modified polyester-glass fiber	499

CHEMICAL	NFPA Doc. No.
styrene monomer	77, 491
styrene monomer, inhibited	49
styrene oxide	325
styrene-acrylonitrile (70-30)	499
styrene-butadiene latex (75% styrene)	499
styrene-maleic anhydride copolymer	499
succinonitrile	77, 325
sucrose	499
sugar, powdered	499
sulfamic acid	491
sulfate dihydrate 100 lb (45 kg) V	432
sulfolane	77, 325, 491
sulfonyl chloride (25°C)	77
sulfur	77, 325, 491, 499
sulfur chloride	49, 325
sulfur dichloride	325, 491
sulfur dioxide	491
sulfur dioxide, liquefied	49
sulfur hexafluoride	491
sulfur, molten	49
sulfur monochloride	491
sulfur trioxide	491
sulfuric acid	49, 491
sulfuric acid (25°C)	77
sulfuryl chloride	49, 491
sweet oil	325
sylvan	325
tallow	325
tallow oil	325
tannic acid	325
tantalum	499
tantalum pentoxide	491
tartaric acid	491
tartaric acid (d, l)	325
tellurium	491
tellurium diethyl	491
terbium	491
terephthalic acid	325, 499
terephthaloyl chloride	325
o-terphenyl	325
m-terphenyl	325
terpineol	325
terpinyl acetate	325
tetraamylbenzene	325
tetrabromoethane	49
1,1,2,2-tetrabromoethane	325
tetrachlorobenzene	325
1,2,4,5-tetrachlorobenzene	325
tetrachlorobenzene	491
tetrachloroethane	491
tetrachloroethylene	49, 491
tetradecane	325
tetradecanol	325
1-tetradecene	325

CHEMICAL	NFPA Doc. No.
tert-tetradecyl mercaptan	325
tetraethoxypropane	325
tetra(2-ethylbutyl) silicate	325
tetra(2-ethylhexyl) silicate	325
tetraethyl lead	325
tetraethyl orthosilicate	325
tetraethylene glycol	325
tetraethylene glycol dibutyl ether	325
tetraethylene glycol dimethyl ether	325
tetraethylene pentamine	77, 325
tetrafluoroethylene	325, 491
tetrafluoroethylene, inhibited	49
tetrafluoromethane	491
tetraglycol dichloride	325
1,2,3,6-tetrahydrobenzaldehyde	325
endo-tetrahydrodicyclopentadiene	325
tetrahydrofuran	49, 77, 325, 491, 497
tetrahydrofurfuryl alcohol	325
tetrahydrofurfuryl oleate	325
tetrahydronaphthalene	325, 497
tetrahydropyran	77, 325
tetrahydropyran-2-methanol	325
tetrahydropyrrole	325
tetraiodoethylene	491
tetralin	325
1,1,3,3-tetramethoxypropane	325
tetramethoxysilane	49
tetramethyl lead	325, 497
tetramethyl tin	325
1,2,3,5-tetramethylbenzene, 85.5%	325
1,2,3,4-tetramethylbenzene, 95%	325
1,2,4,5-tetramethylbenzene, 95%	325
tetramethylene	325
tetramethylene glycol	325
tetramethylene oxide	325
2,2,3,3-tetramethylpentane	325
2,2,3,4-tetramethylpentane	325
tetramethylsilicane	491
tetramethylurea	77
tetranitromethane	430, 491
tetraphenyl tin	325
tetrapropionyl glucosyl propionate	325
tetryl	491
thallic oxide	491
thallium	491
thallium chlorate	430
thallous bromide	491
thallous chloride	491
thialdine	325
2,2-thiodiethanol	325
thiodiethylene glycol	325
thiodiglycol	325, 491
thionyl chloride	49, 491
thiophene	77, 325, 491
thiourea	491

CHEMICAL	NFPA Doc. No.
1,4-thioxane	325
thorium	491, 499
thulium	491
tin	491, 499
titanium	491
titanium, 99% TI	499
titanium carbide	491
titanium dichloride	491
titanium disulfide	491
titanium dioxide	491
titanium hydride	499
titanium tetrachloride	49, 491
toluene	49, 77, 325, 491, 497
toluene diisocyanate	49
toluene-2,4-diisocyanate	325
p-toluenesulfonic acid	325
toluhydroquinone	325
toluidine	491
m-toluidine	77, 325
o-toluidine	49
p-toluidine	49, 77
toluol	325
m-tolydiethanolamine	325
tolyl chloride	491
o-tolyl p-toluene sulfonate	325
o-tolyl phosphate	325
2,4-tolylene diisocyanate	325
transformer oil	325
transil oil	325
tri-n-butyl borate	325
tri-o-cresyl phosphate	325
triacetin	325
triamyl borate	325
triamylbenzene	325
tributyl citrate	325
tributyl phosphate	325
tributyl phosphite	325
tributylamine	49, 325
tributylphosphine	325, 491
trichloro-s-triazinetrione (trichloroisocyanuric) (acid all forms)	430
trichloroacetic acid (25°C)	77
1,2,4-trichlorobenzene	77, 325
1,1,1-trichloroethane	49
1,1,2-trichloroethane	49, 77, 325
1-trichloroethane	491
trichloroethylene	49, 77, 325, 491
trichloroethysilane	491
trichlorofluoromethane	491
trichloroisocyanuric acid, dry	49
trichloromelamine	491
trichloromethylsilane	491
1,2,3-trichloropropane	325
trichlorosilane	49, 77, 325
trichlorotriethyldialuminum	491
1,2-trichlorotrifluoroethane	491
trichlorovinylsilane	491
tridecanal	491
tridecanol	325
2-tridecanone	325
n-tridecene	497
tridecyl acrylate	325
tridecyl alcohol	325
tridecyl phosphite	325
triethanolamine	325
triethylarsine	491
1,1,3-triethoxyhexane	325
triethyl citrate	325
triethyl phosphate	325
triethylaluminum	49, 325, 491
triethylamine	49, 77, 325, 497
1,2,4-triethylbenzene	325
triethylbenzene	497
triethylborane	325, 491
triethylene glycol	77, 325
triethylene glycol diacetate	325
triethylene glycol dimethyl ether	325
triethylene glycol ethyl ether	325
triethylene glycol methyl ether	325
triethylene glycol monobutyl ether	325
triethylenetetramine	49, 77, 325
trifluorochloroethylene	325
triglycol dichloride	325
trihexyl phosphite	325
triisobutyl borate	325
triisobutylaluminum	49, 325, 491
triisopropanolamine	325
triisopropyl borate	325
triisopropylbenzene	325
trilauryl trithiophosphite	325
trimanganese tetroxide	491
trimethoxysilane	49
trimethyl borate	325
2,2,3-trimethyl butane	77
trimethyl carbinol	325
trimethyl phosphite	325, 491
2,3,3-trimethyl-1-butene	325
3,3,5-trimethyl-1-cyclohexanol	325
2,3,4-trimethyl-1-pentene	325
2,4,4-trimethyl-1-pentene	325
2,2,4-trimethyl-1,3-pentanediol	325
2,2,4-trimethyl-1,3-pentanediol diisobutyrate	325
2,2,4-trimethyl-1,3-pentanediol isobutyrate	325
2,4,4-trimethyl-2-pentene	325
3,4,4-trimethyl-2-pentene	325
2,6,8-trimethyl-4-nonanol	325
2,6,8-trimethyl-4-nonanone	325

CHEMICAL	NFPA Doc. No.
trimethylaluminum	325, 491
trimethylamine	49, 77, 325
trimethylarsine	491
1,2,3-trimethylbenzene	325
1,2,4-trimethylbenzene	325
1,3,5-trimethylbenzene	325
1,2,3-trimethylbenzene, 90.5%	325
2,2,3-trimethylbutane	325, 497
2,2,4-trimethylbutane	497
trimethylchlorosilane	325
1,3,5-trimethylcyclohexane	325
trimethylcyclohexanol	325
trimethylene	325
trimethylene glycol	325
trimethylenediamine	325
trimethylethylene	325
trimethylgallium	491
2,5,5-trimethylheptane	325
2,2,5-trimethylhexane	325
3,5,5-trimethylhexanol	325
trimethylolpropane triacrylate	325
2,2,3-trimethylpentane	325
2,2,4-trimethylpentane	325
2,3,3-trimethylpentane	325, 497
2,2,4-trimethylpentanediol isobutyrate benzoate	325
trimethylphosphine	491
trimethylstibine	491
trioctyl phosphite	325
trioxane	325
tripentylamine	49, 325
triphenyl phosphate	325
triphenyl phosphite	325
triphenylmethane	325
triphenylphosphine	325
triphenylphosphorus	325
tripropyl aluminum	325, 491
tripropylamine	325, 497
tripropylene	325
tripropylene glycol	325
tripropylene glycol methyl ether	325
tris(2-ethylhexyl) phosphite	325
trithiobisdimethylthio-formamide	499
tung, kernels, oil-free	499
tung oil	325
tungsten	491
tungsten carbide	491
tungsten trioxide	491
turbine oil	325
turbo fuels	325
turkey red oil	325
turpentine	77, 325, 497
ultrasene	325
undecane	325
undecanol	325

CHEMICAL	NFPA Doc. No.
n-undecene	497
uranium dicarbide	491
uranium dioxide	491
urea	491
urea formaldehyde molding compound	499
urea formaldehyde-phenol formaldehyde	499
urea hydrogen peroxide	430
valeraldehyde	325, 497
valeric acid	325
vanadium	491, 499
vanadium pentoxide	491
vanadium sesquioxide	491
vanadium tetrachloride	49
vanillin	491
vinyl 2-chloroethyl ether	325
vinyl 2-ethylhexoate	325
vinyl 2-ethylhexyl ether	325
vinyl 2-methoxyethyl ether	325
vinyl acetate	77, 325, 491, 497
vinyl acetate, inhibited	49
vinyl acetylene	49, 77, 325
vinyl allyl ether	325
vinyl bromide	325
vinyl butyl ether	325
vinyl butyrate	325
vinyl chloride	325, 491, 497
vinyl chloride, inhibited	49
vinyl chloride-acrylonitrile copolymer	499
vinyl crotonate	325
vinyl cyanide	325
4-vinyl cyclohexene	325
vinyl ether	49, 325
vinyl ethyl alcohol	325
vinyl ethyl ether	325
vinyl fluoride	325
vinyl isobutyl ether	325
vinyl isooctyl ether	325
vinyl isopropyl ether	325
vinyl methyl ether	325
vinyl octadecyl ether	325
vinyl propionate	325
vinyl toluene	325, 497
vinyl toluene, inhibited mixed isomers	49
vinyl toluene-acrylonitrile butadiene	499
vinyl trichlorosilane	325
vinyl-2-pyrrolidone	325
2-vinyl-5-ethylpyridine	325
vinylaceto-β-lactone	325
vinylbenzene	325
vinylbenzylchloride	325
vinylethylene oxide	325

CHEMICAL	NFPA Doc. No.
vinylidene chloride	325, 491, 497
vinylidene chloride, inhibited	49
vinylidene fluoride	325
1-vinylpyrrolidone	325
vinyltrimethoxysilane (<2% methanol)	77
violet 200 dye	499
vitamin b1, mononitrate	499
vitamin c	499
viton a	491
walnut shell, black	499
water (air distilled)	77
water (extremely pure)	77
water gas	325
wax, microcrystalline	325
wax, ozocerite	325
wax, paraffin	325
whale oil	325
wheat	499
wheat flour	499
wheat gluten, gum	499
wheat starch	499
wheat straw	499
whiskey	325
white tar	325
wines	325
wood alcohol	325
wood flour	499
wood tar oil	325
woodbark, ground	499

CHEMICAL	NFPA Doc. No.
wool grease	325
xylene	77, 497
m-xylene	325
o-xylene	325
p-xylene	325
xylidine	497
o-xylidine	325
xylidines, solid or solution	49
o-xylol	325
yeast, torula	499
zinc	491
zinc bromate	430
zinc chlorate	430, 491
zinc chloride	491
zinc cyanide	49, 491
zinc diethyl	325
zinc fluoride	491
zinc iodide	491
zinc nitrate	491
zinc oxide	491
zinc permanganate	430
zinc peroxide	430, 491
zinc phosphide	49, 491
zinc stearate	325
zinc sulfide	491
zirconium	499
zirconium carbide	491
zirconium dihydride	491
zirconium hydride	499
zirconium tetrachloride	49, 491

Synonym Cross Reference

SYNONYM	CHEMICAL	NFPA Doc. No.
abalyn	methyl abietate	325
acetaldehydediethylacetal	acetal	325
acetamide	acetanilide	49
acetic acid anhydride	acetic anhydride	49
acetic acid methyl ester	methyl acetate	325
acetic acid, n-propyl ester	propyl acetate	325
acetic aldehyde	acetaldehyde	49
acetic aldehyde	acetaldehyde	325
p-acetaldehyde	paraldehyde	49
acetic chloride	acetyl chloride	49
acetic ester	ethyl acetate	325
acetoacetic acid, ethyl ester	ethyl acetoacetate	325
o-acetoacetotoluidide	acetoacet-ortho-toluidide	325
acetoethylamide	n-ethylacetamide	325
acetone-free, commercial	diacetone alcohol	325
p-acetotoluene	p-methyl acetophenone	325
acetyl acetone	2,4-pentanedione	325
acetyl ethylene	methyl vinyl ketone	49
acetyl hydroperoxide	peracetic acid (less than 40%)	49
acetyl ketene	diketene, inhibited	49
acetyl oxide	acetic anhydride	49
acetylene dichloride	dichloroethylene	49
acetylene tetrabromide	tetrabromoethane; 1,1,2,2-tetrabromoethane	49; 325
acetylenogen	calcium carbide	49
acetylphenol	phenyl acetate	325
acquinite	chloropicrin	49
acraldehyde	acrolein, inhibited	49
acroleic acid	acrylic acid, inhibited	49
acrylaldehyde	acrolein, inhibited	49
acrylic acid, methyl ester	methyl acrylate, inhibited	49
acrylic acid, n-butyl ester	butylacrylate	49
acrylic aldehyde	acrolein, inhibited; acrolein	49; 325
acrylic amide	acrylamide	49
adipic acid dinitrile	adiponitrile	325
adipic ketone	cyclopentanone	325
adipyl chloride	adipoyl chloride	325
adipyldinitrile	adiponitrile	325
aldehyde collidine	2-methyl-5-ethylpyridine	49
aldehydine	2-methyl-5-ethylpyridine	49, 325
aldol ether	3-methoxybutyraldehyde	325
alkane	dodecyl benzene	325
allyl chlorocarbonate	allyl chloroformate	49, 325
allyl diglycol carbonate	diethylene glycol bis(allylcarbonate)	325
allyl hexanoate	allyl caproate	325
allyl isothiocyanate	mustard oil	325
allyl trichloride	1,2,3-trichloropropane	325
allyl vinyl ether	vinyl allyl ether	325
4-allyl-1,2-dimethoxybenzene	methyl eugenol	325
4-allyl-1,2-methylene-dioxybenzene	safrole	325
4-allyl veratrole	methyl eugenol	325
allylene	propyne	325
allylpropenyl	1,4-hexadiene	325

SYNONYM	CHEMICAL	NFPA Doc. No.
alpha-chloroallyl chloride	dichloropropene	49
alpha-crotonic acid	crotonic acid	49
alpha-methylcrylic acid	methacrylic acid, inhibited	49
aluminum lithium hydride	lithium aluminum hydride	49
aluminum monophosphide	aluminum phosphide	49
aluminum triethyl	triethylaluminum	49
aluminum, tris (2-methylpropyl)	triisobutylaluminum	49
amenoethylene	ethylenimine, inhibited	49
1-amino butane	butylamine	325
amino cyclohexane, hexahydroaniline	cyclohexylamine	325
1-amino-3,4-dichlorobenzene	dichloroanilines, solid or liquid	49
1-amino-4-ethoxybenzene	p-phenetidine	325
m-amino-α-methylbenzyl alcohol	(m-aminophenyl) methyl carbinol	325
2-amino-4-methylpentane	1,3-dimethylbutylamine	325
3-amino-propene	allylamine	49
aminobenzene	aniline	49
aminobenzene	aniline	325
2-aminobiphenyl	2-biphenylamine	325
1-aminobutane	n-butylamine	49
(4-aminobutyl)diethoxymethyl-silane	silane, (4-aminobutyl)-diethoxymethyl	49
aminobutylmethyl diethoxysilane	silane, (4-aminobutyl)-diethoxymethyl	49
aminocyclohexane	cyclohexylamine	49
1-aminodecane	decylamine	325
aminoethane	ethylamine	49
	ethylamine, 70%	325
2-aminoethanol	ethanolamine or ethanolamine solutions	49
2-aminoethanol	ethanolamine	325
aminoethylethanolamine	2-aminoethylethanolamine	325
β-aminoethyl alcohol	ethanolamine or ethanolamine solutions	49
n-aminoethylpiperazine	1-(2-aminoethyl)piperazine	325
1-aminoheptane	heptylamine	325
α-aminoisopropyl alcohol	1-amino-2-propanol	325
4-aminonitro-benzene	nitroanilines (o-, m-, p-)	49
p-aminonitrobenzene	nitroanilines (o-, m-, p-)	49
1-aminooctane	octylamine	325
2-aminopentane	sec-amylamine	325
o-amino-phenetole	o-phenetidine	325
p-aminophenetole	p-phenetidine	325
2-aminopropane	isopropylamine	49
1-aminopropane	propylamine	49
3-aminopropylene	allylamine	49
2-aminotoluene	o-toluidine	49
4-aminotoluene	p-toluidine	49
ammonium bichromate	ammonium dichromate	49
ammonium salt	ammonium nitrate	49
amoxybenzene	amyl phenyl ether	325
tert-n-amyl alcohol	3-pentanol	325
amyl carbinol	hexyl alcohol	325
n-amyl mercaptan	amyl mercaptans	49
n-amyl nitrate	amyl nitrate	325
amyl nitrite	isoamyl nitrite	325
p-tert-amyl phenol	pentaphen	325
amyl phthalate	diamyl phthalate	325

SYNONYM	CHEMICAL	NFPA Doc. No.
amylene	1-pentene	325
amylene chloride	1,5-dichloropentane	325
anesthetic ether	diethyl ether	49
anhydrous aluminum chloride	aluminum chloride, anhydrous	49
anhydrous hydrofluoric acid	hydrogen fluoride, anhydrous	49
2-anilinoethanol	n-phenylethanolamine	325
β-anilinoethanol ethoxyaniline	n-phenylethanolamine	325
o-anisaldehyde	o-methoxybenzaldehyde	325
anol	cyclohexanol	325
antimonal sulfide	antimony sulfide	49
antimony chloride	antimony pentachloride, liquid	49
antimony hydride	stibine	49
antimony pentasulfide	antimony sulfide	49
antimony perchloride	antimony pentachloride, liquid	49
antimony red	antimony sulfide	49
antimony (V) fluoride	antimony pentafluoride	49
aquafortis	nitric acid	49
arheol	santalol	325
arsenic anhydride	arsenic pentoxide	49
arsenic butter	arsenic trichloride	49
arsenic chloride	arsenic trichloride	49
arsenic (III) sulfide	arsenic trisulfide	49
arsenic pentaoxide	arsenic pentoxide	49
arsenic trihydride	arsine	49
arsenic (V) oxide	arsenic pentoxide	49
arsenolite	arsenic trioxide	49
arsenous acid anhydride	arsenic trioxide	49
arsenous chloride	arsenic trichloride	49
arsenous oxide, white arsenic	arsenic trioxide	49
arsenous sulfide	arsenic trisulfide	49
arsenous trichloride	arsenic trichloride	49
artificial almond oil	benzaldehyde	325
artificial essential oil of almond	benzaldehyde	49
azabenzene	pyridine	49
azacyclohexane	piperidine	49
azacyclopropane	ethylenimine, inhibited	49
azine	pyridine	49
azirane	ethylenimine, inhibited	49
aziridine	ethylenimine, inhibited	49
aziridine	ethylenimine	325
azole	pyrrole	325
azotic acid	nitric acid	49
banana oil	isoamyl acetate	325
barium chlorate anhydrous	barium chlorate	49
battery acid	sulfuric acid	49
BCME	dichlorodimethyl ether, symmetrical	49
benzenamine	aniline	49
benzene	benzotrichloride	49
benzene, 1-methylethyl-	cumene	49
benzene, 1,2-dichloro	o-dichlorobenzene	49
benzene carbonyl chloride	benzoyl chloride	325
benzene chloride	chlorobenzene	49
benzene (trifluoromethyl)	benzotrifluoride	49
benzenecarbonol	benzaldehyde	325
benzenecarbonyl chloride	benzoyl chloride	49

SYNONYM	CHEMICAL	NFPA Doc. No.
1,4-benzenedicarbonyl chloride	terephthaloyl chloride	325
1,4-benzenedicarboxylic acid	terephthalic acid	325
1,3-benzenediol	resorcinol	325
benzenyl trichloride	benzotrichloride	49
benzine	petroleum ether	325
benzoic aldehyde	benzaldehyde	49
benzol	benzene	49
benzol	benzene	325
benzyl carbinol	phenethyl alcohol	325
benzyl ether	dibenzyl ether	325
benzyl salicylate	benzyl salicilate	325
2-benzyloxyethanol	glycol benzyl ether	325
bergamol	lynalyl acetate, synthetic	325
bertholite	chlorine	49
beryllium	beryllium, powder (often from machining operations)	49
beryllium dust	beryllium, powder (often from machining operations)	49
beta-methacrylic acid	crotonic acid	49
beta-methylacrolein	crotonaldehyde, stabilized	49
betula oil	methyl salicylate	325
bis(2-aminoethyl)amine	diethylenetriamine	49
n,n′-bis(2-aminotheyl) 1,2-ethane-diamine	triethylenetetramine	49
bis(2-chloroethyl) ether	2,2-dichlorodiethyl ether	49
bis[2-(ethoxyethoxy)ethyl] phthalate	diethylene glycol ethyl ether phthalate	325
bis-(chloromethyl) ether	dichlorodimethyl ether, symmetrical	49
bis(2-chloro-1-methylethyl) ether	dichloroisopropyl ether	325
bis(β-chloroisopropyl) ether	dichloroisopropyl ether	325
bis(beta-hydroxyethyl) sulfide	thiodiglycol	325
bis(β-methylpropyl) amine	diisobutylamine	325
bis-CME	dichlorodimethyl ether, symmetrical	49
bis(2-ethylhexyl) adipate	dioctyl adipate	325
bis(2-ethylhexyl) azelate	dioctyl azelate	325
bis(2-ethylhexyl) phthalate	dioctyl phthalate	325
bis(2-methoxyethyl) phthalate	dimethoxyethyl phthalate	325
1,3-bis(ethylamino) butane	n,n-diethyl-1,3-butanediamine	325
bis(trichlorophenyl) ether	hexachlorodiphenyl oxide	325
borneo camphor, l-borneol, d-borneol	borneol	325
boroethane	diborane	49
borofluoric acid	fluoboric acid	49
boron fluoride	boron trifluoride	49
boron hydride	diborane	49
brazil wax	carnauba wax	325
brimstone	sulfur, molten	49
bromallylene	allyl bromide	49
bromine cyanide	cyanogen bromide	49
1-bromo butane	butyl bromide	325
3-bromo-1-propene	allyl bromide	49
3-bromo-1-propyne	3-bromopropyne	49
1-bromo-2-butene	1-crotyl bromide	325
bromoethane	ethyl bromide	325
sym-dibromoethane	ethylene dibromide	49
bromomethane	methyl bromide	49, 325
1-bromopentane	amyl bromide	325
1-bromopropane	n-propyl bromide	325

SYNONYM	CHEMICAL	NFPA Doc. No.
3-bromopropene	allyl bromide	325
3-bromopropylene	allyl bromide	49
bunker oil bunker C	fuel oil no. 6	325
1,3-butadiene	butadienes, inhibited	49
butanal	butyraldehyde	49, 325
butanal oxime	butyraldoxime	325
1-butanamine	n-butylamine	49
butane nitrile	butyronitrile	49
1,2-butanediol	α-butylene glycol	325
butanoic acid	butyric acid	49
2-butanol	sec-butyl alcohol	325
1-butanol	butyl alcohol	325
2-butanone	methyl ethyl ketone	325
3-buten-1-ol	vinyl ethyl alcohol	325
2-buten-1-ol	crotonyl alcohol	325
3-buten-2-one	methyl vinyl ketone	49
1-buten-3-yne	vinyl acetylene	49
1-buten-3-yne	vinyl acetylene	325
2-butenal	crotonaldehyde, stabilized	49
2-butenal	crotonaldehyde	325
2-butene-1,4-diol	butenediol	325
3-butene-beta-lactone	diketene, inhibited	49
cis-butenedioic anhydride	maleic anhydride	49
2-butenenitrile	crotononitrile	325
2-butenoic acid	crotonic acid	49
Δ^3-2-butenone	methyl vinyl ketone	49
butoxybenzene	butyl phenyl ether	325
1-butoxybutane, butyl ether	dibutyl ether	325
butoxy diethylene glycol	diethylene glycol monobutyl ether	325
2-butoxyethanol ethylene glycol	ethylene glycol monobutyl ether	325
2-butoxyethanol	ethylene glycol n-butyl ether	325
n-butyl ether butyl cellosolve	ethylene glycol monobutyl ether	325
butoxyethyl diglycol carbonate	diethylene glycol bis(2-butyoxyethyl carbonate)	325
butoxyl	3-methoxybutyl acetate	325
butter of antimony	antimony pentachloride, liquid	49
n-butyl acrylate	butylacrylate	49
butyl aldehyde	butyraldehyde	49
butyl benzyl phthalate	benzyl butyl phthalate	325
butyl cellosolve	ethylene glycol n-butyl ether	325
n-butyl-1-butanamine	di-n-butylamine	49
butyl diglycol carbonate	diethylene glycol bis(butyl carbonate)	325
butyl ethanedioate	butyl oxalate	325
n-butyl ester of acrylic acid	butylacrylate	49
n-butyl ether	dibutyl ethers	49
butyl ethyl ether	ethyl butyl ether	325
butyl ethylene	1-hexene	325
butyl isocyanate	n-butyl isocyanate	325
butyl mercaptan	1-butanethiol	325
sec-butyl mercaptan	2-butanethiol	325
tert-butyl mercaptan	2-methyl-2-propanethiol	325
butyl methanoate	butyl formate	325
butyl phosphate	tributyl phosphate	325
n-butyl-2-propenoate	butylacrylate	49
butyl sebacate	dibutyl sebacate	325

SYNONYM	CHEMICAL	NFPA Doc. No.
butyl vinyl ether	vinyl butyl ether	325
butylamine	n-butylamine	49
butylcarbamic acid, ethyl ester	n-butylurethane	325
α-butylene	1-butene	325
β-butylene	2-butene-trans	325
2-butylene dichloride	1,4-dichlorobutane	49
β-butylene glycol	1,3-butanediol	325
γ-butylene	2-methylpropene	325
1,2-butylene oxide	1,2-butylene oxide, stabilized	49
butylethanoate n-butyl acetate	butyl acetate	325
butylethylacetaldehyde	2-ethylhexanal	325
butyric acid, ethyl ester	ethyl butyrate	325
butyric acid nitrile	butyronitrile	49
butyric aldehyde	butyraldehyde	49, 325
butyric ester	ethyl butyrate	325
butyrin	glyceryl tributyrate	325
2,2-(tert-butylimino) diethanol	tert-butyldiethanolamine	325
butyrone	4-heptanone	325
CAA	cyanoacetic acid	49
cal hypo	calcium hypochlorite, dry or calcium hypochlorite, mixtures, dry	49
calcia	calcium oxide	49
calcium acetylide	calcium carbide	49
calcyanide	calcium cyanide	49
caproaldehyde	hexanal	325
caprylic aldehyde	caprylaldehyde	325
carbazotic acid	picric acid, wet, with not less than 10% water	49
carbitol phthalate	diethylene glycol ethyl ether phthalate	325
carbolic acid	phenol, solid phenol, molten phenol solutions	49, 325
carbon bisulfide	carbon disulfide	49, 325
carbon oxychloride	phosgene	49
carbon tet	carbon tetrachloride	49
carbonic acid, dimethyl ester	dimethylcarbonate	49
carbonic oxide	carbon monoxide	49
carbonochloridic acid, ethyl ester	ethyl chloroformate	49
carbonyl chloride	phosgene	49
carbonyl sulfide	carbon oxysulfide	325
castor oil, sulfated	turkey red oil	325
caustic potash	potassium hydroxide, solid potassium hydroxide, solution	49
caustic soda	sodium hydroxide, solid sodium hydroxide solution	49
cellosolve acetate	2-ethoxyethyl acetate	325
cellulose nitrate	nitrocellulose	325
cetane	hexadecane	325
chamber acid	sulfuric acid	49
CHDM	1,4-cyclohexane dimethanol	325
china wood oil	tung oil	325
chloracetyl chloride	chloroacetyl chloride	49
chlorallylene	allyl chloride	49
chlorex 2,2′-dichloroethyl ether	bis(2-chloroethyl) ether	325
chloride of phosphorus	phosphorus trichloride	49
chlorinated biphenyls	polychlorinated biphenyls	49
2-chloro-α,α,α-trifluoro-5-nitrotoluene	2-chloro-5-nitrobenzotrifluoride	325

SYNONYM	CHEMICAL	NFPA Doc. No.
o-chloro-α,α,α-trifluorotoluene	o-chlorobenzotrifluoride	325
3-chloro-1-propene	allyl chloride	49
1-chloro-1-propene	1-chloropropylene	325
1-chloro-2-butene	1-crotyl chloride	325
1-chloro-1,1-difluoroethane	difluoro-1-chloroethane	325
1-chloro-2-hydroxybenzene	chlorophenols, liquid	49
2-chloro-2-methyl-propane	tert-butyl chloride	325
2-chloro-2-methylbutane	tert-amyl chloride	325
1-chloro-2,3-epoxy propane	epichlorohydrin	49
1-chloro-2,4-dinitrobenzene	chlorodinitrobenzenes	49
1-chloro-3-methylbutane	isoamyl chloride	325
1-chloro-3-methylpropane	isobutyl chloride	325
1-chloro-3-nitrobenzene	chloronitrobenzenes; propyl formates (class 3, un 1281)	49
1-chloro-4-hydroxybenzene	chlorophenols, solid	49
1-chloro-4-nitrobenzene	chloronitrobenzenes; propyl formates (class 3, un 1281); p-nitrochlorobenzene	49, 325
chloro-o-nitrobenzene	chloronitrobenzenes; propyl formates (class 3, un 1281)	49
chlorobenzol	chlorobenzene	49, 325
chlorobiphenyls	polychlorinated biphenyls	49
chlorobutadiene	2-chloro-1,3-butadiene	325
1-chlorobutane	butyl chloride	325
2-chlorobutane	sec-butyl chloride	325
chlorocyclohexane	cyclohexyl chloride	325
chlorodiethylaluminum	diethylaluminum chloride	49, 325
chlorodinitrobenzene	dinitrochlorobenzene	325
chloroethane	1,1,1-trichloroethane	49
chloroethane	ethyl chloride	325
chloroethanoic acid	chloroacetic acid, solid	49
2-chloroethanol	ethylene chlorohydrin	49
chloroethene	vinyl chloride, inhibited	49
2-chloroethyl alcohol	ethylene chlorohydrin	49
2-chloroethyl alcohol	2-chloroethanol	325
2-chloroethyl vinyl ether	vinyl 2-chloroethyl ether	325
chloroethylene	vinyl chloride, inhibited; vinyl chloride	49, 325
chloroformic acid ethyl ester	ethyl chloroformate	49
chloroformyl chloride	phosgene	49
chlorohydrin	ethylene chlorohydrin	49
chloroisocyanuric acid	monochloro-s- triazinetrione acid	49
chloroisopropyl alcohol	1-chloro-2-propanol	325
chloromethane	methyl chloride	325
chloromethoxymethane	methylchloromethyl ether	49
chloromethyl methyl ether	methylchloromethyl ether	49
chloromethyloxirane	epichlorohydrin	49
2-(chloro-methyl)oxirane	epichlorohydrin	49
chloronitrobenzene (o-, m-, p-)	chloronitrobenzenes; propyl formates (class 3, un 1281)	49
1-chloropentane	amyl chloride	325
o-chlorophenol	chlorophenols, liquid	49
p-chlorophenol	chlorophenols, solid	49
2-chlorophenol	chlorophenols, liquid	49
4-chlorophenol	chlorophenols, solid	49
chloroprene	2-chloro-1,3-butadiene	325
2-chloropropane	isopropyl chloride	325

SYNONYM	CHEMICAL	NFPA Doc. No.
1-chloropropane	propyl chloride	325
2-chloropropene	2-chloropropylene	325
3-chloropropene	allyl chloride	325
2-chloropropionic acid	α-chloropropionic acid	325
β-chloropropyl alcohol	2-chloro-1-propanol	325
β-chloropropylene	2-chloropropylene	325
chloropropylene oxide	epichlorohydrin	49
3-chloropropylene oxide, γ-chloropropylene oxide	epichlorohydrin	325
chlorosilanes	dichlorosilane	49
chlorosulfuric acid	chlorosulfonic acid	49
α-chlorotoluene	benzyl chloride	325
chlorotrifluoroethylene	trifluorochloroethylene	325
chromic anhydride	chromic acid, solid	49
chromic oxychloride	chromium oxychloride	49
chromium chloride	chromic chloride	49
chromium dioxychloride	chromium oxychloride	49
chromium trichloride	chromic chloride	49
chromium trioxide	chromic acid, solid	49
chromium (VI) oxide	chromic acid, solid	49
chromyl chloride	chromium oxychloride	49
cianurina	mercury cyanide	49
cinene	dipentene	325
cinnamene	styrene monomer, inhibited	49
citronellal hydrate	hydroxycitronellal	325
CMME	methylchloromethyl ether	49
cobalt naphthenate	cobalt naphtha	325
colamine	ethanolamine or ethanolamine solutions	49
cologne spirits	ethyl alcohol	325
columbian spirits	methyl alcohol	325
colza oil	rapeseed oil	325
cooking	corn oil	325
cooking	cottonseed oil	325
p-cresyl methyl ether	methyl p-cresol	325
p-methoxy toluene	methyl p-cresol	325
crotonic aldehyde	crotonaldehyde	325
o-, m-, p- cresylic acid	cresols (o-, m-, p-)	49
crotonylene	2-butyne	325
crotyl alcohol	crotonyl alcohol	325
cumol	cumene	49
cumol	cumene	325
cyanide of sodium	sodium cyanide	49
cyanoethylene	acrylonitrile, inhibited	49
cyanogas	calcium cyanide	49
cyanomethane	acetonitrile	49
α-cyclocitrylideneacetone	α-ionone	325
β-cyclocitrylideneacetone	β-ionone	325
3-cyclohexene-1-carboxaldehyde	1,2,3,6-tetrahydrobenzaldehyde	325
1-cyclohexylbutane	butylcyclohexane	325
2-cyclohexylbutane	sec-butylcyclohexane	325
n-cyclohexylcyclohexanamine	dicyclohexylamine	49
cyclohexylmercaptan	cyclohexanethiol	325
cyclohexylmethane	methylcyclohexane	325
cyclopentimine	piperidine	49
1-cyclopentylpropane	propylcyclopentane	325

SYNONYM	CHEMICAL	NFPA Doc. No.
cypentil	piperidine	49
DCA	dichloroanilines, solid or liquid	49
DCB	1,4-dichlorobutane	49
DCEE	2,2-dichlorodiethyl ether	49
DCS	dichlorosilane	49
DDVP	dichlorvos	325
DEAE	diethylethanolamine	49
decaborane(14)	decaborane	49
decaboron tetra-decahydride	decaborane	49
decalin	decahydronaphthalene	325
decanedioic dibutyl ester butyl sebacate	dibutyl sebacate	325
decyl alcohol	decanol	325
decyl ether	didecyl ether	325
DETA	diethylenetriamine	49
detergent alkylate	dodecyl benzene	325
DHA	dehydroacetic acid	325
di-(2-chloroethyl) formal 2,2-dichloroethyl formal	bis(2-chloroethyl) formal	325
di-methylene oxide	ethylene oxide	49
di-n-pentylamine	di-n-amylamine	49
di(2-ethylhexyl) adipate	dioctyl adipate	325
di(2-ethylhexyl) azelate	dioctyl azelate	325
di(2-ethylhexyl) maleate	bis(2-ethylhexyl) maleate	325
di(2-ethylhexyl) phosphoric acid	bis(2-ethylhexyl) phosphoric acid	325
di(2-ethylhexyl) phthalate	dioctyl phthalate	325
di(2-ethylhexyl) succinate	bis(2-ethylhexyl) succinate	325
diacetone	diacetone alcohol	325
diacetyl	2,3-butanedione	325
diallyl ether	allyl ether	325
diamide	hydrazine, anhydrous	49
diamine	hydrazine, anhydrous	49
2,2-diamino-diethylamine	diethylenetriamine	49
p,p′-diamniodi-phenylmethane	methylenedianiline	325
1,2-diaminobenzene	o-phenylenediamine	325
1,3-diaminobutane	1,3-butanediamine	325
diaminodiphenyl	diamylbiphenyl	325
p,p′-diamniodi-phenylmethane	methylenedianiline	325
1,2-diaminoethane	ethylenediamine	49
1,3-diaminopropane	1,3-propanediamine	325
diamyl ether pentyloxypentane	amyl ether	325
diamyl oxalate	amyl oxalate	325
diamylamine	di-n-amylamine	49
diarsenic pentoxide	arsenic pentoxide	49
diarsenic trisulfide	arsenic trisulfide	49
3,6-diazaoctane-1,8-diamine	triethylenetetramine	49
diboron hexa-hydride	diborane	49
1,2-dibromoethane	ethylene dibromide	49
dibutoxy diethylene, glycol	diethylene glycol, dibutyl ether	325
n-dibutyl ether	dibutyl ethers	49
dibutyl oxide	dibutyl ethers	49
n-dibutylamine	di-n-butylamine	49
dibutyl-d-2,3-dihydroxybutanedioate	n-dibutyl tartrate	325
dibutyl-o-phthalate	dibutyl phthalate	325
dicaproate	triethylene glycol	325
dichloracetyl chloride	dichloroacetyl chloride	49
1,2-dichloro-benzene	o-dichlorobenzene	49

SYNONYM	CHEMICAL	NFPA Doc. No.
dichloro-dioxochromium	chromium oxychloride	49
1,2-dichloro-ethene	dichloroethylene	49
dichloro-propylene	dichloropropene	49
3,4-dichloroaniline	dichloroanilines, solid or liquid	49
3,4-dichlorobenzeneamine	dichloroanilines, solid or liquid	49
o-dichlorobenzol	o-dichlorobenzene	325
sym-dichlorodimethylether	dichlorodimethyl ether, symmetrical	49
dichlorodimethylsilane	dimethyldichlorosilane	49, 325
sym-dichloroethane	ethylene dichloride	49
1,2-dichloroethane	ethylene dichloride	49
1,1-dichloroethane	1,1-ethylidene dichloride	325
1,2-dichloroethane	ethylene dichloride	325
dichloroethanoyl chloride	dichloroacetyl chloride	49, 325
1,1-dichloroethene	vinylidene chloride, inhibited	49
dichloroethylaluminum	ethylaluminum dichloride	325
asym-dichloroethylene	vinylidene chloride, inhibited	49
sym-dichloroethyl ether	2,2-dichlorodiethyl ether	49
sym-dichloroethylene	1,2-dichloroethylene	325
1,2-dichloroethylene	dichloroethylene	49
1,1-dichloroethylene	vinylidene chloride, inhibited	49
1,1-dichloroethylene	vinylidene chloride	325
dichloromethane	methylene chloride	325
dichloromethyl ether	dichlorodimethyl ether, symmetrical	49
dichloromethylsilane	methyldichlorosilane	49
1,2-dichloropropane	propylene dichloride	49, 325
1,3-dichloropropene	dichloropropene	49
1,3-dichloropropylene	dichloropropene	49
dicyan	cyanogen, liquefied	49
1,4-dicyanobutane	adiponitrile	49
dicyanogen	cyanogen, liquefied	49
dicyclohexyl	bicyclohexyl	325
diethenylbenzene	divinylbenzene	49
1,2-diethoxyethane	diethyl glycol	325
diethyl acetaldehyde	2-ethylbutyraldehyde	325
diethyl acetic acid	2-ethylbutyric acid	325
diethyl carbinol	sec-amyl alcohol	325
diethyl ether	ethyl ether	325
diethyl oxalate	ethyl oxalate	325
diethyl oxide	diethyl ether	49
diethyl oxide	ethyl ether	325
n,n-diethyl-1,3-propanediamine	3-(diethylamino)propylamine	325
p-diethyl phthalate	diethyl terephthalate	325
3,9-diethyl-6-tridecanol	heptadecanol	325
2-(diethylamino) ethanol	n,n-diethylethanolamine	325
diethylaminoethanol	diethylethanolamine	49
diethylchlorosilane	chlorodiethyl silane	49
diethylene dioxide	dioxane	49
1,4-diethylene dioxide	dioxane	49
diethylene dioxide	p-dioxane	325
diethylene ether	dioxane	49
diethylene glycol monobutyl ether acetate	diethylene glycol butyl ether acetate	325
diethylene glycol monoethyl ether carbitol	diethylene glycol ethyl ether	325
diethylene glycol monomethyl ether	diethylene glycol methyl ether	325
diethylene glycol n-butyl ether butoxy diethylene glycol	diethylene glycol monobutyl ether	325
diethylene oxide	tetrahydrofuran	49

SYNONYM	CHEMICAL	NFPA Doc. No.
diethylene oximide	morpholine	49
diethylenimide oxide	morpholine	49
diethylhexylamine	bis(2-ethylhexyl) amine	325
diethylhexylethanolamine	bis(2-ethylhexyl) ethanolamine	325
diethylmonoethanolamine	diethylethanolamine	49
3,5-diethyltoluene	1-methyl-3,5-diethylbenzene	325
dihexyl	dodecane	325
dihexyl ether	hexyl ether	325
dihydropentaborane	pentaborane	49
m-dihydroxybenzene	4-isopropylheptane	325
dihydroxybenzol	resorcinol	325
p-dihydroxybenzene	hydroquinone	325
1,2-dihydroxybutane	1,2-butanediol	325
2,2-dihydroxyethyl ether	diethylene glycol	325
dihydroxyethyl sulfide	thiodiglycol	325
2,5-dihydroxyhexane	2,5-hexanediol	325
diisobutylene	2,4,4-trimethyl-1-pentene	325
2,4-diisocyanatotoluene	toluene diisocyanate	49
diisopropyl	2,3-dimethylbutane	325
diisopropyl ether	isopropyl ether	325
diisopropyl oxide	diisopropyl ether	49
diisopropylmethanol	2,4-dimethyl-3-pentanol	325
dimazine	dimethylhydrazine, unsymmetrical	49
1,2-dimethoxyethane	ethylene glycol dimethyl ether	325
1,2-dimethoxy-4-allylbenzene	methyl eugenol	325
o-dimethoxybenzidine	o-dianisidine	325
3,3′-dimethoxybenzidine	o-dianisidine	325
dimethoxymethane, formal	methylal	325
dimethyl carbinol	isopropyl alcohol, 88%	325
o-dimethylaniline	o-xylidine	325
dimethyl carbonate	methyl carbonate	325
dimethyl ether, methyl oxide	methyl ether	325
dimethyl ethyl carbinol	2-methyl-2-butanol	325
dimethyl ketone 2-propanone	acetone	325
dimethyl monosulfate	dimethyl sulfate	49
3,7-dimethyl-7-hydroxyoctanal	hydroxycitronellal	325
3,5-dimethyl-1-hexyn-3-ol	dimethyl hexynol	325
2,2-dimethyl-1-propanol	tert-butyl carbinol	325
2,2-dimethyl-1,3-propanediol	neopentyl glycol	325
dimethyl-1,4-benzenedicarboxylate	dimethyl terephthalate	325
3,7-dimethyl-1,6-octadiene-3,1	linalool, synthetic	325
3,7-dimethyl-2,6-octadienal	citral	325
trans-3,7-dimethyl-2,6-octadien-1-ol	geraniol	325
2,6-dimethyl-4-heptanone	diisobutyl ketone	325
3,7-dimethyl-6-octen-1-ol	citronellol	325
3,7-dimethyl-6-octenal	citronellel	325
2,3-dimethyl-benzenamine	xylidines, solid or solution	49
dimethyl-o,o-dichloro-vinyl-2,2-phosphate	dichlorvos (DDVP)	325
di(methylamyl) maleate	bis(2,4-dimethylbutyl) maleate	325
2,3-dimethylaniline	xylidines, solid or solution	49
o-dimethylaniline	o-xylidine	325
1,3-dimethylbenzene	m-xylene	325
1,2-dimethylbenzene	o-xylene	325
1,4-dimethylbenzene	p-xylene	325
1,3-dimethylbutanol	4-methyl-2-pentanol	325

SYNONYM	CHEMICAL	NFPA Doc. No.
1,3-dimethylbutyl acetate	4-methyl-2-pentanol acetate	325
dimethylene oxide	ethylene oxide	325
dimethylenimine	ethylenimine, inhibited	49
dimethylethanolamine	2-(dimethylamino)ethanol	325
n,n-dimethylhydrazine	dimethylhydrazine, unsymmetrical	49
1,1-dimethylhydrazine	dimethylhydrazine, unsymmetrical	49
dimethylhydrazine, unsymmetrical	1,1-dimethylhydrazine	325
α,α-dimethylphenethyl acetate	dimethylbenzylcarbinyl acetate	325
dinitrile	adiponitrile	49
2,4-dinitro-1-aminobenzene	dinitroanilines	49
2,4-dinitro-1-chlorobenzene	chlorodinitrobenzenes	49
dinitro-chlorobenzene	chlorodinitrobenzenes	49
2,4-dinitrobenzenamine	dinitroanilines	49
o-dinitrobenzene	dinitrobenzenes	49
1,2-dinitrobenzol	dinitrobenzenes	49
1,2-dinitrobenzol	o-dinitrobenzene	325
2,4-dinitrotoluol	dinitrotoluenes, molten dinitrotoluenes, liquid or solid commercially available 2,4 to 2,6 ratio 4/1 with <5% other isomers	49
dinitrotoluol	dinitrotoluenes, molten dinitrotoluenes, liquid or solid commercially available 2,4 to 2,6 ratio 4/1 with <5% other isomers	49
dioctyl adipate	di-2-ethylhexyl adipate	325
dioctylamine	bis(2-ethylhexyl) amine	325
p-dioxane	dioxane	49
1,4-dioxane	dioxane	49
dioxonium perchlorate	perchloric acid (50% <72%)	49
1,3-dioxophthalan	phthalic anhydride	49
DIPA	diisopropylamine	49
diphenyl ether	diphenyl oxide	325
diphenyl	biphenyl	325
1,3-diphenyl-2-buten-1-one	dypnone	325
dipropyl ether	n-propyl ether	325
dipropyl ketone	4-heptanone	325
disulfur dichloride	sulfur chlorides	49
ditane	diphenylmethane	325
divinyl	butadienes, inhibited	49
divinyl oxide	vinyl ether	49
DMA	dimethylamine, anhydrous dimethylamine solution	49
DMAC	dimethylacetamide	325
DMS	dimethyl sulfate	49
DMSO	dimethyl sulfoxide	325
DMT	dimethyl terephthalate	325
DNA	dinitroanilines	49
DNCB	chlorodinitrobenzenes	49
2,4-DNT	dinitrotoluenes, molten, liquid or solid	49
DNT		
DOA	di-2-ethylhexyl adipate	325
dodeca-hydrodiphenylamine	dicyclohexylamine	49
1-dodecane	α-dodecylene	325
dodecyl bromide	lauryl bromide	325
dodecyl mercaptan	1-dodecanethiol	325
dop	dioctyl phthalate	325

SYNONYM	CHEMICAL	NFPA Doc. No.
DS	diethyl sulfate	49
DTBHQ	2,5-di-tert-butylhydroquinone	325
durene	1,2,4,5-tetramethylbenzene, 95%	325
DVB	divinylbenzene	49
EB	ethylbenzene	49
EDB	ethylene dibromide	49
EDC	ethylene dichloride	49
EI	ethylenimine, inhibited	49
EO	ethylene oxide	49
1,2-epoxybutane	1,2-butylene oxide, stabilized	49
1,2-epoxyethane		
1,2-epoxypropane	propylene oxide	49
erythrene	1,3-butadiene	325
essence of mirbane	nitrobenzene	49
ethanal	acetaldehyde	49
ethanamine	ethylamine	49
ethane trichloride	1,1,2-trichloroethane	49
1,2-ethanediamine	ethylenediamine	49
ethanedinitrile	cyanogen, liquefied	49
ethanedioic acid	oxalic acid (as dihydrate)	49
1,2-ethanediol	ethylene glycol	325
ethanenitrile	acetonitrile	49
ethaneperoxoic acid	peracetic acid (less than 40%)	49
ethanethiol	ethyl mercaptan	325
ethanoic acid	acetic acid	49, 325
ethanoic anhydride	acetic anhydride	49, 325
ethanol	ethyl alcohol	325
ethanol, 2-(diethylamino)-	diethylethanolamine	49
ethanoyl chloride	acetyl chloride	49, 325
ethene	ethylene	49, 325
ethene, 1,2-dichloro-	dichloroethylene	49
ethenyl ethanoate	vinyl acetate	325
ethenyloxyethene	vinyl ether	49
ethenyloxyethene	divinyl ether	325
ether	diethyl ether	49
ether	ethyl ether	325
ethine	acetylene, dissolved	49
ethine ethyne	acetylene	325
2-ethoxyaniline	o-phenetidine	325
2-ethoxyethanol	ethylene glycol ethyl ether	325
ethoxymethane	ethyl methyl ether	49
1-ethoxypropane	ethyl propyl ether	325
3-ethoxypropionaldehyde	3-ethoxypropanal	325
ethyl butanoate	ethyl butyrate	325
ethyl butylcarbamate	n-butylurethane	325
ethyl caprate	ethyl decanoate	325
ethyl carbonate	diethyl carbonate	325
ethyl chlorocarbonate	ethyl chloroformate	49
ethyl chlorocarbonate	ethyl chloroformate	325
ethyl chloromethanoate	ethyl chloroformate	325
ethyl dimethyl methane	isopentane	325
ethyl ester of acrylic acid	ethyl acrylate, inhibited	49
ethyl ethanoate	ethyl acetate	325
ethyl ether	diethyl ether	49
ethyl glycol	ethylene chlorohydrin	49

SYNONYM	CHEMICAL	NFPA Doc. No.
ethyl glycol acetate	2-ethoxyethyl acetate	325
ethyl glycolate acetate	ethyl acetyl glycolate	325
ethyl hexanoate	ethyl caproate	325
ethyl hexoate	ethyl caproate	325
2-ethyl hexoic acid	2-ethylhexanoic acid	325
2-ethyl isohexyl alcohol, 2-ethyl-4-methyl pentanol	2-ethylisohexanol	325
ethyl malonate	diethyl malonate	325
ethyl methanoate	ethyl formate	325
ethyl methyl acrylate	ethyl methacrylate	325
ethyl methyl ether	methyl ethyl ether	325
ethyl methyl ketone	methyl ethyl ketone	325
ethyl n-propyl ketone	3-hexanone	325
ethyl octanoate	ethyl caprylate	325
ethyl octoate	ethyl caprylate	325
ethyl orthosilicate	ethyl silicate	325
ethyl 3-oxobutanoate	ethyl acetoacetate	325
ethyl oxide	diethyl ether	49
ethyl oxide	ethyl ether	325
ethyl phenyl ether	ethoxybenzene	325
ethyl phosphate	triethyl phosphate	325
ethyl propenoate	ethyl acrylate, inhibited	49
ethyl silicon trichloride	ethyltrichlorosilane	49
ethyl sulfate	diethyl sulfate	325
ethyl sulfhydrate	ethyl mercaptan	325
3-ethyltoluene	m-ethyltoluene	325
4-ethyltoluene	p-ethyltoluene	325
ethyl vinyl ether	vinyl ethyl ether	325
2-ethyl-1-butanol	2-ethylbutyl alcohol	325
4-ethyl-2-methylhexane	2-methyl-4-ethylhexane	325
3-ethyl-2-methylpentane	2-methyl-3-ethylpentane	325
2-ethyl-4-methyl pentanol	2-ethylisohexanol	325
5-ethyl-2-methylpyridine	2-methyl-5-ethylpyridine	49
5-ethyl-2-picoline	2-methyl-5-ethylpyridine	49
3-ethyl-2,4-dimethylpentane	2,4-dimethyl-3-ethylpentane	325
3-ethyl-4-methylhexane	3-methyl-4-ethylhexane	325
ethyl-phenylamine	n-ethylaniline	49
ethylacetic acid	butyric acid	49
ethylaldehyde	acetaldehyde	49
ethylaminoethanol	n-ethylethanolamine	325
2-(ethylamino) ethanol	n-ethylethanolamine	325
ethylaniline	n-ethylaniline	49
n-ethylbenzenamine	n-ethylaniline	49
ethylbenzol	ethylbenzene	49
ethylbenzol	ethylbenzene	325
2-ethylbutanal	2-ethylbutyraldehyde	325
2-(2-ethylbutoxy)ethanol	2-ethyl butyl glycol	325
2-ethylcaproaldehyde	2-ethylhexanal	325
ethylene acetate	glycol diacetate	325
ethylene bromide	ethylene dibromide	49
ethylene chloride	ethylene dichloride	49
ethylene chlorohydrin	2-chloroethanol	325
ethylene dicyanide	succinonitrile	325
2,2-ethylenedioxydiethanol	triethylene glycol	325
ethylene formate	1,2-ethanediol diformate	325
ethylene glycol	2-ethoxyethyl acetate	325

SYNONYM	CHEMICAL	NFPA Doc. No.
ethylene glycol diaceate	glycol diacetate	325
ethylene glycol diformate	1,2-ethanediol diformate	325
ethylene glycol monoacrylate	2-hydroxyethyl acrylate	325
ethylene glycol monobutyl ether	ethylene glycol n-butyl ether	325
ethylene tetrachloride	tetrachloroethylene	49
ethylene trichloride	trichloroethylene	49
ethylethylene glycol	1,2-butanediol	325
2-ethylhexaldehyde	2-ethylhexanal	325
2-ethylhexenal	2-ethyl-3-propylacrolein	325
2-ethylhexyl alcohol	2-ethylhexanol	325
2-ethylhexyl vinyl ether	vinyl 2-ethylhexyl ether	325
2-ethylhexyl-2-propenoate	2-ethylhexyl acrylate	49
ethylimine	ethylenimine, inhibited	49
ethylisobutylmethane	isoheptane	325
4-ethylphenol	p-ethylphenol	325
2-ethyltoluene	o-ethyltoluene	325
ethyne	acetylene, dissolved	49
ethynylcarbinol	propargyl alcohol	49
ethynylmethanol	propargyl alcohol	49
EtO	ethylene oxide	49
eugenyl methyl ether	methyl eugenol	325
exhaust gas	carbon monoxide	49
fertilizer acid	sulfuric acid	49
flue gas	carbon monoxide	49
fluohydric acid	hydrogen fluoride, anhydrous	49
fluoroboric acid	fluoboric acid	49
1-fluoroethane	ethyl fluoride	325
formalin	formaldehyde, solutions formaldehyde, solutions, flammable	49
formalin methylene oxide	formaldehyde 37%, 15% methanol	325
formic acid, butyl ester	butyl formate	325
formic acid, ethyl ester	ethyl formate	325
formic acid, isopropyl ester	isopropyl formate	49
formic acid, methyl ester	methyl formate	49
formic aldehyde	formaldehyde, solutions formaldehyde, solutions, flammable	49
formonitrile	hydrogen cyanide, anhydrous, stabilized, hydrogen cyanide, anhydrous, stabilized absorbed in a porous inert material	49
fuming nitric acid	nitric acid	49
fuming spirit of libavius	stannic chloride, anhydrous	49
fural	furfural	49
2-furaldehyde	furfural	49
2-furaldehyde	furfural	325
2,5-furandione	maleic anhydride	49
furfuraldehyde	furfural	49
furfuran	furan	325
furfurol	furfural	49
furol	furfural	325
fusel oil	isoamyl alcohol	325
gallium (3+) chloride	gallium trichloride	49
gallium monoarsenide	gallium arsenide	49
gasoline, natural	gasoline, casinghead	325
gaultheria oil	methyl salicylate	325
GDMA	glycol dimercaptoacetate	325

SYNONYM	CHEMICAL	NFPA Doc. No.
geranial	citral	325
geraniol acetate	geranyl acetate	325
geraniol butyrate	geranyl butyrate	325
geraniol formate	geranyl formate	325
geraniol propionate	geranyl propionate	325
germanium tetrahydride	germane	49
glacial acrylic acid	acrylic acid, inhibited	49
glucinium	beryllium, powder (often from machining operations)	49
α,β-glycerin dichlorohydrin	2,3-dichloro-1-propanol	325
glycerol	glycerine	325
glycerol tributyrate	glyceryl tributyrate	325
glyceryl trichlorohydrin	1,2,3-trichloropropane	325
glyceryl trinitrate	nitroglycerine	325
Glycol	ethylene glycol	325
glycol chlorohydrin	ethylene chlorohydrin	49
glycol cyanohydrin	ethylene cyanohydrin	49
glycol dichloride	ethylene dichloride	325
glycol diformate	1,2-ethanediol diformate	325
glycol monoacetate	ethylene glycol acetate	325
grain alcohol	ethyl alcohol	325
gum camphor	camphor	325
HEA	2-hydroxyethyl acrylate	325
heavy hydrogen	deuterium	325
hemellitol	1,2,3-trimethylbenzene	325
hemimellitine	1,2,3-trimethylbenzene, 90.5%	325
3-heptanone	ethyl butyl ketone	325
2-heptanone	methyl amyl ketone	325
1-heptene	heptylene	325
2-heptene-trans	heptylene-2-trans	325
3-heptylene	3-heptene (mixed cis and trans)	325
heptylene	2,3,3-trimethyl-1-butene	325
hexadecyl-tert-mercaptan	tert-hexadecanethiol	325
hexadecylene-1	1-hexadecene	325
1,5-hexadien-3-yne	divinyl acetylene	325
hexahydroaniline	cyclohexylamine	49
hexahydrobenzene	cyclohexane	325
hexahydrocumene	isopropylcyclohexane	325
hexahydroindane	indan	325
hexahydromesitylene	1,3,5-trimethylcyclohexane	325
hexahydropyridine	piperidine	49, 325
hexahydroxylene	1,3-dimethylcyclohexane	325
hexahydroxylol	1,4-dimethylcyclohexane	325
hexahydroxytoluene	methylcyclohexane	325
hexaldehyde	hexanal	325
hexalin	cyclohexanol	325
hexalin acetate	cyclohexyl acetate	325
hexamethylene	cyclohexane	325
hexanedinitrile	adiponitrile	49
1,2-hexanediol	hexylene glycol	325
2,5-hexanedione	acetonyl acetone	325
hexanoic acid	caproic acid	325
1-hexanol	hexyl alcohol	325
2-hexanol	sec-hexyl alcohol	325
2-hexanone	methyl butyl ketone	325

SYNONYM	CHEMICAL	NFPA Doc. No.
hexazane	piperidine	49
3-hexen-1-ol	3-hexenol-cis	325
hexone	methyl isobutyl ketone	49
hexone	methyl isobutyl ketone	325
hexyl chloride	1-chlorohexane	325
hexyl cinnamaldehyde	hexyl cinnamic aldehyde	325
hexyl hydride	hexane	325
2-hexyne	methyl propyl acetylene	325
HFA	hydrogen fluoride, anhydrous	49
hittorf's phosphorus	phosphorus, amorphous; phosphorus, white, molten	49
HMDS	hexamethyldisilazane	49
HMDZ	hexamethyldisilazane	49
HQ	hydroquinone	325
HQMME	hydroquinone monomethyl ether	325
hydra-crylonitrile	ethylene cyanohydrin	49
hydracrylonitrile	ethylene cyanohydrin	325
hydralin	cyclohexanol	325
hydrazine, 1,1-dimethyl-	dimethylhydrazine, unsymmetrical	49
hydrazine base	hydrazine, anhydrous	49
hydrazomethane	methylhydrazine	49
hydrindene	indan	325
hydro-borofluoric acid	fluoboric acid	49
2-, 3-, or 4-hydro-xytoluene	cresols	49
hydrochloric ether	ethyl chloride	325
hydrocinnamic alcohol	phenylpropyl alcohol	325
hydrocinnamic aldehyde	phenylpropyl aldehyde	325
hydrocyanic acid	hydrogen cyanide, anhydrous, stabilized, hydrogen cyanide, anhydrous, stabilized absorbed in a porous inert material	49
hydrofluoboric acid	fluoboric acid	49
hydrofluoric acid gas	hydrogen fluoride, anhydrous	49
hydrogen antimonide	stibine	49
hydrogen arsenide	arsine	49
hydrogen bromide	hydrobromic acid solution	49
hydrogen dioxide	hydrogen peroxide, aqueous solutions (40% to 60%)	49
	hydrogen peroxide, aqueous solutions, stabilized (60%)	49
hydrogen iodide solution	hydriodic acid, solution	49
hydrogen phosphide	phosphine	49
hydrosulfuric acid	hydrogen sulfide, liquefied	49
1-hydroxy-2-methoxy-4-propenylbenzene	isoeugenol	325
2-hydroxy-2-methyl propionitrile	acetone cyanohydrin	325
2-hydroxy-2-methylpropanenitrile	acetone cyanohydrin, stabilized	49
hydroxyanisole	hydroquinone monomethyl ether	325
β-hydroxy naphthalene	β-naphthol	325
o-hydroxybenzaldehyde	salicylaldehyde	325
4-hydroxy-4-methyl-2-pentanone	diacetone alcohol	325
hydroxybenzene	phenol, solid phenol, molten phenol solutions	49
3-hydroxybutanal	aldol	325
β-hydroxybuteraldehyde	aldol	325
n-(2-hydroxyethyl)acetamide	n-acetyl ethanolamine	325
2-hydroxyethyl diethylamine	diethylethanolamine	49

SYNONYM	CHEMICAL	NFPA Doc. No.
β-hydroxyethylaniline	n-phenylethanolamine	325
[n-2-hydroxyethylethylenediamine]	2-aminoethylethanolamine	325
2-hydroxyisobutyronitrile	acetone cyanohydrin, stabilized	49
4-hydroxynitro-benzene	p-nitrophenol	49
3-hydroxypropanenitrile	ethylene cyanohydrin	49
3-hydroxypropionitrile	ethylene cyanohydrin	49
hydroxypropyl acrylate	propylene glycol acrylate	325
o-hydroxytoluene	o-cresol	325
irone	methyl ionone	325
isoacetophorone	isophorone	49
1,3-isobenzo-furandione	phthalic anhydride	49
isobutene	2-methylpropene	325
1-isobutenyl methyl ketone	mesityl oxide	49
isobutyl carbinol	isoamyl alcohol	325
isobutyl vinyl ether	vinyl isobutyl ether	325
isobutylene	2-methylpropene	325
sec-isoamyl mercaptan	3-methyl-2-butanethiol	325
tert-isoamyl alcohol	2-methyl-2-butanol	325
isocyanate methyl methane	methyl isocyanate	49
3-isocyanatomethyl-3,5,5-trimethyl cyclohexylisocyanate	isophorone diisocyanate	49
isocyanic acid, methyl ester	methyl isocyanate	49
isodurene	1,2,3,5-tetramethylbenzene, 85.5%	325
isohexane	2-methylpentane	325
isohexyl alcohol	2-methyl-1-pentanol	325
isooctanol	isooctyl alcohol	325
isooctyl vinyl ether	vinyl isooctyl ether	325
isopentyl butyrate	isoamyl butyrate	325
isophorone diaminediisocyanate	isophorone diisocyanate	49
isopropanol	isopropyl alcohol, 88%	325
isopropanolamine	1-amino-2-propanol	325
2-isopropoxypropane	isopropyl ether	325
isopropyl benzene	cumene	325
isopropyl carbinol	isobutyl alcohol	325
isopropyl ether	diisopropyl ether	49
isopropyl methanoate	isopropyl formate	325
isopropyl vinyl ether	vinyl isopropyl ether	325
isopropyl-2-hydroxypropionate	isopropyl lactate	325
4-isopropyl-1-methyl benzene	p-cymene	325
isopropylcyanide	isobutyronitrile	325
isopropylethylene	3-methyl-1-butene	325
isovaleraldehyde	isopentaldehyde	325
isovaleric acid	isopentanoic acid	325
isovalerone	diisobutyl ketone	325
jet fuel A	fuel oil no. 1	325
kalium	potassium	49
katchung oil	peanut oil (cooking)	325
kerosene range oil	fuel oil no. 1	325
LAH	lithium aluminum hydride	49
lauryl alcohol	1-dodecanol	325
lauryl mercaptan	1-dodecanethiol	325
leaf alcohol	3-hexenol-cis	325
light heavy	fuel oil no. 5	325
lime	calcium oxide	49
limonene	dipentene	325
linalol	linalool, synthetic	325

SYNONYM	CHEMICAL	NFPA Doc. No.
linalyl alcohol	linalool, synthetic	325
liquid camphor	camphor oil	325
lithium monohydride	lithium hydride	49
lithium tetrahydroaluminate	lithium aluminum hydride	49
LN	nitrogen, refrigerated liquid	49
LNG	natural gas, liquefied	49
losantin	calcium hypochlorite, dry or calcium hypochlorite, mixtures, dry	49
LOX	oxygen, refrigerated liquid	49
lye	sodium hydroxide, solid sodium hydroxide solution	49
malonic mononitrile	cyanoacetic acid	49
marsh gas	methane	325
MCA	chloroacetic acid, solid	49
MCP	methyl cyclopentane	49
MDA	methylenedianiline	325
p-mentha-1(7), 2-diene	β-phellandrene	325
mercaptomethane	methyl mercaptan	49
mercuric cyanide	mercury cyanide	49
mercury (II) cyanide	mercury cyanide	49
mesitylene	1,3,5-trimethylbenzene	325
methacrolein	2-methylpropenal	325
α-methyl acrolein	2-methylpropenal	325
methacrylic acid, methyl ester	methyl methacrylate monomer, inhibited	49
methanal	formaldehyde, solutions formaldehyde, solutions, flammable	49
methanamine, n-methyl-	dimethylamine, anhydrous dimethylamine solution	49
methane, tetrachloro-	carbon tetrachloride	49
methane, trichloro-	chloroform	49
methanethiol	methyl mercaptan	49
methanethiol	methyl mercaptan	325
methanoic acid	formic acid	49
methanol	methyl alcohol	325
methox	methoxyethyl phthalate	325
4-methoxy phenol	hydroquinone monomethyl ether	325
1-methoxy-2-propanol	propylene glycol methyl ether	325
1-methoxy-2-vinyloxyethane	vinyl 2-methoxyethyl ether	325
2-methoxyaniline	o-anisidine	325
4-methylanisole	methyl p-cresol	325
methoxybenzene	anisole	325
methoxyethane	ethyl methyl ether	49
2-methoxyethanol	ethylene glycol methyl ether	325
2-(2-methoxyethoxy)ethanol	diethylene glycol methyl ether	325
2-methoxyethyl acetate	ethylene glycol methyl ether acetate	325
methyl 2-octynoate	methyl heptine carbonate	325
methyl acetic ester	methyl acetate	325
methyl aldehyde	formaldehyde, solutions formaldehyde, solutions, flammable	49
methyl carbonimide	methyl isocyanate	325
methyl cellosolve acetate	ethylene glycol methyl ether acetate	325
methyl chloroethanoate	methylchloroacetate	325
methyl chloroform	1,1,1-trichloroethane	325
methyl cyanide	acetonitrile	325
methyl ethyl carbinol	sec-butyl alcohol	325

SYNONYM	CHEMICAL	NFPA Doc. No.
methyl ethyl ether	ethyl methyl ether	49
methyl ethylene glycol	propylene glycol	325
methyl isobutyl carbinol	4-methyl-2-pentanol	325
methyl isobutyl carbinol	2-methyl-1-pentanol	325
methyl isobutenylketone	mesityl oxide	49
methyl methanoate	methyl formate	49
n-methyl methyl anthranilate	dimethyl anthranilate	325
methyl para-tolyl ketone	p-methyl acetophenone	325
methyl pentanal	methylpentaldehyde	325
o-methyl phenol	o-cresol	325
methyl phenyl ether	anisole	325
methyl propenoate	methyl acrylate, inhibited	49
methyl propyl carbinol	sec-amyl alcohol	325
β-methyl propyl ethanoate	isobutyl acetate	325
methyl sebacate	dimethyl sebacate	325
methyl silico chloroform	methyltrichlorosilane	325
methyl styrene	vinyl toluene, inhibited mixed isomers	49
methyl sulfate	dimethyl sulfate	325
methyl sulfhydrate	methyl mercaptan	49
methyl vinyl ether	vinyl methyl ether	325
α-methyl-benzyl acetate	methyl phenyl carbinyl acetate	325
α-methylbenzyl alcohol	methylphenyl carbinol	325
2-methyl-1,3-butadiene	isoprene, inhibited	49
2-methyl-1,3-butadiene	isoprene	325
3-methyl-1-butanol	isoamyl alcohol	325
3-methyl-1-butanol acetate	isoamyl acetate	325
2-methyl butyl ethanoate	isoamyl acetate	325
1-methyl-2-ethylbenzene	o-ethyltoluene	325
α-methyl-p-isopropylphenylpropylaldehyde	cyclamen aldehyde	325
[α-methyl-4-1-methylethylbenzenepropanol]	cyclamen aldehyde	325
methyl-2-methyl-2-propenoate	methyl methacrylate monomer, inhibited	49
4-methyl-2-nitroaniline	2-nitro-p-toluidine	325
5-methyl-2-octanone	methyl heptyl ketone	325
4-methyl-2-pentanol	4-methyl-2-pentanol	325
4-methyl-2-pentanone	methyl isobutyl ketone	49
2-methyl-1-propanol	isobutyl alcohol	325
2-methyl-2-propanol	tert-butyl alcohol	325
2-methyl-2-propenoic acid	methacrylic acid, inhibited	49
n-methyl-2-pyrrolidone	1-methyl-2-pyrrolidinone	325
1-methyl-3-ethylbenzene	m-ethyltoluene	325
3-methyl-3-pentanol	tert-isohexyl alcohol	325
1-methyl-4-ethylbenzene	p-ethyltoluene	325
6-methyl-5-hepten-2-one	methylheptenone	325
methyl-o-amino benzoate	methyl anthranilate	325
methylacetic acid	propionic acid	49
methylacetic acid anhydride	propionic anhydride	49
methylacetylene	propyne	325
methylacetopyranone	dehydroacetic acid	325
2-(methylamino) ethanol	n-methylethanolamine	325
methylamyl acetate	hexyl acetate	325
methylamyl alcohol	4-methyl-2-pentanol	325
methylamyl alcohol	2-methyl-1-pentanol	325
2-methylaniline	o-toluidine	49
2-(n-methylaniline)-ethanol	phenylmethylethanolamine	325

SYNONYM	CHEMICAL	NFPA Doc. No.
4-methylaniline	p-toluidine	49
2-methylaniline	o-toluidine	325
4-methylaniline	p-toluidine	325
p-methylanisole	methyl p-cresol	325
methylbenzene	toluene	49
methylbenzene	toluene	325
2-methylbiphenyl	o-phenyltoluene	325
β-methylbivinyl	isoprene, inhibited	49
2-methylbutane	isopentane	325
methylchloroform	1,1,1-trichloroethane	49
methylene acetone	methyl vinyl ketone	49
methylene chloride	dichloromethane	49
methylene dichloride	dichloromethane	49
methylene oxide	formaldehyde, solutions formaldehyde, solutions, flammable	49
4-methylene-2-oxetanone	diketene, inhibited	49
1-methylethenyl benzine	α-methylstyrene	325
n-(1-methylethyl)-2-propanamine	diisopropylamine	49
(1-methylethyl)benzene	cumene	49
2-methylhexane	isoheptane	325
methylhydroquinone	toluhydroquinone	325
methylisobutylcarbinol acetate	4-methyl-2-pentanol acetate	325
2-methyllactonitrile	acetone cyanohydrin, stabilized	49
n-methylmethanamine	dimethylamine, anhydrous dimethylamine solution	49
methylnitrobenzene	nitrotoluenes, liquid o-, m-, p- nitrotoluenes, solid o-, m-, p-	49
2-methylnonane	isodecanes, mixed	325
2-methyloctane	iso-nonane	325
3-methyloctane	iso-nonane	325
4-methyloctane	iso-nonane	325
methyloxirane	propylene oxide	49
2-methyl-2,4-pentanediol	hexylene glycol	325
2-, 3-, or 4-methylphenol	cresols (o-, m-, p-)	49
1-methyl-1-phenylethene	α-methylstyrene	325
2-methylpropanal	isobutyraldehyde	325
2-methylpropane	isobutane	325
2-methylpropanenitrile	isobutyronitrile	325
methylpropylcarbinylamine	sec-amylamine	325
2-methylpyridine	2-picoline	325
methylsulfate	dimethyl sulfate	49
3-(methylthio) propionaldehyde	β-methyl mercaptopropionaldehyde	325
2-methylvaleraldehyde	methylpentaldehyde	325
1-methylvinyl acetate	isopropenyl acetate	325
MIBK	methyl isobutyl ketone	49
MIC	methyl isocyanate	49
mineral wax	wax, ozocerite	325
mixture of isomeric amyl acetates and amyl alcohols	pent-acetate	325
MMA	methylamine, anhydrous methylamine, aqueous solution	49
MMH	methylhydrazine	49
mono-chloroacetic acid	chloroacetic acid, solid	49
monochlorobenzene	chlorobenzene	49, 325
monochloromethyl ether	methylchloromethyl ether	49
monochlorophenol	chlorophenols, liquid	49

SYNONYM	CHEMICAL	NFPA Doc. No.
monochlorophenol	chlorophenols, solid	49
monoethanolamine	ethanolamine or ethanolamine solutions	49
monoethylamine	ethylamine	49
monoethyl ether acetate	2-ethoxyethyl acetate	325
monogermane	germane	49
monoisopropylamine	isopropylamine	49
monomethyl-hydrazine	methylhydrazine	49
monomethylamine	methylamine, anhydrous methylamine, aqueous solution	49
monosilane	silane	49
monoxide	carbon monoxide	49
moth flakes	naphthalene, crude or refined	49
MTDEA	m-tolydiethanolamine	325
muriatic ether	ethyl chloride	325
muthmann's liquid	tetrabromoethane	49
MVK	methyl vinyl ketone	49
NaH 80	sodium hydride	49
NAL	nitroanilines (o-, m-, p-)	49
naphtha, petroleum	petroleum ether	325
naphthalin	naphthalene, crude or refined	49
naphthene	naphthalene, crude or refined	49
2-naphthol	β-naphthol	325
natrium	sodium	49
natural gas	gas, natural	325
NBD	2,5-norbornadiene	325
neohexane	2,2-dimethylbutane	325
neopentane	2,2-dimethylpropane	325
neutral ammonium fluoride	ammonium fluoride	49
nevoli oil, artificial	methyl anthranilate	325
nickel tetracarbonyl	nickel carbonyl	49
niobe oil	methyl benzoate	325
nitram	ammonium nitrate	49
nitric acid ammonium salt	ammonium nitrate	49
nitric acid propyl ester	n-propyl nitrate	49
nitric ether	ethyl nitrate	325
2,2′,2′-nitrilotriethanol	triethanolamine	325
4-nitro-aniline	nitroanilines (o-, m-, p-)	49
3-nitroaniline	nitroanilines (o-, m-, p-)	49
2-nitroaniline	nitroanilines (o-, m-, p-)	49
nitrobenzol	nitrobenzene	49
nitrobenzol	nitrobenzene	325
nitrocarbol	nitromethane	49
nitrochlorobenzene	chloronitrobenzenes	49
	propyl formates (class 3, un 1281)	49
m-nitrochlorobenzene	chloronitrobenzenes; propyl formates (class 3, un 1281)	49
nitrochloroform	chloropicrin	49
1,1′,1′′-nitrolotri-2-propanol	triisopropanolamine	325
nitrophenol	p-nitrophenol	49
4-nitrophenol	p-nitrophenol	49
sec-nitropropane	2-nitropropane	325
2-sec-nitropropane	nitropropanes	49
2-nitropropane	nitropropanes	49
1-nitropropane	nitropropanes	49

SYNONYM	CHEMICAL	NFPA Doc. No.
4-nitrotoluene	nitrotoluenes, liquid o-, m-, p- nitrotoluenes, solid o-, m-, p-	49
3-nitrotoluene	nitrotoluenes, liquid o-, m-, p- nitrotoluenes, solid o-, m-, p-	49
2-nitrotoluene	nitrotoluenes, liquid o-, m-, p- nitrotoluenes, solid o-, m-, p-	49
nitrotoluol	nitrotoluenes, liquid o-, m-, p- nitrotoluenes, solid o-, m-, p-	49
nitrous acid ethyl ester	ethyl nitrite solutions	49
nitrous ether	ethyl nitrite solutions	49
nitrous ether	ethyl nitrite	325
nitroxanthic acid	picric acid, wet, with not less than 10% water	49
NMT	nitromethane	49
nonyl alcohol	diisobutyl carbinol	325
nonylene	nonene	325
normanthane	isopropylcyclohexane	325
norway saltpeter	ammonium nitrate	49
NTB	nitrobenzene	49
NTM	naphthalene, crude or refined	49
NXX	nitrogen, refrigerated liquid	49
n-octadecane	octadecane	325
1-octadecanol	stearyl alcohol	325
1-octadecene	α-octadecylene	325
octadecyl vinyl ether	vinyl octadecyl ether	325
octahydroindene	indan	325
octanal	caprylaldehyde	325
56–60 octane 73 octane, 92 octane, 100 octane	gasoline	325
1-octanol	octyl alcohol	325
octanone	methyl hexyl ketone	325
2-octanone	methyl hexyl ketone	325
octyl acetate	2-ethylhexyl acetate	325
octyl alcohol	2-ethylhexanol	325
octyl ether	dioctyl ether	325
n-octyl mercaptan	1-octanethiol	325
octylene glycol	2-ethyl-1,3-hexanediol	325
oil of mirbane	nitrobenzene	49, 325
oil of vitriol	sulfuric acid	49
oil of wintergreen	methyl salicylate	325
olefiant gas	ethylene, compressed	49
ortho-methylaniline	o-toluidine	49
orthophosphoric acid	phosphoric acid	49
oxalic acid dinitrile	cyanogen, liquefied	49
oxalic ether	ethyl oxalate	325
oxalonitrile	cyanogen, liquefied	49
oxammonium	hydroxylamine	49
oxammonium	hydroxylamine	325
1,4-oxathiane	1,4-thioxane	325
oxirane	ethylene oxide	49
1,1-oxy-bis-ethene	vinyl ether	49
1,1-oxybis(2-chloroethane)	2,2-dichlorodiethyl ether	49
1,1-oxybis [butane]	dibutyl ethers	49
oxygen	oxygen, refrigerated liquid	49
oxymethylene	formaldehyde, solutions formaldehyde, solutions, flammable	49
palm butter	palm oil	325

SYNONYM	CHEMICAL	NFPA Doc. No.
palm nut oil	palm kernel oil	325
PAN	phthalic anhydride	49
para-methylaniline	p-toluidine	49
para-phthalic acid	terephthalic acid	325
paracetaldehyde	paraldehyde	49
paraffin oil, includes motor oil	lubricating oil, mineral (C20-C50)	325
paraform	paraformaldehyde	49
PCBS	polychlorinated biphenyls	49
PCP	pentachlorophenol	49
pebble lime	calcium oxide	49
penta	pentachlorophenol	49
pentaborane(9)	pentaborane	49
pentaboron nonahydride	pentaborane	49
pentaboron undecahydride	pentaborane	49
pentachlorol	pentachlorophenol	49
pentamethylbenzene	1,2,3,4,5-pentamethylbenzene, 95%	325
pentamethylene dichloride	1,5-dichloropentane	325
pentamethylene glycol	1,5-pentanediol	325
pentamethyleneamine	piperidine	49
pentanal	valeraldehyde	325
pentanethiol	amyl mercaptans	49
1-pentanethiol	n-amyl mercaptan	325
1-pentanol	amyl alcohol	325
2-pentanol	sec-amyl alcohol	325
2-pentanol acetate	sec-amyl acetate	325
1-pentanol acetate, comm.	amyl acetate	325
3-pentanone	diethyl ketone	325
2-pentanone	methyl propyl ketone	325
2-pentanone, 4-methyl-	methyl isobutyl ketone	49
pentapropionyl glucose	glucose pentapropionate	325
2-pentene-cis	β-amylene-cis	325
2-pentene-trans	β-amylene-trans	325
pentyl mercaptan	amyl mercaptans	49
pentyl pentylamine	di-n-amylamine	49
pentyl propionate	amyl propionate	325
1-pentylamine	amylamines	49
	mono-(trichloro) tetra-(monopotassium dichloro)-penta -s-triazinetrione, dry	49
pentylamine	amylamine	325
per-chloriate solution	perchloric acid (>50% <72%)	49
perc perchloroethene tetrachloroethylene	perchloroethylene;tetrachloroethylene	325
perchloric acid solution	perchloric acid (>50% <72%)	49
perchloro-ethylene	tetrachloroethylene	49
perfluoroethylene	tetrafluoroethylene	325
perhydrodiphenylamine	dicyclohexylamine	49
peroxide	hydrogen peroxide, aqueous solutions (40% to 60%)	49
	hydrogen peroxide, aqueous solutions, stabilized (60%)	49
peroxyacetic acid	peracetic acid (less than 40%)	49
petroleum pitch	asphalt (typical)	325
phenacyl chloride	chloroacetophenone	325
phenanthrin	phenanthrene	325
sec-phenethyl alcohol	methylphenyl carbinol	325

SYNONYM	CHEMICAL	NFPA Doc. No.
phenetole	ethoxybenzene	325
phenol, 2-chloro-	chlorophenols, liquid	49
2-phenoxyethanol	ethylene glycol phenyl ether	325
2-phenoxyethanol	phenoxy ethyl alcohol	325
β-phenylethylacetate	β-phenylethyl acetate	325
β-phenoxyethyl chloride	β-chlorophenetole	325
n-phenyl	acetanilide	49
phenyl acetonitrile	benzyl cyanide	325
phenyl bromide	bromobenzene	325
phenyl carbinol	benzyl alcohol	325
phenyl cellosolve	phenoxy ethyl alcohol	325
phenyl chloride	chlorobenzene	49, 325
phenyl chloroform	benzotrichloride	325
phenyl diglycol carbonate	diethylene glycol bis(phenylcarbonate)	325
1-phenyl isopropyl amine	benzedrine	325
n-phenylacetamide	acetanilide	49
phenyl methyl ketone	acetophenone	325
2-phenyl propane	cumene	325
3-phenyl-l-propanol	phenylpropyl alcohol	325
phenylamine	aniline	49, 325
phenylaniline	diphenylamine	325
phenylbenzene	biphenyl	325
phenylchloroform	benzotrichloride	49
phenylcyclohexane	cyclohexylbenzene	325
phenyldiethylamine	n,n-diethylaniline	325
phenylethane	ethylbenzene	49
phenylethylene	styrene monomer, inhibited	49, 325
sec-phenylethyl acetate	methyl phenyl carbinyl acetate	325
phenylethyl alcohol	phenethyl alcohol	325
phenylethyl carbinol	phenylpropyl alcohol	325
phenylethyl carbinol	phenylpropyl alcohol	325
phenylfluoroform	benzotrifluoride	49
phenylmercury acetate	phenylmercuric acetate	49
phenylmethane	toluene	49, 325
phenyl methylcarbinyl acetate	methyl phenyl carbinyl acetate	325
phenylpentane	amylbenzene	325
phenylpropane	propylbenzene	325
3-phenylpropionaldehyde	phenylpropyl aldehyde	325
phenyltrichloromethane	benzotrichloride	49
phosphorated hydrogen	phosphine	49
phosphoric acid, 2,2-dichlorovinyl dimethyl ester	dichlorvos (DDVP)	325
phosphoric chloride	phosphorus pentachloride	49
phosphoric sulfide	phosphorus pentasulfide	49
phosphorous hydride	phosphine	49
phosphorus bromide	phosphorus tribromide	49
phosphorus chloride	phosphorus trichloride	49
phosphorus oxytrichloride	phosphorus oxychloride	49
phosphorus perchloride	phosphorus pentachloride	49
phosphorus persulfide	phosphorus pentasulfide	49
phosphoryl chloride	phosphorus oxychloride	49
phthalandione	phthalic anhydride	49
m-phthalyl dichloride	isophthaloyl chloride	325
p-phthalyl dichloride	terephthaloyl chloride	325
picro-nitric acid	picric acid, wet, with not less than 10% water	49

SYNONYM	CHEMICAL	NFPA Doc. No.
pimelic ketone	cyclohexanone	325
piperylene	1,3-pentadiene (mixture of cis and trans isomers)	325
PMA	phenylmercuric acetate	49
PMAC	phenylmercuric acetate	49
PMAS	phenylmercuric acetate	49
PNP	p-nitrophenol	49
pogy oil	menhaden oil	325
polyoxymethylene	paraformaldehyde	49
potash lye	potassium hydroxide, solid potassium hydroxide, solution	49
potassium dichloroisocyanurate	potassium dichloro-s-triazinetrione	49
potassium monosulfide	potassium sulfide, anhydrous	49
potassium superoxide	potassium peroxide	49
prehnitene	1,2,3,4-tetramethylbenzene, 95%	325
propanal	propionaldeyhde	49, 325
2-propanol	isopropyl alcohol, 88%	325
2-propanamine	isopropylamine	49
1-propanamine	propylamine	49
1,2-propanediol	propylene glycol	325
1,3-propanediol	trimethylene glycol	325
propanenitrile, 2-hydroxy-2-methyl-	acetone cyanohydrin, stabilized	49
propanoic acid	propionic acid	49
propanoic anhydride	propionic anhydride	49
1-propanol	propyl alcohol	325
n-propanolamine	3-aminopropanol	325
propanoyl chloride	propionyl chloride	325
propargyl bromide	3-bromopropyne	49
propargyl bromide	3-bromopropyne	325
2-propen-1-amine	allylamine	49
2-propen-1-ol	allyl alcohol	49
2-propenal	acrolein, inhibited	49
2-propenamide	acrylamide	49
propene	propylene	325
propene oxide	propylene oxide	49
propenenitrile	acrylonitrile	325
2-propenenitrile	acrylonitrile, inhibited	49
2-propenoic acid	acrylic acid, inhibited	49
2-propenoic acid ethyl ether	ethyl acrylate, inhibited	49
2-propenol	allyl alcohol	49
propenyl guaiacol	methyl isoeugenol	325
2-propenyl hexanoate	allyl caproate	325
2-propenylamine	allylamine	325
propionic aldehyde	propionaldeyhde	49
propionitrile	propionic nitrile	325
propionyl-oxide	propionic anhydride	49
propiophenone	ethyl phenyl ketone	325
n-propyl acetylene	1-pentyne	325
propyl carbinol	butyl alcohol	325
propyl cyanide	butyronitrile	49
propyl-aldehyde	propionaldeyhde	49
propyl methanol	butyl alcohol	325
99% pure	propylene glycol methyl ether acetate	325
n-propylamine	propylamine	49
propylene aldehyde	crotonaldehyde	325

SYNONYM	CHEMICAL	NFPA Doc. No.
propylene chlorohydrin	2-chloro-1-propanol	325
sec-propylene chlorohydrin	1-chloro-2-propanol	325
propylene trimer	tripropylene	325
2-propyn-1-ol	propargyl alcohol	49
2-propyn-1-ol	propargyl alcohol	325
1-propyne-3-ol	propargyl alcohol	49
3-propynol	propargyl alcohol	49
protium	hydrogen, refrigerated liquid	49
prussiate of soda	sodium cyanide	49
prussic acid	hydrogen cyanide, anhydrous, stabilized, hydrogen cyanide, anhydrous, stabilized absorbed in a porous inert material	49
prussic acid, hydrogen cyanide	hydrocyanic acid, 96%	325
pseudocumene	1,2,4-trimethylbenzene	325
pyrocatechol catechol	o-dihydroxybenzene	325
quicklime	calcium oxide	49
quinol hydroquinol	hydroquinone	325
quinone	p-benzoquinone	325
R-1113	trifluorochloroethylene	325
R-142b	difluoro-1-chloroethane	325
raney alloy	nickel catalyst	49
raney nickel	nickel catalyst	49
red oil distilled	oleic acid	325
red phosphorus	phosphorus, amorphous	49
	phosphorus, white, molten	49
refined crude	cocoanut oil	325
rhodinal	citronellel	325
ricinus oil	castor oil	325
roach salt	sodium fluoride	49
salycilic acid benzyl ester	benzyl salicilate	325
sherry and port high	wines	325
signal oil	mineral seal oil	325
silane, dichloro-dimethyl-	dimethyldichlorosilane	49
silicane	silane	49
silicochloroform	trichlorosilane	49
silicon chloride	silicon tetrachloride	49
silicon fluoride	silicon tetrafluoride	49
silicon hydride	silane	325
silicon tetrahydride	silane	49
sodium dichloroisocyanurate	sodium dichloro-s- triazinetrione dihydrate	49
sodium hyposulfite	sodium hydrosulfite	49
sodium monosulfide	sodium sulfide, anhydrous	49
sodium sulfoxylate	sodium hydrosulfite	49
sodium sulfuret	sodium sulfide, anhydrous	49
sodium sulphide	sodium sulfide, anhydrous	49
sodium superoxide	sodium peroxide	49
solid crotonic acid	crotonic acid	49
solution of nitrated cellulose in ether-alcohol	collodion	325
spindle oil	lubricating oil, spindle	325
styralyl acetate	methyl phenyl carbinyl acetate	325
styralyl alcohol	methylphenyl carbinol	325
styrol	styrene monomer, inhibited	49
sulfinyl chloride	thionyl chloride	49

SYNONYM	CHEMICAL	NFPA Doc. No.
sulfonyl chloride	sulfuryl chloride	49
sulfur monochloride	sulfur chlorides	49
sulfur subchloride	sulfur chlorides	49
sulfureted hydrogen	hydrogen sulfide, liquefied	49
sulfuric acid diethyl ester	diethyl sulfate	49
sulfuric acid dimethyl ester	dimethyl sulfate	49
sulfuric chlorohydrin	chlorosulfonic acid	49
sulfuric oxy-chloride	sulfuryl chloride	49
sulfurous acid anhydride	sulfur dioxide, liquefied	49
sulfurous anhydride	sulfur dioxide, liquefied	49
sulfurous oxide	sulfur dioxide, liquefied	49
sulfurous oxychloride	thionyl chloride	49
sulphur	sulfur, molten	49
sweet-birch oil	methyl salicylate	325
sweet oil	olive oil	325
sylvan	2-methylfuran	325
symclosene	trichloroisocyanuric acid, dry	49
tannin, digallic acid	tannic acid	325
tar camphor	naphthalene, crude or refined	49
TBE	tetrabromoethane	49
TCCA	trichloroisocyanuric acid, dry	49
TDAC	triethylene glycol diacetate	325
TDI	toluene diisocyanate	49
TDI 2,4-tolylene diisocyanate	toluene-2,4-diisocyanate	325
TEA	triethylamine	49
tellurium ethide	diethyl telluride	49
tellurium ethyl	diethyl telluride	49
TEN	triethylamine	49
terephthalyl dichloride	terephthaloyl chloride	325
terpilenol	terpineol	325
1,4,7,10-tetra-azadecane	triethylenetetramine	49
1,1,2,2-tetrabromoethane,	tetrabromoethane	49
tetracap	tetrachloroethylene	49
tetrachloroethylene	perchloroethylene	325
tetrachloromethane	carbon tetrachloride	49
tetrachlorosilane	silicon tetrachloride	49
tetradecahydrophenanthrene	perhydrophenanthrene	325
tetraethyl orthosilicate	ethyl silicate	325
tetraethylene glycol, dibutyl ether	dibutoxy tetraglycol	325
tetraethylene glycol, dimethyl ether	dimethoxy tetraglycol	325
tetraethylene glycol dichloride	bis[2-(2-chloroethoxy)ethyl] ether	325
tetrafluoroborate	fluoboric acid	49
tetrafluoroboric acid	fluoboric acid	49
tetrafluoroethene	tetrafluoroethylene, inhibited	49
tetrafluorosilane	silicon tetrafluoride	49
tetraglycol dichloride	bis[2-(2-chloroethoxy)ethyl] ether	325
tetrahydro-1,4-isoxazine	morpholine	49
tetrahydropyran	pentamethylene oxide	325
tetrahydropyrrole	pyrrolidine	325
tetrahydrothiophene-1,1-dioxide	sulfolane	325
tetrakis2-ethylhexyl orthosilicate	tetra(2-ethylhexyl) silicate	325
tetralin	tetrahydronaphthalene	325
tetramethyl orthosilicate	tetramethoxysilane	49
1,1,3,3-tetramethylbutylamine	tert-octylamine	325
tetramethylene	cyclobutane	325

SYNONYM	CHEMICAL	NFPA Doc. No.
tetramethylene dichloride	1,4-dichlorobutane	49
tetramethylene glycol	1,4-butanediol	325
tetramethylene oxide	tetrahydrofuran	49, 325
tetramethylene sulfone	sulfolane	325
tetramethylethylene	2,3-dimethyl-2-butene	325
tetrapropionyl glucosyl propionate	glucose pentapropionate	325
TFE	tetrafluoroethylene	325
2,2-thiodiethanol	thiodiglycol	325
THF	tetrahydrofuran	49, 325
thiodiethylene glycol	thiodiglycol	325
thiomethanol	methyl mercaptan	49
thiomethyl alcohol	methyl mercaptan	49
thionyl dichloride	thionyl chloride	49
thiophosphoric anhydride	phosphorus pentasulfide	49
tin (IV) chloride	stannic chloride, anhydrous	49
tin perchloride	stannic chloride, anhydrous	49
tin tetrachloride	stannic chloride, anhydrous	49
titanic chloride	titanium tetrachloride	49
titanium (IV) chloride	titanium tetrachloride	49
TMA	trimethylamine, anhydrous	49
toluene, α,α,α-trichloro	benzotrichloride	325
toluene diisocyanate	toluene-2,4-diisocyanate	325
toluene trichloride	benzotrichloride	49
toluene trifluoride	benzotrifluoride	49
α-toluenethiol	benzyl mercaptan	325
α-toluic acid	phenylacetic acid	325
α-toluic aldehyde	phenylacetaldehyde	325
1,2-toluidine	o-toluidine	49
α-tolunitrile	benzyl cyanide	325
toluol	toluene	49, 325
p-tolyl acetate	p-cresyl acetate	325
tolyl chloride	chlorotoluene	325
o-tolyl phosphate	tri-o-cresyl phosphate	325
2,4-tolylene diisocyanate	toluene diisocyanate	49
TPA	terephthalic acid	325
transil oil	transformer oil	325
tri-chloroimino-cyanuric acid	trichloroisocyanuric acid, dry	49
tri-isobutylalane	triisobutylaluminum	49
tri-n-butylamine	tributylamine	49
triacetin	glyceryl triacetate	325
trialkylaluminum	aluminum alkyls	49
triamylamine	tripentylamine	49
triamylamine	tripentylamine	325
tribromo-phosphine	phosphorus tribromide	49
tributyrinbutyrin	glyceryl tributyrate	325
trichlor	trichloroethylene	49
trichloro	trichloroisocyanuric acid, dry	49
trichloro ethenylsilane	ethyltrichlorosilane	49
trichloro-nitromethane	chloropicrin	49
trichloro-s-triazinetrione	trichloroisocyanuric acid, dry	49
trichloroarsine	arsenic trichloride	49
trichlorochromium	chromic chloride	49
1,2,2-trichloroethane	1,1,2-trichloroethane	49
trichloroethylsilane	ethyltrichlorosilane	49
trichloromethane	chloroform	49

SYNONYM	CHEMICAL	NFPA Doc. No.
trichloromethyl benzene	benzotrichloride	49
trichloromethylsilane	methyltrichlorosilane	49, 325
trichloromonosilane	trichlorosilane	49
trichlorooctadecylsilane	octadecyltrichlorosilane	325
trichloro(phenyl)silane	phenyl trichloro silane	325
trichloropropylsilane	propyltrichlorosilane	49
tricyclodecane	endo-tetrahydrodicyclopentadiene	325
tridecanol	tridecyl alcohol	325
2-tridecanone	methyl undecyl ketone	325
tridodecyl trithiophosphite	trilauryl trithiophosphite	325
triethyl orthoformate	o-ethyl formate	325
triethylene glycol, ethyl ether	ethoxytriglycol	325
triethylene glycol, methyl ether	methoxy triglycol	325
trifluoroboron	boron trifluoride	49
α,α,α-trifluoronitrotoluene	1,3-nitrobenzotrifluoride	325
triisobutyl phosphate	isobutyl phosphate	325
trimethyl borate	methyl borate	325
trimethyl carbinol	tert-butyl alcohol	325
2,4,6-trimethyl-1,3,5-trioxone	paraldehyde	49
3,5,5-trimethyl-2-cyclohexene-1-one	isophorone	49
4-(2,6,6-trimethyl-2-cyclohexen-1-yl)-3-buten-2-one	α-ionone	325
4-(2,6,6-trimethyl-1-cyclohexen-1-yl)-3-buten-2-one]	β-ionone	325
2,6,8-trimethyl-4-nonanone	isobutyl heptyl ketone	325
2,4,8-trimethyl-6-nonanol	2,6,8-trimethyl-4-nonanol	325
trimethylene	cyclopropane	325
trimethylenediamine	1,3-propanediamine	325
trimethylethylene	2-methyl-2-butene	325
2,2,4-trimethylpentane	isooctane	325
2,4,6-trinitrophenol	picric acid, wet, with not less than 10% water	49
triphenylphosphine	triphenylphosphorus	325
tripropionin	glyceryl tripropionate	325
triptane—an isomer of heptane	2,2,3-trimethylbutane	325
tris(2-ethylhexyl) phosphite	trioctyl phosphite	325
troclosene potassium	potassium dichloro-s-triazinetrione	49
turbine oil	lubricating oil, turbine	325
UDMH	dimethylhydrazine, unsymmetrical	49
ultrasene	kerosene, deodorized	325
undecane	hendecane	325
unsymmetrical dimethylhydrazine	dimethylhydrazine, unsymmetrical	49
upper coal tar distillate	coal tar light oil	325
valeric acid	pentanoic acid	325
VAM	vinyl acetate, inhibited	49
vanadium (IV) chloride	vanadium tetrachloride	49
VCM	vinyl chloride, inhibited	49
villiaumite	sodium fluoride	49
vinegar acid	acetic acid, glacial	49
vinyl A monomer	vinyl acetate, inhibited	49
vinyl carbonal	allyl alcohol	49
vinyl cyanide	acrylonitrile, inhibited	49
vinyl cyanide	acrylonitrile	325
vinyl-2-pyrrolidone	1-vinylpyrrolidone	325
vinyl benzene	styrene monomer, inhibited	49, 325
vinyl ether	divinyl ether	325
vinylaceto-β-lactone	diketene	325

SYNONYM	CHEMICAL	NFPA Doc. No.
vinylethylene	butadienes, inhibited	49
vinylethylene oxide	butadiene monoxide	325
vinylformic acid	acrylic acid, inhibited	49
vinylidene chloride	vinylidene chloride, inhibited	49
vinylstyrene	divinylbenzene	49
VyAc	vinyl acetate, inhibited	49
white phosphoric acid	phosphoric acid	49
white tar	naphthalene, crude or refined	49
white tar	naphthalene	325
wood alcohol	methyl alcohol	325
wood tar oil	pine tar oil	325
wool grease	lanolin	325
2,3-xylylamine	xylidines, solid or solution	49
m-xylol	m-xylene	325
o-xylol	o-xylene	325
p-xylol	p-xylene	325
zinc diethyl	diethylzinc	49, 325
zinc ethide	diethylzinc	49
zirconium chloride	zirconium tetrachloride	49

CAS Number Cross Reference

CAS #	CHEMICAL	NFPA Doc. No.
50-00-0	formaldehyde	49, 325, 491, 497
50-21-5	lactic acid	491
50-99-7	dextrose	491
54-11-5	nicotine	325
55-63-0	nitroglycerine	325, 491
56-23-5	carbon tetrachloride	49, 491
56-38-2	parathion	491
56-81-5	glycerine	325
57-06-78007-40-7	mustard oil	325
57-11-4	stearic acid	325
57-13-6	urea	491
57-14-7	dimethylhydrazine	49, 325, 491, 497
57-55-6	propylene glycol	325
57-57-8	propiolactone	325, 491, 497
60-01-5	glyceryl tributyrate	325
60-12-8	phenethyl alcohol	325
60-24-2	2-mercaptoethanol	325
60-29-7	diethyl ether	49, 325, 491, 497
	ethyl ether	49, 325, 491, 497
60-34-4	methylhydrazine	49, 325, 491, 497
62-38-4	phenylmercuric acetate	49
62-53-3	aniline	49, 325, 491, 497
62-56-6	thiourea	491
62-73-7	dichloros	325
64-17-5	ethyl alcohol	491
	ethanol	497
64-18-6	formic acid	49, 325, 491, 497
64-19-7	acetic acid	49, 325, 491, 497
64-67-5	diethyl sulfate	49, 325, 491
65-85-0	benzoic acid	325
66-25-1	hexanal	325
67-56-1	methyl alcohol	325, 491, 497
	methanol	325, 491, 497
67-63-0	isopropyl alcohol	325, 491, 497
	2-propanol	325, 491, 497
67-64-1	acetone	325, 491, 497
67-66-3	chloroform	49, 491
67-68-5	dimethyl sulfoxide	325, 491
68-12-2	n,n-dimethylformamide	325, 497
69-72-7	salicylic acid	325
71-23-8	propyl alcohol	325, 491, 497
	1-propanol	325, 491, 497
71-36-3	butyl alcohol	325, 497
	1-butanol	325, 497
71-36-5	2-butanol	497
71-41-0	amyl alcohol	325, 491, 497
	1-pentanol	325, 491, 497
71-43-2	benzene	49, 325, 491, 497
71-55-6	1,1,1-trichloroethane	49, 325, 491
	methyl chloroform	49, 325, 491
72-20-8	endrin	491
74-82-8	methane	325, 491, 497
74-82-8	natural gas, liquefied (methane)	49
74-83-9	methyl bromide	49, 325, 491
74-84-0	ethane	325, 491, 497
74-85-1	ethylene	49, 325, 491, 497
74-86-2	acetylene	49, 325, 491, 497
74-87-3	methyl chloride	325, 491, 497
74-89-5	methylamine; anhydrous methylamine; aqueous solution	49, 325, 497
74-90-8	hydrogen cyanide	49, 325, 491, 497
74-93-1	methyl mercaptan	49, 325, 497
74-96-4	ethyl bromide	325
74-98-6	propane	325, 491, 497
74-99-7	propyne	325, 491, 497
	methylacetylene	325, 491, 497
75-00-3	ethyl chloride	325, 497
75-01-4	vinyl chloride	49, 325, 491, 497
75-02-5	vinyl fluoride	325
75-04-7	ethylamine	49, 325, 497
75-05-8	acetonitrile	49, 325, 491, 497

CAS #	CHEMICAL	NFPA Doc. No.
75-07-0	acetaldehyde	49, 325, 491, 497
75-08-1	ethyl mercaptan	325, 497
75-09-2	dichloromethane	49, 325
	methylene chloride	49, 325
75-11-6	methylene iodide	491
75-12-7	formamide	325
75-15-0	carbon disulfide	49, 325, 491, 497
75-18-3	dimethyl sulfide	325
75-19-4	cyclopropane	325, 497
75-20-7	calcium carbide	49, 491
75-21-8	ethylene oxide	49, 325, 491, 497
75-24-1	trimethylaluminum	325, 491
75-25-2	bromoform	491
75-28-5	isobutane	325, 497
75-29-6	isopropyl chloride	325
75-31-0	isopropylamine	49, 325, 497
75-34-3	1,1-ethylidene dichloride	325
75-35-4	vinylidene chloride	49, 325, 491, 497
75-36-5	acetyl chloride	49, 325, 491
75-38-7	vinylidene fluoride	325
75-44-5	phosgene	49, 491
75-47-8	iodoform	491
75-50-3	trimethylamine	49, 325
75-52-5	nitromethane	49, 325, 497
75-54-7	methyldichlorosilane	49, 325
75-56-9	propylene oxide	49, 325, 491, 497
75-64-9	tert-butylamine	325
75-65-0	tert-butyl alcohol	325, 491, 497
	methyl-2-propanol	325, 491, 497
75-66-1	2-methyl-2-propanethiol	325
75-68-3	difluoro-1-chloroethane	325
75-69-4	trichlorofluoromethane	491
75-71-8	dichlorodifluoromethane	491
75-72-9	chlorotrifluoromethane	491
75-73-0	tetrafluoromethane	491
75-74-1	tetramethyl lead	325, 497
75-76-3	tetramethylsilicane	491
75-77-4	trimethylchlorosilane	325
75-78-5	dimethyldichlorosilane	49, 325, 491
75-79-6	methyltrichlorosilane	49, 325, 491
	trichloromethylsilane	49, 325, 491
75-83-2	2,2-dimethylbutane	325, 497
75-84-3	tert-butyl carbinol	325
75-85-4	2-methyl-2-butanol	325
75-86-5	acetone cyanohydrin	49, 325, 491, 497
75-91-2	tert-butyl hydroperoxide	325
75-94-5	vinyl trichlorosilane	325, 491
	trichlorovinylsilane	325, 491
76-01-7	pentachlorethane	491
76-06-2	chloropicrin	49, 491
76-13-1	1, 2-trichlorotrifluoroethane	491
76-22-2	camphor	325, 491
77-73-6	dicyclopentadiene	325, 497
77-75-8	3-methyl-1-pentynol	325
77-76-9	2-dimethoxypropane	491
77-78-1	dimethyl sulfate	49, 325, 491, 497
77-93-0	triethyl citrate	325
77-94-1	tributyl citrate	325
78-00-2	tetraethyl lead	325
78-10-4	ethyl silicate	325, 497
78-30-8	tri-o-cresyl phosphate	325
78-40-0	triethyl phosphate	325
78-59-1	isophorone	49, 325, 497
78-67-1	a, a'-azodiisobutyronitrile	325, 491
78-70-6	linalool, synthetic	325
78-78-4	isopentane	325, 497
78-79-5	isoprene	49, 325, 491, 497
78-80-8	isopropenyl acetylene	325
78-81-9	isobutylamine	325
78-82-0	isobutyronitrile	325
78-83-1	isobutyl alcohol	325, 497
78-84-2	isobutyraldehyde	325, 497
78-85-3	2-methylpropenal	325
78-86-4	sec-butyl chloride	325
78-87-5	propylene dichloride	49, 325, 491, 497
	1, 2-dichloropropane	49, 325, 491, 497
78-88-6	2,3-dichloropropene	325
78-89-7	2-chloro-1-propanol	325
78-90-0	propylenediamine	325
78-92-2	sec-butyl alcohol	325
78-93-3	methyl ethyl ketone	325, 491, 497
	ethyl methyl ketone	325, 491, 497
78-94-4	methyl vinyl ketone	49, 325
78-95-5	chloroacetone	491
78-96-6	1-amino-2-propanol	325, 497
	monoisopropanolamine	325, 497
78-97-3	lactonitrile	325
79-00-5	trichloroethane	49, 491
79-01-6	trichloroethylene	49, 325, 491

CAS #	CHEMICAL	NFPA Doc. No.
79-03-8	propionyl chloride	325
79-04-9	chloroacetyl chloride	49
79-06-1	acrylamide	49, 491
79-09-4	propionic acid	49, 325, 497
79-10-7	acrylic acid	49, 325, 491, 497
79-11-8	chloroacetic acid	49, 325
79-20-9	methyl acetate	325, 497
79-21-0	peracetic acid	49, 325, 491
	peroxyacetic acid	49, 325, 491
79-24-3	nitroethane	49, 325, 491, 497
79-27-6	tetrabromoethane	49, 325
79-29-8	2,3-dimethylbutane	325
79-31-2	isobutyric acid	325
79-34-5	tetrachloroethane	491
79-36-7	dichloroacetyl chloride	49, 325
79-37-8	oxalyl chloride	491
79-38-9	trifluorochloroethylene	325
79-41-4	methacrylic acid	49, 325
79-46-9	2-nitropropane	325, 491, 497
80-10-4	diphenyldichlorosilane	325
80-15-9	cumene hydroperoxide	325, 491
80-26-2	terpinyl acetate	325
80-39-7	ethyl p-toluene sulfonamide	325
80-40-0	ethyl p-toluene sulfonate	325
80-46-6	pentaphen	325
80-48-8	methyl toluene sulfonate	325
80-56-8	α-pinene	325
80-62-6	methyl methacrylate	49, 325, 491, 497
84-15-1	o-terphenyl	325
84-62-8	diphenyl phthalate	325
84-65-1	anthraquinone	325
84-66-2	diethyl phthalate	325
84-69-5	diisobutyl phthalate	325
84-74-2	dibutyl phthalate	325, 491
85-01-8	phenanthrene	325
85-44-9	phthalic anhydride	49, 325, 491
85-68-7	benzyl butyl phthalate	325
85-70-1	butyl phthalyl butyl glycolate	325
85-98-3	1,3-diethyl-1,3-diphenyl urea	325
86-57-7	1-nitronaphthalene	325
87-59-2	xylidines, solid or solution	49, 325
87-68-3	hexachlorobutadiene	325
87-69-4	tartaric acid	491
87-86-5	pentachlorophenol	49
87-90-1	trichloroisocyanuric acid, dry	49
87-91-2	diethyl tartrate	325
87-92-3	n-dibutyl tartrate	325

CAS #	CHEMICAL	NFPA Doc. No.
87-69-4	tartaric acid (d)	325
133-37-9	tartaric acid (L)	325
88-09-5	2-ethylbutyric acid	325
88-10-8	diethyl carbamyl chloride	325
88-12-0	1-vinylpyrrolidone	325
88-16-4	o-chlorobenzotrifluoride	325
88-72-2	o-nitrotoluene	325
88-89-1	picric acid, wet	49, 491
88-99-3	phthalic acid	325, 491
o: 88-72-2 m: 99-08-1 p: 99-99-0	nitrotoluenes, liquid o-, m-, p- nitrotoluenes, solid o-, m-, p-	49
89-62-3	2-nitro-p-toluidine	325
89-63-4	4-chloro-2-nitroaniline	491
90-02-8	salicylaldehyde	325
90-12-0	1-methylnaphthalene	325
90-13-1	1-chloronaphthalene	325
90-41-5	2-biphenylamine	325
90-43-7	o-phenylphenol	325
91-17-8	decahydronaphthalene	325
91-20-3	naphthalene	49, 325, 491
91-22-5	quinoline	325, 491
91-23-6	nitroanisole	491
91-49-6	n-butylacetanilide	325
91-66-7	n,n-diethylaniline	325
92-04-6	2-chloro-4-phenylphenol	325
92-06-8	m-terphenyl	325
92-15-9	o-acetoacet anisidide	325
92-50-2	n-phenyl-n-ethylethanolamine	325
92-51-3	bicyclohexyl	325
92-52-4	biphenyl	325
92-53-5	4-phenylmorpholine	325
92-59-1	ethylbenzylaniline	325
92-66-0	4-bromodiphenyl	325
93-15-2	methyl eugenol	325
93-16-3	methyl isoeugenol	325
93-55-0	ethyl phenyl ketone	325
93-58-3	methyl benzoate	325
93-68-5	acetoacet-ortho-toluidide	325
93-89-0	ethyl benzoate	325
93-92-5	methyl phenyl carbinyl acetate	325
93-96-9	α-methylbenzyl ether	325
94-02-0	ethyl benzoylacetate	325
94-14-0	3-methylpentane	497
94-36-0	benzoyl peroxide	491
94-59-7	safrole	325
94-70-2	o-phenetidine	325
94-96-2	2-ethyl-1,3-hexanediol	325
95-46-5	o-bromotoluene	325
95-47-6	o-xylene	325
95-48-7	o-cresol	325
95-50-1	dichlorobenzene	49, 325, 491
95-53-4	o-toluidine	49, 325

CAS #	CHEMICAL	NFPA Doc. No.
95-54-5	o-phenylenediamine	325
95-57-8	chlorophenols, liquid	49, 325
95-63-6	1,2,4-trimethylbenzene	325
95-71-6	toluhydroquinone	325
95-76-1	dichloroanilines, solid or liquid	49, 325
95-92-1	ethyl oxalate	325
95-93-2	1,2,4,5-tetramethylbenzene, 95%	325
95-94-3	tetrachlorobenzene	325, 491
96-09-3	styrene oxide	325
96-10-6	diethylaluminum chloride	49, 325, 491
	chlorodiethylaluminum	49, 325, 491
96-14-0	3-methylpentane	325
96-17-3	2-methyl butyraldehyde	49, 325
96-18-4	1,2,3-trichloropropane	325
96-20-8	2-amino-1-butanol	325
96-22-0	diethyl ketone	325
96-23-1	1,3-dichloro-2-propanol	325
96-29-7	methyl ethyl ketoxime	325
96-33-3	methyl acrylate	49, 325, 497
96-34-4	methylchloroacetate	325
96-37-7	methylcyclopentane	49, 325
96-41-3	cyclopentanol	325
96-47-9	2-methyltetrahydrofuran	325
96-48-0	butyrolactone	325
96-49-1	ethylene carbonate	325
96-50-4	2-aminothiazole	491
96-54-8	methylpyrrole	325
96-80-0	n,n-diisopropylethanolamine	325
97-00-7	chlorodinitrobenzenes	49, 325, 491
	dinitrochlorobenzene	49, 325, 491
97-02-9	dinitroanilines	49, 325
97-36-9	m-acetoacet xylidide	325
97-53-0 and 97-54-1	isoeugenol	325
97-61-0	2-methylpentanoic acid	325
97-62-1	ethyl isobutyrate	325
97-63-2	ethyl methacrylate	325
97-64-3	ethyl lactate	325
97-72-3	isobutyric anhydride	325
97-85-8	isobutyl isobutyrate	325
97-88-1	butyl methacrylate	325
97-93-8	triethylaluminum	49, 325, 491
97-94-9	triethylborane	325, 491
97-95-0	2-ethylbutyl alcohol	325, 497
	ethyl butanol	325, 497
97-96-1	2-ethylbutyraldehyde	325
97-97-2	dimethyl chloracetal	325

CAS #	CHEMICAL	NFPA Doc. No.
97-99-4	tetrahydrofurfuryl alcohol	325
98-00-0	furfuryl alcohol	325, 491, 497
98-01-1	furfural	49, 325, 497
98-06-6	tert-butylbenzene	325
98-07-7	benzotrichloride	49, 325
98-08-8	benzotrifluoride	49, 325
98-09-9	benzenesulfonyl chloride	491
98-12-4	cyclohexyltrichlorosilane	325
98-13-5	phenyltrichlorosilane	325
98-15-7	chlorobenzotrifluoride	325
98-27-1	p-tert-butyl-o-cresol	325
98-28-2	4-tert-butyl-2-chlorophenol	325
98-29-3	4-tert-butyl catechol	325
98-46-4	1,3-nitrobenzotrifluoride	325
98-51-1	para tert.-butyl toluene	497
98-82-8	cumene	49, 325, 491, 497
98-83-9	α-methyl styrene	497
98-85-1	methylphenyl carbinol	325
98-86-2	acetophenone	325
98-87-3	benzyl chloride	497
98-88-4	benzoyl chloride	49, 325, 491
98-89-0	α-methylbenzylamine	325
98-95-3	nitrobenzene	49, 325, 491, 497
99-08-1	m-nitrotoluene	325
99-63-8	isophthaloyl chloride	325
99-87-6	p-cymene	325, 497
99-99-0	p-nitrotoluene	325, 491
100-00-5	p-nitrochlorobenzene	325
100-01-6	nitroanilines (o-, m-, p-)	49, 325
100-02-7	p-nitrophenol	49
100-07-2	anisoyl chloride	491
100-20-9	terephthaloyl chloride	325
100-21-0	terephthalic acid	325
100-37-8	diethylethanolamine	49, 325, 497
	diethylaminoethanol	49, 325, 497
100-40-3	4-vinyl cyclohexene	325
100-41-4	ethylbenzene	49, 325, 497
100-42-5	styrene	49, 325, 491, 497
100-44-7	benzyl chloride	49, 325, 491
	tolyl chloride	49, 325, 491
100-50-5	1,2,3,6-tetrahydrobenzaldehyde	325
100-51-6	benzyl alcohol	325, 491
100-52-7	benzaldehyde	49, 325, 491

CAS #	CHEMICAL	NFPA Doc. No.
100-53-8	benzyl mercaptan	325
100-61-8	monomethyl aniline	497
100-63-0	phenylhydrazine	325, 491, 497
100-66-3	anisole	325
100-67-2	2-ethylisohexanol	325
100-73-2	acrolein dimer	325
100-74-3	ethylmorpholine	325, 497
100-79-8646-06-0	dioxolane	325
100-99-2	triisobutylaluminum	49, 325, 491
101-02-0	triphenyl phosphite	325
101-77-9	methylenedianiline	325
101-81-5	diphenylmethane	325
101-83-7	dicyclohexylamine	49, 325
101-84-8	diphenyl oxide	325
101-86-0	hexyl cinnamic aldehyde	325
101-96-2	n,n'-di-sec-butyl-p-phenylenediamine	325
101-97-3	ethyl phenylacetate	325
102-01-2	acetoacetanilide	325
102-52-3	1,1,3,3-tetramethoxypropane	325
102-56-7	2,5-dimethoxyaniline	325
102-67-0	tripropyl aluminum	325, 491
102-69-2	tripropylamine	325, 497
102-71-6	triethanolamine	325
102-76-1	glyceryl triacetate	325
102-79-4	n-butyldiethanolamine	325
102-81-8	dibutylaminoethanol	325
102-82-9	tributylamine	49, 325
102-85-2	tributyl phosphite	325
103-09-3	2-ethylhexyl acetate	325
103-11-7	2-ethylhexyl acrylate	49, 325, 497
103-23-1	di-2-ethylhexyl adipate	325
103-24-2	dioctyl azelate	325
103-29-7	1,2-diphenylethane (sym)	325
103-50-4	dibenzyl ether	325
103-65-1	propylbenzene	325
103-69-5	n-ethylaniline	49
103-71-9	phenyl isocyanate	491
103-75-3	2-ethoxy-3,4-dihydro-2-pyran	325
103-76-4	1-(2-hydroxyethyl) piperazine	325
103-82-2	phenylacetic acid	325
103-84-4	acetanilide	49, 325
103-89-9	p-acetotoluidide	325
103-95-7	cyclamen aldehyde	325
104-01-8	p-methoxybenzyl formate	491
104-03-0	o-nitrophenylacetic acid	491
104-15-4	p-toluenesulfonic acid	325
104-38-1	hydroquinone di-(β-hydroxyethyl) ether	325
104-51-8	butylbenzene	325
104-53-0	phenylpropyl aldehyde	325
104-72-3	decylbenzene	325

CAS #	CHEMICAL	NFPA Doc. No.
104-75-6	2-ethylhexylamine	325
104-76-7	2-ethylhexanol	325, 497
104-78-9	3-(diethylamino)propylamine	325
104-88-1	p-chlorobenzaldehyde	325
104-90-5	2-methyl-5-ethylpyridine	49, 325, 491, 497
	5-ethyl-2-methylpyridine	49, 325, 491, 497
104-91-6	nitrosophenol	491
104-93-8	methyl p-cresol	325
105-05-5	p-diethylbenzene	325
105-08-8	1,4-cyclohexane dimethanol	325
105-30-6	2-methyl-1-pentanol	325
105-36-2	ethyl bromoacetate	325
105-37-3	ethyl propionate	325
105-38-4	vinyl propionate	325
105-39-5	ethyl chloroacetate	325
105-45-3	methyl acetoacetate	325
105-46-4	sec-butyl acetate	325, 497
105-53-3	diethyl malonate	325
105-54-4	ethyl butyrate	325
105-56-6	ethyl cyanoacetate	325
105-57-7	acetal	325
105-58-8	diethyl carbonate	325
105-59-9	n-methyldiethanolamine	325
105-64-6	diisopropyl peroxydicarbonate	325, 491
105-66-8	n-propyl butyrate	325
105-76-0	dibutyl maleate	325
105-86-2	geranyl formate	325
105-87-3	geranyl acetate	325
105-90-8	geranyl propionate	325
106-20-7	bis(2-ethylhexyl) amine	325
106-22-9	citronellol	325
106-23-0	citronellel	325
106-24-1	geraniol	325
106-27-4	isoamyl butyrate	325
106-29-6	geranyl butyrate	325
106-31-0	butyric anhydride	325
106-32-1	ethyl caprylate	325
106-35-4	ethyl butyl ketone	325, 497
106-36-5	propyl propionate	325
106-38-7	p-bromotoluene	325
106-42-3	p-xylene	325
106-46-7	p-dichlorobenzene	325
106-48-9	chlorophenols	49, 325
106-49-0	p-toluidine	49, 325
106-51-4	p-benzoquinone	325
106-63-8	isobutyl acrylate	325, 497
106-69-4	1,2,6-hexanetriol	325
106-79-6	dimethyl sebacate	325
106-88-7	1,2-butylene oxide	49, 325
106-89-8	epichlorohydrin	49, 325, 491
106-90-1	glycidyl acrylate	325

CAS #	CHEMICAL	NFPA Doc. No.
106-92-3	allyl glycidyl ether	497
106-93-4	ethylene dibromide	49
106-94-5	n-propyl bromide	325
106-95-6	allyl bromide	49, 325
106-96-7	bromopropyne	49, 325, 491, 497
106-97-8	butane	325, 491
106-98-9	1-butene	325
106-99-0	butadiene	49, 325, 491, 497
107-02-8	acrolein	49, 325, 491, 497
107-03-9	1-propanethiol	491
107-05-1	allyl chloride	49, 325, 491, 497
107-06-2	ethylene dichloride	49, 325, 491, 497
107-07-3	ethylene chlorohydrin	49, 325, 491, 497
	2-chloroethanol	49, 325, 491, 497
107-10-8	propylamine	49, 325
107-11-9	allylamine	49, 325
107-12-0	propionic nitrile	325
107-13-1	acrylonitrile	49, 325, 491, 497
107-14-2	chloroacetonitrile	49
107-15-3	ethylenediamine	49, 325, 491, 497
107-18-6	allyl alcohol	49, 325, 491, 497
107-19-7	propargyl alcohol	49, 325, 491
	2-propyn-1-ol	49, 325, 491
107-20-0	chloroacetaldehyde	497
107-21-1	ethylene glycol	325, 491
107-22-2	glyoxal	491
107-25-5	vinyl methyl ether	325
107-30-2	methylchloromethyl ether	49
107-31-3	methyl formate	49, 325, 497
107-37-9	allyl trichlorosilane	325
107-39-1	2,4,4-trimethyl-1-pentene	325
107-40-4	2,4,4-trimethyl-2-pentene	325
107-41-5	2-methyl-2,4-pentanediol	325
107-45-9	tert-octylamine	325
107-71-1	tert-butyl peracetate	325, 491
	t-butyl peroxyacetate	325, 491
107-72-2	amyl trichlorosilane	325
107-75-5	hydroxycitronellal	325
107-83-5	methylpentane	325, 497
	dimethylpentane	325, 497
107-83-5	isohexane (mixture of hexane isomers)	325
107-84-6	isoamyl chloride	325
107-87-9	methyl propyl ketone	325, 497
	2-pentanone	325, 497
107-88-0	1,3-butanediol	325
107-89-1	aldol	325
107-92-6	butyric acid	49, 325, 491, 497
107-98-2	propylene glycol methyl ether	325
108-01-0	2-(dimethylamino)ethanol	325
108-03-2	nitropropane	49, 325, 491, 497
108-05-4	vinyl acetate	49, 325, 491, 497
108-08-7	2,4-dimethylpentane	325
108-09-8	1,3-dimethylbutylamine	325
108-10-1	methyl isobutyl ketone	49, 325
108-11-2	4-methyl-2-pentanol	325, 497
	methyl amyl alcohol	325, 497
108-16-7	n,n-dimethylisopropanolamine	325
108-18-9	diisopropylamine	49, 325, 497
108-20-3	diisopropyl ether	49, 325, 491, 497
	isopropyl ether	49, 325, 491, 497
108-21-4	isopropyl acetate	325, 497
108-22-5	isopropenyl acetate	325
108-23-6	isopropyl chloroformate	491
108-24-7	acetic anhydride	49, 325, 491, 497
108-31-6	maleic anhydride	49, 325, 491
108-32-7	propylene carbonate	325
108-38-3	m-xylene	325
108-39-4 (m-cresol) 106-44-5 (p-cresol)	m- or p-cresol	325
108-44-1	toluidine	491
108-46-3	resorcinol	325
108-60-1	dichloroisopropyl ether	325
108-62-3	metaldehyde	325
108-65-6	propylene glycol methyl ether acetate	325
108-67-8	1,3,5-trimethylbenzene	325
	mesitylene	491
108-77-0	cyanuric chloride	491
108-83-8	diisobutyl ketone	325, 497
108-84-9	4-methyl-2-pentanol acetate	325, 497
	sec-hexyl acetate	325, 497
108-86-1	bromobenzene	325
108-87-2	methylcyclohexane	325
108-88-3	toluene	49, 325, 491, 497
108-89-4	4-picoline	325

CAS #	CHEMICAL	NFPA Doc. No.
108-90-7	chlorobenzene	49, 325, 491, 497
108-91-8	cyclohexylamine	49, 325
108-93-0	cyclohexanol	325, 491, 497
108-94-1	cyclohexanone	325, 491, 497
108-95-2	phenol	49, 325, 491
109-01-3	1-methyl piperazine	325
109-02-4	4-methylmorpholine	325
109-06-8	2-picoline	325
109-08-0	2-methylpyrazine	325
109-19-3	butyl isovalerate	325
109-21-7	butyl butyrate	325
109-43-3	dibutyl sebacate	325
109-47-7	dibutyl phosphate	325
109-52-4	pentanoic acid	325
109-53-5	vinyl isobutyl ether	325
109-55-7	3-(dimethylamino)propylamine	325
109-59-1	ethylene glycol isopropyl ether	325
109-60-4	propyl acetate	325, 497
109-63-7	boron trifluoride etherate	325, 491
109-65-9	butyl bromide	325
109-66-0	pentane	325, 497
109-67-1	1-pentene	325, 497
109-68-2	2-pentene	497
109-69-3	butyl chloride	325
109-72-8	butyllithium	491
109-73-9	butylamine	49, 325, 497
109-74-0	butyronitrile	49, 325
109-76-2	1,3-propanediamine	325
109-78-4	ethylene cyanohydrin	49, 325
	2-cyanoethanol, 3-hydroxypropionitrile	491
109-79-5	1-butanethiol	325, 491, 497
	butyl mercaptan	325, 491, 497
109-83-1	n-methylethanolamine	325
109-86-4	ethylene glycol methyl ether	325, 491, 497
	2-methoxyethanol	325, 491, 497
109-87-5	methylal	325, 497
109-89-7	diethylamine	49, 325, 491, 497
109-92-2	vinyl ethyl ether	325
109-93-3	vinyl ether	49, 325, 491
	divinyl ether	49, 325, 491
109-94-4	ethyl formate	325, 497

CAS #	CHEMICAL	NFPA Doc. No.
109-95-5	ethyl nitrite	49, 325, 491
109-97-7	pyrrole	325
109-99-9	tetrahydrofuran	49, 325, 491, 497
110-00-9	furan	325
110-02-1	thiophene	325, 491
110-05-4	di-tert-butyl peroxide	325
110-12-3	methyl isoamyl ketone	325
110-13-4	acetonyl acetone	325
110-19-0	isobutyl acetate	325, 497
110-22-5	acetyl peroxide	325, 491
110-38-3	ethyl decanoate	325
110-43-0	methyl amyl ketone	325, 497
110-46-3	isoamyl nitrite	325, 491
110-47-4	3-isopropoxypropionitrile	325
110-49-6	ethylene glycol methyl ether acetate	325
110-50-2	adipoyl chloride	325
110-53-2	amyl bromide	325
110-54-3	hexane	325, 497
110-56-5	1,4-dichlorobutane	49, 325
110-58-7	amylamine	325
110-61-2	succinonitrile	325
110-62-3	valeraldehyde	325, 497
	n-butyl formal	325, 497
110-63-4	1,4-butanediol	325
110-64-5	butenediol	325
110-66-7	amyl mercaptans	49, 325
110-67-8	3-methoxypropionitrile	325
110-68-9	n-methylbutylamine	325
110-69-0	butyraldoxime	325
110-71-4	ethylene glycol dimethyl ether	325
110-73-6	n-ethylethanolamine	325
110-74-7	propyl formate	325, 491
110-75-8	vinyl 2-chloroethyl ether	325
110-80-5	ethylene glycol ethyl ether	325, 497
110-82-7	cyclohexane	325, 491, 497
110-83-8	cyclohexene	325, 497
110-85-0	piperazine	325
110-86-1	pyridine	49, 325, 491, 497
110-87-2	dihydropyran	325
110-88-3	trioxane	325
110-89-4	piperidine	49, 325, 491
110-91-8	morpholine	49, 325, 497
110-96-3	diisobutylamine	325
110-97-4	diisopropanolamine	325
110-98-5	dipropylene glycol	325
111-12-6	methylheptenone	325
111-13-7	methyl hexyl ketone	325

CAS #	CHEMICAL	NFPA Doc. No.
111-15-9	2-ethoxyethyl acetate	325, 497
	ethylene glycol monoethyl ether acetate	325, 497
111-21-7	triethylene glycol diacetate	325
111-26-2	hexylamine	325
111-27-3	hexyl alcohol	325, 497
	hexanol	325, 497
111-29-5	1,5-pentanediol	325
111-34-2	vinyl butyl ether	325
111-36-4	n-butyl isocyanate	325
111-40-0	diethylenetriamine	49, 325
111-41-1	2-aminoethylethanolamine	325
111-42-2	diethanolamine	325
111-43-3	n-propyl ether	325, 497
111-44-4	2,2-dichlorodiethyl ether	49, 325
	bis(2-chloroethyl) ether	49, 325
111-46-6	diethylene glycol	325
111-48-8	thiodiglycol	325, 491
	thiodiglycol	491
111-55-7	glycol diacetate	325
111-64-8	caprylyl chloride	325
111-65-0	1-octene	325
111-65-9	n-octane	325, 497
111-67-1	2-octene (mixed cis and trans isomers)	325
111-68-2	heptylamine	325
111-69-3	adiponitrile	49, 325, 497
111-74-0	n,n-diethylethylenediamine	325
111-75-1	n-butyl ethanolamine	325
111-76-2	ethylene glycol n-butyl ether	325, 497
111-77-3	diethylene glycol methyl ether	325, 491, 497
	2(2-methoxyethoxy) ethanol	325, 491, 497
	methyl carbitol	325, 491, 497
111-78-4	1,5-cyclooctadiene	325
111-84-2	nonane	325, 497
111-85-3	octyl chloride	325
111-86-4	octylamine	325
111-87-5	octyl alcohol	325, 497
111-88-6	1-octanethiol	325
111-90-0	diethylene glycol ethyl ether	325
111-91-1	bis(2-chloroethyl) formal	325
111-92-2	dibutylamine	49, 325
111-96-6	diethylene glycol dimethyl ether	325, 491
	bis(2-methoxyethyl) ether	325, 491
112-04-9	octadecyltrichlorosilane	325
112-07-2	ethylene glycol monobutyl ether acetate	325, 497
112-12-9	methyl nonyl ketone	325
112-15-2	diethylene glycol monoethyl ether acetate	325
112-24-3	triethylenetetramine	49, 325
112-26-5	triglycol dichloride	325
112-27-6	triethylene glycol	325
112-30-1	decanol	325, 497
112-31-2	n-decaldehyde	497
112-34-5	diethylene glycol monobutyl ether	325, 497
112-35-6	methoxy triglycol	325
112-36-7	diethylene glycol diethyl ether	325
112-40-3	dodecane	325
112-48-1	ethylene glycol dibutyl ether	325
112-49-2	triethylene glycol dimethyl ether	325
112-50-5	ethoxytriglycol	325
112-53-8	1-dodecanol	325
112-55-0	1-dodecanethiol	325
112-57-2	tetraethylene pentamine	325
112-58-3	hexyl ether	325
112-60-7	tetraethylene glycol	325
112-61-8	methyl stearate	325
112-70-9	tridecanol	325
112-72-1	tetradecanol	325
112-73-2	diethylene glycol dibutyl ether	325
112-80-1	oleic acid	325
112-88-9	α-octadecylene	325
112-92-5	stearyl alcohol	325
112-95-8	eicosane	325
112-98-1	dibutoxy tetraglycol	325
115-07-1	propylene	325, 491, 497
115-10-6	methyl ether	325, 491, 497
	dimethyl ether	325, 491, 497
115-11-7	2-methylpropene	325
115-19-5	3-methyl butynol	325
115-21-9	ethyltrichlorosilane	49, 325, 491
	trichloroethysilane	49, 325, 491
115-76-4	2,2-diethyl-1,3-propanediol	325
115-82-2	tetra(2-ethylhexyl) silicate	325
115-86-6	triphenyl phosphate	325
115-87-7	bis(p-tert-butylphenyl)phenyl phosphate	325
115-95-7	lynalyl acetate, synthetic	325
116-02-9	3,3,5-trimethyl-1-cyclohexanol	325
116-14-3	tetrafluoroethylene	49, 325, 491
117-82-8	dimethyl glycol phthalate	325
117-83-9	dibutoxy ethyl phthalate	325
117-84-0	dioctyl phthalate	325
118-58-1	benzyl salicilate	325
118-74-1	hexachlorobenzene	491
119-06-2	ditridecyl phthalate	325

CAS #	CHEMICAL	NFPA Doc. No.
119-36-8	methyl salicylate	325
119-42-6	o-cyclohexylphenol	325
119-64-2	tetrahydronaphthalene	325, 497
119-90-4	o-dianisidine	325
120-07-7	n-phenyldiethanolamine	325
120-12-7	anthracene	325, 491
120-13-6	isobutyl phenylacetate	325
120-51-4	benzyl benzoate	325
120-55-8	diethylene glycol dibenzoate	325
120-61-6	dimethyl terephthalate	325
120-80-9	o-dihydroxybenzene	325
120-82-1	1,2,4-trichlorobenzene	325
120-83-2	2,4-dichlorophenol	325
120-92-3	cyclopentanone	325
120-94-5	methylpyrrolidine	325
121-14-2	2,4-dinitrotoluene	325
121-14-2	dinitrotoluenes	49
121-33-5	vanillin	491
121-43-7	methyl borate	325
121-44-8	triethylamine	49, 325, 497
121-45-9	trimethyl phosphite	325, 491
121-46-0	2,5-norbornadiene	325
121-69-7	n,n-dimethylaniline	325, 497
121-73-3	m-nitrochlorobenzene	325
122-00-9	p-methyl acetophenone	325
122-04-3	4 nitrobenzoyl chloride	491
122-20-3	triisopropanolamine	325
122-39-4	diphenylamine	325, 491
122-78-1	phenylacetaldehyde	325
122-79-2	phenyl acetate	325
122-82-7	acetoacet-para-phenetide	325
122-97-4	phenylpropyl alcohol	325
122-98-5	n-phenylethanolamine	325
122-99-6	ethylene glycol phenyl ether	325
123-00-2	n-(3-aminopropyl) morpholine	325
123-01-3	dodecyl benzene	325
123-04-6	2-ethylhexyl chloride	325
123-05-7	2-ethylhexanal	325, 497
	2-ethylhexaldehyde	325, 497
123-07-9	p-ethylphenol	325
123-15-9	methylpentaldehyde	325
123-17-1	2,6,8-trimethyl-4-nonanol	325
123-18-2	2,6,8-trimethyl-4-nonanone	325
123-19-3	4-heptanone	325
123-20-6	vinyl butyrate	325
123-25-1	diethyl succinate	325
123-31-9	hydroquinone	325, 491
123-32-0	2,5-dimethylpyrazine	325
123-38-6	propionaldeyhde	49, 325, 497
123-39-7	methyl formamide	491
123-42-2	diacetone alcohol	325, 497
123-51-3	isoamyl alcohol	325, 497
123-54-6	2,4-pentanedione	325
123-62-6	propionic anhydride	49, 325, 497
123-63-7	paraldehyde	49, 325
123-66-0	ethyl caproate	325
123-68-2	allyl caproate	325
123-72-8	butyraldehyde	49, 325, 491, 497
123-75-1	pyrrolidine	325
123-81-9	glycol dimercaptoacetate	325
123-86-4	butyl acetate	325, 491, 497
123-91-1	dioxane	49, 325, 491, 497
123-92-2	isoamyl acetate	325, 497
123-95-5	butyl stearate	325
123-96-6	2-octanol	325
124-04-9	adipic acid	325
124-13-0	caprylaldehyde	325
124-16-3	1-(butoxyethoxy)-2-propanol	325
124-17-4	diethylene glycol butyl ether acetate	325
124-18-5	decane	325
124-40-3	dimethylamine	49, 325, 497
124-41-4	sodium methoxide	491
124-68-5	2-amino-2-methyl-1-propanol	325
125-12-2	isobornyl acetate	325
126-30-7	neopentyl glycol	325
126-33-0	sulfolane	325, 491
126-39-6	2-methyl-2-ethyl-1,3-dioxolane	325
126-71-6	isobutyl phosphate	325
126-73-8	tributyl phosphate	325
126-98-7	methacrylonitrile	325
126-99-8	2-chloro-1,3-butadiene	325, 497
	chloroprene	325, 497
127-00-4	1-chloro-2-propanol	325
127-09-3	sodium acetate	491
127-18-4	tetrachloroethylene	49, 325, 491
	perchloroethylene	49, 325, 491
127-19-5	dimethylacetamide	325
127-25-3	methyl abietate	325
128-37-0	di-tert-butyl-p-cresol	325
131-11-3	dimethyl phthalate	325
131-15-7	dicapryl phthalate	325
131-17-9	diallyl phthalate	325
131-18-0	diamyl phthalate	325
131-74-8	ammonium picrate	491
132-29-6	diphenyl (o-xenyl) phosphate	325
133-37-9	tetra(2-ethylbutyl) silicate	325
134-20-3	methyl anthranilate	325
134-32-7	1-naphthylamine	325

CAS #	CHEMICAL	NFPA Doc. No.
135-01-3	o-diethylbenzene	325
135-02-4	o-methoxybenzaldehyde	325
135-19-3	β-naphthol	325
135-98-8	sec-butylbenzene	325
136-60-7	butyl benzoate	325
136-81-2	o-amyl phenol	325
137-32-6	2-methyl-1-butanol	325
138-22-7	butyl lactate	325
138-86-3	dipentene	325, 491, 497
	limonene	325, 491, 497
139-45-7	glyceryl tripropionate	325
139-87-7	n-ethyldiethanolamine	325
140-04-5	butyl acetyl ricinoleate	325
140-11-4	benzyl acetate	325
140-29-4	benzyl cyanide	325
140-31-8	1-(2-aminoethyl)piperazine	325
140-39-6	p-cresyl acetate	325
140-88-5	ethyl acrylate	49, 325, 491, 497
140-89-6	potassium xanthate	325
141-05-9	diethyl maleate	325
141-20-8	diglycol laurate	325
141-32-2	butylacrylate	49, 325, 497
141-43-5	ethanolamine	49, 325, 491
	2-aminoethanol	49, 325, 491
141-57-1	propyltrichlorosilane	49, 325
141-59-3	tert-octyl mercaptan	325
141-78-6	ethyl acetate	325, 491, 497
141-79-7	mesityl oxide	49, 325, 491
108-10-1	methyl isobutyl ketone	497
141-91-3	2,6-dimethylmorpholine	325
141-93-5	m-diethylbenzene	325
141-97-9	ethyl acetoacetate	325, 491
142-04-1	aniline hydrochloride	325
142-09-6	hexyl methacrylate	325
142-16-5	bis(2-ethylhexyl) maleate	325
142-22-3	diethylene glycol bis(allylcarbonate)	325
142-24-7	n-acetyl ethanolamine	325
142-29-0	cyclopentene	325
142-62-1	caproic acid	325
142-68-7	pentamethylene oxide	325
142-77-8	butyl oleate	325
142-82-5	heptane	325, 491, 497
142-83-6	2,4-hexadienal	325
142-84-7	dipropylamine	325, 497
142-92-7	hexyl acetate	325

CAS #	CHEMICAL	NFPA Doc. No.
142-96-1	dibutyl ethers	49, 325, 491
142-83-6	hexachlorodiphenyl oxide	325
143-08-8	diisobutyl carbinol	325
	nonyl alcohol	497
143-13-5	nonyl acetate	325
143-15-7	lauryl bromide	325
143-16-8	dihexylamine	325
143-22-6	triethyleneglycol monobutyl ether	325
143-24-8	dimethoxy tetraglycol	325
143-33-9	sodium cyanide	49, 491
144-19-4	2,2,4-trimethyl-1,3-pentanediol	325
144-55-8	sodium bicarbonate	491
144-62-7	oxalic acid	49, 491
148-53-8	vanillin	491
149-31-5	2-methyl-1,3-pentanediol	325
149-91-7	gallic acid	491
150-76-5	hydroquinone monomethyl ether	325
151-05-3	dimethylbenzylcarbinyl acetate	325
151-13-3	butyl ricinoleate	325
151-50-8	potassium cyanide	49, 491
151-56-4	ethylenimine	49, 325, 491, 497
	ethyleneimine	49, 325, 491, 497
156-43-4	p-phenetidine	325
156-59-2	1,2-dichloroethylene	497
156-62-7	cyanamide	325
156-87-6	3-aminopropanol	325
208-87-2	methylcyclohexane	497
287-23-0	cyclobutane	325
287-92-3	cyclopentane	325
291-64-5	cycloheptane	325
298-00-0	methyl parathion	491
298-07-7 and 2915-57-3	bis(2-ethylhexyl) phosphoric acid	325
298-14-6	potassium bicarbonate	491
300-62-9	benzedrine	325
301-04-2	lead acetate	491
302-01-2	hydrazine	49, 325, 491, 497
334-88-3	diazomethane	491
353-36-6	ethyl fluoride	325
372-09-8	cyanoacetic acid	49, 491
431-03-8	2,3-butanedione	325
460-19-5	cyanogen	49, 325, 491
462-06-6	fluorobenzene	325
463-49-0	allene	491
463-58-1	carbon oxysulfide	325
463-82-1	2,2-dimethylpropane	325, 497
	neopentane	325, 497

CAS #	CHEMICAL	NFPA Doc. No.
464-06-2	2,2,3-trimethylbutane	325
464-45-9 (l-borneol) 507-70-0 (d-borneol)	borneol	325
471-34-1	calcium carbonate	491
473-55-2	pinane	325
479-45-8	tetryl	491
488-23-3	1,2,3,4-tetramethylbenzene, 95%	325
493-02-7	decahydronaphthalene-trans	325
496-03-7	butyraldol	325
496-11-7	indan	325
497-19-8	sodium carbonate	491
503-17-3	2-butyne	325
503-74-2	isopentanoic acid	325
504-20-1	phorone	325
504-60-9	1,3-pentadiene (mixture of cis and trans isomers)	325
504-63-2	trimethylene glycol	325
506-64-9	silver cyanide	491
506-65-0	gold cyanide	491
506-68-3	cyanogen bromide	49
506-78-5	cyanogen iodide	491
506-93-4	guanidine nitrate (self-reactive)	491
506-96-7	acetyl bromide	491
507-20-0	tert-butyl chloride	325
507-25-5	carbon tetraiodide	491
509-14-8	tetranitromethane	491
513-35-9	2-methyl-2-butene	325
513-36-0	isobutyl chloride	325
513-42-8	methallyl alcohol	325
513-53-1	2-butanethiol	325
513-85-9	2,3-butanediol	325
513-92-8	tetraiodoethylene	491
517-25-9	nitroform, trinitromethane	491
519-73-3	triphenylmethane	325
520-45-6	dehydroacetic acid	325
526-73-8	1,2,3-trimethylbenzene	325
527-53-7	1,2,3,5-tetramethylbenzene, 85.5%	325
528-29-0	dinitrobenzenes	49, 325
532-27-4	chloroacetophenone	325
534-15-6	methyl formal	497
534-22-5	2-methylfuran	325
538-68-1	amylbenzene	325
538-93-2	isobutylbenzene	325
539-90-2	isobutyl butyrate	325
540-18-1	amyl butyrate	325
540-54-5	1-chloropropane	325
540-59-0	dichloroethylene	49, 325, 491
540-67-0	ethyl methyl ether	49, 325, 491
	methyl ethyl ether	49, 325, 491
540-84-1	2,2,4-trimethylpentane	325
540-88-5	acetic acid-tert.-butyl ester	497
541-41-3	ethyl chloroformate	49, 325
541-85-5	ethyl sec-amyl ketone	497
542-18-7	cyclohexyl chloride	325
542-55-2	isobutyl formate	325
542-58-5	2-chloroethyl acetate	325
542-59-6	ethylene glycol acetate	325
542-75-6	dichloropropene	49, 325
542-76-7	3-chloropropionitrile	325
542-88-1	dichlorodimethyl ether, symmetrical	49
543-49-7	2-heptanol	325
543-59-9	amyl chloride	325
544-10-5	1-chlorohexane	325
544-76-3	hexadecane	325
544-92-3	cuprous cyanide	491
547-64-8	methyl lactate	325
554-12-1	methyl propionate	325
554-13-2	lithium carbonate	491
555-10-2	β-phellandrene	325
557-05-1	zinc stearate	325
557-18-6	diethylmagnesium	491
557-19-7	nickel cyanide	491
557-20-0	diethylzinc	49, 325, 491
557-21-1	zinc cyanide	49, 491
557-31-3	ethyl propenyl ether	325
557-40-4	allyl ether	325
557-98-2	2-chloropropylene	325
558-13-4	carbon tetrabromide	491
563-43-9	ethylaluminum dichloride	325
563-45-1	3-methyl-1-butene	325
563-46-2	2-methyl-1-butene (technical grade)	325
563-47-3	methallyl chloride	325
563-79-1	2,3-dimethyl-2-butene	325
565-59-3	2,3-dimethylpentane	325
577-92-4	4-tert-butyl-2-phenylphenol	325
578-54-1	o-ethylaniline	325
583-59-5	2-methylcyclohexanol	325
583-60-8	methylcyclohexanone	325, 497
584-02-1	3-pentanol	325
584-03-2	1,2-butanediol	325
584-08-7	potassium carbonate	491
584-84-9	toluene diisocyanate	49
589-34-4	3-methylhexane	325, 497
589-38-8	3-hexanone	325
589-82-2	3-heptanol	325
589-90-2	1,4-dimethylcyclohexane	325
589-91-3	4-methylcyclohexanol	325
589-92-4	4-methylcyclohexanone	491
590-01-2	butyl propionate	325

CAS #	CHEMICAL	NFPA Doc. No.
590-18-1	2-butene-cis	325
590-21-6	1-chloropropylene	325
590-86-3	isopentaldehyde	325
590-88-5	1,3-butanediamine	325
591-23-1	3-methylcyclohexanol	325
591-47-9	4-methylcyclohexene	325
591-51-5	phenyl lithium	491
591-60-6	butyl acetoacetate	325
591-62-8	n-butylurethane	325
591-76-4	isoheptane	325
591-78-6	methyl butyl ketone	325, 497
	2-hexanone	325, 497
591-87-7	allyl acetate	325
591-97-9	1-crotyl chloride	325
592-01-8	calcium cyanide	49
592-04-1	mercury cyanide	49, 491
592-05-2	lead cyanide	491
592-27-8	isooctane	325
592-41-6	hexene	325, 497
592-45-0	1,4-hexadiene	325
592-84-7	butyl formate	325
593-08-8	methyl undecyl ketone	325
593-45-3	octadecane	325
593-60-2	vinyl bromide	325
593-88-4	trimethylarsine	491
594-09-2	trimethylphosphine	491
594-10-5	trimethylstibine	491
594-27-4	tetramethyl tin	325
594-36-5	tert-amyl chloride	325
594-71-8	2-chloro-2-nitropropane	325
594-72-9	1,1-dichloro-1-nitroethane	325, 497
595-90-4	tetraphenyl tin	325
598-63-0	lead carbonate	491
598-78-7	α-chloropropionic acid	325
598-92-5	1-chloro-1-nitroethane	325
598-96-9	3,4,4-trimethyl-2-pentene	325
600-25-9	1-chloro-1-nitropropane	325
600-36-2	2,4-dimethyl-3-pentanol	325
603-35-0	triphenylphosphorus	325
611-14-3	o-ethyltoluene	325
612-00-0	1,1-diphenylethane (uns)	325
613-29-6	n,n-dibutylaniline	325
614-45-9	tert-butyl perbenzoate	325, 491
	t-butyl peroxybenzoate	325, 491
616-23-9	2,3-dichloro-1-propanol	325
616-29-5	1,3-diamino-2-propanol	325
616-38-6	dimethylcarbonate	49
	methyl carbonate	325
616-45-5	2-pyrrolidone	325
617-51-6	isopropyl lactate	325
617-75-4	triethlyarsine	491
617-89-0	furfurylamine	325
620-14-4	m-ethyltoluene	325
621-77-2	tripentylamine	49, 325

CAS #	CHEMICAL	NFPA Doc. No.
621-78-3	triamyl borate	325
622-08-2	ethylene glycol monobenzyl ether	325
622-40-2	4-(2-hydroxyethyl) morpholine	325
622-45-7	cyclohexyl acetate	325
622-86-6	β-chlorophenetole	325
622-96-8	p-ethyltoluene	325
623-17-6	furfuryl acetate	325
623-42-7	methyl butyrate	325
623-70-1	ethyl crotonate	325
623-91-6	diethyl fumarate	325
624-29-3	1,4-dimethylcyclohexane-cis	325
624-48-6	dimethyl maleate	325
624-54-4	amyl propionate	325
624-64-6	2-butene-trans	325
624-83-9	methyl isocyanate	49, 325, 497
625-30-9	sec-amylamine	325
625-50-3	n-ethylacetamide	325
625-55-8	isopropyl formate	49, 325
625-58-1	ethyl nitrate	325
625-86-5	2,5-dimethylfuran	325
626-23-3	di-sec-butylamine	325
626-38-0	sec-amyl acetate	325, 497
627-13-4	propyl nitrate	49, 325, 497
627-19-0	1-pentyne	325
627-20-3	β-amylene-cis	325
627-27-0	vinyl ethyl alcohol	325
627-53-2	diethyl selenide	325
627-54-3	diethyl telluride	49, 491
	tellurium diethyl	49, 491
628-32-0	ethyl propyl ether	325
628-37-5	diethyl peroxide	325
628-61-5	octyl chloride	325
628-63-7	amyl acetate	325, 497
628-68-2	diethylene glycol diacetate	325
628-76-2	1,5-dichloropentane	325
628-81-9	ethyl butyl ether	325
628-89-7	diglycol chlorohydrin	325
629-14-1	ethylene glycol diethyl ether	325
629-15-2	1,2-ethanediol diformate	325
629-59-4	tetradecane	325
629-82-3	dioctyl ether	325
629-92-5	nonadecane	325
630-08-0	carbon monoxide	49, 325, 491, 497
631-61-8	ammonium acetate	491
636-09-9	diethyl terephthalate	325
638-17-5	thialdine	325
638-49-3	amyl formate	325
638-56-2	bis[2-(2-chloroethoxy)ethyl] ether	325
645-62-5	2-ethyl-3-propylacrolein	325, 497

CAS #	CHEMICAL	NFPA Doc. No.
646-04-8	β-amylene-trans	325
674-82-8	diketene	49, 325, 491
681-84-5	tetramethoxysilane	49
684-93-5	n-methyl-n-nitroso urea	491
688-74-4	tri-n-butyl borate	325
689-97-4	vinyl acetylene	49, 325
691-37-2	4-methyl-1-pentene	325
692-42-2	diethylarsine	491
693-65-2	amyl ether	325
696-29-7	isopropylcyclohexane	325
702-03-4	n-(2-cyanoethyl) cyclohexylamine	325
717-74-8	triisopropylbenzene	325
719-79-9	1,1-diphenylbutane	325
760-21-4	2-ethyl-1-butene	325
763-29-1	2-methyl-1-pentene	325
772-54-3	n-benzyldiethylamine	325
777-37-7	2-chloro-5-nitrobenzotrifluoride	325
782-44-7	oxygen (liquid)	491
814-78-8	methyl isopropenyl ketone	325
818-61-1	2-hydroxyethyl acrylate	325
821-08-9	divinyl acetylene	325
821-55-6	methyl heptyl ketone	325
822-06-0	hexamethylene diisocyanate	491
827-52-1	cyclohexylbenzene	325
865-47-4	potassium tert.-butoxide	491
869-29-4	allylidene diacetate	325
871-27-2	diethylaluminum hydride	325
872-05-9	decene	325, 497
872-10-6	amyl sulfides (mixed)	325
872-50-4	1-methyl-2-pyrrolidinone	325
877-44-1	1,2,4-triethylbenzene	325
917-54-4	methyl lithium	491
926-56-7	4-methyl-1,3-pentadiene	325
926-57-8	1,3-dichloro-2-butene	325
926-65-8	vinyl isopropyl ether	325
927-07-1	tert-butyl peroxypivalate	325
927-80-0	ethoxyacetylene	325
928-45-0	butyl nitrate	325
928-55-2	propenyl ethyl ether	325
928-96-1	3-hexenol-cis	325
930-02-9	vinyl octadecyl ether	325
930-22-3	butadiene monoxide	325
930-68-7	cyclohexenone	325
939-48-0	isopropyl benzoate	325
955-50-1	o-dichlorobenzene	497
998-40-3	tributylphosphine	325, 491
999-61-1	propylene glycol acrylate	325
999-97-3	hexamethyldisilazane	49
1002-16-0	amyl nitrate	49, 325
1071-26-7	3,3-dimethylheptane	497
1081-77-2	nonylbenzene	325

CAS #	CHEMICAL	NFPA Doc. No.
1118-58-7	2-methyl-1,3-pentadiene	325
1119-49-9	n-butyl acetamide	325
1120-21-4	hendecane	325
1122-60-7	nitrocyclohexane	325
1126-78-9	n-butylaniline	325
1126-79-0	butyl phenyl ether	325
1191-15-7	diisobutylaluminum hydride	325
1195-42-2	isopropylcyclohexylamine	325
1254-78-0	phenyl didecyl phosphite	325
1271-19-8	titanium dichloride	491
1299-86-1	aluminum carbide	491
1300-21-6	1,1-dichloroethane	497
1302-30-3	lithium aluminum hydride	49, 491
1303-00-0	gallium arsenide	49
1303-28-2	arsenic pentoxide	49, 491
	arsenic oxide	49, 491
1303-32-8	arsenic disulfide	491
1303-33-9	arsenic trisulfide	49, 491
1304-28-5	barium oxide	491
1304-29-6	barium peroxide	491
1304-56-9	beryllium oxide	491
1304-76-3	bismuth trioxide	491
1305-62-0	calcium hydroxide	491
1305-78-8	calcium oxide	49, 491
1305-79-9	calcium peroxide	491
1305-99-3	calcium phosphide	491
1306-19-0	cadmium oxide	491
1306-23-6	cadmium sulfide	491
1309-42-8	magnesium hydroxide	491
1309-48-4	magnesium oxide	491
1309-60-0	lead dioxide	491
1310-58-3	potassium hydroxide	49, 491
1310-73-2	sodium hydroxide	49, 491
1312-73-8	potassium sulfide, anhydrous	49
1312-81-8	lanthanum oxide	491
1313-13-9	manganese dioxide	491
1313-59-3	sodium monoxide, sodium oxide	491
1313-60-6	sodium peroxide	49, 491
1313-82-2	sodium sulfide, anhydrous	49
1313-99-1	nickel monoxide	491
1314-13-2	zinc oxide	491
1314-22-3	zinc peroxide	491
1314-32-5	thallic oxide	491
1314-34-7	vanadium sesquioxide	491
1314-35-8	tungsten trioxide	491
1314-56-3	phosphorus pentoxide	491
1314-62-1	vanadium pentoxide	491
1314-80-3	phosphorus pentasulfide	49, 491
1314-84-7	zinc phosphide	49, 491
1314-87-0	lead sulfide	491
1314-98-3	zinc sulfide	491
1315-04-4	antimony sulfide	49, 491
1317-33-5	molybdenum trioxide	491

CAS #	CHEMICAL	NFPA Doc. No.
1317-35-7	trimanganese tetroxide	491
1317-36-8	lead oxide	491
1317-37-9	ferrous sulfide	491
1317-38-0	cupric oxide	491
1317-40-4	cupric sulfide	491
1317-65-3	limestone (crushed)	491
1319-77-3	cresol	491, 497
1319-77-3 all isomers meta 108-39-4 ortho 95-48-7 para 106-44-5	cresols (o-, m-, p-)	49
1320-01-0	amyl toluene	325
1320-21-4	amyl xylyl ether	325
1321-60-4	trimethylcyclohexanol	325
1321-74-0	divinylbenzene	49, 325
1327-53-3	arsenic trioxide	49, 491
1330-20-7	xylene	497
1331-11-9	3-ethoxypropionic acid	325
1332-37-2	iron oxide	491
1333-13-7	tert-butyl-m-cresol	325
1333-74-0	hydrogen	49, 325, 491, 497
1333-82-0	chromic acid, solid	49, 491
	chromic anhydride	49, 491
1335-31-5	mercuric cyanide oxide	491
1336-21-6	ammonium hydroxide	491
1336-36-3	polychlorinated biphenyls	49
1344-08-7	sodium polysulfide	491
1344-09-8	sodium silicate	491
1344-28-1	aluminum oxide	491
1344-43-0	manganous oxide	491
1344-48-5	mercuric sulfide	491
1344-57-6	uranium dioxide	491
1345-04-6	antimony trisulfide	491
1401-55-4	tannic acid	325
1445-79-0	trimethylgallium	491
1459-93-4	dimethylisophthalate	325
1467-79-4	dimethylcyanamide	325
1559-35-9	ethylene glycol ethylhexyl ether	325
1563-90-2	n,n-dibutylacetamide	325
1569-69-3	cyclohexanethiol	325
1590-87-0	disilane (silicoethane)	491
1609-19-4	chlorodiethyl silane	49
1634-04-4	methyl tertiary butyl ether	497
1638-16-0	tripropylene glycol	325
1640-89-7	ethylcyclopentane	325
1653-19-6	2,3-dichlorobutadiene-1,3	325
1656-63-9	trilauryl trithiophosphite	325
1663-35-0	vinyl 2-methoxyethyl ether	325
1678-91-7	ethylcyclohexane	325
1678-92-8	propylcyclohexane	325
1678-93-9	butylcyclohexane	325
1696-20-4	n-acetyl morpholine	325

CAS #	CHEMICAL	NFPA Doc. No.
1762-95-4	ammonium thiocyanate	491
1789-58-8	ethyl dichlorosilane	325
2016-57-1	decylamine	325
2049-92-5	p-tert-amylaniline	325
2050-08-0	amyl salicylate	325
2050-24-0	1-methyl-3,5-diethylbenzene	325
2050-60-4	dibutyl oxalate	325
2050-92-2	diamylamine	49, 325
2084-18-6	3-methyl-2-butanethiol	325
2100-42-7	2,5-dimethoxychlorobenzene	325
2109-64-0	dibutylisopropanolamine	325
2156-96-9	decyl acrylate	325
2160-93-2	tert-butyldiethanolamine	325
2202-98-4	diethylene glycol phthalate	325
2216-32-2	2-methyloctane	497
2216-33-3	3-methyloctane	497
2216-34-4	4-methyloctane	497
2235-46-3	n,n-diethylacetoacetamide	325
2244-21-5	potassium dichloro-s-triazinetrione	49
2425-66-3	1-chloro-1-nitropropane	497
2426-54-2	2-(diethylamino)ethyl acrylate	325
2437-56-1	n-tridecene	497
2449-49-2	α-methylbenzyl dimethyl amine	325
2456-28-2	didecyl ether	325
2487-90-3	trimethoxysilane	49
2517-43-3	3-methoxybutanol	325
2541-75-5	heptadecanol	325
2551-62-4	sulfur hexafluoride	491
2568-90-3	dibutoxymethane	325
2681-52-9	sodium hypochlorite	491
2696-92-6	nitrosyl chloride	491
2806-85-1	3-ethoxypropanal	325
2825-83-4	endo-tetrahydrodicyclopenta-diene	325
2842-38-8	n-(2-hydroxyethyl) cyclohexylamine	325
2867-47-2	2-(dimethylamino)ethyl methacrylate	325
2893-78-9	sodium dichloro-s-triazinetrione dihydrate	49
2915-57-3	bis(2-ethylhexyl) succinate	325
2917-26-2	tert-hexadecanethiol	325
2935-44-6	2,5-hexanediol	325
2937-50-0	allyl chloroformate	49, 325
2999-74-8	dimethylmagnesium	491
3037-72-7	silane, (4-aminobutyl)-diethoxymethyl	49
3081-14-9	n,n1-bis-(1,4-dimethylpentyl) p-phenylenediamine	325
3121-61-7	2-methoxyethyl acrylate	325
3126-90-7	dibutyl isophthalate	325
3132-64-7	epichlorohydrin	497
3178-22-1	tert-butylcyclohexane	325

CAS #	CHEMICAL	NFPA Doc. No.
3221-61-2	2-methyloctane	497
3251-23-8	cupric nitrate	491
3268-49-3	β-methyl mercaptopropionaldehyde	325
3312-60-5	n-(3-aminopropyl) cyclohexylamine	325
3352-87-2	n,n-diethyllauramide	325
3452-97-9	3,5,5-trimethylhexanol	325
3522-94-9	2,2,5-trimethylhexane	325
3583-47-9	n-butane	497
3610-27-3	methoxytriglycol acetate	325
3724-65-0	crotonic acid	49, 325
3775-90-4	tert-butylaminoethyl methacrylate	325
	potassium chlorate	491
3917-15-5	vinyl allyl ether	325
4016-14-2	isopropyl glycidyl ether	497
4050-45-7 (trans)	2-hexene	325
4098-71-9	isophorone diisocyanate	49
4109-96-0	dichlorosilane	49, 325, 491
4170-30-3	crotonaldehyde	49, 325, 491, 497
4292-92-6	amylcyclohexane	325
4324-38-3	3-ethoxypropionic acid	325
4435-53-4	3-methoxybutyl acetate	325
4439-24-1	ethylene glycol monoisobutyl ether	325
4461-41-0	2-chlorobutene-2	325
4784-77-4	1-crotyl bromide	325
4786-20-3	crotononitrile	325
4806-61-5	ethylcyclobutane	325
4904-61-4	1,5,9-cyclododecatriene	325
5329-14-6	sulfamic acid	491
5332-73-0	3-methoxypropylamine	325
5392-40-5	citral	325
5419-55-6	triisopropyl borate	325
5459-93-8	n-ethylcyclohexylamine	325
5743-97-5	perhydrophenanthrene	325
5881-17-4	3-ethyloctane	325
5894-60-0	hexadecyltrichlorosilane	325
6032-29-7	sec-amyl alcohol	325
6095-42-7	trihexyl phosphite	325
6100-20-5	potassium tetroxide	491
6117-91-5	crotonyl alcohol	325
6382-13-4	amyl stearate	325
6484-52-2	ammonium nitrate	49, 491
6531-86-8	cyclohexylcyclohexanol	325
6812-78-8	rhodinol	325
6842-15-5	dodecene	497
6920-22-5	hexylene glycol	325
7085-85-0	2-cyanoethyl acrylate	325
7397-62-8	butyl glycolate	325
73513-42-5	isohexane (mixture of hexane isomers)	325

CAS #	CHEMICAL	NFPA Doc. No.
7429-90-5	aluminum powder, uncoated	49
7439-88-5	iridium	491
7439-89-6	iron	491
7439-91-0	lanthanum	491
7439-92-1	lead	491
7439-93-2	lithium	49, 491
7439-94-3	lutetium	491
7439-95-4	magnesium	49, 491
7439-96-5	manganese	491
7439-97-6	mercury	491
7439-98-7	molybdenum	491
7440-00-8	neodymium	491
7440-02-0	nickel	49, 491
7440-03-0	niobium (columbium)	491
7440-04-2	osmium	491
7440-05-3	palladium	491
7440-06-4	platinum	491
7440-09-7	potassium	49, 491
7440-10-0	praseodymium	491
7440-15-5	rhenium	491
7440-16-6	rhodium	491
7440-17-7	rubidium	491
7440-18-8	ruthenium	491
7440-19-9	samarium	491
7440-21-3	silicon	491
7440-22-4	silver	491
7440-23-5	sodium	49
7440-25-7	tantalum pentoxide	491
7440-27-9	terbium	491
7440-28-0	thallium	491
7440-29-1	thorium	491
7440-30-4	thulium	491
7440-31-5	tin	491
7440-32-6	titanium	491
7440-33-7	tungsten	491
7440-36-0	antimony	491
7440-38-2	arsenic	491
7440-41-7	beryllium	49, 491
7440-42-8	boron	491
7440-43-9	cadmium	491
7440-44-0	carbon	491
7440-45-1	cerium	491
7440-46-2	cesium	491
7440-47-3	chromium	491
7440-48-4	cobalt	491
7440-50-8	copper	491
7440-52-0	erbium	491
7440-53-1	europium	491
7440-54-2	gadolinium	491
7440-56-4	germanium	491
7440-57-5	gold	491
7440-60-0	holmium	491
7440-62-2	vanadium	491
7440-66-6	zinc	491

CAS #	CHEMICAL	NFPA Doc. No.
7440-70-2	calcium	49, 491
7440-74-6	indium	491
7446-09-05	sulfur dioxide	49, 491
7446-11-9	sulfur trioxide	491
7446-14-2	lead sulfate	491
7446-70-0	aluminum chloride	49, 491
7447-39-4	cupric chloride	491
7447-40-7	potassium chloride	491
7447-41-8	lithium chloride	491
7487-94-7	mercuric chloride	491
7521-80-4	butyl trichlorosilane	325
7546-30-7	mercurous chloride	491
7550-45-0	titanium tetrachloride	49, 491
7553-56-2	iodine	491
7568-93-6	(m-aminophenyl) methyl carbinol	325
7572-29-4	dichloracetylene	491
7580-67-8	lithium hydride	49, 491
7581-97-7	2,3-dichlorobutane	325
7601-89-0	sodium perchlorate	491
7601-90-3	perchloric acid	49, 491
7616-94-6	perchloryl fluoride	491
7631-86-9	silica (silica dioxide)	491
7631-99-4	sodium nitrate	491
7632-00-0	sodium nitrite	491
7632-51-1	vanadium tetrachloride	49
7646-69-7	sodium hydride	49, 491
7646-78-8	stannic chloride	49, 491
7646-85-7	zinc chloride	491
7647-01-0	hydrogen chloride	49, 491
	hydrochloric acid	49, 491
7647-14-5	sodium chloride	491
7647-15-6	sodium bromide	491
7647-17-8	cesium chloride	491
7647-18-9	antimony pentachloride, liquid	49, 491
	antimonyl chloride	49, 491
7664-38-2	phosphoric acid	49
7664-39-3	hydrogen fluoride, anhydrous	49, 491
	hydrofluoric acid	49, 491
7664-41-7	ammonia	49, 325, 491, 497
7664-93-9	sulfuric acid	49, 491
7673-09-8	trichloromelamine	491
7681-11-0	potassium iodide	491
7681-49-4	sodium fluoride	49
7681-53-0	sodium hypophosphite	491
7681-55-2	sodium iodate	491
7681-82-5	sodium iodide	491
7688-21-3	2-hexene-cis	325
7693-27-8	magnesium hydride	491
7697-37-2	nitric acid	49, 491
7704-34-9	sulfur	49, 325, 491
7704-99-6	zirconium dihydride	491
7718-54-9	nickel chloride	491
7719-09-7	thionyl chloride	49, 491
7719-12-2	phosphorus trichloride	49, 491
7722-64-7	potassium permanganate	491
7722-76-1	ammonium phosphate, monoammonium phosphate	491
7722-84-1	hydrogen peroxide	49, 491
7722-86-3	permonosulfuric acid (caro's acid)	491
7723-14-0	phosphorus	49, 491
7726-95-6	bromine	49, 491
7727-21-1	potassium persulfate	491
7727-37-9	nitrogen	49, 491
7727-43-7	barium sulfate	491
7727-54-0	ammonium persulfate	491
7757-79-1	potassium nitrate	491
7757-82-6	sodium sulfate	491
7758-01-2	potassium bromate	491
7758-02-3	potassium bromide	491
7758-05-6	potassium iodate	491
7758-09-0	potassium nitrite	491
7758-19-2	sodium chlorite	49, 491
7758-89-6	cuprous chloride	491
7758-94-3	ferrous chloride	491
7758-97-6	lead chromate	491
7758-98-7	cupric sulfate	491
7761-88-8	silver nitrate	491
7772-98-7	sodium thiosulfate	491
7772-99-8	stannous chloride	491
7773-01-5	manganous chloride	491
7774-29-0	mercuric iodide	491
7775-09-9	sodium chlorate	491
7775-14-6	sodium hydrosulfite	49, 491
7778-50-9	potassium dichromate	491
7778-54-3	calcium hypochlorite	49, 491
7778-74-7	potassium perchlorate	491
7778-80-5	potassium sulfate	491
7779-88-6	zinc nitrate	491
7782-39-0	deuterium	325
7782-41-4	fluorine	49, 491
7782-42-5	graphite	491
7782-44-7	oxygen	49, 491
7782-49-2	selenium	491
7782-50-5	chlorine	49, 491
7782-65-2	germane	49, 491
7782-78-7	nitrosylsulfuric acid	491
7782-89-0	lithium amide	491
7782-92-5	sodium amide	491
7783-06-4	hydrogen sulfide	49, 491
7783-07-5	hydrogen selenide	491
7783-18-8	ammonium thiosulfate	491
7783-20-2	ammonium sulfate	491
7783-46-2	lead fluoride	491
7783-49-5	zinc fluoride	491

CAS #	CHEMICAL	NFPA Doc. No.
7783-54-2	nitrogen trifluoride	491
7783-55-3	phosphorus trifluoride	491
7783-61-1	silicon tetrafluoride	49
7783-66-6	iodine pentafluoride	491
7783-70-2	antimony pentafluoride	49, 491
7783-90-6	silver chloride	491
7783-93-9	silver perchlorate	491
7783-95-1	silver fluoride	491
7783-96-2	silver iodide	491
7784-18-1	aluminum fluoride	491
7784-21-6	aluminum hydride	491
7784-34-1	arsenic trichloride	49, 491
7784-36-3	arsenic pentafluoride	49
7784-42-1	arsine	49, 491
7784-45-4	arsenic triiodide	491
7786-30-3	magnesium chloride	491
7787-60-2	bismuth trichloride	491
7787-70-4	cuprous bromide	491
7787-71-5	bromine trifluoride	49, 491
7789-09-5	ammonium dichromate	49, 491
7789-23-3	potassium fluoride	491
7789-30-2	bromine pentafluoride	49, 491
7789-33-5	iodine monobromide	491
7789-38-0	sodium bromate	491
7789-40-4	thallous bromide	491
7789-42-6	cadmium bromide	491
7789-45-9	cupric bromide	491
7789-47-1	mercuric bromide	491
7789-60-8	phosphorus tribromide	49, 491
7789-61-9	antimony tribromide	491
7789-67-5	stannic bromide	491
7789-78-8	calcium hydride	491
7789-79-9	calcium hypophosphite	491
7790-33-2	manganous iodide	491
7790-44-5	antimony triiodide	491
7790-47-8	stannic iodide	491
7790-79-6	cadmium fluoride	491
7790-80-9	cadmium iodide	491
7790-89-8	chlorine monofluoride	491
7790-91-2	chlorine trifluoride	49, 491
7790-93-4	chloric acid	491
7790-94-5	chlorosulfonic acid	49, 491
	chlorosulfuric acid	49, 491
7790-98-9	ammonium perchlorate	49, 491
7791-10-8	strontium chlorate	491
7791-11-9	rubidium chloride	491
7791-12-0	thallous chloride	491
7791-21-1	chlorine monoxide	325, 491
7791-23-3	selenium oxychloride	491
7791-25-5	sulfuryl chloride	49, 491
7803-49-8	hydroxylamine	49, 325, 491
7803-51-2	phosphine	49, 325, 491
7803-52-3	stibine	49, 491
7803-62-5	silane	49, 325, 491
8000-41-7	terpineol	325
8001-20-5	tung oil	325
8001-22-7	soy bean oil	325
8001-25-0	olive oil	325
8001-26-1	linseed oil	325, 491
8001-29-4	cottonseed oil	325
8001-30-7	corn oil	325
8001-31-8	cocoanut oil	325
8001-58-9	creosote oil	325
8001-69-2	cod liver oil	325
8001-78-3	castor oil (hydrogenated)	325
8001-79-4	castor oil	325
8002-13-9	rapeseed oil	325
8002-16-2	rosin oil	325
8002-24-2	sperm oil no. 1	325
8002-33-3	turkey red oil	325
8002-50-4	menhaden oil	325
8002-64-0	neatsfoot oil	325
8002-74-2	wax, paraffin	325
8002-75-3	palm oil	325
8006-14-2	gas, natural	325
8006-20-0	gas, producer	325
8006-54-0	lanolin	325
8006-61-9	gasoline	325, 497
8006-64-2	turpentine	497
8007-45-2	coal tar pitch	325
8008-20-6	fuel oil no. 1	325, 497
8008-51-3	camphor oil	325
8008-74-0	sesame oil	325
8011-48-1	pine tar	325
8012-95-1	mineral oil	325
8015-86-9	carnauba wax	325
8016-28-2	lard oil (commercial or animal)	325
8021-55-4	wax, ozocerite	325
8023-79-8	palm kernel oil	325
8030-30-6	naphtha (coal tar)	497
8032-32-4	naphtha v.m. & p.	325
8052-41-3	stoddard solvent	325
8052-42-4	asphalt	325, 491
9002-84-0	polytetrafluoroethylene, teflon (polytetrafluoroethylene)	491
9002-88-4	polyethylene	491
9002-89-5	polyvinyl alcohol	325
9002-92-0	polyoxyethylene lauryl ether	325
9003-07-0	polypropylene	491
9003-27-4	polyisobutylene	491
9003-35-4	phenol-formaldehyde resin	491
9004-34-6	cellulose	491
9004-70-0	collodion	325
9005-90-7	turpentine	325

CAS #	CHEMICAL	NFPA Doc. No.
9006-04-6	rubber	491
9010-98-4	neoprene	491
9011-14-7	lucite, methyl methacrylate polymer	491
9011-17-0	viton a	491
10022-31-8	barium nitrate	491
10024-97-2	nitrous oxide	491
10025-67-9	sulfur chlorides	49, 491
10025-67-9	sulfur dichloride	325
10025-73-7	chromic chloride	49
10025-78-2	trichlorosilane	49, 325
10025-85-1	nitrogen trichloride	491
10025-87-3	phosphorus oxychloride	49, 491
	phosphoryl chloride	49, 491
10025-91-9	antimony trichloride	491
10026-04-7	silicon tetrachloride	49, 491
10026-11-6	zirconium tetrachloride	49, 491
10026-13-8	phosphorus pentachloride	49, 491
10028-15-6	ozone	491
10028-18-9	nickel fluoride	491
10031-87-5	2-ethylbutyl acetate	325
10034-81-8	magnesium perchlorate	491
10034-85-2	hydriodic acid, solution	49, 491
10035-10-6	hydrogen bromide	49, 491
10038-98-9	germanium tetrachloride	491
10043-11-5	boron nitride	491
10043-35-3	boric acid	491
10043-52-4	calcium chloride	491
10045-94-0	mercuric nitrate	491
10049-04-4	chlorine dioxide	491
10061-02-6	1,3-dichloropropene	497
10097-28-6	silicon monoxide	491
10099-70-4	diisopropyl maleate	325
10099-71-5	diamyl maleate	325
10099-74-8	lead nitrate	491
10102-43-9	nitric oxide	491
10102-44-0	nitrogen dioxide	491
10108-56-2	n-butylcyclohexylamine	325
10108-64-2	cadmium chloride	491
10137-74-3	calcium chlorate	491
10139-47-6	zinc iodide	491
10217-52-4	hydrazine hydrate	491
10294-33-4	boron tribromide	49, 491
10294-34-5	boron trichloride	491
10308-82-4	aminoguanidine nitrate	491
10326-21-3	magnesium chlorate	491
10361-29-2	ammonimum carbonate	491
10361-37-2	barium chloride	491
10361-95-2	zinc chlorate	491
10377-60-3	magnesium nitrate	491
10415-75-5	mercurous nitrate	491
10450-60-9	periodic acid	491
10476-85-4	strontium chloride	491
10476-86-5	strontium iodide	491

CAS #	CHEMICAL	NFPA Doc. No.
10486-19-8	tridecanal	491
10544-72-6	nitrogen peroxide, nitrogen tetroxide	491
10544-73-7	nitrogen trioxide	491
10545-99-0	sulfur chloride	325, 491
10588-01-9	sodium dichromate	491
11031-45-1	santalol	325
11071-47-9	isooctenes	325
11104-28-2	polychlorinated biphenyl	491
11113-50-1	boric acid	491
11135-81-2	potassium-sodium alloys	49, 491
	sodium-potassium alloy	49, 491
12013-56-8	calcium silicide	491
12013-82-0	calcium nitride	491
12027-06-4	ammonium iodide	491
12029-98-0	iodine pentoxide	491
12030-88-5	potassium superoxide	491
12033-89-5	silicon nitride	491
12039-13-3	titanium disulfide	491
12057-74-8	magnesium phosphide	491
12058-85-4	sodium phosphide	491
12063-98-8	gallium phosphide	49
12070-08-5	titanium carbide	491
12070-12-1	tungsten carbide	491
12070-14-3	zirconium carbide	491
12071-33-9	uranium dicarbide	491
12075-68-2	ethylaluminum sesquichloride	325, 491
	trichlorotriethyldialuminum	325, 491
12124-97-9	ammonium bromide	491
12125-01-8	ammonium fluoride	49
12125-02-9	ammonium chloride	491
12136-45-7	potassium oxide	491
12164-94-2	ammonium azide	491
12263-85-3	methylaluminum sesquibromide	325
12504-16-4	strontium phosphide	491
12542-85-7	methylaluminum sesquichloride	325
12674-11-2	polychlorinated biphenyl	491
12771-08-3	sulfur dichloride	325
13057-78-8	monochloro-s- triazinetrione acid	49
13360-63-9	ethylbutylamine	325
13424-46-9	lead azide	491
13444-85-4	nitrogen iodide, nitrogen triiodide	491
13446-10-1	ammonium permanganate	49, 491
13450-90-3	gallium trichloride	49
13462-88-9	nickel bromide	491
13463-39-3	nickel carbonyl	49, 325, 491
13463-40-6	iron carbonyl	325, 491
	iron pentacarbonyl	325, 491
13463-67-7	titanium dixoide	491
13465-95-7	barium perchlorate	491

CAS #	CHEMICAL	NFPA Doc. No.
13477-00-4	barium chlorate	49, 491
13477-09-3	barium hydride	491
13494-80-9	tellurium	491
13637-76-8	lead perchlorate	491
13746-66-2	potassium ferricyanide	491
13762-51-1	potassium tetrahydroborate	491
13779-96-2	sodium tetrahydroaluminate	491
13818-89-8	digermane	491
13943-58-3	potassium ferrocyanide	491
13952-84-6	sec-butylamine	325
13973-87-0	bromine azide	491
13981-16-3	plutonium	491
14038-43-8	ferric ferrocyanide	491
14258-49-2	ammonium oxalate	491
14519-17-6	magnesium bromate	491
14674-72-7	calcium chlorite	491
14861-06-4	vinyl crotonate	325
14901-07-6	β-ionone	325
14977-61-8	chromium oxychloride	49, 491
	chromyl chloride	49, 491
15117-48-3	plutonium	491
15219-34-8	oxalyl bromide	491
15245-44-0	lead styphnate	491
15625-89-5	trimethylolpropane triacrylate	325
15829-53-5	mercurous oxide	491
15869-86-0	4-ethyloctane	325
15980-15-1	1,4-thioxane	325
16721-80-5	sodium bisulfide	491
16853-85-3	lithium aluminum hydride	491
16872-11-0	fluoboric acid	49, 491
16940-66-2	sodium tetrahydroborate	491
16949-15-8	lithium tetrahydroborate	491
17014-71-0	potassium peroxide	49, 491
17242-52-3	potassium amide	491
17702-41-9	decaborane	49, 325, 491
18282-10-5	stannic oxide	491
19287-45-7	diborane	49, 325, 491
19594-40-2	isobutyl heptyl ketone	325
19597-69-4	lithium azide	491
19624-22-7	pentaborane	49, 325, 491
20548-54-3	calcium sulfide	491
20667-12-3	silver oxide	491
20762-60-1	potassium azide	491
20859-73-8	aluminum phosphide	49, 491
21109-95-5	barium sulfide	491
21490-63-1	2,3-butylene oxide	325
21645-51-2	aluminum hydroxide	491
21651-19-4	stannous oxide	491
21908-53-2	mercuric oxide	491
24800-44-0	tripropylene glycol	325
25013-15-4	vinyl toluene	49, 325, 497
25103-52-0	isooctanoic acid	325
25103-58-6	tert-dodecyl mercaptan	325
25136-55-4	dimethyldioxane	325
25154-52-3	nonylphenol	325
25154-55-6	o-nitrophenol	491
25167-67-3	butylene	497
25167-70-8	diisobutylene	325, 491, 497
25168-05-2	chlorotoluene	325
25265-77-4	2,2,4-trimethyl-1,3-pentanediol isobutyrate	325
25321-09-9	diisopropylbenzene	325
25322-68-3	polyethylene glycols	325
25322-69-4	polypropylene glycols	325
25339-56-4	heptylene	325
25340-17-4	diethyl benzene	497
25340-18-5	triethylbenzene	497
25340-18-5	1,2,4-triethylbenzene	325
25360-10-5	tert-nonyl mercaptan	325
25377-83-7	octene	497
25498-49-1	tripropylene glycol methyl ether	325
25584-83-2	propylene glycol acrylate	325
25630-42-3	methylcyclohexanol	497
25640-78-2	2-isopropylbiphenyl	325
25735-67-5	p-sec-amylphenol	325
26094-13-3	butylamine oleate	325
26403-17-8	isodecanoic acid	325
26444-49-5	cresyl diphenyl phosphate	325
26628-22-8	sodium azide	491
26761-40-0	diisodecyl phthalate	325
26952-13-6	1-tetradecene	325
26952-14-7	1-hexadecene	325
26952-21-6	isooctyl alcohol	325
27178-16-1	diisodecyl adipate	325
27193-86-8	dodecyl phenol	325
27193-93-7	nonylnaphthalene	325
27214-95-8	nonene	497
27215-95-8	nonene	325
27554-26-3	diisooctyl phthalate	325
27846-30-6	methylacetylene-propadiene	497
28469-92-3	2,6-dichlorostyrene	325
28682-72-4	2-methylbiphenyl	325
28761-27-5	n-undecene	497
28983-37-1	tert-tetradecyl mercaptan	325
29191-52-4	o-anisidine	325
30174-58-4	tert-decylmercaptan	325
30232-11-2	methylcyclohexyl acetate	325
30525-89-4	paraformaldehyde	49, 325, 491
30586-10-8	dichloropentanes (mixed)	325
31242-93-0	heptylene-2-trans	325
31394-54-4	2,3-dimethylhexane	497
32280-46-9	n,n-diethyl-1,3-butanediamine	325
32480-00-5	nitromethane	491

CAS #	CHEMICAL	NFPA Doc. No.
32749-94-3	2,3-dimethylpentaldehyde	325
34590-94-8	dipropylene glycol methyl ether	325, 497
37211-05-5	nickel chloride	491
38232-63-2	mercurous azide	491
42350-99-2	2-chloro-4,6-di-tert-amylphenol	325
61789-51-3	cobalt naphtha	325
61789-97-7	tallow	325
63148-62-9	polydimethylsiloxane	491
63231-60-7	wax, microcrystalline	325
64037-54-3	3,4-dichlorobutene-1	325
64475-85-0	petroleum ether	325
64741-44-2	gas oil	325
64742-06-9	mineral seal oil	325
64742-34-3	straw oil	325
64742-88-7	mineral spirits	325
65996-68-1	gas, blast furnace	325
65996-77-2	coke	491
65996-81-8	gas, coke-oven	325

CAS #	CHEMICAL	NFPA Doc. No.
65996-91-0	coal tar light oil	325
68132-21-8	perilla oil	325
68187-82-6	fish oil (bisulfated mix)	325
68334-30-5	diesel fuel oil no. 1-d	325
68425-31-0	gasoline, casinghead	325
68476-26-6	gas, oil gas	325
68476-30-2	fuel oil no. 2	325
68476-31-3	fuel oil no. 4	325
68476-34-6	diesel fuel oil no. 2-d	325
68476-85-7	liquified petroleum gas	497
68553-00-4	fuel oil no. 6	325
68605-68-5	menhaden oil	325
70892-11-4	fuel oil no. 5	325
72623-85-9	lubricating oil, mineral (c20-c50)	325
73090-68-3	tert-butyl tetralin	325
73090-69-4	chloro-4-tert-amylphenol	325
73513-42-5	isohexane (mixture of hexane isomers)	325
81624-04-6	n-heptene	497

NFPA 49

1994 Edition

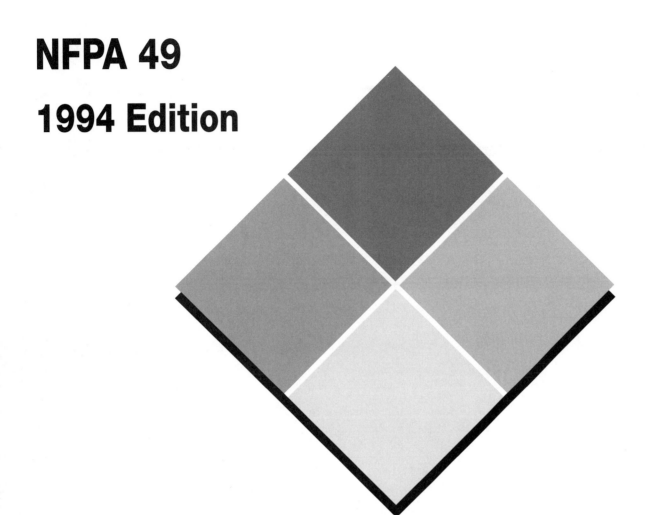

Hazardous Chemicals Data

NFPA 49

Hazardous Chemicals Data

1994 Edition, Amended 2001

This edition of NFPA 49, *Hazardous Chemicals Data,* was revised by NFPA Staff and the Technical Committee on Classification and Properties of Hazardous Chemicals Data. At the NFPA Fall Meeting held November 15–18, 1998 in Atlanta, GA, the document was withdrawn from the National Fire Codes®, along with NFPA 325, and later NFPA 491. Many of the recent revisions to NFPA 49, 325, and 491 were generated by the Committee with the prompting of staff, since few if any public proposals or comments were received. The Committee wished to note that this, coupled with concern of the speed in updating the data (which was not possible in a 3 to 5 year cycle), were the sole reasons the documents were withdrawn.

Origin and Development of NFPA 49

The compilation of information on hazardous chemicals was originated by the NFPA Committee on Hazardous Chemicals and Explosives in cooperation with the American Chemical Society. A Table of Common Hazardous Chemicals (NFPA 49) was adopted in 1928. Revisions were adopted in 1929, 1931, 1935, 1938, 1939, 1941, 1942, 1944, 1946, and 1950.

A complete revision, prepared by the Sectional Committee on Properties of Hazardous Chemicals, was adopted in 1961 under the new title, *Hazardous Chemicals Data* (NFPA 49M). Amendments were adopted in 1962, 1963, 1964, 1965, 1966, 1967, 1968, 1969, 1971, 1972, 1973, 1975, and 1991. Starting with the 1964 edition, the identifying number of *Hazardous Chemicals Data* has been NFPA 49.

The 1994 edition represented a complete revision of the document. Many of the chemicals were re-rated in accordance with the 1990 edition of NFPA 704, *Standard System for the Identification of the Fire Hazards of Materials,* which contained more quantitative criteria for the ratings. Up-to-date chemical data were used to rate the chemicals, which is easily and more readily available in this age of electronic databases.

New data included in this edition of the *Guide* are NFPA 30/OSHA flammable and combustible liquid classifications and Chemical Abstracts Service (CAS) numbers.

Technical Committee on Classification and Properties of Hazardous Chemical Data

Gary Robinson, *Chair*
LMG Property Engineering, IL [I]
Rep. The Alliance of American Insurers

Robert A. Michaels, *Secretary*
RAM TRAC Corporation, NY [SE]

Laurence G. Britton, Union Carbide Corporation, WV [M]
Lance "Skip" Edwards, National paint & Coatings Association, DC [M]
Richard Gowland, Dow Chemical, Great Britain [M]
Ronald Keefer, Menlo Park Fire Protection District, CA [E]
Ron A. Kirsch, OHS Associates, Inc., TN [SE]
Arthur A. Krawetz, Phoenix Chemical Laboratory, Inc., IL [RT]
F. Owen Kubias, Rocky River, OH [SE]
Roland J. Land, Risk Control Consultants, LLC, NJ [SE]
Jennifer L. Nelson, AT&T — EH&S, NY [U]
Rep. NFPA Industrial Fire Protection Section
Curtis G. Payne, U.S. Coast Guard, DC [U]
David F. Peterson, Madison, WI Fire Department, WI [E]
Thomas A. Salamone, Health Care & Life Safety Concepts, NY [I]
William J. Satterfield, III, RODE & Associates, LLC, RI [I]

Nonvoting

Whitney Fay Long, c/o CDR Long SACLANTCEN, APO AE
Ira Wainless, U.S. Department of Labor/OSHA, DC

Amy B. Spencer, NFPA Staff Liaison

This list represents the membership at the time the Committee was balloted on the text of this edition. Since that time, changes in the membership may have occurred.

NOTE: Membership on a committee shall not in and of itself constitute an endorsement of the Association or any document developed by the committee on which the member serves.

Committee Scope: This Committee shall have primary responsibility for documents on the classification of the relative hazards of all chemical solids, liquids, and gases and to compile data on the hazard properties of these hazardous chemicals.

Contents

NFPA 49

Hazardous Chemicals Data

1994 Edition, Amended 2001

Chapter 1 General Information

1.1 Scope. The information presented in this document is intended for use by personnel who have a basic knowledge of the chemistry of hazardous materials. The information contained herein offers guidance on storage and fire fighting techniques that can be used in an emergency or in disaster planning. It is not intended as a guide for workplace exposure or for relative indices of toxicity.

1.2 Purpose.

1.2.1 The National Fire Protection Association Committee on Classification and Properties of Hazardous Chemicals Data recognizes the continuing need to provide guidance on the hazards of chemicals to emergency personnel, safety professionals, inspection and enforcement officials, and architects, designers, and engineers. The committee has developed this publication to respond to needs that may not be fully met by other publications, including material safety data sheets.

1.2.2 Chapter 2 describes the criteria used by the committee to select the chemicals herein. Undoubtedly there are chemicals meeting this criteria that have not yet been considered by the committee. Any reader who wishes to propose a chemical for inclusion in the Fire Protection Guide to Hazardous Materials may do so using the data sheet and instructions provided in Appendix B. The completed data sheet should be sent to Amy Beasley Spencer, FPG Engineer, c/o NFPA, 1 Batterymarch Park, P.O. Box 9101, Quincy, MA 02269-9101.

1.3 Definitions.

Active Metals. Examples include aluminum, beryllium, lithium, magnesium, potassium, and sodium.

Acute Exposure. A single, short-term exposure to a hazardous substance.

Allergen. A substance capable of sensitizing susceptible individuals and thereby eliciting a dermal and/or respiratory response (termed an allergic response); see also sensitizer.

Anemia. A condition wherein the number of red blood cells per unit volume of blood, or the amount of hemoglobin per red blood cell, is reduced below normal.

Anesthesia. A state characterized by loss of sensation, resulting from pharmacological depression of nerve function or from neurological disease.

Arrhythmia. Irregularity of heartbeat.

Asphyxiation. Production of asphyxia; that is, impaired or absent exchange of oxygen and carbon dioxide in breathing.

Asthma. Bronchial asthma, a condition of the lungs in which widespread airway narrowing occurs over short time periods either spontaneously or caused by treatments resulting in respiratory muscle spasm, edema of the respiratory mucosa, or mucus in the bronchi and bronchioles; asthma may be allergically or chemically induced.

Ataxia. Muscular incoordination in voluntary movement.

Autoignition Temperature. The minimum temperature of a solid, liquid, or gas required to initiate or cause self-sustained combustion in air with no other source of ignition. Data are apparatus- and procedure-dependent.

BLEVE (Boiling Liquid Expanding Vapor Explosion). A type of rapid phase transition in which a liquid contained above its atmospheric boiling point is rapidly depressurized, causing a nearly instantaneous transition from a liquid to a vapor with a corresponding energy release. A BLEVE is often accompanied by a large fireball if a flammable liquid is involved, since an external fire impinging on the vapor space of a pressure vessel is a common BLEVE scenario. However, it is not necessary for the liquid to be flammable to have a BLEVE occur.

Boiling Point. The temperature at which the vapor pressure of a liquid equals the ambient atmospheric pressure.

Bronchitis. Inflammation of the mucus membranes of the airways known as bronchi or bronchial tubes.

Carbon Dioxide (extinguishing agent). A colorless, odorless, electrically nonconductive inert gas suitable for extinguishing fires. Commonly referred to as CO_2.

Carboy. A large cylindrical container for the transport and storage of liquids, 5–13 gallons in size, and made of glass, plastic, metal, earthenware, clay, or stoneware and cushioned in a special container.

Carcinogen. Substance capable of producing cancer; see also oncogen.

Cardiovascular. Referring to the heart and blood vessel or to the circulatory system.

Central Nervous System (CNS). The brain and spinal cord.

Chloracne. An acne-like skin eruption induced by dermal contact with certain chlorinated compounds.

Chronic Exposure. A repeated or long-term exposure to a hazardous substance.

Coma. State of profound unconsciousness from which an individual cannot be roused.

Combustible. A substance that will burn.

Conjunctivitis. Inflammation of the conjunctiva, which is the mucus membrane covering the anterior surface of the eyeball and lining of the eyelids.

Cornea. Transparent tissue constituting the anterior sixth of the outer wall of the eye.

Corrosive. Any solid, liquid, or gaseous substance that burns or destructively attacks body tissues.

Cyanosis. Dark bluish or purplish coloration of skin and mucus membrane due to insufficient oxygenation of the blood.

Decomposition. To undergo chemical breakdown, separating into constituent parts or elements or into simpler compounds.

Defatting. Removal of fat.

Dermatitis. Skin inflammation, sometimes of allergic origin, as in contact dermatitis.

Diaphoresis. Perspiration.

Dry Chemical. A fire-extinguishing agent, usually of sodium bicarbonate, potassium bicarbonate, urea-based potassium bicarbonate, potassium chloride, or monoammonium phosphate, with added particulate material supplemented by special treatment to provide resistance to packing, resistance to moisture absorption (caking), and proper flow capabilities. It extinguishes a fire by interfering with the combustion reaction.

Dry Powder. A powder mixture (typically sodium chloride) used as an extinguishing agent for combustible metal fires, such as sodium, titanium, uranium, zirconium, lithium, magnesium, and sodium-potassium alloys. It extinguishes a fire by forming an air-tight coating over the metal.

Dyspnea. Shortness of breath, difficulty breathing.

Edema. Swelling due to accumulation of excessive amounts of watery fluid in cells, tissues, or serum-containing cavities.

Equimolar. Of equal molarity, that is, mass concentration measured in gram molecular weight units.

Erythema. Skin reddening.

Etiologic. Referring to etiology, or disease causation; an etiologic agent is an agent of disease.

Evaporation. The change of a sustance from the solid or liquid phase to the gaseous phase.

Exothermic. A process or chemical reaction that is accompanied by release of heat.

Explosion. The bursting or rupture of an enclosure or container due to the development of internal pressure.

Deflagration. Propagation of a reaction zone at a velocity that is less than the speed of sound in the unreacted medium.

Detonation. Propagation of a reaction zone at a velocity that is more than the speed of sound in the unreacted medium.

Explosive. A substance capable of sudden high-velocity reaction with the generation of high pressures. Explosives are classified as deflagrating (low explosive) and detonating (high explosive). Depending on their sensitivity, explosives are set off by fire (heat), by friction, by concussion, by percussion, or by detonation.

Flammability. The ease with which a material (gas, liquid, or solid) will ignite, either spontaneously (pyrophoric), from exposure to a high temperature environment (autoignition), or to a spark or open flame.

Flammable Limits. The minimum and maximum concentrations of vapor in air below and above which propagation of flame does not occur, usually expressed in terms of percent by volume of the vapor or gas in air.

Lower Flammable Limit (LFL). The lowest concentration of a flammable vapor or gas/air mixture that will ignite and burn with a flame.

Upper Flammable Limit (UFL). The highest concentration of a flammable vapor or gas/air mixture that will ignite and burn with a flame.

NOTE: The word "explosive" is often substituted for "flammable"; LEL and UEL are considered to be interchangeable with LFL and UFL for practical applications.

Flash Point. The minimum temperature at which the liquid gives off sufficient vapor to form an ignitible mixture with air near the surface of the liquid or within the test vessel used. Data are apparatus- and procedure-dependent.

Foam, Fire Fighting. Material that smothers the flames of a burning liquid consisting of minute stable and heat resistant bubbles applied to the surface of the liquid.

Alcohol-resistant foam. A fire fighting foam that can be employed to combat fires in polar solvents, such as alcohols.

Aqueous foam. A fire fighting foam using fluorocarbon surfactants to control vaporization of flammable liquids. Also known as "light water" or "AFFF."

Health Hazard. A substance or formulation of mixed substances that, as a result of acute exposure typical of emergency conditions, is capable of causing adverse health effects in members of the general public or in emergency response personnel not equipped with adequate protective clothing and equipment. Adverse effects associated with chronic (long-term) exposure are excluded, except to the degree that substantial risks of such effects may also have been demonstrated to exist as a result of acute exposure.

Degrees of health hazard include:

(a) *Severe.* Hazards that, under emergency conditions, may be lethal. Numerical rating = 4.

(b) *Serious.* Hazards that, under emergency conditions, may cause serious or permanent injury, such as tissue corrosion or irreversible eye damage. Numerical rating = 3.

(c) *Moderate.* Hazards that, under emergency conditions, may cause temporary incapacitation or reversible residual injury, such as irritation of skin, eyes, or mucous membranes. Numerical rating = 2.

(d) *Slight.* Hazards that, under emergency conditions, may cause significant irritation to skin, eyes, or mucous membranes only during exposure, with only insignificant residual irritation or injury, which is rapidly resolved following cessation of exposure. Numerical rating = 1.

(e) *Minimal.* Hazards that, under emergency conditions, are not severe, serious, moderate, or slight health hazards. Numerical rating = 0.

Hypotension. Subnormal pressure, "low" blood pressure.

Inert Material. Material, such as sand, that can be used to adsorb hazardous materials for safe disposal.

Inerting. The use of an inert gas to render the atmosphere of an enclosure substantially oxygen-free or to reduce the oxygen content to a point at which combustion cannot take place.

Irritant. An agent capable of causing irritation; that is, inflammation of tissue in response to injury.

Jaundice. Yellowish staining of skin and underlying tissues due to accumulation of bile pigments.

Lachrymation. Tearing of the eyes, possibly caused by a lachrymator.

Laryngitis. Inflammation of the larynx, that is, the "voice box."

Metal Fume Fever. Syndrome resulting from inhalation of oxide fumes of such metals as copper, iron, magnesium, and zinc; usually beginning with chills and fever, profuse sweating, and weakness.

Methemoglobinemia. Presence in the blood of methemoglobin (metHb), an abnormal oxidation product of oxyhemoglobin produced by poisoning with substances, for example, acetanilide and potassium chlorate; oxygen is firmly bound to the altered (oxy)hemoglobin molecule, rendering it unavailable to tissues.

Monomer. A simple molecule that is capable of combining with a number of other molecules to form a polymer.

Motor Weakness. Reduced strength of voluntary muscles.

Mutagen. An agent capable of causing mutation, that is, alteration of the genetic material.

Narcosis. A state of stupor, unconsciousness, or arrested activity produced by the influence of chemicals.

Necrosis. Pathological death of cells or portions of tissues or organs resulting from irreversible damage.

Neoplasm. Abnormal tissue that grows by abnormally rapid cellular proliferation and fails to cease growing upon removal of the growth-initiating stimulus.

Neurotoxic. Toxic to, or capable of adversely affecting, nerve cells.

Oncogen. A substance capable of producing neoplasms.

Oxidation. (1) A process in which oxygen or other oxidizing material combines with another substance. (2) A reaction in which electrons are transferred to or from an atom or group of atoms.

Oxidizer. (1) A sustance that readily gives up oxygen. (2) A substance that gains electrons. Examples include bromine, chlorine, and fluorine.

Pneumonia. Inflammation of the lung, specifically the parenchyma tissue of the lung; inflammation may include the bronchial tubes in broncho-pneumonia or may be caused by pathogens (such as streptococcus pneumoniae as in pneumococcal pneumonia) or chemicals, as in chemical pneumonia.

Polymerization. The chemical reaction that produces polymers by bonding two or more monomers.

Protected Locations. An area where fire fighters will be protected from the pressure rupture of a container or ignition of flammable material suddenly released from a ruptured container.

Pulmonary. Referring to the lung(s).

Pyrolysis. The breaking apart of complex molecules into simpler units by the use of heat.

Pyrophoric Material. A substance capable of self-ignition upon short exposure to air under ordinary atmospheric conditions.

Renal. Referring to the kidney(s).

Sensitizer. An agent, usually an antibody, capable of causing dermatitis or an allergic respiratory response only after alteration (sensitization) of the skin or lungs by previous exposure to the agent.

Static Electricity. A charge of electricity on non-conducting materials when two dissimilar non-conducting materials are rapidly separated.

Suffocation. The act or condition of suffocating; asphyxiation; witholding oxygen; impeding respiration or breathing.

Tachycardia. Elevated heartbeat, usually over 100 beats per minute.

Teratogen. Agent capable of causing birth defects.

Ulceration. Formation of an ulcer, that is, a lesion on the surface of the skin or mucus membrane caused by superficial loss of tissue, usually with inflammation.

Vapor Pressure. The pressure exerted by a separated vapor above its own liquid in a closed container.

Vertigo. Sensation of irregular or whirling motion, either of oneself, as in subjective vertigo, or of external objects, as in objective vertigo.

Chapter 2 Requirements for Listing of Chemicals

2.1 The following requirements apply to listing chemicals.

(a) Only chemicals that are considered to be commercially significant have been included in NFPA 49. To meet this initial criterion, a chemical must be available in containers of 5 gal (18.9 L) capacity or larger, in compressed gas cylinders, or in pallet-load quantities or must otherwise be considered commercially significant. Once this criterion is met, the chemical must pose a distinct hazard by meeting one or more of the following criteria (listed in order of priority):

(b) Chemicals having a Health Hazard Rating of 2 or higher, based on NFPA 704, *Standard System for the Identification of the Hazards of Materials for Emergency Response.*

(c) Chemicals having an NFPA 704 Instability Rating of 1 or higher.

2.2 Chemicals in the following categories will not be addressed:

(a) Chemicals whose only hazard is mild oxidizing ability.

(b) Commercial explosives and blasting agents.

(c) Chemicals whose only hazard is flammability.

(d) Commercial formulations of organic peroxides. (Information on organic peroxide formulations is available in NFPA 432, *Code for the Storage of Organic Peroxide Formulations.*)

(e) Chemicals whose only hazard is one of chronic health hazard.

(f) Teratogens, mutagens, oncogens, etiologic agents, and other similar hazards.

(g) (For information on NFPA 704, Standard System for the Identification of the Hazards of Materials for Emergency Response, see Appendix B.)

Chapter 3 Arrangement of Information

3.1 Starting with the hazard signal indicating the numerical ratings for the hazards of health, flammability, and instability, with the lower diamond reserved for special hazards, twelve categories of specific and generalized statements with data are listed in this numerical order. When no data are available or are not pertinent the appropriate category is omitted.

(1) Identity
(2) Statement of Hazards
(3) Emergency Response Personal Protective Equipment
(4) Spill and Leak Procedures
(5) Fire Fighting Procedures
(6) Health Hazards
(7) Fire and Explosion Hazards

(8) Instability and Reactivity Hazards
(9) Storage Recommendations
(10) Usual Shipping Containers
(11) Physical Properties
(12) Electrical Equipment Group Classification (if appropriate).

Refer to Appendix A for a more complete explanation for each of the 12 categories including the data presented and its significance.

Chapter 4 Additional Hazardous Chemical Information Sources

4.1 Five national organizations were established to assist telephone callers with specifics. They are:

4.1.1 National Chemical Response and Information Center. The National Chemical Response and Information Center was established by the Chemical Manufacturers Association (CMA) in March 1985 to provide the public and emergency response personnel with information about chemicals and advice and assistance in handling emergencies. The center accomplishes these objectives through three programs: CHEMTREC, the Chemical Referral Center, and Emergency Response Training.

4.1.1.1 CHEMTREC. The CHEMical TRansportation Emergency Center provides information and assistance to those involved in responding to chemical incidents. CHEMTREC operates in two stages: first, it provides immediate advice on the nature of a specific chemical, its hazards, and specific response recommendations; second, it will promptly contact the shipper of the material for more detailed information and appropriate follow-up, including on-site assistance, where feasible. CHEMTREC operates 24 hours a day, seven days a week. The telephone number for the continental U.S. is 1-800-424-9300.

CHEMTREC serves as the communications center for emergency response systems for most of the private sector, including major shippers, carriers, industry groups, and mutual aid groups. CHEMTREC maintains extensive files on more than 90,000 chemicals and trade name products. This information is continually updated to reflect the most accurate information possible. CHEMTREC maintains 24-hour contact numbers for shippers and carriers. The center will also augment its capability to provide emergency medical advice to physicians treating those exposed to chemicals by providing direct contact with the manufacturers' medical personnel.

4.1.1.2 Chemical Referral Center. The Chemical Referral Center is designed to enable users, transportation personnel, and the general public to obtain safety and health information about chemicals. The Center operates from 8:00 a.m. to 9:00 p.m. at 1-800-262-8200 in Washington, DC. Based on the information provided by the caller, the Center's operators will provide the caller with a point of contact within the manufacturing company that can provide the needed information. In most cases, this information will be the same as that provided by the material safety data sheet.

4.1.1.3 Regional Poison Control Centers. Poison control centers are located in various cities throughout the United States. They are 24-hour emergency telephone services that provide assistance to the public and to police, fire, and emergency medical personnel who are involved in poisonings or medical emergencies involving hazardous materials. The centers are staffed by physicians, nurses, and pharmacists specially trained to handle these types of emergencies. The centers' staffs provide first-aid and referral assistance and then provide the treating physician with the most recent and most accurate information available on treatment of the specific exposure. A typical large center serving a major metropolitan area will handle 50,000 to 75,000 calls each year. The centers are operated by the American Association of Poison Control Centers. The Association also sponsors a certification program for regional centers and a testing and certification program for the information specialists who staff the regional centers.

Chapter 5 Hazardous Chemical Data Sheets

NAME: **ACETALDEHYDE**

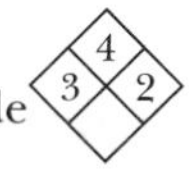

SYNONYMS: acetic aldehyde; ethanal; ethylaldehyde

FORMULA: CH_3CHO

NFPA 30/OSHA CLASSIFICATION: IA

DOT CLASS: Class 3, Flammable and combustible liquid

SHIPPING LABEL: FLAMMABLE LIQUID

ID NO.: UN 1089

CAS NO.: 75-07-0

MOL. WT.: 44.0

STATEMENT OF HAZARDS: Flammable and corrosive liquid. Serious health hazard. Oxidizes readily in air to form unstable peroxides that may explode spontaneously. Reacts with oxidizers, halogens, amines, strong bases, and acids.

EMERGENCY RESPONSE PERSONAL PROTECTIVE EQUIPMENT: Wear special protective clothing and positive pressure self-contained breathing apparatus.

SPILL OR LEAK PROCEDURES: Eliminate all ignition sources. Stop or control the leak, if this can be done without undue risk. Use water spray to cool and disperse vapors, protect personnel, and dilute spills to form nonflammable mixtures. Control runoff and isolate discharged material for proper disposal.

FIRE FIGHTING PROCEDURES: Fight fire from protected location or maximum possible distance. Use dry chemical, "alcohol resistant" foam, or carbon dioxide. Water may be ineffective. Use water spray to keep fire-exposed containers cool.

HEALTH HAZARDS: Corrosive. Causes severe eye and skin burns. Serious health hazard. Irritating to skin, eyes, and respiratory system. Narcosis, nausea, and loss of conciousness may result from exposure to high concentrations of vapor.

FIRE AND EXPLOSION HAZARDS: Flammable liquid. Oxidizes readily in air to form unstable peroxides that may explode spontaneously. Vapors are heavier than air and may travel to a source of ignition and flash back. Combustion may produce irritants and toxic gases. Closed containers may rupture violently when heated.

FLASH POINT: −36°F (−38°C)

AUTOIGNITION TEMPERATURE: 347°F (175°C)

FLAMMABLE LIMITS: LOWER: 4.0% UPPER: 60.0%

INSTABILITY AND REACTIVITY HAZARDS: Hazardous polymerization may occur. Reacts with oxidizing materials, halogens, amines, strong alkalies, and acids.

STORAGE RECOMMENDATIONS: Store in a cool, dry, well-ventilated location. Inside storage should be in a standard flammable liquids storage warehouse, room, or cabinet. Separate from oxidizing materials and other reactive hazards. Store bulk quantities in detached tanks provided with refrigeration and inert gas cover.

USUAL SHIPPING CONTAINERS: Glass pressure bottles, metal drums, and insulated tank cars, tank trucks, and tank barges.

PHYSICAL PROPERTIES: Colorless, mobile liquid with strong, pungent, fruity odor. Rapidly volatilizes at room temperature.

MELTING POINT: −190°F (−123°C)

BOILING POINT: 69°F (21°C)

SPECIFIC GRAVITY: 0.78

SOLUBILITY IN WATER: soluble

VAPOR DENSITY: 1.52

VAPOR PRESSURE: 750 mm Hg @ 20°C

ELECTRICAL EQUIPMENT: Class I, Group C

NAME: **ACETANILIDE**

SYNONYMS: acetamide; N-phenyl: N-phenylacetamide

FORMULA: $C_6H_5NH(COCH_3)$

NFPA 30/OSHA CLASSIFICATION: IIIB

CAS NO.: 103-84-4

MOL. WT.: 135.2

STATEMENT OF HAZARDS: Combustible solid. Moderate health hazard. Under fire conditions decomposition products include oxides of nitrogen.

EMERGENCY RESPONSE PERSONAL PROTECTIVE EQUIPMENT: Wear full protective clothing and positive pressure self-contained breathing apparatus.

SPILL OR LEAK PROCEDURES: Adsorb in noncombustible material for proper disposal; shovel into suitable dry container.

FIRE FIGHTING PROCEDURES: Use water spray, dry chemical, foam, or carbon dioxide. Use water spray to keep fire-exposed containers cool.

HEALTH HAZARDS: Moderate health hazard. May be harmful if inhaled. Irritating to eyes, skin, and respiratory system. May cause edema of the lungs and severe dermatitis. Under fire conditions decomposition products include oxides of nitrogen.

FIRE AND EXPLOSION HAZARDS: Combustible solid. Combustion may produce irritants and toxic gases.

FLASH POINT: 345°F (174°C)

INSTABILITY AND REACTIVITY HAZARDS: Reacts with strong bases and oxidizing materials.

STORAGE RECOMMENDATIONS: Store in a cool, dry, well-ventilated location. Outside or detached storage is preferred. Store away from heat, oxidizing materials, and strong bases.

USUAL SHIPPING CONTAINERS: Bottles and fiber drums.

PHYSICAL PROPERTIES: Gray, odorless solid in chip form.

MELTING POINT: 235 to 239°F (113 to 115°C)

BOILING POINT: 579°F (304°C)

SOLUBILITY IN WATER: not soluble

VAPOR PRESSURE: 1 mm Hg @ 114°C

NAME: **ACETIC ACID, GLACIAL**

SYNONYMS: ethanoic acid; vinegar acid

FORMULA: CH_3COOH

NFPA 30/OSHA CLASSIFICATION: II

DOT CLASS: Class 8, Corrosive material

SHIPPING LABEL: CORROSIVE

ID NO.: UN 2789

CAS NO.: 64-19-7

MOL. WT.: 60.1

STATEMENT OF HAZARDS: Corrosive and combustible liquid. Serious health hazard. Reacts with oxidizing and alkali materials.

EMERGENCY RESPONSE PERSONAL PROTECTIVE EQUIPMENT: Wear special protective clothing and positive pressure self-contained breathing apparatus.

SPILL OR LEAK PROCEDURES: Use water spray to cool and disperse vapors, protect personnel, and dilute spills to form nonflammable mixtures. Use soda ash to neutralize spills. Control runoff and isolate discharged material for proper disposal.

FIRE FIGHTING PROCEDURES: Use water spray, dry chemical, "alcohol resistant" foam, or carbon dioxide. Use water spray to keep fire-exposed containers cool.

HEALTH HAZARDS: Corrosive. Causes severe eye and skin burns. Serious health hazard. May be harmful if inhaled. Irritating to skin, eyes, and respiratory system.

FIRE AND EXPLOSION HAZARDS: Combustible liquid. Combustion may produce irritants and toxic gases.

FLASH POINT: 103°F (39°C)

AUTOIGNITION TEMPERATURE: 961°F (516°C)

FLAMMABLE LIMITS: LOWER: 4.0% UPPER: 19.9%

INSTABILITY AND REACTIVITY HAZARDS: May react with alkaline substances and oxidizing materials such as peroxides, nitric acid, and chromic acid.

STORAGE RECOMMENDATIONS: Store in a dry, well-ventilated place. Separate from oxidizing materials and alkaline substances.

USUAL SHIPPING CONTAINERS: Glass bottles, carboys, lined drums, and tank trucks or tank cars.

PHYSICAL PROPERTIES: Clear, colorless liquid with pungent odor of vinegar. Forms ice-like solid below 62°F (17°C).

MELTING POINT: 62°F (17°C)

BOILING POINT: 244°F (118°C)

SPECIFIC GRAVITY: 1.05

SOLUBILITY IN WATER: soluble

VAPOR PRESSURE: 11 mm Hg @ 20°C

ELECTRICAL EQUIPMENT: Class I, Group D

NAME: **ACETIC ANHYDRIDE**

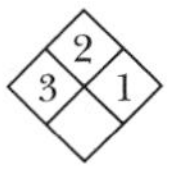

SYNONYMS: acetic acid anhydride; acetyl oxide; ethanoic anhydride

FORMULA: $(CH_3CO)_2O$

NFPA 30/OSHA CLASSIFICATION: II

DOT CLASS: Class 8, Corrosive material

SHIPPING LABEL: CORROSIVE

ID NO.: UN 1715

CAS NO.: 108-24-7

MOL. WT.: 102.1

STATEMENT OF HAZARDS: Corrosive and combustible liquid. Serious health hazard. Reacts with alcohol, oxidizing materials, and alkaline materials.

EMERGENCY RESPONSE PERSONAL PROTECTIVE EQUIPMENT: Wear special protective clothing and positive pressure self-contained breathing apparatus.

SPILL OR LEAK PROCEDURES: Use water spray to cool and disperse vapors, protect personnel, and dilute spills to form nonflammable mixtures. Control runoff and isolate discharged material for proper disposal. Neutralize spill and washings with soda ash or lime.

FIRE FIGHTING PROCEDURES: Use water spray, dry chemical, "alcohol resistant" foam, or carbon dioxide. Use water spray to keep fire-exposed containers cool. Use flooding quantities of water.

HEALTH HAZARDS: Corrosive. Causes severe eye and skin burns. Serious health hazard. May be harmful if inhaled. Irritating to eyes, skin, and respiratory system.

FIRE AND EXPLOSION HAZARDS: Combustible liquid. Combustion may produce irritants and toxic gases.

FLASH POINT: 126°F (52°C)

AUTOIGNITION TEMPERATURE: 630°F (332°C)

FLAMMABLE LIMITS: LOWER: 2.9% UPPER: 10.3%

INSTABILITY AND REACTIVITY HAZARDS: Reacts with oxidizing materials, water, alcohols, and alkaline materials. Reacts with water to form acetic acid.

STORAGE RECOMMENDATIONS: Store in a cool, dry, well-ventilated location. Outside or detached storage is preferred. Store away from heat, oxidizers, and sunlight. Exclude moisture from vapor space in storage tanks.

USUAL SHIPPING CONTAINERS: Glass bottles, carboys, lined drums, and tank trucks or tank cars.

PHYSICAL PROPERTIES: Clear, colorless liquid with strong, pungent, acetic odor.

MELTING POINT: −101°F (−74°C)

BOILING POINT: 282°F (139°C)

SPECIFIC GRAVITY: 1.08

SOLUBILITY IN WATER: partly soluble (reacts, decomposes)

VAPOR PRESSURE: 4 mm Hg @ 20°C

ELECTRICAL EQUIPMENT: Class I, Group D

NAME: **ACETONE CYANOHYDRIN, Stabilized**

SYNONYMS: 2-hydroxyisobutyronitrile; 2-hydroxy-2-methylpropanenitrile; 2-methyllactonitrile; propanenitrile; 2-hydroxy-2-methyl-

FORMULA: $(CH_3)_2C(OH)CN$

NFPA 30/OSHA CLASSIFICATION: IIIA

DOT CLASS: Class 6.1, Poisonous material

SHIPPING LABEL: POISON

ID NO.: UN 1541

CAS NO.: 75-86-5

MOL. WT.: 85.1

STATEMENT OF HAZARDS: Severe health hazard. Combustible liquid. Evolves hydrogen cyanide during decomposition.

EMERGENCY RESPONSE PERSONAL PROTECTIVE EQUIPMENT: Wear special protective clothing and positive pressure self-contained breathing apparatus.

SPILL OR LEAK PROCEDURES: Releases may require isolation or evacuation. Use water spray to cool and disperse vapors, protect personnel, and dilute spills to form nonflammable mixtures. Control runoff and isolate discharged material for proper disposal.

FIRE FIGHTING PROCEDURES: Use dry chemical, "alcohol resistant" foam, carbon dioxide, or water spray. Approach fire from upwind to avoid hazardous vapors and toxic decomposition products.

HEALTH HAZARDS: Severe health hazard. May be fatal if absorbed through skin or inhaled. Irritating to skin, eyes, and respiratory system. Readily forms hydrogen cyanide, which is a severe health hazard by all routes of entry.

FIRE AND EXPLOSION HAZARDS: Combustible liquid. Decomposes readily to emit hydrogen cyanide gas, which is flammable. See hydrogen cyanide. Combustion by-products include: oxides of nitrogen, hydrogen cyanide.

FLASH POINT: 165°F (74°C)

AUTOIGNITION TEMPERATURE: 1270°F (688°C)

FLAMMABLE LIMITS: LOWER: 2.2% UPPER: 12%

INSTABILITY AND REACTIVITY HAZARDS: Decomposes readily to form hydrogen cyanide. Reacts with acids, strong alkalies, oxidizing materials, and reducing agents.

STORAGE RECOMMENDATIONS: Separate from acids, alkalies, oxidizing materials, and reducing agents. Store in a cool, dry, well-ventilated location.

USUAL SHIPPING CONTAINERS: Carboys, drums, tank barges.

PHYSICAL PROPERTIES: Light yellow liquid.

MELTING POINT: −2°F (−19°C)

BOILING POINT: 203°F (95°C)

SPECIFIC GRAVITY: 0.93

SOLUBILITY IN WATER: soluble

VAPOR PRESSURE: 1.0 mm Hg @ 20°C

ELECTRICAL EQUIPMENT: Class I, Group D

NAME: **ACETONITRILE**

DOT SHIPPING NAME: **METHYL CYANIDE**

SYNONYMS: cyanomethane; ethanenitrile

FORMULA: CH_3CN

NFPA 30/OSHA CLASSIFICATION: IB

DOT CLASS: Class 3, Flammable and combustible liquid

SHIPPING LABEL: FLAMMABLE LIQUID AND POISON

ID NO.: UN 1648

CAS NO.: 75-05-8

MOL. WT.: 41.0

STATEMENT OF HAZARDS: Flammable liquid. Moderate health hazard. Combustion by-products may include hydrogen cyanide and oxides of nitrogen.

EMERGENCY RESPONSE PERSONAL PROTECTIVE EQUIPMENT: Wear full protective clothing and positive pressure self-contained breathing apparatus.

SPILL OR LEAK PROCEDURES: Eliminate all ignition sources. Approach release from upwind. Stop or control the leak, if this can be done without undue risk. Use water spray to cool and disperse vapors, protect personnel, and dilute spills to form nonflammable mixtures. Control runoff and isolate discharged material for proper disposal.

FIRE FIGHTING PROCEDURES: Approach fire from upwind to avoid hazardous vapors and toxic decomposition products. Use water spray, dry chemical, "alcohol resistant" foam, or carbon dioxide. Use water spray to keep fire-exposed containers cool.

HEALTH HAZARDS: Moderate health hazard. May be harmful if absorbed through skin or inhaled. Irritating to eye, skin, and respiratory system. Combustion by-products may include hydrogen cyanide and oxides of nitrogen.

FIRE AND EXPLOSION HAZARDS: Flammable liquid. Vapors are heavier than air and may travel to a source of ignition and flash back. Combustion by-products include hydrogen cyanide and oxides of nitrogen.

FLASH POINT: 42°F (6°C) (oc)

AUTOIGNITION TEMPERATURE: 975°F (524°C)

FLAMMABLE LIMITS: LOWER: 4.4% UPPER: 16.0%

INSTABILITY AND REACTIVITY HAZARDS: Reacts with oxidizing materials.

STORAGE RECOMMENDATIONS: Inside storage should be in a standard flammable liquids storage warehouse, room, or cabinet. Separate from oxidizing materials. Outside or detached storage is preferred.

USUAL SHIPPING CONTAINERS: Glass bottles, drums, tanks on trucks, rail cars, barges.

PHYSICAL PROPERTIES: Colorless liquid with ethereal odor.

MELTING POINT: −50°F (−46°C)

BOILING POINT: 179°F (82°C)

SPECIFIC GRAVITY: 0.79

SOLUBILITY IN WATER: soluble

VAPOR PRESSURE: 73 mm Hg @ 20°C

ELECTRICAL EQUIPMENT: Class I, Group D

NAME: **ACETYL CHLORIDE**

SYNONYMS: acetic chloride; ethanoyl chloride

FORMULA: CH_3COCl

NFPA 30/OSHA CLASSIFICATION: IB

DOT CLASS: Class 3, Flammable and combustible liquid

SHIPPING LABEL: FLAMMABLE LIQUID and CORROSIVE

ID NO.: UN 1717

CAS NO.: 75-36-5

MOL. WT.: 78.5

STATEMENT OF HAZARDS: Corrosive and flammable liquid. Serious health hazard. Reacts violently with water.

EMERGENCY RESPONSE PERSONAL PROTECTIVE EQUIPMENT: Wear special protective clothing and positive pressure self-contained breathing apparatus.

SPILL OR LEAK PROCEDURES: Eliminate all ignition sources. Stop or control the leak, if this can be done without undue risk. Approach release from upwind. Control runoff and isolate discharged material for proper disposal.

FIRE FIGHTING PROCEDURES: DO NOT use water or foam directly on spilled material. Violent reaction may result. Use dry chemical or carbon dioxide only. Approach fire from upwind to avoid hazardous vapors and toxic decomposition products. Fight fire from protected location or maximum possible distance.

HEALTH HAZARDS: Corrosive. Causes severe eye and skin burns. Serious health hazard. Irritating to skin, eyes, and respiratory system.

FIRE AND EXPLOSION HAZARDS: Flammable liquid. Vapors are heavier than air and may travel to a source of ignition and flash back. Decomposes at fire temperature with release of hydrogen chloride and phosgene. Closed containers may rupture violently when heated.

FLASH POINT: 40°F (4°C)

AUTOIGNITION TEMPERATURE: 734°F (390°C)

FLAMMABLE LIMITS: LOWER: 5.0% UPPER: not determined

INSTABILITY AND REACTIVITY HAZARDS: Water reactive. Violent exothermic decomposition with water produces corrosive hydrochloric and acetic acids. Reacts violently with alcohols, alkalies, amines, and strong oxidizing materials.

STORAGE RECOMMENDATIONS: Separate from alcohols, alkalies, amines, and strong oxidizing materials. Store in a cool, dry, well-ventilated location. Outside or detached storage is preferred. Inside storage should be in a standard flammable liquids storage warehouse, room, or cabinet.

USUAL SHIPPING CONTAINERS: Glass bottles or carboys inside wooden box.

PHYSICAL PROPERTIES: Colorless to pale yellow fuming liquid with a strong pungent odor.

MELTING POINT: −170°F (−112°C)

BOILING POINT: 124°F (51°C)

SPECIFIC GRAVITY: 1.10

SOLUBILITY IN WATER: reacts violently

VAPOR PRESSURE: 135 mm Hg @ 8°C

ELECTRICAL EQUIPMENT: Class I, Group D

NAME: **ACETYLENE, Dissolved**

SYNONYMS: ethine; ethyne

FORMULA: HC ≡ CH

NFPA 30/OSHA CLASSIFICATION:

DOT CLASS: Class 2.1, Flammable gas

SHIPPING LABEL: FLAMMABLE GAS

ID NO.: UN 1001

CAS NO.: 74-86-2

MOL. WT.: 26.0

STATEMENT OF HAZARDS: Flammable gas. Forms explosive mixtures with air over a very wide range. Low ignition energy. Reacts with active metals to form explosive compounds.

EMERGENCY RESPONSE PERSONAL PROTECTIVE EQUIPMENT: Wear full protective clothing and positive pressure self-contained breathing apparatus.

SPILL OR LEAK PROCEDURES: Eliminate all ignition sources. Stop or control the leak, if this can be done without undue risk. Use water spray to cool and disperse vapors and protect personnel.

FIRE FIGHTING PROCEDURES: Stop flow of gas before extinguishing fire. Use water spray to keep fire-exposed containers cool. Approach fire from upwind to avoid hazardous vapors and toxic decomposition products. Fight fire from protected location or maximum possible distance. Use water spray, dry chemical, foam, or carbon dioxide.

HEALTH HAZARDS: Simple asphyxiant.

FIRE AND EXPLOSION HAZARDS: Flammable gas. Forms explosive mixtures with air over a very wide range. Closed containers may rupture violently when heated.

AUTOIGNITION TEMPERATURE: 581°F (305°C)

FLAMMABLE LIMITS: LOWER: 2.5% UPPER: 100%

INSTABILITY AND REACTIVITY HAZARDS: Acetylene not dissolved in acetone may deflagrate above about 760 mm Hg absolute and becomes unstable at elevated pressures. It may decompose into hydrogen and carbon with explosive violence. Reacts with active metals (copper, silver, and mercury) to form explosive acetylide compounds. Reacts with chlorine to form acetylene chloride.

STORAGE RECOMMENDATIONS: Outside or detached storage is preferred. Isolate from oxidizing gases, especially chlorine. Store in a cool, dry, well-ventilated location. Store cylinders upright.

USUAL SHIPPING CONTAINERS: Steel cylinders. Usually contains porous material and acetone.

PHYSICAL PROPERTIES: Colorless gas with slight garlic-like odor.

MELTING POINT: −116°F (−82°C)

BOILING POINT: −118°F (−83°C)

SOLUBILITY IN WATER: not soluble

VAPOR DENSITY: 0.9

ELECTRICAL EQUIPMENT: Class I, Group A

NAME: **ACROLEIN, inhibited**

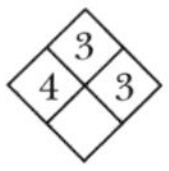

SYNONYMS: acrylaldehyde; acrylic aldehyde; acraldehyde; 2-propenal

FORMULA: $CH_2 = CHCHO$

NFPA 30/OSHA CLASSIFICATION: IB

DOT CLASS: Class 6.1, Poisonous material

SHIPPING LABEL: POISON and FLAMMABLE LIQUID

ID NO.: UN 1092

CAS NO.: 107-02-8

MOL. WT.: 56.1

STATEMENT OF HAZARDS: Severe health hazard. Flammable liquid. Low ignition energy. May polymerize explosively. Forms peroxides.

EMERGENCY RESPONSE PERSONAL PROTECTIVE EQUIPMENT: Wear special protective clothing and positive pressure self-contained breathing apparatus.

SPILL OR LEAK PROCEDURES: Releases may require isolation or evacuation. Eliminate all ignition sources. Use water spray to cool and disperse vapors, protect personnel, and dilute spills to form nonflammable mixtures.

FIRE FIGHTING PROCEDURES: Use water spray, dry chemical, "alcohol resistant" foam, or carbon dioxide. Use water spray to keep fire-exposed containers cool. Approach fire from upwind to avoid hazardous vapors and toxic decomposition products. Fight fire from protected location or maximum possible distance.

HEALTH HAZARDS: Severe health hazard. May be fatal if inhaled. May be harmful if absorbed through skin. Irritating to eyes, skin and respiratory system. Causes severe tearing. Sensitizer. Inhalation may result in pulmonary edema.

FIRE AND EXPLOSION HAZARDS: Flammable liquid. Combustion may produce irritants and toxic gases. Vapors are heavier than air and may travel to a source of ignition and flash back. Closed containers may rupture violently when heated.

FLASH POINT: −15°F (−26°C)

AUTOIGNITION TEMPERATURE: 455°F (235°C)

FLAMMABLE LIMITS: LOWER: 2.8% UPPER: 31%

INSTABILITY AND REACTIVITY HAZARDS: May polymerize explosively. Polymerization may be caused by elevated temperature, oxidizers, peroxides, acids, alkalies, or sunlight. Uninhibited monomer vapor may form polymer in vents and other confined spaces. May form shock sensitive peroxides or acids over time.

STORAGE RECOMMENDATIONS: Separate from oxidizing materials, peroxides, acids, and alkalies. Store in a cool, dry, well-ventilated location, protected from sunlight. Outside or detached storage is preferred. Inside storage should be in a standard flammable liquids storage warehouse, room, or cabinet. Do not store uninhibited acrolein.

USUAL SHIPPING CONTAINERS: Glass bottles, carboys, drums, and tank trucks or tank cars.

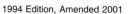

PHYSICAL PROPERTIES: Clear, colorless to yellowish, volatile liquid with piercing, disagreeable odor. Soluble in water, alcohol, ether.

MELTING POINT: −126°F (−88°C)

BOILING POINT: 127°F (53°C)

SPECIFIC GRAVITY: 0.84

SOLUBILITY IN WATER: soluble

VAPOR PRESSURE: 210 mm Hg @ 20°C

ELECTRICAL EQUIPMENT: Class I, Group B (C)

NAME: **ACRYLAMIDE**

SYNONYMS: acrylic amide; 2-propenamide

FORMULA: $CH_2=CHCONH_2$

NFPA 30/OSHA CLASSIFICATION:

DOT CLASS: Class 6.1, Poisonous material

SHIPPING LABEL: KEEP AWAY FROM FOOD

ID NO.: UN 2074

CAS NO.: 79-06-1

MOL. WT.: 71.1

STATEMENT OF HAZARDS: Moderate health hazard. Combustible solid. May polymerize explosively if heated to the melting point.

EMERGENCY RESPONSE PERSONAL PROTECTIVE EQUIPMENT: Wear full protective clothing and positive pressure self-contained breathing apparatus.

SPILL OR LEAK PROCEDURES: Prompt cleanup and removal are necessary.

FIRE FIGHTING PROCEDURES: Use dry chemical, foam, carbon dioxide, or water spray. Approach fire from upwind to avoid hazardous vapors and toxic decomposition products. Fight fire from protected location or maximum possible distance.

HEALTH HAZARDS: Moderate health hazard. May be harmful if absorbed through skin or inhaled. Irritating to eye, skin, and respiratory system. Penetrates the skin easily. Affects central nervous system; may cause tremors, hallucinations, and paralysis.

FIRE AND EXPLOSION HAZARDS: Combustible solid. Decomposes/polymerizes above 184°F (85°C) with release of ammonia and hydrogen gases. Combustion will produce irritants and toxic gases. Closed containers may rupture violently when heated.

AUTOIGNITION TEMPERATURE: 464°F (240°C)

INSTABILITY AND REACTIVITY HAZARDS: May polymerize explosively. Thermally unstable. Polymerization may be caused by elevated temperature, oxidizers, or peroxides.

STORAGE RECOMMENDATIONS: Separate from oxidizing materials and peroxides. Store in a cool, dry, well-ventilated location. Store away from heat, sunlight, acids, and alkalies.

USUAL SHIPPING CONTAINERS: Metal cans, pails, drums. Bulk packaging in trucks and rail cars and bulk in tank barges.

PHYSICAL PROPERTIES: Colorless to white flakes or crystals.

MELTING POINT: 184°F (85°C) (decomposes/polymerizes)

SPECIFIC GRAVITY: 1.22

SOLUBILITY IN WATER: soluble

VAPOR PRESSURE: 1.6 mm Hg @ 85°C

ELECTRICAL EQUIPMENT: Class II, Group G

NAME: **ACRYLIC ACID, inhibited**

SYNONYMS: acroleic acid; glacial acrylic acid; 2-propenoic acid; vinylformic acid

FORMULA: $H_2C=CHCOOH$

NFPA 30/OSHA CLASSIFICATION: II

DOT CLASS: Class 8, Corrosive material

SHIPPING LABEL: CORROSIVE

ID NO.: UN 2218

CAS NO.: 79-10-7

MOL. WT.: 72.1

STATEMENT OF HAZARDS: Corrosive and combustible liquid. Serious health hazard. Material may polymerize explosively.

EMERGENCY RESPONSE PERSONAL PROTECTIVE EQUIPMENT: Wear special protective clothing and positive pressure self-contained breathing apparatus.

SPILL OR LEAK PROCEDURES: Use water spray to cool and disperse vapors, protect personnel, and dilute spill to form nonflammable mixtures. Control runoff and isolate discharged material for proper disposal.

FIRE FIGHTING PROCEDURES: Use water spray, dry chemical, "alcohol resistant" foam, or carbon dioxide. Use water spray to keep fire-exposed containers cool. Fight fire from protected location or maximum possible distance.

HEALTH HAZARDS: Corrosive. Causes severe eye and skin burns. Serious health hazard. May be harmful if absorbed through skin. Irritating to skin, eye, and respiratory system. Inhalation may cause headache, nausea, vomiting, confusion, dizziness, and unconsciousness.

FIRE AND EXPLOSION HAZARDS: Combustible liquid. Material may polymerize explosively. Closed containers may rupture violently when heated.

FLASH POINT: 124°F (51°C)

AUTOIGNITION TEMPERATURE: 820°F (438°C)

FLAMMABLE LIMITS: LOWER: 2.0% UPPER: 8.0%

INSTABILITY AND REACTIVITY HAZARDS: Hazardous polymerization may occur. Decomposes at 392°F (200°C) with release of CO, carbon dioxide, and acrid fumes. Usually contains inhibitors to prevent polymerization. Polymerization may be caused by elevated temperature, oxidizers, peroxides, or sunlight. Material will react with strong acids and alkalies. Uninhibited monomer vapor may form polymer in vents and other confined spaces.

STORAGE RECOMMENDATIONS: Separate from oxidizing materials, peroxides, initiators, acids, and alkalies. Store in cool, dry, well-ventilated location. Outside or detached storage is preferred.

USUAL SHIPPING CONTAINERS: Glass bottles, carboys, lined drums, and tank trucks or tank cars.

PHYSICAL PROPERTIES: Colorless liquid with acrid, repulsive odor. Freezes to solid at 56°F (14°C).

MELTING POINT: 56°F (14°C)

BOILING POINT: 286°F (141°C)

SPECIFIC GRAVITY: 1.05

SOLUBILITY IN WATER: soluble

VAPOR PRESSURE: 3 mm Hg @ 20°C

ELECTRICAL EQUIPMENT: Class I, Group D

NAME: **ACRYLONITRILE, inhibited**

SYNONYMS: cyanoethylene; 2-propenenitrile; vinyl cyanide

FORMULA: $CH_2=CHCN$

NFPA 30/OSHA CLASSIFICATION: IB

DOT CLASS: Class 3, Flammable and combustible liquid

SHIPPING LABEL: FLAMMABLE LIQUID and POISON

ID NO.: UN 1093

CAS NO.: 107-13-1

MOL. WT.: 53.1

STATEMENT OF HAZARDS: Severe health hazard. Flammable liquid. Low ignition energy. Hazardous polymerization may occur.

EMERGENCY RESPONSE PERSONAL PROTECTIVE EQUIPMENT: Wear special protective clothing and positive pressure self-contained breathing apparatus.

SPILL OR LEAK PROCEDURES: Releases may require isolation or evacuation. Eliminate all ignition sources. Stop or control the leak, if this can be done without undue risk. Use water spray to cool and disperse vapors, and protect personnel. Control runoff and isolate discharged material for proper disposal.

FIRE FIGHTING PROCEDURES: Approach fire from upwind to avoid hazardous vapors and toxic decomposition products. Use water spray, dry chemical, "alcohol resistant" foam, or carbon dioxide. Use water spray to keep fire-exposed containers cool. Fight fire from protected location or maximum possible distance.

HEALTH HAZARDS: Severe health hazard. May be fatal if absorbed through skin or inhaled. Causes cyanosis. Irritating to skin, eye, and respiratory system.

FIRE AND EXPLOSION HAZARDS: Flammable liquid. Vapors are heavier than air and may travel to a source of ignition and flash back. Liquid may float on water. Combustion by-products include hydrogen cyanide and oxides of nitrogen. Closed containers may rupture violently when heated.

FLASH POINT: 32°F (0°C)

AUTOIGNITION TEMPERATURE: 898°F (481°C)

FLAMMABLE LIMITS: LOWER: 3.1% UPPER: 17.0%

INSTABILITY AND REACTIVITY HAZARDS: Hazardous polymerization may occur. Polymerization may be caused by elevated temperature or alkalies. Uninhibited monomer vapor may form polymer in vents and other confined spaces.

STORAGE RECOMMENDATIONS: Isolate from alkalies and oxidizing materials. Inside storage should be in a standard flammable liquids storage warehouse, room, or cabinet. Outside or detached storage is preferred. Do not store uninhibited acrylonitrile.

USUAL SHIPPING CONTAINERS: Pails, drums; tanks on trucks, rail cars, barges.

PHYSICAL PROPERTIES: Colorless to pale yellow liquid with faintly pungent odor that is above the toxic threshold.

MELTING POINT: −118°F (−84°C)

BOILING POINT: 171°F (77°C)

SPECIFIC GRAVITY: 0.81

SOLUBILITY IN WATER: not soluble

VAPOR PRESSURE: 83 mm Hg @ 20°C

ELECTRICAL EQUIPMENT: Class I, Group D

NAME: **ADIPONITRILE**

SYNONYMS: 1,4-dicyanobutane; dinitrile; hexanedinitrile

FORMULA: $CN(CH_2)_4CN$

NFPA 30/OSHA CLASSIFICATION:

DOT CLASS: Class 6.1, Poisonous material

SHIPPING LABEL: KEEP AWAY FROM FOOD

ID NO.: UN 2205

CAS NO.: 111-69-3

MOL. WT.: 108.1

STATEMENT OF HAZARDS: Moderate health hazard. Combustible liquid.

EMERGENCY RESPONSE PERSONAL PROTECTIVE EQUIPMENT: Wear full protective clothing and positive pressure self-contained breathing apparatus.

SPILL OR LEAK PROCEDURES: Stop or control the leak, if this can be done without undue risk. Use water spray to cool and disperse vapors and protect personnel. Approach release from upwind. Absorb in noncombustible material for proper disposal.

FIRE FIGHTING PROCEDURES: Use water spray, dry chemical, foam, or carbon dioxide. Use water spray to keep fire-exposed containers cool. Approach fire from upwind to avoid hazardous vapors and toxic decomposition products.

HEALTH HAZARDS: Moderate health hazard. May be harmful if absorbed through skin or inhaled. Irritating to skin, eye, and respiratory system. May cause cyanosis.

FIRE AND EXPLOSION HAZARDS: Combustible liquid. Products of combustion may be more hazardous than the material itself. By-products include hydrogen cyanide and irritants.

FLASH POINT: 200°F (93°C) (oc)

AUTOIGNITION TEMPERATURE: 1022°F (550°C)

FLAMMABLE LIMITS: LOWER: 1.0% UPPER: not determined

INSTABILITY AND REACTIVITY HAZARDS: Reacts violently with oxidizers.

STORAGE RECOMMENDATIONS: Separate from strong acids. Store in a cool, dry, well-ventilated location. Outside or detached storage is preferred.

USUAL SHIPPING CONTAINERS: Glass bottle inside wooden box. Tank barges and tank cars.

PHYSICAL PROPERTIES: White, watery liquid. Practically odorless.

MELTING POINT: 34°F (1°C)

BOILING POINT: 563°F (295°C)

SPECIFIC GRAVITY: 0.97

SOLUBILITY IN WATER: soluble

ELECTRICAL EQUIPMENT: Class I, Group D

NAME: **ALLYL ALCOHOL**

SYNONYMS: 2-propenol; 2-propen-1-ol; vinyl carbonal

FORMULA: $CH_2{=}CHCH_2OH$

NFPA 30/OSHA CLASSIFICATION: IB

DOT CLASS: Class 6.1, Poisonous material

SHIPPING LABEL: POISON and FLAMMABLE LIQUID

ID NO.: UN 1098

CAS NO.: 107-18-6

MOL. WT.: 58.1

STATEMENT OF HAZARDS: Severe health hazard. Flammable liquid.

EMERGENCY RESPONSE PERSONAL PROTECTIVE EQUIPMENT: Wear special protective clothing and positive pressure self-contained breathing apparatus.

SPILL OR LEAK PROCEDURES: Releases may require isolation or evacuation. Stop or control the leak, if this can be done without undue risk. Use water spray to cool and disperse vapors, protect personnel, and dilute spills to form nonflammable mixtures. Approach release from upwind. Eliminate all ignition sources. Control runoff and isolate discharged material for proper disposal.

FIRE FIGHTING PROCEDURES: Use water spray, dry chemical, "alcohol resistant" foam, or carbon dioxide. Water may be ineffective. Use water spray to keep fire-exposed containers cool.

HEALTH HAZARDS: Severe health hazard. May be fatal if absorbed through skin or inhaled. Irritating to skin, eye, and respiratory system. May cause pulmonary edema if inhaled. Health effects may be delayed.

FIRE AND EXPLOSION HAZARDS: Flammable liquid. Vapors are heavier than air and may travel to a source of ignition and flash back. Combustion may produce irritants and toxic gases.

FLASH POINT: 72°F (22°C)

AUTOIGNITION TEMPERATURE: 713°F (378°C)

FLAMMABLE LIMITS: LOWER: 2.5% UPPER: 18.0%

INSTABILITY AND REACTIVITY HAZARDS: Reacts with strong oxidizers. Polymerization may be caused by elevated temperature, oxidizers, peroxides.

STORAGE RECOMMENDATIONS: Separate from strong oxidizing materials. Store in a cool, dry, well-ventilated location.

USUAL SHIPPING CONTAINERS: Bottles, cans, drums, and tank trucks or tank cars.

PHYSICAL PROPERTIES: Colorless liquid with a pungent mustard-like odor. Floats and mixes with water.

MELTING POINT: −200°F (−129°C)

BOILING POINT: 207°F (97°C)

SPECIFIC GRAVITY: 0.85

SOLUBILITY IN WATER: soluble

VAPOR PRESSURE: 17 mm Hg @ 20°C

ELECTRICAL EQUIPMENT: Class I, Group D

NAME: **ALLYLAMINE**

SYNONYMS: 3-amino-propene; 3-aminopropylene; 2-propen-1-amine

FORMULA: $CH_2{=}CHCH_2NH_2$

NFPA 30/OSHA CLASSIFICATION: IB

DOT CLASS: Class 6.1, Poisonous material

SHIPPING LABEL: POISON and FLAMMABLE LIQUID

ID NO.: UN 2334

CAS NO.: 107-11-9

MOL. WT.: 57.1

STATEMENT OF HAZARDS: Severe health hazard. Corrosive. Flammable liquid.

EMERGENCY RESPONSE PERSONAL PROTECTIVE EQUIPMENT: Wear special protective clothing and positive pressure self-contained breathing apparatus.

SPILL OR LEAK PROCEDURES: Releases may require isolation or evacuation. Stop or control the leak, if this can be done without undue risk. Eliminate all ignition sources. Use water spray to cool and disperse vapors, protect personnel, and dilute spills to form nonflammable mixtures. Approach release from upwind. Absorb in noncombustible material for proper disposal.

FIRE FIGHTING PROCEDURES: Use water spray, dry chemical, "alcohol resistant" foam, or carbon dioxide. Use water spray to keep fire-exposed containers cool. Solid streams of water may be ineffective and spread material.

HEALTH HAZARDS: Severe health hazard. May be fatal if inhaled or absorbed through skin. Corrosive. Causes severe eye and skin burns even in a single, short exposure. Irritating to skin, eyes, and respiratory system. May cause severe tearing, conjunctivitis, corneal edema, coughing, nausea, and pulmonary edema.

FIRE AND EXPLOSION HAZARDS: Flammable liquid. Vapors are heavier than air and may travel to a source of ignition and flash back. Combustion may produce irritants and toxic gases, including oxides of nitrogen.

FLASH POINT: −4°F (−20°C)

AUTOIGNITION TEMPERATURE: 705°F (374°C)

FLAMMABLE LIMITS: LOWER: 2.2% UPPER: 22.0%

INSTABILITY AND REACTIVITY HAZARDS: Reacts with acids, oxidizing materials, chlorine, hypochlorite, halogenated compounds, and reactive organic compounds. May react with active metals. Products of decomposition include carbon monoxide, carbon dioxide, hydrocarbons, and oxides of nitrogen as well as amine vapors. Polymerization may be caused by elevated temperature, oxidizers, peroxides.

STORAGE RECOMMENDATIONS: Separate from oxidizing materials, acids, and sources of halogen. Outside or detached storage is preferred. Store in a cool, dry, well-ventilated location.

USUAL SHIPPING CONTAINERS: Glass bottles, cans, drums, and tank cars.

PHYSICAL PROPERTIES: Colorless liquid with strong ammonia-like odor.

MELTING POINT: −127°F (−88°C)

BOILING POINT: 128°F (53°C)

SPECIFIC GRAVITY: 0.76

SOLUBILITY IN WATER: soluble

VAPOR DENSITY: 1.97

ELECTRICAL EQUIPMENT: Class I, Group D

NAME: **ALLYL BROMIDE**

SYNONYMS: bromallylene; 3-bromo-1-propene; 3-bromopropylene

FORMULA: $CH_2=CHCH_2Br$

NFPA 30/OSHA CLASSIFICATION: IB

DOT CLASS: Class 3, Flammable and combustible liquid

SHIPPING LABEL: FLAMMABLE LIQUID and POISON

ID NO.: UN 1099

CAS NO.: 106-95-6

MOL. WT.: 121.0

STATEMENT OF HAZARDS: Corrosive and flammable liquid.

EMERGENCY RESPONSE PERSONAL PROTECTIVE EQUIPMENT: Wear special protective clothing and positive pressure self-contained breathing apparatus.

SPILL OR LEAK PROCEDURES: Releases may require isolation or evacuation. Eliminate all ignition sources. Stop or control the leak, if this can be done without undue risk. Use appropriate foam to blanket release and suppress vapors. Absorb in noncombustible material for proper disposal.

FIRE FIGHTING PROCEDURES: Use dry chemical, foam, carbon dioxide, or water spray. Water may be ineffective. Use water spray to keep fire-exposed containers cool. Approach fire from upwind to avoid hazardous vapors and toxic decomposition products.

HEALTH HAZARDS: Corrosive. Causes severe eye and skin burns. Serious health hazard. May be harmful if absorbed through skin or inhaled. Irritating to eyes, skin, and respiratory system.

FIRE AND EXPLOSION HAZARDS: Flammable liquid. Vapors are heavier than air and may travel to a source of ignition and flash back. Combustion by-products include hydrogen bromide.

FLASH POINT: 28°F (−2°C)

AUTOIGNITION TEMPERATURE: 563°F (280°C)

FLAMMABLE LIMITS: LOWER: 4.4% UPPER: 7.3%

INSTABILITY AND REACTIVITY HAZARDS: Reacts with oxidizing materials, alkalies. Polymerization may be caused by elevated temperature, oxidizers, peroxides.

STORAGE RECOMMENDATIONS: Separate from oxidizing materials, alkalies. Store in a cool, dry, well-ventilated location.

USUAL SHIPPING CONTAINERS: Glass bottles, carboys.

PHYSICAL PROPERTIES: Colorless liquid with pungent, unpleasant odor.

MELTING POINT: −182°F (−119°C)

BOILING POINT: 160°F (71°C)

SPECIFIC GRAVITY: 1.40

SOLUBILITY IN WATER: not soluble

VAPOR DENSITY: 4.17

ELECTRICAL EQUIPMENT: Class I, Group D

NAME: **ALLYL CHLORIDE**

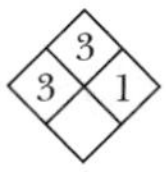

SYNONYMS: chlorallylene; 3-chloro-1-propene

FORMULA: $CH_2=CHCH_2Cl$

NFPA 30/OSHA CLASSIFICATION: IB

DOT CLASS: Class 3, Flammable and combustible liquid

SHIPPING LABEL: FLAMMABLE LIQUID and POISON

ID NO.: UN 1100

CAS NO.: 107-05-1

MOL. WT.: 76.5

STATEMENT OF HAZARDS: Corrosive and flammable liquid.

EMERGENCY RESPONSE PERSONAL PROTECTIVE EQUIPMENT: Wear special protective clothing and positive pressure self-contained breathing apparatus.

SPILL OR LEAK PROCEDURES: Eliminate all ignition sources. Approach release from upwind. Stop or control the leak, if this can be done without undue risk. Control runoff and isolate discharged material for proper disposal.

FIRE FIGHTING PROCEDURES: Approach fire from upwind to avoid hazardous vapors and toxic decomposition products. Use water spray, dry chemical, foam, or carbon dioxide. Use water spray to keep fire-exposed containers cool. Fight fire from a protected location or maximum possible distance.

HEALTH HAZARDS: Corrosive. Causes severe eye and skin burns. Serious health hazard. May be harmful if absorbed through skin or inhaled. Irritating to eyes, skin, and respiratory system.

FIRE AND EXPLOSION HAZARDS: Flammable liquid. Vapors are heavier than air and may travel to a source of ignition and flash back. Liquid floats on water and may travel to a source of ignition and spread fire. Combustion may produce irritants and toxic gases.

FLASH POINT: −20°F (−29°C)

AUTOIGNITION TEMPERATURE: 737°F (392°C)

FLAMMABLE LIMITS: LOWER: 3.3% UPPER: 11.1%

INSTABILITY AND REACTIVITY HAZARDS: Polymerization may be caused by elevated temperature, acid catalysts, oxidizers, peroxides. Reacts with amines and active metals.

STORAGE RECOMMENDATIONS: Store in a cool, dry, well-ventilated location. Inside storage should be in a standard flammable liquids storage warehouse, room, or cabinet. Isolate from acid catalysts. Outside or detached storage is preferred. Immediately remove and properly dispose of any spilled material.

USUAL SHIPPING CONTAINERS: Drums; tanks on trucks, rail cars, barges.

PHYSICAL PROPERTIES: Colorless liquid with a sharp, irritating odor.

MELTING POINT: −209°F (−134°C)

BOILING POINT: 113°F (45°C)

SPECIFIC GRAVITY: 0.94

SOLUBILITY IN WATER: not soluble

VAPOR DENSITY: 2.66

VAPOR PRESSURE: 295 mm Hg @ 20°C

ELECTRICAL EQUIPMENT: Class I, Group D

NAME: **ALLYL CHLOROFORMATE**

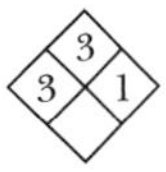

SYNONYMS: allyl chlorocarbonate

FORMULA: $CH_2=CHCH_2COOCl$

NFPA 30/OSHA CLASSIFICATION: IC

DOT CLASS: Class 8, Corrosive material

SHIPPING LABEL: CORROSIVE and POISON

ID NO.: UN 1722

CAS NO.: 2937-50-0

MOL. WT.: 120.5

STATEMENT OF HAZARDS: Serious health hazard. Flammable liquid. Reacts with water to produce chloroformic acid and allyl alcohol.

EMERGENCY RESPONSE PERSONAL PROTECTIVE EQUIPMENT: Wear special protective clothing and positive pressure self-contained breathing apparatus.

SPILL OR LEAK PROCEDURES: Eliminate all ignition sources. Keep water away from release. Stop or control the leak, if this can be done without undue risk. Use appropriate foam to blanket release and suppress vapors. Absorb in noncombustible material for proper disposal.

FIRE FIGHTING PROCEDURES: Use dry chemical, foam, carbon dioxide, or water spray. Water may be ineffective. Use water spray to keep fire-exposed containers cool. Approach fire from upwind to avoid hazardous vapors and toxic decomposition products.

HEALTH HAZARDS: Serious health hazard. May be harmful if absorbed through skin or inhaled. Irritating to skin, eye, and respiratory system. Reaction with water produces chloroformic acid and allyl alcohol, causing severe burns and tearing.

FIRE AND EXPLOSION HAZARDS: Flammable liquid. Vapors are heavier than air and may travel to a source of ignition and flash back. Combustion by-products include hydrogen chloride and other irritants and toxic gases.

FLASH POINT: 88°F (31°C)

INSTABILITY AND REACTIVITY HAZARDS: Reacts with water to produce chloroformic acid and allyl alcohol. Polymerization may be caused by elevated temperature, oxidizers, peroxides.

STORAGE RECOMMENDATIONS: Separate from acids, alkalies, amines, alcohols, oxidizing materials, and water. Store in a cool, dry, well-ventilated location. Normally refrigerated. Outside or detached storage is preferred.

USUAL SHIPPING CONTAINERS: Glass bottle inside wooden box. Glass or polyethylene bottles, carboys, polyethylene-lined drums.

PHYSICAL PROPERTIES: Colorless watery liquid. Extremely irritating odor.

BOILING POINT: 235°F (113°C)

SPECIFIC GRAVITY: 1.14

SOLUBILITY IN WATER: not soluble (decomposes)

VAPOR PRESSURE: 256 mm Hg @ 60°C
20 mm Hg @ 25°C

ELECTRICAL EQUIPMENT: Class I, Group D

NAME: **ALUMINUM ALKYLS**

SYNONYMS: trialkylaluminum

FORMULA: R_xAl ($x=2,3$) (R = alkyl radical)

NFPA 30/OSHA CLASSIFICATION:

DOT CLASS: Class 4.2, Spontaneously combustible material

SHIPPING LABEL: SPONTANEOUSLY COMBUSTIBLE

ID NO.: UN 3051

CAS NO.: VARIES

MOL. WT.: VARIES

STATEMENT OF HAZARDS: Pyrophoric; may ignite spontaneously on exposure to air. Corrosive and flammable liquid. Water reactive.

EMERGENCY RESPONSE PERSONAL PROTECTIVE EQUIPMENT: Wear special protective clothing and positive pressure self-contained breathing apparatus.

SPILL OR LEAK PROCEDURES: Keep water away from release. Spills may ignite spontaneously if solvent evaporates. Absorb in noncombustible material for proper disposal; shovel into suitable dry container.

FIRE FIGHTING PROCEDURES: Stop flow of liquid before extinguishing fire. Use dry chemical or carbon dioxide. DO NOT use water as straight stream directly on spilled material. Water fog can be used to control fire. DO NOT use halogenated extinguishing agents on spilled material. Violent reaction may result. Use water spray to keep fire-exposed containers cool. Fight fire from protected location or maximum possible distance.

HEALTH HAZARDS: Corrosive. Causes severe eye and skin burns. Serious health hazard. Harmful if absorbed through skin or inhaled. Inhalation of fumes can cause metal fume fever.

FIRE AND EXPLOSION HAZARDS: Pyrophoric material in flammable solvent. Vapors are heavier than air and may travel to a source of ignition and flash back. Decomposition begins at 350°F (177°C), releasing alkenes and aluminum by-products. Closed containers may rupture violently when heated.

INSTABILITY AND REACTIVITY HAZARDS: Reacts violently with a broad range of materials including air and water.

STORAGE RECOMMENDATIONS: Separate from air, water, halocarbons, alcohols. Store in a cool, dry, well-ventilated location. Outside or detached storage is preferred. Inside storage should be in a standard flammable liquids storage warehouse, room, or cabinet.

USUAL SHIPPING CONTAINERS: Bottles packed in insulating material. Metal cans, pails, drums. Tanks on trucks, rail cars, barges. Packaged under nitrogen gas.

PHYSICAL PROPERTIES: Colorless liquid or solid. Typically in solution with hydrocarbon solvent. Aluminum alkyls are generally supplied as solutions of 20% or less of the material. Properties are dependent upon the solvent.

NAME: **ALUMINUM CHLORIDE, anhydrous**

SYNONYMS: anhydrous aluminum chloride

FORMULA: $AlCl_3$

NFPA 30/OSHA CLASSIFICATION:

DOT CLASS: Class 8, Corrosive material

SHIPPING LABEL: CORROSIVE

ID NO.: UN 1726

CAS NO.: 7446-70-0

MOL. WT.: 133.3

STATEMENT OF HAZARDS: Corrosive. Contact with water causes release of hydrogen chloride and heat.

EMERGENCY RESPONSE PERSONAL PROTECTIVE EQUIPMENT: Wear special protective clothing and positive pressure self-contained breathing apparatus.

SPILL OR LEAK PROCEDURES: Keep water away from release. Prompt cleanup and removal is necessary. Shovel into suitable dry container.

FIRE FIGHTING PROCEDURES: DO NOT use water. Violent reaction may result. Extinguish fire using agent suitable for surrounding fire. Extinguish adjacent fires with dry chemical, carbon dioxide, or foam. Use water spray to keep fire-exposed containers cool.

HEALTH HAZARDS: Corrosive. Causes severe eye and skin burns. Irritating to skin, eye, and respiratory system.

FIRE AND EXPLOSION HAZARDS: Not combustible, but heating may produce irritants and toxic gases. Reacts violently with water producing hydrochloric acid and heat.

INSTABILITY AND REACTIVITY HAZARDS: Reacts violently with water to form hydrogen chloride. Reacts with organic materials.

STORAGE RECOMMENDATIONS: Store in cool, dry, well-ventilated location. Separate from organic materials.

USUAL SHIPPING CONTAINERS: Glass bottles, metal pails and drums, bulk package containers of rubberized fabric.

PHYSICAL PROPERTIES: Yellow-orange to grayish-white crystals or powder. Odor of hydrogen chloride formed by reaction with moisture in air. Sublimes at 358°F (181°C).

MELTING POINT: 381°F (194°C) @ 5.2 atm

SUBLIMES AT: 358°F (181°C)

SPECIFIC GRAVITY: 2.44

SOLUBILITY IN WATER: soluble/reacts violently

NAME: **ALUMINUM PHOSPHIDE**

SYNONYMS: aluminum monophosphide

FORMULA: AlP

NFPA 30/OSHA CLASSIFICATION:

DOT CLASS: Class 4.3, Dangerous when wet material

SHIPPING LABEL: DANGEROUS WHEN WET and POISON

ID NO.: UN 1397

CAS NO.: 20859-73-8

MOL. WT.: 58.0

STATEMENT OF HAZARDS: Pyrophoric. Severe health hazard. Liberates pyrophoric phosphine gas if exposed to moisture.

EMERGENCY RESPONSE PERSONAL PROTECTIVE EQUIPMENT: Wear special protective clothing and positive pressure self-contained breathing apparatus.

SPILL OR LEAK PROCEDURES: Blanket release with dry sand, clay, or ground limestone. Shovel into suitable dry container.

FIRE FIGHTING PROCEDURES: Smother with dry sand, dry clay, dry ground limestone, or use approved Class D extinguishers. DO NOT use water. Violent reaction may result. Where access to the area is strictly controlled, it may be best to allow the release to burn.

HEALTH HAZARDS: Severe health hazard. May be fatal if inhaled. Liberates pyrophoric phosphine gas if exposed to moisture.

FIRE AND EXPLOSION HAZARDS: Liberates pyrophoric, poisonous phosphine gas on contact with moist air, water, steam. Phosphine ignites on contact with air. Combustion by-products include toxic oxides of phosphorus, aluminum fumes.

INSTABILITY AND REACTIVITY HAZARDS: Reacts with water and reacts violently with strong acids to liberate phosphine gas.

STORAGE RECOMMENDATIONS: Always keep container closed, dry. Store in a noncombustible, nonsprinklered building away from all combustible material. Isolate from strong acids.

USUAL SHIPPING CONTAINERS: Packaged in fiber boxes, bags.

PHYSICAL PROPERTIES: Dark gray or yellow crystals. In moist air has fishy odor.

MELTING POINT: 1832°F (>1000°C)

SPECIFIC GRAVITY: 2.40 to 2.85

SOLUBILITY IN WATER: decomposes

NAME: **ALUMINUM POWDER, uncoated**

FORMULA: Al

NFPA 30/OSHA CLASSIFICATION:

DOT CLASS: Class 4.3, Dangerous when wet material

SHIPPING LABEL: DANGEROUS WHEN WET

ID NO.: UN 1396

CAS NO.: 7429-90-5

MOL. WT.: 27.0

STATEMENT OF HAZARDS: Flammable solid if finely divided. Easily ignited.

EMERGENCY RESPONSE PERSONAL PROTECTIVE EQUIPMENT: Wear full protective clothing and positive pressure self-contained breathing apparatus.

SPILL OR LEAK PROCEDURES: Shovel into suitable dry container. Eliminate all ignition sources.

FIRE FIGHTING PROCEDURES: Smother with dry sand, dry clay, dry ground limestone, or use approved Class D extinguishers. DO NOT use carbon dioxide or halogenated extinguishing agents. DO NOT use water.

HEALTH HAZARDS: May cause minor irritation to lungs and eyes.

FIRE AND EXPLOSION HAZARDS: Flammable solid if finely divided. Forms explosive mixtures in a dust cloud in air. Bulk dust when damp with water may heat spontaneously. Hazard greater as fineness increases.

AUTOIGNITION TEMPERATURE: 1400°F (760°C)

INSTABILITY AND REACTIVITY HAZARDS: Reacts with strong acids, strong alkalies to release hydrogen gas. Reacts with oxidizing materials, acid chlorides, metal salts, other materials.

STORAGE RECOMMENDATIONS: Store in a cool, dry, well-ventilated location. Separate from acids, alkalies, halogenated compounds, oxidizers, combustible materials.

USUAL SHIPPING CONTAINERS: Fiber cans, boxes, drums; steel drums.

PHYSICAL PROPERTIES: Gray to silver powdered metal. Metallic odor when dust is inhaled.

MELTING POINT: 1221°F (660°C)

BOILING POINT: 4473°F (2467°C)

SPECIFIC GRAVITY: 2.70

SOLUBILITY IN WATER: not soluble

ELECTRICAL EQUIPMENT: Class II, Group E

NAME: **AMMONIA, anhydrous, liquefied**

FORMULA: NH_3

NFPA 30/OSHA CLASSIFICATION:

DOT CLASS: Class 2.2, Nonflammable compressed gas

SHIPPING LABEL: NONFLAMMABLE GAS

ID NO.: UN 1005

CAS NO.: 7664-41-7

MOL. WT.: 17.0

STATEMENT OF HAZARDS: Corrosive. May be an explosion hazard in a confined space.

EMERGENCY RESPONSE PERSONAL PROTECTIVE EQUIPMENT: Wear special protective clothing and positive pressure self-contained breathing apparatus.

SPILL OR LEAK PROCEDURES: Releases may require isolation or evacuation. Stop or control the leak, if this can be done without undue risk. Use water spray to cool, absorb, and disperse vapors, and protect personnel. Approach release from upwind.

FIRE FIGHTING PROCEDURES: Use water spray to keep fire-exposed containers cool. Extinguish fire using agent suitable for surrounding fire.

HEALTH HAZARDS: Corrosive. Liquid and vapor will burn skin and eyes severely. Serious health hazard. May be harmful if inhaled. Irritating to eyes, skin, and respiratory system. Symptoms of exposure include pulmonary edema and convulsions. Liquid ammonia may cause frostbite. Aqueous solutions of ammonia have considerable vapor pressure and present hazards of gas and liquid.

FIRE AND EXPLOSION HAZARDS: No flash point determined in conventional closed cup tester. May be an explosion hazard in a confined space.

AUTOIGNITION TEMPERATURE: 1204°F (651°C)

DECOMPOSITION: Begins at 928°F (498°C)

FLAMMABLE LIMITS: LOWER: 15% UPPER: 28%

INSTABILITY AND REACTIVITY HAZARDS: Reacts with acids and oxidizing materials. Corrosive to copper, zinc, and many metal surfaces. Reacts with hypochlorite or other halogen sources to form explosive compounds that are sensitive to pressure or increases in temperature.

STORAGE RECOMMENDATIONS: Separate from other chemicals, particularly oxidizing materials, acids, and halogens. Store in a cool, dry, well-ventilated location.

USUAL SHIPPING CONTAINERS: Barges, rail cars, tank trucks, and cylinders.

PHYSICAL PROPERTIES: Colorless gas with penetrating suffocating characteristic odor. Liquid released under pressure floats and boils on water. Forms aqueous solutions with high vapor pressure.

MELTING POINT: −108°F (−78°C)

BOILING POINT: −28°F (−33°C)

SPECIFIC GRAVITY: 0.68 @ −33°C

SOLUBILITY IN WATER: soluble

VAPOR DENSITY: 0.59 @ 32°F

VAPOR PRESSURE: 400 mm Hg @ 45°C
6658 mmHg @ 21°C

ELECTRICAL EQUIPMENT: Class I, Group D

NAME: **AMMONIUM DICHROMATE**

SYNONYMS: ammonium bichromate

FORMULA: $(NH_4)_2Cr_2O_7$

NFPA 30/OSHA CLASSIFICATION:

DOT CLASS: Class 5.1, Oxidizer

SHIPPING LABEL: OXIDIZER

ID NO.: UN 1439

CAS NO.: 7789-09-5

MOL. WT.: 252.1

STATEMENT OF HAZARDS: Serious health hazard. Combustible solid. Strong oxidizer.

EMERGENCY RESPONSE PERSONAL PROTECTIVE

EQUIPMENT: Wear full protective clothing and positive pressure self-contained breathing apparatus.

SPILL OR LEAK PROCEDURES: Blanket spill with dry sand, clay, or ground limestone. Place material in noncombustible containers. Immediately remove and properly dispose of any spilled material.

FIRE FIGHTING PROCEDURES: Use flooding quantities of water. Use water spray to keep fire-exposed containers cool.

HEALTH HAZARDS: Serious health hazard. Irritating to eyes, skin, and respiratory system. May cause ulcers of the nasal passages and pulmonary edema.

FIRE AND EXPLOSION HAZARDS: Strong oxidizer. Combustible solid. Material swells dramatically, and closed containers may rupture violently when heated. Combustion by-products include chromic oxide.

AUTOIGNITION TEMPERATURE: 437°F (225°C)

INSTABILITY AND REACTIVITY HAZARDS: Reacts with strong acids, reducing agents, alcohols.

STORAGE RECOMMENDATIONS: Separate from acids, combustibles, alcohols, and reducing agents. See also NFPA 430, Code for the Storage of Liquid and Solid Oxidizers.

USUAL SHIPPING CONTAINERS: Glass bottles, fiber boxes or bags, barrels, drums.

PHYSICAL PROPERTIES: Orange to red odorless crystals.

MELTING POINT: 338°F (170°C) (decomposes)

BOILING POINT: decomposes

SPECIFIC GRAVITY: 2.15

SOLUBILITY IN WATER: soluble

NAME: **AMMONIUM FLUORIDE**

SYNONYMS: neutral ammonium fluoride

FORMULA: NH_4F

NFPA 30/OSHA CLASSIFICATION:

DOT CLASS: Class 6.1, Poisonous material

SHIPPING LABEL: KEEP AWAY FROM FOOD

ID NO.: UN 2505

CAS NO.: 12125-01-8

MOL. WT.: 37.0

STATEMENT OF HAZARDS: Serious health hazard. Combustion by-products may include hydrogen fluoride, ammonia, and oxides of nitrogen.

EMERGENCY RESPONSE PERSONAL PROTECTIVE EQUIPMENT: Wear special protective clothing and positive pressure self-contained breathing apparatus.

SPILL OR LEAK PROCEDURES: Isolate the area. Stop or control the leak, if this can be done without undue risk. Shovel into suitable dry container.

FIRE FIGHTING PROCEDURES: Use appropriate extinguishing agents on nearby combustible fires. Use water spray to knock down acid vapors.

HEALTH HAZARDS: Serious health hazard. May be harmful if inhaled. Irritating to eyes, skin, and respiratory system. Under fire conditions may produce ammonia, hydrogen fluoride, oxides of nitrogen and other toxic and corrosive gases and aerosols.

FIRE AND EXPLOSION HAZARDS: Not combustible, but if involved in a fire decomposes to produce ammonia, hydrogen fluoride, and oxides of nitrogen.

INSTABILITY AND REACTIVITY HAZARDS: Reacts with acids to produce hydrogen fluoride. Reacts with alkalies, soluble calcium salts to produce ammonia gas. Decomposes with heat. Corrodes glass, cement, most metals.

STORAGE RECOMMENDATIONS: Separate from acids, alkalies. Store in a cool, dry, well-ventilated location.

USUAL SHIPPING CONTAINERS: Polyethylene, fluorocarbon, or wax-lined bottles, barrels.

PHYSICAL PROPERTIES: Colorless crystals or white powder. Odorless.

MELTING POINT: decomposes

SPECIFIC GRAVITY: 1.01

SOLUBILITY IN WATER: soluble

NAME: **AMMONIUM NITRATE**

SYNONYMS: ammonium salt; nitram; nitric acid ammonium salt; norway saltpeter

FORMULA: NH_4NO_3

NFPA 30/OSHA CLASSIFICATION:

DOT CLASS: Class 5.1, Oxidizer

SHIPPING LABEL: OXIDIZER

ID NO.: UN 1942

CAS NO.: 6484-52-2

MOL. WT.: 80.0

STATEMENT OF HAZARDS: Strong oxidizer. Combustion by-products include oxides of nitrogen and ammonia. If subjected to strong shocks or heated under confinement causing a pressure buildup, may undergo detonation.

EMERGENCY RESPONSE PERSONAL PROTECTIVE EQUIPMENT: Wear full protective clothing and positive pressure self-contained breathing apparatus.

SPILL OR LEAK PROCEDURES: Prompt cleanup and removal are necessary in order to prevent contamination with combustible materials.

FIRE FIGHTING PROCEDURES: Use flooding quantities of water. Fight fire from protected location or maximum possible distance. Approach fire from upwind to avoid hazardous vapors and toxic decomposition products. Fire situations may require evacuation.

HEALTH HAZARDS: The oxides of nitrogen gases (except nitrous oxide) emitted on decomposition of ammonium nitrate are serious health hazard.

FIRE AND EXPLOSION HAZARDS: Strong oxidizer. If heated under confinement, material may explode. Ammonium nitrate of any grade, including fertilizer, when contaminated with oil, charcoal, or other organic materials should be considered an explosive capable of detonation by combustion or by explosion of adjacent explosive materials. Combustion by-products include oxides of nitrogen, ammonia. Closed containers may rupture violently when heated.

INSTABILITY AND REACTIVITY HAZARDS: Reacts violently with reducing agents, strong acids, powdered metals, organic materials.

STORAGE RECOMMENDATIONS: Separate from acids, alkalies, reducing agents, combustible materials. Store in a cool, dry, well-ventilated location. See also NFPA 490, Code for the Storage of Ammonium Nitrate, and NFPA 430, Code for the Storage of Liquid and Solid Oxidizers.

USUAL SHIPPING CONTAINERS: Fiber bags and drums, steel drums, and bulk packaging in trucks and rail cars and bulk in tank barges.

PHYSICAL PROPERTIES: White to gray to brown odorless beads, pellets, or flakes.

MELTING POINT: 336°F (169°C) decomposes @ 410°F (210°C)

SPECIFIC GRAVITY: 1.72

SOLUBILITY IN WATER: soluble

NAME: **AMMONIUM PERCHLORATE**

FORMULA: NH_4ClO_4

NFPA 30/OSHA CLASSIFICATION:

DOT CLASS: Class 5.1, Oxidizer

SHIPPING LABEL: OXIDIZER

ID NO.: UN 1442

CAS NO.: 7790-98-9

MOL. WT.: 117.5

STATEMENT OF HAZARDS: Strong oxidizer. Contact with combustible material will increase fire and explosion hazard. Shock sensitive. Slight health hazard. Combustion may produce irritants and toxic gases.

EMERGENCY RESPONSE PERSONAL PROTECTIVE EQUIPMENT: Wear full protective clothing and positive pressure self-contained breathing apparatus.

SPILL OR LEAK PROCEDURES: Prompt cleanup and removal are necessary in order to prevent contamination with combustible materials.

FIRE FIGHTING PROCEDURES: Explosive decomposition may occur under fire conditions. Fight fire from protected location or maximum possible distance. Use flooding quantities of water. Use water spray to keep fire-exposed containers cool. Fire situations may require evacuation.

HEALTH HAZARDS: Slight health hazard. The oxides of nitrogen (except nitrous oxide), hydrogen chloride, and ammonia emitted on decomposition of ammonium perchlorate are serious health hazard. Irritating to skin, eyes, and respiratory system.

FIRE AND EXPLOSION HAZARDS: Strong oxidizer. Heat or shock may cause explosion. Combustion by-products include oxides of nitrogen, ammonia, hydrogen chloride. Closed containers may rupture violently when heated.

INSTABILITY AND REACTIVITY HAZARDS: Strong oxidizer. Decomposes violently with shock. Reacts violently and can detonate with reducing agents, strong acids, powdered metals, or if mixed with organic materials.

STORAGE RECOMMENDATIONS: Separate from acids, alkalies, reducing agents, combustible materials. Store in a cool, dry, well-ventilated location. See also NFPA 430, Code for the Storage of Liquid and Solid Oxidizers.

USUAL SHIPPING CONTAINERS: Fiber bags and drums, steel drums, and tote bins.

PHYSICAL PROPERTIES: White, odorless crystals.

MELTING POINT: 464°F (240°C) (decomposes)

SPECIFIC GRAVITY: 1.95

SOLUBILITY IN WATER: soluble

NAME: **AMMONIUM PERMANGANATE**

DOT SHIPPING NAME: **PERMANGANATES, INORGANIC, n.o.s.**

FORMULA: NH_4MnO_4

NFPA 30/OSHA CLASSIFICATION:

DOT CLASS: Class 5.1, Oxidizer

SHIPPING LABEL: OXIDIZER

ID NO.: UN 1482

CAS NO.: 13446-10-1

MOL. WT.: 137.0

STATEMENT OF HAZARDS: Strong oxidizer. Contact with combustible material will increase fire hazard. Shock sensitive at elevated temperatures. Combustion may produce irritants and toxic gases.

EMERGENCY RESPONSE PERSONAL PROTECTIVE EQUIPMENT: Wear full protective clothing and positive pressure self-contained breathing apparatus.

SPILL OR LEAK PROCEDURES: Prompt cleanup and removal are necessary in order to prevent contamination with combustible materials.

FIRE FIGHTING PROCEDURES: Explosive decomposition may occur under fire conditions. Fight fire from protected location or maximum possible distance. Use flooding quantities of water. Use water spray to keep fire-exposed containers cool. Fire situations may require evacuation.

HEALTH HAZARDS: The oxides of nitrogen (except nitrous oxide) emitted on decomposition of ammonium permanganate are serious health hazard.

FIRE AND EXPLOSION HAZARDS: Strong oxidizer. Heat or shock may cause explosion. Combustion by-products include oxides of nitrogen and ammonia. Closed containers may rupture violently when heated.

INSTABILITY AND REACTIVITY HAZARDS: Strong oxidizer. When mixed with organic materials or reducing agents, shock or friction may initiate a violent reaction.

STORAGE RECOMMENDATIONS: Separate from acids, alkalies, reducing agents, and combustible materials. Store in a cool, dry, well-ventilated location. See also NFPA 430, Code for the Storage of Liquid and Solid Oxidizers.

USUAL SHIPPING CONTAINERS: Fiber bags and drums, steel drums.

PHYSICAL PROPERTIES: Purple crystals. Odorless.

MELTING POINT: 230°F (110°C)

SPECIFIC GRAVITY: 2.21

SOLUBILITY IN WATER: soluble

NAME: **AMYLAMINES**

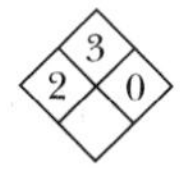

SYNONYMS: 1-pentylamine

FORMULA: $CH_3(CH_2)_4NH_2$

NFPA 30/OSHA CLASSIFICATION: IB

DOT CLASS: Class 3, Flammable and combustible liquid

SHIPPING LABEL: FLAMMABLE LIQUID

ID NO.: UN 1106

CAS NO.: N/A

MOL. WT.: 87.2

STATEMENT OF HAZARDS: Flammable liquid. Moderate health hazard.

EMERGENCY RESPONSE PERSONAL PROTECTIVE EQUIPMENT: Wear full protective clothing and positive pressure self-contained breathing apparatus.

SPILL OR LEAK PROCEDURES: Eliminate all ignition sources. Stop or control the leak, if this can be done without undue risk. Use water spray to cool and disperse vapors, protect personnel, and dilute spills to form nonflammable mixtures. Control runoff and isolate discharged material for proper disposal.

FIRE FIGHTING PROCEDURES: Use water spray, dry chemical, "alcohol resistant" foam, or carbon dioxide. Water may be ineffective. Use water spray to keep fire-exposed containers cool.

HEALTH HAZARDS: Moderate health hazard. May be harmful if absorbed through skin or inhaled. Irritating to eye, skin, and respiratory system.

FIRE AND EXPLOSION HAZARDS: Flammable liquid. Vapors are heavier than air and may travel to a source of ignition and flash back.

FLASH POINT: 30°F (−1°C)

FLAMMABLE LIMITS: LOWER: 2.2% UPPER: 22%

INSTABILITY AND REACTIVITY HAZARDS: Reacts with oxidizing materials.

STORAGE RECOMMENDATIONS: Store in a cool, dry, well-ventilated location. Store away from heat, oxidizers, and sunlight. Outside or detached storage is preferred. Separate from oxidizing materials. Inside storage should be in a standard flammable liquids storage warehouse, room, or cabinet.

USUAL SHIPPING CONTAINERS: 1- to 5-gallon cans, 55-gallon drums, tank cars.

PHYSICAL PROPERTIES: Colorless, volatile liquid with ammonia-like odor.

MELTING POINT: −67°F (−55°C)

BOILING POINT: 210°F (99°C)

SPECIFIC GRAVITY: 0.8

SOLUBILITY IN WATER: soluble

ELECTRICAL EQUIPMENT: Class I, Group D

NAME: **AMYL MERCAPTANS**

SYNONYMS: n-amyl mercaptan; pentanethiol; pentyl mercaptan

FORMULA: $CH_3(CH_2)_3CH_2SH$

NFPA 30/OSHA CLASSIFICATION: IB

DOT CLASS: Class 3, Flammable and combustible liquid

SHIPPING LABEL: FLAMMABLE LIQUID

ID NO.: UN 1111

CAS NO.: 110-66-7

MOL. WT.: 104.2

STATEMENT OF HAZARDS: Flammable liquid. Moderate health hazard.

EMERGENCY RESPONSE PERSONAL PROTECTIVE EQUIPMENT: Wear full protective clothing and positive pressure self-contained breathing apparatus.

SPILL OR LEAK PROCEDURES: Eliminate all ignition sources. Stop or control the leak, if this can be done without undue risk. Control runoff and isolate discharged material for proper disposal.

FIRE FIGHTING PROCEDURES: Use water spray, dry chemical, foam, or carbon dioxide. Water may be ineffective. Use water spray to keep fire-exposed containers cool.

HEALTH HAZARDS: Moderate health hazard. May be harmful if inhaled. Irritating to skin, eye, and respiratory system.

FIRE AND EXPLOSION HAZARDS: Flammable liquid. Vapors are heavier than air and may travel to a source of ignition and flash back. Liquid floats on water and may travel to a source of ignition and spread fire.

FLASH POINT: 65°F (18°C)

INSTABILITY AND REACTIVITY HAZARDS: Reacts with oxidizing materials.

STORAGE RECOMMENDATIONS: Store in a cool, dry, well-ventilated location. Separate from oxidizing materials. Outside or detached storage is preferred. Inside storage should be in a standard flammable liquids storage warehouse, room, or cabinet.

USUAL SHIPPING CONTAINERS: 1- to 5-gallon cans and 55-gallon drums.

PHYSICAL PROPERTIES: Colorless to light-yellow liquid with very disagreeable odor.

MELTING POINT: −105°F (−76°C)

BOILING POINT: 260°F (127°C)

SPECIFIC GRAVITY: 0.8

SOLUBILITY IN WATER: not soluble

VAPOR PRESSURE: 14 mm Hg @ 25°C

ELECTRICAL EQUIPMENT: Class I, Group D

NAME: **AMYL NITRATE**

FORMULA: $CH_3(CH_2)_4NO_3$

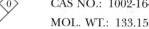

NFPA 30/OSHA CLASSIFICATION: II

DOT CLASS: Class 3, Flammable and combustible liquid

SHIPPING LABEL: FLAMMABLE LIQUID

ID NO.: UN 1112

CAS NO.: 1002-16-0

MOL. WT.: 133.15

STATEMENT OF HAZARDS: Combustible liquid. Moderate health hazard. Products of combustion may be more hazardous than the material itself. Strong oxidizer.

EMERGENCY RESPONSE PERSONAL PROTECTIVE EQUIPMENT: Wear full protective clothing and positive pressure self-contained breathing apparatus.

SPILL OR LEAK PROCEDURES: Stop or control the leak, if this can be done without undue risk. Use water spray to cool and disperse vapors and protect personnel.

FIRE FIGHTING PROCEDURES: Use water spray, dry chemical, foam, or carbon dioxide. Use water spray to keep fire-exposed containers cool.

HEALTH HAZARDS: Moderate health hazard. May be harmful if inhaled. Combustion by-products include oxides of nitrogen and may be more hazardous than the material itself.

FIRE AND EXPLOSION HAZARDS: Combustible liquid. Strong oxidizer.

FLASH POINT: 118°F (48°C)

INSTABILITY AND REACTIVITY HAZARDS: Strong oxidizer. Combustion by-products include oxides of nitrogen.

STORAGE RECOMMENDATIONS: Store in a cool, dry, well-ventilated location. Outside or detached storage is preferred. Inside storage should be in a standard flammable liquids storage warehouse, room, or cabinet. See also NFPA 430, Code for the Storage of Liquid and Solid Oxidizers.

USUAL SHIPPING CONTAINERS: 55-gallon drums, tank trucks, tank cars.

PHYSICAL PROPERTIES: Colorless liquid with an ethereal odor.

BOILING POINT: 306 to 315°F (153 to 157°C)

SPECIFIC GRAVITY: 1.0

SOLUBILITY IN WATER: not soluble

ELECTRICAL EQUIPMENT: Class I, Group Undesignated

NAME: **ANILINE**

SYNONYMS: aminobenzene; benzenamine; phenylamine

FORMULA: $C_6H_5NH_2$

NFPA 30/OSHA CLASSIFICATION: IIIA

DOT CLASS: Class 6.1, Poisonous material

SHIPPING LABEL: POISON

ID NO.: UN 1547

CAS NO.: 62-53-3

MOL. WT.: 93.1

STATEMENT OF HAZARDS: Serious health hazard. Combustible liquid.

EMERGENCY RESPONSE PERSONAL PROTECTIVE EQUIPMENT: Wear special protective clothing and positive pressure self-contained breathing apparatus.

SPILL OR LEAK PROCEDURES: Approach release from upwind. Stop or control the leak, if this can be done without undue risk. Use water spray to cool and disperse vapors and protect personnel. Control runoff and isolate discharged material for proper disposal.

FIRE FIGHTING PROCEDURES: Use water spray, dry chemical, foam, or carbon dioxide. Use water spray to keep fire-exposed containers cool.

HEALTH HAZARDS: Serious health hazard. May be harmful if absorbed through skin and inhaled. Vapors are readily absorbed through the skin. Causes chemical asphyxiation.

FIRE AND EXPLOSION HAZARDS: Combustible liquid. Combustion by-products include nitrogen oxides as well as other materials.

FLASH POINT: 158°F (70°C)

AUTOIGNITION TEMPERATURE: 1139°F (615°C)

FLAMMABLE LIMITS: LOWER: 1.3% UPPER: 11%

INSTABILITY AND REACTIVITY HAZARDS: Reacts with oxidizing materials, acids, and alkalies. See NFPA 491M, Manual for Hazardous Chemical Reactions, for details of other hazardous chemical reactions involving aniline.

STORAGE RECOMMENDATIONS: Store in cool, dry, well-ventilated location away from fire hazards and reactive materials.

USUAL SHIPPING CONTAINERS: Bottles, cans, drums, and tank vehicles, tank cars, and tank vessels.

PHYSICAL PROPERTIES: Colorless to brown oily liquid with amine odor.

MELTING POINT: 21°F (−6°C)

BOILING POINT: 364°F (184°C)

SPECIFIC GRAVITY: 1.02

SOLUBILITY IN WATER: not soluble

VAPOR PRESSURE: 1 mm Hg @ 20°C

ELECTRICAL EQUIPMENT: Class I, Group D

NAME: **ANTIMONY PENTACHLORIDE, liquid**

SYNONYMS: antimony chloride; antimony perchloride; butter of antimony

FORMULA: $SbCl_5$

NFPA 30/OSHA CLASSIFICATION:

DOT CLASS: Class 8, Corrosive material

SHIPPING LABEL: CORROSIVE

ID NO.: UN 1730

CAS NO.: 7647-18-9

MOL. WT.: 299.0

STATEMENT OF HAZARDS: Corrosive.

EMERGENCY RESPONSE PERSONAL PROTECTIVE EQUIPMENT: Wear special protective clothing and positive pressure self-contained breathing apparatus.

SPILL OR LEAK PROCEDURES: Stop or control the leak, if this can be done without undue risk. Use water spray to cool and disperse vapors and protect personnel.

FIRE FIGHTING PROCEDURES: Use appropriate extinguishing agents on nearby combustible fires. Use water spray to knock down acid vapors.

HEALTH HAZARDS: Corrosive. Causes severe eye and skin burns. Vapors resulting from contact with water or moist air may burn skin, eyes, and respiratory system. May be harmful if absorbed through skin or inhaled. Combustion by-products may include antimony fumes and hydrogen chloride.

FIRE AND EXPLOSION HAZARDS: Not combustible, but if involved in a fire decomposes to produce fumes of antimony and hydrogen chloride.

INSTABILITY AND REACTIVITY HAZARDS: Decomposes with heat, acids, or on contact with water or moist air to produce hydrogen chloride and antimony pentoxide.

STORAGE RECOMMENDATIONS: Separate from acids, alkalies. Store in a cool, dry, well-ventilated location.

USUAL SHIPPING CONTAINERS: Glass bottles, carboys, metal drums.

PHYSICAL PROPERTIES: Colorless to red-yellow oily liquid. Unpleasant odor.

MELTING POINT: 37°F (2.8°C)

BOILING POINT: decomposes

SPECIFIC GRAVITY: 2.34

SOLUBILITY IN WATER: decomposes

VAPOR PRESSURE: 1 mm Hg @ 22.7°C

NAME: **ANTIMONY PENTAFLUORIDE**

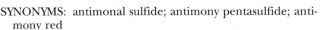

SYNONYMS: antimony (V) fluoride

FORMULA: SbF_5

NFPA 30/OSHA CLASSIFICATION:

DOT CLASS: Class 8, Corrosive material

SHIPPING LABEL: CORROSIVE and POISON

ID NO.: UN 1732

CAS NO.: 7783-70-2

MOL. WT.: 216.7

STATEMENT OF HAZARDS: Severe health hazard. Corrosive. Reacts with water to produce hydrogen fluoride.

EMERGENCY RESPONSE PERSONAL PROTECTIVE EQUIPMENT: Wear special protective clothing and positive pressure self-contained breathing apparatus.

SPILL OR LEAK PROCEDURES: Keep water away from release. Approach release from upwind. Stop or control the leak, if this can be done without undue risk. Control runoff and isolate discharged material for proper disposal.

FIRE FIGHTING PROCEDURES: Approach fire from upwind to avoid hazardous vapors and toxic decomposition products. Use dry chemical, carbon dioxide, or flooding quantities of water as spray on fire involved material.

HEALTH HAZARDS: Severe health hazard. May be fatal if absorbed through skin or inhaled. Corrosive. Causes severe eye and skin burns. Irritating to skin, eyes, and respiratory system. Reacts with water to produce hydrogen fluoride.

FIRE AND EXPLOSION HAZARDS: Not combustible, but if involved in a fire decomposes to produce fumes of antimony and hydrogen fluoride. Contact with combustible materials may increase the fire hazard. Closed containers may rupture violently when heated.

INSTABILITY AND REACTIVITY HAZARDS: Hydrofluoric acid is formed from reaction with water and moisture, which may react with metals forming hydrogen gas.

STORAGE RECOMMENDATIONS: Store in a cool, dry, well-ventilated location. Outside or detached storage is preferred. Separate from organic or siliceous materials.

USUAL SHIPPING CONTAINERS: Stainless steel cylinders.

PHYSICAL PROPERTIES: Oily colorless liquid. Hygroscopic. Fumes readily upon contact with moist air.

MELTING POINT: 45°F (7°C)

BOILING POINT: 301°F (150°C)

SPECIFIC GRAVITY: 2.99

SOLUBILITY IN WATER: soluble

VAPOR PRESSURE: 10 mm Hg @ 25°C

NAME: **ANTIMONY SULFIDE**

DOT SHIPPING NAME: **ANTIMONY COMPOUNDS, INORGANIC SOLID, N.O.S.**

SYNONYMS: antimonal sulfide; antimony pentasulfide; antimony red

FORMULA: Sb_2S_5

NFPA 30/OSHA CLASSIFICATION:

DOT CLASS: Class 6.1, Poisonous material

SHIPPING LABEL: POISON or KEEP AWAY FROM FOOD

ID NO.: UN 1549

CAS NO.: 1315-04-4

MOL. WT.: 403.8

STATEMENT OF HAZARDS: Combustible solid. Slight health hazard. Combustion by-products include hydrogen sulfide, antimony oxides, and sulfur dioxide.

EMERGENCY RESPONSE PERSONAL PROTECTIVE EQUIPMENT: Wear full protective clothing and positive pressure self-contained breathing apparatus.

SPILL OR LEAK PROCEDURES: Shovel into suitable dry container.

FIRE FIGHTING PROCEDURES: Extinguish fire using agent suitable for surrounding fire. Use flooding quantities of water as spray. Approach fire from upwind to avoid hazardous vapors and toxic decomposition products.

HEALTH HAZARDS: Slight health hazard. Products of combustion or reaction products with water or acids include hydrogen sulfide and sulfur dioxide, which may be more hazardous than the material itself.

FIRE AND EXPLOSION HAZARDS: Combustible solid. Combustion by-products include antimony oxides, sulfur dioxide, and hydrogen sulfide.

INSTABILITY AND REACTIVITY HAZARDS: Reacts with water or acids to produce toxic gas. Reacts with oxidizing materials.

STORAGE RECOMMENDATIONS: Separate from acids, oxidizing materials. Store in a cool, dry, well-ventilated location.

USUAL SHIPPING CONTAINERS: Cans and fiber drums.

PHYSICAL PROPERTIES: Orange-yellow odorless powder.

MELTING POINT: 167°F (75°C) (decomposes)

SPECIFIC GRAVITY: 4.12

SOLUBILITY IN WATER: not soluble/decomposes

NAME: **ARSENIC PENTAFLUORIDE**

FORMULA: AsF_5

NFPA 30/OSHA CLASSIFICATION:

DOT CLASS: N/A

ID NO.: N/A

CAS NO.: 7784-36-3

MOL. WT.: 169.9

STATEMENT OF HAZARDS: Corrosive gas.

EMERGENCY RESPONSE PERSONAL PROTECTIVE EQUIPMENT: Wear special protective clothing and positive pressure self-contained breathing apparatus.

SPILL OR LEAK PROCEDURES: Stop or control the leak, if this can be done without undue risk. Use water spray to disperse vapors and protect personnel. Control runoff and isolate discharged material for proper disposal.

FIRE FIGHTING PROCEDURES: Use appropriate extinguishing agents on nearby combustible fires. Carefully use water spray to knock down acid vapors.

HEALTH HAZARDS: Corrosive. Causes severe eye and skin burns. Irritating to skin, eyes, and respiratory system.

FIRE AND EXPLOSION HAZARDS: Not combustible, but if involved in a fire decomposes to produce fumes of arsenic and hydrogen fluoride.

INSTABILITY AND REACTIVITY HAZARDS: Decomposes on contact with water or moist air to produce hydrogen fluoride and arsenic pentoxide. Behaves like hydrogen fluoride once wet.

STORAGE RECOMMENDATIONS: Separate from acids, alkalies. Store in a cool, dry, well-ventilated location.

USUAL SHIPPING CONTAINERS: Cylinders.

PHYSICAL PROPERTIES: Colorless gas. Forms white fumes in moist air.

MELTING POINT: −112°F (−80°C)

BOILING POINT: −63°F (−53°C)

SOLUBILITY IN WATER: decomposes

VAPOR DENSITY: 5.86

NAME: **ARSENIC PENTOXIDE**

SYNONYMS: arsenic anhydride; arsenic (V) oxide; arsenic pentaoxide; diarsenic pentoxide

FORMULA: As_2O_5

NFPA 30/OSHA CLASSIFICATION:

DOT CLASS: Class 6.1, Poisonous material

SHIPPING LABEL: POISON

ID NO.: UN 1559

CAS NO.: 1303-28-2

MOL. WT.: 229.8

STATEMENT OF HAZARDS: Serious health hazard.

EMERGENCY RESPONSE PERSONAL PROTECTIVE EQUIPMENT: Wear special protective clothing and positive pressure self-contained breathing apparatus.

SPILL OR LEAK PROCEDURES: Prompt cleanup and removal are necessary.

FIRE FIGHTING PROCEDURES: Use flooding quantities of water as spray. Control runoff and isolate discharged material for proper disposal. Extinguish fire using agent suitable for surrounding fire.

HEALTH HAZARDS: Serious health hazard. May be harmful if absorbed through skin or inhaled. Irritating to skin, eyes, and respiratory system.

FIRE AND EXPLOSION HAZARDS: Not combustible, but if involved in a fire decomposes to produce arsenic fumes.

INSTABILITY AND REACTIVITY HAZARDS: Reacts with acids, halogens, aluminum, and zinc.

STORAGE RECOMMENDATIONS: Separate from acids, halogens, aluminum, and zinc. Store in a cool, dry, well-ventilated location.

USUAL SHIPPING CONTAINERS: Lined fiber bags, drums, steel drums.

PHYSICAL PROPERTIES: White, hygroscopic, odorless powder.

MELTING POINT: 1472°F (800°C) (decomposes)

BOILING POINT: decomposes

SPECIFIC GRAVITY: 4.32

SOLUBILITY IN WATER: soluble

NAME: **ARSENIC TRICHLORIDE**

SYNONYMS: arsenic butter; arsenic chloride; arsenous chloride; arsenous trichloride; trichloroarsine

FORMULA: $AsCl_3$

NFPA 30/OSHA CLASSIFICATION:

DOT CLASS: Class 6.1, Poisonous material

SHIPPING LABEL: POISON

ID NO.: UN 1560

CAS NO.: 7784-34-1

MOL. WT.: 181.3

STATEMENT OF HAZARDS: Corrosive liquid.

EMERGENCY RESPONSE PERSONAL PROTECTIVE EQUIPMENT: Wear special protective clothing and positive pressure self-contained breathing apparatus.

SPILL OR LEAK PROCEDURES: Stop or control the leak, if this can be done without undue risk. Use water spray to disperse vapors and protect personnel. Control runoff and isolate discharged material for proper disposal.

FIRE FIGHTING PROCEDURES: Use appropriate extinguishing agents on nearby combustible fires. Use water spray to knock down acid vapors.

HEALTH HAZARDS: Corrosive. Causes severe eye and skin burns. Irritating to skin, eyes, and respiratory system.

FIRE AND EXPLOSION HAZARDS: Not combustible, but if involved in a fire decomposes to produce fumes of arsenic and hydrogen chloride.

INSTABILITY AND REACTIVITY HAZARDS: Decomposes

with sunlight or on contact with water or moist air to produce hydrogen chloride and arsenic trioxide.

STORAGE RECOMMENDATIONS: Separate from acids, alkalies. Store in a cool, dark, dry, well-ventilated location.

USUAL SHIPPING CONTAINERS: Glass bottles, cans, drums.

PHYSICAL PROPERTIES: Colorless to pale yellow oily liquid. Unpleasant odor. Fumes in moist air.

MELTING POINT: 16.7°F (−8°C)

BOILING POINT: 266°F (130°C)

SPECIFIC GRAVITY: 2.15

SOLUBILITY IN WATER: decomposes

VAPOR PRESSURE: 10 mm Hg @ 23.5°C

NAME: **ARSENIC TRIOXIDE**

SYNONYMS: arsenolite; arsenous acid anhydride; arsenous oxide, white arsenic

FORMULA: As_2O_3

NFPA 30/OSHA CLASSIFICATION:

DOT CLASS: Class 6.1, Poisonous material

SHIPPING LABEL: POISON

ID NO.: UN 1561

CAS NO.: 1327-53-3

MOL. WT.: 197.8

STATEMENT OF HAZARDS: Serious health hazard.

EMERGENCY RESPONSE PERSONAL PROTECTIVE EQUIPMENT: Wear special protective clothing and positive pressure self-contained breathing apparatus.

SPILL OR LEAK PROCEDURES: Prompt cleanup and removal are necessary. Shovel into suitable dry container.

FIRE FIGHTING PROCEDURES: Extinguish fire using agent suitable for surrounding fire. Use flooding quantities of water as spray. Control runoff and isolate discharged material for proper disposal.

HEALTH HAZARDS: Serious health hazard. May be harmful if absorbed through skin or inhaled. Irritating to skin, eyes, and respiratory system.

FIRE AND EXPLOSION HAZARDS: Not combustible, but if involved in a fire decomposes to produce arsenic fumes.

INSTABILITY AND REACTIVITY HAZARDS: Reacts with acids, halogens, aluminum, and zinc.

STORAGE RECOMMENDATIONS: Store in a cool, dry, well-ventilated location. Separate from acids, halogens, and iron salts.

USUAL SHIPPING CONTAINERS: Lined fiber bags. Metal cans, pails, drums. Bulk in trucks, rail cars, barges.

PHYSICAL PROPERTIES: Colorless to white crystals.

MELTING POINT: 379°F (193°C) (sublimes)

BOILING POINT: sublimes

SPECIFIC GRAVITY: 3.74

SOLUBILITY IN WATER: not soluble

VAPOR PRESSURE: 66 mm Hg @ 312°C

NAME: **ARSENIC TRISULFIDE**

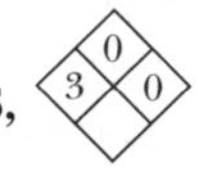

DOT SHIPPING NAME: **ARSENIC COMPOUNDS, SOLID, n.o.s. (UN 1557)**

SYNONYMS: arsenic (III) sulfide; arsenous sulfide; diarsenic trisulfide

FORMULA: As_2S_3

NFPA 30/OSHA CLASSIFICATION:

DOT CLASS: Class 6.1, Poisonous material

SHIPPING LABEL: POISON

ID NO.: NA 1557

CAS NO.: 1303-33-9

MOL. WT.: 246.0

STATEMENT OF HAZARDS: Serious health hazard.

EMERGENCY RESPONSE PERSONAL PROTECTIVE EQUIPMENT: Wear special protective clothing and positive pressure self-contained breathing apparatus.

SPILL OR LEAK PROCEDURES: Prompt cleanup and removal are necessary. Control runoff and isolate discharged material for proper disposal.

FIRE FIGHTING PROCEDURES: Extinguish fire using agent suitable for surrounding fire. Use flooding quantities of water as spray. Control runoff and isolate discharged material for proper disposal.

HEALTH HAZARDS: Serious health hazard. May be harmful if absorbed through skin or inhaled. Irritating to skin, eyes, and respiratory system.

FIRE AND EXPLOSION HAZARDS: Not combustible, but if involved in a fire may decompose to produce sulfur oxides and arsenic compounds.

INSTABILITY AND REACTIVITY HAZARDS: Reacts with acids, oxidizing materials, halogens. Reacts with water or steam to produce hydrogen sulfide.

STORAGE RECOMMENDATIONS: Store in a cool, dry, well-ventilated location. Separate from acids, oxidizing materials, halogens.

USUAL SHIPPING CONTAINERS: Lined fiber bags; metal cans, pails, drums.

PHYSICAL PROPERTIES: Yellow or red crystalline solid. Odorless.

MELTING POINT: 594°F (312°C)

BOILING POINT: 1305°F (707°C)

SPECIFIC GRAVITY: 3.43

SOLUBILITY IN WATER: not soluble

NAME: **ARSINE**

SYNONYMS: arsenic trihydride; hydrogen arsenide

FORMULA: AsH_3

NFPA 30/OSHA CLASSIFICATION:

DOT CLASS: Class 2.3, Poisonous gas

SHIPPING LABEL: POISON GAS and FLAMMABLE GAS

ID NO.: UN 2188

CAS NO.: 7784-42-1

MOL. WT.: 77.9

STATEMENT OF HAZARDS: Severe health hazard. Low ignition energy.

EMERGENCY RESPONSE PERSONAL PROTECTIVE EQUIPMENT: Wear special protective clothing and positive pressure self-contained breathing apparatus.

SPILL OR LEAK PROCEDURES: Releases may require isolation or evacuation. Approach release from upwind. Eliminate all ignition sources. Stop or control the leak, if this can be done without undue risk. Use water spray to cool and disperse vapors and protect personnel.

FIRE FIGHTING PROCEDURES: Stop flow of gas before extinguishing fire. Approach fire from upwind to avoid hazardous vapors and toxic decomposition products. Fight fire from protected location or maximum possible distance. Use fine spray or fog to control fire by preventing its spread and absorbing some of its heat. Use water spray to keep fire-exposed containers cool.

HEALTH HAZARDS: Severe health hazard. May be fatal if absorbed through skin or inhaled, even in very low doses. Inhalation causes headache, vomiting, anoxia, nervousness, abdominal pains, chills, death. Symptoms may appear up to a few hours after exposure.

FIRE AND EXPLOSION HAZARDS: Flammable gas. Decomposes at 572°F (300°C) with deposition of arsenic, which vaporizes at 752°F (400°C). Gas is heavier than air and may travel to a source of ignition and flash back. Closed containers may rupture violently when heated.

FLAMMABLE LIMITS: LOWER: 5.1% UPPER: 78%

INSTABILITY AND REACTIVITY HAZARDS: Reacts violently with oxidizing materials, acids, halogens. Reacts with light to deposit arsenic.

STORAGE RECOMMENDATIONS: Separate from oxidizing materials, acids, halogens. Store in a cool, dry, well-ventilated location. Outside or detached storage is preferred.

USUAL SHIPPING CONTAINERS: Steel cylinders.

PHYSICAL PROPERTIES: Colorless, neutral gas with disagreeable garlic odor.

MELTING POINT: −179°F (−117°C)

BOILING POINT: −81°F (−62°C)

SOLUBILITY IN WATER: not soluble

VAPOR DENSITY: 2.66

VAPOR PRESSURE: >760 mm Hg @ 20°C

NAME: **BARIUM CHLORATE**

SYNONYMS: barium chlorate anhydrous

FORMULA: $Ba(ClO_3)_2$

NFPA 30/OSHA CLASSIFICATION:

DOT CLASS: Class 5.1, Oxidizer

SHIPPING LABEL: OXIDIZER and POISON

ID NO.: UN 1445

CAS NO.: 13477-00-4

MOL. WT.: 304.3

STATEMENT OF HAZARDS: Moderate health hazard. Strong oxidizer.

EMERGENCY RESPONSE PERSONAL PROTECTIVE EQUIPMENT: Wear full protective clothing and positive pressure self-contained breathing apparatus.

SPILL OR LEAK PROCEDURES: Prompt cleanup and removal is necessary in order to prevent contamination with combustible materials.

FIRE FIGHTING PROCEDURES: Use flooding quantities of water. Use water spray to keep fire-exposed containers cool.

HEALTH HAZARDS: Moderate health hazard. May be harmful if inhaled. Irritating to skin, eyes, and respiratory system. May cause muscle spasms, slow pulse, irritation of throat, eyes, skin.

FIRE AND EXPLOSION HAZARDS: Strong oxidizer. Releases oxygen above 482°F (250°C). Not combustible, but if involved in a fire decomposes to produce barium oxides.

INSTABILITY AND REACTIVITY HAZARDS: Strong oxidizer. May react violently with reducing agents, strong acids, powdered metals. Contact with combustible material will increase the fire hazard.

STORAGE RECOMMENDATIONS: Separate from acids, alkalies, reducing agents, combustibles, ammonium compounds. Store in a cool, dry, well-ventilated location. See also NFPA 430, Code for the Storage of Liquid and Solid Oxidizers.

USUAL SHIPPING CONTAINERS: Fiber bags, boxes, and drums; wooden kegs.

PHYSICAL PROPERTIES: Colorless to white odorless crystals or powder.

MELTING POINT: 482°F (250°C) (loses oxygen) 777°F (414°C) (melts)

SPECIFIC GRAVITY: 3.18

SOLUBILITY IN WATER: soluble

NAME: **BENZALDEHYDE**

DOT SHIPPING NAME: **ALDEHYDE, n.o.s.**

SYNONYMS: artificial essential oil of almond; benzoic aldehyde

FORMULA: $(C_6H_5)CHO$

NFPA 30/OSHA CLASSIFICATION: IIIA

DOT CLASS: Class 3, Flammable and combustible liquid

SHIPPING LABEL: FLAMMABLE LIQUID

ID NO.: UN 1989

CAS NO.: 100-52-7

MOL. WT.: 106.1

STATEMENT OF HAZARDS: Moderate health hazard. Combustible liquid.

EMERGENCY RESPONSE PERSONAL PROTECTIVE EQUIPMENT: Wear full protective clothing and positive pressure self-contained breathing apparatus.

SPILL OR LEAK PROCEDURES: Stop or control the leak, if this can be done without undue risk. Use water spray to cool and disperse vapors and protect personnel. Absorb in noncombustible material for proper disposal.

FIRE FIGHTING PROCEDURES: Use water spray, dry chemical, foam, or carbon dioxide. Use water spray to keep fire-exposed containers cool.

HEALTH HAZARDS: Moderate health hazard. May be harmful if absorbed through skin or inhaled. Narcotic in high concentrations. Acts as local anesthetic. Irritating to skin, eyes, and respiratory system.

FIRE AND EXPLOSION HAZARDS: Combustible liquid. Combustion may produce irritants and toxic gases.

FLASH POINT: 148°F (64°C)

AUTOIGNITION TEMPERATURE: 378°F (192°C)

FLAMMABLE LIMITS: LOWER: 1.4% UPPER: not determined

INSTABILITY AND REACTIVITY HAZARDS: Reacts with a broad range of materials.

STORAGE RECOMMENDATIONS: Store in a cool, dry, dark, well-ventilated location. Separate from oxidizing materials, reducing agents, alkalies.

USUAL SHIPPING CONTAINERS: Glass bottle or metal can inside wooden box; carboys; drums; tanks on trucks, rail cars, barges.

PHYSICAL PROPERTIES: Yellow liquid. Odor of almonds. Burning, aromatic taste.

MELTING POINT: −69°F (−56°C)

BOILING POINT: 354°F (179°C)

SPECIFIC GRAVITY: 1.04

SOLUBILITY IN WATER: not soluble

VAPOR PRESSURE: 1 mm Hg @ 26°C

ELECTRICAL EQUIPMENT: Class I, Group D

NAME: **BENZENE**

SYNONYMS: benzol

FORMULA: C_6H_6

NFPA 30/OSHA CLASSIFICATION: IB

DOT CLASS: Class 3, Flammable and combustible liquid

SHIPPING LABEL: FLAMMABLE LIQUID

ID NO.: UN 1114

CAS NO.: 71-43-2

MOL. WT.: 78.1

STATEMENT OF HAZARDS: Flammable liquid. May accumulate static electricity. Moderate health hazard.

EMERGENCY RESPONSE PERSONAL PROTECTIVE EQUIPMENT: Wear full protective clothing and positive pressure self-contained breathing apparatus.

SPILL OR LEAK PROCEDURES: Eliminate all ignition sources. Stop or control the leak, if this can be done without undue risk. Use water spray to cool and disperse vapors, protect personnel, and dilute spills to form nonflammable mixtures. Absorb in noncombustible material for proper disposal. Control runoff and isolate discharged material for proper disposal.

FIRE FIGHTING PROCEDURES: Approach fire from upwind to avoid hazardous vapors. Use water spray, dry chemical, foam, or carbon dioxide. Use water spray to keep fire-exposed containers cool.

HEALTH HAZARDS: Moderate health hazard. May be harmful if absorbed through skin or inhaled. Irritating to eye, skin, and respiratory system.

FIRE AND EXPLOSION HAZARDS: Flammable liquid. Vapors are heavier than air and may travel to a source of ignition and flash back. Liquid floats on water and may travel to a source of ignition and spread fire.

FLASH POINT: 12°F (−11°C)

AUTOIGNITION TEMPERATURE: 928°F (498°C)

FLAMMABLE LIMITS: LOWER: 1.3% UPPER: 7.1%

INSTABILITY AND REACTIVITY HAZARDS: Reacts with oxidizing materials.

STORAGE RECOMMENDATIONS: Outside or detached storage is preferred. Inside storage should be in a standard flammable liquids storage warehouse, room, or cabinet. Separate from oxidizing materials.

USUAL SHIPPING CONTAINERS: Glass bottles, cans, drums, and tanks on trucks, rail cars, barges.

PHYSICAL PROPERTIES: Colorless liquid with aromatic odor.

MELTING POINT: 42°F (6°C)

BOILING POINT: 176°F (80°C)

SPECIFIC GRAVITY: 0.88

SOLUBILITY IN WATER: not soluble

VAPOR PRESSURE: 75 mm Hg @ 20°C

ELECTRICAL EQUIPMENT: Class I, Group D

NAME: **BENZOTRICHLORIDE**

SYNONYMS: benzene, (trichloromethyl)-; benzenyl trichloride; phenylchloroform; phenyltrichloromethane; toluene trichloride

FORMULA: $C_6H_5CCl_3$

NFPA 30/OSHA CLASSIFICATION: IIIB

DOT CLASS: Class 8, Corrosive material

SHIPPING LABEL: CORROSIVE

ID NO.: UN 2226

CAS NO.: 98-07-7

MOL. WT.: 195.5

STATEMENT OF HAZARDS: Serious health hazard. Corrosive and combustible liquid. Reacts with water.

EMERGENCY RESPONSE PERSONAL PROTECTIVE EQUIPMENT: Wear special protective clothing and positive pressure self-contained breathing apparatus.

SPILL OR LEAK PROCEDURES: Use water spray to cool and disperse vapors, protect personnel. Control runoff and isolate discharged material for proper disposal.

FIRE FIGHTING PROCEDURES: Use dry chemical, foam, or carbon dioxide. The use of water should be avoided as hydrochloric acid will be liberated. If water must be use, flood with large amounts to absorb liberated hydrogen chloride. Use water spray to keep fire-exposed containers cool.

Approach fire from upwind to avoid hazardous vapors and toxic decomposition products.

HEALTH HAZARDS: Serious health hazard. Corrosive. Causes severe eye and skin burns. Irritating to the eyes, skin, and respiratory system. May cause pulmonary edema or other lung damage. Skin sensitization may occur.

FIRE AND EXPLOSION HAZARDS: Combustible liquid. Combustion by-products include hydrogen chloride and carbon dioxide.

FLASH POINT: 260°F (127°C)

AUTOIGNITION TEMPERATURE: 412°F (211°C)

INSTABILITY AND REACTIVITY HAZARDS: Reacts with water to produce hydrogen chloride. Contact with acid evolves chlorine fumes.

STORAGE RECOMMENDATIONS: Separate from acids. Store in a cool, dry, well-ventilated location.

PHYSICAL PROPERTIES: Colorless to yellowish, oily liquid, which fumes in air and has a penetrating odor.

MELTING POINT: 23°F (−5°C)

BOILING POINT: 429°F (221°C)

SPECIFIC GRAVITY: 1.38

SOLUBILITY IN WATER: reacts

VAPOR PRESSURE: 0.23 mm Hg @ 20°C

NAME: **BENZOTRIFLUORIDE**

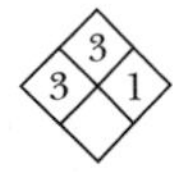

SYNONYMS: benzene (trifluoromethyl); phenylfluoroform; toluene trifluoride,

FORMULA: $C_6H_5CF_3$

NFPA 30/OSHA CLASSIFICATION: IB

DOT CLASS: Class 3, Flammable and combustible liquid

SHIPPING LABEL: FLAMMABLE LIQUID

ID NO.: UN 2338

CAS NO.: 98-08-8

MOL. WT.: 146.1

STATEMENT OF HAZARDS: Corrosive and flammable liquid. Reacts with water to produce hydrogen fluoride.

EMERGENCY RESPONSE PERSONAL PROTECTIVE EQUIPMENT: Wear special protective clothing and positive pressure self-contained breathing apparatus.

SPILL OR LEAK PROCEDURES: Eliminate all ignition sources. Approach release from upwind. Stop or control the leak, if this can be done without undue risk. Keep water away from release to avoid hydrogen fluoride formation.

FIRE FIGHTING PROCEDURES: Use water as spray, dry chemical, foam, or carbon dioxide. Water may be ineffective. Approach fire from upwind to avoid hazardous vapors and toxic decomposition products. Use water spray to keep fire-exposed containers cool.

HEALTH HAZARDS: Serious health hazard. May be harmful if absorbed through skin or inhaled. Corrosive. Causes severe eye and skin burns. Forms toxic and corrosive hydrogen fluoride on contact with water.

FIRE AND EXPLOSION HAZARDS: Flammable liquid. Vapors are heavier than air and may travel to a source of ignition and flash back. Combustion may produce irritants and toxic gases including hydrogen fluoride.

FLASH POINT: 54°F (12°C)

AUTOIGNITION TEMPERATURE: 1148°F (620°C)

INSTABILITY AND REACTIVITY HAZARDS: Reacts with water or moisture in air to form benzoic acid and hydrogen fluoride. Decomposition may release hydrogen fluoride.

STORAGE RECOMMENDATIONS: Store in a cool, dry, well-ventilated location. Inside storage should be in a standard flammable liquids storage warehouse, room, or cabinet. Separate from oxidizing materials.

USUAL SHIPPING CONTAINERS: 55-gallon drums.

PHYSICAL PROPERTIES: Watery white liquid with aromatic odor.

MELTING POINT: −20°F (−29.1°C)

BOILING POINT: 216°F (102°C)

SPECIFIC GRAVITY: 1.19

SOLUBILITY IN WATER: not soluble; reacts with water

VAPOR PRESSURE: 40 mm Hg @ 26°C

ELECTRICAL EQUIPMENT: Class I, Group D

NAME: **BENZOYL CHLORIDE**

SYNONYMS: benzenecarbonyl chloride

FORMULA: $(C_6H_5)COCl$

NFPA 30/OSHA CLASSIFICATION: IIIA

DOT CLASS: Class 8, Corrosive material

SHIPPING LABEL: CORROSIVE

ID NO.: UN 1736

CAS NO.: 98-88-4

MOL. WT.: 140.6

STATEMENT OF HAZARDS: Corrosive and combustible liquid. Water reactive.

EMERGENCY RESPONSE PERSONAL PROTECTIVE EQUIPMENT: Wear special protective clothing and positive pressure self-contained breathing apparatus.

SPILL OR LEAK PROCEDURES: Keep water away from release. Stop or control the leak, if this can be done without undue risk. Approach release from upwind. Absorb in noncombustible material for proper disposal.

FIRE FIGHTING PROCEDURES: Extinguish fire using agent suitable for surrounding fire with dry chemical or carbon dioxide. DO NOT use water. Violent reaction may result. Carefully use water spray to keep fire-exposed containers cool.

HEALTH HAZARDS: Corrosive. Causes severe eye and skin burns. May be harmful if absorbed through skin or inhaled. Irritating to eyes, skin, and respiratory system. Causes severe tearing. May cause pulmonary edema.

FIRE AND EXPLOSION HAZARDS: Combustible liquid. Combustion by-products include hydrogen chloride and other irritants.

FLASH POINT: 162°F (72°C) (oc)

FLAMMABLE LIMITS: LOWER: 1.2% UPPER: 4.9%

INSTABILITY AND REACTIVITY HAZARDS: Water reactive. Reacts violently with a broad range of materials.

STORAGE RECOMMENDATIONS: Store in a cool, dry, well-ventilated location. Separate from alkalies, oxidizing materials, alcohols, and water.

USUAL SHIPPING CONTAINERS: Glass bottles, carboys; tanks on trucks, rail cars, barges. Packaged under nitrogen gas.

PHYSICAL PROPERTIES: Colorless liquid. Acrid, penetrating odor.

MELTING POINT: 30°F (−1°C)

BOILING POINT: 387°F (197°C)

SPECIFIC GRAVITY: 1.21

SOLUBILITY IN WATER: decomposes

VAPOR PRESSURE: 1 mm Hg @ 20°C

NAME: **BENZYL CHLORIDE**

FORMULA: $C_6H_5CH_2Cl$

NFPA 30/OSHA CLASSIFICATION: IIIA

DOT CLASS: Class 8, Corrosive material

SHIPPING LABEL: CORROSIVE

ID NO.: UN 1738

CAS NO.: 100-44-7

MOL. WT.: 112.6

STATEMENT OF HAZARDS: Corrosive and combustible liquid. May undergo hazardous polymerization.

EMERGENCY RESPONSE PERSONAL PROTECTIVE EQUIPMENT: Wear special protective clothing and positive pressure self-contained breathing apparatus.

SPILL OR LEAK PROCEDURES: Stop or control leak, if this can be done without undue risk. Use water spray to cool and protect personnel. Approach release from upwind. Absorb in noncombustible material for proper disposal.

FIRE FIGHTING PROCEDURES: Use water spray, dry chemical, foam, or carbon dioxide. Use water spray to keep fire-exposed containers cool. Approach fire from upwind to avoid hazardous vapors and toxic decomposition products.

HEALTH HAZARDS: Corrosive. Causes severe eye and skin burns. May be harmful if absorbed through skin or inhaled. Irritating to eyes, skin, and respiratory system. May cause severe tearing, lung damage, pulmonary edema, and paralysis of the extremities.

FIRE AND EXPLOSION HAZARDS: Combustible liquid. Unstabilized benzyl chloride may violently decompose with the rupture of its container in the presence of copper, aluminum, iron, zinc, magnesium, and other catalysts.

FLASH POINT: 153°F (67°C)

AUTOIGNITION TEMPERATURE: 1161°F (627°C)

FLAMMABLE LIMITS: LOWER: 1.3% UPPER: 7.1%

INSTABILITY AND REACTIVITY HAZARDS: May undergo hazardous polymerization. Unstabilized benzyl chloride undergoes a self-condensation reaction in the presence of all common metals (except nickel and lead) with the liberation of heat and hydrogen chloride. Decomposition and polymerization reactions are inhibited to a limited extent by addition of triethylamine, propylene oxide, or sodium carbonate.

STORAGE RECOMMENDATIONS: Store in a cool, dry, well-ventilated location. Outside or detached storage is preferred. Store away from oxidizing materials.

USUAL SHIPPING CONTAINERS: Glass carboys, nickel drums, lined-steel drums, and nickel tank trucks and tank cars.

PHYSICAL PROPERTIES: Clear, colorless, tear-producing liquid with an unpleasant, pungent, aromatic odor.

MELTING POINT: −39°F (−39°C)

BOILING POINT: 355°F (179°C)

SPECIFIC GRAVITY: 1.1

SOLUBILITY IN WATER: not soluble

VAPOR PRESSURE: 11.8 mm Hg @ 25°C

ELECTRICAL EQUIPMENT: Class I, Group D

NAME: **BERYLLIUM, powder**

(often from machining operations)

SYNONYMS: beryllium; beryllium dust; glucinium

FORMULA: Be

NFPA 30/OSHA CLASSIFICATION:

DOT CLASS: Class 6.1, Poisonous material

SHIPPING LABEL: POISON and FLAMMABLE SOLID

ID NO.: UN 1567

CAS NO.: 7440-41-7

MOL. WT.: 9.0

STATEMENT OF HAZARDS: Serious health hazard and combustible solid.

EMERGENCY RESPONSE PERSONAL PROTECTIVE EQUIPMENT: Wear special protective clothing and positive pressure self-contained breathing apparatus.

SPILL OR LEAK PROCEDURES: Place contaminated materials into appropriate containers for disposal.

FIRE FIGHTING PROCEDURES: In case of fire, smother with dry sand, dry clay, dry ground limestone, or use approved Class D extinguishers. DO NOT use carbon dioxide or halogenated extinguishing agents. DO NOT use water.

HEALTH HAZARDS: Serious health hazard. May be harmful if inhaled. Severe respiratory irritant. Contact with skin, eyes, mucous membranes may result in dermatitis, conjunctivitis, corneal burns, nonhealing ulcers.

FIRE AND EXPLOSION HAZARDS: Combustible solid.

INSTABILITY AND REACTIVITY HAZARDS: Reacts with acids and alkalies to liberate highly flammable hydrogen gas.

STORAGE RECOMMENDATIONS: Store in a cool, dry, well-ventilated, location. Separate from acids, bases, halocarbons, oxidizing materials.

USUAL SHIPPING CONTAINERS: Steel and fiber drums.

PHYSICAL PROPERTIES: Gray shiny metal powder or fine granules, resembles powdered aluminum.

MELTING POINT: 2332°F (1278°C)

BOILING POINT: 5378°F (2970°C)

SPECIFIC GRAVITY: 1.85

SOLUBILITY IN WATER: not soluble

ELECTRICAL EQUIPMENT: Class II, Group E

NAME: **BORON TRIBROMIDE**

FORMULA: BBr_3

NFPA 30/OSHA CLASSIFICATION:

DOT CLASS: Class 8, Corrosive material

SHIPPING LABEL: CORROSIVE and POISON

ID NO.: UN 2692

CAS NO.: 10294-33-4

MOL. WT.: 250.6

STATEMENT OF HAZARDS: Corrosive. Water reactive.

EMERGENCY RESPONSE PERSONAL PROTECTIVE EQUIPMENT: Wear special protective clothing and positive pressure self-contained breathing apparatus.

SPILL OR LEAK PROCEDURES: Releases may require isolation or evacuation. Keep water away from release. Stop or control the leak, if this can be done without undue risk. Approach release from upwind. Absorb in noncombustible material for proper disposal.

FIRE FIGHTING PROCEDURES: Extinguish fire using agent suitable for surrounding fire. Use dry chemical or carbon dioxide. DO NOT use water. Violent reaction may result.

HEALTH HAZARDS: Corrosive. Causes severe eye and skin burns. Serious health hazard. Inhalation results in bronchial spasm, extreme irritation, death. Combines with moisture in the lungs to form hydrobromic acid.

FIRE AND EXPLOSION HAZARDS: Not combustible, but contact with fire or water produces hydrogen bromide, boron oxides, and other irritants.

INSTABILITY AND REACTIVITY HAZARDS: Reacts with water and various metals.

STORAGE RECOMMENDATIONS: Separate from alkalies, oxidizing materials, alcohols, ethers, alkali metals, phosphorus, wood. Store in a cool, dry, well-ventilated location.

USUAL SHIPPING CONTAINERS: Glass bottle or metal can inside wooden box; steel or nickel cylinders, tanks. Packaged under nitrogen gas.

PHYSICAL PROPERTIES: Colorless fuming liquid with acrid odor.

MELTING POINT: −51°F (−46°C)

BOILING POINT: 196°F (91°C)

SPECIFIC GRAVITY: 2.70

SOLUBILITY IN WATER: reacts

NAME: **BORON TRIFLUORIDE**

SYNONYMS: boron fluoride; trifluoroboron

FORMULA: BF_3

NFPA 30/OSHA CLASSIFICATION:

DOT CLASS: Class 2.3, Poisonous gas

SHIPPING LABEL: POISON GAS

ID NO.: UN 1008

CAS NO.: 7637-07-2

MOL. WT.: 67.8

STATEMENT OF HAZARDS: Severe health hazard and corrosive. Compressed gas.

EMERGENCY RESPONSE PERSONAL PROTECTIVE EQUIPMENT: Wear special protective clothing and positive pressure self-contained breathing apparatus.

SPILL OR LEAK PROCEDURES: Approach release from upwind. Stop or control the leak, if this can be done without undue risk. Use water spray to cool and disperse vapors and protect personnel. Avoid wetting leak or spill area. Releases may require isolation or evacuation.

FIRE FIGHTING PROCEDURES: Approach fire from upwind to avoid hazardous vapors and toxic decomposition products. Use water spray to keep fire-exposed containers cool. Extinguish fire using agent suitable for surrounding fire.

HEALTH HAZARDS: Severe health hazard. May be fatal if inhaled. Corrosive. Causes severe eye and skin burns.

FIRE AND EXPLOSION HAZARDS: Nonflammable compressed gas. May be shipped and stored as ethyl ether complex, which will greatly increase the fire hazard.

INSTABILITY AND REACTIVITY HAZARDS: Water reactive. Hydrolyzes to produce boric acid, hydrofluoric acid, and fluoboric acid. Catalyst for many polymerization reactions. Incompatible with many active metals.

STORAGE RECOMMENDATIONS: Store in a cool, dry, well-ventilated location. Outside or detached storage is preferred. Separate from water, active metals, monomers.

USUAL SHIPPING CONTAINERS: Steel cylinders; pressurized tanks on trucks, rail cars, barges.

PHYSICAL PROPERTIES: Colorless gas with pungent, irritating odor. May be shipped and stored as ethyl ether complex.

MELTING POINT: −197°F (−127°C)

BOILING POINT: −148°F (−100°C)

SPECIFIC GRAVITY: 2.99

SOLUBILITY IN WATER: reacts

VAPOR DENSITY: 2.34

NAME: **BROMINE**
BROMINE SOLUTIONS

FORMULA: Br_2

NFPA 30/OSHA CLASSIFICATION:

DOT CLASS: Class 8, Corrosive material

SHIPPING LABEL: CORROSIVE and POISON

ID NO.: UN 1744

CAS NO.: 7726-95-6

MOL. WT.: 159.8

STATEMENT OF HAZARDS: Corrosive and fuming liquid. Strong oxidizer.

EMERGENCY RESPONSE PERSONAL PROTECTIVE EQUIPMENT: Wear special protective clothing and positive pressure self-contained breathing apparatus.

SPILL OR LEAK PROCEDURES: Stop or control the leak, if this can be done without undue risk. Use water spray to cool and disperse vapors and protect personnel. Use soda ash to neutralize liquid. Control runoff and isolate discharged material for proper disposal.

FIRE FIGHTING PROCEDURES: Use water spray to keep fire-exposed containers cool. Use appropriate extinguishing agents on nearby combustible fires.

HEALTH HAZARDS: Corrosive and fuming liquid. May be harmful if inhaled. Liquid and vapor cause severe eye and skin burns even in short single exposure. Respiratory damage occurs at low vapor concentrations.

FIRE AND EXPLOSION HAZARDS: Strong oxidizer. Heat of reaction may ignite combustibles on contact. May accelerate combustion reactions.

INSTABILITY AND REACTIVITY HAZARDS: Strong oxidizer. Reacts with alkalies, reactive metals, and other reducing agents.

STORAGE RECOMMENDATIONS: Store in cool, dry, well-ventilated location. Separate from oxidizing materials. See also NFPA 430, Code for the Storage of Liquid and Solid Oxidizers.

USUAL SHIPPING CONTAINERS: Glass bottles, lead lined drums or tanks. Special alloy drums.

PHYSICAL PROPERTIES: Reddish-brown fuming liquid. Suffocating odor. Heavier than water.

MELTING POINT: 19°F (−7°C)

BOILING POINT: 138°F (59°C)

SPECIFIC GRAVITY: 3.12

SOLUBILITY IN WATER: not soluble

VAPOR PRESSURE: 175 mm Hg @ 20°C

NAME: **BROMINE PENTAFLUORIDE**

FORMULA: BrF_5

NFPA 30/OSHA CLASSIFICATION:

DOT CLASS: Class 5.1, Oxidizer

SHIPPING LABEL: OXIDIZER and POISON and CORROSIVE

ID NO.: UN 1745

CAS NO.: 7789-30-2

MOL. WT.: 174.9

STATEMENT OF HAZARDS: Severe health hazard. Corrosive and fuming liquid. Strong oxidizer. Water reactive.

EMERGENCY RESPONSE PERSONAL PROTECTIVE EQUIPMENT: Wear special protective clothing and positive pressure self-contained breathing apparatus.

SPILL OR LEAK PROCEDURES: Isolate the area until the release is under full control. Use water spray to cool and disperse vapors and protect personnel.

FIRE FIGHTING PROCEDURES: DO NOT use water directly on spilled material or violent reaction may result. Use appropriate extinguishing agents on nearby fires. Use dry chemical, dry sand, or carbon dioxide. Use water spray to keep fire-exposed containers cool.

HEALTH HAZARDS: Severe health hazard. May be fatal if inhaled. Corrosive. Causes severe eye and skin burns. Irritating to skin, eyes, and respiratory system.

FIRE AND EXPLOSION HAZARDS: Strong oxidizer. Not combustible, but if involved in a fire decomposes to produce toxic gases.

INSTABILITY AND REACTIVITY HAZARDS: Reacts violently with water, hydrogen-containing materials. Reacts with almost all elements except inert gases. Incompatible with acids, alkalies, halogens, salts, metals, organic matter.

STORAGE RECOMMENDATIONS: Separate from acids, alkalies, halogens, salts, metals, organic matter. Store in a cool, dry, well-ventilated location. Keep cylinders restrained. See also NFPA 430, Code for the Storage of Liquid and Solid Oxidizers.

USUAL SHIPPING CONTAINERS: Cylinders.

PHYSICAL PROPERTIES: Colorless, fuming liquid. Irritating odor.

MELTING POINT: −78°F (−61°C)

BOILING POINT: 106°F (41°C)

SPECIFIC GRAVITY: 2.47 @ 25°C

SOLUBILITY IN WATER: decomposes

NAME: **BROMINE TRIFLUORIDE**

FORMULA: BrF_3

NFPA 30/OSHA CLASSIFICATION:

DOT CLASS: Class 5.1, Oxidizer

SHIPPING LABEL: OXIDIZER and POISON and CORROSIVE

ID NO.: UN 1746

CAS NO.: 7787-71-5

MOL. WT.: 136.9

STATEMENT OF HAZARDS: Severe health hazard and corrosive liquid. Strong oxidizer. Water reactive.

EMERGENCY RESPONSE PERSONAL PROTECTIVE EQUIPMENT: Wear special protective clothing and positive pressure self-contained breathing apparatus.

SPILL OR LEAK PROCEDURES: Isolate the area until the release is under full control. Use water spray to cool and disperse vapors and protect personnel.

FIRE FIGHTING PROCEDURES: DO NOT use water directly on this material or violent reaction may result. Use appropriate extinguishing agents on nearby combustible fires. Use dry chemical, dry sand, or carbon dioxide. Use water spray to keep fire-exposed containers cool.

HEALTH HAZARDS: Severe health hazard. May be fatal if inhaled. Corrosive. Causes severe eye and skin burns. Irritating to skin, eyes, and respiratory system.

FIRE AND EXPLOSION HAZARDS: Not combustible, but if involved in a fire decomposes to produce hydrogen fluoride and hydrogen bromide.

INSTABILITY AND REACTIVITY HAZARDS: Reacts violently with water, organic matter. Reacts with acids, alkalies, halogens, salts, metal oxides.

STORAGE RECOMMENDATIONS: Separate from acids, alkalies, halogens, salts, metal oxides. Store in a cool, dry, well-ventilated location. Keep cylinders restrained. See also NFPA 430, Code for the Storage of Liquid and Solid Oxidizers.

USUAL SHIPPING CONTAINERS: Cylinders.

PHYSICAL PROPERTIES: Colorless to pale yellow fuming liquid. Highly irritating odor.

MELTING POINT: 48°F (9°C)

BOILING POINT: 275°F (135°C)

SPECIFIC GRAVITY: 2.80 @ 25°C

SOLUBILITY IN WATER: decomposes

NAME: **3-BROMOPROPYNE**

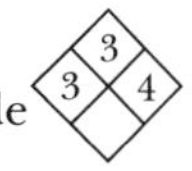

SYNONYMS: 3-bromo-1-propyne; propargyl bromide

FORMULA: $CH \equiv CCH_2Br$

NFPA 30/OSHA CLASSIFICATION: IB

DOT CLASS: Class 3, Flammable and combustible liquid

SHIPPING LABEL: FLAMMABLE LIQUID

ID NO.: UN 2345

CAS NO.: 106-96-7

MOL. WT.:

STATEMENT OF HAZARDS: Flammable liquid. Serious health hazard.

EMERGENCY RESPONSE PERSONAL PROTECTIVE EQUIPMENT: Wear special protective clothing and positive pressure self-contained breathing apparatus.

SPILL OR LEAK PROCEDURES: Eliminate all ignition sources. Stop or control the leak, if this can be done without undue risk. Use water spray to cool and disperse vapors, and protect personnel. Control runoff and isolate discharged material for proper disposal. Fire situations may require evacuation.

FIRE FIGHTING PROCEDURES: Use water spray, dry chemical, foam, or carbon dioxide. Use fine spray or fog to control fire by preventing its spread and absorbing some of its heat. Application of a water blanket may be effective for extinguishment. Use water spray to keep fire-exposed containers cool. Fight fire from protected location or maximum possible distance. Approach fire from upwind to avoid hazardous vapors and toxic decomposition products.

HEALTH HAZARDS: Serious health hazard. May be harmful if absorbed through skin or inhaled. Irritating to skin, eyes, and respiratory system. Causes severe tearing.

FIRE AND EXPLOSION HAZARDS: Flammable liquid. Combustion may produce irritants and toxic gases. Closed containers may rupture violently when heated. May be decomposed by mild shock. Decomposes when heated; if diluted with toluene, its explosive properties are practically eliminated.

FLASH POINT: 50°F (10°C)

AUTOIGNITION TEMPERATURE: 615°F (324°C)

FLAMMABLE LIMITS: LOWER: 3% UPPER: not determined

INSTABILITY AND REACTIVITY HAZARDS: May be decomposed by mild shock. Decomposes when heated under confinement. Dilution with toluene reduces the explosive tendency of the material.

STORAGE RECOMMENDATIONS: Unstabilized material should be stored like an explosive. If diluted, material should be stored like a flammable material. Store in a cool, dry, well-ventilated location. Outside or detached storage is preferred. Separate from oxidizing materials. Inside storage should be in a standard flammable liquids storage warehouse, room, or cabinet.

USUAL SHIPPING CONTAINERS: Glass carboys and metal drums.

PHYSICAL PROPERTIES: Colorless to light-amber liquid.

MELTING POINT: −76°F (−60°C)

BOILING POINT: 185°F (85°C)

SPECIFIC GRAVITY: 1.57

SOLUBILITY IN WATER: not soluble

ELECTRICAL EQUIPMENT: Class I, Group D

NAME: **BUTADIENES, inhibited**

SYNONYMS: 1,3-butadiene; divinyl; vinylethylene

FORMULA: $CH_2{=}CHCH{=}CH_2$

NFPA 30/OSHA CLASSIFICATION: IA

DOT CLASS: Class 2.1, Flammable and combustible gas

SHIPPING LABEL: FLAMMABLE GAS

ID NO.: UN 1010

CAS NO.: 106-99-0

MOL. WT.: 54.1

STATEMENT OF HAZARDS: Flammable gas. Low ignition energy. May polymerize explosively. Forms explosive peroxides in absence of inhibitors. Moderate health hazard.

EMERGENCY RESPONSE PERSONAL PROTECTIVE EQUIPMENT: Wear full protective clothing and positive pressure self-contained breathing apparatus.

SPILL OR LEAK PROCEDURES: Eliminate all ignition sources. Approach release from upwind. Stop or control the leak, if this can be done without undue risk. Use water spray to cool and disperse vapors and protect personnel.

FIRE FIGHTING PROCEDURES: Fight fire from protected location or maximum possible distance. Stop flow of gas before extinguishing fire. Use water spray to keep fire-exposed containers cool. Use flooding quantities of water as fog or spray. Dry chemical or carbon dioxide extinguishers may be appropriate.

HEALTH HAZARDS: Moderate health hazard. Rapid evaporation of liquid causes frostbite damage to eyes and skin. May be harmful if inhaled. Narcotic. Liquefied material and vapor are eye, skin, and respiratory system irritant.

FIRE AND EXPLOSION HAZARDS: Flammable gas. Vapors are heavier than air and may travel to a source of ignition and flash back. Closed containers may rupture violently when heated.

FLASH POINT: −105°F (−76°C)

AUTOIGNITION TEMPERATURE: 788°F (420°C)

FLAMMABLE LIMITS: LOWER: 2.0% UPPER: 11.5%

INSTABILITY AND REACTIVITY HAZARDS: Hazardous polymerization may occur. Usually contains inhibitors to prevent polymerization. Uninhibited monomer vapor may form polymer in vents and other confined spaces. Forms explosive peroxides in air in absence of inhibitors.

STORAGE RECOMMENDATIONS: Outside or detached storage is preferred. Store in a cool, dry, well-ventilated location. Isolate from oxidizing materials.

USUAL SHIPPING CONTAINERS: Steel cylinders; pressurized tanks on trucks, rail cars, barges.

PHYSICAL PROPERTIES: Colorless gas with mildly aromatic or gasoline-like odor. Usually shipped as a liquefied compressed gas under its vapor pressure.

MELTING POINT: −164°F (−109°C)

BOILING POINT: 24°F (−4°C)

SPECIFIC GRAVITY: 0.65 @ −6°C

SOLUBILITY IN WATER: not soluble

VAPOR DENSITY: 1.87

VAPOR PRESSURE: gas

ELECTRICAL EQUIPMENT: Class I, Group B (D)

NAME: **BUTYLACRYLATE**

SYNONYMS: acrylic acid n-butyl ester; n-butyl acrylate; n-butyl ester of acrylic acid, n-butyl-2-propenoate,

FORMULA: $CH_2{=}CHCOOC_4H_9$

NFPA 30/OSHA CLASSIFICATION: II

DOT CLASS: Class 3, Flammable and combustible liquid

SHIPPING LABEL: FLAMMABLE LIQUID

ID NO.: UN 2348

CAS NO.: 141-32-2

MOL. WT.: 128.2

STATEMENT OF HAZARDS: Combustible liquid. Thermally unstable. Polymerizes when exposed to heat. Moderate health hazard.

EMERGENCY RESPONSE PERSONAL PROTECTIVE EQUIPMENT: Wear full protective clothing and positive pressure self-contained breathing apparatus.

SPILL OR LEAK PROCEDURES: Eliminate all ignition sources. Stop or control the leak, if this can be done without undue risk. Use water spray to cool and disperse vapors and protect personnel. Control runoff and isolate discharged material for proper disposal.

FIRE FIGHTING PROCEDURES: Use water spray to keep fire-exposed containers cool. Solid streams of water may be ineffective or may cause frothing. Use water spray, dry chemical, foam, or carbon dioxide. Fight fire from protected location or maximum possible distance.

HEALTH HAZARDS: Moderate health hazard. Contact with liquid causes irritation of skin and burning of eyes. May be harmful if inhaled. Vapor is irritating and may cause dizziness, headache, nausea, vomiting, and narcosis.

FIRE AND EXPLOSION HAZARDS: Combustible liquid. Heat may cause material to polymerize explosively and may cause violent rupture of closed containers.

FLASH POINT: 103°F (39°C)

AUTOIGNITION TEMPERATURE: 534°F (279°C)

FLAMMABLE LIMITS: LOWER: 1.3% UPPER: 9.9%

INSTABILITY AND REACTIVITY HAZARDS: Hazardous polymerization may occur. Polymerization may be caused by elevated temperature, oxidizers, peroxides, or sunlight. Material will react with strong acids and alkalies. Usually contains inhibitors to prevent polymerization. Uninhibited monomer vapor may form polymer in vents and other confined spaces.

STORAGE RECOMMENDATIONS: Separate from any oxidizing materials, peroxides, or other initiators. Store in a cool, dry, well-ventilated location. Outside or detached storage is preferred.

USUAL SHIPPING CONTAINERS: Bottles, cans, drums, and tank trucks or tank cars.

PHYSICAL PROPERTIES: Clear, colorless liquid with sharp, biting characteristic odor.

MELTING POINT: −83°F (−64°C)

BOILING POINT: 300°F (149°C)

SPECIFIC GRAVITY: 0.90

SOLUBILITY IN WATER: not soluble

VAPOR PRESSURE: 3 mm Hg @ 20°C

ELECTRICAL EQUIPMENT: Class I, Group D

NAME: **n-BUTYLAMINE**

SYNONYMS: 1-aminobutane; 1-butanamine; butylamine

FORMULA: $CH_3CH_2CH_2CH_2NH_2$

NFPA 30/OSHA CLASSIFICATION: IB

DOT CLASS: Class 3, Flammable and combustible liquid

SHIPPING LABEL: FLAMMABLE LIQUID

ID NO.: UN 1125

CAS NO.: 109-73-9

MOL. WT.: 73.1

STATEMENT OF HAZARDS: Corrosive and flammable liquid.

EMERGENCY RESPONSE PERSONAL PROTECTIVE EQUIPMENT: Wear special protective clothing and positive pressure self-contained breathing apparatus.

SPILL OR LEAK PROCEDURES: Stop or control the leak, if this can be done without undue risk. Eliminate all ignition sources. Use water spray to cool and disperse vapors, protect personnel, and dilute spills to form nonflammable mixtures. Sand, clay, earth, or other absorbent material may be used to contain liquid.

FIRE FIGHTING PROCEDURES: Use water spray, dry chemical, "alcohol resistant" foam, or carbon dioxide. Use water spray to keep fire-exposed containers cool. Approach fire from upwind to avoid hazardous vapors and toxic decomposition products.

HEALTH HAZARDS: Corrosive. Causes severe eye and skin burns. Irritating to skin, eyes, and respiratory system.

FIRE AND EXPLOSION HAZARDS: Flammable liquid. Vapors are heavier than air and may travel to a source of ignition and flash back.

FLASH POINT: 10°F (−12°C)

AUTOIGNITION TEMPERATURE: 594°F (312°C)

FLAMMABLE LIMITS: LOWER: 1.7% UPPER: 9.8%

INSTABILITY AND REACTIVITY HAZARDS: Reacts with acids, oxidizing materials, chlorine, hypochlorite, halogenated compounds, and reactive organic compounds. Products of decomposition include carbon monoxide, carbon dioxide, hydrocarbons, and toxic oxides of nitrogen as well as toxic amine vapors. Ammonia vapors are liberated upon decomposition.

STORAGE RECOMMENDATIONS: Outside or detached storage is preferred. Separate from oxidizing materials, acids, and sources of halogens. Store in a cool, dry, well-ventilated location.

USUAL SHIPPING CONTAINERS: Glass bottles, cans, drums, and tank cars.

PHYSICAL PROPERTIES: Colorless liquid with odor like ammonia or fish.

MELTING POINT: −58°F (−50°C)

BOILING POINT: 171°F (77°C)

SPECIFIC GRAVITY: 0.74

SOLUBILITY IN WATER: soluble

VAPOR PRESSURE: 82 mm Hg @ 20°C

ELECTRICAL EQUIPMENT: Class I, Group D

NAME: **1,2-BUTYLENE OXIDE, stabilized**

SYNONYMS: 1,2-butylene oxide; 1,2-epoxybutane

FORMULA: $CH_3CH_2—CH—CH_2$
\ /
O

NFPA 30/OSHA CLASSIFICATION: IB

DOT CLASS: Class 3, Flammable and combustible liquid

SHIPPING LABEL: FLAMMABLE LIQUID

ID NO.: UN 3022

CAS NO.: 106-88-7

MOL. WT.: 72.1

STATEMENT OF HAZARDS: Flammable liquid. Low ignition energy. May polymerize explosively. Moderate health hazard.

EMERGENCY RESPONSE PERSONAL PROTECTIVE EQUIPMENT: Wear full protective clothing and positive pressure self-contained breathing apparatus.

SPILL OR LEAK PROCEDURES: Eliminate all ignition sources. Stop or control the leak, if this can be done without undue risk. Use water spray to cool and disperse vapors and protect personnel. Adsorb in sand for proper disposal.

FIRE FIGHTING PROCEDURES: Use water spray, dry chemical, foam, or carbon dioxide. Water may be ineffective. Fight fire from protected location or maximum possible distance. Use water spray to keep fire-exposed containers cool.

HEALTH HAZARDS: Moderate health hazard. May be harmful if absorbed through skin or inhaled. Irritating to skin, eyes, and respiratory system.

FIRE AND EXPLOSION HAZARDS: Flammable liquid. Vapors are heavier than air and may travel to a source of ignition and flash back. Combustion may produce irritants and toxic gases. Closed containers may rupture violently when heated.

FLASH POINT: −7°F (−22°C)

AUTOIGNITION TEMPERATURE: 822°F (439°C)

FLAMMABLE LIMITS: LOWER: 1.7% UPPER: 19%

INSTABILITY AND REACTIVITY HAZARDS: Hazardous polymerization may occur. Usually contains inhibitors to prevent polymerization. Uninhibited monomer vapor may form polymer in vents and other confined spaces. Reacts with metal chlorides, oxides, hydroxides, and acids.

STORAGE RECOMMENDATIONS: Store in a cool, dry, well-ventilated location. Store away from heat, oxidizing materials, and sunlight.

USUAL SHIPPING CONTAINERS: Glass bottles; metal cans, pails, drums. Tanks on trucks, rail cars, barges. Packaged under nitrogen gas.

PHYSICAL PROPERTIES: Colorless liquid. Sharp, penetrating odor.

BOILING POINT: 145°F (63°C)

SPECIFIC GRAVITY: 0.826 @ 77°F (25°C)

SOLUBILITY IN WATER: not soluble

ELECTRICAL EQUIPMENT: Class I, Group D

NAME: **BUTYLLITHIUM**

DOT SHIPPING NAME: **LITHIUM ALKYLS**

(Class 4.2, SPONTANEOUSLY COMBUSTIBLE)

FORMULA: $CH_3(CH_2)_3Li$

NFPA 30/OSHA CLASSIFICATION:

DOT CLASS: N/A

ID NO.: N/A

CAS NO.: Various

MOL. WT.: Various

STATEMENT OF HAZARDS: Pyrophoric; will ignite spontaneously on exposure to air. Normally shipped in flammable hydrocarbon solvents. Corrosive. Water reactive.

EMERGENCY RESPONSE PERSONAL PROTECTIVE EQUIPMENT: Wear special protective clothing and positive pressure self-contained breathing apparatus.

SPILL OR LEAK PROCEDURES: Keep water away from release. Spills may ignite spontaneously if solvent evaporates. Absorb in noncombustible material for proper disposal. Shovel into suitable dry container.

FIRE FIGHTING PROCEDURES: DO NOT use water directly on this material or violent reaction may result. Use water spray to keep fire-exposed containers cool. Fight fire from protected location or maximum possible distance. Use dry chemical, foam, carbon dioxide, or water spray.

HEALTH HAZARDS: Corrosive. Causes severe eye and skin burns. Serious health hazard. May be harmful if absorbed through skin or inhaled.

FIRE AND EXPLOSION HAZARDS: Pyrophoric material in flammable solvent. Solvent vapors are heavier than air and may travel to a source of ignition and flash back. Combustion may produce irritants and toxic gases. Closed containers may rupture violently when heated.

INSTABILITY AND REACTIVITY HAZARDS: Reacts violently with a broad range of materials including water and air.

STORAGE RECOMMENDATIONS: Store in a cool, dry, well-ventilated location. Separate from air, water, oxidizing materials, halocarbons, and organic matter. Outside or detached storage is preferred. Immediately remove and properly dispose of any spilled material.

USUAL SHIPPING CONTAINERS: Bottles packed in insulating material. Metal cans, pails, drums. Tanks on trucks, rail cars, barges. Packaged under nitrogen gas.

PHYSICAL PROPERTIES: Colorless hydrocarbon solution. Commonly used solvents for butyllithium are pentane, hexane, and heptane. Properties are primarily dependent upon the properties of the solvent.

ELECTRICAL EQUIPMENT: Class I, Group D

NAME: **BUTYRALDEHYDE**

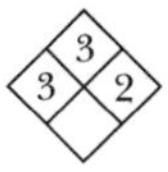

SYNONYMS: butanal; butyl aldehyde; butyric aldehyde

FORMULA: $CH_3(CH_2)_2CHO$

NFPA 30/OSHA CLASSIFICATION: IB

DOT CLASS: Class 3, Flammable and combustible liquid

SHIPPING LABEL: FLAMMABLE LIQUID

ID NO.: UN 1129

CAS NO.: 123-72-8

MOL. WT.: 72.1

STATEMENT OF HAZARDS: Corrosive and flammable liquid. Forms peroxides in absence of inhibitors. Hazardous polymerization may occur.

EMERGENCY RESPONSE PERSONAL PROTECTIVE EQUIPMENT: Wear full protective clothing and positive pressure self-contained breathing apparatus.

SPILL OR LEAK PROCEDURES: Eliminate all ignition sources. Stop or control the leak, if this can be done without undue risk. Use water spray to cool and disperse vapors and protect personnel. Control runoff and isolate discharged material for proper disposal.

FIRE FIGHTING PROCEDURES: Fight fire from protected location or maximum possible distance. Use dry chemical, foam, carbon dioxide. Water may be ineffective. Use water spray to keep fire-exposed containers cool.

HEALTH HAZARDS: Corrosive. Causes severe eye and skin burns. May be harmful if inhaled. Irritating to skin, eyes, and respiratory system. Narcosis, nausea, and loss of consciousness may result from exposure to high concentrations of vapor.

FIRE AND EXPLOSION HAZARDS: Flammable liquid. Forms explosive peroxides. Vapors are heavier than air and may travel to a source of ignition and flash back. Combustion may produce irritants and toxic gases. Closed containers may rupture violently when heated.

FLASH POINT: 10°F (−12°C)

AUTOIGNITION TEMPERATURE: 446°F (230°C)

FLAMMABLE LIMITS: LOWER: 2.5% UPPER: 12.5%

INSTABILITY AND REACTIVITY HAZARDS: Hazardous polymerization may occur. Explosive peroxides may be formed in air. Reacts with oxidizing materials, amines, strong alkalies, and acids.

STORAGE RECOMMENDATIONS: Store in cool, dry, well-ventilated location. Separate from oxidizing materials, amines, strong alkalies, acids, and other reactive hazards. Inside storage should be in a standard flammable liquids storage warehouse, room, or cabinet. Bulk storage should be blanketed with inert gas.

USUAL SHIPPING CONTAINERS: Glass bottles, metal drums, tank cars, tank trucks, and tank barges.

PHYSICAL PROPERTIES: Colorless liquid with suffocating fruity odor.

MELTING POINT: −146°F (−99°C)

BOILING POINT: 168°F (76°C)

SPECIFIC GRAVITY: 0.80

SOLUBILITY IN WATER: not soluble

VAPOR PRESSURE: 88.5 mm Hg @ 20°C

ELECTRICAL EQUIPMENT: Class I, Group C

NAME: **BUTYRIC ACID**

SYNONYMS: butanoic acid; ethylacetic acid

FORMULA: $CH_3CH_2CH_2COOH$

NFPA 30/OSHA CLASSIFICATION: IIIA

DOT CLASS: Class 8, Corrosive material

SHIPPING LABEL: CORROSIVE

ID NO.: UN 2820

CAS NO.: 107-92-6

MOL. WT.: 88.1

STATEMENT OF HAZARDS: Corrosive and combustible liquid.

EMERGENCY RESPONSE PERSONAL PROTECTIVE EQUIPMENT: Wear special protective clothing and positive pressure self-contained breathing apparatus.

SPILL OR LEAK PROCEDURES: Eliminate all ignition sources. Use water spray to cool and disperse vapors, protect personnel, and dilute spills to form nonflammable mixtures. Control runoff and isolate discharged material for proper disposal. Neutralize spill and washings with soda ash or lime.

FIRE FIGHTING PROCEDURES: Use water spray, dry chemical, "alcohol resistant" foam, or carbon dioxide. Use water spray to keep fire-exposed containers cool. On large fires, solid streams of water may not be effective.

HEALTH HAZARDS: Corrosive. Causes severe eye and skin burns. Irritating to skin, eyes, and respiratory system.

FIRE AND EXPLOSION HAZARDS: Combustible liquid.

FLASH POINT: 161°F (72°C)

AUTOIGNITION TEMPERATURE: 846°F (452°C)

FLAMMABLE LIMITS: LOWER: 2.0% UPPER: 10.0%

INSTABILITY AND REACTIVITY HAZARDS: Reacts with oxidizing materials and alkalies. Products of combustion include carbon dioxide and carbon monoxide as well as irritating fumes.

STORAGE RECOMMENDATIONS: Outside or detached storage is preferred. Separate from heat, oxidizers, and sunlight.

USUAL SHIPPING CONTAINERS: Glass bottles, carboys, lined drums, and tank trucks or tank cars.

PHYSICAL PROPERTIES: Colorless, oily liquid with pungent odor of rancid butter.

MELTING POINT: 17°F (−8°C)

BOILING POINT: 326°F (164°C)

SPECIFIC GRAVITY: 0.96

SOLUBILITY IN WATER: soluble

VAPOR PRESSURE: 0.43 mm Hg @ 20°C

ELECTRICAL EQUIPMENT: Class I, Group D

NAME: **BUTYRONITRILE**

SYNONYMS: butane nitrile; butyric acid nitrile; propyl cyanide

FORMULA: $CH_3(CH_2)_2CN$

NFPA 30/OSHA CLASSIFICATION: IC

CAS NO.: 109-74-0

MOL. WT.: 69.1

STATEMENT OF HAZARDS: Serious health hazard. Flammable liquid.

EMERGENCY RESPONSE PERSONAL PROTECTIVE EQUIPMENT: Wear special protective clothing and positive pressure self-contained breathing apparatus.

SPILL OR LEAK PROCEDURES: Use water spray to cool and disperse vapors, protect personnel, and dilute spills to form nonflammable mixtures. Control runoff and isolate discharged material for proper disposal.

FIRE FIGHTING PROCEDURES: Use dry chemical, foam, carbon dioxide, or water spray. Approach fire from upwind to avoid hazardous vapors and toxic decomposition products.

HEALTH HAZARDS: Serious health hazard. May be harmful if absorbed through skin or inhaled. Irritating to eye, skin, and respiratory system. Symptoms of overexposure include dizziness, rapid respiration, drowsiness, rapid pulse, and unconsciousness, possibly leading to convulsions.

FIRE AND EXPLOSION HAZARDS: Flammable liquid.

FLASH POINT: 79°F (26°C) (oc)

AUTOIGNITION TEMPERATURE: 935°F (501°C)

FLAMMABLE LIMITS: LOWER: 1.65% UPPER: not determined

INSTABILITY AND REACTIVITY HAZARDS: Reacts exothermically with strong oxidizers and acids. Hydrogen cyanide may be liberated from reactions with acids.

STORAGE RECOMMENDATIONS: Store in a cool, dry, well-ventilated location. Outside or detached storage is preferred. Separate from strong oxidizers and acids.

USUAL SHIPPING CONTAINERS: Drums and tank cars.

PHYSICAL PROPERTIES: Colorless liquid.

MELTING POINT: FREEZING POINT: −170°F (−112°C)

BOILING POINT: 244°F (118°C)

SPECIFIC GRAVITY: 0.80

SOLUBILITY IN WATER: not soluble

NAME: **CALCIUM**

FORMULA: Ca

NFPA 30/OSHA CLASSIFICATION:

DOT CLASS: Class 4.3, Dangerous when wet material

SHIPPING LABEL: DANGEROUS WHEN WET

ID NO.: UN 1401

CAS NO.: 7440-70-2

MOL. WT.: 40.1

STATEMENT OF HAZARDS: Flammable when finely divided. Reacts with water to liberate hydrogen. Corrosive. Causes eye and skin burns.

EMERGENCY RESPONSE PERSONAL PROTECTIVE EQUIPMENT: Wear special protective clothing and positive pressure self-contained breathing apparatus.

SPILL OR LEAK PROCEDURES: Keep water away from release. Shovel into suitable dry container.

FIRE FIGHTING PROCEDURES: Use approved Class D extinguishers or smother with dry sand, dry clay, or dry ground limestone. DO NOT use carbon dioxide or halogenated extinguishing agents. DO NOT use water. Violent reaction may result.

HEALTH HAZARDS: Corrosive. Causes severe eye, mucous membrane, and skin burns. May be harmful if inhaled. Irritating to skin, eyes, and respiratory system.

FIRE AND EXPLOSION HAZARDS: Flammable when finely divided. Evolves hydrogen on contact with water. Combustion may produce irritants and toxic gases.

INSTABILITY AND REACTIVITY HAZARDS: Reacts readily when finely divided with a broad range of materials, including air and water.

STORAGE RECOMMENDATIONS: Store in a cool, dry, well-ventilated location. Separate from water, alcohols, acids, and halogens. Immediately remove and properly dispose of any spilled material.

USUAL SHIPPING CONTAINERS: Glass bottles, hermetically sealed can inside wooden box, drums.

PHYSICAL PROPERTIES: Lustrous, silver-white metallic solid. Odorless.

MELTING POINT: 1542°F (842°C)

BOILING POINT: 4755°F (1440°C)

SPECIFIC GRAVITY: 1.54

SOLUBILITY IN WATER: reacts

VAPOR PRESSURE: 10 mm Hg @ 983°C

NAME: **CALCIUM CARBIDE**

SYNONYMS: acetylenogen; calcium acetylide

FORMULA: CaC_2

NFPA 30/OSHA CLASSIFICATION:

DOT CLASS: Class 4.3, Dangerous when wet material

SHIPPING LABEL: DANGEROUS WHEN WET

ID NO.: UN 1402

CAS NO.: 75-20-7

MOL. WT.: 64.1

STATEMENT OF HAZARDS: Corrosive. Reacts with water to produce highly flammable acetylene gas.

EMERGENCY RESPONSE PERSONAL PROTECTIVE EQUIPMENT: Wear full protective clothing and positive pressure self-contained breathing apparatus.

SPILL OR LEAK PROCEDURES: Keep water away from release. Shovel into suitable dry container.

FIRE FIGHTING PROCEDURES: Use approved Class D extinguishers or smother with dry sand, dry clay, or dry ground limestone. DO NOT use carbon dioxide or halogenated extinguishing agents. DO NOT use water. Violent reaction may result.

HEALTH HAZARDS: Corrosive. Causes severe eye and skin burns. May be harmful if inhaled. Irritating to skin, eye, and respiratory system.

FIRE AND EXPLOSION HAZARDS: On contact with water, evolves highly flammable acetylene, which will ignite.

INSTABILITY AND REACTIVITY HAZARDS: Reacts with water producing acetylene gas and lime. Also reacts with oxidizing materials.

STORAGE RECOMMENDATIONS: Store in a cool, dry, well-ventilated location. Separate from oxidizing materials, water. Immediately remove and properly dispose of any spilled material.

USUAL SHIPPING CONTAINERS: Metal cans, drums.

PHYSICAL PROPERTIES: Grayish-black irregular lumps. Slight garlic odor.

MELTING POINT: 4172°F (2300°C)

SPECIFIC GRAVITY: 2.22

SOLUBILITY IN WATER: reacts

NAME: **CALCIUM CYANIDE**

SYNONYMS: calcyanide; cyanogas

FORMULA: $Ca(CN)_2$

NFPA 30/OSHA CLASSIFICATION:

DOT CLASS: Class 6.1, Poisonous material

SHIPPING LABEL: POISON

ID NO.: UN 1575

CAS NO.: 592-01-8

MOL. WT.: 92.1

STATEMENT OF HAZARDS: Serious health hazard. Releases hydrogen cyanide on contact with water and acids.

EMERGENCY RESPONSE PERSONAL PROTECTIVE EQUIPMENT: Wear special protective clothing and positive pressure self-contained breathing apparatus.

SPILL OR LEAK PROCEDURES: Isolate the area until the release is under full control. Place contaminated materials into appropriate containers for disposal. Keep material out of drains, sewers, streams.

FIRE FIGHTING PROCEDURES: Extinguish fire using agent suitable for surrounding fire. Approach fire from upwind to avoid hazardous vapors and toxic decomposition products. Use water spray to keep fire-exposed containers cool.

HEALTH HAZARDS: Serious health hazard. May be harmful if absorbed through skin or inhaled. Irritating to skin, eyes, and respiratory system. Releases hydrogen cyanide on contact with water and acids.

FIRE AND EXPLOSION HAZARDS: Not combustible, but if involved in a fire decomposes to produce oxides of nitrogen. Decomposes at about 662°F (350°C).

INSTABILITY AND REACTIVITY HAZARDS: Reacts with water and acids evolving highly toxic hydrogen cyanide.

STORAGE RECOMMENDATIONS: Store in a cool, dry, well-ventilated location. Separate from acids, oxidizing materials.

USUAL SHIPPING CONTAINERS: Glass bottles up to 5 lb, metal cans inside boxes up to 25 lb. Metal drums, fiber boxes with plastic lining.

PHYSICAL PROPERTIES: White to grey to black solid. Almond odor.

MELTING POINT: 662°F (350°C); decomposes

SPECIFIC GRAVITY: 1.85

SOLUBILITY IN WATER: soluble

NAME: **CALCIUM HYPOCHLORITE, dry**
CALCIUM HYPOCHLORITE, mixtures, dry

SYNONYMS: cal hypo; losantin

FORMULA: $Ca(OCl)_2$

NFPA 30/OSHA CLASSIFICATION:

DOT CLASS: Class 5.1, Oxidizer

SHIPPING LABEL: OXIDIZER

ID NO.: UN 2880 hydrated

UN 1748 mixture, dry

UN 2208

CAS NO.: 7778-54-3

MOL. WT.: 143.0

STATEMENT OF HAZARDS: Strong oxidizer. Evolves chlorine in reaction with water and acids. Thermally unstable. Decomposes at 350°F (177°C) releasing oxygen. Corrosive.

EMERGENCY RESPONSE PERSONAL PROTECTIVE EQUIPMENT: Wear full protective clothing and positive pressure self-contained breathing apparatus.

SPILL OR LEAK PROCEDURES: Keep water away from release. Prompt cleanup and removal is necessary. Containerize all spilled material in a clean dry container using only clean dedicated equipment for cleanup and remove to a well ventilated area being sure to not seal tightly. Control runoff and isolate discharged material for proper disposal.

FIRE FIGHTING PROCEDURES: Approach fire from upwind to avoid hazardous vapors and toxic decomposition products. Use flooding quantities of water as fog or spray. Use water spray to keep fire-exposed containers cool. Fight fire from protected location or maximum possible distance. Do not use dry chemical fire extinguishers containing ammonium compounds.

HEALTH HAZARDS: Corrosive. Causes severe eye and skin burns. May be harmful if inhaled. Irritating to skin, eyes, and respiratory system. Chlorine gas released when wet.

FIRE AND EXPLOSION HAZARDS: Not combustible. Contact with combustible materials will increase fire hazard. May undergo accelerated decomposition with release of heat above 350°F (177°C).

INSTABILITY AND REACTIVITY HAZARDS: Reacts with water and with acids releasing chlorine. Forms explosive compounds with ammonia and amines. Strong oxidizer. Other incompatible materials include organics, nitrogen containing compounds, dry chemical fire extinguishers containing mono-ammonium phosphate, combustible or flammable materials.

STORAGE RECOMMENDATIONS: Store in a cool, dry, well-ventilated location at a temperature below 120°F (50°C) to avoid slow decomposition. Separate from oxidizing materials, acids, ammonia, amines, and other chlorinating agents. Immediately remove and properly dispose of any spilled material. See also, NFPA 430, Code for the Storage of Liquid and Solid Oxidizers.

USUAL SHIPPING CONTAINERS: Plastic bottles, lined drums of fiber or steel, pails.

PHYSICAL PROPERTIES: Granular white solid with slight chlorine odor.

MELTING POINT: Decomposes above 350°F (177°C)

SPECIFIC GRAVITY: 2.35

SOLUBILITY IN WATER: soluble, reacts slowly releasing chlorine gas

NAME: **CALCIUM OXIDE**

SYNONYMS: calcia; lime; pebble lime; quicklime

FORMULA: CaO

NFPA 30/OSHA CLASSIFICATION:

DOT CLASS: Class 8, Corrosive material

SHIPPING LABEL: CORROSIVE

ID NO.: UN 1910

CAS NO.: 1305-78-8

MOL. WT.: 56.1

STATEMENT OF HAZARDS: Corrosive. Reacts with water releasing heat and forming alkaline solution.

EMERGENCY RESPONSE PERSONAL PROTECTIVE EQUIPMENT: Wear special protective clothing and positive pressure self-contained breathing apparatus.

SPILL OR LEAK PROCEDURES: Shovel into suitable dry container. Use water spray to control dust, protect personnel.

FIRE FIGHTING PROCEDURES: Extinguish fire using agent suitable for surrounding fire. Use flooding quantities of water as spray. DO NOT use carbon dioxide or halogenated extinguishing agents.

HEALTH HAZARDS: Corrosive. Causes severe eye and skin burns. May be harmful if inhaled. Irritating to skin, eyes, and respiratory system. When combined with water or sweat, produces highly irritating alkaline solution and burning sensation.

FIRE AND EXPLOSION HAZARDS: Not combustible, but bulk powder may heat spontaneously when damp with water.

INSTABILITY AND REACTIVITY HAZARDS: Reacts with water to produce heat and calcium hydroxide (alkaline) solution. Reacts with acids.

STORAGE RECOMMENDATIONS: Store in a cool, dry, well-ventilated location.

USUAL SHIPPING CONTAINERS: Lined fiber bags; bulk packaging in trucks and rail cars, and bulk in tank barges.

PHYSICAL PROPERTIES: White, pale yellow, or pale gray odorless powder.

MELTING POINT: 4737°F (2614°C)

BOILING POINT: 5162°F (2850°C)

SPECIFIC GRAVITY: 3.37

SOLUBILITY IN WATER: reacts

NAME: **CARBON DISULFIDE**

SYNONYMS: carbon bisulfide

FORMULA: CS_2

NFPA 30/OSHA CLASSIFICATION: IB

DOT CLASS: Class 3, Flammable and combustible liquid

SHIPPING LABEL: FLAMMABLE LIQUID and POISON

ID NO.: UN 1131

CAS NO.: 75-15-0

MOL. WT.: 76.1

STATEMENT OF HAZARDS: Flammable and corrosive liquid. May accumulate static electricity. Low ignition energy.

EMERGENCY RESPONSE PERSONAL PROTECTIVE EQUIPMENT: Wear special protective clothing and positive pressure self-contained breathing apparatus.

SPILL OR LEAK PROCEDURES: Select protected position upwind. Eliminate all ignition sources. Stop or control the leak, if this can be done without undue risk. Releases may require isolation or evacuation. Use water spray to cool and disperse vapors and protect personnel. Control runoff and isolate discharged material for proper disposal.

FIRE FIGHTING PROCEDURES: Use water spray, dry chemical, foam, or carbon dioxide. Blanket with water to extinguish fire. Use water spray to keep fire-exposed containers cool.

HEALTH HAZARDS: Corrosive. Causes severe eye and skin burns. May be harmful if absorbed through skin or inhaled. Affects central nervous system. Defats tissue. Irritating to eyes, skin, and respiratory system.

FIRE AND EXPLOSION HAZARDS: Flammable liquid. Forms explosive mixtures with air over a wide range. Vapors are heavier than air and may travel to a source of ignition and flash back. Combustion produces toxic gases and irritants including carbon monoxide and oxides of sulfur.

FLASH POINT: −22°F (−30°C)

AUTOIGNITION TEMPERATURE: 194°F (90°C)

FLAMMABLE LIMITS: LOWER: 1.3% UPPER: 50.0%

INSTABILITY AND REACTIVITY HAZARDS: Reacts with strong oxidizing materials to produce oxides of sulfur and carbon monoxide.

STORAGE RECOMMENDATIONS: Store small containers in a cool, dry, well-ventilated location. Store bulk quantities under water or inert gas blanket. Outside or detached storage preferred.

USUAL SHIPPING CONTAINERS: Glass bottles, metal cans and drums, tank trucks, tank cars, and tank barges.

PHYSICAL PROPERTIES: Colorless to yellow liquid with an unpleasant odor of rotten eggs in commercial and reagent grades and sweet odor in pure form.

MELTING POINT: −168°F (−111°C)

BOILING POINT: 115°F (46°C)

SPECIFIC GRAVITY: 1.26

SOLUBILITY IN WATER: not soluble

VAPOR PRESSURE: 300 mm Hg @ 20°C

ELECTRICAL EQUIPMENT: Cannot be classified in conventional Groups A, B, C, or D, owing to the exceptional flammable properties

NAME: **CARBON MONOXIDE**

SYNONYMS: carbonic oxide; exhaust gas; flue gas; monoxide

FORMULA: CO

NFPA 30/OSHA CLASSIFICATION:

DOT CLASS: Class 2.3, Poisonous gas

SHIPPING LABEL: POISON GAS and FLAMMABLE GAS

ID NO.: UN 1016

CAS NO.: 630-08-0

MOL. WT.: 28.0

STATEMENT OF HAZARDS: Flammable gas. Serious health hazard.

EMERGENCY RESPONSE PERSONAL PROTECTIVE EQUIPMENT: Wear special protective clothing and positive pressure self-contained breathing apparatus.

SPILL OR LEAK PROCEDURES: Use water spray to disperse vapors and protect personnel. With cryogenic liquids, releases may require isolation or evacuation.

FIRE FIGHTING PROCEDURES: Stop flow of gas before extinguishing fire. Use water spray. Use water spray to keep fire-exposed containers cool. Fire situations may require evacuation.

HEALTH HAZARDS: Serious health hazard. May be harmful if inhaled. Carbon monoxide can cause headache, dizziness, mental dullness, weakness, sleepiness, nausea, vomiting, unconsciousness, and death. Rapid release of compressed gas may cause frostbite.

FIRE AND EXPLOSION HAZARDS: Flammable gas.

AUTOIGNITION TEMPERATURE: 1292°F (700°C)

FLAMMABLE LIMITS: LOWER: 12% UPPER: 75%

INSTABILITY AND REACTIVITY HAZARDS: Reacts with strong oxidizing materials, halogen compounds.

STORAGE RECOMMENDATIONS: Store in a cool, dry, well-ventilated location.

USUAL SHIPPING CONTAINERS: Use steel cylinders when shipped as pressurized gas; ship as cryogenic liquid in portable tanks, refrigerated tanks on trucks, rail cars, or barges.

PHYSICAL PROPERTIES: Colorless, odorless, tasteless gas.

MELTING POINT: −337°F (−205°C)

BOILING POINT: −313°F (−192°C)

SOLUBILITY IN WATER: not soluble

VAPOR DENSITY: 0.97

VAPOR PRESSURE: >760 mm Hg @ 20°C

ELECTRICAL EQUIPMENT: Class I, Group C

NAME: **CARBON TETRACHLORIDE**

SYNONYMS: carbon tet; methane, tetrachloro-; tetrachloromethane

FORMULA: CCl_4

NFPA 30/OSHA CLASSIFICATION:

DOT CLASS: Class 6.1, Poisonous material

SHIPPING LABEL: POISON

ID NO.: UN 1846

CAS NO.: 56-23-5

MOL. WT.: 153.8

STATEMENT OF HAZARDS: Serious health hazard. When involved in a fire may produce toxic and irritating gases.

EMERGENCY RESPONSE PERSONAL PROTECTIVE EQUIPMENT: Wear special protective clothing and positive pressure self-contained breathing apparatus.

SPILL OR LEAK PROCEDURES: Stop or control the leak, if this can be done without undue risk. Control runoff and isolate discharged material for proper disposal.

FIRE FIGHTING PROCEDURES: Use water spray to keep fire-exposed containers cool. Extinguish fire using agent suitable for surrounding fire.

HEALTH HAZARDS: Serious health hazard. Vapor and liquid irritating to eyes, skin, and respiratory system. May be harmful if inhaled. May cause central nervous system depression. Will defat tissue. Combustion by-products may include hydrochloric acid and phosgene.

FIRE AND EXPLOSION HAZARDS: Not combustible, but reacts under fire conditions producing hydrochloric acid and phosgene.

INSTABILITY AND REACTIVITY HAZARDS: Reacts explosively with alkali metals.

STORAGE RECOMMENDATIONS: Store in a cool, dry, well-ventilated location. Separate from alkali metals.

USUAL SHIPPING CONTAINERS: Glass bottles, cans, drums, tank trucks, and tank cars.

PHYSICAL PROPERTIES: Colorless liquid with ethereal, sweet odor.

MELTING POINT: −9°F (−23°C)

BOILING POINT: 170°F (77°C)

SOLUBILITY IN WATER: not soluble

SPECIFIC GRAVITY: 1.59

VAPOR DENSITY: 5.31

VAPOR PRESSURE: 91 mm Hg @ 20°C

NAME: **CHLORINE**

SYNONYMS: Bertholite

FORMULA: Cl_2

NFPA 30/OSHA CLASSIFICATION:

DOT CLASS: Class 2.3, Poisonous gas

SHIPPING LABEL: POISON GAS

ID NO.: UN 1017

CAS NO.: 7782-50-5

MOL. WT.: 70.9

STATEMENT OF HAZARDS: Severe health hazard. Corrosive gas that may be shipped as a liquid. Strong oxidizer. Most combustibles will burn in chlorine as they do in oxygen.

EMERGENCY RESPONSE PERSONAL PROTECTIVE EQUIPMENT: Wear special protective clothing and positive pressure self-contained breathing apparatus.

SPILL OR LEAK PROCEDURES: Approach release from upwind. Stop or control the leak, if this can be done without undue risk. Use water spray to cool and disperse vapors and protect personnel. Apply vapor suppression foam to limit vaporization from liquid release. Control runoff and isolate discharged material for proper disposal.

FIRE FIGHTING PROCEDURES: Strong oxidizer. Use water spray to keep fire-exposed containers cool. Extinguish fire using agent suitable for surrounding fire.

HEALTH HAZARDS: Severe health hazard. May be fatal if inhaled. Corrosive. Causes severe eye and skin burns. Irritating and corrosive to all living tissue. Causes severe or permanent eye damage. Causes collapse of respiratory system.

FIRE AND EXPLOSION HAZARDS: Strong oxidizer. Most combustibles will burn in chlorine, forming irritating and toxic gases. Cylinders may vent rapidly or explode when heated. Flame impingement upon steel chlorine container will result in iron/chlorine fire causing rupture of the container.

INSTABILITY AND REACTIVITY HAZARDS: Strong oxidizer. Reacts with organic materials, active metals, reducing agents, and ammonia. Reacts with water to form corrosive, acidic solutions.

STORAGE RECOMMENDATIONS: Store in a cool, dry, well-ventilated location. Separate from combustible, organic, or easily oxidizable materials. Isolate from acetylene, ammonia, hydrogen, hydrocarbons, ether, turpentine, and finely divided metals. Outside or detached storage is preferred. See also NFPA 430, Code for the Storage of Liquid and Solid Oxidizers.

USUAL SHIPPING CONTAINERS: Shipped in steel cylinders as a liquid under its own vapor pressure. Tank cars and tank barges.

PHYSICAL PROPERTIES: Greenish-yellow gas with bleach-like choking odor.

MELTING POINT: −150°F (−101°C)

BOILING POINT: −29°F (−34°C)

SPECIFIC GRAVITY: 1.57 @ 34°C

SOLUBILITY IN WATER: not soluble

VAPOR DENSITY: 2.44

VAPOR PRESSURE: gas

NAME: **CHLORINE TRIFLUORIDE**

FORMULA: ClF_3

NFPA 30/OSHA CLASSIFICATION:

DOT CLASS: Class 2.3, Poisonous gas

SHIPPING LABEL: POISON GAS and OXIDIZER and CORROSIVE

ID NO.: UN 1749

CAS NO.: 7790-91-2

MOL. WT.: 92.5

STATEMENT OF HAZARDS: Severe health hazard. Corrosive gas shipped as a liquid. Strong oxidizer. Water reactive.

EMERGENCY RESPONSE PERSONAL PROTECTIVE EQUIPMENT: Wear special protective clothing and positive pressure self-contained breathing apparatus.

SPILL OR LEAK PROCEDURES: Use water spray to disperse vapors. Material is water reactive, do not apply water spray directly over top of spilled pools of liquid. Protect personnel.

FIRE FIGHTING PROCEDURES: DO NOT use water. Violent reaction may result. Use appropriate extinguishing agents on nearby combustible fires. Use of dry chemical or carbon dioxide preferred.

HEALTH HAZARDS: Severe health hazard. May be fatal if inhaled. Corrosive. Causes severe eye and skin burns. Irritating to skin, eyes, and respiratory system. Vapors cause severe burns to skin, eyes.

FIRE AND EXPLOSION HAZARDS: Not combustible, but if involved in a fire by-products include hydrogen fluoride and hydrogen chloride. Causes spontaneous combustion on contact with organic or silicon containing materials.

INSTABILITY AND REACTIVITY HAZARDS: Reacts violently with water, organic matter, glass, asbestos, sand, chlorofluorocarbons, acids, alkalies, halogens, salts, metal oxides, as well as many other materials.

STORAGE RECOMMENDATIONS: Store in a cool, dry, well-ventilated location. Keep cylinders restrained. Separate from water, organic matter, glass, asbestos, sand, chlorofluorocarbons, acids, alkalies, halogens, salts, metal oxides. Outside or detached storage is preferred. See also NFPA 430, Code for the Storage of Liquid and Solid Oxidizers.

USUAL SHIPPING CONTAINERS: Steel cylinders, tank cars, special casks.

PHYSICAL PROPERTIES: Greenish-yellow fuming liquid or colorless gas. Sweet, irritating odor.

MELTING POINT: −105°F (−83°C)

BOILING POINT: 53°F (11°C)

SPECIFIC GRAVITY: 1.77 @ 13°C

SOLUBILITY IN WATER: decomposes

VAPOR DENSITY: 3.19

VAPOR PRESSURE: gas

NAME: **CHLOROACETIC ACID, solid**

SYNONYMS: chloroethanoic acid; MCA; monochloroacetic acid

FORMULA: $ClCH_2COOH$

NFPA 30/OSHA CLASSIFICATION: IIIB

DOT CLASS: Class 8, Corrosive material

SHIPPING LABEL: CORROSIVE

ID NO.: UN 1751 solid

CAS NO.: 79-11-8

MOL. WT.: 94.5

STATEMENT OF HAZARDS: Corrosive and combustible solid.

EMERGENCY RESPONSE PERSONAL PROTECTIVE EQUIPMENT: Wear special protective clothing and positive pressure self-contained breathing apparatus.

SPILL OR LEAK PROCEDURES: Approach release from upwind. Absorb in noncombustible material for proper disposal.

FIRE FIGHTING PROCEDURES: Use water spray, dry chemical, "alcohol resistant" foam, or carbon dioxide. Water or foam may cause frothing. Use water spray to keep fire-exposed containers cool. Approach fire from upwind to avoid hazardous vapors and toxic decomposition products.

HEALTH HAZARDS: Corrosive. Causes severe eye and skin burns. May be harmful if absorbed through skin or inhaled. Irritating to skin, eyes, and respiratory system.

FIRE AND EXPLOSION HAZARDS: Combustible solid. Combustion may produce hydrogen chloride and other irritants and toxic gases.

FLASH POINT: 259°F (126°C)

FLAMMABLE LIMITS: LOWER: 8% UPPER: not determined

INSTABILITY AND REACTIVITY HAZARDS: Corrosive to metals. Reacts with a broad range of materials.

STORAGE RECOMMENDATIONS: Store in a cool, dry, well-ventilated location. Separate from alkalies, alcohols, oxidizing materials, reducing agents, and metals.

USUAL SHIPPING CONTAINERS: Glass or polyethylene bottles, polyethylene-lined drums. Tanks on trucks, rail cars, barges. Nickel or stainless cylinders. Commonly shipped as solid or solution.

PHYSICAL PROPERTIES: Colorless or white crystals. Vinegar odor.

MELTING POINT: 142 to 145°F (61 to 63°C)

BOILING POINT: 372°F (189°C)

SPECIFIC GRAVITY: 1.40

SOLUBILITY IN WATER: soluble

VAPOR PRESSURE: 1 mm Hg @ 43°C

3 mm Hg @ 55°C

NAME: **CHLOROACETONITRILE**

FORMULA: ClCH$_2$C N

NFPA 30/OSHA CLASSIFICATION: II

DOT CLASS: Class 6.1, Poisonous material

SHIPPING LABEL: POISON

ID NO.: UN 2668

CAS NO.: 107-14-2

MOL. WT.: 75.5

STATEMENT OF HAZARDS: Serious health hazard. Combustible liquid.

EMERGENCY RESPONSE PERSONAL PROTECTIVE EQUIPMENT: Wear special protective clothing and positive pressure self-contained breathing apparatus.

SPILL OR LEAK PROCEDURES: Releases may require isolation or evacuation. Eliminate all ignition sources. Stop or control the leak, if this can be done without undue risk. Use water spray or foam to cool and disperse vapors and protect personnel. Approach release from upwind. Control runoff and isolate discharged material for proper disposal.

FIRE FIGHTING PROCEDURES: Use water spray, dry chemical, foam, or carbon dioxide. Use water spray to keep fire-exposed containers cool. Approach fire from upwind to avoid hazardous vapors and toxic decomposition products.

HEALTH HAZARDS: Serious health hazard. May be harmful if absorbed through skin or inhaled. Irritating to skin, eyes, and respiratory system. Causes severe tearing.

FIRE AND EXPLOSION HAZARDS: Combustible liquid. Combustion by-products include oxides of nitrogen, hydrogen cyanide, and hydrogen chloride.

FLASH POINT: 118°F (47°C)

STORAGE RECOMMENDATIONS: Store in a cool, dry, well-ventilated location. Separate from acids, alkalies, oxidizing materials, and reducing agents. Outside or detached storage is preferred.

USUAL SHIPPING CONTAINERS: Glass bottle inside wooden box.

PHYSICAL PROPERTIES: Colorless liquid.

BOILING POINT: 259°F (126°C)

SPECIFIC GRAVITY: 1.19

SOLUBILITY IN WATER: not soluble

VAPOR PRESSURE: 8 mm Hg @ 20°C

ELECTRICAL EQUIPMENT: Class I, Group D

NAME: **CHLOROACETYL CHLORIDE**

SYNONYMS: chloracetyl chloride

FORMULA: $ClCH_2COCl$

NFPA 30/OSHA CLASSIFICATION:

DOT CLASS: Class 8, Corrosive material

SHIPPING LABEL: CORROSIVE and POISON

ID NO.: UN 1752

CAS NO.: 79-04-9

MOL. WT.: 112.9

STATEMENT OF HAZARDS: Corrosive. Serious health hazard.

EMERGENCY RESPONSE PERSONAL PROTECTIVE EQUIPMENT: Wear special protective clothing and positive pressure self-contained breathing apparatus.

SPILL OR LEAK PROCEDURES: Approach release from upwind. Keep water away from release. Stop or control the leak, if this can be done without undue risk. Prompt cleanup and removal is necessary. Control runoff and isolate discharged material for proper disposal.

FIRE FIGHTING PROCEDURES: Approach fire from upwind to avoid hazardous vapors and toxic decomposition products. Use water spray to keep fire-exposed containers cool. Extinguish fire using agent suitable for surrounding fire.

HEALTH HAZARDS: Corrosive. Causes severe eye and skin burns. Serious health hazard. May be harmful if inhaled. Irritating to skin, eyes, and respiratory system.

FIRE AND EXPLOSION HAZARDS: Not combustible, but if involved in a fire decomposes to produce hydrogen chloride.

INSTABILITY AND REACTIVITY HAZARDS: Reacts with water to produce hydrochloric and monochloroacetic acids. Reacts with alkalies and alcohols.

STORAGE RECOMMENDATIONS: Store in a cool, dry, well-ventilated location. Separate from combustibles, alkalies, alcohols.

USUAL SHIPPING CONTAINERS: Glass bottles, drums.

PHYSICAL PROPERTIES: Colorless to light yellow liquid with sharp, extremely irritating odor.

MELTING POINT: −8°F (−22°C)

BOILING POINT: 225°F (107°C)

SPECIFIC GRAVITY: 1.42

SOLUBILITY IN WATER: reacts

VAPOR DENSITY: 3.9

VAPOR PRESSURE: 19 mm Hg @ 20°C

NAME: **CHLOROBENZENE**

SYNONYMS: benzene chloride; chlorobenzol; mono-chlorobenzene; phenyl chloride

FORMULA: C_6H_5Cl

NFPA 30/OSHA CLASSIFICATION: IC

DOT CLASS: Class 3, Flammable and combustible liquid

SHIPPING LABEL: FLAMMABLE LIQUID

ID NO.: UN 1134

CAS NO.: 108-90-7

MOL. WT.: 112.6

STATEMENT OF HAZARDS: Flammable liquid. Moderate health hazard. Products of combustion may be more hazardous than the material itself.

EMERGENCY RESPONSE PERSONAL PROTECTIVE EQUIPMENT: Wear full protective clothing and positive pressure self-contained breathing apparatus.

SPILL OR LEAK PROCEDURES: Eliminate all ignition sources. Stop or control the leak, if this can be done without undue risk. Use water spray to cool and disperse vapors. Control runoff and isolate discharged material for proper disposal.

FIRE FIGHTING PROCEDURES: Approach fire from upwind to avoid hazardous vapors and toxic decomposition products. Water may be ineffective. Use water spray, dry chemical, foam, or carbon dioxide. Use water spray to keep fire-exposed containers cool.

HEALTH HAZARDS: Moderate health hazard. May be harmful if inhaled. Irritating to skin, eyes, and respiratory system. Products of combustion may be more hazardous than the material itself.

FIRE AND EXPLOSION HAZARDS: Flammable liquid. Vapors are heavier than air and may travel to a source of ignition and flash back. Combustion by-products include phosgene and hydrogen chloride gases.

FLASH POINT: 82°F (29°C)

AUTOIGNITION TEMPERATURE: 1180°F (638°C)

FLAMMABLE LIMITS: LOWER: 1.3% UPPER: 9.6%

INSTABILITY AND REACTIVITY HAZARDS: Reacts with strong oxidizing materials.

STORAGE RECOMMENDATIONS: Inside storage should be in a standard flammable liquids storage warehouse, room, or cabinet. Outside or detached storage is preferred. Separate from strong oxidizing materials.

USUAL SHIPPING CONTAINERS: Small glass bottles, drums; tanks on trucks, rail cars, barges.

PHYSICAL PROPERTIES: Colorless, refractive liquid with sweet almond odor.

MELTING POINT: −49°F (−45°C)

BOILING POINT: 270°F (132°C)

SPECIFIC GRAVITY: 1.11

SOLUBILITY IN WATER: not soluble

VAPOR PRESSURE: 12 mm Hg @ 25°C

ELECTRICAL EQUIPMENT: Class I, Group D

NAME: **CHLORODIETHYL SILANE**

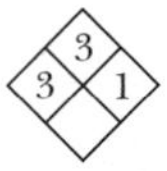

SYNONYMS: diethylchlorosilane

FORMULA: $(C_2H_5)_2SiHCl$

NFPA 30/OSHA CLASSIFICATION: IC

DOT CLASS: N/A

ID NO.: N/A

CAS NO.: 1609-19-4

MOL. WT.: 122.7

STATEMENT OF HAZARDS: Corrosive and flammable liquid.

EMERGENCY RESPONSE PERSONAL PROTECTIVE EQUIPMENT: Wear special protective clothing and positive pressure self-contained breathing apparatus.

SPILL OR LEAK PROCEDURES: Eliminate all ignition sources. Stop or control the leak, if this can be done without undue risk. Use water spray to cool and disperse vapors and protect personnel. Control runoff and isolate discharged material for proper disposal.

FIRE FIGHTING PROCEDURES: Use dry chemical, foam, carbon dioxide, or water spray. Water may be ineffective. Use water spray to keep fire-exposed containers cool. Approach fire from upwind to avoid hazardous vapors and toxic decomposition products.

HEALTH HAZARDS: Corrosive. Causes severe eye and skin burns. May be harmful if absorbed through skin or inhaled. Irritating to skin, eyes, and respiratory system. Strong sensitizer.

FIRE AND EXPLOSION HAZARDS: Flammable liquid. Vapors are heavier than air and may travel to a source of ignition and flash back. Evolves hydrogen and may ignite on contact with alkali. Combustion by-products include hydrogen chloride and other irritants and toxic gases.

FLASH POINT: 90°F (32°C)

INSTABILITY AND REACTIVITY HAZARDS: Reacts with water to produce hydrogen chloride. Reacts with a broad range of materials.

STORAGE RECOMMENDATIONS: Store in a cool, dry, well-ventilated location. Separate from acids, alkalies, oxidizing materials, and water. Outside or detached storage is preferred.

USUAL SHIPPING CONTAINERS: Glass bottle inside wooden box. Metal cans, pails, drums. Packaged under nitrogen gas.

PHYSICAL PROPERTIES: Colorless liquid.

SPECIFIC GRAVITY: 1.0

SOLUBILITY IN WATER: not soluble

VAPOR DENSITY: 4.23 (decomposes)

ELECTRICAL EQUIPMENT: Class I, Group D

NAME: **CHLORODINITROBENZENES**

SYNONYMS: 1-chloro-2,4-dinitrobenzene;dinitrochlorobenzene; 2,4-dinitro-1-chlorobenzene; DNCB

FORMULA: $(C_6H_3)(NO_2)_2Cl$

NFPA 30/OSHA CLASSIFICATION: IIIB

DOT CLASS: Class 6.1, Poisonous material

SHIPPING LABEL: POISON

ID NO.: UN 1577

CAS NO.: 97-00-7

MOL. WT.: 202.6

STATEMENT OF HAZARDS: Shock and heat sensitive. Air is not required for explosive decomposition. Serious health hazard. Combustible solid.

EMERGENCY RESPONSE PERSONAL PROTECTIVE EQUIPMENT: Wear special protective clothing and positive pressure self-contained breathing apparatus.

SPILL OR LEAK PROCEDURES: Shovel into suitable dry container.

FIRE FIGHTING PROCEDURES: Use water spray, dry chemical, or carbon dioxide. Use water spray to keep fire-exposed containers cool. Fight fire from protected location or maximum possible distance.

HEALTH HAZARDS: Serious health hazard. May be harmful if absorbed through skin or inhaled. Causes delayed nausea, vomiting, and cyanosis, up to 2 to 4 hours after exposure.

FIRE AND EXPLOSION HAZARDS: Air is not required for explosive decomposition. Combustible solid. Explodes when heated in confinement. Combustion may produce irritants and toxic gases. Closed containers may rupture violently when heated.

FLASH POINT: 382°F (194°C)

FLAMMABLE LIMITS: LOWER: 2% UPPER: 22%

INSTABILITYAND REACTIVITYHAZARDS: Shock and heat sensitive. Reacts with alkalies, oxidizing materials. Has been known to detonate at about 300°F (149°C).

STORAGE RECOMMENDATIONS: Separate from alkalies and oxidizing materials. Store in a cool, dry, well-ventilated location. Outside or detached storage is preferred.

USUAL SHIPPING CONTAINERS: Drums; bulk packaging in trucks and rail cars and bulk in tank barges.

PHYSICAL PROPERTIES: Yellow crystals.

MELTING POINT: 109°F (43°C)

BOILING POINT: 599°F (315°C)

SPECIFIC GRAVITY: 1.70

SOLUBILITY IN WATER: not soluble

NAME: **CHLOROFORM**

SYNONYMS: methane, trichloro-; trichloromethane

FORMULA: $CHCl_3$

NFPA 30/OSHA CLASSIFICATION:

DOT CLASS: Class 6.1, Poisonous material

SHIPPING LABEL: POISON

ID NO.: UN 1888

CAS NO.: 67-66-3

MOL. WT.: 119.4

STATEMENT OF HAZARDS: Serious health hazard. Not combustible, but if involved in a fire the decomposition products may be more hazardous than the material itself.

EMERGENCY RESPONSE PERSONAL PROTECTIVE EQUIPMENT: Wear special protective clothing and positive pressure self-contained breathing apparatus.

SPILL OR LEAK PROCEDURES: Approach release from upwind. Stop or control the leak, if this can be done without undue risk. Control runoff and isolate discharged material for proper disposal.

FIRE FIGHTING PROCEDURES: Use water spray to keep fire-exposed containers cool. Extinguish fire using agent suitable for surrounding fire.

HEALTH HAZARDS: Serious health hazard. May be harmful if absorbed through skin or inhaled. Irritating to skin, eyes, and respiratory system. Symptoms include headache, nausea, dizziness, or loss of consciousness. Will defat tissue.

FIRE AND EXPLOSION HAZARDS: Not combustible, but if involved in a fire reacts to produce hydrogen chloride and phosgene.

INSTABILITY AND REACTIVITY HAZARDS: Reacts with strong alkalies and aluminum.

STORAGE RECOMMENDATIONS: Store in cool, dry, well-ventilated location. Separate from strong alkalies and strong mineral acids.

USUAL SHIPPING CONTAINERS: Glass bottles, drums, tank trucks, and tank cars.

PHYSICAL PROPERTIES: Colorless liquid with pleasant, sweet odor.

MELTING POINT: −82°F (−63°C)

BOILING POINT: 143°F (62°C)

SPECIFIC GRAVITY: 1.48

SOLUBILITY IN WATER: not soluble

VAPOR DENSITY: 4.13

VAPOR PRESSURE: 160 mm Hg @ 20°C

NAME: **CHLORONITROBENZENES**

SYNONYMS: 1-chloro-3-nitrobenzene; chloronitrobenzene (o-,m-, p-); 1-chloro-4-nitrobenzene; chloro-o-nitrobenzene; nitrochlorobenzene; m-nitrochlorobenzene;

FORMULA: $C_6H_4ClNO_2$

NFPA 30/OSHA CLASSIFICATION: IIIB

DOT CLASS: Class 6.1, Poisonous material

SHIPPING LABEL: POISON

ID NO.: UN 1578

CAS NO.: m-: 121-73-3

p-: 100-00-5

o-: 88-73-3

MOL. WT.: 157.6

STATEMENT OF HAZARDS: Corrosive. Combustible solid.

EMERGENCY RESPONSE PERSONAL PROTECTIVE EQUIPMENT: Wear special protective clothing and positive pressure self-contained breathing apparatus.

SPILL OR LEAK PROCEDURES: Stop or control the leak, if this can be done without undue risk. Cover with noncombustible material for proper disposal.

FIRE FIGHTING PROCEDURES: Water may cause foaming or frothing. Use water spray, dry chemical, foam, or carbon dioxide.

HEALTH HAZARDS: Corrosive. Causes severe eye and skin burns. Irritating to skin, eyes, and respiratory system. May cause cyanosis and pulmonary edema.

FIRE AND EXPLOSION HAZARDS: Combustible solids. Combustion by-products include nitrogen oxides, hydrogen chloride.

FLASH POINT: 261°F (128°C) (p-)

AUTOIGNITION TEMPERATURE: 500°F (260°C) (m-)

FLAMMABLE LIMITS: LOWER: 1.4% UPPER: 8.7% (m-)

INSTABILITY AND REACTIVITY HAZARDS: Reacts with alkalies, oxidizing materials.

STORAGE RECOMMENDATIONS: Store in a cool, dry, well-ventilated location. Separate from alkalies and oxidizing materials.

USUAL SHIPPING CONTAINERS: Glass bottles, steel drums.

PHYSICAL PROPERTIES: Pale yellow aromatic crystals.

MELTING POINT: 90 to 183°F (32 to 84°C) (range for all isomers)

BOILING POINT: 457 to 475°F (236 to 246°C) (range for all isomers)

SPECIFIC GRAVITY: 1.30 to 1.53 (range for all isomers)

SOLUBILITY IN WATER: not soluble

VAPOR PRESSURE: <1 mm Hg @ 20°C

NAME: **CHLOROPHENOLS, liquid**

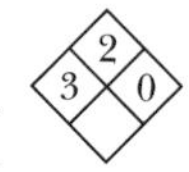

SYNONYMS: 1-chloro-2-hydroxybenzene; o-chlorophenol; 2-chlorophenol; monochlorophenol; phenol, 2-chloro-

FORMULA: C_6H_4ClOH

NFPA 30/OSHA CLASSIFICATION: IIIA

DOT CLASS: Class 6.1, Poisonous material

SHIPPING LABEL: KEEP AWAY FROM FOOD

ID NO.: UN 2021

CAS NO.: 95-57-8

MOL. WT.: 128.6

STATEMENT OF HAZARDS: Corrosive and combustible liquid.

EMERGENCY RESPONSE PERSONAL PROTECTIVE EQUIPMENT: Wear special protective clothing and positive pressure self-contained breathing apparatus.

SPILL OR LEAK PROCEDURES: Stop or control the leak, if this can be done without undue risk. Use water spray to cool and disperse vapors and protect personnel. Absorb in noncombustible material for proper disposal.

FIRE FIGHTING PROCEDURES: Use dry chemical, foam, carbon dioxide, or water spray. Approach fire from upwind to avoid hazardous vapors and toxic decomposition products. Use water spray to keep fire-exposed containers cool.

HEALTH HAZARDS: Corrosive. Causes severe eye and skin burns. May be harmful if absorbed through skin or inhaled. Symptoms of overexposure include muscle weakness, tremors, and convulsions. Contact may cause chloracne.

FIRE AND EXPLOSION HAZARDS: Combustible liquid. Combustion may produce irritants and toxic gases.

FLASH POINT: 147°F (64°C)

INSTABILITY AND REACTIVITY HAZARDS: Reacts with some oxidizing materials, organic acids.

STORAGE RECOMMENDATIONS: Store in a cool, dry, well-ventilated location. Separate from oxidizing materials, organic acids.

USUAL SHIPPING CONTAINERS: Glass bottles, steel drums, tanks.

PHYSICAL PROPERTIES: White to straw colored liquid with heavy medicinal (phenolic) odor.

MELTING POINT: 49°F (9°C)

BOILING POINT: 347°F (175°C)

SPECIFIC GRAVITY: 1.26

SOLUBILITY IN WATER: not soluble

ELECTRICAL EQUIPMENT: Class I, Group D

NAME: **CHLOROPHENOLS, solid**

SYNONYMS: 1-chloro-4-hydroxybenzene; p-chlorophenol; 4-chlorophenol; monochlorophenol

FORMULA: C_6H_4ClOH

NFPA 30/OSHA CLASSIFICATION: IIIB

DOT CLASS: Class 6.1, Poisonous material

SHIPPING LABEL: KEEP AWAY FROM FOOD

ID NO.: UN 2020

CAS NO.: 106-48-9

MOL. WT.: 128.6

STATEMENT OF HAZARDS: Corrosive and combustible solid.

EMERGENCY RESPONSE PERSONAL PROTECTIVE EQUIPMENT: Wear special protective clothing and positive pressure self-contained breathing apparatus.

SPILL OR LEAK PROCEDURES: Shovel into suitable dry container.

FIRE FIGHTING PROCEDURES: Use dry chemical, foam, carbon dioxide, or water spray. Approach fire from upwind to avoid hazardous vapors and toxic decomposition products.

HEALTH HAZARDS: Corrosive. Causes severe eye and skin burns. May be harmful if absorbed through skin or inhaled. Symptoms of overexposure include muscle weakness and liver dysfunction. Contact may cause chloracne, tremors, and convulsions.

FIRE AND EXPLOSION HAZARDS: Combustible solid. Combustion may produce irritants and toxic gases.

FLASH POINT: >230°F (>110°C)

INSTABILITY AND REACTIVITY HAZARDS: Reacts with some oxidizing materials, organic acids.

STORAGE RECOMMENDATIONS: Store in a cool, dry, well-ventilated location. Separate from oxidizing materials, organic acids.

USUAL SHIPPING CONTAINERS: Glass bottles, metal cans, pails, drums.

PHYSICAL PROPERTIES: White to pale yellow crystalline solid with heavy medicinal (phenolic) odor.

MELTING POINT: 110°F (43°C)

BOILING POINT: 428°F (220°C)

SPECIFIC GRAVITY: 1.22

SOLUBILITY IN WATER: not soluble

NAME: **CHLOROPICRIN**

SYNONYMS: acquinite; nitrochloroform; trichloronitromethane

FORMULA: CCl_3NO_2

NFPA 30/OSHA CLASSIFICATION:

DOT CLASS: Class 6.1, Poisonous material

SHIPPING LABEL: POISON

ID NO.: UN 1580

CAS NO.: 76-06-2

MOL. WT.: 164.4

STATEMENT OF HAZARDS: Severe health hazard. May decompose explosively at elevated temperatures.

EMERGENCY RESPONSE PERSONAL PROTECTIVE EQUIPMENT: Wear special protective clothing and positive pressure self-contained breathing apparatus.

SPILL OR LEAK PROCEDURES: Releases may require isolation or evacuation. Stop or control the leak, if this can be done without undue risk. Use water spray to cool and disperse vapors and protect personnel. Absorb in noncombustible material for proper disposal.

FIRE FIGHTING PROCEDURES: Extinguish fire using agent suitable for surrounding fire. Use dry chemical, foam, carbon dioxide, or water spray. Water may be ineffective. Explosive decomposition may occur under fire conditions. Fight fire from protected location or maximum possible distance. Use water spray to keep fire-exposed containers cool. Approach fire from upwind to avoid hazardous vapors and toxic decomposition products.

HEALTH HAZARDS: Severe health hazard. May be fatal if absorbed through skin or inhaled. Causes tearing. Irritating to skin, eyes, and respiratory system. Symptoms include nausea and vomiting.

FIRE AND EXPLOSION HAZARDS: Not combustible, but material if contaminated may explode when heated under confinement. Closed containers may rupture violently when heated.

INSTABILITY AND REACTIVITY HAZARDS: Decomposes explosively at elevated temperatures. Can become shock sensitive.

STORAGE RECOMMENDATIONS: Store in a cool, dry, well-ventilated location. Separate from oxidizing materials. Outside or detached storage is preferred.

USUAL SHIPPING CONTAINERS: Bottles packed in insulating material, metal drums up to 30 gallons (113.6 liters).

PHYSICAL PROPERTIES: Slightly oily, colorless liquid. Intense odor causes eye watering.

MELTING POINT: −83°F (−64°C)

BOILING POINT: 234°F (112°C)

SPECIFIC GRAVITY: 1.65

SOLUBILITY IN WATER: not soluble

VAPOR PRESSURE: 20 mm Hg @ 20°C

NAME: **CHLOROSILANES, n.o.s.**

FORMULA: R_xSiCl_y $(x + y = 4)$ $(x \neq o)$ (Note: R represents an alkyl group)

NFPA 30/OSHA CLASSIFICATION:

DOT CLASS: Various

ID NO.: Various

CAS NO.: Various

MOL. WT.: Various

STATEMENT OF HAZARDS: Corrosive and flammable liquid. Low ignition energy. Water reactive.

EMERGENCY RESPONSE PERSONAL PROTECTIVE EQUIPMENT: Wear special protective clothing and positive pressure self-contained breathing apparatus.

SPILL OR LEAK PROCEDURES: Eliminate all ignition sources. Stop or control the leak, if this can be done without undue risk. Use water spray to cool and disperse vapors and protect personnel. Control runoff and isolate discharged material for proper disposal.

FIRE FIGHTING PROCEDURES: Use dry chemical, medium expansion foam, carbon dioxide, or water spray. Water may be ineffective. Use water spray to keep fire-exposed containers cool. Approach fire from upwind to avoid hazardous vapors and toxic decomposition products.

HEALTH HAZARDS: Corrosive. Causes severe eye and skin burns. May be harmful if absorbed through skin or inhaled. Irritating to skin, eyes, and respiratory system.

FIRE AND EXPLOSION HAZARDS: Flammable liquid. Vapors are heavier than air and may travel to a source of ignition and flash back. Evolves hydrogen and may ignite on contact with alkali. Combustion by-products include hydrogen chloride, other irritants, and toxic gases.

FLASH POINT: <100°F (<38°C) (typically)

INSTABILITY AND REACTIVITY HAZARDS: Reacts with water to produce hydrogen chloride.

STORAGE RECOMMENDATIONS: Store in a cool, dry, well-ventilated location. Separate from acids, alkalies, oxidizing materials, and water. Outside or detached storage is preferred.

USUAL SHIPPING CONTAINERS: Glass bottle inside wooden box. Metal cans, pails, drums. Packaged under nitrogen gas.

PHYSICAL PROPERTIES: Colorless, fuming liquid.

MELTING POINT: <−148°F (<−100°C) (typically)

BOILING POINT: 122 to 212°F (50 to 100°C) (typically)

SOLUBILITY IN WATER: not soluble (decomposes)

ELECTRICAL EQUIPMENT: Class I, Group B

NAME: **CHLOROSULFONIC ACID**

SYNONYMS: chlorosulfuric acid; sulfuric chlorohydrin

FORMULA: $HClSO_3$

NFPA 30/OSHA CLASSIFICATION:

DOT CLASS: Class 8, Corrosive material

SHIPPING LABEL: CORROSIVE and POISON

ID NO.: UN 1754

CAS NO.: 7790-94-5

MOL. WT.: 116.5

STATEMENT OF HAZARDS: Severe health hazard. Corrosive. Water reactive. Strong oxidizer.

EMERGENCY RESPONSE PERSONAL PROTECTIVE EQUIPMENT: Wear special protective clothing and positive pressure self-contained breathing apparatus.

SPILL OR LEAK PROCEDURES: Releases may require isolation or evacuation. Keep water away from release. Approach release from upwind. Stop or control the leak, if this can be done without undue risk. Absorb in noncombustible material for proper disposal.

FIRE FIGHTING PROCEDURES: Extinguish fire using agent suitable for surrounding fire. Fight fire from protected location or maximum possible distance. Use water spray, dry chemical, foam, or carbon dioxide. DO NOT allow water to make contact with material, as highly acidic run-off will be formed. Use water spray to keep fire-exposed containers cool. Closed containers may rupture violently when heated.

HEALTH HAZARDS: Severe health hazard. May be fatal if absorbed through skin or inhaled. Inhalation may produce spasms, pulmonary edema, death. Corrosive. Causes severe eye and skin burns. Irritating to skin, eyes, and respiratory system. Forms strong acids on contact with water. See hydrogen chloride, sulfuric acid.

FIRE AND EXPLOSION HAZARDS: Not combustible, but if involved in a fire decomposes rapidly to produce hydrogen chloride, sulfur dioxide, sulfuric acid. Evolves hydrogen on contact with moist metals. Closed containers may rupture violently when heated.

STORAGE RECOMMENDATIONS: Store in a cool, dry, well-ventilated location. Separate from water, acids, alkalies, alcohols. See also NFPA 430, Code for the Storage of Liquid and Solid Oxidizers.

USUAL SHIPPING CONTAINERS: Glass bottle inside wooden box, drums; tanks on trucks, rail cars, barges. Packaged under nitrogen gas.

PHYSICAL PROPERTIES: Colorless to pale yellow liquid. Fumes in air. Pungent, acrid odor.

MELTING POINT: −112°F (−80°C)

BOILING POINT: 304°F (152°C)

SPECIFIC GRAVITY: 1.75

SOLUBILITY IN WATER: soluble

VAPOR PRESSURE: 1 mm Hg @ 25°C

NAME: **CHROMIC ACID, solid**

SYNONYMS: chromic anhydride; chromium (VI) oxide; chromium trioxide

FORMULA: CrO_3

NFPA 30/OSHA CLASSIFICATION:

DOT CLASS: Class 5.1, Oxidizer

SHIPPING LABEL: OXIDIZER and CORROSIVE

ID NO.: NA 1463

CAS NO.: 1333-82-0

MOL. WT.: 100.0

STATEMENT OF HAZARDS: Corrosive. Strong oxidizer.

EMERGENCY RESPONSE PERSONAL PROTECTIVE EQUIPMENT: Wear special protective clothing and positive pressure self-contained breathing apparatus.

SPILL OR LEAK PROCEDURES: Shovel into suitable dry container. Control runoff and isolate discharged material for proper disposal.

FIRE FIGHTING PROCEDURES: Extinguish fire using agent suitable for surrounding fire. Use flooding quantitites of water as spray.

HEALTH HAZARDS: Corrosive. Causes severe eye and skin burns. May be harmful if inhaled. Sensitizer. May cause nasal ulcerations. May cause severe allergic respiratory reaction.

FIRE AND EXPLOSION HAZARDS: Strong oxidizer. Decomposes at 482°F (250°C) with release of oxygen. Not combustible, but if involved in a fire decomposes to produce chromium fumes.

INSTABILITY AND REACTIVITY HAZARDS: Strong oxidizer. Reacts with a broad range of materials. Material is corrosive to many metals.

STORAGE RECOMMENDATIONS: Store in a cool, dry, well-ventilated location. Separate from combustible materials, halogens, sulfides, metals. See also NFPA 430, Code for the Storage of Liquid and Solid Oxidizers.

USUAL SHIPPING CONTAINERS: Glass or polyethylene bottles, lined drums.

PHYSICAL PROPERTIES: Dark red odorless crystals.

MELTING POINT: 387°F (197°C)

BOILING POINT: 482°F (250°C) (decomposes)

SPECIFIC GRAVITY: 2.70

SOLUBILITY IN WATER: soluble

NAME: **CHROMIC CHLORIDE**

SYNONYMS: chromium chloride; chromium trichloride; trichlorochromium

FORMULA: $CrCl_3$

NFPA 30/OSHA CLASSIFICATION:

DOT CLASS: N/A

ID NO.: N/A

CAS NO.: 10025-73-7

MOL. WT.: 158.4

STATEMENT OF HAZARDS: Corrosive.

EMERGENCY RESPONSE PERSONAL PROTECTIVE EQUIPMENT: Wear special protective clothing and positive pressure self-contained breathing apparatus.

SPILL OR LEAK PROCEDURES: Absorb in noncombustible material for proper disposal. Control runoff and isolate discharged material for proper disposal.

FIRE FIGHTING PROCEDURES: Extinguish fire using agent suitable for surrounding fire. Use flooding quantities of water. Approach fire from upwind to avoid hazardous vapors and toxic decomposition products.

HEALTH HAZARDS: Corrosive. Causes severe eye and skin burns. May be harmful if absorbed through skin or inhaled. Irritating to skin, eyes, and respiratory system.

FIRE AND EXPLOSION HAZARDS: Not combustible, but if involved in a fire decomposes to produce irritants and toxic gases.

INSTABILITY AND REACTIVITY HAZARDS: Reacts with water and oxidizing materials.

STORAGE RECOMMENDATIONS: Store in a cool, dry, well-ventilated location. Separate from oxidizing materials and water.

USUAL SHIPPING CONTAINERS: Lined fiber bags. Metal cans, pails, drums. Bulk packaging in trucks and rail cars and bulk in tank barges.

PHYSICAL PROPERTIES: Violet crystals. Odorless. Greenish black or violet deliquescent crystals are soluble.

MELTING POINT: 2106°F (1152°C)

BOILING POINT: 2372°F (1300°C)

SPECIFIC GRAVITY: 2.76 @ 15°C

SOLUBILITY IN WATER: not soluble (reacts)

NAME: **CHROMIUM OXYCHLORIDE**

SYNONYMS: chromic oxychloride; chromium dioxy-chloride; chromyl chloride; dichloro-dioxochromium

FORMULA: CrO_2Cl_2

NFPA 30/OSHA CLASSIFICATION:

DOT CLASS: Class 8, Corrosive material

SHIPPING LABEL: CORROSIVE

ID NO.: UN 1758

CAS NO.: 14977-61-8

MOL. WT.: 154.9

STATEMENT OF HAZARDS: Corrosive. Water reactive.

EMERGENCY RESPONSE PERSONAL PROTECTIVE EQUIPMENT: Wear special protective clothing and positive pressure self-contained breathing apparatus.

SPILL OR LEAK PROCEDURES: Isolate the area until the release is under full control. Use water spray to cool and disperse vapors and protect personnel.

FIRE FIGHTING PROCEDURES: Use appropriate extinguishing agents on surrounding fires. Use water spray to knock down acid vapors.

HEALTH HAZARDS: Corrosive. Causes severe eye and skin burns. May be harmful if inhaled. Sensitizer. May cause severe allergic respiratory reaction.

FIRE AND EXPLOSION HAZARDS: Not combustible, but if involved in a fire decomposes to produce hydrogen chloride, chromic acid. May increase the fire hazard on mixture with organic matter.

INSTABILITYAND REACTIVITYHAZARDS: Reacts violently with water and ammonia. Explodes on contact with nonmetal halides, hydrides. Reacts with reducing agents, alcohols, organic matter. Decomposes on contact with light.

STORAGE RECOMMENDATIONS: Store in a cool, dry, dark, well-ventilated location. Separate from water, ammonia, organic matter.

USUAL SHIPPING CONTAINERS: Amber glass bottles, carboys, steel drums, tanks.

PHYSICAL PROPERTIES: Dark red mobile liquid. Appears black with reflected light. Unpleasant odor. Fumes in moist air.

MELTING POINT: −142°F (−96°C)

BOILING POINT: 243°F (117°C)

SPECIFIC GRAVITY: 1.91

SOLUBILITY IN WATER: decomposes

NAME: **CRESOLS (o-, m-, p-)**

SYNONYMS: m-, p- cresylic acid; 2-, 3-, or 4-hydro-xytoluene; 2-, 3-, or 4-methylphenol

FORMULA: $CH_3C_6H_4OH$

NFPA 30/OSHA CLASSIFICATION: IIIA

DOT CLASS: Class 6.1, Poisonous material

SHIPPING LABEL: POISON

ID NO.: UN 2076

CAS NO.: 1319-77-3 all isomers
meta 108-39-4
ortho 95-48-7
para 106-44-5

MOL. WT.: 108.1

STATEMENT OF HAZARDS: Corrosive and combustible liquid.

EMERGENCY RESPONSE PERSONAL PROTECTIVE EQUIPMENT: Wear special protective clothing and positive pressure self-contained breathing apparatus.

SPILL OR LEAK PROCEDURES: Approach release from upwind. Control runoff and isolate discharged material for proper disposal.

FIRE FIGHTING PROCEDURES: Use water spray, dry chemical, foam, or carbon dioxide. Use water spray to keep fire-exposed containers cool.

HEALTH HAZARDS: Corrosive. Causes severe eye and skin burns. May be harmful if absorbed through skin or inhaled. Irritating to skin, eyes, and respiratory system. Symptoms include severe irritation of eyes with tearing, conjunctivitis, and corneal edema. May act as a skin sensitizer.

FIRE AND EXPLOSION HAZARDS: Combustible liquid. Products of combustion include fumes of cresols and other aromatic degradation products.

FLASH POINT: o: 178°F (81°C)

m: 187°F (86°C)

p: 187°F (86°C)

AUTOIGNITION TEMPERATURE: o: 1100°F (599°C)

m: 1038°F(558°C)

p: 1038°F (558°C)

FLAMMABLE LIMITS: LOWER: 1.0% (m,p) 1.4%(o) UPPER: not determined

INSTABILITY AND REACTIVITY HAZARDS: Reacts with oxidizing materials.

STORAGE RECOMMENDATIONS: Store in a cool, dry, well-ventilated location. Separate from oxidizing materials.

USUAL SHIPPING CONTAINERS: Shipped in bottles, drums, and bulk packaging in trucks and rail cars.

PHYSICAL PROPERTIES: Colorless crystals or liquid becoming dark with age and exposure to air and light. Phenolic odor.

MELTING POINT: 53°F (12°C) (o); 53°F (12°C) (m)

BOILING POINT: 375°F (191°C) (o); 396°F (202°C) (m)

SPECIFIC GRAVITY: 1.05 (o); 1.03 (m)

SOLUBILITY IN WATER: not soluble

VAPOR PRESSURE: 1 mm Hg @ 38 to 53°C 0.357 @ 20°C

ELECTRICAL EQUIPMENT: Class I, Group D

NAME: **CROTONALDEHYDE, stabilized**

SYNONYMS: 2-butenal; beta-methylacrolein

FORMULA: $CH_3CH=CHCHO$

NFPA 30/OSHA CLASSIFICATION: IB

DOT CLASS: Class 3, Flammable and combustible liquid

SHIPPING LABEL: FLAMMABLE LIQUID and POISON

ID NO.: UN 1143

CAS NO.: 4170-30-3

MOL. WT.: 70.1

STATEMENT OF HAZARDS: Severe health hazard. Flammable and corrosive liquid. May polymerize explosively. Forms explosive peroxides.

EMERGENCY RESPONSE PERSONAL PROTECTIVE EQUIPMENT: Wear special protective clothing and positive pressure self-contained breathing apparatus.

SPILL OR LEAK PROCEDURES: Releases may require isolation or evacuation. Eliminate all ignition sources. Stop or control the leak, if this can be done without undue risk. Use water spray to cool and disperse vapors and protect personnel. Control runoff and isolate discharged material for proper disposal.

FIRE FIGHTING PROCEDURES: Approach fire from upwind to avoid hazardous vapors and toxic decomposition products. Use water spray, dry chemical, "alcohol resistant" foam, or carbon dioxide. Use water spray to keep fire-exposed containers cool. Fight fire from protected location or maximum possible distance.

HEALTH HAZARDS: Severe health hazard. May be fatal if absorbed through skin or inhaled. Corrosive. Causes severe eye and skin burns. Irritating to skin, eyes, and respiratory system.

FIRE AND EXPLOSION HAZARDS: Flammable liquid. Vapors are heavier than air and may travel to a source of ignition and flash back. Combustion may produce irritants and toxic gases. Closed containers may rupture violently when heated. May form explosive peroxides.

FLASH POINT: 55°F (13°C)

AUTOIGNITION TEMPERATURE: 450°F (232°C)

FLAMMABLE LIMITS: LOWER: 2.1% UPPER: 15.5%

INSTABILITY AND REACTIVITY HAZARDS: Hazardous polymerization may occur. Polymerization may be caused by elevated temperatures and alkalies. May form explosive peroxides.

STORAGE RECOMMENDATIONS: Outside or detached storage is preferred. Inside storage should be in a standard flammable liquids storage warehouse, room, or cabinet. Isolate from alkalies and oxidizing materials.

USUAL SHIPPING CONTAINERS: 10-gallon (37.9-liter) boxed carboys.

PHYSICAL PROPERTIES: Clear, colorless to yellow watery liquid with a pungent odor.

MELTING POINT: −100°F (−75°C)

BOILING POINT: 216°F (102°C)

SPECIFIC GRAVITY: 0.85

SOLUBILITY IN WATER: partly soluble

VAPOR PRESSURE: 30 mm Hg @ 20°C

ELECTRICAL EQUIPMENT: Class I, Group C

NAME: **CROTONIC ACID**

DOT SHIPPING NAME: **CROTONIC ACID, liquid**

CROTONIC ACID, solid

SYNONYMS: 2-butenoic acid; alpha-crotonic acid; beta-methacrylic acid;

solid crotonic acid

FORMULA: $C_4H_6O_2$

NFPA 30/OSHA CLASSIFICATION: IIIA

DOT CLASS: Class 8, Corrosive material

SHIPPING LABEL: CORROSIVE

ID NO.: UN 2823

CAS NO.: 3724-65-0

MOL. WT.: 86.1

STATEMENT OF HAZARDS: Corrosive and combustible solid. Serious health hazard.

EMERGENCY RESPONSE PERSONAL PROTECTIVE EQUIPMENT: Wear special protective clothing and positive pressure self-contained breathing apparatus.

SPILL OR LEAK PROCEDURES: Control runoff and isolate discharged material for proper disposal. Neutralize spill and washings with soda ash or lime. Adsorb solid material in noncombustible material for proper disposal; shovel into suitable dry container.

FIRE FIGHTING PROCEDURES: Use dry chemical, "alcohol resistant" foam, carbon dioxide, or water spray. Use water spray to keep fire-exposed containers cool.

HEALTH HAZARDS: Corrosive. Causes severe eye and skin burns. Serious health hazard. Irritating to skin, eyes, and respiratory system.

FIRE AND EXPLOSION HAZARDS: Combustible solid. When exposed to heat can produce acrid smoke and irritating fumes.

FLASH POINT: 190°F (88°C) (oc)

AUTOIGNITION TEMPERATURE: 745°F (396°C)

INSTABILITY AND REACTIVITY HAZARDS: Reacts with oxidizing materials.

STORAGE RECOMMENDATIONS: Store in a cool, dry, well-ventilated location. Outside or detached storage is preferred. Store away from heat and oxidizing materials.

USUAL SHIPPING CONTAINERS: Glass bottles and fiber drums.

PHYSICAL PROPERTIES: Colorless, needle-like crystalline solid.

MELTING POINT: 162°F (72°C)

BOILING POINT: 365°F (185°C)

SPECIFIC GRAVITY: 1.02

SOLUBILITY IN WATER: soluble

VAPOR PRESSURE: 0.19 mm Hg @ 20°C

NAME: **CUMENE**

DOT SHIPPING NAME: **ISOPROPYLBENZENE**

SYNONYMS: benzene; 1-methylethyl-; cumol; (1-methylethyl)benzene

FORMULA: $(CH_3)_2CHC_6H_5$

NFPA 30/OSHA CLASSIFICATION: IC

DOT CLASS: Class 3, Flammable and combustible liquid

SHIPPING LABEL: FLAMMABLE LIQUID

ID NO.: UN 1918

CAS NO.: 98-82-8

MOL. WT.: 120.2

STATEMENT OF HAZARDS: Flammable liquid. May accumulate static electricity. Moderate health hazard. Forms explosive peroxides.

EMERGENCY RESPONSE PERSONAL PROTECTIVE EQUIPMENT: Wear full protective clothing and positive pressure self-contained breathing apparatus.

SPILL OR LEAK PROCEDURES: Eliminate all ignition sources. Stop or control the leak, if this can be done without undue risk. Use water spray to cool and disperse vapors and protect personnel. Absorb in noncombustible material for proper disposal. Control runoff and isolate discharged material for proper disposal.

FIRE FIGHTING PROCEDURES: Use water spray, dry chemical, foam, or carbon dioxide. Use water spray to keep fire-exposed containers cool.

HEALTH HAZARDS: Moderate health hazard. May be harmful if absorbed through skin or inhaled. Irritating to skin, eyes, and respiratory system. Narcotic effects possible.

FIRE AND EXPLOSION HAZARDS: Flammable liquid. Combustion may produce irritants and toxic gases.

FLASH POINT: 92°F (33°C)

AUTOIGNITION TEMPERATURE: 797°F (425°C)

FLAMMABLE LIMITS: LOWER: 0.9% UPPER: 6.5%

INSTABILITY AND REACTIVITY HAZARDS: Reacts with oxidizing materials. Reacts with nitric acid and sulfuric acid with release of energy. Forms cumene hydroperoxide upon prolonged exposure to air.

STORAGE RECOMMENDATIONS: Outside or detached storage is preferred. Inside storage should be in a standard flammable liquids storage warehouse, room, or cabinet. Separate from oxidizing materials, nitric acid, sulfuric acid.

USUAL SHIPPING CONTAINERS: Glass bottles, cans, drums, and tanks on trucks, rail cars, barges.

PHYSICAL PROPERTIES: Colorless liquid with sharp, penetrating aromatic odor.

MELTING POINT: −141°F (−96°C)

BOILING POINT: 306°F (152°C)

SPECIFIC GRAVITY: 0.86

SOLUBILITY IN WATER: not soluble

VAPOR DENSITY: 4.14

VAPOR PRESSURE: 3.2 mm Hg @ 20°C

ELECTRICAL EQUIPMENT: Class I, Group D

NAME: **CYANOACETIC ACID**

DOT SHIPPING NAME: **CORROSIVE LIQUID, n.o.s.**

SYNONYMS: CAA; malonic mononitrile

FORMULA: $N \equiv CCH_2COOH$

NFPA 30/OSHA CLASSIFICATION: IIIB

DOT CLASS: Class 8, Corrosive material

SHIPPING LABEL: CORROSIVE

ID NO.: UN 1759

CAS NO.: 372-09-8

MOL. WT.: 85.1

STATEMENT OF HAZARDS: Corrosive and combustible solid.

EMERGENCY RESPONSE PERSONAL PROTECTIVE EQUIPMENT: Wear special protective clothing and positive pressure self-contained breathing apparatus.

SPILL OR LEAK PROCEDURES: Stop or control the leak, if this can be done without undue risk. Absorb in noncombustible material for proper disposal.

FIRE FIGHTING PROCEDURES: Use water spray, dry chemical, or carbon dioxide. Use water spray to keep fire-exposed containers cool. Control corrosive runoff and isolate discharged material for proper disposal. Approach fire from upwind to avoid hazardous vapors and toxic decomposition products.

HEALTH HAZARDS: Corrosive. Causes severe eye and skin burns. May be harmful if absorbed through skin or inhaled. Irritating to skin, eyes, and respiratory system.

FIRE AND EXPLOSION HAZARDS: Combustible solid. Decomposes at 320°F (160°C) with release of acetonitrile. Combustion may produce irritants and toxic gases.

FLASH POINT: 226°F (107°C)

STORAGE RECOMMENDATIONS: Store in a cool, dry, well-ventilated location. Separate from acids, alkalies, oxidizing materials, reducing agents.

USUAL SHIPPING CONTAINERS: Glass or polyethylene bottles, polyethylene-lined drums.

PHYSICAL PROPERTIES: Moist, white crystals. Also, frequently found as yellow-brown solution. Unpleasant odor.

MELTING POINT: 158°F (70°C)

BOILING POINT: 226°F (108°C)

SPECIFIC GRAVITY: >1.1 @ 20°C

SOLUBILITY IN WATER: soluble

NAME: **CYANOGEN, liquefied**

SYNONYMS: dicyan; dicyanogen; ethanedinitrile; oxalic acid dinitrile; oxalonitrile,

FORMULA: $N \equiv C{=}mC \equiv N$

NFPA 30/OSHA CLASSIFICATION:

DOT CLASS: Class 2.3, Poisonous gas

SHIPPING LABEL: POISON GAS and FLAMMABLE GAS

ID NO.: UN 1026

CAS NO.: 460-19-5

MOL. WT.: 52.0

STATEMENT OF HAZARDS: Severe health hazard. Corrosive and flammable gas shipped as a liquid. Thermally unstable. Low ignition energy.

EMERGENCY RESPONSE PERSONAL PROTECTIVE EQUIPMENT: Wear special protective clothing and positive pressure self-contained breathing apparatus.

SPILL OR LEAK PROCEDURES: Releases may require isolation or evacuation. Eliminate all ignition sources. Stop or control the leak, if this can be done without undue risk. Use water spray to cool and disperse vapors, protect personnel, and dilute spills to form nonflammable mixtures. Approach release from upwind. Control runoff and isolate discharged material for proper disposal.

FIRE FIGHTING PROCEDURES: Stop flow of gas before extinguishing fire. Use fine spray or fog to control fire by preventing its spread and absorbing some of its heat. Use water spray to keep fire-exposed containers cool. Fight fire from protected location or maximum possible distance. Control runoff and isolate discharged material for proper disposal.

HEALTH HAZARDS: Severe health hazard. May be fatal if inhaled or absorbed through skin. Corrosive. Causes severe eye and skin burns. Causes weakness, headache, confusion, and chemical asphyxiation. Rapid release of compressed gas may cause frostbite.

FIRE AND EXPLOSION HAZARDS: Flammable gas. Vapors are heavier than air and may travel to a source of ignition and flash back. Closed containers may rupture violently when heated. Combustion by-products include hydrogen cyanide and oxides of nitrogen.

FLAMMABLE LIMITS: LOWER: 6.6% UPPER: 32%

INSTABILITY AND REACTIVITY HAZARDS: Reacts with acids.

STORAGE RECOMMENDATIONS: Store in a cool, dry, well-ventilated location. Isolate from acids. Outside or detached storage is preferred.

USUAL SHIPPING CONTAINERS: Steel cylinders; pressurized tanks on trucks, rail cars, barges.

PHYSICAL PROPERTIES: Colorless gas. Odor of almonds; acrid and pungent when in lethal concentrations.

MELTING POINT: −18°F (−28°C)

BOILING POINT: −6°F (−21°C)

SPECIFIC GRAVITY: 0.95

SOLUBILITY IN WATER: soluble

VAPOR DENSITY: 1.79

ELECTRICAL EQUIPMENT: Class I, Group B

NAME: **CYANOGEN BROMIDE**

SYNONYMS: bromine cyanide

FORMULA: $BrC \equiv N$

NFPA 30/OSHA CLASSIFICATION:

DOT CLASS: Class 6.1, Poisonous material

SHIPPING LABEL: POISON and CORROSIVE

ID NO.: UN 1889

CAS NO.: 506-68-3

MOL. WT.: 105.9

STATEMENT OF HAZARDS: Severe health hazard. Thermally unstable. Solid vaporizes at room temperature.

EMERGENCY RESPONSE PERSONAL PROTECTIVE EQUIPMENT: Wear special protective clothing and positive pressure self-contained breathing apparatus.

SPILL OR LEAK PROCEDURES: Releases may require isolation or evacuation. Place contaminated materials into appropriate containers for disposal.

FIRE FIGHTING PROCEDURES: Extinguish fire using agent suitable for surrounding fire. Use water spray to keep fire-exposed containers cool.

HEALTH HAZARDS: Severe health hazard. May be fatal if inhaled. Irritating to skin, eyes, and respiratory system. May cause acute or delayed pulmonary edema.

FIRE AND EXPLOSION HAZARDS: Not combustible, but if involved in a fire decomposes to produce toxic gases.

INSTABILITY AND REACTIVITY HAZARDS: Reacts with acids, water to release highly toxic hydrogen cyanide. May decompose with oxidizing materials or heat with release of toxic gases.

STORAGE RECOMMENDATIONS: Store in a cool, dry, well-ventilated location. Separate from acids.

USUAL SHIPPING CONTAINERS: Metal can or glass bottle inside wooden box, not to exceed 25 lb.

PHYSICAL PROPERTIES: White crystals, volatile at room temperature.

MELTING POINT: 125°F (52°C)

BOILING POINT: 142°F (61°C)

SPECIFIC GRAVITY: 2.02

SOLUBILITY IN WATER: soluble

VAPOR PRESSURE: 100 mm Hg @ 22.6°C

NAME: **CYCLOHEXYLAMINE**

SYNONYMS: aminocyclohexane; hexahydroaniline

FORMULA: $C_6H_{11}NH_2$

NFPA 30/OSHA CLASSIFICATION: IC

DOT CLASS: Class 8, Corrosive material

SHIPPING LABEL: CORROSIVE and FLAMMABLE LIQUID

ID NO.: UN 2357

CAS NO.: 108-91-8

MOL. WT.: 99.2

STATEMENT OF HAZARDS: Corrosive and flammable liquid.

EMERGENCY RESPONSE PERSONAL PROTECTIVE EQUIPMENT: Wear special protective clothing and positive pressure self-contained breathing apparatus.

SPILL OR LEAK PROCEDURES: Stop or control the leak, if this can be done without undue risk. Eliminate all ignition sources. Use water spray to cool and disperse vapors, protect personnel, and dilute spills to form nonflammable mixtures. Approach release from upwind. Absorb in noncombustible material for proper disposal.

FIRE FIGHTING PROCEDURES: Use water spray, dry chemical, "alcohol resistant" foam, or carbon dioxide. Use water spray to keep fire-exposed containers cool. Solid streams of water may be ineffective and spread material.

HEALTH HAZARDS: Corrosive. Causes severe eye and skin burns. Irritating to skin, eyes, and respiratory system. Symptoms include tearing, conjunctivitis, and corneal edema. Inhalation may cause difficulties ranging from coughing and nausea to pulmonary edema. Sensitizer. May cause severe allergic reaction.

FIRE AND EXPLOSION HAZARDS: Flammable liquid. Vapors are heavier than air and may travel to a source of ignition and flash back.

FLASH POINT: 88°F (31°C)

AUTOIGNITION TEMPERATURE: 560°F (293°C)

FLAMMABLE LIMITS: LOWER: 1.5% UPPER: 9.4%

INSTABILITY AND REACTIVITY HAZARDS: Avoid contact with acids, oxidizing materials, chlorine, hypochlorite, halogenated compounds, and reactive organic compounds. Products of decomposition include carbon monoxide, carbon dioxide, hydrocarbons, and oxides of nitrogen as well as amine vapors and ammonia.

STORAGE RECOMMENDATIONS: Outside or detached storage is preferred. Avoid oxidizing materials, acids, and sources of halogen. Store in a cool, dry, well-ventilated location.

USUAL SHIPPING CONTAINERS: Glass bottles, cans, drums, and tank cars.

PHYSICAL PROPERTIES: Colorless to yellow liquid with odor like ammonia.

MELTING POINT: 0.1°F (−18°C)

BOILING POINT: 275°F (135°C)

SPECIFIC GRAVITY: 0.87

SOLUBILITY IN WATER: soluble

VAPOR PRESSURE: 10 mm Hg @ 24°C

ELECTRICAL EQUIPMENT: Class I, Group D

NAME: **DECABORANE**

SYNONYMS: decaborane(14); decaboron tetradecahydride

FORMULA: $B_{10}H_{14}$

NFPA 30/OSHA CLASSIFICATION:

DOT CLASS: Class 4.1, Flammable solid

SHIPPING LABEL: FLAMMABLE SOLID and POISON

ID NO.: UN 1868

CAS NO.: 17702-41-9

MOL. WT.: 122.3

STATEMENT OF HAZARDS: Corrosive and combustible solid.

EMERGENCY RESPONSE PERSONAL PROTECTIVE EQUIPMENT: Wear special protective clothing and positive pressure self-contained breathing apparatus.

SPILL OR LEAK PROCEDURES: Absorb in noncombustible material for proper disposal.

FIRE FIGHTING PROCEDURES: Smother fire with dry sand or dry clay or spray with water. DO NOT use carbon dioxide or halocarbons. Use water spray to keep fire-exposed containers cool. Approach fire from upwind to avoid hazardous vapors and toxic decomposition products.

HEALTH HAZARDS: Corrosive. Causes severe eye and skin burns. May be harmful if absorbed through skin or inhaled. Irritating to skin, eyes, and respiratory system. Symptoms of overexposure include dizziness, nausea, vomiting, and muscular tremors. Onset of symptoms may be delayed for up to one or two days after exposure.

FIRE AND EXPLOSION HAZARDS: Combustible solid. Combustion by-products include boron fumes, irritants, and other toxic gases.

AUTOIGNITION TEMPERATURE: 300°F (149°C)

INSTABILITY AND REACTIVITY HAZARDS: Reacts with a broad range of materials. Forms shock-sensitive explosive with carbon tetrachloride.

STORAGE RECOMMENDATIONS: Store in a cool, dry, well-ventilated location. Separate from oxidizing materials, halocarbons, and water.

USUAL SHIPPING CONTAINERS: Bottles, metal cans, pails, drums.

PHYSICAL PROPERTIES: Colorless crystals. Pungent, chocolate-like odor.

MELTING POINT: 211°F (100°C)

BOILING POINT: 415°F (213°C)

SPECIFIC GRAVITY: 0.94

SOLUBILITY IN WATER: not soluble

VAPOR PRESSURE: < 1 mm Hg @ 25°C
19 mm Hg @ 100°C

NAME: **DI-n-AMYLAMINE**

SYNONYMS: diamylamine; di-n-pentylamine; pentyl pentylamine

FORMULA: $(C_5H_{11})_2NH$

NFPA 30/OSHA CLASSIFICATION: II

DOT CLASS: Class 6.1, Poisonous material

SHIPPING LABEL: KEEP AWAY FROM FOOD

ID NO.: UN 2841

CAS NO.: 2050-92-2

MOL. WT.: 157.3

STATEMENT OF HAZARDS: Corrosive and combustible liquid.

EMERGENCY RESPONSE PERSONAL PROTECTIVE EQUIPMENT: Wear special protective clothing and positive pressure self-contained breathing apparatus.

SPILL OR LEAK PROCEDURES: Releases may require isolation or evacuation. Stop or control the leak, if this can be done without undue risk. Use water spray to cool and disperse vapors and protect personnel. Absorb in noncombustible material for proper disposal.

FIRE FIGHTING PROCEDURES: Use dry chemical, foam, or carbon dioxide. Water may be ineffective. Use water spray to keep fire-exposed containers cool. Approach fire from upwind to avoid hazardous vapors and toxic decomposition products.

HEALTH HAZARDS: Corrosive. Causes severe eye and skin burns. May be harmful if absorbed through skin or inhaled. Irritating to skin, eyes, and respiratory system. Other symptoms include nausea, vomiting, lung irritation, visual disturbances.

FIRE AND EXPLOSION HAZARDS: Combustible liquid. Combustion by-products include oxides of nitrogen.

FLASH POINT: 124°F (51°C)

INSTABILITY AND REACTIVITY HAZARDS: Strong alkali. Reacts with strong oxidizing agents and strong acids.

STORAGE RECOMMENDATIONS: Store in a cool, dry, well-ventilated location. Separate from acids and oxidizing materials.

USUAL SHIPPING CONTAINERS: Metal cans, pails, drums, tanks.

PHYSICAL PROPERTIES: Colorless to water-white to pale yellow liquid. Characteristic amine odor (fishy-ammonia).

BOILING POINT: 396°F (202°C)

SPECIFIC GRAVITY: 0.78

SOLUBILITY IN WATER: not soluble

NAME: **DIBORANE**

SYNONYMS: boroethane; boron hydride; diboron hexa-hydride

FORMULA: B_2H_6

NFPA 30/OSHA CLASSIFICATION: IA

DOT CLASS: Class 2.3, Poisonous gas

SHIPPING LABEL: POISON GAS and FLAMMABLE GAS

ID NO.: UN 1911

CAS NO.: 19287-45-7

MOL. WT.: 27.7

STATEMENT OF HAZARDS: Pyrophoric. Flammable gas. Low ignition energy. Severe health hazard. Water reactive. Thermally unstable.

EMERGENCY RESPONSE PERSONAL PROTECTIVE EQUIPMENT: Wear special protective clothing and positive pressure self-contained breathing apparatus.

SPILL OR LEAK PROCEDURES: Stop or control the leak, if this can be done without undue risk. Use water spray to cool and disperse vapors and protect personnel. Approach release from upwind.

FIRE FIGHTING PROCEDURES: Do not use halocarbons. Use fine spray or fog to control fire by preventing its spread and absorbing some of its heat. Stop flow of gas before extinguishing fire. Liquid nitrogen may be effective for cooling and extinguishing diborane fires. Use water spray to keep fire-exposed containers cool. Explosive decomposition may occur under fire conditions. Fight fire from protected location or maximum possible distance. Approach fire from upwind to avoid hazardous vapors and toxic decomposition products.

HEALTH HAZARDS: Severe health hazard. May be fatal if absorbed through skin or inhaled. Irritating to skin, eyes, and respiratory system. Inhalation causes pulmonary edema. Onset of symptoms may be delayed up to two days. Rapid release of compressed gas may cause frostbite.

FIRE AND EXPLOSION HAZARDS: Flammable gas. Evolves hydrogen and ignites on contact with water or moist air. Pyrophoric; may ignite spontaneously on exposure to air. May accumulate then explode in air without a source of ignition. Combustion may produce irritants and toxic gases. Closed containers may rupture violently when heated.

FLASH POINT: −130°F (−90°C)

AUTOIGNITION TEMPERATURE: 104 to 122°F (40 to 50°C)

FLAMMABLE LIMITS: LOWER: 0.8% UPPER: 98%

INSTABILITY AND REACTIVITY HAZARDS: Decomposes in air at room temperature. Reacts violently with a broad range of materials.

STORAGE RECOMMENDATIONS: Store in a cool, dry, well-ventilated location. Isolate from air, moisture, halogens, alkali metals, aluminum, and rust. Outside or detached storage is preferred. Normally refrigerated.

USUAL SHIPPING CONTAINERS: Steel cylinders.

PHYSICAL PROPERTIES: Colorless gas. Repulsive, sickly-sweet odor.

MELTING POINT: −265°F (−165°C)

BOILING POINT: −135°F (−93°C)

SPECIFIC GRAVITY: 0.45

SOLUBILITY IN WATER: not soluble (decomposes)

VAPOR DENSITY: 0.95

VAPOR PRESSURE: 224 mm Hg @ −112°C

NAME: **DI-n-BUTYLAMINE**

SYNONYMS: N-butyl-1-butanamine; n-dibutylamine

FORMULA: $(C_4H_9)_2NH$

NFPA 30/OSHA CLASSIFICATION: II

DOT CLASS: Class 8, Corrosive material

SHIPPING LABEL: CORROSIVE and FLAMMABLE LIQUID

ID NO.: UN 2248

CAS NO.: 111-92-2

MOL. WT.: 129.3

STATEMENT OF HAZARDS: Corrosive and combustible liquid.

EMERGENCY RESPONSE PERSONAL PROTECTIVE EQUIPMENT: Wear special protective clothing and positive pressure self-contained breathing apparatus.

SPILL OR LEAK PROCEDURES: Use water spray to cool and disperse vapors and protect personnel. Approach release from upwind. Sand, clay, earth, or other absorbent material may be used to contain liquid.

FIRE FIGHTING PROCEDURES: Use water spray, dry chemical, foam, or carbon dioxide. Use water spray to keep fire-exposed containers cool.

HEALTH HAZARDS: Corrosive. Causes severe eye and skin burns. May be harmful if inhaled. Irritating to skin, eyes, and respiratory system. Vapors cause irritation of eyes with severe tearing, conjunctivitis, and corneal edema. Inhalation may cause difficulties ranging from coughing and nausea to pulmonary edema.

FIRE AND EXPLOSION HAZARDS: Combustible liquid.

FLASH POINT: 117°F (47°C)

FLAMMABLE LIMITS: LOWER: 1.1% UPPER: not determined

INSTABILITY AND REACTIVITY HAZARDS: Reacts with acids, oxidizing materials, chlorine, hypochlorite, halogenated compounds, and reactive organic compounds. Products of decomposition include carbon monoxide, carbon dioxide, hydrocarbons, and oxides of nitrogen as well as amine vapors.

STORAGE RECOMMENDATIONS: Separate from oxidizing materials, acids, and sources of halogens. Store in a cool, dry, well-ventilated location. Outside or detached storage is preferred.

USUAL SHIPPING CONTAINERS: Glass bottles, cans, drums, and tank cars.

PHYSICAL PROPERTIES: Colorless liquid with ammonia-like or fishy odor.

MELTING POINT: −74°F (−59°C)

BOILING POINT: 319°F (159°C)

SPECIFIC GRAVITY: 0.76

SOLUBILITY IN WATER: not soluble

VAPOR PRESSURE: 2 mm Hg @ 20°C

ELECTRICAL EQUIPMENT: Class I, Group C

NAME: **DIBUTYL ETHERS**

SYNONYMS: n-butyl ether; n-dibutyl ether; dibutyl oxide; 1,1-oxybis [butane]

FORMULA: $(C_4H_9)_2O$

NFPA 30/OSHA CLASSIFICATION: IC

DOT CLASS: Class 3, Flammable and combustible liquid

SHIPPING LABEL: FLAMMABLE LIQUID

ID NO.: UN 1149

CAS NO.: 142-96-1

MOL. WT.: 130.2

STATEMENT OF HAZARDS: Flammable liquid. May accumulate static electricity. Moderate health hazard. Forms explosive peroxides.

EMERGENCY RESPONSE PERSONAL PROTECTIVE EQUIPMENT: Wear full protective clothing and positive pressure self-contained breathing apparatus.

SPILL OR LEAK PROCEDURES: Eliminate all ignition sources. Stop or control the leak, if this can be done without undue risk. Use appropriate foam to blanket release and suppress vapors. Absorb in noncombustible material for proper disposal.

FIRE FIGHTING PROCEDURES: Use dry chemical, foam, carbon dioxide, or water spray. Water may be ineffective. Use water spray to keep fire-exposed containers cool.

HEALTH HAZARDS: Moderate health hazard. May be harmful if absorbed through skin or inhaled. Irritating to skin, eyes, and respiratory system. Inhalation causes dizziness, suffocation.

FIRE AND EXPLOSION HAZARDS: Flammable liquid. Vapors are heavier than air and may travel to a source of ignition and flash back. Liquid floats on water and may travel to a source of ignition and spread fire. Combustion may produce irritants and toxic gases.

FLASH POINT: 92°F (33°C) (oc)

AUTOIGNITION TEMPERATURE: 382°F (194°C)

FLAMMABLE LIMITS: LOWER: 1.5% UPPER: 7.6%

INSTABILITY AND REACTIVITY HAZARDS: Forms shock-sensitive peroxides over time. Peroxide formation may occur in containers that have been opened and remain in storage. Peroxides can be detonated by friction, impact, or heating. Reacts with acids.

STORAGE RECOMMENDATIONS: Store in a cool, dry, well-ventilated location. Store away from heat, oxidizing materials, sunlight, and acids.

USUAL SHIPPING CONTAINERS: Metal cans, pails, drums; tanks on trucks, rail cars, barges.

PHYSICAL PROPERTIES: Colorless liquid with mild, ethereal odor.

MELTING POINT: −144°F (−98°C)

BOILING POINT: 288°F (142°C)

SPECIFIC GRAVITY: 0.77

SOLUBILITY IN WATER: not soluble

NAME: **DICHLOROACETYL CHLORIDE**

SYNONYMS: dichloracetyl chloride; dichloroethanoyl chloride

FORMULA: $Cl_2CHCOCl$

NFPA 30/OSHA CLASSIFICATION: IIIA

DOT CLASS: Class 8, Corrosive material

SHIPPING LABEL: CORROSIVE

ID NO.: UN 1765

CAS NO.: 79-36-7

MOL. WT.: 147.4

STATEMENT OF HAZARDS: Corrosive and combustible liquid. Water reactive.

EMERGENCY RESPONSE PERSONAL PROTECTIVE EQUIPMENT: Wear special protective clothing and positive pressure self-contained breathing apparatus.

SPILL OR LEAK PROCEDURES: Keep water away from release. Stop or control the leak, if this can be done without undue risk. Approach release from upwind. Cover with water-free noncombustible material for proper disposal.

FIRE FIGHTING PROCEDURES: Extinguish fire using agent suitable for surrounding fire with dry chemical, foam, or carbon dioxide. DO NOT use water directly on spilled material or violent reaction may result. Carefully use water spray to keep fire-exposed containers cool.

HEALTH HAZARDS: Corrosive. Causes severe eye and skin burns. May be harmful if inhaled. Irritating to skin, eyes, and respiratory system.

FIRE AND EXPLOSION HAZARDS: Combustible liquid. Combustion by-products include hydrogen chloride and other irritants.

FLASH POINT: 151°F (66°C)

INSTABILITY AND REACTIVITY HAZARDS: Water reactive.

STORAGE RECOMMENDATIONS: Store in a cool, dry, well-ventilated location. Separate from alkalies, oxidizing materials, alcohols, and water.

USUAL SHIPPING CONTAINERS: Glass bottles, carboys; tanks on trucks, rail cars, barges. Packaged under nitrogen gas.

PHYSICAL PROPERTIES: Colorless to pale yellow liquid. Fumes in moist air. Acrid, penetrating odor.

BOILING POINT: 226 to 230°F (108 to 110°C)

SPECIFIC GRAVITY: 1.53

SOLUBILITY IN WATER: decomposes

ELECTRICAL EQUIPMENT: Class I, Group D

NAME: **DICHLOROANILINES, solid liquid**

SYNONYMS: 1-amino-3,4-dichlorobenzene; DCA; 3,4-dichloroaniline; 3,4-dichlorobenzeneamine

FORMULA: $Cl_2(C_6H_3)NH_2$

NFPA 30/OSHA CLASSIFICATION: IIIB

DOT CLASS: Class 6.1, Poisonous material

SHIPPING LABEL: POISON

ID NO.: UN 1590

CAS NO.: 95-76-1

MOL. WT.: 162.0

STATEMENT OF HAZARDS: Serious health hazard. Combustible solid.

EMERGENCY RESPONSE PERSONAL PROTECTIVE EQUIPMENT: Wear special protective clothing and positive pressure self-contained breathing apparatus.

SPILL OR LEAK PROCEDURES: Prompt cleanup and removal are necessary. Shovel into suitable dry container.

FIRE FIGHTING PROCEDURES: Use water spray, dry chemical, foam, or carbon dioxide. Water or foam may cause frothing. Use water spray to keep fire-exposed containers cool. Approach fire from upwind to avoid hazardous vapors and toxic decomposition products.

HEALTH HAZARDS: Serious health hazard. May be harmful if absorbed through skin or inhaled. Irritating to skin, eyes, and respiratory system. Onset of symptoms may be delayed for two to four hours.

FIRE AND EXPLOSION HAZARDS: Combustible solid. Combustion by-products include oxides of nitrogen, aniline, and other irritants and toxic gases.

FLASH POINT: 331°F (166°C) (oc)

AUTOIGNITION TEMPERATURE: 509°F (265°C)

FLAMMABLE LIMITS: LOWER: 2.8% UPPER: 7.2%

INSTABILITY AND REACTIVITY HAZARDS: Reacts with acids and oxidizing materials.

STORAGE RECOMMENDATIONS: Store in a cool, dry, well-ventilated location. Separate from acids, oxidizing materials, and combustibles.

USUAL SHIPPING CONTAINERS: Fiber or steel drums.

PHYSICAL PROPERTIES: Light brown crystals.

MELTING POINT: 160°F (72°C)

BOILING POINT: 522°F (272°C)

SOLUBILITY IN WATER: not soluble

VAPOR PRESSURE: 1 mm Hg @ 80°C

NAME: **o-DICHLOROBENZENE**

SYNONYMS: benzene; 1,2-dichloro; 1,2-dichlorobenzene

FORMULA: $C_6H_4Cl_2$

NFPA 30/OSHA CLASSIFICATION: IIIA

DOT CLASS: Class 6.1, Poisonous material

SHIPPING LABEL: KEEP AWAY FROM FOOD

ID NO.: UN 1591

CAS NO.: 95-50-1

MOL. WT.: 147.0

STATEMENT OF HAZARDS: Combustible liquid. Moderate health hazard. Combustion by-products include hydrogen chloride.

EMERGENCY RESPONSE PERSONAL PROTECTIVE EQUIPMENT: Wear full protective clothing and positive pressure self-contained breathing apparatus.

SPILL OR LEAK PROCEDURES: Approach release from upwind. Stop or control the leak, if this can be done without undue risk. Control runoff and isolate discharged material for proper disposal.

FIRE FIGHTING PROCEDURES: Approach fire from upwind to avoid hazardous vapors and toxic decomposition products. Use water spray, dry chemical, foam, or carbon dioxide. Use water spray to keep fire-exposed containers cool. Extinguish fire using agent suitable for surrounding fire.

HEALTH HAZARDS: Moderate health hazard. May be harmful if absorbed through skin or inhaled. Irritating to skin, eyes, and respiratory system.

FIRE AND EXPLOSION HAZARDS: Combustible liquid. Combustion may produce irritants and toxic gases. Combustion by-products include hydrogen chloride, phosgene, and chlorocarbons. Fire may be smoky due to incomplete combustion.

FLASH POINT: 151°F (66°C)

AUTOIGNITION TEMPERATURE: 1198°F (648°C)

FLAMMABLE LIMITS: LOWER: 2.2% UPPER: 9.2%

INSTABILITY AND REACTIVITY HAZARDS: Avoid oxidizing materials.

STORAGE RECOMMENDATIONS: Store in a cool, dry, well-ventilated location. Separate from oxidizing materials.

USUAL SHIPPING CONTAINERS: Glass bottles, drums; tanks on trucks, rail cars, barges.

PHYSICAL PROPERTIES: Colorless liquid with pleasant aromatic odor.

MELTING POINT: 1°F (−17°C)

BOILING POINT: 357°F (180°C)

SPECIFIC GRAVITY: 1.30

SOLUBILITY IN WATER: not soluble

VAPOR PRESSURE: 1.2 mm Hg @ 20°C

ELECTRICAL EQUIPMENT: Class I, Group D

NAME: **1,4-DICHLOROBUTANE**

SYNONYMS: 2-butylene dichloride; tetramethylene dichloride, DCB

FORMULA: $ClCH_2(CH_2)_2CH_2Cl$

NFPA 30/OSHA CLASSIFICATION: II

DOT CLASS: N/A

ID NO.: N/A

CAS NO.: 110-56-5

MOL. WT.: 127.0

STATEMENT OF HAZARDS: Corrosive and combustible liquid.

EMERGENCY RESPONSE PERSONAL PROTECTIVE EQUIPMENT: Wear special protective clothing and positive pressure self-contained breathing apparatus.

SPILL OR LEAK PROCEDURES: Stop or control the leak, if this can be done without undue risk. Use appropriate foam to blanket release and suppress vapors. Absorb in noncombustible material for proper disposal.

FIRE FIGHTING PROCEDURES: Use dry chemical, foam, carbon dioxide, or water spray. Use water spray to keep fire-exposed containers cool.

HEALTH HAZARDS: Corrosive. Causes severe eye and skin burns.

FIRE AND EXPLOSION HAZARDS: Combustible liquid. Combustion may produce irritants and toxic gases.

FLASH POINT: 126°F (52°C)

FLAMMABLE LIMITS: LOWER: 1.5% UPPER: 4.0%

INSTABILITY AND REACTIVITY HAZARDS: Reacts with oxidizing materials and alkalies.

STORAGE RECOMMENDATIONS: Store in a cool, dry, well-ventilated location. Separate from oxidizing materials and alkalies. Inside storage should be in a standard flammable liquids storage warehouse, room, or cabinet.

USUAL SHIPPING CONTAINERS: Glass bottles; metal cans, pails, drums; tanks on trucks, rail cars, barges.

PHYSICAL PROPERTIES: Colorless liquid with distinct odor.

MELTING POINT: −35°F (−37°C)

BOILING POINT: 309°F (154°C)

SPECIFIC GRAVITY: 1.14

SOLUBILITY IN WATER: not soluble

ELECTRICAL EQUIPMENT: Class I, Group D

NAME: **2,2-DICHLORODIETHYL ETHER**

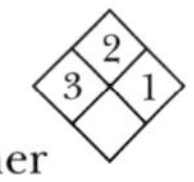

SYNONYMS: bis(2-chloroethyl) ether; DCEE; 1,1-oxybis(2-chloroethane); sym-dichloroethyl ether

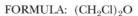

FORMULA: $(ClCH_2CH_2)_2O$

NFPA 30/OSHA CLASSIFICATION: II

DOT CLASS: Class 6.1, Poisonous material

SHIPPING LABEL: POISON and FLAMMABLE LIQUID

ID NO.: UN 1916

CAS NO.: 111-44-4

MOL. WT.: 143.0

STATEMENT OF HAZARDS: Serious health hazard. Combustible liquid. Forms peroxides in absence of inhibitors.

EMERGENCY RESPONSE PERSONAL PROTECTIVE EQUIPMENT: Wear special protective clothing and positive pressure self-contained breathing apparatus.

SPILL OR LEAK PROCEDURES: Eliminate all ignition sources. Stop or control the leak, if this can be done without undue risk. Use water spray to cool and disperse vapors and protect personnel. Absorb in noncombustible material for proper disposal.

FIRE FIGHTING PROCEDURES: Use dry chemical, foam, carbon dioxide, or water spray. Use water spray to keep fire-exposed containers cool.

HEALTH HAZARDS: Serious health hazard. May be harmful if absorbed through skin or inhaled. Irritating to skin, eyes, and respiratory system. Symptoms include severe tearing, coughing, nausea, and vomiting.

FIRE AND EXPLOSION HAZARDS: Combustible liquid. Combustion by-products may include hydrogen chloride.

FLASH POINT: 131°F (55°C)

AUTOIGNITION TEMPERATURE: 696°F (369°C)

FLAMMABLE LIMITS: LOWER: 2.7% UPPER: not determined

INSTABILITY AND REACTIVITY HAZARDS: Peroxide formation may occur in containers that have been opened and remain in storage. Peroxides can be detonated by friction, impact, or heating. Usually contains inhibitors to prevent polymerization. Reacts with strong acids and oxidizing materials.

STORAGE RECOMMENDATIONS: Store in a cool, dry, well-ventilated location. Store away from heat, oxidizing materials, strong acids, and sunlight.

USUAL SHIPPING CONTAINERS: Glass bottles. Metal cans, pails, drums. Tanks on trucks, rail cars, barges.

PHYSICAL PROPERTIES: Colorless liquid. Pungent odor.

MELTING POINT: −62°F (−52°C)

BOILING POINT: 352°F (179°C)

SPECIFIC GRAVITY: 1.22

SOLUBILITY IN WATER: not soluble

VAPOR PRESSURE: 0.7 mm Hg @ 20°C

ELECTRICAL EQUIPMENT: Class I, Group C

NAME: **DICHLORODIMETHYL ETHER, symmetrical**

SYNONYMS: BCME; bis-(chloromethyl) ether; bis-CME; dichloromethyl ether; sym-dichlorodimethylether,

FORMULA: $(CH_2Cl)_2O$

NFPA 30/OSHA CLASSIFICATION: IB

DOT CLASS: Class 6.1, Poisonous material

SHIPPING LABEL: POISON

ID NO.: UN 2249

CAS NO.: 542-88-1

MOL. WT.: 115.0

STATEMENT OF HAZARDS: Severe health hazard. Flammable liquid.

EMERGENCY RESPONSE PERSONAL PROTECTIVE EQUIPMENT: Wear special protective clothing and positive pressure self-contained breathing apparatus.

SPILL OR LEAK PROCEDURES: Eliminate all ignition sources. Keep water away from release. Stop or control the leak, if this can be done without undue risk. Absorb in noncombustible material for proper disposal. Control runoff and isolate discharged material for proper disposal.

FIRE FIGHTING PROCEDURES: Use dry chemical, foam, carbon dioxide, or water spray. Use water spray to keep fire-exposed containers cool. Water or foam may cause frothing.

HEALTH HAZARDS: Severe health hazard. May be fatal if inhaled. Symptoms of overexposure include irritation of the skin, eyes, and respiratory system; pulmonary edema.

FIRE AND EXPLOSION HAZARDS: Flammable liquid. Vapors are heavier than air and may travel to a source of ignition and flash back. Combustion may produce irritants and toxic gases.

FLASH POINT: <66°F (<19°C)

INSTABILITY AND REACTIVITY HAZARDS: Formation of shock-sensitive compounds may be caused by oxidizing materials, peroxides, or sunlight.

STORAGE RECOMMENDATIONS: Store in a cool, dry, well-ventilated location. Must be stored in a dry location. Outside or detached storage is preferred.

USUAL SHIPPING CONTAINERS: Glass bottle inside wooden box. Nickel cans, pails, drums.

PHYSICAL PROPERTIES: Colorless liquid. Suffocating odor.

MELTING POINT: −43°F (−42°C)

BOILING POINT: 219°F (104°C)

SPECIFIC GRAVITY: 1.32

SOLUBILITY IN WATER: not soluble (decomposes)

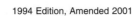

VAPOR PRESSURE: 30 mm Hg @ 22°C

ELECTRICAL EQUIPMENT: Class I, Group C

NAME: **DICHLOROETHYLENE**

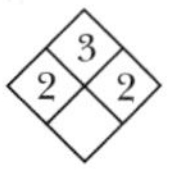

SYNONYMS: acetylene dichloride; 1,2-dichloroethene; 1,2-dichloroethylene;

ethene, 1,2-dichloro-

FORMULA: ClCH = CHCl

NFPA 30/OSHA CLASSIFICATION: IB

DOT CLASS: Class 3, Flammable and combustible liquid

SHIPPING LABEL: FLAMMABLE LIQUID

ID NO.: UN 1150

CAS NO.: 540-59-0

MOL. WT.: 97.0

STATEMENT OF HAZARDS: Flammable liquid. Moderate health hazard. Combustion by-products may include hydrogen chloride and phosgene.

EMERGENCY RESPONSE PERSONAL PROTECTIVE EQUIPMENT: Wear full protective clothing and positive pressure self-contained breathing apparatus.

SPILL OR LEAK PROCEDURES: Eliminate all ignition sources. Stop or control the leak, if this can be done without undue risk. Use appropriate foam to blanket release and suppress vapors. Absorb in noncombustible material for proper disposal.

FIRE FIGHTING PROCEDURES: Use dry chemical, foam, carbon dioxide, or water spray. Use flooding quantities of water to blanket the fire. Water may be ineffective. Use water spray to keep fire-exposed containers cool. Fight fire from protected location or maximum possible distance.

HEALTH HAZARDS: Moderate health hazard. May be harmful if absorbed through skin or inhaled. Inhalation may cause central nervous system depression, narcosis. Irritating to skin, eyes, and respiratory system.

FIRE AND EXPLOSION HAZARDS: Flammable liquid. Vapors are heavier than air and may travel to a source of ignition and flash back. Combustion by-products may include hydrogen chloride, phosgene. Closed containers may rupture violently when heated.

FLASH POINT: 36 to 39°F (18 to 21°C)

AUTOIGNITION TEMPERATURE: 860°F (460°C)

FLAMMABLE LIMITS: LOWER: 9.7% UPPER: 12.8%

INSTABILITY AND REACTIVITY HAZARDS: Hazardous polymerization may occur. Polymerization may be caused by elevated temperature, oxidizing materials, peroxides, or sunlight. Usually contains inhibitors to prevent polymerization. Uninhibited monomer vapor may form polymer in vents and other confined spaces. May form organic peroxides following prolonged contact with air. Reacts with alkalies and alkali metals, such as aluminum.

STORAGE RECOMMENDATIONS: Store in a cool, dry, well-ventilated location. Separate from air, light, heat, strong oxidizing materials.

USUAL SHIPPING CONTAINERS: Glass bottles; metal cans, pails, drums; tanks on trucks, rail cars, barges.

PHYSICAL PROPERTIES: Colorless liquid with ethereal odor.

MELTING POINT: −113°F (−80°C)

BOILING POINT: 140°F (60°C)

SPECIFIC GRAVITY: 1.28

SOLUBILITY IN WATER: not soluble

VAPOR PRESSURE: 180-265 mm Hg @ 20°C

ELECTRICAL EQUIPMENT: Class I, Group D

NAME: **DICHLOROMETHANE**

SYNONYMS: methylene chloride; methylene dichloride

FORMULA: $ClCH_2Cl$

NFPA 30/OSHA CLASSIFICATION:

DOT CLASS: Class 6.1, Poisonous material

SHIPPING LABEL: KEEP AWAY FROM FOOD

ID NO.: UN 1593

CAS NO.: 75-09-2

MOL. WT.: 84.9

STATEMENT OF HAZARDS: Moderate health hazard. Combustion by-products may include hydrogen chloride and phosgene.

EMERGENCY RESPONSE PERSONAL PROTECTIVE EQUIPMENT: Wear full protective clothing and positive pressure self-contained breathing apparatus.

SPILL OR LEAK PROCEDURES: Stop or control the leak, if this can be done without undue risk. Control runoff and isolate discharged material for proper disposal.

FIRE FIGHTING PROCEDURES: Use dry chemical, carbon dioxide, foam, or water spray. Use water spray to keep fire-exposed containers cool.

HEALTH HAZARDS: Moderate health hazard. May be harmful if inhaled. Irritating to skin, eyes, and respiratory system. Narcotic in high concentrations. Combustion by-products may include hydrogen chloride and phosgene.

FIRE AND EXPLOSION HAZARDS: No flash point in conventional closed tester, but forms flammable vapor-air mixtures in larger volumes and may be an explosion hazard in a confined space. Combustion may produce irritants and toxic gases. Combustion by-products include hydrogen chloride and phosgene.

AUTOIGNITION TEMPERATURE: 1033°F (556°C)

FLAMMABLE LIMITS: LOWER: 13% UPPER: 23%

INSTABILITY AND REACTIVITY HAZARDS: Reacts violently with active metals.

STORAGE RECOMMENDATIONS: Store in a cool, dry, well-ventilated location. Isolate from active metals.

USUAL SHIPPING CONTAINERS: Glass bottles, steel drums; tanks on trucks, rail cars, barges.

PHYSICAL PROPERTIES: Colorless volatile liquid with sweet odor like chloroform.

MELTING POINT: −142°F (−97°C)

BOILING POINT: 104°F (40°C)

SPECIFIC GRAVITY: 1.33

SOLUBILITY IN WATER: not soluble

VAPOR DENSITY: 2.93

VAPOR PRESSURE: 350 mm Hg @ 20°C

ELECTRICAL EQUIPMENT: Class I, Group D

NAME: **DICHLOROPROPENE**

SYNONYMS: alpha-chloroallyl chloride; dichloropropylene; 1,3-dichloropropene; 1,3-dichloropropylene

FORMULA: $ClCH_2CH=CHCl$

NFPA 30/OSHA CLASSIFICATION: IC

DOT CLASS: Class 3, Flammable and combustible liquid

SHIPPING LABEL: FLAMMABLE LIQUID

ID NO.: UN 2047

CAS NO.: 542-75-6

MOL. WT.: 111.0

STATEMENT OF HAZARDS: Flammable liquid. Moderate health hazard. Combustion by-products may include hydrogen chloride.

EMERGENCY RESPONSE PERSONAL PROTECTIVE EQUIPMENT: Wear full protective clothing and positive pressure self-contained breathing apparatus.

SPILL OR LEAK PROCEDURES: Eliminate all ignition sources. Approach release from upwind. Stop or control the leak, if this can be done without undue risk. Control runoff and isolate discharged material for proper disposal.

FIRE FIGHTING PROCEDURES: Approach fire from upwind to avoid hazardous vapors and toxic decomposition products. Stop flow of liquid before extinguishing fire. Use water spray, dry chemical, foam, or carbon dioxide. Use water spray to keep fire-exposed containers cool.

HEALTH HAZARDS: Moderate health hazard. May be harmful if absorbed through skin or inhaled. Irritating to skin, eyes, and respiratory system. Combustion by-products may include hydrogen chloride.

FIRE AND EXPLOSION HAZARDS: Flammable liquid. Vapors are heavier than air and may travel to a source of ignition and flash back. Combustion may produce irritants and toxic gases. Combustion by-products include hydrogen chloride.

FLASH POINT: 95°F (35°C)

FLAMMABLE LIMITS: LOWER: 5.3% UPPER: 14.5%

INSTABILITY AND REACTIVITY HAZARDS: Oxidizable. Reacts with active metals.

STORAGE RECOMMENDATIONS: Outside or detached storage is preferred. Inside storage should be in a standard flammable liquids storage warehouse, room, or cabinet. Separate from oxidizing materials and active metals.

USUAL SHIPPING CONTAINERS: Glass bottles, drums; tanks on trucks, rail cars, barges.

PHYSICAL PROPERTIES: Colorless liquid with odor like chloroform.

BOILING POINT: 219°F (103°C) for lower boiling isomer

SPECIFIC GRAVITY: 1.22

SOLUBILITY IN WATER: not soluble

VAPOR PRESSURE: 40-52 mm Hg @ 20°C

ELECTRICAL EQUIPMENT: Class I, Group D

NAME: **DICHLOROSILANE**

SYNONYMS: chlorosilanes; DCS

FORMULA: H_2SiCl_2

NFPA 30/OSHA CLASSIFICATION: IA

DOT CLASS: Class 2.3, Poisonous gas

SHIPPING LABEL: POISON GAS and FLAMMABLE GAS

ID NO.: UN 2189

CAS NO.: 4109-96-0

MOL. WT.: 101.0

STATEMENT OF HAZARDS: Pyrophoric. Flammable gas. Severe health hazard. Corrosive. May accumulate static electricity. Low ignition energy. Water reactive.

EMERGENCY RESPONSE PERSONAL PROTECTIVE EQUIPMENT: Wear special protective clothing and positive pressure self-contained breathing apparatus.

SPILL OR LEAK PROCEDURES: Stop or control the leak, if this can be done without undue risk. Use water spray to cool and disperse vapors and protect personnel. Approach release from upwind. Do not use absorbent spill control materials because self-heating and ignition may result.

FIRE FIGHTING PROCEDURES: Do not use halocarbons. Use water spray for small spills. Water, foam, and CO_2 may be ineffective. Use water spray to keep fire-exposed containers cool. Approach fire from upwind to avoid hazardous vapors and toxic decomposition products. Material may reignite.

HEALTH HAZARDS: Severe health hazard. May be fatal if absorbed through skin or inhaled. Corrosive. Causes severe eye and skin burns. Irritating to skin, eyes, and respiratory system.

FIRE AND EXPLOSION HAZARDS: Pyrophoric. Flammable gas. Combustion by-products include hydrogen chloride and other irritants and toxic gases.

FLASH POINT: −62°F (−52°C)

AUTOIGNITION TEMPERATURE: 111°F (44°C)

FLAMMABLE LIMITS: LOWER: 4.7% UPPER: 96%

INSTABILITY AND REACTIVITY HAZARDS: Reacts with water to produce corrosive hydrogen chloride. Reacts violently with a broad range of materials. May explode with halocarbons when ignited. Explodes on contact with strong oxidizers.

STORAGE RECOMMENDATIONS: Store in a cool, dry, well-ventilated location. Separate from acids, alkalies, oxidizing materials, and water. Outside or detached storage is preferred.

USUAL SHIPPING CONTAINERS: Carbon steel cylinders.

PHYSICAL PROPERTIES: Colorless gas. Acrid odor. Fumes in moist air. Pressurized liquefied gas normally stored under its own vapor pressure.

MELTING POINT: −188°F (−122°C)

BOILING POINT: 47°F (8°C)

SPECIFIC GRAVITY: 1.22

SOLUBILITY IN WATER: not soluble (decomposes)

VAPOR DENSITY: 3.48

VAPOR PRESSURE: 1230 mm Hg @ 20°C

NAME: **DICYCLOHEXYLAMINE**

SYNONYMS: N-cyclohexylcyclohexanamine; dodeca-hydrodiphenylamine; perhydrodiphenylamine

FORMULA: $(C_6H_{11})_2NH$

NFPA 30/OSHA CLASSIFICATION: IIIB

DOT CLASS: Class 8, Corrosive material

SHIPPING LABEL: CORROSIVE

ID NO.: UN 2565

CAS NO.: 101-83-7

MOL. WT.: 181.3

STATEMENT OF HAZARDS: Corrosive and combustible liquid. Serious health hazard. Decomposes at 255°C.

EMERGENCY RESPONSE PERSONAL PROTECTIVE EQUIPMENT: Wear special protective clothing and positive pressure self-contained breathing apparatus.

SPILL OR LEAK PROCEDURES: Use water spray to cool and disperse vapors and protect personnel. Control runoff and isolate discharged material for proper disposal.

FIRE FIGHTING PROCEDURES: Use dry chemical, foam, carbon dioxide, or water spray. Use water spray to keep fire-exposed containers cool.

HEALTH HAZARDS: Corrosive. Causes severe eye and skin burns. Sensitizer. Serious health hazard. May be harmful if inhaled. Irritating to skin, eyes, and respiratory system. Symptoms of overexposure include nausea, vomiting, weakness, and irritation of gastrointestinal tract.

FIRE AND EXPLOSION HAZARDS: Combustible liquid. Decomposes at 250°C.

FLASH POINT: >210°F (>99°C)

INSTABILITY AND REACTIVITY HAZARDS: Reacts with oxidizers and air. Decomposes at 250°C.

STORAGE RECOMMENDATIONS: Separate from oxidizing materials. Store in a cool, dry, well-ventilated location.

PHYSICAL PROPERTIES: Clear yellow liquid.

MELTING POINT: 68°F (20°C)

BOILING POINT: 493°F (256°C)

SPECIFIC GRAVITY: 0.91

SOLUBILITY IN WATER: not soluble

NAME: **DIETHYLALUMINUM CHLORIDE**

SYNONYMS: chlorodiethylaluminum

FORMULA: $(C_2H_5)_2AlCl$

NFPA 30/OSHA CLASSIFICATION:

DOT CLASS: N/A

ID NO.: N/A

CAS NO.: 96-10-6

MOL. WT.: 110.6

STATEMENT OF HAZARDS: Pyrophoric. Flammable liquid. Corrosive. Water reactive.

EMERGENCY RESPONSE PERSONAL PROTECTIVE EQUIPMENT: Wear special protective clothing and positive pressure self-contained breathing apparatus.

SPILL OR LEAK PROCEDURES: Approach release from upwind. Keep water away from release. Do not use foam to blanket release or suppress vapors. Stop or control the leak, if this can be done without undue risk. Control runoff and isolate discharged material for proper disposal.

FIRE FIGHTING PROCEDURES: Fight fire from protected location or maximum possible distance. DO NOT use water. Violent reaction may result. Use graphite powder, soda ash, or powdered sodium chloride to extinguish fire. On solvent based materials use dry chemical, foam, or carbon dioxide. Use water spray cautiously to keep fire-exposed containers cool.

HEALTH HAZARDS: Corrosive. Causes severe eye and skin burns. Irritating to skin, eyes, and respiratory system. May be harmful if absorbed through skin or inhaled. "Metal fume fever" may result from inhalation of fumes.

FIRE AND EXPLOSION HAZARDS: Flammable liquid. Pyrophoric; may ignite spontaneously on exposure to air. Water reactive. Combustion may produce irritants and toxic gases. Closed containers may rupture violently when heated. Material is flammable in air at all temperatures.

INSTABILITY AND REACTIVITY HAZARDS: Reacts violently with air and water. Reacts with oxidizing materials, water, acids, and alcohols.

STORAGE RECOMMENDATIONS: Separate from oxidizing materials, acids, and alcohols. Store in a cool, dry, well-ventilated location. Must be stored in a dry location. Outside or detached storage is preferred. Inside storage should be in a standard flammable liquids storage warehouse, room, or cabinet.

USUAL SHIPPING CONTAINERS: Bottles, cylinders; tank trucks and tank cars containing a blanket of nitrogen gas.

PHYSICAL PROPERTIES: Clear, colorless liquid. Aluminum alkyls are generally supplied as 20% solutions in selected solvents so as to be less reactive. Properties may depend on solvent. Solvent may evaporate during spill or exposure.

BOILING POINT: 417°F (214°C)

SPECIFIC GRAVITY: 0.97

SOLUBILITY IN WATER: reacts violently

VAPOR PRESSURE: 1.93 mm Hg @ 60°C

NAME: **DIETHYLAMINE**

FORMULA: $(C_2H_5)_2NH$

NFPA 30/OSHA CLASSIFICATION: IB

DOT CLASS: Class 3, Flammable and combustible liquid

SHIPPING LABEL: FLAMMABLE LIQUID

ID NO.: UN 1154

CAS NO.: 109-89-7

MOL. WT.: 73.1

STATEMENT OF HAZARDS: Corrosive and flammable liquid.

EMERGENCY RESPONSE PERSONAL PROTECTIVE EQUIPMENT: Wear special protective clothing and positive pressure self-contained breathing apparatus.

SPILL OR LEAK PROCEDURES: Eliminate all ignition sources. Approach release from upwind. Use water spray to cool and disperse vapors, protect personnel, and dilute spills to form nonflammable mixtures. Absorb in noncombustible material for proper disposal. Control runoff and isolate discharged material for proper disposal.

FIRE FIGHTING PROCEDURES: Use water spray to keep fire-exposed containers cool. Use water spray, dry chemical, or "alcohol resistant" foam. Aqueous solutions will burn unless diluted thoroughly with spray.

HEALTH HAZARDS: Corrosive. Causes severe eye and skin burns. Irritating to skin, eyes, and respiratory system. May cause conjunctivitis and corneal damage. May be harmful if inhaled. Inhalation may cause coughing, nausea, and pulmonary edema.

FIRE AND EXPLOSION HAZARDS: Flammable liquid. Vapors are heavier than air and may travel to a source of ignition and flash back. Aqueous solutions are flammable unless diluted extensively.

FLASH POINT: −18°F (−28°C)

AUTOIGNITION TEMPERATURE: 594°F (312°C)

FLAMMABLE LIMITS: LOWER: 1.8% UPPER: 10.1%

INSTABILITY AND REACTIVITY HAZARDS: May react with acids, oxidizing materials, chlorine, hypochlorite, halogenated compounds, reactive organic compounds, and some metals. Products of decomposition include carbon monoxide, carbon dioxide, hydrocarbons, and toxic oxides of nitrogen as well as toxic amine vapors.

STORAGE RECOMMENDATIONS: Separate from oxidizing materials, acids, and sources of halogens. Store in cool, dry, well-ventilated, noncombustible location.

USUAL SHIPPING CONTAINERS: Glass bottles, cans, drums, and tank cars.

PHYSICAL PROPERTIES: Colorless liquid with strong ammonia-like odor. Miscible with water. May be in water solutions as shipped or used.

MELTING POINT: −58°F (−50°C)

BOILING POINT: 132°F (56°C)

SPECIFIC GRAVITY: 0.71

SOLUBILITY IN WATER: soluble

VAPOR PRESSURE: 194 mm Hg @ 20°C

ELECTRICAL EQUIPMENT: Class I, Group C

NAME: **DIETHYLENETRIAMINE**

SYNONYMS: bis(2-aminoethyl)amine; 2,2-diaminodiethylamine; DETA

FORMULA: $NH_2CH_2CH_2NHCH_2CH_2NH_2$

NFPA 30/OSHA CLASSIFICATION: IIIB

DOT CLASS: Class 8, Corrosive material

SHIPPING LABEL: CORROSIVE

ID NO.: UN 2079

CAS NO.: 111-40-0

MOL. WT.: 103.2

STATEMENT OF HAZARDS: Corrosive and combustible liquid.

EMERGENCY RESPONSE PERSONAL PROTECTIVE EQUIPMENT: Wear special protective clothing and positive pressure self-contained breathing apparatus.

SPILL OR LEAK PROCEDURES: Stop or control the leak, if this can be done without undue risk. Use water spray to cool and disperse vapors, protect personnel, and dilute spills to form nonflammable mixtures. Approach release from upwind. Absorb in noncombustible material for proper disposal.

FIRE FIGHTING PROCEDURES: Use water spray, dry chemical, "alcohol resistant" foam, or carbon dioxide. Use water spray to keep fire-exposed containers cool. Solid streams may be ineffective and spread material, but becomes soluble when fine water spray is applied.

HEALTH HAZARDS: Corrosive. Causes severe eye and skin burns. May cause severe irritation of eyes with corneal injury and permanent eye damage. Irritating to skin, eyes, and respiratory system.

FIRE AND EXPLOSION HAZARDS: Combustible liquid.

FLASH POINT: 215°F (101°C)

AUTOIGNITION TEMPERATURE: 750°F (395°C)

FLAMMABLE LIMITS: LOWER: 1.9% @ 302°F (150°C) UPPER: 11.6% @ 302°F (150°C)

INSTABILITY AND REACTIVITY HAZARDS: Avoid contact with acids, oxidizing materials, chlorine, hypochlorite, halogenated compounds, and reactive organic compounds. Products of decomposition include carbon monoxide, carbon dioxide, hydrocarbons, and oxides of nitrogen as well as amine vapors.

STORAGE RECOMMENDATIONS: Outside or detached storage is preferred. Avoid oxidizing materials, acids, and sources of halogens. Store in a cool, dry, well-ventilated location.

USUAL SHIPPING CONTAINERS: Glass bottles, cans, drums, and tank cars.

PHYSICAL PROPERTIES: Colorless to yellow hygroscopic liquid with odor of ammonia.

MELTING POINT: −31°F (−39°C)

BOILING POINT: 390°F (199°C)

SPECIFIC GRAVITY: 0.95

SOLUBILITY IN WATER: soluble

VAPOR DENSITY: 3.56

VAPOR PRESSURE: 0.22 mm Hg @ 20°C

NAME: **DIETHYLETHANOLAMINE**

DOT SHIPPING NAME: **DIETHYLAMINOETHANOL**

SYNONYMS: DEAE; diethylaminoethanol; diethylmonoethanolamine; ethanol, 2-(diethylamino)-; 2-hydroxyethyl diethylamine

FORMULA: $HOCH_2CH_2N(C_2H_5)_2$

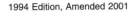

NFPA 30/OSHA CLASSIFICATION: IIIA

DOT CLASS: Class 3, Flammable and combustible liquid

SHIPPING LABEL: FLAMMABLE LIQUID

ID NO.: UN 2686

CAS NO.: 100-37-8

MOL. WT.: 117.2

STATEMENT OF HAZARDS: Corrosive and combustible liquid. Serious health hazard.

EMERGENCY RESPONSE PERSONAL PROTECTIVE EQUIPMENT: Wear special protective clothing and positive pressure self-contained breathing apparatus.

SPILL OR LEAK PROCEDURES: Use water spray to cool and disperse vapors and protect personnel. Control runoff and isolate discharged material for proper disposal.

FIRE FIGHTING PROCEDURES: Use dry chemical, "alcohol resistant" foam, carbon dioxide, or water spray. Water or foam may cause frothing. Use water spray to keep fire-exposed containers cool. Approach fire from upwind to avoid hazardous vapors and toxic decomposition products.

HEALTH HAZARDS: Corrosive. Causes severe eye and skin burns. Serious health hazard. May be harmful if absorbed through skin or inhaled. Irritating to skin, eyes, and respiratory system. Symptoms of overexposure include dizziness, nausea, and pulmonary edema.

FIRE AND EXPLOSION HAZARDS: Combustible liquid. Products of combustion may be toxic.

FLASH POINT: 140°F (60°C) (oc)

AUTOIGNITION TEMPERATURE: 608°F (320°C)

FLAMMABLE LIMITS: LOWER: 6.7% UPPER: 11.7%

INSTABILITY AND REACTIVITY HAZARDS: Avoid contact with strong acids and oxidizing materials. Avoid excessive heat.

STORAGE RECOMMENDATIONS: Separate from strong acids and oxidizing materials. Store in a cool, dry, well-ventilated location.

PHYSICAL PROPERTIES: Colorless, hygroscopic liquid with nauseating ammonia-like odor.

MELTING POINT: −94°F (−70°C)

BOILING POINT: 324°F (163°C)

SPECIFIC GRAVITY: 0.89

SOLUBILITY IN WATER: soluble

VAPOR PRESSURE: 21 mm Hg @ 20°C

ELECTRICAL EQUIPMENT: Class I, Group C

NAME: **DIETHYL ETHER**

SYNONYMS: anesthetic ether; diethyl oxide; ether; ethyl ether; ethyl oxide

FORMULA: $C_2H_5OC_2H_5$

NFPA 30/OSHA CLASSIFICATION: IA

DOT CLASS: Class 3, Flammable and combustible liquid

SHIPPING LABEL: FLAMMABLE LIQUID

ID NO.: UN 1155

CAS NO.: 60-29-7

MOL. WT.: 74.1

STATEMENT OF HAZARDS: Flammable liquid. Containers that have been opened may contain dangerous explosive peroxides. May accumulate static electricity. Low ignition energy. Slight health hazard.

EMERGENCY RESPONSE PERSONAL PROTECTIVE EQUIPMENT: Wear full protective clothing and positive pressure self-contained breathing apparatus.

SPILL OR LEAK PROCEDURES: Eliminate all ignition sources. Stop or control the leak, if this can be done without undue risk. Use water spray to cool and disperse vapors protect personnel and dilute spills to form nonflammable mixtures. Control runoff and isolate discharged material for proper disposal.

FIRE FIGHTING PROCEDURES: Water may be ineffective. Use water spray to keep fire-exposed containers cool. Use water spray, dry chemical, foam, or carbon dioxide.

HEALTH HAZARDS: Slight health hazard. Inhalation may cause confusion, dizziness, lack of coordination, and unconsciousnesss.

FIRE AND EXPLOSION HAZARDS: Flammable liquid. Vapors are heavier than air and may travel to a source of ignition and flash back. Liquid floats on water and may travel to a source of ignition and spread fire.

FLASH POINT: −49°F (−45°C)

AUTOIGNITION TEMPERATURE: 320°F (160°C)

FLAMMABLE LIMITS: LOWER: 1.9% UPPER: 36%

INSTABILITY AND REACTIVITY HAZARDS: Peroxide formation may occur in ether containers that have been opened and remain in storage for more than six months. Peroxides can be detonated by friction, impact, or heating.

STORAGE RECOMMENDATIONS: Separate from oxidizing materials. Store in cool, dry, well-ventilated area. Avoid sunlight.

USUAL SHIPPING CONTAINERS: Bottles, cans, or drums.

PHYSICAL PROPERTIES: Clear volatile liquid with sweet odor. Floats on water.

MELTING POINT: −177°F (−116°C)

BOILING POINT: 94°F (35°C)

SPECIFIC GRAVITY: 0.71

SOLUBILITY IN WATER: not soluble

VAPOR DENSITY: 2.56

VAPOR PRESSURE: 442 mm Hg @ 20°C

ELECTRICAL EQUIPMENT: Class I, Group C

NAME: **DIETHYL SULFATE**

SYNONYMS: DS; sulfuric acid diethyl ester

FORMULA: $(C_2H_5)_2SO_4$

NFPA 30/OSHA CLASSIFICATION: IIIB

DOT CLASS: Class 6.1, Poisonous material

SHIPPING LABEL: POISON

ID NO.: UN 1594

CAS NO.: 64-67-5

MOL. WT.: 154.2

STATEMENT OF HAZARDS: Corrosive and combustible liquid.

EMERGENCY RESPONSE PERSONAL PROTECTIVE EQUIPMENT: Wear special protective clothing and positive pressure self-contained breathing apparatus.

SPILL OR LEAK PROCEDURES: Stop or control the leak, if this can be done without undue risk. Use water spray to cool and disperse vapors and protect personnel. Approach release from upwind. Absorb in noncombustible material for proper disposal. Prompt cleanup and removal are necessary.

FIRE FIGHTING PROCEDURES: Use dry chemical, foam, carbon dioxide, or water spray. Use water spray to keep fire-exposed containers cool. Approach fire from upwind to avoid hazardous vapors and toxic decomposition products.

HEALTH HAZARDS: Corrosive. Causes severe eye and skin burns. May be harmful if absorbed through skin or inhaled. Symptoms of overexposure include coughing, wheezing, headache, nausea, and vomiting.

FIRE AND EXPLOSION HAZARDS: Combustible liquid. Combustion may produce irritants and toxic gases. Decomposes at elevated temperature forming ethyl ether, which is more flammable than the material itself.

FLASH POINT: 220°F (104°C)

AUTOIGNITION TEMPERATURE: 817°F (436°C)

FLAMMABLE LIMITS: LOWER: 4.1% UPPER: not determined

INSTABILITY AND REACTIVITY HAZARDS: Reacts with a broad range of materials. Slowly decomposes with water.

STORAGE RECOMMENDATIONS: Store in a cool, dry, well-ventilated location. Separate from bases, oxidizing materials, water, and air.

USUAL SHIPPING CONTAINERS: Metal cans, pails, drums. Tanks on trucks, rail cars, barges.

PHYSICAL PROPERTIES: Colorless (but darkens with age), oily liquid. Peppermint odor.

MELTING POINT: −32°F (−25°C)

BOILING POINT: 409°F (210°C) (decomposes)

SPECIFIC GRAVITY: 1.18

SOLUBILITY IN WATER: decomposes

VAPOR PRESSURE: 1 mm Hg @ 47°C

NAME: **DIETHYL TELLURIDE**

SYNONYMS: tellurium ethide; tellurium ethyl

FORMULA: $Te(C_2H_5)_2$

NFPA 30/OSHA CLASSIFICATION:

DOT CLASS: N/A

ID NO.: N/A

CAS NO.: 627-54-3

MOL. WT.: 185.7

STATEMENT OF HAZARDS: Pyrophoric. Flammable liquid. Water reactive. Contact with water or moist air may cause fire by release of flammable vapors and heat. Thermally unstable. Slight health hazard.

EMERGENCY RESPONSE PERSONAL PROTECTIVE EQUIPMENT: Wear full protective clothing and positive pressure self-contained breathing apparatus.

SPILL OR LEAK PROCEDURES: Keep water away from release. Stop or control the leak, if this can be done without undue risk. Approach release from upwind.

FIRE FIGHTING PROCEDURES: Use dry chemical and sand to extinguish fire. DO NOT use water. Where access to the area is strictly controlled, it may be best to allow the release to burn spontaneously. Use extreme caution in applying cooling streams of water to fire-exposed containers from a safe distance or from a protected location. Fight fire from protected location or maximum possible distance.

HEALTH HAZARDS: Slight health hazard. May cause irritation of skin, eyes, and respiratory system.

FIRE AND EXPLOSION HAZARDS: Ignites on contact with air, giving blue flame. Explodes with heating. Releases flammable gases on contact with water. Closed containers may rupture violently when heated.

INSTABILITY AND REACTIVITY HAZARDS: Reacts violently with water, methanol, oxidizing materials, halogens. Decomposes on contact with air.

STORAGE RECOMMENDATIONS: Store in a cool, dry, well-ventilated location. Isolate from air, water, oxidizing materials, organic peroxides. Separate from flammable materials. Keep material under carbon dioxide, nitrogen, or other inert gas.

USUAL SHIPPING CONTAINERS: Steel, nickel cylinders.

PHYSICAL PROPERTIES: Red-yellow odorous mobile liquid.

BOILING POINT: 280°F (138°C)

SOLUBILITY IN WATER: decomposes

NAME: **DIETHYLZINC**

SYNONYMS: zinc diethyl; zinc ethide

FORMULA: $Zn(C_2H_5)_2$

NFPA 30/OSHA CLASSIFICATION:

DOT CLASS: Class 4.2, Spontaneously combustible material

SHIPPING LABEL: SPONTANEOUSLY COMBUSTIBLE

ID NO.: UN 1366

CAS NO.: 557-20-0

MOL. WT.: 123.5

STATEMENT OF HAZARDS: Pyrophoric. Flammable liquid. Corrosive. Water reactive. Contact with water or moist air may cause fire by release of flammable vapors and heat. Thermally unstable. Decomposes explosively at 248°F (120°C).

EMERGENCY RESPONSE PERSONAL PROTECTIVE EQUIPMENT: Wear special protective clothing and positive pressure self-contained breathing apparatus.

SPILL OR LEAK PROCEDURES: Isolate the area until the release is under full control. Keep water away from release. Blanket release with dry sand, clay, or ground limestone.

FIRE FIGHTING PROCEDURES: Use dry chemical, sand, and graphite to extinguish fire. DO NOT use water. Where access to the area is strictly controlled, it may be best to allow the release to burn spontaneously. Fight fire from protected location or maximum possible distance.

HEALTH HAZARDS: Corrosive. Causes severe eye and skin burns. May be harmful if inhaled. Irritating to skin, eyes, and respiratory system. May cause pulmonary edema.

FIRE AND EXPLOSION HAZARDS: Pyrophoric. Ignites on contact with air, giving blue flame. Explodes when heated above 248°F (120°C). Releases flammable gases on contact with water. Closed containers may rupture violently when heated.

INSTABILITY AND REACTIVITY HAZARDS: Reacts violently with water, methanol, oxidizing materials, halogens. Decomposes on contact with air.

STORAGE RECOMMENDATIONS: Store in a cool, dry, well-ventilated location. Separate from air, water, oxidizing materials, organic peroxides, flammable materials. Keep material under carbon dioxide, nitrogen, or other inert gas.

USUAL SHIPPING CONTAINERS: Steel, nickel cylinders.

PHYSICAL PROPERTIES: Colorless, mobile liquid. Odor of garlic in air.

MELTING POINT: −18°F (−28°C)

BOILING POINT: 243°F (117°C)

SPECIFIC GRAVITY: 1.21

SOLUBILITY IN WATER: decomposes

NAME: **DIISOPROPYLAMINE**

SYNONYMS: DIPA; N-(1-methylethyl)-2-propanamine

FORMULA: $[(CH_3)_2CH]_2NH$

NFPA 30/OSHA CLASSIFICATION: IB

DOT CLASS: Class 3, Flammable and combustible liquid

SHIPPING LABEL: FLAMMABLE LIQUID

ID NO.: UN 1158

CAS NO.: 108-18-9

MOL. WT.: 101.2

STATEMENT OF HAZARDS: Corrosive and flammable liquid.

EMERGENCY RESPONSE PERSONAL PROTECTIVE EQUIPMENT: Wear special protective clothing and positive pressure self-contained breathing apparatus.

SPILL OR LEAK PROCEDURES: Eliminate all ignition sources. Stop or control the leak, if this can be done without undue risk. Use water spray to cool and disperse vapors, protect personnel, and dilute spills to form nonflammable mixtures. Absorb in noncombustible material for proper disposal.

FIRE FIGHTING PROCEDURES: Use dry chemical, "alcohol resistant" foam, carbon dioxide, or water spray. Water may be ineffective. Use water spray to keep fire-exposed containers cool. Approach fire from upwind to avoid hazardous vapors and toxic decomposition products.

HEALTH HAZARDS: Corrosive. Causes severe eye and skin burns. May be harmful if absorbed through skin or inhaled. Irritating to skin, eyes, and respiratory system. Other symptoms include nausea, vomiting, and visual disturbances.

FIRE AND EXPLOSION HAZARDS: Flammable liquid. Vapors are heavier than air and may travel to a source of ignition and flash back. Combustion by-products include oxides of nitrogen.

FLASH POINT: 21°F (−6°C) (oc)

AUTOIGNITION TEMPERATURE: 600°F (316°C)

FLAMMABLE LIMITS: LOWER: 0.8% UPPER: 7.1%

INSTABILITY AND REACTIVITY HAZARDS: Reacts with strong alkalies.

STORAGE RECOMMENDATIONS: Store in a cool, dry, well-ventilated location. Separate from acids and oxidizing materials.

USUAL SHIPPING CONTAINERS: Metal cans, pails, drums; tanks on trucks, rail cars, barges.

PHYSICAL PROPERTIES: Colorless to pale yellow liquid. Characteristic amine odor (fishy-ammonia).

MELTING POINT: −141°F (−96°C)

BOILING POINT: 183°F (84°C)

SPECIFIC GRAVITY: 0.72

SOLUBILITY IN WATER: soluble

VAPOR PRESSURE: 60 mm Hg @ 20°C

ELECTRICAL EQUIPMENT: Class I, Group C

NAME: **DIISOPROPYL ETHER**

SYNONYMS: diisopropyl oxide; isopropyl ether

FORMULA: $(CH_3)_2CHOCH(CH_3)_2$

NFPA 30/OSHA CLASSIFICATION: IB

DOT CLASS: Class 3, Flammable and combustible liquid

SHIPPING LABEL: FLAMMABLE LIQUID

ID NO.: UN 1159

CAS NO.: 108-20-3

MOL. WT.: 102.2

STATEMENT OF HAZARDS: Flammable liquid. May accumulate static electricity. Previously opened containers are most likely to contain explosive peroxides. Slight health hazard.

EMERGENCY RESPONSE PERSONAL PROTECTIVE EQUIPMENT: Wear full protective clothing and positive pressure self-contained breathing apparatus.

SPILL OR LEAK PROCEDURES: Stop or control the leak, if this can be done without undue risk. Eliminate all ignition sources. Use water spray to cool and disperse vapors and protect personnel. Approach release from upwind.

FIRE FIGHTING PROCEDURES: Water may be ineffective. Use water spray to keep fire-exposed containers cool. Use water spray, dry chemical, foam, or carbon dioxide.

HEALTH HAZARDS: Slight health hazard. Inhalation may cause anesthesia, nausea, headache, dizziness, irritation of skin, eyes, and respiratory system.

FIRE AND EXPLOSION HAZARDS: Flammable liquid. Vapors are heavier than air and may travel to a source of ignition and flash back. Liquid floats on water and may travel to a source of ignition and spread fire. Ether tends to form unstable, explosive peroxides on standing.

FLASH POINT: −18°F (−28°C)

AUTOIGNITION TEMPERATURE: 830°F (443°C)

FLAMMABLE LIMITS: LOWER: 1.4% UPPER: 7.9%

INSTABILITY AND REACTIVITY HAZARDS: Peroxide formation is likely to occur when ether containers have been opened and remain in storage for more than six months. Isopropyl ether is especially susceptible to the formation of peroxides, which are shock sensitive. Peroxides can be detonated by friction, impact, or heating.

STORAGE RECOMMENDATIONS: Inside storage should be in a standard flammable liquids storage warehouse, room, or cabinet. Outside or detached storage is preferred. Avoid sunlight.

USUAL SHIPPING CONTAINERS: Bottles, cans, or drums.

PHYSICAL PROPERTIES: Clear liquid with sweet anesthetic odor. Not soluble in water. Floats on water.

MELTING POINT: −124°F (−87°C)

BOILING POINT: 156°F (69°C)

SPECIFIC GRAVITY: 0.72

SOLUBILITY IN WATER: not soluble

VAPOR PRESSURE: 119 mm Hg @ 20°C

ELECTRICAL EQUIPMENT: Class I, Group C

NAME: **DIKETENE, inhibited**

SYNONYMS: acetyl ketene; 3-butene-beta-lactone; 4-methylene-2-oxetanone

–O–

FORMULA: $CH_2{=}CCH_2C{=}O$

NFPA 30/OSHA CLASSIFICATION: IC

DOT CLASS: Class 3, Flammable and combustible liquid

SHIPPING LABEL: FLAMMABLE LIQUID and POISON

ID NO.: UN 2521

CAS NO.: 674-82-8

MOL. WT.: 84.1

STATEMENT OF HAZARDS: Severe health hazard. Corrosive and flammable liquid. Thermally unstable.

EMERGENCY RESPONSE PERSONAL PROTECTIVE EQUIPMENT: Wear special protective clothing and positive pressure self-contained breathing apparatus.

SPILL OR LEAK PROCEDURES: Eliminate all ignition sources. Approach release from upwind. Use water spray to cool and disperse vapors, protect personnel, and dilute spills to form nonflammable mixtures. Stop or control the leak, if this can be done without undue risk. Control runoff and isolate discharged material for proper disposal. Releases may require isolation or evacuation.

FIRE FIGHTING PROCEDURES: Approach fire from upwind to avoid hazardous vapors and toxic decomposition products. Fight fire from protected location or maximum possible distance. Use water spray to keep fire-exposed containers cool. Use flooding quantities of water as fog or spray. Carbon dioxide may be used. Extinguish fire using agent suitable for surrounding fire.

HEALTH HAZARDS: Severe health hazard. May be fatal if inhaled. Corrosive. Causes severe eye and skin burns. Vapor is irritating to eye, skin, and respiratory system.

FIRE AND EXPLOSION HAZARDS: Flammable liquid. Vapors are heavier than air and may travel to a source of ignition and flash back. Closed containers may rupture violently when heated. Thermally unstable.

FLASH POINT: 93°F (34°C)

AUTOIGNITION TEMPERATURE: 590°F (310°C)

INSTABILITY AND REACTIVITY HAZARDS: Hazardous polymerization may occur with heat, mineral acids, alkalies, or amines. Reacts with water to form acetone and carbon dioxide. Begins to react and decompose exothermically at 208°F (98°C) or lower if contaminated.

STORAGE RECOMMENDATIONS: Store at 32°F (0°C) in a standard flammable liquids storage warehouse, room, or cabinet. Special vented containers may be required. Separate from oxidizing materials, acids, and alkalies.

USUAL SHIPPING CONTAINERS: Refrigerated and insulated special vented containers held at 32°F (0°C) or below.

PHYSICAL PROPERTIES: Light colored liquid with irritating odor.

MELTING POINT: 18°F (−7°C)

BOILING POINT: 261°F (127°C)

SPECIFIC GRAVITY: 1.07

SOLUBILITY IN WATER: soluble; reacts to form acetone and carbon dioxide

VAPOR PRESSURE: 8 mm Hg @ 20°C

ELECTRICAL EQUIPMENT: Class I, Group C

NAME: **DIMETHYLAMINE, anhydrous DIMETHYLAMINE solution**

SYNONYMS: DMA; methanamine; N-methyl-; N-methylmethanamine

FORMULA: $(CH_3)_2NH$

NFPA 30/OSHA CLASSIFICATION:

DOT CLASS: Class 2.1, Flammable gas

Class 3, Flammable and combustible liquid

SHIPPING LABEL: FLAMMABLE GAS FLAMMABLE LIQUID

ID NO.: UN 1032 FLAMMABLE GAS

UN 1160 FLAMMABLE LIQUID

CAS NO.: 124-40-3

MOL. WT.: 45.1

STATEMENT OF HAZARDS: Flammable gas. Gases or vapors from aqueous solutions are corrosive.

EMERGENCY RESPONSE PERSONAL PROTECTIVE EQUIPMENT: Wear special protective clothing and positive pressure self-contained breathing apparatus.

SPILL OR LEAK PROCEDURES: Releases may require isolation or evacuation. Eliminate all ignition sources. Approach release from upwind. Use water spray to cool and disperse vapors, protect personnel, and dilute spills to form nonflammable mixtures. Five percent sulfuric acid may be used to neutralize diluted pools. Absorb spills involving aqueous solutions in noncombustible material for proper disposal. Control runoff and isolate discharged material for proper disposal.

FIRE FIGHTING PROCEDURES: Stop flow of gas before extinguishing fire. Use water spray to keep fire-exposed containers cool. Use water spray, dry chemical, or "alcohol resistant" foam on fires involving aqueous solutions.

HEALTH HAZARDS: Corrosive. Gases or vapors from aqueous solutions cause severe eye and skin burns. May cause irritation to skin, eyes, and respiratory system. May cause conjunctivitis and corneal damage. May be harmful if inhaled. Inhalation may cause coughing, nausea, and pulmonary edema.

FIRE AND EXPLOSION HAZARDS: Flammable gas. Vapors are heavier than air and may travel to a source of ignition and flash back. Aqueous solutions are flammable unless diluted extensively.

AUTOIGNITION TEMPERATURE: 806°F (430°C)

FLAMMABLE LIMITS: LOWER: 2.8% UPPER: 14.4%

INSTABILITY AND REACTIVITY HAZARDS: May react with acids, oxidizing materials, chlorine, hypochlorite, halogenated compounds, reactive organic compounds, some metals, and mercury and nitrosating compounds. Products of decomposition include carbon monoxide, carbon dioxide, hydrocarbons, and toxic oxides of nitrogen as well as toxic amine vapors.

STORAGE RECOMMENDATIONS: Avoid oxidizing materials, acids, and sources of halogens. Store in cool, dry, well-ventilated, noncombustible location.

USUAL SHIPPING CONTAINERS: For gases: steel cylinders, tank cars, and tank trucks. For solutions: steel drums, tank cars, tank trucks, and tank barges.

PHYSICAL PROPERTIES: Anhydrous gas. Very soluble in water forming very strong alkaline solutions. May be in water solution as shipped or used. Anhydrous material floats and boils on water as it mixes. Strong fishy or ammonia-like odor.

MELTING POINT: −134°F (−92°C)

BOILING POINT: 44°F (7°C)

SPECIFIC GRAVITY: liq. 0.68 at 0°C

SOLUBILITY IN WATER: soluble

VAPOR DENSITY: 1.55

VAPOR PRESSURE: 1500 mm Hg @ 25°C Aqueous solutions will boil 65 to 85°F (40 to 50°C) higher and freeze at proportionately higher temperatures. Vapor pressure of aqueous solutions will range from 215 to 500 mm Hg. Specific gravity values for aqueous solutions will be 0.83 to 0.93.

ELECTRICAL EQUIPMENT: Class I, Group C

NAME: **DIMETHYLCARBONATE**

SYNONYMS: carbonic acid; dimethyl ester; methyl carbonate

FORMULA: $CO(OCH_3)_2$

NFPA 30/OSHA CLASSIFICATION: IB

DOT CLASS: Class 3, Flammable and combustible liquid

SHIPPING LABEL: FLAMMABLE LIQUID

ID NO.: UN 1161

CAS NO.: 616-38-6

MOL. WT.: 90.0

STATEMENT OF HAZARDS: Flammable liquid. Corrosive.

EMERGENCY RESPONSE PERSONAL PROTECTIVE EQUIPMENT: Wear full protective clothing and positive pressure self-contained breathing apparatus.

SPILL OR LEAK PROCEDURES: Use water spray to cool and disperse vapors and protect personnel. Control runoff and isolate discharged material for proper disposal.

FIRE FIGHTING PROCEDURES: Use water spray, dry chemical, foam, or carbon dioxide. Water may be ineffective. Use water spray to keep fire-exposed containers cool.

HEALTH HAZARDS: Corrosive. Causes severe eye and skin burns. May be harmful if inhaled. Irritating to skin, eye, and respiratory system. May cause pulmonary edema.

FIRE AND EXPLOSION HAZARDS: Flammable liquid. Combustion may produce irritants and toxic gases.

FLASH POINT: 64°F (18°C)

STORAGE RECOMMENDATIONS: Store in a cool, dry, well-ventilated location. Outside or detached storage is preferred.

PHYSICAL PROPERTIES: Colorless liquid with pleasant odor.

MELTING POINT: 31°F (−0.5°C)

BOILING POINT: 196°F (91°C)

SPECIFIC GRAVITY: 1.07

SOLUBILITY IN WATER: not soluble

NAME: **DIMETHYLDICHLOROSILANE**

SYNONYMS: dichlorodimethylsilae; silane, dichloro-dimethyl-

FORMULA: $(CH_3)_2SiCl_2$

NFPA 30/OSHA CLASSIFICATION: IB

DOT CLASS: Class 3, Flammable and combustible liquid

SHIPPING LABEL: FLAMMABLE LIQUID and CORROSIVE

ID NO.: UN 1162

CAS NO.: 75-78-5

MOL. WT.: 129.1

STATEMENT OF HAZARDS: Flammable and corrosive liquid. Serious health hazard. Reacts with water to produce hydrogen chloride.

EMERGENCY RESPONSE PERSONAL PROTECTIVE EQUIPMENT: Wear special protective clothing and positive pressure self-contained breathing apparatus.

SPILL OR LEAK PROCEDURES: Use water spray to cool and disperse vapors and protect personnel. Control runoff and isolate discharged material for proper disposal.

FIRE FIGHTING PROCEDURES: Use dry chemical or carbon dioxide. Approach fire from upwind to avoid hazardous vapors and toxic decomposition products. Use water spray to keep fire-exposed containers cool.

HEALTH HAZARDS: Corrosive. Causes severe eye and skin burns. Serious health hazard. May be harmful if inhaled. Irritating to eye, skin, and respiratory system.

FIRE AND EXPLOSION HAZARDS: Flammable liquid. Vapors are heavier than air and may travel to sources of ignition and flash back. Combustion by-products include hydrogen chloride.

FLASH POINT: 16°F (−9°C) (oc)

AUTOIGNITION TEMPERATURE: 716°F (380°C)

FLAMMABLE LIMITS: LOWER: 3.4% UPPER: 9.5%

INSTABILITY AND REACTIVITY HAZARDS: Reacts with water to liberate hydrogen chloride.

STORAGE RECOMMENDATIONS: Store in a cool, dry, well-ventilated location. Keep dry.

PHYSICAL PROPERTIES: Colorless liquid.

MELTING POINT: −105°F (−76°C)

BOILING POINT: 158°F (70°C)

SPECIFIC GRAVITY: 1.1

SOLUBILITY IN WATER: reacts

VAPOR PRESSURE: 110 mm Hg @ 20°C

NAME: **DIMETHYL ETHER**

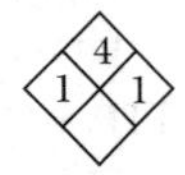

SYNONYMS: methyl ether; methyl oxide; oxibismethane

FORMULA: CH_3OCH_3

NFPA 30/OSHA CLASSIFICATION:

DOT CLASS: Class 2.1, Flammable gas

SHIPPING LABEL: FLAMMABLE GAS

ID NO.: UN 1033

CAS NO.: 115-10-6

MOL. WT.: 46.1

STATEMENT OF HAZARDS: Flammable gas. May accumulate static electricity. Containers that have been opened may contain dangerous explosive peroxides. Slight health hazard.

EMERGENCY RESPONSE PERSONAL PROTECTIVE EQUIPMENT: Wear full protective clothing and positive pressure self-contained breathing apparatus.

SPILL OR LEAK PROCEDURES: Eliminate all ignition sources. Stop or control the leak, if this can be done without undue risk. Use water spray to cool and disperse vapors, protect personnel, and dilute spills to form nonflammable mixtures. Control runoff and isolate discharged material for proper disposal.

FIRE FIGHTING PROCEDURES: Stop flow of gas before extinguishing fire. Use water spray to keep fire-exposed containers cool. Use dry chemical, carbon dioxide, water spray, or "alcohol resistant" foam.

HEALTH HAZARDS: Slight health hazard. Inhalation may cause confusion, dizziness, lack of coordination, and unconsciousness.

FIRE AND EXPLOSION HAZARDS: Flammable gas. Vapors are heavier than air and may travel to a source of ignition and flash back.

AUTOIGNITION TEMPERATURE: 662°F (350°C)

FLAMMABLE LIMITS: LOWER: 3.4% UPPER: 27%

INSTABILITY AND REACTIVITY HAZARDS: Peroxide formation may occur in ether containers that have been opened and remain in storage for more than six months. Peroxides can be detonated by friction, impact, or heating.

STORAGE RECOMMENDATIONS: Separate from oxidizing materials. Store in cool, dry, well-ventilated area. Avoid sunlight.

USUAL SHIPPING CONTAINERS: Gas cylinders.

PHYSICAL PROPERTIES: Colorless gas with ethereal odor.

MELTING POINT: −217°F (−139°C)

BOILING POINT: −11°F (−24°C)

SOLUBILITY IN WATER: soluble

VAPOR DENSITY: 1.62

ELECTRICAL EQUIPMENT: Class I, Group C

NAME: **DIMETHYLHYDRAZINE, unsymmetrical**

SYNONYMS: dimazine; 1,1-dimethylhydrazine; N,N-dimethylhydrazine; hydrazine, 1,1-dimethyl-; UDMH; unsymmetrical dimethylhydrazine

FORMULA: $(CH_3)_2NNH_2$

NFPA 30/OSHA CLASSIFICATION: IB

DOT CLASS: Class 6.1, Poisonous material

SHIPPING LABEL: POISON and FLAMMABLE LIQUID and CORROSIVE

ID NO.: UN 1163

CAS NO.: 57-14-7

MOL. WT.: 60.1

STATEMENT OF HAZARDS: Severe health hazard. Corrosive and flammable liquid.

EMERGENCY RESPONSE PERSONAL PROTECTIVE EQUIPMENT: Wear special protective clothing and positive pressure self-contained breathing apparatus.

SPILL OR LEAK PROCEDURES: Releases may require isolation or evacuation. Eliminate all ignition sources. Stop or control the leak, if this can be done without undue risk. Use water spray to cool and disperse vapors, protect personnel, and dilute spills to form nonflammable mixtures. Absorb in noncombustible material for proper disposal.

FIRE FIGHTING PROCEDURES: Use flooding quantities of water as spray, dry chemical, "alcohol resistant" foam, or carbon dioxide. Use water spray to keep fire-exposed containers cool.

HEALTH HAZARDS: Severe health hazard. May be fatal if absorbed through skin or inhaled. Corrosive. Causes severe eye and skin burns. May cause pulmonary edema.

FIRE AND EXPLOSION HAZARDS: Flammable liquid. Vapors are heavier than air and may travel to a source of ignition and flash back. Combustion by-products include oxides of nitrogen. Mixes with air to form flammable mixture over a wide range.

FLASH POINT: 5°F (−15°C)

AUTOIGNITION TEMPERATURE: 480°F (249°C)

FLAMMABLE LIMITS: LOWER: 2% UPPER: 95%

INSTABILITY AND REACTIVITY HAZARDS: Strong organic alkali. Reacts violently with oxidizers.

STORAGE RECOMMENDATIONS: Store in a cool, dry, well-ventilated location. Isolate from oxidizing materials, strong acids, halogens, and copper, iron, and mercury metals and compounds. Inside storage should be in a standard flammable liquids storage warehouse, room, or cabinet.

USUAL SHIPPING CONTAINERS: Glass bottles or carboys inside wooden box; stainless steel cans, drums, tanks.

PHYSICAL PROPERTIES: Colorless to pale yellow mobile liquid. Fumes in air with odor of ammonia.

MELTING POINT: −72°F (−58°C)

BOILING POINT: 147°F (64°C)

SPECIFIC GRAVITY: 0.78

SOLUBILITY IN WATER: soluble

VAPOR PRESSURE: 103 mm Hg @ 20°C

ELECTRICAL EQUIPMENT: Class I, Group C

NAME: **DIMETHYL SULFATE**

SYNONYMS: dimethyl monosulfate; DMS; methylsulfate; sulfuric acid dimethyl ester

FORMULA: $(CH_3)_2SO_4$

NFPA 30/OSHA CLASSIFICATION: IIIA

DOT CLASS: Class 6.1, Poisonous material

SHIPPING LABEL: POISON and CORROSIVE

ID NO.: UN 1595

CAS NO.: 77-78-1

MOL. WT.: 126.1

STATEMENT OF HAZARDS: Severe health hazard. Corrosive and combustible liquid.

EMERGENCY RESPONSE PERSONAL PROTECTIVE EQUIPMENT: Wear special protective clothing and positive pressure self-contained breathing apparatus.

SPILL OR LEAK PROCEDURES: Stop or control the leak, if this can be done without undue risk. Use water spray to cool and disperse vapors and protect personnel. Approach release from upwind. Absorb in noncombustible material for proper disposal. Prompt cleanup and removal are necessary.

FIRE FIGHTING PROCEDURES: Use dry chemical, foam, carbon dioxide, or water spray. Use water spray to keep fire-exposed containers cool. Approach fire from upwind to avoid hazardous vapors and toxic decomposition products.

HEALTH HAZARDS: Severe health hazard. May be fatal if absorbed through skin or inhaled. Corrosive. Causes severe eye and skin burns. Irritating to skin, eyes, and respiratory system. Symptoms of exposure include visual disturbance and pulmonary edema.

FIRE AND EXPLOSION HAZARDS: Combustible liquid. Combustion may produce irritants and toxic gases.

FLASH POINT: 182°F (83°C)

AUTOIGNITION TEMPERATURE: 370°F (188°C)

INSTABILITY AND REACTIVITY HAZARDS: Reacts with a broad range of materials, including water. Corrodes steel when wet.

STORAGE RECOMMENDATIONS: Store in a cool, dry, well-ventilated location. Separate from bases, oxidizing materials, water, and metal.

USUAL SHIPPING CONTAINERS: Glass bottle inside wooden box. Metal cans, pails, drums. Tanks on trucks, rail cars, barges.

PHYSICAL PROPERTIES: Colorless, oily liquid. Faint onion odor.

MELTING POINT: −25°F (−32°C)

BOILING POINT: 370°F (188°C) (decomposes)

SPECIFIC GRAVITY: 1.33

SOLUBILITY IN WATER: not soluble

VAPOR PRESSURE: < 1 mm Hg @ 20°C

ELECTRICAL EQUIPMENT: Class I, Group D

NAME: **DINITROANILINES**

SYNONYMS: 2,4-dinitro-1-aminobenzene; 2,4-dinitrobenzenamine; DNA

FORMULA: $(NO_2)_2C_6H_3NH_2$

NFPA 30/OSHA CLASSIFICATION: IIIB

DOT CLASS: Class 6.1, Poisonous material

SHIPPING LABEL: POISON

ID NO.: UN 1596

CAS NO.: 97-02-9

MOL. WT.: 183.1

STATEMENT OF HAZARDS: Corrosive and combustible solid. Explosive decomposition may occur under fire conditions.

EMERGENCY RESPONSE PERSONAL PROTECTIVE EQUIPMENT: Wear special protective clothing and positive pressure self-contained breathing apparatus.

SPILL OR LEAK PROCEDURES: Shovel into suitable dry container with extreme caution.

FIRE FIGHTING PROCEDURES: Fight fire from protected location or maximum possible distance. Use water spray, dry chemical, foam, or carbon dioxide. Water or foam may cause frothing. Approach fire from upwind to avoid hazardous vapors and toxic decomposition products.

HEALTH HAZARDS: Corrosive. Causes severe eye and skin burns. May be harmful if absorbed through skin or inhaled. Irritating to skin, eyes, and respiratory system. Symptoms of overexposure include headache, nausea, dizziness, and stupor. Onset of symptoms may be delayed two to four hours.

FIRE AND EXPLOSION HAZARDS: Explosive decomposition may occur under fire conditions. Air or oxygen is not required for decomposition. Combustible solid. Combustion by-products include oxides of nitrogen and other irritants and toxic gases. Closed containers may rupture violently when heated.

FLASH POINT: 435°F (224°C)

STORAGE RECOMMENDATIONS: Store in a cool, dry, well-ventilated location. Separate from acids and oxidizing materials. Detached storage must be used.

USUAL SHIPPING CONTAINERS: Metal can inside wooden box or steel drums.

PHYSICAL PROPERTIES: Yellow to greenish-yellow needle-like crystals.

MELTING POINT: 370°F (188°C)

SPECIFIC GRAVITY: 1.62

SOLUBILITY IN WATER: not soluble

NAME: **DINITROBENZENES**

SYNONYMS: o-dinitrobenzene; 1,2-dinitrobenzol

FORMULA: $C_6H_4(NO_2)_2$

NFPA 30/OSHA CLASSIFICATION: IIIB

DOT CLASS: Class 6.1, Poisonous material

SHIPPING LABEL: POISON

ID NO.: UN 1597

CAS NO.: 528-29-0

MOL. WT.: 168.1

STATEMENT OF HAZARDS: Shock and friction sensitive. Serious health hazard. Combustible solid. Explosive decomposition may occur under fire conditions.

EMERGENCY RESPONSE PERSONAL PROTECTIVE EQUIPMENT: Wear special protective clothing and positive pressure self-contained breathing apparatus.

SPILL OR LEAK PROCEDURES: Shovel into suitable dry container with extreme caution.

FIRE FIGHTING PROCEDURES: Use extreme caution. Fight fire from protected location or maximum possible distance. Use water spray, foam, dry chemical, or carbon dioxide. Water or foam may cause frothing. Approach fire from upwind to avoid hazardous vapors and toxic decomposition products.

HEALTH HAZARDS: Serious health hazard. May be harmful if absorbed through skin or inhaled. Irritating to skin, eyes and respiratory system. Symptoms of overexposure include headache, vertigo, and vomiting followed by exhaustion, staggering, and collapse.

FIRE AND EXPLOSION HAZARDS: Combustible solid. Combustion by-products include oxides of nitrogen. Explosive decomposition may occur under fire conditions. Air or oxygen is not required for decomposition. Closed containers may rupture violently when heated.

FLASH POINT: 302°F (150°C)

INSTABILITY AND REACTIVITY HAZARDS: Shock and friction sensitive.

STORAGE RECOMMENDATIONS: Store in a cool, dry, well-ventilated location. Separate from metals, oxidizing materials, reducing agents. Detached storage must be used. See also NFPA 495, Explosive Materials Code.

USUAL SHIPPING CONTAINERS: Metal can inside wooden box. Fiber or steel drums.

PHYSICAL PROPERTIES: Colorless to yellow needle-like or plate-like crystals.

MELTING POINT: 245°F (119°C)

BOILING POINT: 606°F (319°C)

SPECIFIC GRAVITY: 1.57

SOLUBILITY IN WATER: not soluble

VAPOR PRESSURE: < 1 mm Hg @ 20°C

NAME: **DINITROTOLUENES, molten**
DINITROTOLUENES, liquid or solid commercially available 2,4 to 2,6 ratio 4/1 with <5% other isomers

SYNONYMS: dinitrotoluol; 2,4-dinitrotoluol; DNT; 2,4-DNT

FORMULA: $C_6H_3CH_3(NO_2)_2$

NFPA 30/OSHA CLASSIFICATION: IIIB

DOT CLASS: Class 6.1, Poisonous material

SHIPPING LABEL: POISON

ID NO.: UN 1600 (molten)

UN 2038 (solid or liquid)

CAS NO.: 121-14-2 (for 2,4-)

MOL. WT.: 182.1

STATEMENT OF HAZARDS: Serious health hazard. Corrosive and combustible solid. Explosive hazard if confined and heated.

EMERGENCY RESPONSE PERSONAL PROTECTIVE EQUIPMENT: Wear special protective clothing and positive pressure self-contained breathing apparatus.

SPILL OR LEAK PROCEDURES: Spilled solid should be placed in steel drum for removal. Flush area with hot water to remove solid DNT; cool and settle solid for disposal in drums.

FIRE FIGHTING PROCEDURES: Use water spray, dry chemical, or carbon dioxide. Fight fire from protected location or maximum possible distance. Use water spray to keep fire-exposed containers cool.

HEALTH HAZARDS: Corrosive. Causes severe eye and skin burns. May be harmful if inhaled or absorbed through skin. Effects may be immediate or delayed. Can cause anemia, methemoglobinemia, and cyanosis.

FIRE AND EXPLOSION HAZARDS: Combustible solid. Spontaneously decomposes above 536°F (280°C) and will cause an explosion if confined. Explosive energy of DNT is approximately 85% of TNT. Air or oxygen is not required for decomposition or oxidation. Combustion by-products include oxides of nitrogen. Contamination of DNT with organic materials lowers decomposition temperature and increases risk of explosion. Closed containers may rupture violently when heated.

FLASH POINT: 404°F (207°C)

INSTABILITY AND REACTIVITY HAZARDS: Potentially explosive if heated to decomposition temperatures in confined spaces or detonated. Generally insensitive to impact shock unless from high energy source. Liquid is less sensitive to shock than solid. Organic contaminants lower decomposition temperatures and increase risk of explosion.

STORAGE RECOMMENDATIONS: Normally stored as a molten liquid. Separate from strong oxidizing materials and reducing agents. Hot water coils should not exceed 194°F (90°C).

USUAL SHIPPING CONTAINERS: Shipped molten in tank cars or in drums as cast solid.

PHYSICAL PROPERTIES: Orange-yellow crystalline solid. May be shipped in molten state. Anaerobic decomposition begins at 482°F (250°C) although not self-sustaining until 536°F (280°C).

MELTING POINT: 158°F (70°C)

BOILING POINT: 482°F (250°C)

SPECIFIC GRAVITY: 1.3 (1iquid)

1.5 (solid)

SOLUBILITY IN WATER: not soluble

VAPOR PRESSURE: 1 mm Hg @ 20°C

NAME: **DIOXANE**

SYNONYMS: 1,4-diethylene dioxide; diethylene ether; diethylene dioxide; p-dioxane; 1,4-dioxane

FORMULA: $CH_2CH_2OCH_2CH_2O$

NFPA 30/OSHA CLASSIFICATION: IB

DOT CLASS: Class 3, Flammable and combustible liquid

SHIPPING LABEL: FLAMMABLE LIQUID

ID NO.: UN 1165

CAS NO.: 123-91-1

MOL. WT.: 88.1

STATEMENT OF HAZARDS: Flammable liquid. May accumulate static electricity. Peroxide formation may occur in containers that have been opened and remain in storage. Peroxides can be detonated by friction, impact, or heating. Moderate health hazard.

EMERGENCY RESPONSE PERSONAL PROTECTIVE EQUIPMENT: Wear full protective clothing and positive pressure self-contained breathing apparatus.

SPILL OR LEAK PROCEDURES: Eliminate all ignition sources. Approach release from upwind. Stop or control the leak, if this can be done without undue risk. Use water spray to cool and disperse vapors, protect personnel, and dilute spills to form nonflammable mixtures. Control runoff and isolate discharged material for proper disposal.

FIRE FIGHTING PROCEDURES: Approach fire from upwind to avoid hazardous vapors and toxic decomposition products. Use water spray, dry chemical, "alcohol resistant" foam, or carbon dioxide. Use water spray to keep fire-exposed containers cool.

HEALTH HAZARDS: Moderate health hazard. May be harmful if absorbed through skin or inhaled. Irritating to eye, skin, and respiratory system. Inhalation of vapor may produce narcotic effects.

FIRE AND EXPLOSION HAZARDS: Flammable liquid. Vapors are heavier than air and may travel to a source of ignition and flash back. Peroxide formation may occur in containers that have been opened and remain in storage. Peroxides can be detonated by friction, impact, or heating.

FLASH POINT: 54°F (12°C)

AUTOIGNITION TEMPERATURE: 356°F (180°C)

FLAMMABLE LIMITS: LOWER: 2.0% UPPER: 22.0%

INSTABILITY AND REACTIVITY HAZARDS: Forms peroxides in absence of inhibitors. Peroxide formation may occur in containers that have been opened and remain in storage. Peroxides can be detonated by friction, impact, or heating. Reacts with oxidizing materials.

STORAGE RECOMMENDATIONS: Store in a cool, dry, well-ventilated location. Store away from heat, oxidizing materials, and sunlight. Outside or detached storage is preferred. Inside storage should be in a standard flammable liquids storage warehouse, room, or cabinet.

USUAL SHIPPING CONTAINERS: Bottles, cans, drums.

PHYSICAL PROPERTIES: Colorless liquid with faint ethereal odor.

MELTING POINT: 53°F (12°C)

BOILING POINT: 214°F (101°C)

SPECIFIC GRAVITY: 1.03

SOLUBILITY IN WATER: soluble

VAPOR PRESSURE: 29 mm Hg @ 20°C

ELECTRICAL EQUIPMENT: Class I, Group C

NAME: **DIVINYLBENZENE**

SYNONYMS: diethenylbenzene; DVB; vinylstyrene

FORMULA: $C_6H_4(CH{=}CH_2)_2$

NFPA 30/OSHA CLASSIFICATION: IIIA

DOT CLASS: N/A

ID NO.: N/A

CAS NO.: 1321-74-0

MOL. WT.: 130.2

STATEMENT OF HAZARDS: Combustible liquid. May accumulate static electricity. Thermally unstable. Polymerizes when heated. Slight health hazard.

EMERGENCY RESPONSE PERSONAL PROTECTIVE EQUIPMENT: Wear full protective clothing and positive pressure self-contained breathing apparatus.

SPILL OR LEAK PROCEDURES: Stop or control the leak, if this can be done without undue risk. Adsorb in noncombustible material (e.g., sand) for proper disposal. Use water spray to cool and disperse vapors and protect personnel. Control runoff and isolate discharged material for proper disposal.

FIRE FIGHTING PROCEDURES: Use water spray, dry chemical, foam, or carbon dioxide. Use water spray to keep fire-exposed containers cool. Fight fire from protected location or maximum possible distance. Use remote equipment wherever possible.

HEALTH HAZARDS: Slight health hazard. Irritating to skin, eyes, and respiratory system. May cause dizziness, anesthetic, and narcotic effects.

FIRE AND EXPLOSION HAZARDS: Combustible liquid. Closed containers may rupture violently when heated.

FLASH POINT: 157°F (69°C)

AUTOIGNITION TEMPERATURE: 878°F (470°C)

FLAMMABLE LIMITS: LOWER: 0.7% @ 185°F UPPER: 6.2% @ 248°F

INSTABILITY AND REACTIVITY HAZARDS: Hazardous polymerization may occur. Reacts with acids, oxidizing materials, peroxides, metal salts such as iron chloride or aluminum chloride, or polymer initiators. Usually contains inhibitors to prevent polymerization. Uninhibited monomer vapor may form polymer in vents and other confined spaces.

STORAGE RECOMMENDATIONS: Store in a cool, dry, well-ventilated location. Outside or detached storage is preferred.

USUAL SHIPPING CONTAINERS: Drums and tank cars.

PHYSICAL PROPERTIES: Yellowish to water-white liquid. Not soluble in water. Floats on water.

MELTING POINT: −89°F (−67°C)

BOILING POINT: 388°F (198°C)

SPECIFIC GRAVITY: 0.9

SOLUBILITY IN WATER: not soluble

VAPOR DENSITY: 4.5

VAPOR PRESSURE: 0.9 mm Hg @ 30°C

ELECTRICAL EQUIPMENT: Class I, Group D

NAME: **EPICHLOROHYDRIN**

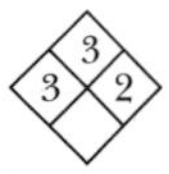

SYNONYMS: 1-chloro-2,3-epoxy propane; chloromethyl-oxirane, 2-(chloro-methyl)oxirane; chloropropylene oxide

FORMULA: $ClCH_2$—CH—CH_2 (with O bridging CH and CH_2)

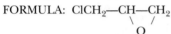

NFPA 30/OSHA CLASSIFICATION: IC

DOT CLASS: Class 6.1, Poisonous material

SHIPPING LABEL: POISON

ID NO.: UN 2023

CAS NO.: 106-89-8

MOL. WT.: 92.5

STATEMENT OF HAZARDS: Corrosive and flammable liquid.

EMERGENCY RESPONSE PERSONAL PROTECTIVE EQUIPMENT: Wear special protective clothing and positive pressure self-contained breathing apparatus.

SPILL OR LEAK PROCEDURES: Eliminate all ignition sources. Approach release from upwind. Releases may require isolation or evacuation. Use appropriate foam to blanket release and suppress vapors. Use water spray to cool and disperse vapors, protect personnel, and dilute spills to form nonflammable mixtures. Do not use clay absorbents in cleanup. Control runoff and isolate discharged material for proper disposal.

FIRE FIGHTING PROCEDURES: Approach fire from upwind to avoid hazardous vapors and toxic decomposition products. Fight fire from protected location or maximum possible distance. Use water spray, dry chemical, "alcohol resistant" foam, or carbon dioxide. Use water spray to keep fire-exposed containers cool.

HEALTH HAZARDS: Corrosive. Causes severe eye and skin burns. May be harmful if absorbed through skin or inhaled. Irritating to skin, eyes, and respiratory system.

FIRE AND EXPLOSION HAZARDS: Flammable liquid. Vapors are heavier than air and may travel to a source of ignition and flash back. Closed containers may rupture violently when heated. Combustion may produce irritants and toxic gases. Combustion by-products include hydrogen chloride.

FLASH POINT: 88°F (31°C)

AUTOIGNITION TEMPERATURE: 772°F (411°C)

FLAMMABLE LIMITS: LOWER: 3.8% UPPER: 21.0%

INSTABILITY AND REACTIVITY HAZARDS: Hazardous polymerization may occur. Reacts with acids, alkalies, salts, and water.

STORAGE RECOMMENDATIONS: Separate from acids, alkalies, salts, water, and oxidizers. Store in a cool, dry, well-ventilated location. Inside storage should be in a standard flammable liquids storage warehouse, room, or cabinet.

USUAL SHIPPING CONTAINERS: Drums; tanks on trucks, rail cars, barges.

PHYSICAL PROPERTIES: Colorless liquid with an irritating odor like chloroform.

MELTING POINT: −54°F (−48°C)

BOILING POINT: 241°F (116°C)

SPECIFIC GRAVITY: 1.18

SOLUBILITY IN WATER: not soluble

VAPOR PRESSURE: 13 mm Hg @ 20°C

ELECTRICAL EQUIPMENT: Class I, Group C

NAME: **ETHANOLAMINE**
ETHANOLAMINE SOLUTIONS

SYNONYMS: 2-aminoethanol; b-aminoethyl alcohol; colamine; monoethanolamine

FORMULA: $HO(CH_2)_2NH_2$

NFPA 30/OSHA CLASSIFICATION: IIIA

DOT CLASS: Class 8, Corrosive material

SHIPPING LABEL: CORROSIVE

ID NO.: UN 2491

CAS NO.: 141-43-5

MOL. WT.: 61.1

STATEMENT OF HAZARDS: Corrosive and combustible liquid.

EMERGENCY RESPONSE PERSONAL PROTECTIVE EQUIPMENT: Wear special protective clothing and positive pressure self-contained breathing apparatus.

SPILL OR LEAK PROCEDURES: Absorb in noncombustible material for proper disposal.

FIRE FIGHTING PROCEDURES: Use water spray, dry chemical, "alcohol resistant" foam, or carbon dioxide. Use water spray to keep fire-exposed containers cool.

HEALTH HAZARDS: Corrosive. Causes severe eye and skin burns. May be harmful if absorbed through skin or inhaled. Irritating to skin, eyes, respiratory system.

FIRE AND EXPLOSION HAZARDS: Combustible liquid. Combustion may produce irritants and toxic gases.

FLASH POINT: 185°F (85°C)

AUTOIGNITION TEMPERATURE: 770°F (410°C)

FLAMMABLE LIMITS: LOWER: 3% UPPER: 23.5% @ 140°C

INSTABILITY AND REACTIVITY HAZARDS: Strong alkali. Reacts with oxidizing materials, acids, halogenated hydrocarbons to produce heat. Reacts with iron producing an unstable and pyrophoric complex trisethanolaminoiron.

STORAGE RECOMMENDATIONS: Separate from oxidizing materials, acids, and halogens. Store in a cool, dry, well-ventilated location.

USUAL SHIPPING CONTAINERS: Metal cans, pails, drums. Tanks on trucks, rail cars, barges.

PHYSICAL PROPERTIES: Clear to yellowish viscous liquid. Odor of ammonia.

MELTING POINT: 51°F (10°C)

BOILING POINT: 339°F (171°C)

SPECIFIC GRAVITY: 1.01

SOLUBILITY IN WATER: soluble

VAPOR DENSITY: 2.1

VAPOR PRESSURE: <1 mm Hg @ 20°C

ELECTRICAL EQUIPMENT: Class I, Group D

NAME: **ETHYL ACRYLATE, inhibited**

SYNONYMS: ethyl ester of acrylic acid; ethyl propenoate; 2-propenoic acid ethyl ether

FORMULA: $CH_2{=}CHCO_2C_2H_5$

NFPA 30/OSHA CLASSIFICATION: IB

DOT CLASS: Class 3, Flammable and combustible liquid

SHIPPING LABEL: FLAMMABLE LIQUID

ID NO.: UN 1917

CAS NO.: 140-88-5

MOL. WT.: 100.1

STATEMENT OF HAZARDS: Flammable liquid. Thermally unstable. Polymerizes when exposed to heat. Moderate health hazard.

EMERGENCY RESPONSE PERSONAL PROTECTIVE EQUIPMENT: Wear full protective clothing and positive pressure self-contained breathing apparatus.

SPILL OR LEAK PROCEDURES: Eliminate all ignition sources. Stop or control the leak, if this can be done without undue risk. Use water spray to cool and disperse vapors and protect personnel. Control runoff and isolate discharged material for proper disposal.

FIRE FIGHTING PROCEDURES: Use water spray to keep fire-exposed containers cool. Use fine spray or fog to control fire by preventing its spread and absorbing some of its heat. Solid streams of water may be ineffective or may cause frothing. Use water spray, dry chemical, foam, or carbon dioxide. Fight fire from protected location or maximum possible distance.

HEALTH HAZARDS: Moderate health hazard. Irritating to skin, eyes, and respiratory system. Skin sensitizer. May cause severe allergic reaction.

FIRE AND EXPLOSION HAZARDS: Flammable liquid. Closed containers may rupture violently when heated. Vapors are heavier than air and may travel to a source of ignition and flash back. Liquid floats on water and may travel to a source of ignition and spread fire.

FLASH POINT: 48°F (9°C)

AUTOIGNITION TEMPERATURE: 702°F (372°C)

FLAMMABLE LIMITS: LOWER: 1.4% UPPER: 14.0%

INSTABILITY AND REACTIVITY HAZARDS: Hazardous polymerization may occur. Polymerization may be caused by elevated temperature, oxidizers, peroxides. Material will react with strong acids and alkalies. Uninhibited monomer vapor may form polymer in vents and other confined spaces.

STORAGE RECOMMENDATIONS: Store away from heat, oxidizers, and sunlight. Outside or detached storage is preferred. Separate from any oxidizers, peroxides, or other initiators.

USUAL SHIPPING CONTAINERS: Bottles, cans, drums, and tank trucks or tank cars.

PHYSICAL PROPERTIES: Colorless liquid with acrid penetrating odor.

MELTING POINT: −98°F (−72°C)

BOILING POINT: 211°F (100°C)

SPECIFIC GRAVITY: 0.94

SOLUBILITY IN WATER: not soluble

VAPOR PRESSURE: 31 mm Hg @ 20°C

ELECTRICAL EQUIPMENT: Class I, Group D

NAME: **ETHYLAMINE**

SYNONYMS: aminoethane; ethanamine; monoethylamine

FORMULA: $C_2H_5NH_2$

NFPA 30/OSHA CLASSIFICATION:

DOT CLASS: Class 2.1, Flammable gas

SHIPPING LABEL: FLAMMABLE GAS

ID NO.: UN 1036

CAS NO.: 75-04-7

MOL. WT.: 45.1

STATEMENT OF HAZARDS: Flammable gas. Pure material and aqueous solutions are corrosive.

EMERGENCY RESPONSE PERSONAL PROTECTIVE EQUIPMENT: Wear special protective clothing and positive pressure self-contained breathing apparatus.

SPILL OR LEAK PROCEDURES: Eliminate all ignition sources. Approach release from upwind. Use water spray to cool and disperse vapors, protect personnel, and dilute spills to form nonflammable mixtures. Absorb in noncombustible material for proper disposal. Control runoff and isolate discharged material for proper disposal.

FIRE FIGHTING PROCEDURES: Stop flow of gas before extinguishing fire. Use water spray to keep fire-exposed containers cool. Use water spray, dry chemical, or "alcohol resistant" foam. Aqueous solutions will burn unless diluted thoroughly with spray.

HEALTH HAZARDS: Corrosive. Causes severe eye and skin burns. Irritating to skin, eyes, and respiratory system. Inhalation may cause coughing, nausea, and pulmonary edema.

FIRE AND EXPLOSION HAZARDS: Flammable gas above 62°F (17°C). Vapors are heavier than air and may travel to a source of ignition and flash back. Aqueous solutions are flammable unless diluted extensively.

AUTOIGNITION TEMPERATURE: 725°F (385°C)

FLAMMABLE LIMITS: LOWER: 3.5% UPPER: 14.0%

INSTABILITY AND REACTIVITY HAZARDS: Reacts with acids, oxidizing materials, chlorine, hypochlorite, halogenated compounds, reactive organic compounds, and some metals. Products of decomposition include oxides of nitrogen as well as amine vapors.

STORAGE RECOMMENDATIONS: Separate from oxidizing materials, acids, and sources of halogens. Store in cool, dry, well-ventilated, noncombustible location.

USUAL SHIPPING CONTAINERS: Glass bottles, cans, drums, and tank cars.

PHYSICAL PROPERTIES: Flammable gas with strong ammonia-like odor [above 62°F (17°C)]. May be in water solutions as shipped or used.

MELTING POINT: −114°F (−81°C)

BOILING POINT: 62°F (17°C)

SPECIFIC GRAVITY: 0.69

SOLUBILITY IN WATER: soluble

VAPOR DENSITY: 1.55

VAPOR PRESSURE: 873 mm Hg @ 20°C

ELECTRICAL EQUIPMENT: Class I, Group D

NAME: **N-ETHYLANILINE**

SYNONYMS: ethylaniline; N-ethylbenzenamine; ethyl-phenylamine

FORMULA: $(C_6H_5)NHC_2H_5$

NFPA 30/OSHA CLASSIFICATION: IIIA

DOT CLASS: Class 6.1, Poisonous material

SHIPPING LABEL: KEEP AWAY FROM FOOD

ID NO.: UN 2272

CAS NO.: 103-69-5

MOL. WT.: 121.2

STATEMENT OF HAZARDS: Serious health hazard. Combustible liquid.

EMERGENCY RESPONSE PERSONAL PROTECTIVE EQUIPMENT: Wear special protective clothing and positive pressure self-contained breathing apparatus.

SPILL OR LEAK PROCEDURES: Approach release from upwind. Stop or control the leak, if this can be done without undue risk. Use appropriate foam to blanket release and suppress vapors. Absorb in noncombustible material for proper disposal. Control runoff and isolate discharged material for proper disposal.

FIRE FIGHTING PROCEDURES: Use water spray, dry chemical, foam, or carbon dioxide. Use water spray to keep fire-exposed containers cool. Approach fire from upwind to avoid hazardous vapors and toxic decomposition products.

HEALTH HAZARDS: Serious health hazard. May be harmful if absorbed through skin or inhaled. Symptoms of overexposure include respiratory distress, impairment of red blood cells, vertigo, headache, and confusion.

FIRE AND EXPLOSION HAZARDS: Combustible liquid. Condensed vapors may deposit solid ethylaniline. Combustion by-products include oxides of nitrogen, aniline, and other irritants and toxic gases.

FLASH POINT: 185°F (85°C) (oc)

FLAMMABLE LIMITS: LOWER: 1.6% UPPER: 9.5%

INSTABILITY AND REACTIVITY HAZARDS: Decomposes on contact with air or light. Reacts with a broad range of materials.

STORAGE RECOMMENDATIONS: Store away from heat, oxidizing materials, and sunlight in a dry, well-ventiliated location. Outside or detached storage is preferred.

USUAL SHIPPING CONTAINERS: Amber glass bottles, steel drums, tanks.

PHYSICAL PROPERTIES: Colorless to pale yellow to brown, oily liquid. Becomes brown on exposure to light. Odor of aniline (somewhat pleasant, medicinal).

MELTING POINT: −83°F (−64°C)

BOILING POINT: 400°F (204°C)

SPECIFIC GRAVITY: 0.96

SOLUBILITY IN WATER: not soluble

VAPOR PRESSURE: 1 mm Hg @ 38°C

ELECTRICAL EQUIPMENT: Class I, Group D

NAME: **ETHYLBENZENE**

SYNONYMS: EB; ethylbenzol; phenylethane

FORMULA: $C_6H_5C_2H_5$

NFPA 30/OSHA CLASSIFICATION: IB

DOT CLASS: Class 3, Flammable and combustible liquid

SHIPPING LABEL: FLAMMABLE LIQUID

ID NO.: UN 1175

CAS NO.: 100-41-4

MOL. WT.: 106.2

STATEMENT OF HAZARDS: Flammable liquid. May accumulate static electricity. Moderate health hazard.

EMERGENCY RESPONSE PERSONAL PROTECTIVE EQUIPMENT: Wear full protective clothing and positive pressure self-contained breathing apparatus.

SPILL OR LEAK PROCEDURES: Eliminate all ignition sources. Stop or control the leak, if this can be done without undue risk. Use water spray to cool and disperse vapors and protect personnel. Absorb in noncombustible material for proper disposal. Control runoff and isolate discharged material for proper disposal.

FIRE FIGHTING PROCEDURES: Approach fire from upwind to avoid hazardous vapors and toxic decomposition products. Use water spray, dry chemical, foam, or carbon dioxide. Use water spray to keep fire-exposed containers cool.

HEALTH HAZARDS: Moderate health hazard. May be harmful if absorbed through skin or inhaled. Irrtitating to skin, eyes, and respiratory system.

FIRE AND EXPLOSION HAZARDS: Flammable liquid. Vapors are heavier than air and may travel to a source of ignition and flash back. Liquid floats on water and may travel to a source of ignition and spread fire. Combustion may produce irritants and toxic gases.

FLASH POINT: 70°F (21°C)

AUTOIGNITION TEMPERATURE: 810°F (432°C)

FLAMMABLE LIMITS: LOWER: 1.0% UPPER: 6.7%

INSTABILITY AND REACTIVITY HAZARDS: Reacts with oxidizing materials.

STORAGE RECOMMENDATIONS: Outside or detached storage is preferred. Inside storage should be in a standard flammable liquids storage warehouse, room, or cabinet. Separate from oxidizing materials.

USUAL SHIPPING CONTAINERS: Glass bottles, cans, drums, and tanks on trucks, rail cars, barges.

PHYSICAL PROPERTIES: Colorless liquid with aromatic odor.

MELTING POINT: −139°F (−95°C)

BOILING POINT: 277°F (136°C)

SPECIFIC GRAVITY: 0.87

SOLUBILITY IN WATER: not soluble

VAPOR DENSITY: 3.66

VAPOR PRESSURE: 7 mm Hg @ 20°C

ELECTRICAL EQUIPMENT: Class I, Group D

NAME: **ETHYL CHLOROFORMATE**

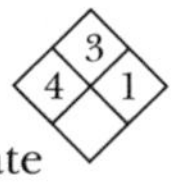

SYNONYMS: carbonochloridic acid ethyl ester; chloroformic acid ethyl ester; ethyl chlorocarbonate

FORMULA: $ClCOOC_2H_5$

NFPA 30/OSHA CLASSIFICATION: IB

DOT CLASS: Class 6.1, Poisonous material

SHIPPING LABEL: POISON and FLAMMABLE LIQUID and CORROSIVE

ID NO.: UN 1182

CAS NO.: 541-41-3

MOL. WT.: 108.5

STATEMENT OF HAZARDS: Severe health hazard. Corrosive and flammable liquid.

EMERGENCY RESPONSE PERSONAL PROTECTIVE EQUIPMENT: Wear special protective clothing and positive pressure self-contained breathing apparatus.

SPILL OR LEAK PROCEDURES: Releases may require isolation or evacuation. Eliminate all ignition sources. Stop or control the leak, if this can be done without undue risk. Use water spray to cool and disperse vapors and protect personnel. Absorb in noncombustible material for proper disposal.

FIRE FIGHTING PROCEDURES: Use dry chemical, foam, carbon dioxide, or water spray. Water may be ineffective. Use water spray to keep fire-exposed containers cool. Approach fire from upwind to avoid hazardous vapors and toxic decomposition products.

HEALTH HAZARDS: Severe health hazard. May be fatal if inhaled. Corrosive. Causes severe eye and skin burns. Irritating to skin, eyes, and respiratory system. Symptoms of overexposure include coughing, wheezing, laryngitis, headache, nausea, and vomiting.

FIRE AND EXPLOSION HAZARDS: Flammable liquid. Vapors are heavier than air and may travel to a source of ignition and flash back. Combustion by-products include hydrogen chloride and other irritants and toxic gases.

FLASH POINT: 61°F (16°C)

AUTOIGNITION TEMPERATURE: 932°F (500°C)

INSTABILITY AND REACTIVITY HAZARDS: Reacts with water to produce ethyl alcohol and chloroformic acid. Reacts with a broad range of materials, including moist air.

STORAGE RECOMMENDATIONS: Store in a cool, dry, well-ventilated location. Separate from acids, alkalies, amines, alcohols, oxidizing materials, and water. Normally kept refrigerated.

USUAL SHIPPING CONTAINERS: Glass bottles inside wooden box. Glass or polyethylene bottles, carboys, polyethylene-lined drums. Tanks on trucks, rail cars, barges.

PHYSICAL PROPERTIES: Colorless to light yellow liquid. Irritating odor.

MELTING POINT: −113°F (−81°C)

BOILING POINT: 203°F (95°C)

SPECIFIC GRAVITY: 1.14

SOLUBILITY IN WATER: not soluble (decomposes)

VAPOR PRESSURE: 53 mm Hg @ 20°C

95 mm Hg @ 40°C

ELECTRICAL EQUIPMENT: Class I, Group D

NAME: **ETHYLENE, compressed**

SYNONYMS: ethene; olefiant gas

FORMULA: $CH_2{=}CH_2$

NFPA 30/OSHA CLASSIFICATION:

DOT CLASS: Class 2.1, Flammable gas

SHIPPING LABEL: FLAMMABLE GAS

ID NO.: UN 1962

CAS NO.: 74-85-1

MOL. WT.: 28.1

STATEMENT OF HAZARDS: Flammable gas. Low ignition energy. May undergo explosive decomposition at elevated pressures when heated or ignited. Hazardous polymerization may occur. Simple asphyxiant.

EMERGENCY RESPONSE PERSONAL PROTECTIVE EQUIPMENT: Wear full protective clothing and positive pressure self-contained breathing apparatus.

SPILL OR LEAK PROCEDURES: Eliminate all ignition sources. Stop or control the leak, if this can be done without undue risk. Use water spray to cool and disperse vapors.

FIRE FIGHTING PROCEDURES: Stop flow of gas before extinguishing fire. Use water spray to keep fire-exposed containers cool. Use fine spray or fog to control fire by preventing its spread and absorbing some of its heat. Dry chemical or carbon dioxide can be used. Fight fire from protected location or maximum possible distance. Use remote equipment wherever possible.

HEALTH HAZARDS: Slight health hazard. Simple asphyxiant. Rapid release of compressed gas may cause frostbite.

FIRE AND EXPLOSION HAZARDS: Flammable gas. Closed containers may rupture violently when heated. At room temperature may decompose explosively at high pressure.

AUTOIGNITION TEMPERATURE: 914°F (490°C)

FLAMMABLE LIMITS: LOWER: 2.7% UPPER: 36.0%

INSTABILITY AND REACTIVITY HAZARDS: Reacts with oxidizing materials. Hazardous polymerization may occur.

STORAGE RECOMMENDATIONS: Store in a cool, dry, well-ventilated location. Protect against static electricity and lightning. Isolate from oxidizing materials, halogens, and other combustibles.

USUAL SHIPPING CONTAINERS: Steel cylinders; pressurized tanks on trucks, rail cars, barges.

PHYSICAL PROPERTIES: Colorless gas with sweet odor and taste. May exist as a cryogenic liquid.

MELTING POINT: −272°F (−169°C)

BOILING POINT: −155°F (−104°C)

SPECIFIC GRAVITY: 1.26 @ 0°C

SOLUBILITY IN WATER: not soluble

VAPOR DENSITY: 0.97

ELECTRICAL EQUIPMENT: Class I, Group C

NAME: **ETHYLENE CHLOROHYDRIN**

SYNONYMS: 2-chloroethanol; 2-chloroethyl alcohol; chlorohydrin; ethyl glycol; glycol chlorohydrin

FORMULA: $Cl(CH_2)_2OH$

NFPA 30/OSHA CLASSIFICATION: IIIA

DOT CLASS: Class 6.1, Poisonous material

SHIPPING LABEL: POISON

ID NO.: UN 1135

CAS NO.: 107-07-3

MOL. WT.: 80.5

STATEMENT OF HAZARDS: Severe health hazard. Combustible liquid.

EMERGENCY RESPONSE PERSONAL PROTECTIVE EQUIPMENT: Wear special protective clothing and positive pressure self-contained breathing apparatus.

SPILL OR LEAK PROCEDURES: Releases may require isolation or evacuation. Stop or control the leak, if this can be done without undue risk. Use water spray to cool and disperse vapors, protect personnel, and dilute spills to form nonflammable mixtures. Approach release from upwind.

FIRE FIGHTING PROCEDURES: Use water spray, dry chemical, "alcohol resistant" foam, or carbon dioxide. Use water spray to keep fire-exposed containers cool.

HEALTH HAZARDS: Severe health hazard. May be fatal if absorbed through skin or inhaled. Symptoms of overexposure include nausea, vomiting, pain in the head and chest, vertigo, and respiratory paralysis. Irritating to skin, eyes, and respiratory system.

FIRE AND EXPLOSION HAZARDS: Combustible liquid.

FLASH POINT: 140°F (60°C)

AUTOIGNITION TEMPERATURE: 797°F (425°C)

FLAMMABLE LIMITS: LOWER: 4.9% UPPER: 15.9%

INSTABILITY AND REACTIVITY HAZARDS: Reacts with oxidizing materials, acids, bases.

STORAGE RECOMMENDATIONS: Store in a cool, dry, well-ventilated location. Inside storage should be in a standard flammable liquids storage warehouse, room, or cabinet. Separate from oxidizing materials, acids, and bases.

USUAL SHIPPING CONTAINERS: Metal cans, pails, drums. Glass or polyethylene bottles, carboys, polyethylene-lined drums.

PHYSICAL PROPERTIES: Colorless liquid with a faint ethereal odor.

MELTING POINT: −90°F (−68°C)

BOILING POINT: 262 to 266°F (128 to 130°C)

SPECIFIC GRAVITY: 1.20

SOLUBILITY IN WATER: soluble

VAPOR PRESSURE: 5 mm Hg @ 20°C

ELECTRICAL EQUIPMENT: Class I, Group D

NAME: **ETHYLENE CYANOHYDRIN**

SYNONYMS: glycol cyanohydrin; hydracrylonitrile; 3-hydroxypropanenitrile; 3-hydroxypropio-nitrile

FORMULA: $HO(CH_2)_2CN$

NFPA 30/OSHA CLASSIFICATION: IIIB

DOT CLASS: N/A

ID NO.: N/A

CAS NO.: 109-78-4

MOL. WT.: 71.1

STATEMENT OF HAZARDS: Combustible liquid. Hazardous polymerization may occur. Slight health hazard. Combustion by-products may include hydrogen cyanide.

EMERGENCY RESPONSE PERSONAL PROTECTIVE EQUIPMENT: Wear full protective clothing and positive pressure self-contained breathing apparatus.

SPILL OR LEAK PROCEDURES: Stop or control the leak, if this can be done without undue risk. Use water spray to cool and disperse vapors, protect personnel, and dilute spills to form nonflammable mixtures. Absorb in noncombustible material for proper disposal.

FIRE FIGHTING PROCEDURES: Use water spray, dry chemical, "alcohol resistant" foam, or carbon dioxide. Water or foam may cause frothing. Use water spray to keep fire-exposed containers cool. Fight fire from protected location or maximum possible distance. Approach fire from upwind to avoid hazardous vapors and toxic decomposition products.

HEALTH HAZARDS: Slight health hazard. Irritating to skin, eyes, and respiratory system.

FIRE AND EXPLOSION HAZARDS: Combustible liquid. Products of combustion may be more hazardous than the material itself. By-products include highly flammable and toxic hydrogen cyanide and other irritants. Decomposition begins at 442°F (228°C). Closed containers may rupture violently when heated.

FLASH POINT: 265°F (129°C) (oc)

AUTOIGNITION TEMPERATURE: 922°F (494°C)

FLAMMABLE LIMITS: LOWER: 2.3% UPPER: 12.1%

INSTABILITY AND REACTIVITY HAZARDS: Hazardous polymerization may occur. Reacts violently with oxidizing materials.

STORAGE RECOMMENDATIONS: Store in a cool, dry, well-ventilated location. Separate from oxidizing materials. Outside or detached storage is preferred.

USUAL SHIPPING CONTAINERS: Metal cans, pails, drums. Tanks on trucks, rail cars, barges.

PHYSICAL PROPERTIES: Colorless to yellow-brown liquid. Odorless to weak odor.

MELTING POINT: −51°F (−46°C)

BOILING POINT: 442°F (228°C) (decomposes)

SPECIFIC GRAVITY: 1.04

SOLUBILITY IN WATER: soluble

ELECTRICAL EQUIPMENT: Class I, Group D

NAME: **ETHYLENE DIBROMIDE**

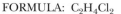

SYNONYMS: 1,2-dibromoethane; sym-dibromoethane; EDB; ethylene bromide

FORMULA: $C_2H_4Br_2$

NFPA 30/OSHA CLASSIFICATION:

DOT CLASS: Class 6.1, Poisonous material

SHIPPING LABEL: POISON

ID NO.: UN 1605

CAS NO.: 106-93-4

MOL. WT.: 187.9

STATEMENT OF HAZARDS: Serious health hazard.

EMERGENCY RESPONSE PERSONAL PROTECTIVE EQUIPMENT: Wear special protective clothing and positive pressure self-contained breathing apparatus.

SPILL OR LEAK PROCEDURES: Stop or control the leak, if this can be done without undue risk. Use appropriate foam to blanket release and suppress vapors. Absorb in noncombustible material for proper disposal.

FIRE FIGHTING PROCEDURES: Extinguish fire using agent suitable for surrounding fire. Use water to keep fire-exposed containers cool.

HEALTH HAZARDS: Serious health hazard. May be harmful if absorbed through skin or inhaled. Irritating to skin, eyes, and respiratory system. Symptoms of overexposure may include pulmonary lesions, central nervous system depression, dermatitis.

FIRE AND EXPLOSION HAZARDS: Not combustible, but if involved in a fire decomposes to produce hydrogen bromide.

INSTABILITY AND REACTIVITY HAZARDS: Reacts with oxidizing materials, alkali metals, ammonia.

STORAGE RECOMMENDATIONS: Store in a cool, dry, dark, well-ventilated location. Separate from oxidizing materials, alkali metals, ammonia.

USUAL SHIPPING CONTAINERS: Glass bottles; metal cans, pails, drums; tanks on trucks, rail cars, barges.

PHYSICAL PROPERTIES: Colorless, heavy liquid. Odor similar to chloroform (sweet, pleasant).

MELTING POINT: 50°F (10°C)

BOILING POINT: 268 to 270°F (131 to 132°C)

SPECIFIC GRAVITY: 2.18

SOLUBILITY IN WATER: not soluble

VAPOR PRESSURE: 11 mm Hg @ 25°C

NAME: **ETHYLENE DICHLORIDE**

SYNONYMS: 1,2-dichloroethane; sym-dichloroethane; EDC; ethylene chloride

FORMULA: $C_2H_4Cl_2$

NFPA 30/OSHA CLASSIFICATION: IB

DOT CLASS: Class 3, Flammable and combustible liquid

SHIPPING LABEL: FLAMMABLE LIQUID and POISON

ID NO.: UN 1184

CAS NO.: 107-06-2

MOL. WT.: 99.0

STATEMENT OF HAZARDS: Flammable liquid. Moderate health hazard. Combustion by-products may include hydrogen chloride and phosgene.

EMERGENCY RESPONSE PERSONAL PROTECTIVE EQUIPMENT: Wear full protective clothing and positive pressure self-contained breathing apparatus.

SPILL OR LEAK PROCEDURES: Eliminate all ignition sources. Use appropriate foam to blanket release and suppress vapors. Absorb in noncombustible material for proper disposal.

FIRE FIGHTING PROCEDURES: Use dry chemical, foam, carbon dioxide, or water spray. Water may be ineffective. Use water spray to keep fire-exposed containers cool. Approach fire from upwind to avoid hazardous vapors and toxic decomposition products.

HEALTH HAZARDS: Moderate health hazard. May be harmful if absorbed through skin or inhaled. Irritating to skin, eyes, and respiratory system. Symptoms of overexposure include dizziness, narcosis, abdominal cramps, central nervous system depression.

FIRE AND EXPLOSION HAZARDS: Flammable liquid. Vapors are heavier than air and may travel to a source of ignition and flash back. Combustion by-products include hydrogen chloride and phosgene. Forms dense soot.

FLASH POINT: 56°F (13°C)

AUTOIGNITION TEMPERATURE: 775°F (413°C)

FLAMMABLE LIMITS: LOWER: 6.2% UPPER: 15.9%

INSTABILITY AND REACTIVITY HAZARDS: Reacts with alkalies, amines, and alkali metals, such as aluminum.

STORAGE RECOMMENDATIONS: Store in a cool, dry, well-ventilated location. Separate from oxidizing materials, aluminum, ammonia.

USUAL SHIPPING CONTAINERS: Metal cans, pails, drums; tanks on trucks, rail cars, barges. Normally packaged under nitrogen gas.

PHYSICAL PROPERTIES: Colorless, heavy liquid. Odor similar to chloroform (sweet, pleasant). Sweet taste.

MELTING POINT: −32°F (−35°C)

BOILING POINT: 181 to 183°F (83 to 84°C)

SPECIFIC GRAVITY: 1.26

SOLUBILITY IN WATER: not soluble

VAPOR PRESSURE: 100 mm Hg @ 29°C

ELECTRICAL EQUIPMENT: Class I, Group D

NAME: **ETHYLENE OXIDE**

SYNONYMS: di-methylene oxide; EO; EtO; 1,2-epoxyethane; oxirane

FORMULA: H_2C—CH_2 (with O bridging the two carbons: O / \ above)

NFPA 30/OSHA CLASSIFICATION: IA

DOT CLASS: Class 2.3, Poisonous gas

SHIPPING LABEL: POISON GAS and FLAMMABLE GAS

ID NO.: UN 1040

CAS NO.: 75-21-8

MOL. WT.: 44.0

STATEMENT OF HAZARDS: Flammable gas. Low ignition energy. Explosive decomposition may occur. Hazardous polymerization may occur. Serious health hazard.

EMERGENCY RESPONSE PERSONAL PROTECTIVE EQUIPMENT: Wear special protective clothing and positive pressure self-contained breathing apparatus.

SPILL OR LEAK PROCEDURES: Eliminate all ignition sources. Releases may require isolation or evacuation. Approach release from upwind. Stop or control the leak, if this can be done without undue risk. Use water spray to cool and disperse vapors, protect personnel, and dilute spills to form nonflammable mixtures. Water solutions no longer flammable in open areas when diluted as 1 part in 22 parts water. In enclosed areas such as sewers, dilution to 1 part in 100 parts water may be required to eliminate flash potential. Control runoff and isolate discharged material for proper disposal.

FIRE FIGHTING PROCEDURES: Use flooding quantities of water as fog. Use water spray, dry chemical, "alcohol resistant" foam, or carbon dioxide. Use water spray to keep fire-exposed containers cool. Explosive decomposition may occur under fire conditions. Fight fire from protected location or maximum possible distance.

HEALTH HAZARDS: Serious health hazard. May be harmful if absorbed through skin or inhaled. Pulmonary edema may result. Irritating to skin, eyes, and respiratory system.

FIRE AND EXPLOSION HAZARDS: Flammable gas. Volatile flammable liquid below room temperature. Explosive decomposition may occur in vapor or liquid phases. Vapor forms explosive mixtures with air over a wide range. Vapors are heavier than air and may travel to a source of ignition and flash back. Closed containers may rupture violently when heated.

FLASH POINT: −4°F (−20°C)

AUTOIGNITION TEMPERATURE: 804°F (429°C) [AIT in the absence of air is 1058°F (570°C)]

FLAMMABLE LIMITS: LOWER: 3.0% UPPER: 100.0%

INSTABILITY AND REACTIVITY HAZARDS: Highly reactive. Hazardous polymerization may occur especially if contaminated. Reacts with acids, alkalies, salts, combustible materials. May undergo runaway reaction with water. Many materials may accelerate this reaction.

STORAGE RECOMMENDATIONS: Store in a cool, dry, well-ventilated location. Store away from heat, oxidizing materials, and sunlight. Separate from acids, alkalies, salts, and combustible materials. Outside or detached storage is preferred. May react in insulation forming low molecular weight polyethylene glycols that can spontaneously heat and ignite at less than 212°F (100°C).

USUAL SHIPPING CONTAINERS: Insulated steel cylinders; pressurized tanks on trucks, rail cars, barges. Safety relief valves required.

PHYSICAL PROPERTIES: Colorless gas with sweet ether-like odor.

MELTING POINT: −170°F (−112°C)

BOILING POINT: 51°F (11°C)

SPECIFIC GRAVITY: 0.89 @ 0°C

SOLUBILITY IN WATER: soluble

VAPOR DENSITY: 1.51

VAPOR PRESSURE: 1095 mm Hg @ 20°C

ELECTRICAL EQUIPMENT: Class I, Group B (C)

NAME: **ETHYLENEDIAMINE**

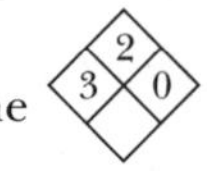

SYNONYMS: 1,2-diaminoethane; 1,2-ethanediamine

FORMULA: $NH_2CH_2CH_2NH_2$

NFPA 30/OSHA CLASSIFICATION: II

DOT CLASS: Class 8, Corrosive material

SHIPPING LABEL: CORROSIVE and FLAMMABLE LIQUID

ID NO.: UN 1604

CAS NO.: 107-15-3

MOL. WT.: 60.1

STATEMENT OF HAZARDS: Corrosive and combustible liquid.

EMERGENCY RESPONSE PERSONAL PROTECTIVE EQUIPMENT: Wear special protective clothing and positive pressure self-contained breathing apparatus.

SPILL OR LEAK PROCEDURES: Stop or control the leak, if this can be done without undue risk. Use water spray to cool and disperse vapors, protect personnel, and dilute spills to form nonflammable mixtures. Absorb in noncombustible material for proper disposal.

FIRE FIGHTING PROCEDURES: Use water spray, dry chemical, "alcohol resistant" foam, or carbon dioxide. Use water spray to keep fire-exposed containers cool. Solid streams may be ineffective and spread material.

HEALTH HAZARDS: Corrosive. Causes severe eye and skin burns. May be harmul if inhaled. Irritating to skin, eyes, and respiratory system. Sensitizer. May cause severe allergic reaction.

FIRE AND EXPLOSION HAZARDS: Combustible liquid.

FLASH POINT: 110°F (43°C)

AUTOIGNITION TEMPERATURE: 725°F (385°C)

FLAMMABLE LIMITS: LOWER: 1.1% UPPER: 5.8%

2.5% to 12% @ 212°F (100°C)

INSTABILITY AND REACTIVITY HAZARDS: Avoid contact with acids, oxidizing materials, chlorine, hypochlorite, halogenated compounds, and reactive organic compounds. Products of decomposition include carbon monoxide, carbon dioxide, hydrocarbons, and toxic oxides of nitrogen as well as toxic amine vapors. See NFPA 491M, Manual of Hazardous Chemical Reactions, for listed reactions with selected acids and unsaturated compounds where temperature rise and pressure increase are noted.

STORAGE RECOMMENDATIONS: Outside or detached storage is preferred. Avoid oxidizing materials, acids, and sources of halogens. Store in a cool, dry, well-ventilated location.

USUAL SHIPPING CONTAINERS: Glass bottles, cans, drums, and tank cars.

PHYSICAL PROPERTIES: Colorless hygroscopic liquid with odor of ammonia.

MELTING POINT: 47°F (9°C)

BOILING POINT: 239°F (115°C)

SPECIFIC GRAVITY: 0.90

SOLUBILITY IN WATER: soluble

VAPOR DENSITY: 2.07

VAPOR PRESSURE: 10 mm Hg @ 20°C

ELECTRICAL EQUIPMENT: Class I, Group D

NAME: **ETHYLENIMINE, inhibited**

SYNONYMS: amenoethylene; azacyclopropane; azirane; aziridine; dimethylenimine; EI; ethylimine

H
N
/ \
FORMULA: $H_2C—CH_2$

NFPA 30/OSHA CLASSIFICATION: IB

DOT CLASS: Class 6.1, Poisonous material

SHIPPING LABEL: POISON and FLAMMABLE LIQUID

ID NO.: UN 1185

CAS NO.: 151-56-4

MOL. WT.: 43.1

STATEMENT OF HAZARDS: Severe health hazard. Corrosive and flammable liquid. May polymerize explosively.

EMERGENCY RESPONSE PERSONAL PROTECTIVE EQUIPMENT: Wear special protective clothing and positive pressure self-contained breathing apparatus.

SPILL OR LEAK PROCEDURES: Releases may require isolation or evacuation. Eliminate all ignition sources. Stop or control the leak, if this can be done without undue risk. Use water spray to cool and disperse vapors, protect personnel, and dilute spills to form nonflammable mixtures. Absorb in noncombustible material for proper disposal.

FIRE FIGHTING PROCEDURES: Use dry chemical, "alcohol resistant" foam, carbon dioxide, or water spray. Water may be ineffective. Use water spray to keep fire-exposed containers cool. Approach fire from upwind to avoid hazardous vapors and toxic decomposition products. Explosive decomposition may occur under fire conditions. Fight fire from protected location or maximum possible distance.

HEALTH HAZARDS: Severe health hazard. May be fatal if absorbed through skin or inhaled. Corrosive. Causes severe eye and skin burns. Other symptoms include nausea, vomiting, dizziness, pulmonary edema. Effects may be delayed.

FIRE AND EXPLOSION HAZARDS: Flammable liquid. Vapors are heavier than air and may travel to a source of ignition and flash back. Closed containers may rupture violently when heated. Combustion by-products include oxides of nitrogen.

FLASH POINT: 12°F (−11°C)

AUTOIGNITION TEMPERATURE: 608°F (320°C)

FLAMMABLE LIMITS: LOWER: 3.3% UPPER: 54.8%

INSTABILITY AND REACTIVITY HAZARDS: May polymerize explosively. Usually contains inhibitors to prevent polymerization. Polymerization may be caused by elevated temperature, oxidizers, peroxides, or sunlight. Uninhibited monomer vapor may form polymer in vents and other confined spaces.

STORAGE RECOMMENDATIONS: Store in a cool, dry, well-ventilated location. Store away from heat, oxidizing materials, and sunlight. Separate from oxidizing materials and peroxides.

USUAL SHIPPING CONTAINERS: Metal can inside wooden box; drums; tanks on trucks, rail cars.

PHYSICAL PROPERTIES: Colorless, oily, volatile liquid. Ammonia odor.

MELTING POINT: −98°F (−72°C)

BOILING POINT: 135°F (57°C)

SPECIFIC GRAVITY: 0.83

SOLUBILITY IN WATER: soluble

VAPOR PRESSURE: 160 mm @ 20°C

ELECTRICAL EQUIPMENT: Class I, Group C

NAME: **2-ETHYLHEXYL ACRYLATE**

SYNONYMS: 2-ethylhexyl-2-propenoate

FORMULA: $CH_2=CHCO_2CH_2CH(C_2H_5)C_4H_9$

NFPA 30/OSHA CLASSIFICATION: IIIA

DOT CLASS: N/A

ID NO.: N/A

CAS NO.: 103-11-7

MOL. WT.: 184.3

STATEMENT OF HAZARDS: Combustible liquid. Thermally unstable. Polymerizes when exposed to heat. Peroxides or other initiators may cause polymerization. Moderate health hazard.

EMERGENCY RESPONSE PERSONAL PROTECTIVE EQUIPMENT: Wear full protective clothing and positive pressure self-contained breathing apparatus.

SPILL OR LEAK PROCEDURES: Stop or control the leak, if this can be done without undue risk. Use water spray to cool and disperse vapors, protect personnel. Control runoff and isolate discharged material for proper disposal.

FIRE FIGHTING PROCEDURES: Use water spray, dry chemical, foam, or carbon dioxide. Use water spray to keep fire-exposed containers cool. Water or foam may cause frothing. Fight fire from protected location or maximum possible distance.

HEALTH HAZARDS: Moderate health hazard. May be harmful if inhaled. Irritating to skin, eyes, and respiratory system. Skin sensitizer. May cause severe allergic reaction.

FIRE AND EXPLOSION HAZARDS: Combustible liquid. Closed containers may rupture violently when heated.

FLASH POINT: 180°F (82°C) (oc)

FLAMMABLE LIMITS: LOWER: 0.7% UPPER: 8.2%

INSTABILITY AND REACTIVITY HAZARDS: Hazardous polymerization may occur. Polymerization may be caused by elevated temperature, oxidizers, peroxides. Usually contains inhibitors to prevent polymerization. Material will react with strong acids and alkalies.

STORAGE RECOMMENDATIONS: Separate from heat, oxidizers, and sunlight. Store in a cool, dry, well-ventilated location. Outside or detached storage is preferred.

USUAL SHIPPING CONTAINERS: Bottles, cans, drums, and tank trucks or tank cars.

PHYSICAL PROPERTIES: Clear, colorless liquid with strong, acrid, musty odor.

MELTING POINT: −130°F (−90°C)

BOILING POINT: 363°F (184°C)

SPECIFIC GRAVITY: 0.88

SOLUBILITY IN WATER: not soluble

VAPOR PRESSURE: 0.14 mm Hg @ 20°C

ELECTRICAL EQUIPMENT: Class I, Group D

NAME: **ETHYL METHYL ETHER**

SYNONYMS: ethoxymethane; methoxyethane; methyl ethyl ether

FORMULA: $CH_3OC_2H_5$

NFPA 30/OSHA CLASSIFICATION: IA

DOT CLASS: Class 2.1, Flammable gas

SHIPPING LABEL: FLAMMABLE GAS

ID NO.: UN 1039

CAS NO.: 540-67-0

MOL. WT.: 60.1

STATEMENT OF HAZARDS: Flammable gas. May accumulate static electricity. Previously opened containers may contain dangerous explosive peroxides. Slight health hazard.

EMERGENCY RESPONSE PERSONAL PROTECTIVE EQUIPMENT: Wear full protective clothing and positive pressure self-contained breathing apparatus.

SPILL OR LEAK PROCEDURES: Stop or control the leak, if this can be done without undue risk. Eliminate all ignition sources. Use water spray to cool and disperse vapors, protect personnel, and dilute spills to form nonflammable mixtures. Approach release from upwind.

FIRE FIGHTING PROCEDURES: Use water spray to keep fire-exposed containers cool. Use water spray, dry chemical, "alcohol resistant" foam, or carbon dioxide. Solid water streams may spread fire.

HEALTH HAZARDS: Slight health hazard. Inhalation causes anesthesia, nausea, headache, dizziness, and irritation of eyes, skin, and respiratory system.

FIRE AND EXPLOSION HAZARDS: Flammable gas. Volatile flammable liquid below room temperature. Vapors are heavier than air and may travel to a source of ignition and flash back. Ether tends to form unstable, explosive peroxides on standing in presence of air.

FLASH POINT: −35°F (−37°C)

AUTOIGNITION TEMPERATURE: 374°F (190°C)

FLAMMABLE LIMITS: LOWER: 2% UPPER: 10.1%

INSTABILITY AND REACTIVITY HAZARDS: Peroxide formation is likely to occur when ether containers have been opened and remain in storage for more than six months.

STORAGE RECOMMENDATIONS: Outside or detached storage is preferred. Inside storage should be in a standard flammable liquids storage warehouse, room, or cabinet. Avoid sunlight.

USUAL SHIPPING CONTAINERS: Bottles, cans, or drums.

PHYSICAL PROPERTIES: Clear gas with sweet anesthetic odor.

BOILING POINT: 51°F (11°C)

SPECIFIC GRAVITY: 0.70

SOLUBILITY IN WATER: soluble

VAPOR DENSITY: 2.07

ELECTRICAL EQUIPMENT: Class I, Group C

NAME: **ETHYL NITRITE solutions**

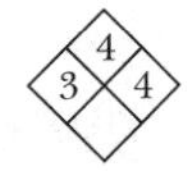

SYNONYMS: nitrous acid ethyl ester; nitrous ether

FORMULA: C_2H_5ONO

NFPA 30/OSHA CLASSIFICATION: IA

DOT CLASS: Class 3, Flammable and combustible liquid

SHIPPING LABEL: FLAMMABLE LIQUID and POISON

ID NO.: UN 1194

CAS NO.: 109-95-5

MOL. WT.: 75.1

STATEMENT OF HAZARDS: Flammable liquid. Thermally unstable. Decomposes explosively at 194°F (90°C). Corrosive.

EMERGENCY RESPONSE PERSONAL PROTECTIVE EQUIPMENT: Wear special protective clothing and positive pressure self-contained breathing apparatus.

SPILL OR LEAK PROCEDURES: Eliminate all ignition sources. Stop or control the leak, if this can be done without undue risk. Use appropriate foam to blanket release and suppress vapors. Absorb in noncombustible material for proper disposal.

FIRE FIGHTING PROCEDURES: Use water spray, dry chemical, foam, or carbon dioxide. Use water spray to keep fire-exposed containers cool. Fight fire from protected location or maximum possible distance.

HEALTH HAZARDS: Corrosive. Causes severe eye and skin burns. May be harmful if absorbed through skin or inhaled. Symptoms of overexposure include methemoglobinemia, narcosis, and hypotension.

FIRE AND EXPLOSION HAZARDS: Flammable liquid. Explodes when heated above 194°F (90°C). Air or oxygen is not required for decomposition. Closed containers may rupture violently when heated.

FLASH POINT: −31°F (−35°C)

AUTOIGNITION TEMPERATURE: 194°F (90°C)

FLAMMABLE LIMITS: LOWER: 3% UPPER: >50%

INSTABILITY AND REACTIVITY HAZARDS: Decomposes with air, light, or moisture.

STORAGE RECOMMENDATIONS: Store away from heat, oxidizers, and sunlight. Must be stored in a dry location. Outside or detached storage is preferred.

USUAL SHIPPING CONTAINERS: Bottles or carboys packed in insulating material.

PHYSICAL PROPERTIES: Colorless to yellow liquid. Ether odor. Burning, sweet taste.

BOILING POINT: 63°F (17°C)

SPECIFIC GRAVITY: 0.90

SOLUBILITY IN WATER: not soluble (decomposes)

VAPOR DENSITY: 2.59

ELECTRICAL EQUIPMENT: Class I, Group C

NAME: **ETHYLTRICHLOROSILANE**

SYNONYMS: ethyl silicon trichloride; trichloro ethenylsilane; trichloroethylsilane

FORMULA: $C_2H_5SiCl_3$

NFPA 30/OSHA CLASSIFICATION: IB

DOT CLASS: Class 3, Flammable and combustible liquid

SHIPPING LABEL: FLAMMABLE LIQUID and CORROSIVE

ID NO.: UN 1196

CAS NO.: 115-21-9

MOL. WT.: 163.5

STATEMENT OF HAZARDS: Corrosive and flammable liquid. Water reactive.

EMERGENCY RESPONSE PERSONAL PROTECTIVE EQUIPMENT: Wear special protective clothing and positive pressure self-contained breathing apparatus.

SPILL OR LEAK PROCEDURES: Eliminate all ignition sources. Stop or control the leak, if this can be done without undue risk. Use water spray to cool and disperse vapors and protect personnel. Control runoff and isolate discharged material for proper disposal.

FIRE FIGHTING PROCEDURES: Use dry chemical, "alcohol resistant" foam, carbon dioxide. Use water spray to keep fire-exposed containers cool. Approach fire from upwind to avoid hazardous vapors and toxic decomposition products.

HEALTH HAZARDS: Corrosive. Causes severe eye and skin burns. May be harmful if absorbed through skin or inhaled. Irritating to skin, eyes, and respiratory system.

FIRE AND EXPLOSION HAZARDS: Flammable liquid. Vapors are heavier than air and may travel to a source of ignition and flash back. Evolves hydrogen and may ignite on contact with base. Combustion by-products include hydrogen chloride, other irritants, and toxic gases.

FLASH POINT: 64°F (18°C) (oc)

INSTABILITY AND REACTIVITY HAZARDS: Reacts with water to produce hydrogen chloride. Reacts violently with a broad range of materials.

STORAGE RECOMMENDATIONS: Store in a cool, dry, well-ventilated location. Separate from acids, alkalies, oxidizing materials, and water. Outside or detached storage is preferred.

USUAL SHIPPING CONTAINERS: Glass bottle inside wooden box. Metal cans, pails, drums. Packaged under nitrogen gas.

PHYSICAL PROPERTIES: Colorless liquid. Acrid odor.

MELTING POINT: −158°F (−106°C)

BOILING POINT: 208°F (98°C)

SPECIFIC GRAVITY: 1.24

SOLUBILITY IN WATER: not soluble (decomposes)

ELECTRICAL EQUIPMENT: Class I, Group C

NAME: **FLUOBORIC ACID**

SYNONYMS: borofluoric acid; fluoroboric acid; hydroborofluoric acid; hydrofluoboric acid; tetrafluoroborate; tetrafluoroboric acid

FORMULA: HBF_4

NFPA 30/OSHA CLASSIFICATION:

DOT CLASS: Class 8, Corrosive material

SHIPPING LABEL: CORROSIVE

ID NO.: UN 1775

CAS NO.: 16872-11-0

MOL. WT.: 87.8

STATEMENT OF HAZARDS: Corrosive liquid.

EMERGENCY RESPONSE PERSONAL PROTECTIVE EQUIPMENT: Wear special protective clothing and positive pressure self-contained breathing apparatus.

SPILL OR LEAK PROCEDURES: Stop or control the leak, if this can be done without undue risk. Approach release from upwind. Control runoff and isolate discharged material for proper disposal.

FIRE FIGHTING PROCEDURES: Use appropriate extinguishing agent for surrounding fire. Use water spray to keep fire-exposed containers cool.

HEALTH HAZARDS: Corrosive. Causes severe eye and skin burns. May be harmful if absorbed through skin or inhaled.

FIRE AND EXPLOSION HAZARDS: Not combustible, but material reacts with active metals, releasing flammable hydrogen gas.

INSTABILITY AND REACTIVITY HAZARDS: Reacts with active metals and alkalies to release flammable hydrogen gas.

STORAGE RECOMMENDATIONS: Separate from active metals and alkalies. Outside or detached storage is preferred. Store in a cool, dry, well-ventilated location.

USUAL SHIPPING CONTAINERS: Stainless steel cylinders.

PHYSICAL PROPERTIES: Colorless liquid. Properties shown are for 50% water solution

BOILING POINT: 266°F (130°C) (decomposes)

SPECIFIC GRAVITY: 1.37

SOLUBILITY IN WATER: soluble

VAPOR PRESSURE: 5 to 10 mm Hg @ 20°C

NAME: **FLUORINE, compressed**

FORMULA: F_2

NFPA 30/OSHA CLASSIFICATION:

DOT CLASS: Class 2.3, Poisonous gas

SHIPPING LABEL: POISON GAS and OXIDIZER

ID NO.: UN 1045

CAS NO.: 7782-41-4

MOL. WT.: 38.0

STATEMENT OF HAZARDS: Severe health hazard. Corrosive gas. Very strong oxidizer. Water reactive. Reacts vigorously with most oxidizable materials.

EMERGENCY RESPONSE PERSONAL PROTECTIVE EQUIPMENT: Wear special protective clothing and positive pressure self-contained breathing apparatus.

SPILL OR LEAK PROCEDURES: Keep water away from release. Approach release from upwind. Stop or control the leak, if this can be done without undue risk. Control runoff and isolate discharged material for proper disposal.

FIRE FIGHTING PROCEDURES: Use water spray to keep fire-exposed containers cool. Extinguish associated fire using agent suitable for surrounding fire.

HEALTH HAZARDS: Severe health hazard. May be fatal if inhaled. Corrosive. Causes severe eye and skin burns. Irritating skin, eyes, and respiratory system. May cause respiratory paralysis.

FIRE AND EXPLOSION HAZARDS: Very strong oxidizer. Reacts violently with combustibles, causing fire or explosion. Combustion may produce irritants and toxic gases. Closed containers may rupture violently when heated.

INSTABILITY AND REACTIVITY HAZARDS: Strong oxidizer. Reacts with every known element except helium, neon, and argon. Reacts with all materials except for some Teflons and some metals at low temperatures. Water reactive. Reacts with water to form hydrogen fluoride and oxygen.

STORAGE RECOMMENDATIONS: Store in cool, dry, well-ventilated location. Outside or detached storage is preferred. Isolate from all other storage.

USUAL SHIPPING CONTAINERS: Shipped in special steel cylinders.

PHYSICAL PROPERTIES: Pale-yellow gas with sharp, pungent odor.

MELTING POINT: −363°F (−219°C)

BOILING POINT: −307°F (−188°C)

SPECIFIC GRAVITY: 1.69 (liquid)

SOLUBILITY IN WATER: reacts with water

VAPOR DENSITY: 1.31

NAME: **FORMALDEHYDE, solutions**
FORMALDEHYDE, solutions, flammable

solutions

flammable solutions

SYNONYMS: formalin; formic aldehyde; methanal; methyl aldehyde; methylene oxide; oxymethylene

FORMULA: HCHO

NFPA 30/OSHA CLASSIFICATION: IIIA

DOT CLASS: Class 9 (no label required)

Class 3 , Flammable and combustible liquid

SHIPPING LABEL: FLAMMABLE LIQUID

ID NO.: UN 2209 (Class 9)

UN 1198 (Class 3)

CAS NO.: 50-00-0

MOL. WT.: 30.0

STATEMENT OF HAZARDS: Flammable gas or combustible solutions. Corrosive.

EMERGENCY RESPONSE PERSONAL PROTECTIVE EQUIPMENT: Wear special protective clothing and positive pressure self-contained breathing apparatus.

SPILL OR LEAK PROCEDURES: Approach release from upwind. Use water spray to cool and disperse vapors, protect personnel, and dilute spills to form nonflammable mixtures. Stop or control the leak, if this can be done without undue risk. Control runoff and isolate discharged material for proper disposal.

FIRE FIGHTING PROCEDURES: Approach fire from upwind to avoid hazardous vapors and toxic decomposition products. Use water spray, dry chemical, "alcohol resistant" foam, or carbon dioxide.

HEALTH HAZARDS: Liquid is corrosive. Causes severe eye and skin burns. Vapor is irritating to eye, skin, and respiratory system.

FIRE AND EXPLOSION HAZARDS: Solutions of formaldehyde in water are considered combustible as the flammable vapors escape and form explosive mixtures with air over a wide range.

For aqueous solutions 37 to 56% formaldehyde by weight:

FLASH POINT: 140 to 181°F (60 to 83°C)

AUTOIGNITION TEMPERATURE: 806°F (430°C)

For gas: 572°F (300°C)

FLAMMABLE LIMITS: LOWER: 7.0% UPPER: 73.0%

INSTABILITY AND REACTIVITY HAZARDS: Reacts with alkalies, amines, acids, and oxidizing materials. Some monomers are reactive with formaldehyde.

STORAGE RECOMMENDATIONS: Store in a cool, dry, well-ventilated location. Special temperature control may be required. Separate from oxidizing materials, alkalies, acids, amines.

USUAL SHIPPING CONTAINERS: Bottles, carboys; tanks on trucks, rail cars, barges.

PHYSICAL PROPERTIES: Colorless gas with highly irritating odor. Commercially available in aqueous solutions 37 to 56% formaldehyde by weight. Methyl alcohol may be present up to 15 to inhibit polymerization.

MELTING POINT: −134°F (−92°C)

BOILING POINT: −6°F (−21°C)

SPECIFIC GRAVITY: 0.82 @ −21°C

SOLUBILITY IN WATER: soluble

VAPOR DENSITY: 1.03

VAPOR PRESSURE: gas

For aqueous solutions: 206 to 212°F (96.7 to 100°C)

VAPOR PRESSURE: 17 to 20 mm Hg @ 25°C (77°F)

ELECTRICAL EQUIPMENT: Class I, Group B

NAME: **FORMIC ACID**

SYNONYMS: methanoic acid

FORMULA: HCOOH

NFPA 30/OSHA CLASSIFICATION: II

DOT CLASS: Class 8, Corrosive material

SHIPPING LABEL: CORROSIVE

ID NO.: UN 1779

CAS NO.: 64-18-6

MOL. WT.: 46.0

STATEMENT OF HAZARDS: Corrosive and combustible liquid. Reacts with oxidizing materials.

EMERGENCY RESPONSE PERSONAL PROTECTIVE EQUIPMENT: Wear special protective clothing and positive pressure self-contained breathing apparatus.

SPILL OR LEAK PROCEDURES: Use water spray to cool and disperse vapors and protect personnel. Control runoff and isolate discharged material for proper disposal. Neutralize spill and washings with soda ash or lime.

FIRE FIGHTING PROCEDURES: Use water spray, dry chemical, "alcohol resistant" foam, or carbon dioxide. Use water spray to keep fire-exposed containers cool.

HEALTH HAZARDS: Corrosive. Causes severe eye and skin burns. May be harmful if inhaled. Inhalation causes damage to nasal and respiratory passages.

FIRE AND EXPLOSION HAZARDS: Combustible liquid. Combustion may produce irritants and toxic gases.

FLASH POINT: 122°F (50°C) (90% aqueous solution)

AUTOIGNITION TEMPERATURE: 813°F (601°C)

FLAMMABLE LIMITS: LOWER: 18% UPPER: 57% (90% aqueous solution)

INSTABILITY AND REACTIVITY HAZARDS: May react with alkalies and oxidizing materials such as peroxides, nitric acid, and chromic acid. Formic acid decomposes slowly during storage and more rapidly under fire conditions, forming carbon monoxide.

STORAGE RECOMMENDATIONS: Store in a dry, well-ventilated place. Separate from oxidizing materials and alkaline substances.

USUAL SHIPPING CONTAINERS: Glass bottles, carboys, lined drums and tankers.

PHYSICAL PROPERTIES: Colorless fuming liquid with pungent penetrating odor. Miscible with water. Usually available as 90% aqueous solutions.

MELTING POINT: 47°F (9°C)

BOILING POINT: 213°F (101°C)

SPECIFIC GRAVITY: 1.22

SOLUBILITY IN WATER: soluble

VAPOR PRESSURE: 22 mm Hg @ 20°C

ELECTRICAL EQUIPMENT: Class I, Group D

NAME: **FURFURAL**

SYNONYMS: fural; 2-furaldehyde; furfuraldehyde; furfurol

FORMULA: C_4H_3OCHO

NFPA 30/OSHA CLASSIFICATION: IIIA

DOT CLASS: Class 3, Flammable and combustible liquid

SHIPPING LABEL: FLAMMABLE LIQUID

ID NO.: UN 1199

CAS NO.: 98-01-1

MOL. WT.: 96.1

STATEMENT OF HAZARDS: Serious health hazard. Combustible liquid.

EMERGENCY RESPONSE PERSONAL PROTECTIVE EQUIPMENT: Wear special protective clothing and positive pressure self-contained breathing apparatus.

SPILL OR LEAK PROCEDURES: Stop or control the leak, if this can be done without undue risk. Use water spray to cool and disperse vapors and protect personnel. Control runoff and isolate discharged material for proper disposal.

FIRE FIGHTING PROCEDURES: Use water spray, dry chemical, "alcohol resistant" foam, or carbon dioxide. Use water spray to keep fire-exposed containers cool.

HEALTH HAZARDS: Serious health hazard. May be harmful if absorbed through skin or inhaled. Irritating to eyes, skin, and respiratory system.

FIRE AND EXPLOSION HAZARDS: Combustible liquid. Combustion may produce irritants and toxic gases.

FLASH POINT: 140°F (60°C)

AUTOIGNITION TEMPERATURE: 601°F (316°C)

FLAMMABLE LIMITS: LOWER: 2.1% UPPER: 19.3%

INSTABILITY AND REACTIVITY HAZARDS: Polymerization may occur on contact with strong acids or strong alkalies. Reacts with oxidizing materials.

STORAGE RECOMMENDATIONS: Store in cool, dry, well-ventilated location. Separate from strong oxidizing materials, strong alkalies, and strong acids. Outside or detached storage is preferred.

USUAL SHIPPING CONTAINERS: Bottles, drums, tank cars, and tank trucks.

PHYSICAL PROPERTIES: Colorless to light-brown liquid with odor of almonds.

MELTING POINT: −38°F (−39°C)

BOILING POINT: 323°F (162°C)

SPECIFIC GRAVITY: 1.16

SOLUBILITY IN WATER: partly soluble

VAPOR PRESSURE: 2 mm Hg @ 20°C

ELECTRICAL EQUIPMENT: Class I, Group C

NAME: **GALLIUM ARSENIDE**

SYNONYMS: gallium monoarsenide

FORMULA: GaAs

NFPA 30/OSHA CLASSIFICATION:

DOT CLASS: N/A

ID NO.: N/A

CAS NO.: 1303-00-0

MOL. WT.: 144.6

STATEMENT OF HAZARDS: Serious health hazard. Combustible solid. Combustion by-products may include fumes of gallium, arsenic, and arsine. Water reactive.

EMERGENCY RESPONSE PERSONAL PROTECTIVE EQUIPMENT: Wear special protective clothing and positive pressure self-contained breathing apparatus.

SPILL OR LEAK PROCEDURES: Keep water away from release. Absorb in noncombustible material for proper disposal. Prompt cleanup and removal are necessary.

FIRE FIGHTING PROCEDURES: Extinguish fire using agent suitable for surrounding fire. Use approved Class D extinguishers or smother with dry sand, dry clay, or dry ground limestone. DO NOT use carbon dioxide or halogenated extinguishing agents. DO NOT use water; violent reaction may result. Explosive decomposition may occur under fire conditions. Fight fire from protected location or maximum possible distance.

HEALTH HAZARDS: Serious health hazard. May be harmful if absorbed through skin or inhaled. May cause pulmonary edema. Irritating to skin, eyes, and respiratory system. Gallium exposure results in metallic taste and dermatitis. Combustion by-products may include fumes of gallium, arsenic, and arsine.

FIRE AND EXPLOSION HAZARDS: Combustible solid. Combustion may produce irritants; fumes of gallium, arsenic, and flammable arsine gas; and other toxic gases. Closed containers may rupture violently when heated.

INSTABILITY AND REACTIVITY HAZARDS: Water reactive. Reacts with steam and acids to produce flammable arsine gas.

STORAGE RECOMMENDATIONS: Store in a cool, dry, well-ventilated location. Isolate from water and acids. Outside or detached storage is preferred.

USUAL SHIPPING CONTAINERS: Metal cans, pails, drums.

PHYSICAL PROPERTIES: Dark gray crystals with metallic sheen. May have odor of garlic if moist.

MELTING POINT: 2260°F (1238°C)

SPECIFIC GRAVITY: 5.31

SOLUBILITY IN WATER: not soluble (decomposes)

NAME: **GALLIUM PHOSPHIDE**

FORMULA: GaP

NFPA 30/OSHA CLASSIFICATION:

DOT CLASS: N/A

ID NO.: N/A

CAS NO.: 12063-98-8

MOL. WT.: 100.7

STATEMENT OF HAZARDS: Serious health hazard. Liberates pyrophoric phosphine gas, a severe health hazard, if exposed to water.

EMERGENCY RESPONSE PERSONAL PROTECTIVE EQUIPMENT: Wear special protective clothing and positive pressure self-contained breathing apparatus.

SPILL OR LEAK PROCEDURES: Keep water away from release. Absorb in noncombustible material for proper disposal. Prompt cleanup and removal are necessary.

FIRE FIGHTING PROCEDURES: Use approved Class D extinguishers or smother with dry sand, dry clay, or dry ground limestone. DO NOT use carbon dioxide or halogenated extinguishing agents. DO NOT use water. Violent reaction may result. Where access to the area is strictly controlled, it may be best to allow the release to burn.

HEALTH HAZARDS: Serious health hazard. May be harmful if inhaled. Irritating to respiratory system. Symptoms of exposure to gallium include metallic taste, dermatitis, nausea, and vomiting.

FIRE AND EXPLOSION HAZARDS: On contact with water, generates phosphine gas, which is pyrophoric; ignites spontaneously on exposure to air. Combustion may produce irritants and toxic gases.

INSTABILITY AND REACTIVITY HAZARDS: Reacts with water and acids, releasing toxic, pyrophoric phosphine.

STORAGE RECOMMENDATIONS: Store in a cool, dry, well-ventilated location. Isolate from water and acids. Outside or detached storage is preferred.

USUAL SHIPPING CONTAINERS: Metal cans, pails, drums.

PHYSICAL PROPERTIES: Translucent, amber-colored crystals. May have odor of rotten fish if moist.

MELTING POINT: 2669°F (1465°C)

SOLUBILITY IN WATER: not soluble (decomposes)

NAME: **GALLIUM TRICHLORIDE**

SYNONYMS: gallium (3+) chloride

FORMULA: $GaCl_3$

NFPA 30/OSHA CLASSIFICATION:

DOT CLASS: N/A

ID NO.: N/A

CAS NO.: 13450-90-3

MOL. WT.: 176.1

STATEMENT OF HAZARDS: Corrosive.

EMERGENCY RESPONSE PERSONAL PROTECTIVE EQUIPMENT: Wear special protective clothing and positive pressure self-contained breathing apparatus.

SPILL OR LEAK PROCEDURES: Approach release from upwind. Shovel into suitable dry container.

FIRE FIGHTING PROCEDURES: Extinguish fire using agent suitable for surrounding fire. Approach fire from upwind to avoid hazardous vapors and toxic decomposition products.

HEALTH HAZARDS: Corrosive. Causes severe eye and skin burns. May be harmful if inhaled. Irritating to skin, eyes, and respiratory system. Gallium exposure results in metallic taste, dermatitis, nausea, and vomiting.

FIRE AND EXPLOSION HAZARDS: Not combustible, but if involved in a fire decomposes to produce toxic gallium fumes and hydrogen chloride.

INSTABILITY AND REACTIVITY HAZARDS: May react with alkali metals, water.

STORAGE RECOMMENDATIONS: Keep in a cool, dry, well-ventilated location. Separate from alkali metals, halogenated compounds, water.

USUAL SHIPPING CONTAINERS: Bottles or metal can packed in insulating material. Metal cans, pails, drums.

PHYSICAL PROPERTIES: Colorless to white crystals, may emit acrid odor in moist air.

MELTING POINT: 172°F (78°C)

BOILING POINT: 394°F (201°C)

SPECIFIC GRAVITY: 2.47

SOLUBILITY IN WATER: not soluble (decomposes)

NAME: **GERMANE**

SYNONYMS: germanium tetrahydride; monogermane

FORMULA: GeH_4

NFPA 30/OSHA CLASSIFICATION:

DOT CLASS: Class 2.3, Poisonous gas

SHIPPING LABEL: POISON GAS and FLAMMABLE GAS

ID NO.: UN 2192

CAS NO.: 7782-65-2

MOL. WT.: 76.6

STATEMENT OF HAZARDS: Pyrophoric. Severe health hazard. Flammable gas. May decompose explosively at elevated temperature. May propagate a decomposition flame in the absence of air.

EMERGENCY RESPONSE PERSONAL PROTECTIVE EQUIPMENT: Wear special protective clothing and positive pressure self-contained breathing apparatus.

SPILL OR LEAK PROCEDURES: Keep water away from release. Stop or control the leak, if this can be done without undue risk. Use water spray to cool and disperse vapors and protect personnel. Releases may ignite spontaneously.

FIRE FIGHTING PROCEDURES: Stop flow of gas before extinguishing fire. Use dry chemical, foam, carbon dioxide, or water spray. Use water spray to keep fire-exposed containers cool. Explosive decomposition may occur under fire conditions. Fight fire from protected location or maximum possible distance. Approach fire from upwind to avoid hazardous vapors and toxic decomposition products.

HEALTH HAZARDS: Severe health hazard. May be fatal if inhaled. Symptoms of overexposure include coughing, wheezing, laryngitis, headache, nausea and vomiting, and pulmonary edema.

FIRE AND EXPLOSION HAZARDS: Flammable gas. Pyrophoric; ignites spontaneously on exposure to air. May evolve hydrogen and ignite on contact with water. Combustion may produce irritants and toxic gases. Closed containers may rupture violently when heated.

INSTABILITY AND REACTIVITY HAZARDS: Reacts violently with oxidizing materials and halogens. Can decompose explosively.

STORAGE RECOMMENDATIONS: Store in a cool, dry, well-ventilated location. Separate from air, oxidizing materials, and halogens. Outside or detached storage is preferred.

USUAL SHIPPING CONTAINERS: Steel cylinders.

PHYSICAL PROPERTIES: Colorless gas with pungent odor.

MELTING POINT: −265°F (−165°C)

BOILING POINT: −127°F (−89°C)

SPECIFIC GRAVITY: 1.52

SOLUBILITY IN WATER: not soluble

VAPOR DENSITY: 2.64

VAPOR PRESSURE: 76 mm Hg @ 20°C

NAME: **HEXAMETHYLDISILAZANE**

SYNONYMS: HMDS; HMDZ

FORMULA: $(CH_3)_3SiNHSi(CH_3)_3$

NFPA 30/OSHA CLASSIFICATION: IB

DOT CLASS: N/A

ID NO.: N/A

CAS NO.: 999-97-3

MOL. WT.: 161

STATEMENT OF HAZARDS: Flammable liquid. May accumulate static electricity. Slight health hazard.

EMERGENCY RESPONSE PERSONAL PROTECTIVE EQUIPMENT: Wear full protective clothing and positive pressure self-contained breathing apparatus.

SPILL OR LEAK PROCEDURES: Eliminate all ignition sources. Stop or control the leak, if this can be done without undue risk. Use water spray to cool and disperse vapors and protect personnel. Control runoff and isolate discharged material for proper disposal.

FIRE FIGHTING PROCEDURES: Use dry chemical, "alcohol resistant" foam, or carbon dioxide. Use water spray to keep fire-exposed containers cool. Approach fire from upwind to avoid hazardous vapors and toxic decomposition products.

HEALTH HAZARDS: Slight health hazard. Irritating to skin, eyes, and respiratory system.

FIRE AND EXPLOSION HAZARDS: Flammable liquid. Vapors are heavier than air and may travel to a source of ignition and flash back. Combustion may produce irritants and toxic gases.

FLASH POINT: 48°F (9°C)

FLAMMABLE LIMITS: LOWER: 0.7% UPPER: 31%

INSTABILITY AND REACTIVITY HAZARDS: Reacts with mineral acids and water. Products of combustion include oxides of nitrogen.

STORAGE RECOMMENDATIONS: Store in a cool, dry, well-ventilated location. Separate from acids.

USUAL SHIPPING CONTAINERS: Glass bottles.

PHYSICAL PROPERTIES: Clear liquid, slight amine odor.

MELTING POINT: −94°F (−70°C)

BOILING POINT: 259°F (126°C)

SPECIFIC GRAVITY: 0.77

SOLUBILITY IN WATER: reacts slowly

VAPOR PRESSURE: 23 mm Hg

ELECTRICAL EQUIPMENT: Class I, Group C

NAME: **HYDRAZINE, anhydrous**

SYNONYMS: diamide; diamine; hydrazine base

FORMULA: H_2NNH_2

NFPA 30/OSHA CLASSIFICATION: II

DOT CLASS: Class 3, Flammable and combutible liquid

SHIPPING LABEL: FLAMMABLE LIQUID and POISON and CORROSIVE

ID NO.: UN 2029

CAS NO.: 302-01-2

MOL. WT.: 32.0

STATEMENT OF HAZARDS: Corrosive and flammable liquid. Rocket fuel. Air or oxygen is not required for decomposition. Thermally unstable. Decomposes at room temperature or above depending on surface contacted.

EMERGENCY RESPONSE PERSONAL PROTECTIVE EQUIPMENT: Wear special protective clothing and positive pressure self-contained breathing apparatus.

SPILL OR LEAK PROCEDURES: Eliminate all ignition sources. Approach release from upwind. Use water spray to cool and disperse vapors, protect personnel, and dilute spills to form nonflammable mixtures. Control runoff and isolate discharged material for proper disposal.

FIRE FIGHTING PROCEDURES: Approach fire from upwind to avoid hazardous vapors and toxic decomposition products. Fight fire from protected location or maximum possible distance. Use water spray to keep fire-exposed containers cool. Use flooding quantities of water as fog or spray. Flooding may be necessary to prevent reignition.

HEALTH HAZARDS: Corrosive. Causes severe eye and skin burns. May be harmful if absorbed through skin or inhaled. Irritating to skin, eyes, and respiratory system. Delayed effects are possible. Skin sensitizer. May cause severe allergic reaction.

FIRE AND EXPLOSION HAZARDS: Flammable liquid. Rocket fuel. Flammable over a wide range including 100% pure material. Air or oxygen is not required for decomposition. Closed containers may rupture violently when heated. Thermally unstable. Ignites in air at room temperature on metal oxide surfaces, and in a wide variety of porous materials, such as cellulosic materials.

FLASH POINT: 100°F (38°C)

AUTOIGNITION TEMPERATURE: 518°F (270°C) on glass surface. Autoignition temperature may be as low as 74°F (23°C) depending on surface contacted.

FLAMMABLE LIMITS: LOWER: 2.9% UPPER: 98%

INSTABILITY AND REACTIVITY HAZARDS: Thermally unstable. Powerful reducing agent; reacts vigorously with most oxidizing materials. Strong alkali.

STORAGE RECOMMENDATIONS: Detached storage is preferred. Inside storage should be in a standard flammable liquids storage warehouse, room, or cabinet. Provide water for flushing spills or leaks. Tanks should be located in water-filled dikes. Separate from acids, oxidizing materials, metal oxides. Normally stored under nitrogen.

USUAL SHIPPING CONTAINERS: Glass bottles and carboys in wooden boxes; special cans; drums; tanks on trucks, rail cars, barges.

PHYSICAL PROPERTIES: Colorless oily liquid, fuming in air. Hygroscopic. Ammonia-like odor.

MELTING POINT: 36°F (2°C)

BOILING POINT: 236°F (113°C)

SPECIFIC GRAVITY: 1.00

SOLUBILITY IN WATER: soluble

VAPOR PRESSURE: 10 mm Hg @ 20°C

ELECTRICAL EQUIPMENT: Class I, Group C

NAME: **HYDRIODIC ACID, solution**

SYNONYMS: hydrogen iodide solution

FORMULA: HI

NFPA 30/OSHA CLASSIFICATION:

DOT CLASS: Class 8, Corrosive material

SHIPPING LABEL: CORROSIVE

ID NO.: UN 1787

CAS NO.: 10034-85-2

MOL. WT.: 127.9

STATEMENT OF HAZARDS: Corrosive gas in solution (57% hydrogen iodide).

EMERGENCY RESPONSE PERSONAL PROTECTIVE EQUIPMENT: Wear special protective clothing and positive pressure self-contained breathing apparatus.

SPILL OR LEAK PROCEDURES: Stop or control the leak, if this can be done without undue risk. Absorb in noncombustible material for proper disposal.

FIRE FIGHTING PROCEDURES: Extinguish fire using agent suitable for surrounding fire. Use flooding quantities of water. Use water spray to keep fire-exposed containers cool. Approach fire from upwind to avoid hazardous vapors.

HEALTH HAZARDS: Corrosive. Causes severe eye and skin burns. May be harmful if absorbed through skin or inhaled. Irritating to skin, eyes, and respiratory system. Symptoms of overexposure include burning, coughing, wheezing, laryngitis, headache, nausea, and vomiting.

FIRE AND EXPLOSION HAZARDS: Not combustible, but if involved in a fire decomposes to produce irritants and toxic gases.

INSTABILITY AND REACTIVITY HAZARDS: Strong acid. Reacts with alkalies and steel.

STORAGE RECOMMENDATIONS: Store in a cool, dry, well-ventilated location. Separate from alkalies, amines, oxidizing materials, alkali metals, and steel. Refrigerate at or below 30°F (−1°C).

USUAL SHIPPING CONTAINERS: Glass or polyethylene bottles, carboys, polyethylene-lined drums.

PHYSICAL PROPERTIES: Colorless to yellow/brown liquid. Acrid odor.

MELTING POINT: −59°F (−51°C)

BOILING POINT: −31°F (−35°C)

SPECIFIC GRAVITY: 2.85 @ 40°C

SOLUBILITY IN WATER: soluble

NAME: **HYDROBROMIC ACID** solution

SYNONYMS: hydrogen bromide

FORMULA: HBr

NFPA 30/OSHA CLASSIFICATION:

DOT CLASS: Class 8, Corrosive material

SHIPPING LABEL: CORROSIVE

ID NO.: UN 1788

CAS NO.: 10035-10-6

MOL. WT.: 80.91

STATEMENT OF HAZARDS: Corrosive gas in solution.

EMERGENCY RESPONSE PERSONAL PROTECTIVE EQUIPMENT: Wear special protective clothing and positive pressure self-contained breathing apparatus.

SPILL OR LEAK PROCEDURES: Stop or control the leak, if this can be done without undue risk. Absorb in noncombustible material for proper disposal.

FIRE FIGHTING PROCEDURES: Extinguish fire using agent suitable for surrounding fire. Use flooding quantities of water. Use water spray to keep fire-exposed containers cool. Approach fire from upwind to avoid hazardous vapors.

HEALTH HAZARDS: Corrosive. Causes severe eye and skin burns. Toxic. May be harmful if absorbed through skin or inhaled. Irritating to skin, eyes, and respiratory system. Symptoms include: burning, wheezing, coughing, laryngitis, headache, nausea, and vomiting.

FIRE AND EXPLOSION HAZARDS: Not combustible, but if involved in a fire decomposes to produce irritants and toxic gases.

INSTABILITY AND REACTIVITY HAZARDS: Strong acid. Reacts violently with a broad range of materials, including most metals.

STORAGE RECOMMENDATIONS: Store in a cool, dry, well-ventilated location. Separate from alkalies, oxidizing materials, amines, halogens, and metals.

USUAL SHIPPING CONTAINERS: Glass or polyethylene bottles, carboys, polyethylene-lined drums; tanks on trucks, rail cars, barges.

PHYSICAL PROPERTIES: Colorless to pale yellow to brown liquid.

MELTING POINT: −127°F (−89°C) (gas)

BOILING POINT: 165°F (74°C) (solution)

SPECIFIC GRAVITY: 3.5 (gas) 2.7 (solution)

SOLUBILITY IN WATER: soluble

NAME: **HYDROGEN, refrigerated liquid**

SYNONYMS: protium

FORMULA: H_2

NFPA 30/OSHA CLASSIFICATION:

DOT CLASS: Class 2.1, Flammable gas

SHIPPING LABEL: FLAMMABLE GAS

ID NO.: UN 1966 refrigerated liquid

CAS NO.: 1333-74-0

MOL. WT.: 2.0

STATEMENT OF HAZARDS: Liquefied or compressed flammable gas. Low ignition energy. Burns with practically invisible flame. Reacts vigorously with oxidizers.

EMERGENCY RESPONSE PERSONAL PROTECTIVE EQUIPMENT: Wear special protective clothing and positive pressure self-contained breathing apparatus.

SPILL OR LEAK PROCEDURES: Eliminate all ignition sources. Approach release from upwind. Stop or control the leak, if this can be done without undue risk. Use water spray to disperse vapors and protect personnel.

FIRE FIGHTING PROCEDURES: Approach fire with caution as high-temperature flame is practically invisible. Stop flow of gas before extinguishing fire. Use water spray to keep fire-exposed containers cool. Use flooding quantities of water as fog or spray.

HEALTH HAZARDS: Contact with liquid will cause frostbite or severe burns of the skin. Simple asphyxiant.

FIRE AND EXPLOSION HAZARDS: Liquefied or compressed flammable gas. Easily ignited over a wide range of vapor/air concentrations. Rapid propagation of flame or flashback possible. Burns with practically invisible flame at 3700°F (2038°C), which must be avoided. Flammable or explosive when mixed with chlorine or other oxidizing materials. Liquid hydrogen in exposed piping may condense oxygen out of atmosphere. High pressure releases often ignite with no apparent source of ignition possibly via static electricity.

AUTOIGNITION TEMPERATURE: 752°F (400°C)

FLAMMABLE LIMITS: LOWER: 4.0% UPPER: 75.0%

INSTABILITY AND REACTIVITY HAZARDS: Easily oxidized. Some steels are susceptible to hydrogen attack or embrittlement at high temperature and pressure.

STORAGE RECOMMENDATIONS: Store in a cool, dry, well-ventilated location. Outside or detached storage is preferred. Isolate from oxygen, halogens, other oxidizing materials.

USUAL SHIPPING CONTAINERS: Cylinders and special tank cars.

PHYSICAL PROPERTIES: Colorless, odorless gas. Much lighter than air.

MELTING POINT: −434°F (−259°C)

BOILING POINT: −423°F (−253°C)

SPECIFIC GRAVITY: 0.071

SOLUBILITY IN WATER: not soluble

VAPOR DENSITY: 0.069

VAPOR PRESSURE: gas

ELECTRICAL EQUIPMENT: Class I, Group B

NAME: **HYDROGEN CHLORIDE, anhydrous**
HYDROGEN CHLORIDE, refrigerated liquid

FORMULA: HCl

NFPA 30/OSHA CLASSIFICATION:

DOT CLASS: Class 2.3, Poisonous gas

SHIPPING LABEL: POISON GAS and CORROSIVE

ID NO.: UN 1050 anhydrous

UN 2186 refrigerated liquid

CAS NO.: 7647-01-0

MOL. WT.: 36.5

STATEMENT OF HAZARDS: Corrosive.

EMERGENCY RESPONSE PERSONAL PROTECTIVE EQUIPMENT: Wear special protective clothing and positive pressure self-contained breathing apparatus.

SPILL OR LEAK PROCEDURES: Approach release from upwind. Stop or control the leak, if this can be done without undue risk. Use water fog or spray to knock down and absorb vapors. Releases may require isolation or evacuation. Control runoff and isolate discharged material for proper disposal.

FIRE FIGHTING PROCEDURES: Use water spray to keep fire-exposed containers cool. Extinguish fire using agent suitable for surrounding fire.

HEALTH HAZARDS: Corrosive. Causes severe eye and skin burns. May be harmful if inhaled. Irritating to skin, eyes, and respiratory system. Contact with liquid may cause frostbite.

FIRE AND EXPLOSION HAZARDS: Not combustible. Aqueous hydrochloric acid solutions react with most metals, forming flammable hydrogen gas.

INSTABILITY AND REACTIVITY HAZARDS: Anhydrous hydrogen chloride is rapidly absorbed in water to form corrosive hydrochloric acid. Aqueous hydrochloric acid solutions are quite reactive. Reacts vigorously with alkalies and with many organic materials. Strong oxidizing materials cause release of chlorine.

STORAGE RECOMMENDATIONS: Store in a cool, dry, well-ventilated location. Separate from oxidizing materials, organic materials, and alkalies.

USUAL SHIPPING CONTAINERS: Aqueous solutions in glass bottles and carboys and in rubber-lined tankers. Anhydrous hydrogen chloride in steel cylinders.

PHYSICAL PROPERTIES: Colorless gas with an irritating pungent odor. Hydrochloric acid solutions are colorless or slightly yellow with irritating pungent odor; usually fuming.

MELTING POINT: −174°F (−114°C)

BOILING POINT: −121°F (−85°C)

SPECIFIC GRAVITY: 1.19 @ −85°C

SOLUBILITY IN WATER: soluble

VAPOR DENSITY: 1.26

VAPOR PRESSURE: gas

NAME: **HYDROGEN CYANIDE, anhydrous, stabilized**
HYDROGEN CYANIDE, anhydrous, stabilized absorbed in a porous inert material

SYNONYMS: formonitrile; hydrocyanic acid; prussic acid

FORMULA: HCN

NFPA 30/OSHA CLASSIFICATION: IA

DOT CLASS: Class 6.1, Poisonous material

SHIPPING LABEL: POISON and FLAMMABLE LIQUID

ID NO.: UN 1051 (anhydrous)

UN 1614 (absorbed in a porous material)

CAS NO.: 74-90-8

MOL. WT.: 27.0

STATEMENT OF HAZARDS: Severe health hazard. Flammable liquid. Low ignition energy. May polymerize violently after a period of time.

EMERGENCY RESPONSE PERSONAL PROTECTIVE EQUIPMENT: Wear special protective clothing and positive pressure self-contained breathing apparatus.

SPILL OR LEAK PROCEDURES: Releases may require isolation or evacuation. Eliminate all ignition sources. Stop or control the leak, if this can be done without undue risk. Use vapor-suppressing foam to blanket release.

FIRE FIGHTING PROCEDURES: Fire situations may require evacuation. Allow burning of material until flow of gas can be stopped. Use water spray, dry chemical, "alcohol resistant" foam, or carbon dioxide. Water may be ineffective. Approach fire from upwind. Fight fire from protected location or maximum possible distance.

HEALTH HAZARDS: Severe health hazard. May be fatal if absorbed through skin or inhaled. May cause headache, nausea, vomiting, paralysis, convulsions, unconsciousness, death, cyanosis.

FIRE AND EXPLOSION HAZARDS: Flammable liquid. Burns in air with a blue flame. Closed containers may rupture violently when heated.

FLASH POINT: 0°F (−18°C)

AUTOIGNITION TEMPERATURE: 1004°F (540°C)

FLAMMABLE LIMITS: LOWER: 5.6% UPPER: 40%

INSTABILITY AND REACTIVITY HAZARDS: May violently polymerize spontaneously in absence of inhibitors or if impure.

STORAGE RECOMMENDATIONS: Store in a cool, dry, well-ventilated location. Shelf life not to exceed 90 days or as otherwise specified by manufacturer.

USUAL SHIPPING CONTAINERS: Steel cylinders from lecture bottle size to tank cars. Also dissolved or absorbed into water, inert solutions, or other materials.

PHYSICAL PROPERTIES: Colorless gas or liquid. Distinctive odor of bitter almonds.

MELTING POINT: 7°F (−14°C)

BOILING POINT: 79°F (26°C)

SPECIFIC GRAVITY: 0.69 (liquid)

SOLUBILITY IN WATER: soluble

VAPOR DENSITY: 0.94 (gas)

ELECTRICAL EQUIPMENT: Class I, Group C

NAME: **HYDROGEN FLUORIDE, anhydrous**

SYNONYMS: anhydrous hydrofluoric acid; fluohydric acid; HFA; hydrofluoric acid gas

FORMULA: HF

NFPA 30/OSHA CLASSIFICATION:

DOT CLASS: Class 8, Corrosive material

SHIPPING LABEL: CORROSIVE and POISON

ID NO.: UN 1052

CAS NO.: 7664-39-3

MOL. WT.: 20.0

STATEMENT OF HAZARDS: Severe health hazard. Corrosive.

EMERGENCY RESPONSE PERSONAL PROTECTIVE EQUIPMENT: Wear special protective clothing and positive pressure self-contained breathing apparatus.

SPILL OR LEAK PROCEDURES: Releases may require isolation or evacuation. Stop or control the leak, if this can be done without undue risk. Use water fog or spray to knock down and absorb vapors. Absorb in noncombustible material for proper disposal.

FIRE FIGHTING PROCEDURES: Extinguish fire surrounding anhydrous hydrogen fluoride containers using agent suitable for surrounding fire. Water spray is very effective in absorbing HF fumes escaping from leaking containers of anhydrous hydrogen fluoride. Use flooding quantities of water. Use water spray to keep fire-exposed containers cool. Approach fire from upwind to avoid hazardous vapors.

HEALTH HAZARDS: Severe health hazard. May be fatal if inhaled. May cause pulmonary edema. Corrosive. Causes severe eye and skin burns. Contact with dilute solutions (<20% in water) may produce pain or visible damage; such as erythema within 24 hours after the exposure.

FIRE AND EXPLOSION HAZARDS: Not combustible, but if involved in a fire is extremely irritating. Evolves heat when combined with water.

INSTABILITY AND REACTIVITY HAZARDS: Not compatible with most metals, water, and alkali materials. Reacts to form hydrogen gas on contact with metals. Etches glass.

STORAGE RECOMMENDATIONS: Store in a cool, dry, well-ventilated location. Separate from silica, incompatible metals, concrete, glass, ceramics, and oxidizing materials. Do not put even dilute solutions in glass containers.

USUAL SHIPPING CONTAINERS: Anhydrous gas is shipped in steel cylinders; pressurized tanks on trucks, rail cars, barges. Solutions are shipped in polyethylene, fluorocarbon, or wax-lined bottles.

PHYSICAL PROPERTIES: Colorless gas, fumes in air. Irritating odor.

MELTING POINT: −117°F (−83°C)

BOILING POINT: 67°F (20°C)

SPECIFIC GRAVITY: 0.99

SOLUBILITY IN WATER: soluble

VAPOR DENSITY: 0.69

VAPOR PRESSURE: 760 mm Hg @ 20°C

NAME: **HYDROGEN PEROXIDE, aqueous solutions (40% to 60%)**

SYNONYMS: hydrogen dioxide; peroxide

FORMULA: H_2O_2

NFPA 30/OSHA CLASSIFICATION:

DOT CLASS: Class 5.1, Oxidizer

SHIPPING LABEL: OXIDIZER and CORROSIVE

ID NO.: UN 2014

CAS NO.: 7722-84-1

MOL. WT.: 34.0

STATEMENT OF HAZARDS: Corrosive. Strong oxidizer.

EMERGENCY RESPONSE PERSONAL PROTECTIVE EQUIPMENT: Wear special protective clothing and positive pressure self-contained breathing apparatus.

SPILL OR LEAK PROCEDURES: Stop or control the leak, if this can be done without undue risk. Use water spray to cool and disperse vapors and protect personnel.

FIRE FIGHTING PROCEDURES: Extinguish fire using agent suitable for surrounding fire. Use flooding quantities of water.

HEALTH HAZARDS: Corrosive. Causes severe eye and skin burns. Irritating to skin, eyes, and respiratory system.

FIRE AND EXPLOSION HAZARDS: Strong oxidizer. Not combustible, but promotes combustion in combination with combustibles.

INSTABILITY AND REACTIVITY HAZARDS: Reacts with alkalies, oxidizable materials, finely divided metals, alcohols, permanganates. See also NFPA 430, Code for the Storage of Liquid and Solid Oxidizers.

STORAGE RECOMMENDATIONS: Store in a cool, dry, well-ventilated location. Separate from alkalies, oxidizable materials, finely divided metals, alcohols, permanganates. See also NFPA 430, Code for the Storage of Liquid and Solid Oxidizers.

USUAL SHIPPING CONTAINERS: Glass or polyethylene bottles, carboys, polyethylene-lined or aluminum drums with special vent caps; bulk packaging in aluminum tank trucks or rail cars and bulk in tank barges.

PHYSICAL PROPERTIES: Colorless liquid, slightly acrid odor.

BOILING POINT: 226° to 237°F (108° to 114°C) (35 to 50% solution)

SPECIFIC GRAVITY: 1.13 @ 20°C

SOLUBILITY IN WATER: soluble

VAPOR PRESSURE: 18 to 23 mm Hg (35% to 50% solution) @ 30°C

NAME: **HYDROGEN PEROXIDE, aqueous solutions, stabilized (>60%)**

SYNONYMS: hydrogen dioxide; peroxide

FORMULA: H_2O_2

NFPA 30/OSHA CLASSIFICATION:

DOT CLASS: Class 5.1, Oxidizer

SHIPPING LABEL: OXIDIZER and CORROSIVE

ID NO.: UN 2015

CAS NO.: 7722-84-1

MOL. WT.: 34.0

STATEMENT OF HAZARDS: Corrosive. Strong oxidizer.

EMERGENCY RESPONSE PERSONAL PROTECTIVE EQUIPMENT: Wear special protective clothing and positive pressure self-contained breathing apparatus.

SPILL OR LEAK PROCEDURES: Stop or control the leak, if this can be done without undue risk. Use water spray to cool and disperse vapors and protect personnel.

FIRE FIGHTING PROCEDURES: Extinguish fire using agent suitable for surrounding fire. Use flooding quantities of water. Fight fire from protected location or maximum possible distance.

HEALTH HAZARDS: Corrosive. Causes severe eye and skin burns.

FIRE AND EXPLOSION HAZARDS: Strong oxidizer. Not combustible, but promotes combustion in combination with combustibles. Closed containers may rupture violently when heated. May cause spontaneous combustion if allowed to remain in contact with readily oxidizable materials.

INSTABILITY AND REACTIVITY HAZARDS: Reacts violently with alkalies, oxidizable materials, finely divided metals, alcohols, permanganates. Contaminated hydrogen peroxide can decompose at a rate that will exceed the venting capability of the container. Decomposition can be self-accelerating and result in explosive rupture of the container.

STORAGE RECOMMENDATIONS: Store in a cool, dry, well-ventilated location. Separate from alkalies, oxidizable materials, finely divided metals, alcohols, permanganates. See also NFPA 430, Code for the Storage of Liquid and Solid Oxidizers.

USUAL SHIPPING CONTAINERS: Glass or polyethylene bottles, carboys, polyethylene-lined or aluminum drums with special vent caps; bulk packaging in aluminum tank trucks or rail cars and bulk in tank barges.

PHYSICAL PROPERTIES: Colorless liquid, slightly acrid odor.

BOILING POINT: 258°F (126°C) (70% solution)

SPECIFIC GRAVITY: 1.44 @ 25°C

SOLUBILITY IN WATER: soluble

VAPOR PRESSURE: 8 mm Hg @ 77°F (25°C)

NAME: **HYDROGEN SULFIDE, liquefied**

SYNONYMS: hydrosulfuric acid; sulfureted hydrogen

FORMULA: H_2S

NFPA 30/OSHA CLASSIFICATION:

DOT CLASS: Class 2.3, Poisonous gas

SHIPPING LABEL: POISON GAS and FLAMMABLE GAS

ID NO.: UN 1053

CAS NO.: 7783-06-4

MOL. WT.: 34.1

STATEMENT OF HAZARDS: Severe health hazard. Flammable gas. Low ignition energy.

EMERGENCY RESPONSE PERSONAL PROTECTIVE EQUIPMENT: Wear special protective clothing and positive pressure self-contained breathing apparatus.

SPILL OR LEAK PROCEDURES: Eliminate all ignition sources. Approach release from upwind. Stop or control the leak, if this can be done without undue risk. Use water spray to cool and disperse vapors, protect personnel, and dilute spills to form nonflammable mixtures. Control runoff and isolate discharged material for proper disposal.

FIRE FIGHTING PROCEDURES: Stop flow of gas before extinguishing fire. Use water spray, dry chemical, or carbon dioxide. Use water spray to keep fire-exposed containers cool.

HEALTH HAZARDS: Severe health hazard. May be fatal if inhaled. Irritating to eye and respiratory system. The sense of smell is immediately lost at concentrations of greater than 200 ppm.

FIRE AND EXPLOSION HAZARDS: Flammable gas. Forms explosive mixtures with air over wide range. Combustion produces irritants and toxic gases, including sulfur dioxide.

AUTOIGNITION TEMPERATURE: 500°F (260°C)

FLAMMABLE LIMITS: LOWER: 4.3% UPPER: 46.0%

INSTABILITY AND REACTIVITY HAZARDS: Reacts with strong oxidizing materials.

STORAGE RECOMMENDATIONS: Store in cool, dry, well-ventilated location. Separate from oxidizing materials.

USUAL SHIPPING CONTAINERS: Special steel pressure cylinders. Shipped as a liquid under its own vapor pressure.

PHYSICAL PROPERTIES: Colorless gas with characteristic odor of rotten eggs.

MELTING POINT: −122°F (−86°C)

BOILING POINT: −76°F (−60°C)

SPECIFIC GRAVITY: 1.54 liquefied

SOLUBILITY IN WATER: soluble

VAPOR DENSITY: 1.18

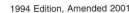

VAPOR PRESSURE: 14,060 mm Hg @ 20°C

ELECTRICAL EQUIPMENT: Class I, Group C

NAME: **HYDROXYLAMINE**

SYNONYMS: oxammonium

FORMULA: NH_2OH

NFPA 30/OSHA CLASSIFICATION:

DOT CLASS: N/A

ID NO.: N/A

CAS NO.: 7803-49-8

MOL. WT.: 33.0

STATEMENT OF HAZARDS: Noncombustible solid that explodes when heated to 265°F (129°C). Usually stored or shipped in liquid form as hydroxylamine sulfate or hydroxylamine hydrochloride. It will decompose at high temperatures and, if confined at 284°F (140°C), will explode. Moderate health hazard.

EMERGENCY RESPONSE PERSONAL PROTECTIVE EQUIPMENT: Wear full protective clothing and positive pressure self-contained breathing apparatus.

SPILL OR LEAK PROCEDURES: Absorb solutions in noncombustible material for proper disposal.

FIRE FIGHTING PROCEDURES: Not combustible. Extinguish fire using agent suitable for surrounding fire. Fight fire from protected location or maximum possible distance. Approach fire from upwind to avoid hazardous vapors and toxic decomposition products. Explosive decomposition may occur under fire conditions.

HEALTH HAZARDS: Moderate health hazard. May be harmful if absorbed through skin or inhaled. Irritating to skin, eyes, and respiratory system.

FIRE AND EXPLOSION HAZARDS: When confined and heated to 284°F (140°C) or higher may decompose with explosive force. Closed containers may rupture violently when heated.

INSTABILITY AND REACTIVITY HAZARDS: Explodes when heated or exposed to open flame. Reacts with oxidizing materials.

STORAGE RECOMMENDATIONS: Separate from oxidizing materials. Store in a cool, dry, well-ventilated location. Store away from heat, oxidizers, and sunlight. Outside or detached storage is preferred.

USUAL SHIPPING CONTAINERS: Lead-lined steel drums.

PHYSICAL PROPERTIES: White crystals or colorless liquid.

MELTING POINT: 93°F (34°C)

BOILING POINT: 158°F (70°C)

SPECIFIC GRAVITY: 1.2

SOLUBILITY IN WATER: soluble

VAPOR PRESSURE: 10 mm Hg @ 47°C

NAME: **ISOPHORONE**

SYNONYMS: isoacetophorone; 3,5,5-trimethyl-2-cyclohexene-1-one

FORMULA: $\overline{C(O)CHC(CH_3)CH_2C(CH_3)_2CH_2}$

NFPA 30/OSHA CLASSIFICATION: IIIA

DOT CLASS: N/A

ID NO.: N/A

CAS NO.: 78-59-1

MOL. WT.: 138.2

STATEMENT OF HAZARDS: Moderate health hazard. Combustible liquid.

EMERGENCY RESPONSE PERSONAL PROTECTIVE EQUIPMENT: Wear full protective clothing and positive pressure self-contained breathing apparatus.

SPILL OR LEAK PROCEDURES: Stop or control the leak, if this can be done without undue risk. Use water spray to cool and disperse vapors, protect personnel. Control runoff and isolate discharged material for proper disposal.

FIRE FIGHTING PROCEDURES: Use water spray to keep fire-exposed containers cool. Use flooding quantities of water as fog or spray, dry chemical, foam, or carbon dioxide

HEALTH HAZARDS: Moderate health hazard. Irritating to skin, eyes, and respiratory system. May be harmful if inhaled.

FIRE AND EXPLOSION HAZARDS: Combustible liquid.

FLASH POINT: 184°F (84°C)

AUTOIGNITION TEMPERATURE: 860°F (460°C)

FLAMMABLE LIMITS: LOWER: 0.8% UPPER: 3.8%

INSTABILITY AND REACTIVITY HAZARDS: Reacts with oxidizing materials, strong alkalies and amines.

STORAGE RECOMMENDATIONS: Store in a cool, dry, well-ventilated location. Outside or detached storage is preferred. Separate from oxidizing materials.

USUAL SHIPPING CONTAINERS: Steel drums.

PHYSICAL PROPERTIES: Colorless or pale liquid with a camphor-like odor.

MELTING POINT: 17°F (−8°C)

BOILING POINT: 419°F (215°C)

SPECIFIC GRAVITY: 0.92

SOLUBILITY IN WATER: not soluble

VAPOR PRESSURE: <1 mm Hg @ 20°C

ELECTRICAL EQUIPMENT: Class I, Group D

NAME: **ISOPHORONE DIISOCYANATE**

SYNONYMS: 3-isocyanatomethyl-3,5,5-trimethyl cyclohexylisocyanate; isophorone diaminediisocyanate

FORMULA:

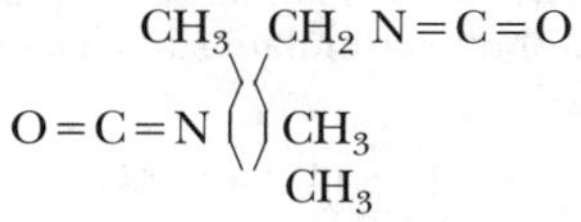

NFPA 30/OSHA CLASSIFICATION: IIIB

DOT CLASS: Class 6.1, Poisonous material

SHIPPING LABEL: KEEP AWAY FROM FOOD

ID NO.: UN 2290

CAS NO.: 4098-71-9

MOL. WT.: 222.3

STATEMENT OF HAZARDS: Moderate health hazard. Combustible liquid. Water reactive.

EMERGENCY RESPONSE PERSONAL PROTECTIVE EQUIPMENT: Wear special protective clothing and positive pressure self-contained breathing apparatus.

SPILL OR LEAK PROCEDURES: Use water spray to cool and disperse vapors and protect personnel. Control runoff and isolate discharged material for proper disposal.

FIRE FIGHTING PROCEDURES: Use water spray, dry chemical, foam, or carbon dioxide. Use water spray to keep fire-exposed containers cool.

HEALTH HAZARDS: Moderate health hazard. May be harmful if absorbed through skin or inhaled. Irritating to skin, eyes, and upper respiratory system.

FIRE AND EXPLOSION HAZARDS: Combustible liquid.

FLASH POINT: 212°F (100°C)

INSTABILITY AND REACTIVITY HAZARDS: Reacts with substances containing active hydrogen such as amines, amides, alcohols, mercaptans, and water.

STORAGE RECOMMENDATIONS: Store in a cool, dry, well-ventilated location. Outside or detached storage is preferred. Avoid contact with amines, amides, alcohols, mercaptans, and water.

PHYSICAL PROPERTIES: Colorless to slightly yellow liquid.

MELTING POINT: −74°F (−60°C)

BOILING POINT: 316°F (158°C)

SPECIFIC GRAVITY: 1.06

SOLUBILITY IN WATER: reacts

VAPOR PRESSURE: 0.0003 mm Hg @ 20°C

NAME: **ISOPRENE, inhibited**

SYNONYMS: b-methylbivinyl; 2-methyl-1,3-butadiene

FORMULA: $CH_2=C(CH_3)CH=CH_2$

NFPA 30/OSHA CLASSIFICATION: IA

DOT CLASS: Class 3, Flammable and combustible liquid

SHIPPING LABEL: FLAMMABLE LIQUID

ID NO.: UN 1218

CAS NO.: 78-79-5

MOL. WT.: 68.1

STATEMENT OF HAZARDS: Flammable liquid. May polymerize explosively. May accumulate static electricity. Toxic. Slight health hazard.

EMERGENCY RESPONSE PERSONAL PROTECTIVE EQUIPMENT: Wear full protective clothing and positive pressure self-contained breathing apparatus.

SPILL OR LEAK PROCEDURES: Eliminate all ignition sources. Stop or control the leak, if this can be done without undue risk. Use appropriate foam to blanket release and suppress vapors. Absorb in noncombustible material for proper disposal.

FIRE FIGHTING PROCEDURES: Use fine spray or fog to control fire by preventing its spread and absorbing some of its heat. Use water spray to keep fire-exposed containers cool. Fight fire from protected location or maximum possible distance.

HEALTH HAZARDS: Slight health hazard. Irritating to skin, eyes, and respiratory system.

FIRE AND EXPLOSION HAZARDS: Flammable liquid. May polymerize explosively. Closed containers may rupture violently when heated. Vapors are heavier than air and may travel to a source of ignition and flash back. Liquid floats on water and may travel to a source of ignition and spread fire.

FLASH POINT: −65°F (−54°C)

AUTOIGNITION TEMPERATURE: 428°F (220°C)

FLAMMABLE LIMITS: LOWER: 2% UPPER: 9%

INSTABILITY AND REACTIVITY HAZARDS: May polymerize explosively. Usually contains inhibitors to prevent polymerization. Polymerization may be caused by elevated temperature, oxidizing materials, peroxides, or sunlight. Uninhibited monomer vapor may form polymer in vents and other confined spaces.

STORAGE RECOMMENDATIONS: Store in a cool, dry, well-ventilated location. Outside or detached storage is preferred. Separate from oxidizing materials.

USUAL SHIPPING CONTAINERS: Metal cans, pails, drums. Tanks on trucks, rail cars, barges.

PHYSICAL PROPERTIES: Colorless, watery liquid. Mild odor.

MELTING POINT: −231°F (−146°C)

BOILING POINT: 93°F (34°C)

SPECIFIC GRAVITY: 0.68

SOLUBILITY IN WATER: not soluble

VAPOR DENSITY: 2.35

VAPOR PRESSURE: 400 mm Hg @ 15°C

ELECTRICAL EQUIPMENT: Class I, Group D

NAME: **ISOPROPYLAMINE**

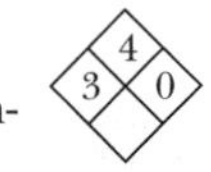

SYNONYMS: 2-aminopropane; monoisopropylamine; 2-propanamine

FORMULA: $(CH_3)_2CHNH_2$

NFPA 30/OSHA CLASSIFICATION: IA

DOT CLASS: Class 3, Flammable and combustible liquid

SHIPPING LABEL: FLAMMABLE LIQUID

ID NO.: UN 1221

CAS NO.: 75-31-0

MOL. WT.: 59.1

STATEMENT OF HAZARDS: Flammable liquid. Corrosive.

EMERGENCY RESPONSE PERSONAL PROTECTIVE EQUIPMENT: Wear special protective clothing and positive pressure self-contained breathing apparatus.

SPILL OR LEAK PROCEDURES: Eliminate all ignition sources. Stop or control the leak, if this can be done without undue risk. Use water spray to cool and disperse vapors, protect personnel, and dilute spills to form nonflammable mixtures. Absorb in noncombustible material for proper disposal.

FIRE FIGHTING PROCEDURES: Use dry chemical, "alcohol resistant" foam, carbon dioxide, or water spray. Water may be ineffective. Use water spray to keep fire-exposed containers cool. Approach fire from upwind to avoid hazardous vapors and toxic decomposition products.

HEALTH HAZARDS: Corrosive. Causes severe eye and skin burns. May be harmful if absorbed through skin or inhaled. Irritating to skin, eyes, and respiratory system. May cause pulmonary edema.

FIRE AND EXPLOSION HAZARDS: Flammable liquid. Vapors are heavier than air and may travel to a source of ignition and flash back. Combustion by-products include oxides of nitrogen.

FLASH POINT: −15°F (−26°C) (oc)

AUTOIGNITION TEMPERATURE: 756°F (402°C)

FLAMMABLE LIMITS: LOWER: 2.0% UPPER: 10.4%

INSTABILITY AND REACTIVITY HAZARDS: Reacts with acids, aldehydes, ketones, epoxides, and oxidizing agents.

STORAGE RECOMMENDATIONS: Store in a cool, dry, well-ventilated location. Separate from strong acids, oxidizing materials.

USUAL SHIPPING CONTAINERS: Metal cans, pails, drums; tanks on trucks, rail cars, barges.

PHYSICAL PROPERTIES: Colorless liquid with strong ammonia odor.

MELTING POINT: −150°F (−101°C)

BOILING POINT: 93°F (34°C)

SPECIFIC GRAVITY: 0.69

SOLUBILITY IN WATER: soluble

VAPOR DENSITY: 2.04

VAPOR PRESSURE: 478 mm Hg @ 20°C

ELECTRICAL EQUIPMENT: Class I, Group D

NAME: **ISOPROPYL FORMATE**

DOT SHIPPING NAME: **PROPYL FORMATES (Class 3, UN 1281)**

SYNONYMS: formic acid isopropyl ester

FORMULA: $HCO_2CH(CH_3)_2$

NFPA 30/OSHA CLASSIFICATION: IB

DOT CLASS: N/A

ID NO.: N/A

CAS NO.: 625-55-8

MOL. WT.: 88.1

STATEMENT OF HAZARDS: Flammable liquid. Moderate health hazard.

EMERGENCY RESPONSE PERSONAL PROTECTIVE EQUIPMENT: Wear full protective clothing and positive pressure self-contained breathing apparatus.

SPILL OR LEAK PROCEDURES: Eliminate all ignition sources. Use water spray to cool and disperse vapors and protect personnel. Absorb in noncombustible material for proper disposal.

FIRE FIGHTING PROCEDURES: Use water spray, dry chemical, "alcohol resistant" foam, or carbon dioxide. Water may be ineffective. Use water spray to keep fire-exposed containers cool. Approach fire from upwind to avoid hazardous vapors and toxic decomposition products.

HEALTH HAZARDS: Moderate health hazard. May be harmful if absorbed through skin or inhaled. Symptoms of overexposure include dizziness and suffocation. Produces formic acid on contact with water, causing painful burning of skin and mucous membranes.

FIRE AND EXPLOSION HAZARDS: Flammable liquid. Vapors are heavier than air and may travel to a source of ignition and flash back. Combustion may produce irritants and toxic gases.

FLASH POINT: 22°F (−6°C)

AUTOIGNITION TEMPERATURE: 813°F (434°C)

INSTABILITY AND REACTIVITY HAZARDS: Gradually decomposed by water into formic acid and isopropyl alcohol. Reacts with oxidizing materials.

STORAGE RECOMMENDATIONS: Store in a cool, dry, well-ventilated location. Separate from strong acids and alkalies, oxidizing materials. Outside or detached storage is preferred.

USUAL SHIPPING CONTAINERS: Bottles packed in insulating material. Metal cans, pails, drums. Tanks on trucks, rail cars, barges.

PHYSICAL PROPERTIES: Colorless liquid. Pleasant odor.

BOILING POINT: 155°F (68°C)

SPECIFIC GRAVITY: 0.87

SOLUBILITY IN WATER: not soluble (decomposes)

VAPOR PRESSURE: 100 mm Hg @ 18°C

ELECTRICAL EQUIPMENT: Class I, Group D

NAME: **LITHIUM**

FORMULA: Li

NFPA 30/OSHA CLASSIFICATION:

DOT CLASS: Class 4.3, Dangerous when wet material

SHIPPING LABEL: DANGEROUS WHEN WET

ID NO.: UN 1415

CAS NO.: 7439-93-2

MOL. WT.: 6.9

STATEMENT OF HAZARDS: Corrosive and flammable solid. Water reactive.

EMERGENCY RESPONSE PERSONAL PROTECTIVE EQUIPMENT: Wear special protective clothing and positive pressure self-contained breathing apparatus.

SPILL OR LEAK PROCEDURES: Eliminate all ignition sources. Keep water away from release. Shovel into suitable dry container.

FIRE FIGHTING PROCEDURES: Use approved Class D extinguishers or smother with dry sand, dry clay, or dry ground limestone. DO NOT use carbon dioxide or halogenated extinguishing agents. DO NOT use water. Violent reaction may result.

HEALTH HAZARDS: Corrosive. Causes severe eye and skin burns.

FIRE AND EXPLOSION HAZARDS: Flammable solid. Evolves hydrogen and ignites on contact with water. Combustion may produce irritants and toxic gases.

AUTOIGNITION TEMPERATURE: 354°F (179°C)

INSTABILITY AND REACTIVITY HAZARDS: Reacts violently with a broad range of materials, including water.

STORAGE RECOMMENDATIONS: Store in a cool, dry, well-ventilated location. Separate from water.

USUAL SHIPPING CONTAINERS: Hermetically sealed can inside wooden box. Metal cans, pails, drums. Packaged under inert gas, mineral oil, or kerosene.

PHYSICAL PROPERTIES: Silvery-white metal; becomes yellow with exposure to air.

MELTING POINT: 357°F (181°C)

BOILING POINT: 2448°F (1342°C)

SPECIFIC GRAVITY: 0.53

SOLUBILITY IN WATER: decomposes

VAPOR PRESSURE: 1 mm Hg @ 723°C

NAME: **LITHIUM ALUMINUM HYDRIDE**

SYNONYMS: aluminum lithium hydride; LAH; lithium tetrahydroaluminate

FORMULA: $LiAlH_4$

NFPA 30/OSHA CLASSIFICATION:

DOT CLASS: Class 4.3, Dangerous when wet material

SHIPPING LABEL: DANGEROUS WHEN WET

ID NO.: UN 1410

CAS NO.: 1302-30-3

MOL. WT.: 37.9

STATEMENT OF HAZARDS: Corrosive and flammable solid. Water reactive.

EMERGENCY RESPONSE PERSONAL PROTECTIVE EQUIPMENT: Wear special protective clothing and positive pressure self-contained breathing apparatus.

SPILL OR LEAK PROCEDURES: Keep water away from release. Shovel into suitable dry container.

FIRE FIGHTING PROCEDURES: Use approved Class D extinguishers or smother with dry sand, dry clay, or dry ground limestone. DO NOT use carbon dioxide or halogenated extinguishing agents. DO NOT use water. Violent reaction may result.

HEALTH HAZARDS: Corrosive. Causes severe eye and skin burns. May be harmful if inhaled. Irritating to skin, eyes, and respiratory system. Symptoms of overexposure include spasms, inflammation and edema of larynx and bronchi, pulmonary edema, coughing, wheezing, laryngitis, nausea, and vomiting.

FIRE AND EXPLOSION HAZARDS: Flammable solid. Evolves hydrogen and ignites on contact with water. Decomposition begins at 257°F (125°C) and releases heat. Combustion may produce irritants and toxic gases.

INSTABILITY AND REACTIVITY HAZARDS: Reacts violently with a broad range of materials, including water.

STORAGE RECOMMENDATIONS: Store in a cool, dry, well-ventilated location. Separate from ketones, aldehydes, nitrogenous organic compounds.

USUAL SHIPPING CONTAINERS: Glass bottles or metal cans inside wooden box. Packaged under nitrogen or argon gas.

PHYSICAL PROPERTIES: White crystalline powder.

MELTING POINT: 257°F (125°C) (decomposes)

BOILING POINT: decomposes

SPECIFIC GRAVITY: 0.92

SOLUBILITY IN WATER: decomposes

ELECTRICAL EQUIPMENT: Class II, Group Undesignated

NAME: **LITHIUM HYDRIDE**

SYNONYMS: lithium monohydride

FORMULA: LiH

NFPA 30/OSHA CLASSIFICATION:

DOT CLASS: Class 4.3, Dangerous when wet material

SHIPPING LABEL: DANGEROUS WHEN WET

ID NO.: UN 1414

CAS NO.: 7580-67-8

MOL. WT.: 7.9

STATEMENT OF HAZARDS: Corrosive and flammable solid. Water reactive.

EMERGENCY RESPONSE PERSONAL PROTECTIVE EQUIPMENT: Wear special protective clothing and positive pressure self-contained breathing apparatus.

SPILL OR LEAK PROCEDURES: Keep water away from release. Shovel into suitable dry container.

FIRE FIGHTING PROCEDURES: Use approved Class D extinguishers or smother with dry sand, dry clay, or dry ground limestone. DO NOT use carbon dioxide or halogenated extinguishing agents. DO NOT use water. Violent reaction may result.

HEALTH HAZARDS: Corrosive. Causes severe eye and skin burns. May be harmful if inhaled. Symptoms of overexposure include nausea, muscular twitches, mental confusion, blurred vision.

FIRE AND EXPLOSION HAZARDS: Flammable solid. Evolves hydrogen and ignites on contact with water. Dust/air mixtures may explode. Combustion may produce irritants and toxic gases.

INSTABILITY AND REACTIVITY HAZARDS: Thermally unstable. Decomposes at 1009°F (400°C). Reacts violently with a broad range of materials, including water.

STORAGE RECOMMENDATIONS: Store in a cool, dry, well-ventilated location. Must be stored in a dry location. Immediately remove and properly dispose of any spilled material.

USUAL SHIPPING CONTAINERS: Metal can inside wooden box or fiber drums. Packaged under argon or nitrogen gas.

PHYSICAL PROPERTIES: Gray cubic crystals that darken rapidly on exposure to light. Odorless.

MELTING POINT: 1256°F (680°C)

BOILING POINT: decomposes

SPECIFIC GRAVITY: 0.82

SOLUBILITY IN WATER: decomposes

VAPOR PRESSURE: 0 mm Hg @ 20°C

ELECTRICAL EQUIPMENT: Class II, Group Undesignated

NAME: **MAGNESIUM**
MAGNESIUM ALLOYS
with more than 50 percent magnesium in pellets, turnings, or ribbons

FORMULA: Mg

NFPA 30/OSHA CLASSIFICATION:

DOT CLASS: Class 4.1, Flammable solid

SHIPPING LABEL: FLAMMABLE SOLID

ID NO.: UN 1869

CAS NO.: 7439-95-4

MOL. WT.: 24.3

STATEMENT OF HAZARDS: Fine powder, thin sheets, chips, and turnings are easily ignited and burn with intense heat and brilliant white flame.

EMERGENCY RESPONSE PERSONAL PROTECTIVE EQUIPMENT: Wear full protective clothing and positive pressure self-contained breathing apparatus.

SPILL OR LEAK PROCEDURES: Eliminate all ignition sources. Shovel into suitable dry container.

FIRE FIGHTING PROCEDURES: Use approved Class D extinguishers or smother with dry sand, dry clay, or dry ground limestone and dry graphite. DO NOT use carbon dioxide or halogenated extinguishing agents. DO NOT use water or foam.

HEALTH HAZARDS: May be irritating to skin, eyes, and respiratory system. Avoid looking at the intense white flame.

FIRE AND EXPLOSION HAZARDS: Fine powder, thin sheets, chips, and turnings are easily ignited and burn with intense heat and brilliant white flame. Powders form explosive mixtures with air that may be ignited by a spark. Finely divided form evolves hydrogen on contact with water. All solid forms react with acids to produce hydrogen gas.

AUTOIGNITION TEMPERATURE: 883°F (473°C) for turnings; may be lower for finer forms

INSTABILITY AND REACTIVITY HAZARDS: Finely divided forms react with water and acids to release hydrogen. Reacts in finely divided form with chlorine, bromine, iodine, and oxidizing agents.

STORAGE RECOMMENDATIONS: Detached storage must be used for finely divided materials. Must be stored in a dry location. Isolate from halogens, acids, and oxidizing materials.

USUAL SHIPPING CONTAINERS: Bars, ribbon, wire, turnings and shavings, and finely divided powders in tightly closed metal or fiber containers.

PHYSICAL PROPERTIES: Silvery solid like aluminum but weighs one third less.

MELTING POINT: 1202°F (650°C)

BOILING POINT: 2025°F (1107°C)

SPECIFIC GRAVITY: 1.74

SOLUBILITY IN WATER: not soluble

ELECTRICAL EQUIPMENT: Class II, Group E

NAME: **MALEIC ANHYDRIDE**

SYNONYMS: cis-butenedioic anhydride; 2,5-furandione

FORMULA: (CH: CHCOOC)O

NFPA 30/OSHA CLASSIFICATION: IIIB

DOT CLASS: Class 8, Corrosive material

SHIPPING LABEL: CORROSIVE

ID NO.: UN 2215

CAS NO.: 108-31-6

MOL. WT.: 98.1

STATEMENT OF HAZARDS: Corrosive. Combustible solid. Dust cloud may be exploded by flame or spark.

EMERGENCY RESPONSE PERSONAL PROTECTIVE EQUIPMENT: Wear special protective clothing and positive pressure self-contained breathing apparatus.

SPILL OR LEAK PROCEDURES: Sweep up or collect solid for disposal or recovery. Control runoff and isolate discharged material for proper disposal.

FIRE FIGHTING PROCEDURES: Water stream or foam may cause frothing. Use dry chemical, carbon dioxide, or water spray.

HEALTH HAZARDS: Corrosive. Causes severe eye and skin burns. May be harmful if absorbed through skin or inhaled. Irritation eyes, skin, and respiratory system. Skin and respiratory system sensitizer. May cause severe allergic reaction.

FIRE AND EXPLOSION HAZARDS: Combustible solid. Dust cloud may be exploded by flame or spark.

FLASH POINT: 215°F (102°C)

AUTOIGNITION TEMPERATURE: 890°F (477°C)

FLAMMABLE LIMITS: LOWER: 1.4% UPPER: 7.1%

INSTABILITY AND REACTIVITY HAZARDS: Reacts with strong alkalies, strong oxidizing agents, and amines. Reacts with water or steam to form maleic acid with release of energy.

STORAGE RECOMMENDATIONS: Outside or detached storage is preferred. Store in a cool, dry, well-ventilated location. Separate from alkalies, alkali metals, amines, and oxidizing materials.

USUAL SHIPPING CONTAINERS: Bags, fiber drums; molten in tank cars and tank trucks.

PHYSICAL PROPERTIES: Colorless or white solid with a penetrating odor. Dissolves in water to form maleic acid. Usually shipped as briquettes.

MELTING POINT: 127°F (53°C)

BOILING POINT: 395°F (202°C)

SPECIFIC GRAVITY: 1.48

SOLUBILITY IN WATER: dissolves to acid

VAPOR PRESSURE: 0.16 mm Hg @ 20°C

NAME: **MERCURY CYANIDE**

SYNONYMS: cianurina; mercuric cyanide; mercury (II) cyanide

FORMULA: $Hg(CN)_2$

NFPA 30/OSHA CLASSIFICATION:

DOT CLASS: Class 6.1, Poisonous material

SHIPPING LABEL: POISON

ID NO.: UN 1636

CAS NO.: 592-04-1

MOL. WT.: 252.6

STATEMENT OF HAZARDS: Serious health hazard.

EMERGENCY RESPONSE PERSONAL PROTECTIVE EQUIPMENT: Wear special protective clothing and positive pressure self-contained breathing apparatus.

SPILL OR LEAK PROCEDURES: Stop or control the leak, if this can be done without undue risk. Shovel into suitable dry container. Control runoff and isolate discharged material for proper disposal.

FIRE FIGHTING PROCEDURES: Approach fire from upwind to avoid hazardous vapors and toxic decomposition products. Extinguish fire using agent suitable for surrounding fire. Use water spray to keep fire-exposed containers cool.

HEALTH HAZARDS: Serious health hazard. May be harmful if inhaled or absorbed through skin. Mercury causes brain damage and accumulates in the body. May release hydrogen cyanide. Neurotoxic.

FIRE AND EXPLOSION HAZARDS: Decomposes prior to melting. Not combustible, but if involved in a fire decomposes to produce hydrogen cyanide, mercury and mercuric oxide fumes, oxides of nitrogen.

INSTABILITY AND REACTIVITY HAZARDS: Reacts with strong acids evolving hydrogen cyanide. May decompose on exposure to light.

STORAGE RECOMMENDATIONS: Store in a cool, dry, well-ventilated location. Separate from acids.

USUAL SHIPPING CONTAINERS: Glass bottles up to 5 lb, metal cans inside boxes up to 25 lb. Metal drums, fiber boxes with plastic lining.

PHYSICAL PROPERTIES: Colorless to white crystals or white powder.

MELTING POINT: decomposes @ 320 °C

BOILING POINT: decomposes

SPECIFIC GRAVITY: 4.00

SOLUBILITY IN WATER: not soluble

NAME: **MESITYL OXIDE**

SYNONYMS: 1-isobutenyl methyl ketone; methyl isobutenylketone

FORMULA: $(CH_3)_2C=CHCOCH_3$

NFPA 30/OSHA CLASSIFICATION: IC

DOT CLASS: Class 3, Flammable and combustible liquid

SHIPPING LABEL: FLAMMABLE LIQUID

ID NO.: UN 1229

CAS NO.: 141-79-7

MOL. WT.: 98.1

STATEMENT OF HAZARDS: Flammable liquid. Moderate health hazard.

EMERGENCY RESPONSE PERSONAL PROTECTIVE EQUIPMENT: Wear full protective clothing and positive pressure self-contained breathing apparatus.

SPILL OR LEAK PROCEDURES: Eliminate all ignition sources. Stop or control the leak, if this can be done without undue risk. Use appropriate foam to blanket release and suppress vapors. Approach release from upwind. Absorb in noncombustible material for proper disposal.

FIRE FIGHTING PROCEDURES: Use dry chemical, foam, carbon dioxide, or water spray. Water may be ineffective. Use water spray to keep fire-exposed containers cool.

HEALTH HAZARDS: Moderate health hazard. May be harmful if absorbed through skin or inhaled. Irritating to skin, eyes, and respiratory system.

FIRE AND EXPLOSION HAZARDS: Flammable liquid. Vapors are heavier than air and may travel to a source of ignition and flash back. Combustion may produce irritants and toxic gases.

FLASH POINT: 87°F (31°C)

AUTOIGNITION TEMPERATURE: 652°F (344°C)

FLAMMABLE LIMITS: LOWER: 1.4% UPPER: 7.2%

INSTABILITY AND REACTIVITY HAZARDS: Polymerization may occur. When heated reacts with oxidizing materials.

STORAGE RECOMMENDATIONS: Store in a cool, dry, well-ventilated location. Store away from heat, oxidizing materials, and sunlight. Outside or detached storage is preferred. Separate from oxidizing materials.

USUAL SHIPPING CONTAINERS: Glass bottle inside wooden box. Metal cans, pails, drums. Tanks on trucks, rail cars, barges.

PHYSICAL PROPERTIES: Colorless, oily liquid. Odor of honey (sweet, heavy).

MELTING POINT: −74°F (−59°C)

BOILING POINT: 266°F (130°C)

SPECIFIC GRAVITY: 0.86

SOLUBILITY IN WATER: not soluble

VAPOR PRESSURE: 9 mm Hg @ 20°C

ELECTRICAL EQUIPMENT: Class I, Group D

NAME: **METHACRYLIC ACID, inhibited**

SYNONYMS: alpha-methylcrylic acid; 2-methyl-2-propenoic acid

FORMULA: $CH_2=C(CH_3)COOH$

NFPA 30/OSHA CLASSIFICATION: IIIA

DOT CLASS: Class 8, Corrosive material

SHIPPING LABEL: CORROSIVE

ID NO.: UN 2531

CAS NO.: 79-41-4

MOL. WT.: 86.1

STATEMENT OF HAZARDS: Corrosive and combustible liquid. Material may polymerize explosively.

EMERGENCY RESPONSE PERSONAL PROTECTIVE EQUIPMENT: Wear special protective clothing and positive pressure self-contained breathing apparatus.

SPILL OR LEAK PROCEDURES: Use water spray to cool and disperse vapors, protect personnel, and dilute spill to form nonflammable mixtures. Control runoff and isolate discharged material for proper disposal.

FIRE FIGHTING PROCEDURES: Use water spray, dry chemical, "alcohol resistant" foam, or carbon dioxide. Use water spray to keep fire-exposed containers cool. Fight fire from protected location or maximum possible distance.

HEALTH HAZARDS: Corrosive. Causes severe eye and skin burns. May be harmful if inhaled. Irritating to skin, eyes, and respiratory system. Inhalation may cause headache, nausea, vomiting, confusion, dizziness, and unconsciousness. May cause skin sensitization.

FIRE AND EXPLOSION HAZARDS: Combustible liquid. Material may polymerize explosively. Closed containers may rupture violently when heated.

FLASH POINT: 171°F (77°C)

AUTOIGNITION TEMPERATURE: 154°F (68°C)

FLAMMABLE LIMITS: LOWER: 1.6% UPPER: 8.8%

INSTABILITY AND REACTIVITY HAZARDS: Hazardous polymerization may occur. Usually contains inhibitors to prevent polymerization. Polymerization may be caused by elevated temperature, oxidizers, peroxides, or sunlight. Material will react with strong acids and alkalies. Hazardous decomposition products include carbon monoxide and acrid fumes. Uninhibited monomer vapor may form polymer in vents and other confined spaces.

STORAGE RECOMMENDATIONS: Separate from oxidizing materials, peroxides, or other initiators. Store in cool, dry, well-ventilated location.

USUAL SHIPPING CONTAINERS: Glass bottles, carboys, lined drums, and tankers.

PHYSICAL PROPERTIES: Colorless liquid with acrid, repulsive odor. Freezes to solid at 61°F (16°C).

MELTING POINT: 61°F (16°C)

BOILING POINT: 325°F (163°C)

SPECIFIC GRAVITY: 1.02

SOLUBILITY IN WATER: soluble

VAPOR PRESSURE: 1 mm Hg @ 20°C

ELECTRICAL EQUIPMENT: Class I, Group C

NAME: **METHYL ACRYLATE, inhibited**

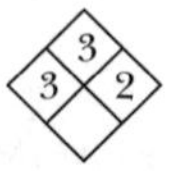

SYNONYMS: acrylic acid methyl ester; methyl propenoate

FORMULA: $CH_2=CHCO_2CH_3$

NFPA 30/OSHA CLASSIFICATION: IB

DOT CLASS: Class 3, Flammable and combustible liquid

SHIPPING LABEL: FLAMMABLE LIQUID

ID NO.: UN 1919

CAS NO.: 96-33-3

MOL. WT.: 86.1

STATEMENT OF HAZARDS: Serious health hazard. Flammable liquid. May polymerize explosively on loss of inhibitor.

EMERGENCY RESPONSE PERSONAL PROTECTIVE EQUIPMENT: Wear special protective clothing and positive pressure self-contained breathing apparatus.

SPILL OR LEAK PROCEDURES: Eliminate all ignition sources. Stop or control the leak, if this can be done without undue risk. Use water spray to cool and disperse vapors and protect personnel. Control runoff and isolate discharged material for proper disposal.

FIRE FIGHTING PROCEDURES: Use water spray, dry chemical, foam, or carbon dioxide. Use water spray to keep fire-exposed containers cool. Fight fire from protected location or maximum possible distance.

HEALTH HAZARDS: Serious health hazard. May be harmful if absorbed through skin or inhaled. Irritating to skin, eyes, and respiratory system. Inhalation may cause headache, nausea, vomiting, confusion, dizziness, and unconsciousness.

FIRE AND EXPLOSION HAZARDS: Flammable liquid. May polymerize explosively. Closed containers may rupture violently when heated. Vapors are heavier than air and may travel to a source of ignition and flash back. Liquid floats on water and may travel to a source of ignition and spread fire.

FLASH POINT: 27°F (−3°C)

AUTOIGNITION TEMPERATURE: 875°F (468°C)

FLAMMABLE LIMITS: LOWER: 2.8% UPPER: 25%

INSTABILITY AND REACTIVITY HAZARDS: Hazardous polymerization may occur above 70°F (21°C). Usually contains inhibitors to prevent polymerization. Inhibitor should be checked periodically. Polymerization may be caused by elevated temperature, oxidizers, peroxides. Material will react with strong acids and alkalies. Hazardous decomposition products include carbon monoxide, and acrid fumes. Uninhibited monomer vapor may form polymer in vents and other confined spaces.

STORAGE RECOMMENDATIONS: Separate from oxidizers, peroxides, or other initiators. Store in cool, dry, well-ventilated place.

USUAL SHIPPING CONTAINERS: Glass bottles, cans, drums, and tankers.

PHYSICAL PROPERTIES: Clear, colorless liquid with a sharp, sweet odor. Floats on water.

MELTING POINT: −106°F (−77°C)

BOILING POINT: 177°F (81°C)

SPECIFIC GRAVITY: 0.96

SOLUBILITY IN WATER: not soluble

VAPOR PRESSURE: 68.2 mm Hg @ 20°C

ELECTRICAL EQUIPMENT: Class I, Group D

NAME: **METHYLAMINE, anhydrous**

METHYLAMINE, aqueous solution

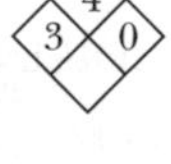

SYNONYMS: MMA; monomethylamine

FORMULA: CH_3NH_2

NFPA 30/OSHA CLASSIFICATION:

DOT CLASS: Class 2.3, Poisonous gas

Class 3, Flammable and combustible liquid

SHIPPING LABEL: POISON GAS

FLAMMABLE GAS

ID NO.: UN 1061 anhydrous UN 1235 aqueous

CAS NO.: 74-89-5

MOL. WT.: 31.1

STATEMENT OF HAZARDS: Flammable gas. Gas and aqueous solutions (25-48%) are corrosive and serious health hazard.

EMERGENCY RESPONSE PERSONAL PROTECTIVE EQUIPMENT: Wear special protective clothing and positive pressure self-contained breathing apparatus.

SPILL OR LEAK PROCEDURES: Releases may require isolation or evacuation. Eliminate all ignition sources. Approach release from upwind. Use water spray to cool and disperse vapors, protect personnel, and dilute spills to form nonflammable mixtures. Five percent sulfuric acid may be used to neutralize diluted pools. Absorb in noncombustible material for proper disposal. Control runoff and isolate discharged material for proper disposal.

FIRE FIGHTING PROCEDURES: Stop flow of gas before extinguishing fire. Use water spray to keep fire-exposed containers cool. Use water spray, dry chemical, or "alcohol resistant" foam. Aqueous solutions will burn unless diluted thoroughly with spray.

HEALTH HAZARDS: Corrosive. Causes severe eye and skin burns. May be harmful if inhaled. Irritating to skin, eyes, and respiratory system. May cause conjunctivitis and corneal damage. Inhalation may cause coughing, nausea, and pulmonary edema.

FIRE AND EXPLOSION HAZARDS: Flammable gas. Aqueous solutions are flammable unless diluted extensively.

AUTOIGNITION TEMPERATURE: 806°F (430°C)

FLAMMABLE LIMITS: LOWER: 4.9% UPPER: 20.7%

INSTABILITY AND REACTIVITY HAZARDS: May react with acids, oxidizing materials, chlorine, hypochlorite, halogenated compounds, reactive organic compounds and some metals, and mercury and nitrosating compounds. Products of decomposition include carbon monoxide, carbon dioxide, hydrocarbons, and toxic oxides of nitrogen as well as toxic amine vapors.

STORAGE RECOMMENDATIONS: Avoid oxidizing materials, acids, and sources of halogens. Store in cool, dry, well-ventilated, noncombustible location.

USUAL SHIPPING CONTAINERS: Glass bottles, cans, drums, and tank cars.

PHYSICAL PROPERTIES: Anhydrous gas or liquid under pressure. Very soluble in water, forming very strong alkaline solutions. May be in water solution as shipped or used. Anhydrous material floats and boils on water as it mixes.

MELTING POINT: −136°F (−94°C)

BOILING POINT: 21°F (−6°C)

SPECIFIC GRAVITY: liquid 0.70 @ 12°F (−11°C)

SOLUBILITY IN WATER: soluble

VAPOR DENSITY: 1.07

VAPOR PRESSURE: 2622 mm Hg @ 25°C

Boiling temperatures will be higher than those listed (by about 65 to 85°F) for aqueous solutions. Freezing temperatures will also be proportionately higher than values listed for gas (anhydrous). Vapor pressure of aqueous solutions will range from 215 to 500 mm Hg. Specific gravity values for aqueous solutions will be 0.83 to 0.93.

ELECTRICAL EQUIPMENT: Class I, Group D

NAME: **METHYL BROMIDE**

SYNONYMS: bromomethane

FORMULA: CH_3Br

NFPA 30/OSHA CLASSIFICATION:

DOT CLASS: Class 2.3, Poisonous gas

SHIPPING LABEL: POISON GAS

ID NO.: UN 1062

CAS NO.: 74-83-9

MOL. WT.: 94.9

STATEMENT OF HAZARDS: Corrosive. Not ordinarily combustible except in the presence of high heat or strong oxidizers.

EMERGENCY RESPONSE PERSONAL PROTECTIVE EQUIPMENT: Wear special protective clothing and positive pressure self-contained breathing apparatus.

SPILL OR LEAK PROCEDURES: Releases may require isolation or evacuation. Approach release from upwind. Stop or control the leak, if this can be done without undue risk. Use water spray to cool and disperse vapors and protect personnel. Control runoff and isolate discharged material for proper disposal.

FIRE FIGHTING PROCEDURES: Approach fire from upwind to avoid hazardous vapors and toxic decomposition products. Extinguish fire using agent suitable for surrounding fire. Use flooding quantities of water as fog. Use water spray to keep fire-exposed containers cool.

HEALTH HAZARDS: Corrosive. Causes severe eye and skin burns. May be harmful if absorbed through skin or inhaled. Causes permanent damage to central nervous system and pulmonary edema. Effects may be delayed from 2-48 hours.

FIRE AND EXPLOSION HAZARDS: Not ordinarily considered to be combustible; however, it will burn in air in the presence of a high energy source of ignition and within a narrow flammability range.

AUTOIGNITION TEMPERATURE: 999°F (537°C)

FLAMMABLE LIMITS: LOWER: 10% UPPER: 16%

INSTABILITY AND REACTIVITY HAZARDS: Reacts with active metals.

STORAGE RECOMMENDATIONS: Store in a cool, dry, well-ventilated location. Outside or detached storage is preferred for cylinders. Isolate from active metals.

USUAL SHIPPING CONTAINERS: Cans, steel cylinders, and tank cars.

PHYSICAL PROPERTIES: Colorless volatile liquid or gas with chloroform-like odor.

MELTING POINT: −135°F (−93°C)

BOILING POINT: 39°F (4°C)

SPECIFIC GRAVITY: 1.73

SOLUBILITY IN WATER: not soluble

VAPOR DENSITY: 3.27

VAPOR PRESSURE: 1250 mm Hg @ 20°C

ELECTRICAL EQUIPMENT: Class I, Group D

NAME: **2-METHYL BUTYRALDEHYDE**

FORMULA: $C_2H_5CH(CH_3)CHO$

NFPA 30/OSHA CLASSIFICATION: IB

DOT CLASS: N/A

ID NO.: N/A

CAS NO.: 96-17-3

MOL. WT.: 86.1

STATEMENT OF HAZARDS: Flammable liquid. Moderate health hazard.

EMERGENCY RESPONSE PERSONAL PROTECTIVE EQUIPMENT: Wear full protective clothing and positive pressure self-contained breathing apparatus.

SPILL OR LEAK PROCEDURES: Eliminate all ignition sources. Stop or control the leak, if this can be done without undue risk. Use water spray to cool and disperse vapors and protect personnel. Absorb in noncombustible material for proper disposal.

FIRE FIGHTING PROCEDURES: Use dry chemical, foam, carbon dioxide, or water spray. Water may be ineffective. Use water spray to keep fire-exposed containers cool.

HEALTH HAZARDS: Moderate health hazard. May be harmful if absorbed through skin or inhaled. Irritating to skin, eyes, and respiratory system.

FIRE AND EXPLOSION HAZARDS: Flammable liquid. Combustion may produce irritants and toxic gases. Vapors are heavier than air and may travel to a source of ignition and flash back. Liquid floats on water and may travel to a source of ignition and spread fire.

FLASH POINT: 40°F (4°C)

INSTABILITY AND REACTIVITY HAZARDS: Reacts with oxidizing materials, strong alkalies, and reducing agents.

STORAGE RECOMMENDATIONS: Store in a cool, dry, well-ventilated location. Separate from alkalies, oxidizing materials, and reducing agents. Inside storage should be in a standard flammable liquids storage warehouse, room, or cabinet.

USUAL SHIPPING CONTAINERS: Metal cans, pails, drums. Tanks on trucks, rail cars, barges.

PHYSICAL PROPERTIES: Colorless liquid.

BOILING POINT: 198°F (92°C)

SPECIFIC GRAVITY: 0.80

SOLUBILITY IN WATER: not soluble

ELECTRICAL EQUIPMENT: Class I, Group C

NAME: **METHYLCHLOROMETHYL ETHER**

SYNONYMS: chloromethoxymethane; chloromethyl methyl ether; CMME; monochloromethyl ether

FORMULA: CH_3OCH_2Cl

NFPA 30/OSHA CLASSIFICATION: IB

DOT CLASS: Class 6.1, Poisonous material

SHIPPING LABEL: POISON and FLAMMABLE LIQUID

ID NO.: UN 1239

CAS NO.: 107-30-2

MOL. WT.: 80.5

STATEMENT OF HAZARDS: Serious health hazard. Flammable liquid.

EMERGENCY RESPONSE PERSONAL PROTECTIVE EQUIPMENT: Wear special protective clothing and positive pressure self-contained breathing apparatus.

SPILL OR LEAK PROCEDURES: Releases may require isolation or evacuation. Eliminate all ignition sources. Stop or control the leak, if this can be done without undue risk. Absorb in noncombustible material for proper disposal. Control runoff and isolate discharged material for proper disposal.

FIRE FIGHTING PROCEDURES: Use dry chemical, foam, carbon dioxide, or water spray. Use water spray to keep fire-exposed containers cool. Fight fire from protected location or maximum possible distance.

HEALTH HAZARDS: Serious health hazard. May be harmful if inhaled. Irritating to skin, eyes, and respiratory system. Symptoms of overexposure include cough, wheezing, pulmonary congestion, bronchial secretions, and pneumonia.

FIRE AND EXPLOSION HAZARDS: Flammable liquid. Vapors are heavier than air and may travel to a source of ignition and flash back. Combustion may produce irritants and toxic gases. Closed containers may rupture violently when heated.

FLASH POINT: 60°F (15°C)

INSTABILITY AND REACTIVITY HAZARDS: Polymerization may be caused by elevated temperature, oxidizers, peroxides, or sunlight. Reacts with water. May form shock-sensitive peroxides upon prolonged exposure to air.

STORAGE RECOMMENDATIONS: Store in a cool, dry, well-ventilated location. Must be stored in a dry location. Outside or detached storage is preferred. Separate from oxidizing materials and peroxides.

USUAL SHIPPING CONTAINERS: Glass bottle inside wooden box. Nickel cans, pails, drums.

PHYSICAL PROPERTIES: Colorless liquid.

MELTING POINT: −154°F (−103°C)

BOILING POINT: 138°F (59°C)

SPECIFIC GRAVITY: 1.06

SOLUBILITY IN WATER: decomposes

ELECTRICAL EQUIPMENT: Class I, Group C

NAME: **METHYL CYCLOPENTANE**

SYNONYMS: MCP

FORMULA: $(C_5H_9)CH_3$

NFPA 30/OSHA CLASSIFICATION: IB

DOT CLASS: Class 3, Flammable and combustible liquid

SHIPPING LABEL: FLAMMABLE LIQUID

ID NO.: UN 2298

CAS NO.: 96-37-7

MOL. WT.: 84.7

STATEMENT OF HAZARDS: Flammable liquid. May accumulate static electricity. Moderate health hazard.

EMERGENCY RESPONSE PERSONAL PROTECTIVE EQUIPMENT: Wear full protective clothing and positive pressure self-contained breathing apparatus.

SPILL OR LEAK PROCEDURES: Eliminate all ignition sources. Stop or control the leak, if this can be done without undue risk. Use water spray to cool and disperse vapors and protect personnel. Absorb in noncombustible material for proper disposal.

FIRE FIGHTING PROCEDURES: Use dry chemical, foam, carbon dioxide, or water spray. Water may be ineffective. Use water spray to keep fire-exposed containers cool.

HEALTH HAZARDS: Moderate health hazard. May be harmful if inhaled. Irritating to skin, eyes, and respiratory system. Symptoms of overexposure include dizziness, nausea, vomiting, collapse, and unconsciousness.

FIRE AND EXPLOSION HAZARDS: Flammable liquid. Vapors are heavier than air and may travel to a source of ignition and flash back. Liquid floats on water and may travel to distant locations or spread fire. Combustion may produce irritants and toxic gases.

FLASH POINT: <20°F (< −7°C)

AUTOIGNITION TEMPERATURE: 496°F (258°C)

FLAMMABLE LIMITS: LOWER: 1.0% UPPER: 8.4%

STORAGE RECOMMENDATIONS: Store in a cool, dry, well-ventilated location. Separate from oxidizing materials. Inside storage should be in a standard flammable liquids storage warehouse, room, or cabinet.

USUAL SHIPPING CONTAINERS: Metal cans, pails, drums. Glass carboys packed in insulating material.

PHYSICAL PROPERTIES: Colorless mobile liquid.

MELTING POINT: −224°F (−142°C)

BOILING POINT: 161°F (72°C)

SPECIFIC GRAVITY: 0.75

SOLUBILITY IN WATER: not soluble

VAPOR PRESSURE: 100 mm Hg @ 18°C

ELECTRICAL EQUIPMENT: Class I, Group D

NAME: **METHYLDICHLOROSILANE**

SYNONYMS: dichloromethylsilane

FORMULA: CH_3SiHCl_2

NFPA 30/OSHA CLASSIFICATION: IB

DOT CLASS: Class 4.3, Dangerous when wet material

SHIPPING LABEL: DANGEROUS WHEN WET and CORROSIVE and FLAMMABLE LIQUID

ID NO.: UN 1242

CAS NO.: 75-54-7

MOL. WT.: 115.0

STATEMENT OF HAZARDS: Corrosive and flammable liquid. Water reactive.

EMERGENCY RESPONSE PERSONAL PROTECTIVE EQUIPMENT: Wear special protective clothing and positive pressure self-contained breathing apparatus.

SPILL OR LEAK PROCEDURES: Eliminate all ignition sources. Stop or control the leak, if this can be done without undue risk. Use water spray to cool and disperse vapors and protect personnel. Control runoff and isolate discharged material for proper disposal.

FIRE FIGHTING PROCEDURES: Use dry chemical, foam, or carbon dioxide. DO NOT use water. Use water spray to keep fire-exposed containers cool. Approach fire from upwind to avoid hazardous vapors and toxic decomposition products.

HEALTH HAZARDS: Corrosive. Causes severe eye and skin burns. May be harmful if absorbed through skin or inhaled. Irritating to skin, eyes, and respiratory system.

FIRE AND EXPLOSION HAZARDS: Flammable liquid. Vapors are heavier than air and may travel to a source of ignition and flash back. Evolves hydrogen and may ignite on contact with base. Combustion by-products include hydrogen chloride, other irritants, and toxic gases. Reignition may occur.

FLASH POINT: 15°F (−9°C)

AUTOIGNITION TEMPERATURE: >600°F (>316°C)

FLAMMABLE LIMITS: LOWER: 6% UPPER: 55%

INSTABILITY AND REACTIVITY HAZARDS: Reacts with water to produce hydrogen chloride.

STORAGE RECOMMENDATIONS: Store in a cool, dry, well-ventilated location. Separate from acids, alkalies, oxidizing materials, and water. Outside or detached storage is preferred.

USUAL SHIPPING CONTAINERS: Glass bottle inside wooden box. Metal cans, pails, drums. Packaged under nitrogen gas.

PHYSICAL PROPERTIES: Colorless liquid. Sharp, irritating odor.

MELTING POINT: −135°F (−93°C)

BOILING POINT: 107°F (42°C)

SPECIFIC GRAVITY: 1.11

SOLUBILITY IN WATER: not soluble (decomposes)

ELECTRICAL EQUIPMENT: Class I, Group C

NAME: **2-METHYL-5-ETHYLPYRIDINE**

SYNONYMS: aldehyde collidine; aldehydine; 5-ethyl-2-methylpyridine; 5-ethyl-2-picoline

FORMULA: $CH_2C_5H_3NC_2H_5$

NFPA 30/OSHA CLASSIFICATION: IIIA

DOT CLASS: Class 6.1, Poisonous material

SHIPPING LABEL: KEEP AWAY FROM FOOD

ID NO.: UN 2300

CAS NO.: 104-90-5

MOL. WT.: 120.2

STATEMENT OF HAZARDS: Moderate health hazard. Combustible liquid. Combustion by-products may include oxides of nitrogen.

EMERGENCY RESPONSE PERSONAL PROTECTIVE EQUIPMENT: Wear full protective clothing and positive pressure self-contained breathing apparatus.

SPILL OR LEAK PROCEDURES: Stop or control the leak, if this can be done without undue risk. Use appropriate foam to blanket release and suppress vapors. Control runoff and isolate discharged material for proper disposal.

FIRE FIGHTING PROCEDURES: Use dry chemical, foam, carbon dioxide, or water spray. Water may be ineffective. Use water spray to keep fire-exposed containers cool. Approach fire from upwind to avoid hazardous vapors and toxic decomposition products.

HEALTH HAZARDS: Moderate health hazard. May be harmful if absorbed through skin or inhaled. Irritating to skin, eyes, and respiratory system. Combustion by-products may include oxides of nitrogen.

FIRE AND EXPLOSION HAZARDS: Combustible liquid. Combustion by-products include oxides of nitrogen, irritants, and toxic gases.

FLASH POINT: 155°F (68°C) (oc)

FLAMMABLE LIMITS: LOWER: 1.1% UPPER: 6.6%

INSTABILITY AND REACTIVITY HAZARDS: Reacts with oxidizing materials.

STORAGE RECOMMENDATIONS: Store in a cool, dry, well-ventilated location. Separate from oxidizing materials, copper, and metal alloys. Outside or detached storage is preferred.

USUAL SHIPPING CONTAINERS: Metal cans, pails, drums. Tanks on trucks, rail cars, barges.

PHYSICAL PROPERTIES: Colorless liquid. Sharp aromatic odor.

BOILING POINT: 352°F (178°C)

SPECIFIC GRAVITY: 0.92

SOLUBILITY IN WATER: not soluble

ELECTRICAL EQUIPMENT: Class I, Group D

NAME: **METHYL FORMATE**

SYNONYMS: formic acid methyl ester; methyl methanoate

FORMULA: CH_3OCHO

NFPA 30/OSHA CLASSIFICATION: IA

DOT CLASS: Class 3, Flammable and combustible liquid

SHIPPING LABEL: FLAMMABLE LIQUID

ID NO.: UN 1243

CAS NO.: 107-31-3

MOL. WT.: 60.1

STATEMENT OF HAZARDS: Flammable liquid. Moderate health hazard.

EMERGENCY RESPONSE PERSONAL PROTECTIVE EQUIPMENT: Wear full protective clothing and positive pressure self-contained breathing apparatus.

SPILL OR LEAK PROCEDURES: Eliminate all ignition sources. Use water spray to cool and disperse vapors, protect personnel, and dilute spills to form nonflammable mixtures. Stop or control the leak, if this can be done without undue risk. Control runoff and isolate discharged material for proper disposal.

FIRE FIGHTING PROCEDURES: Use water spray, dry chemical, "alcohol resistant" foam, or carbon dioxide. Water may be ineffective. Use water spray to keep fire-exposed containers cool.

HEALTH HAZARDS: Moderate health hazard. May be harmful if inhaled. Irritating to skin, eyes, and respiratory system. Symptoms of overexposure include nasal and conjunctival irritation, vomiting, narcosis, dyspnea, central nervous system depression.

FIRE AND EXPLOSION HAZARDS: Flammable liquid. Vapors are heavier than air and may travel to a source of ignition and flash back. Combustion may produce irritants and toxic gases.

FLASH POINT: −2°F (−19°C)

AUTOIGNITION TEMPERATURE: 853°F (456°C)

FLAMMABLE LIMITS: LOWER: 5% UPPER: 23%

INSTABILITY AND REACTIVITY HAZARDS: Reacts slowly with water.

STORAGE RECOMMENDATIONS: Store in a cool, dry, well-ventilated location. Separate from alkalies, oxidizing materials, and moisture. Outside or detached storage is preferred.

USUAL SHIPPING CONTAINERS: Bottles packed in insulating material. Metal cans, pails, drums. Tanks on trucks, rail cars, barges.

PHYSICAL PROPERTIES: Colorless liquid. Agreeable odor.

MELTING POINT: −146°F (−99°C)

BOILING POINT: 89°F (32°C)

SPECIFIC GRAVITY: 0.98

SOLUBILITY IN WATER: soluble

VAPOR DENSITY: 2.07

VAPOR PRESSURE: 476 mm Hg @ 20°C

ELECTRICAL EQUIPMENT: Class I, Group D

NAME: **METHYLHYDRAZINE**

SYNONYMS: hydrazomethane; MMH; monomethylhydrazine

FORMULA: CH_3NHNH_2

NFPA 30/OSHA CLASSIFICATION: IB

DOT CLASS: Class 6.1, Poisonous material

SHIPPING LABEL: POISON and FLAMMABLE LIQUID and CORROSIVE

ID NO.: UN 1244

CAS NO.: 60-34-4

MOL. WT.: 46.1

STATEMENT OF HAZARDS: Severe health hazard. Corrosive and flammable liquid.

EMERGENCY RESPONSE PERSONAL PROTECTIVE EQUIPMENT: Wear special protective clothing and positive pressure self-contained breathing apparatus.

SPILL OR LEAK PROCEDURES: Eliminate all ignition sources. Stop or control the leak, if this can be done without undue risk. Use water spray to cool and disperse vapors and protect personnel. Absorb in noncombustible material for proper disposal.

FIRE FIGHTING PROCEDURES: Use flooding quantities of water. Use water spray to keep fire-exposed containers cool. Fight fire from protected location or maximum possible distance. Approach fire from upwind to avoid hazardous vapors and toxic decomposition products.

HEALTH HAZARDS: Severe health hazard. May be fatal if absorbed through skin or inhaled. Strong sensitizer. Corrosive. Causes severe eye and skin burns. Symptoms of overexposure include convulsions, damage to liver and kidneys, death.

FIRE AND EXPLOSION HAZARDS: Flammable liquid. Vapors are heavier than air and may travel to a source of ignition and flash back. Combustion by-products include oxides of nitrogen. Closed containers may rupture violently when heated.

FLASH POINT: 17°F (−8°C)

AUTOIGNITION TEMPERATURE: 385°F (196°C)

FLAMMABLE LIMITS: LOWER: 2.5% UPPER: 97%

INSTABILITY AND REACTIVITY HAZARDS: Reacts violently with oxidizing materials, oxygen, and peroxides; sometimes resulting in autoignition.

STORAGE RECOMMENDATIONS: Store in a cool, dry, well-ventilated location. Separate from acids, oxidizing materials, halogens, and air. Outside or detached storage is preferred.

USUAL SHIPPING CONTAINERS: Bottles packed in insulating material. Metal cans, pails, drums.

PHYSICAL PROPERTIES: Clear liquid. Odor characteristic of amines (ammonia).

MELTING POINT: −62°F (−52°C)

BOILING POINT: 190°F (88°C)

SPECIFIC GRAVITY: 0.87

SOLUBILITY IN WATER: soluble

VAPOR PRESSURE: 38 mm Hg @ 20°C

206 mm Hg @ 55°C

ELECTRICAL EQUIPMENT: Class I, Group C

NAME: **METHYL ISOBUTYL KETONE**

SYNONYMS: hexone; 4-methyl-2-pentanone; MIBK; 2-pentanone, 4-methyl-

FORMULA: $CH_3COCH_2CH(CH_3)_2$

NFPA 30/OSHA CLASSIFICATION: IB

DOT CLASS: Class 3, Flammable and combustible liquid

SHIPPING LABEL: FLAMMABLE LIQUID

ID NO.: UN 1245

CAS NO.: 108-10-1

MOL. WT.: 100.2

STATEMENT OF HAZARDS: Flammable liquid. Moderate health hazard. May form explosive peroxides with air.

EMERGENCY RESPONSE PERSONAL PROTECTIVE EQUIPMENT: Wear full protective clothing and positive pressure self-contained breathing apparatus.

SPILL OR LEAK PROCEDURES: Use water spray to cool and disperse vapors, protect personnel, and dilute spills to form nonflammable mixtures. Control runoff and isolate discharged material for proper disposal.

FIRE FIGHTING PROCEDURES: Use water spray, dry chemical, "alcohol resistant" foam, or carbon dioxide. Water may be ineffective. Use water spray to keep fire-exposed containers cool.

HEALTH HAZARDS: Moderate health hazard. May be harmful if inhaled. Irritating to eye, skin, and respiratory system. Narcotic in high concentrations leading to central nervous system depression. Symptoms of overexposure include headache, nausea, and vomiting.

FIRE AND EXPLOSION HAZARDS: Flammable liquid. Vapors are heavier than air and may travel to a source of ignition and flash back.

FLASH POINT: 64°F (18°C)

AUTOIGNITION TEMPERATURE: 840°F (448°C)

FLAMMABLE LIMITS: LOWER: 1.2% UPPER: 8.0% (@ 200°F)

INSTABILITY AND REACTIVITY HAZARDS: May form explosive peroxides in air. Incompatible with strong oxidizers and can react vigorously with reducing agents.

STORAGE RECOMMENDATIONS: Store in a cool, dry, well-ventilated location. Outside or detached storage is preferred. Store away from oxidizers and reducing agents.

USUAL SHIPPING CONTAINERS: Cans, drums, and tank cars.

PHYSICAL PROPERTIES: Colorless liquid with a sweet, camphor-like odor.

MELTING POINT: −120°F (−85°C)

BOILING POINT: 242°F (117°C)

SPECIFIC GRAVITY: 0.8

SOLUBILITY IN WATER: not soluble

VAPOR PRESSURE: 16 mm Hg @ 20°C

ELECTRICAL EQUIPMENT: Class I, Group D

NAME: **METHYL ISOCYANATE**

SYNONYMS: isocyanate methyl methane; isocyanic acid methyl ester; MIC

FORMULA: $CH_3N=CO$

NFPA 30/OSHA CLASSIFICATION: IB

DOT CLASS: Class 6.1, Poisonous material

SHIPPING LABEL: POISON and FLAMMABLE LIQUID

ID NO.: UN 2480

CAS NO.: 624-83-9

MOL. WT.: 57.0

STATEMENT OF HAZARDS: Severe health hazard. Flammable liquid. May polymerize explosively. Water reactive.

EMERGENCY RESPONSE PERSONAL PROTECTIVE EQUIPMENT: Wear special protective clothing and positive pressure self-contained breathing apparatus.

SPILL OR LEAK PROCEDURES: Releases may require isolation or evacuation. Eliminate all ignition sources. Stop or control the leak, if this can be done without undue risk. Use water spray to cool and disperse vapors and protect personnel. Approach release from upwind. Absorb in noncombustible material for proper disposal.

FIRE FIGHTING PROCEDURES: Use dry chemical or carbon dioxide. Use water spray to keep fire-exposed containers cool. Approach fire from upwind to avoid hazardous vapors and toxic decomposition products. Fight fire from protected location or maximum possible distance.

HEALTH HAZARDS: Severe health hazard. May be fatal if absorbed through skin or inhaled. Irritating to skin, eyes, and respiratory system. Causes severe tearing. Symptoms of overexposure include coughing, mucous secretions, chest pain, dyspnea, asthma, eye and skin injury.

FIRE AND EXPLOSION HAZARDS: Flammable liquid. Vapors are heavier than air and may travel to a source of ignition and flash back. Closed containers may rupture violently when heated. Combustion by-products include oxides of nitrogen, hydrogen cyanide and other irritants and toxic gases.

FLASH POINT: −19°F (−7°C)

AUTOIGNITION TEMPERATURE: 994°F (534°C)

FLAMMABLE LIMITS: LOWER: 5.3% UPPER: 26%

INSTABILITY AND REACTIVITY HAZARDS: Hazardous polymerization may occur. Usually contains inhibitors to prevent polymerization. Uninhibited monomer vapor may form polymer in vents and other confined spaces. Reacts with water, which may cause runaway reaction. Reacts with a broad range of materials.

STORAGE RECOMMENDATIONS: Store in a cool, dry, well-ventilated location. Store away from heat, oxidizing materials, and sunlight. Separate from acids, bases, amines, oxidizing materials, water, iron, tin, and copper. Outside or detached storage is preferred.

USUAL SHIPPING CONTAINERS: Glass carboys inside wooden box, stainless steel drums. Tanks on trucks, rail cars, barges.

PHYSICAL PROPERTIES: Colorless liquid. Sharp odor.

MELTING POINT: −112°F (−80°C)

BOILING POINT: 102°F (39°C)

SPECIFIC GRAVITY: 0.96

SOLUBILITY IN WATER: reacts vigorously

VAPOR PRESSURE: 348 mm Hg @ 20°C
1399 mm Hg @ 55°C

ELECTRICAL EQUIPMENT: Class I, Group D

NAME: **METHYL MERCAPTAN**

SYNONYMS: mercaptomethane; methanethiol; methyl sulfhydrate; thiomethanol; thiomethyl alcohol

FORMULA: CH_3SH

NFPA 30/OSHA CLASSIFICATION:

DOT CLASS: Class 2.3, Poisonous gas

SHIPPING LABEL: POISON GAS and FLAMMABLE GAS

ID NO.: UN 1064

CAS NO.: 74-93-1

MOL. WT.: 48.0

STATEMENT OF HAZARDS: Severe health hazard. Flammable gas.

EMERGENCY RESPONSE PERSONAL PROTECTIVE EQUIPMENT: Wear special protective clothing and positive pressure self-contained breathing apparatus.

SPILL OR LEAK PROCEDURES: Stop or control the leak, if this can be done without undue risk. Use water spray to cool and disperse vapors, protect personnel, and dilute spills to form nonflammable mixtures. Control runoff and isolate discharged material for proper disposal.

FIRE FIGHTING PROCEDURES: Stop flow of gas before extinguishing fire. Use water spray to control fire by preventing its spread and absorbing some of its heat.

HEALTH HAZARDS: Severe health hazard. May be fatal if inhaled. Irritation to the skin, eyes, and respiratory system. Symptoms include headache, nausea, narcosis, cyanosis, and pulmonary edema. Can cause fatal respiratory paralysis.

FIRE AND EXPLOSION HAZARDS: Flammable gas. Vapors are heavier than air and may travel to a source of ignition and flash back. Combustion will produce irritants and toxic gases.

FLAMMABLE LIMITS: LOWER: 3.9% UPPER: 21.8%

INSTABILITY AND REACTIVITY HAZARDS: Can react dangerously with strong oxidizing agents and mercury (II) oxide.

STORAGE RECOMMENDATIONS: Separate from oxidizing materials. Store in a cool, dry, well-ventilated location.

USUAL SHIPPING CONTAINERS: Stainless steel cylinders.

PHYSICAL PROPERTIES: Colorless gas with odor of rotten cabbage.

MELTING POINT: −184°F (−120°C)

BOILING POINT: 43°F (6°C)

SPECIFIC GRAVITY: 0.87

SOLUBILITY IN WATER: soluble

ELECTRICAL EQUIPMENT: Class I, Group C

NAME: **METHYL METHACRYLATE monomer, inhibited**

SYNONYMS: methacrylic acid, methyl ester; methyl-2-methyl-2-propenoate

FORMULA: $CH_2{=}C(CH_3)CO_2CH_3$

NFPA 30/OSHA CLASSIFICATION: IB

DOT CLASS: Class 3, Flammable and combustible liquid

SHIPPING LABEL: FLAMMABLE LIQUID

ID NO.: UN 1247

CAS NO.: 80-62-6

MOL. WT.: 100.1

STATEMENT OF HAZARDS: Flammable liquid. May polymerize explosively. Moderate health hazard.

EMERGENCY RESPONSE PERSONAL PROTECTIVE EQUIPMENT: Wear full protective clothing and positive pressure self-contained breathing apparatus.

SPILL OR LEAK PROCEDURES: Eliminate all ignition sources. Stop or control the leak, if this can be done without undue risk. Use water spray to cool and disperse vapors and protect personnel. Control runoff and isolate discharged material for proper disposal.

FIRE FIGHTING PROCEDURES: Use water spray, dry chemical, foam, or carbon dioxide. Use water spray to keep fire-exposed containers cool. Fight fire from protected location or maximum possible distance.

HEALTH HAZARDS: Moderate health hazard. May be harmful if inhaled. Irritating skin, eyes, and respiratory system. Inhalation may cause headache, nausea, vomiting, confusion, dizziness, and unconsciousness.

FIRE AND EXPLOSION HAZARDS: Flammable liquid. May polymerize explosively. Closed containers may rupture violently when heated. Vapors are heavier than air and may travel to a source of ignition and flash back. Liquid floats on water and may travel to a source of ignition and spread fire.

FLASH POINT: 50°F (10°C) (oc)

AUTOIGNITION TEMPERATURE: 815°F (435°C)

FLAMMABLE LIMITS: LOWER: 1.7% UPPER: 8.2%

INSTABILITY AND REACTIVITY HAZARDS: Hazardous polymerization may occur. Usually contains inhibitors to prevent polymerization. Polymerization may be caused by elevated temperature, oxidizers, peroxides, or sunlight. Material will react with strong acids and alkalies. Hazardous decomposition products include CO, carbon dioxide, and acrid fumes. Uninhibited monomer vapor may form polymer in vents and other confined spaces.

STORAGE RECOMMENDATIONS: Separate from oxidizing materials, peroxides, or other initiators. Store in cool, dry, well-ventilated place.

USUAL SHIPPING CONTAINERS: Usually shipped in bottles, cans, drums, and tank trucks or tank cars.

PHYSICAL PROPERTIES: Colorless liquid with acrid, fruity odor.

MELTING POINT: −55°F (−48°C)

BOILING POINT: 213°F (100°C)

SPECIFIC GRAVITY: 0.94

SOLUBILITY IN WATER: not soluble

VAPOR PRESSURE: 29 mm Hg @ 20°C

ELECTRICAL EQUIPMENT: Class I, Group D

NAME: **METHYLTRICHLOROSILANE**

SYNONYMS: trichloromethylsilane

FORMULA: CH_3SiCl_3

NFPA 30/OSHA CLASSIFICATION: IB

DOT CLASS: Class 3, Flammable and combustible liquid

SHIPPING LABEL: FLAMMABLE LIQUID and CORROSIVE

ID NO.: UN 1250

CAS NO.: 75-79-6

MOL. WT.: 149.5

STATEMENT OF HAZARDS: Corrosive and flammable liquid. Water reactive.

EMERGENCY RESPONSE PERSONAL PROTECTIVE EQUIPMENT: Wear special protective clothing and positive pressure self-contained breathing apparatus.

SPILL OR LEAK PROCEDURES: Eliminate all ignition sources. Stop or control the leak, if this can be done without undue risk. Use water spray to cool and disperse vapors and protect personnel. Control runoff and isolate discharged material for proper disposal.

FIRE FIGHTING PROCEDURES: Use dry chemical, foam, carbon dioxide, or water spray. Water may be ineffective. Use water spray to keep fire exposed containers cool. Approach fire from upwind to avoid hazardous vapors and toxic decomposition products.

HEALTH HAZARDS: Corrosive. Causes severe eye and skin burns. May be harmful if absorbed through skin or inhaled. Irritating to skin, eyes, and respiratory system. Symptoms of overexposure include coughing, wheezing, laryngitis, headache, nausea, vomiting, spasm, pulmonary inflammation, and edema.

FIRE AND EXPLOSION HAZARDS: Flammable liquid. Vapors are heavier than air and may travel to a source of ignition and flash back. Evolves hydrogen and may ignite on contact with base. Combustion by-products include hydrogen chloride, other irritants, and toxic gases.

FLASH POINT: 15°F (−9°C)

FLAMMABLE LIMITS: LOWER: 7.2% UPPER: 11.9%

INSTABILITY AND REACTIVITY HAZARDS: Reacts with water to produce hydrogen chloride. Reacts with a broad range of materials.

STORAGE RECOMMENDATIONS: Store in a cool, dry, well-ventilated location. Separate from acids, alkalies, oxidizing materials, and water. Outside or detached storage is preferred.

USUAL SHIPPING CONTAINERS: Glass bottle inside wooden box. Metal cans, pails, drums. Packaged under nitrogen gas.

PHYSICAL PROPERTIES: Colorless liquid.

MELTING POINT: −130°F (−90°C)

BOILING POINT: 151°F (66°C)

SPECIFIC GRAVITY: 1.27

SOLUBILITY IN WATER: not soluble (decomposes)

VAPOR PRESSURE: 137 mm Hg @ 20°C

ELECTRICAL EQUIPMENT: Class I, Group Undesignated

NAME: **METHYL VINYL KETONE**

SYNONYMS: acetyl ethylene; 3-buten-2-one; ^{3}-2-butenone; methylene acetone; MVK

FORMULA: $CH_3COCH{=}CH_2$

NFPA 30/OSHA CLASSIFICATION: IB

DOT CLASS: Class 3, Flammable and combustible liquid

SHIPPING LABEL: FLAMMABLE LIQUID

ID NO.: UN 1251

CAS NO.: 78-94-4

MOL. WT.: 70.1

STATEMENT OF HAZARDS: Severe health hazard. Flammable liquid. May polymerize explosively.

EMERGENCY RESPONSE PERSONAL PROTECTIVE EQUIPMENT: Wear special protective clothing and positive pressure self-contained breathing apparatus. Attacks all protective garments except Teflon.

SPILL OR LEAK PROCEDURES: Eliminate all ignition sources. Stop or control the leak, if this can be done without undue risk. Use water spray to cool and disperse vapors, protect personnel, and dilute spills to form nonflammable mixtures. Control runoff and isolate discharged material for proper disposal.

FIRE FIGHTING PROCEDURES: Use dry chemical, "alcohol resistant" foam, carbon dioxide, or water spray. Water may be ineffective. Use water spray to keep fire-exposed containers cool. Fight fire from protected location or maximum possible distance. Approach fire from upwind to avoid hazardous vapors and toxic decomposition products.

HEALTH HAZARDS: Severe health hazard. May be fatal if absorbed through skin or inhaled. Causes severe tearing. Irritating to skin, eyes, and respiratory system.

FIRE AND EXPLOSION HAZARDS: Flammable liquid. Vapors are heavier than air and may travel to a source of ignition and flash back. Closed containers may rupture violently when heated. Reacts violently with a broad range of materials under fire conditions. Combustion may produce irritants and toxic gases.

FLASH POINT: 20°F (−7°C)

AUTOIGNITION TEMPERATURE: 915°F (491°C)

FLAMMABLE LIMITS: LOWER: 2.1% UPPER: 15.6%

INSTABILITY AND REACTIVITY HAZARDS: Usually contains inhibitors to prevent polymerization. Polymerization may be caused by elevated temperature, oxidizing materials, peroxides, or sunlight. Uninhibited monomer vapor may form polymer in vents and other confined spaces. Reacts violently with a broad range of materials.

STORAGE RECOMMENDATIONS: Store in a cool, dry, well-ventilated location. Store away from heat, oxidizing materials, and sunlight. Separate from alkalies, reducing agents. Outside or detached storage is preferred.

USUAL SHIPPING CONTAINERS: Bottles or carboys packed in insulating material. Metal cans, pails, drums.

PHYSICAL PROPERTIES: Colorless liquid. Pungent, irritating odor.

MELTING POINT: 20°F (−7°C)

BOILING POINT: 179°F (81°C)

SPECIFIC GRAVITY: 0.86

SOLUBILITY IN WATER: soluble

VAPOR PRESSURE: 71 mm Hg @ 20°C

310 mm Hg @ 55°C

ELECTRICAL EQUIPMENT: Class I, Group D

NAME: **MONOCHLORO-s-TRIAZINETRIONE ACID**

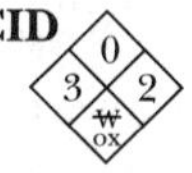

SYNONYMS: chloroisocyanuric acid

FORMULA: $C_3ClH_2N_3O_3$

NFPA 30/OSHA CLASSIFICATION:

DOT CLASS: N/A

ID NO.: N/A

CAS NO.: 13057-78-8

MOL. WT.: 163.5

STATEMENT OF HAZARDS: Serious health hazard. Strong oxidizer. Reacts exothermically with combustible materials, ammonium salts, or foreign materials causing fire or explosion. Reacts with water, releasing chlorine gas and nitrogen trichloride. Thermally unstable. Decomposes at fire temperature.

EMERGENCY RESPONSE PERSONAL PROTECTIVE EQUIPMENT: Wear special protective clothing and positive pressure self-contained breathing apparatus.

SPILL OR LEAK PROCEDURES: Keep water away from release. Approach release from upwind. Isolate leaking containers, if this can be done without undue risk. Prompt cleanup and removal are necessary. Shovel into suitable dry container. Control runoff and isolate discharged material for proper disposal.

FIRE FIGHTING PROCEDURES: Approach fire from upwind to avoid hazardous vapors and toxic decomposition products. Fight fire from protected location or maximum possible distance. Use flooding quantities of water on fire-involved containers. If necessary use water spray to keep fire-exposed containers cool.

HEALTH HAZARDS: Serious health hazard. Irritating to skin, eyes, and respiratory system. May be harmful if inhaled. Water reactive. Releases chlorine gas and nitrogen trichloride.

FIRE AND EXPLOSION HAZARDS: Reacts exothermically with combustible materials, ammonium salts, or foreign substances and may cause explosion or fire. Water reactive. Releases chlorine gas and nitrogen trichloride and in confined spaces increases temperature and pressure to dangerous levels. Closed containers may rupture violently when heated. Thermally unstable. Decomposes at fire temperature.

INSTABILITY AND REACTIVITY HAZARDS: Reacts with water to form nitrogen trichloride, which, if concentrated, will explode. Water introduced into drums will result in an explosion. Reaction with ammonia or amines produces nitrogen trichloride. Reacts with most reducing agents.

STORAGE RECOMMENDATIONS: Store in a cool, dry, well-ventilated location. Outside or detached storage is preferred. Must be stored in a dry location on pallets. Separate from combustibles, oxidizables, ammonia, sodium carbonate (soda ash), calcium hypochlorite, hydrogen peroxide. See also NFPA 430, Code for the Storage of Liquid and Solid Oxidizers.

USUAL SHIPPING CONTAINERS: Moisture-excluding fiber drums with polyethylene bag liner and lined pails. Smaller quantities in glass or polyethylene bottles and in special laminated packets.

PHYSICAL PROPERTIES: White crystalline solid with strong chlorine odor. Thermally unstable. Decomposes at fire temperature.

SOLUBILITY IN WATER: slowly reacts

NAME: **mono-(TRICHLORO) TETRA-(MONOPOTASSIUM DICHLORO)-PENTA-s-TRIAZINETRIONE, dry**

FORMULA: $C_3Cl_3N_3O_3.4KCl_2(NCO)_3$

NFPA 30/OSHA CLASSIFICATION:

DOT CLASS: Class 5.1, Oxidizer

SHIPPING LABEL: OXIDIZER

ID NO.: NA 2468

CAS NO.: N/A

MOL. WT.: 176.5

STATEMENT OF HAZARDS: Serious health hazard. Strong oxidizer. Thermally unstable. Decomposes at fire temperature. Closed containers may rupture violently when heated.

EMERGENCY RESPONSE PERSONAL PROTECTIVE EQUIPMENT: Wear special protective clothing and positive pressure self-contained breathing apparatus.

SPILL OR LEAK PROCEDURES: Keep water away from release. Approach release from upwind. Isolate leaking containers, if this can be done without undue risk. Avoid bulging drums and isolate if possible. Prompt cleanup and removal are necessary. Shovel into suitable dry container. Control runoff and isolate discharged material for proper disposal.

FIRE FIGHTING PROCEDURES: Approach fire from upwind to avoid hazardous vapors and toxic decomposition products. Fight fire from protected location or maximum possible distance. Use flooding quantities of water on fire-involved containers. If necessary use water spray to keep fire-exposed containers cool. Avoid use of water on non-involved material wherever possible.

HEALTH HAZARDS: Serious health hazard. Irritating to skin, eyes, and respiratory system. May be harmful if inhaled. Water reactive. Releases chlorine gas and nitrogen trichloride liquid.

FIRE AND EXPLOSION HAZARDS: Strong oxidizer. Water reactive. Releases chlorine gas and nitrogen trichloride and in confined spaces increases temperature and pressure to dangerous levels. Closed containers may rupture violently when heated. Thermally unstable. Decomposes at fire temperature.

INSTABILITY AND REACTIVITY HAZARDS: Reacts with water to produce nitrogen trichloride, which if concentrated will explode. Water introduced into drums will result in an explosion. Reaction with ammonia or amines produces nitrogen trichloride. Reacts with most reducing agents.

STORAGE RECOMMENDATIONS: Store in a cool, dry, well-ventilated location. Outside or detached storage is preferred. Must be stored in a dry location on pallets arranged according to NFPA 430, Code for Storage of Liquid and Solid Oxidizers. Separate from combustibles, oxidizables, ammonia, sodium carbonate (soda ash), calcium hypochlorite, hydrogen peroxide.

USUAL SHIPPING CONTAINERS: Moisture-excluding fiber drums with polyethylene bag liner and lined pails. Smaller quantities in glass or polyethylene bottles and in special laminated packets.

PHYSICAL PROPERTIES: White crystalline solid with strong chlorine odor.

NAME: **MORPHOLINE**

SYNONYMS: diethylene oximide; diethylenimide oxide; tetrahydro-1,4-isoxazine

FORMULA: $\overline{OCH_2CH_2NHCH_2CH_2}$

NFPA 30/OSHA CLASSIFICATION: IC

DOT CLASS: Class 3, Flammable and combustible liquid

SHIPPING LABEL: FLAMMABLE LIQUID

ID NO.: UN 2054

CAS NO.: 110-91-8

MOL. WT.: 87.1

STATEMENT OF HAZARDS: Corrosive and flammable liquid.

EMERGENCY RESPONSE PERSONAL PROTECTIVE EQUIPMENT: Wear special protective clothing and positive pressure self-contained breathing apparatus.

SPILL OR LEAK PROCEDURES: Eliminate all ignition sources. Stop or control the leak, if this can be done without undue risk. Use water spray to cool and disperse vapors, protect personnel, and dilute spills to form nonflammable mixtures. Control runoff and isolate discharged material for proper disposal.

FIRE FIGHTING PROCEDURES: Use flooding quantities of water as fog or spray, dry chemical, "alcohol resistant" foam, or carbon dioxide. Use water spray to keep fire-exposed containers cool.

HEALTH HAZARDS: Corrosive. Causes severe eye and skin burns. May be harmful if absorbed through skin or inhaled. Irritating to skin, eyes, and respiratory system.

FIRE AND EXPLOSION HAZARDS: Flammable liquid. Vapors are heavier than air and may travel to a source of ignition and flash back. Combustion may produce irritants and toxic gases. Combustion by-products include ammonia and nitrogen oxides.

FLASH POINT: 95°F (35°C)

AUTOIGNITION TEMPERATURE: 590°F (310°C)

FLAMMABLE LIMITS: LOWER: 1.8% UPPER: 11.0%

INSTABILITY AND REACTIVITY HAZARDS: Reacts with acids, oxidizing materials, and nitro compounds.

STORAGE RECOMMENDATIONS: Separate from oxidizing materials and acids. Store in a cool, dry, well-ventilated location. Outside or detached storage is preferred. Inside storage should be in a standard flammable liquids storage warehouse, room, or cabinet.

USUAL SHIPPING CONTAINERS: Glass bottles. Steel drums. May be shipped as anhydrous liquid or as aqueous solution.

PHYSICAL PROPERTIES: Hygroscopic colorless liquid with characteristic fish-like amine odor.

MELTING POINT: 23°F (−5°C)

BOILING POINT: 264°F (129°C)

SPECIFIC GRAVITY: 1.00

SOLUBILITY IN WATER: soluble

VAPOR PRESSURE: 8 mm Hg @ 20°C

ELECTRICAL EQUIPMENT: Class I, Group C

NAME: **NAPHTHALENE,** crude or refined

SYNONYMS: moth flakes; naphthalin; naphthene; NTM; tar camphor; white tar

FORMULA: $C_{10}H_8$

NFPA 30/OSHA CLASSIFICATION: IIIA

DOT CLASS: Class 4.1, Flammable solid

SHIPPING LABEL: FLAMMABLE SOLID

ID NO.: UN 1334

CAS NO.: 91-20-3

MOL. WT.: 128.2

STATEMENT OF HAZARDS: Moderate health hazard. Combustible solid.

EMERGENCY RESPONSE PERSONAL PROTECTIVE EQUIPMENT: Wear full protective clothing and positive pressure self-contained breathing apparatus.

SPILL OR LEAK PROCEDURES: Shovel into suitable dry container.

FIRE FIGHTING PROCEDURES: Use dry chemical, foam, carbon dioxide, or water spray. Water or foam may cause frothing. Use water spray to keep fire-exposed containers cool.

HEALTH HAZARDS: Moderate health hazard. May be harmful if absorbed through skin or inhaled. Irritating to skin, eyes, and respiratory system. Symptoms of overexposure include nausea, vomiting, headache, diaphoresis, fever, convulsions, and coma. Symptoms may appear two to four hours after exposure.

FIRE AND EXPLOSION HAZARDS: Combustible solid. Volatile solid that gives off flammable vapors when heated. Dust may explode in air if provided with ignition source. Combustion may produce irritants and toxic gases.

FLASH POINT: 174°F (79°C)

AUTOIGNITION TEMPERATURE: 979°F (526°C)

FLAMMABLE LIMITS: LOWER: 0.9% UPPER: 5.9%

INSTABILITY AND REACTIVITY HAZARDS: Volatilizes at room temperature. Reacts with oxidizing materials.

STORAGE RECOMMENDATIONS: Store in a cool, dry, well-ventilated location. Separate from oxidizing materials. May be stored under nitrogen gas.

USUAL SHIPPING CONTAINERS: Bottles, boxes, cans, kegs, and drums.

PHYSICAL PROPERTIES: White volatile solid in flake, cake, or powder form.

MELTING POINT: 176°F (80°C)

BOILING POINT: 424°F (218°C)

SPECIFIC GRAVITY: 1.16

SOLUBILITY IN WATER: not soluble

VAPOR PRESSURE: 0.05 mm Hg @ 20°C

1.0 mm Hg @ 53°C

NAME: **NATURAL GAS, LIQUEFIED**

DOT SHIPPING NAME: **METHANE, refrigerated liquid**

SYNONYMS: LNG

FORMULA: CH_4 (approx. 85%)

C_2H_6 (approx. 9%)

NFPA 30/OSHA CLASSIFICATION:

DOT CLASS: Class 2.1, Flammable gas

SHIPPING LABEL: FLAMMABLE GAS

ID NO.: UN 1972 refrigerated liquid

CAS NO.: 74-82-8 (METHANE)

MOL. WT.: 18 (approx.)

STATEMENT OF HAZARDS: Liquefied flammable gas.

EMERGENCY RESPONSE PERSONAL PROTECTIVE EQUIPMENT: Wear special protective clothing and positive pressure self-contained breathing apparatus.

SPILL OR LEAK PROCEDURES: Eliminate all ignition sources. Use water spray to disperse vapors, protect personnel, and increase the rate of evaporation if the increase in vapor evolution can be controlled. Stop or control the leak, if this can be done without undue risk. Approach release from upwind.

FIRE FIGHTING PROCEDURES: Stop flow of gas before extinguishing fire. Use fine spray or fog to control fire by preventing its spread and absorbing some of its heat.

HEALTH HAZARDS: Contact with liquid may cause frostbite or severe burns of the skin. Narcotic in high concentrations. Simple asphyxiant.

FIRE AND EXPLOSION HAZARDS: Liquefied flammable gas. Cold gas that has recently escaped from pressurized tanks may travel close to the ground and flash back.

AUTOIGNITION TEMPERATURE: 999°F (537°C)

FLAMMABLE LIMITS: LOWER: 5.3% UPPER: 14.0%

STORAGE RECOMMENDATIONS: Store in a cool, dry, well-ventilated location. Separate from halogens and oxygen. Outside or detached storage is preferred.

USUAL SHIPPING CONTAINERS: Refrigerated pressurized tanks for liquid.

PHYSICAL PROPERTIES: Colorless gas. Odorless or weak mercaptan (skunk) odor.

MELTING POINT: −297°F (−183°C)

BOILING POINT: −258°F (−161°C)

SPECIFIC GRAVITY: 0.43 @ −162°C

SOLUBILITY IN WATER: not soluble

VAPOR DENSITY: 0.61

ELECTRICAL EQUIPMENT: Class I, Group D

NAME: **NICKEL CARBONYL**

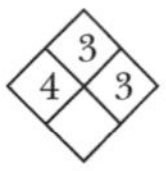

SYNONYMS: nickel tetracarbonyl

FORMULA: $Ni(CO)_4$

NFPA 30/OSHA CLASSIFICATION: IB

DOT CLASS: Class 6.1, Poisonous material

SHIPPING LABEL: POISON and FLAMMABLE LIQUID

ID NO.: UN 1259

CAS NO.: 13463-39-3

MOL. WT.: 170.7

STATEMENT OF HAZARDS: Severe health hazard. Flammable liquid. Thermally unstable. Decomposes violently at 140°F (60°C).

EMERGENCY RESPONSE PERSONAL PROTECTIVE EQUIPMENT: Wear special protective clothing and positive pressure self-contained breathing apparatus.

SPILL OR LEAK PROCEDURES: Stop or control the leak, if this can be done without undue risk. Eliminate all ignition sources. Use appropriate foam to blanket release and suppress vapors. Control runoff and isolate discharged material for proper disposal.

FIRE FIGHTING PROCEDURES: Use water spray, dry chemical, foam, or carbon dioxide. Use water spray to keep fire-exposed containers cool. Fight fire from protected location or maximum possible distance.

HEALTH HAZARDS: Severe health hazard. May be fatal if absorbed through skin or inhaled. Irritating to skin, eyes, and respiratory system. Inhalation of small amounts may cause congestion, pulmonary edema, death. Effects may be delayed.

FIRE AND EXPLOSION HAZARDS: Flammable liquid. Decomposes explosively at 140°F (60°C) with release of nickel fumes. Closed containers may rupture violently when heated.

FLASH POINT: <-4°F (<-20°C)

AUTOIGNITION TEMPERATURE: 140°F (60°C)

FLAMMABLE LIMITS: LOWER: 2% UPPER: 34%

INSTABILITY AND REACTIVITY HAZARDS: Oxidizes in air. Reacts with nitric acid, halogens, oxidizing materials.

STORAGE RECOMMENDATIONS: Store in a cool, dry, well-ventilated location. Keep cylinders restrained.

USUAL SHIPPING CONTAINERS: Steel or nickel cylinders.

PHYSICAL PROPERTIES: Colorless to brownish volatile liquid. Sooty or musty odor.

MELTING POINT: -13°F (-25°C)

BOILING POINT: 109°F (43°C)

SPECIFIC GRAVITY: 1.32 @ 17°C

SOLUBILITY IN WATER: not soluble

VAPOR PRESSURE: 400 mm Hg @ 25.8°C

ELECTRICAL EQUIPMENT: Class I, Group D

NAME: **NICKEL CATALYST**

SYNONYMS: Raney alloy; Raney nickel

FORMULA: Ni

NFPA 30/OSHA CLASSIFICATION:

DOT CLASS: N/A

ID NO.: N/A

CAS NO.: 7440-02-0

MOL. WT.: 58.7

STATEMENT OF HAZARDS: Flammable solid. Pyrophoric when dry. Moderate health hazard.

EMERGENCY RESPONSE PERSONAL PROTECTIVE EQUIPMENT: Wear full protective clothing and positive pressure self-contained breathing apparatus.

SPILL OR LEAK PROCEDURES: Blanket release with dry sand, dry clay, or dry ground limestone. Shovel into suitable dry container.

FIRE FIGHTING PROCEDURES: Smother with dry sand, dry clay, dry ground limestone, or use approved Class D extinguishers. DO NOT use carbon dioxide or halogenated extinguishing agents. Use flooding quantities of water. Fight fire from protected location or maximum possible distance.

HEALTH HAZARDS: Moderate health hazard. May be harmful if inhaled. Irritating to skin, eyes, and respiratory system.

FIRE AND EXPLOSION HAZARDS: Flammable solid. Mixtures of finely divided nickel and air may explode if allowed source of ignition. Pyrophoric when dry. Raney nickel ignites spontaneously in air. Reaction with acid evolves highly flammable hydrogen gas. Closed containers may rupture violently when heated.

INSTABILITY AND REACTIVITY HAZARDS: May cause violent decomposition reactions with acids, oxidizing materials, sulfur, hydrazine, hydrazoic acid, and other materials.

STORAGE RECOMMENDATIONS: Store in a cool, dry, well-ventilated location. Separate from acids, oxidizing materials. Keep activated catalyst (Raney nickel) under inert gas or water.

USUAL SHIPPING CONTAINERS: Cans, boxes, barrels, drums.

PHYSICAL PROPERTIES: Silvery or dark gray metal powder. Raney nickel has appearance of spongy mass.

MELTING POINT: 2651°F (1455°C)

BOILING POINT: 4946°F (2730°C)

SPECIFIC GRAVITY: 8.90

SOLUBILITY IN WATER: not soluble

NAME: **NITRIC ACID**

fuming UN 2032 — >40% UN 2031 — ≤40% NA 1760

SYNONYMS: aquafortis; azotic acid; fuming nitric acid

FORMULA: HNO_3

NFPA 30/OSHA CLASSIFICATION:

DOT CLASS: Class 8, Corrosive material

Class 8, Corrosive material

COMPOSITION: Red fuming

SHIPPING LABEL: Corrosive & Oxidizer & Poison

ID NO.: UN 2031

UN 2032

CAS NO.: 7697-37-2

MOL. WT.: 63.0

STATEMENT OF HAZARDS: Severe health hazard. Corrosive. Strong oxidizer. Fuming nitric acid is more corrosive and reactive.

EMERGENCY RESPONSE PERSONAL PROTECTIVE EQUIPMENT: Wear special protective clothing and positive pressure self-contained breathing apparatus.

SPILL OR LEAK PROCEDURES: Releases may require isolation or evacuation. Approach release from upwind. Stop or control the leak, if this can be done without undue risk. Use water spray to cool and disperse vapors and protect personnel. Avoid solid stream on pooled liquids. Prompt cleanup and removal are necessary. Control runoff and isolate discharged material for proper disposal.

FIRE FIGHTING PROCEDURES: Approach fire from upwind to avoid hazardous vapors and toxic decomposition products. Use flooding quantities of water as spray or fog. Use water spray to keep fire-exposed containers cool. Extinguish fire using agent suitable for surrounding fire.

HEALTH HAZARDS: Severe health hazard. May be fatal if inhaled. May cause pulmonary edema. Corrosive. Causes severe eye and skin burns.

FIRE AND EXPLOSION HAZARDS: Strong oxidizer. Contact of concentrated nitric acid with combustible materials may increase the hazard from fire and may lead to an explosion. Decomposes at fire temperature with release of oxides of nitrogen. Releases hydrogen gas on contact with many metals.

INSTABILITY AND REACTIVITY HAZARDS: Strong oxidizer. Reacts vigorously with combustibles, or readily oxidizable materials, organic solvents, metal powders, carbides, cyanides, sulfides, and alkalies. See NFPA 491M, Manual of Hazardous Chemical Reactions. Reacts with alkalies. Fuming nitric acid dissolves in water, releasing heat. Small quantities of water added to concentrated nitric acid may cause vigorous reaction.

STORAGE RECOMMENDATIONS: Store in a cool, dry, well-ventilated location. Separate from alkalies, metals, organics, and other oxidizing materials. See also NFPA 430, Code for the Storage of Solid and Liquid Oxidizers.

USUAL SHIPPING CONTAINERS: Glass bottles and carboys, special metal drums. Tanks on trucks, rail cars, barges.

PHYSICAL PROPERTIES: Colorless to light brown fuming liquid. Fuming nitric acid is reddish fuming liquid.

MELTING POINT: −44°F (−42°C)

BOILING POINT: 181°F (83°C)

SPECIFIC GRAVITY: 1.50

SOLUBILITY IN WATER: soluble

VAPOR PRESSURE: UN 2032 51 mm Hg @ 25°C

(95-98%) 113 mm Hg @ 38°C

67% 6.8 mm Hg @ 20°C

UN 2031 8 to 11 mm Hg @ 25°C

17 to 25 mm Hg @ 38°C

NAME: **NITROANILINES (o-, m-, p-)**

SYNONYMS: p-aminonitrobenzene; 4-aminonitrobenzene; NAL; 2-nitroaniline; 3-nitroaniline; 4-nitro-aniline

FORMULA: $NO_2(C_6H_4)NH_2$

NFPA 30/OSHA CLASSIFICATION: IIIB

DOT CLASS: Class 6.1, Poisonous material

SHIPPING LABEL: POISON

ID NO.: UN 1661

CAS NO.: 100-01-6

MOL. WT.: 138.1

STATEMENT OF HAZARDS: Serious health hazard. Combustible solid. May decompose explosively in a fire.

EMERGENCY RESPONSE PERSONAL PROTECTIVE EQUIPMENT: Wear special protective clothing and positive pressure self-contained breathing apparatus.

SPILL OR LEAK PROCEDURES: Shovel into suitable dry container.

FIRE FIGHTING PROCEDURES: Use water spray, dry chemical, foam, or carbon dioxide. Fight fire from protected location or maximum possible distance. Approach fire from upwind to avoid hazardous vapors and toxic decomposition products.

HEALTH HAZARDS: Serious health hazard. May be harmful if absorbed through skin or inhaled. Irritating to skin, eyes, and respiratory system. Symptoms of overexposure include irritability, vomiting, diarrhea, cyanosis, ataxia, tachycardia, convulsions, respiratory arrest, and anemia.

FIRE AND EXPLOSION HAZARDS: Combustible solid. Explosive decomposition may occur under fire conditions. Combustion by-products include oxides of nitrogen and other irritants and toxic gases. Closed containers may rupture violently when heated.

FLASH POINT: 309°F (154°C)

INSTABILITY AND REACTIVITY HAZARDS: Reacts vigorously with strong oxidizers, strong reducing agents, strong acids, acid chlorides, and acid anhydrides.

STORAGE RECOMMENDATIONS: Store in a cool, dry, well-ventilated location. Separate from acids, oxidizing materials, and reducing agents.

USUAL SHIPPING CONTAINERS: Fiber or metal drums. Insulated tanks on trucks, rail cars, barges.

PHYSICAL PROPERTIES: Bright yellow powder. Odor of ammonia.

MELTING POINT: 298°F (148°C)

BOILING POINT: 637°F (332°C)

SPECIFIC GRAVITY: 1.42

SOLUBILITY IN WATER: not soluble

VAPOR PRESSURE: 1 mm Hg @ 142°C

NAME: **NITROBENZENE**

SYNONYMS: essence of mirbane; nitrobenzol; NTB; oil of mirbane

FORMULA: $NO_2(C_6H_5)$

NFPA 30/OSHA CLASSIFICATION: IIIA

DOT CLASS: Class 6.1, Poisonous material

SHIPPING LABEL: POISON

ID NO.: UN 1662

CAS NO.: 98-95-3

MOL. WT.: 123.1

STATEMENT OF HAZARDS: Serious health hazard. Combustible liquid.

EMERGENCY RESPONSE PERSONAL PROTECTIVE EQUIPMENT: Wear special protective clothing and positive pressure self-contained breathing apparatus.

SPILL OR LEAK PROCEDURES: Stop or control the leak, if this can be done without undue risk. Use appropriate foam to blanket release and suppress vapors. Cover in noncombustible material for proper disposal. Prompt cleanup and removal are necessary.

FIRE FIGHTING PROCEDURES: Use dry chemical, foam, carbon dioxide, or water spray. Use water spray to keep fire-exposed containers cool. Approach fire from upwind to avoid hazardous vapors and toxic decomposition products.

HEALTH HAZARDS: Serious health hazard. May be harmful if absorbed through skin or inhaled. Irritating to skin, eyes, and respiratory system. Symptoms of overexposure include headache, nausea, drowsiness, vomiting, cyanosis. Symptoms may be delayed.

FIRE AND EXPLOSION HAZARDS: Combustible liquid. Combustion by-products include oxides of nitrogen.

FLASH POINT: 190°F (88°C)

AUTOIGNITION TEMPERATURE: 924°F (496°C)

FLAMMABLE LIMITS: LOWER: 1.8% UPPER: not determined

STORAGE RECOMMENDATIONS: Store in a cool, dry, well-ventilated, dark location. Separate from acids, bases, oxidizing materials, and metals.

USUAL SHIPPING CONTAINERS: Glass or polyethylene bottles, carboys, polyethylene-lined drums. Metal cans, pails, drums.

PHYSICAL PROPERTIES: Colorless to pale yellow, oily liquid. Odor of volatile oil of almond or paste shoe polish.

MELTING POINT: 42°F (6°C)

BOILING POINT: 411°F (211°C)

SPECIFIC GRAVITY: 1.20

SOLUBILITY IN WATER: not soluble

VAPOR PRESSURE: <1 mm Hg @ 20°C

50 mm Hg @ 120°C

ELECTRICAL EQUIPMENT: Class I, Group D

NAME: **NITROETHANE**

FORMULA: $C_2H_5NO_2$

NFPA 30/OSHA CLASSIFICATION: IC

DOT CLASS: Class 3, Flammable and combustible liquid

SHIPPING LABEL: FLAMMABLE LIQUID

ID NO.: UN 2842

CAS NO.: 79-24-3

MOL. WT.: 75.1

STATEMENT OF HAZARDS: Flammable liquid. Combustion by-products may include oxides of nitrogen. May decompose explosively at elevated temperature. Slight health hazard.

EMERGENCY RESPONSE PERSONAL PROTECTIVE EQUIPMENT: Wear full protective clothing and positive pressure self-contained breathing apparatus.

SPILL OR LEAK PROCEDURES: Eliminate all ignition sources. Use water spray to cool and disperse vapors and protect personnel. Control runoff and isolate discharged material for proper disposal.

FIRE FIGHTING PROCEDURES: Use flooding quantities of water. Use dry chemical, foam, or carbon dioxide. Fight fire from protected location or maximum possible distance.

HEALTH HAZARDS: Slight health hazard. Irritating to skin, eyes, and respiratory system. Decomposition products contain oxides of nitrogen.

FIRE AND EXPLOSION HAZARDS: Can explode when heated rapidly to high temperatures. Vapors are heavier than air and may travel to a source of ignition and flash back. Closed containers may rupture violently when heated.

FLASH POINT: 82°F (28°C)

AUTOIGNITION TEMPERATURE: 778°F (414°C)

FLAMMABLE LIMITS: LOWER: 3.4% UPPER: not determined

INSTABILITY AND REACTIVITY HAZARDS: Decomposes at elevated temperatures to form carbon monoxide, carbon dioxide, and oxides of nitrogen. Reacts with many strong alkalies.

STORAGE RECOMMENDATIONS: Detached storage preferred. Separate from other flammables and oxidizing materials.

USUAL SHIPPING CONTAINERS: Glass bottles, drums, tank cars, and tank trucks.

PHYSICAL PROPERTIES: Colorless liquid with mild fruity odor.

MELTING POINT: −130°F (−90°C)

BOILING POINT: 237°F (114°C)

SPECIFIC GRAVITY: 1.05

SOLUBILITY IN WATER: not soluble

VAPOR PRESSURE: 15.6 mm Hg @ 20°C

ELECTRICAL EQUIPMENT: Class I, Group C

NAME: **NITROGEN, refrigerated liquid**

SYNONYMS: NXX; LN

FORMULA: N_2

NFPA 30/OSHA CLASSIFICATION:

DOT CLASS: Class 2.2 , Nonflammable compressed gas

SHIPPING LABEL: NONFLAMMABLE GAS

ID NO.: UN 1977 refrigerated

CAS NO.: 7727-37-9

MOL. WT.: 28.0

STATEMENT OF HAZARDS: Cryogenic liquid.

EMERGENCY RESPONSE PERSONAL PROTECTIVE EQUIPMENT: Wear special protective clothing and positive pressure self-contained breathing apparatus.

SPILL OR LEAK PROCEDURES: Stop or control the leak, if this can be done without undue risk. Flooding quantities of water applied as a spray will hasten evaporation of liquid N_2 spills.

FIRE FIGHTING PROCEDURES: Extinguish fire using agent suitable for surrounding fire. Use water spray to keep fire-exposed containers cool.

HEALTH HAZARDS: Contact with liquid may cause frostbite and severe skin burns. If vaporized, may displace oxygen and cause asphyxiation. Simple asphyxiant.

FIRE AND EXPLOSION HAZARDS: Nonflammable liquid. A pipeline containing liquid nitrogen has the ability to condense liquid oxygen out of the atmosphere and can create a fire or explosion hazard.

STORAGE RECOMMENDATIONS: Store in a cool, dry, well-ventilated location. Outside or detached storage is preferred.

USUAL SHIPPING CONTAINERS: Refrigerated tanks on trucks, rail cars, barges.

PHYSICAL PROPERTIES: Cryogenic liquid. Odorless.

MELTING POINT: −346°F (−210°C)

BOILING POINT: −320°F (−196°C)

SPECIFIC GRAVITY: 0.81

SOLUBILITY IN WATER: not soluble

VAPOR DENSITY: 0.97

NAME: **NITROGEN OXIDES**

SYNONYMS: NO_x; oxides of nitrogen

FORMULA:

NFPA 30/OSHA CLASSIFICATION:

DOT CLASS: Class 2.3, Poisonous gas

SHIPPING LABEL: POISON GAS and OXIDIZER ID NO.

SPECIES	FORMULA	MOL. WT.	CAS NO.	ID NO.	DOT CLASS
NITRIC OXIDE	NO	30.0	10102-43-9	UN 1660	2.3
NITROGEN DIOXIDE, liquefied	NO_2	46.0	10102-44-0	UN 1067	2.3
DINITROGEN TETROXIDE	N_2O_4	92.0	10102-44-0	UN 1067	2.3
NITROGEN TRIOXIDE	N_2O_3	76	10544-73-7	UN 2421	2.3
NITROGEN PENTOXIDE[1]	N_2O_5	108.0	10102-03-1	**	**

**Not subject to hazardous materials regulations.

STATEMENT OF HAZARDS: Serious health hazard. Corrosive. Strong oxidizer.

EMERGENCY RESPONSE PERSONAL PROTECTIVE EQUIPMENT: Wear special protective clothing and positive pressure self-contained breathing apparatus.

SPILL OR LEAK PROCEDURES: Releases may require isolation or evacuation. Stop or control the leak, if this can be done without undue risk. Use water spray to disperse vapors and protect personnel. Approach release from upwind. Runoff of less volatile nitrogen oxides may contain highly corrosive nitric acid.

FIRE FIGHTING PROCEDURES: Extinguish surrounding fire using suitable agent. Use water spray to keep fire-exposed containers cool. Approach fire from upwind to avoid hazardous vapors.

HEALTH HAZARDS: Serious health hazard. May be harmful if inhaled. Corrosive. Causes severe eye and skin burns. Irritating to skin, eyes, and respiratory system. May cause pulmonary edema. Effects may be delayed. Rapid release of compressed gas may cause frostbite.

FIRE AND EXPLOSION HAZARDS: Strong oxidizer. Enhances combustion of organic matter and other combustible materials.

INSTABILITY AND REACTIVITY HAZARDS: Nitrogen oxides have varying instability depending on the species. Nitrogen trioxide and nitrogen pentoxide decompose readily to form nitrogen dioxide and dinitrogen tetroxide. The oxides of nitrogen react with a broad range of materials and decomposition may occur under certain conditions.

STORAGE RECOMMENDATIONS: Store in a cool, dry, well-ventilated location. Separate from oxidizable materials. Outside or detached storage is preferred. See also NFPA 430, Code for the Storage of Liquid and Solid Oxidizers.

USUAL SHIPPING CONTAINERS: Steel cylinders, pressurized tanks on trucks, rail cars, barges.

PHYSICAL PROPERTIES: Colorless to brick red gases. When frozen these may appear as white to bluish-white snow. Irritating odor.

NITRIC OXIDE

MELTING POINT: −263°F (−164°C)

BOILING POINT: −241°F (−52°C)

NITROGEN DIOXIDE

MELTING POINT: 15°F (−9°C)

BOILING POINT: 70°F (15°C)

MELTING POINT: 86°F (30°C)

SOLUBILITY IN WATER: not soluble (decomposes)

VAPOR DENSITY: 1.03 - 3.72

NAME: **NITROMETHANE**

SYNONYMS: nitrocarbol; NMT

FORMULA: CH_3NO_2

NFPA 30/OSHA CLASSIFICATION: IC

DOT CLASS: Class 3, Flammable and combustible liquid

SHIPPING LABEL: FLAMMABLE LIQUID

ID NO.: UN 1261

CAS NO.: 75-52-5

MOL. WT.: 61.0

STATEMENT OF HAZARDS: Flammable liquid. May decompose explosively above 599°F (315°C) in confinement. Slight health hazard.

EMERGENCY RESPONSE PERSONAL PROTECTIVE EQUIPMENT: Wear full protective clothing and positive pressure self-contained breathing apparatus.

SPILL OR LEAK PROCEDURES: Eliminate all ignition sources. Stop or control the leak, if this can be done without undue risk. Use water spray to cool and disperse vapors and protect personnel.

FIRE FIGHTING PROCEDURES: Explosive decomposition may occur under fire conditions. Fight fire from protected location or maximum possible distance. Use water spray, dry chemical, foam, or carbon dioxide. Use water spray to keep fire-exposed containers cool.

HEALTH HAZARDS: Slight health hazard. May be harmful if inhaled. Irritating to skin, eyes, and respiratory system. Causes dermatitis.

FIRE AND EXPLOSION HAZARDS: Flammable liquid. Vapors are heavier than air and may travel to a source of ignition and flash back. Shock- and heat-sensitive. Explosive decomposition begins at 599°F (315°C). May be detonated by nearby explosions. Combustion may produce oxides of nitrogen and other irritants and toxic gases. Closed containers may rupture violently when heated.

FLASH POINT: 95°F (35°C)

AUTOIGNITION TEMPERATURE: 785°F (418°C)

FLAMMABLE LIMITS: LOWER: 7.3% UPPER: not determined

INSTABILITY AND REACTIVITY HAZARDS: Shock- and heat-sensitive. Thermally unstable. Explosively decomposes at 599°F (315°C). Nitromethane is made more sensitive to detonation by contamination with certain other materials such as amines and acids.

STORAGE RECOMMENDATIONS: Store in a cool, dry, well-ventilated location. Separate from amines, acids, bases, oxidizing materials, and metal oxides. Outside or detached storage is preferred.

USUAL SHIPPING CONTAINERS: Bottles packed in insulating material. Metal cans, pails, drums.

PHYSICAL PROPERTIES: Colorless, oily liquid. Disagreeable, fruity odor.

MELTING POINT: −20°F (−29°C)

BOILING POINT: 213°F (101°C)

SPECIFIC GRAVITY: 1.13

SOLUBILITY IN WATER: not soluble

VAPOR PRESSURE: 28 mm Hg @ 20°C

ELECTRICAL EQUIPMENT: Class I, Group C

NAME: **p-NITROPHENOL**

DOT SHIPPING NAME: **NITROPHENOLS (o-, m-, p-)**

SYNONYMS: 4-hydroxynitro-benzene; 4-nitrophenol; nitrophenol; PNP

FORMULA: $NO_2(C_6H_4)OH$

NFPA 30/OSHA CLASSIFICATION:

DOT CLASS: Class 6.1, Poisonous material

SHIPPING LABEL: KEEP AWAY FROM FOOD

ID NO.: UN 1663

CAS NO.: 100-02-7

MOL. WT.: 139.1

STATEMENT OF HAZARDS: Serious health hazard. Combustible solid.

EMERGENCY RESPONSE PERSONAL PROTECTIVE EQUIPMENT: Wear special protective clothing and positive pressure self-contained breathing apparatus.

SPILL OR LEAK PROCEDURES: Shovel into suitable dry container.

FIRE FIGHTING PROCEDURES: Use water spray, dry chemical, foam, or carbon dioxide. Use water spray to keep fire-exposed containers cool. Approach fire from upwind to avoid hazardous vapors and toxic decomposition products. Fight fire from protected loction or maximum possible distance.

HEALTH HAZARDS: Serious health hazard. May be harmful if absorbed through skin or inhaled. Irritating to skin, eyes, and respiratory system. Symptoms of overexposure include headache, drowsiness, nausea, and cyanosis.

FIRE AND EXPLOSION HAZARDS: Decomposes at elevated temperatures to release oxides of nitrogen. Closed containers may rupture violently when heated.

AUTOIGNITION TEMPERATURE: 541°F (283°C)

STORAGE RECOMMENDATIONS: Store in a cool, dry, well-ventilated location. Separate from alkalies and oxidizing materials.

USUAL SHIPPING CONTAINERS: Glass containers, metal cans, pails, drums.

PHYSICAL PROPERTIES: Colorless to yellow crystals. Odorless. Sweetish then burning taste.

MELTING POINT: 239°F (115°C)

BOILING POINT: 534°F (279°C)

SPECIFIC GRAVITY: 1.48

SOLUBILITY IN WATER: not soluble

VAPOR PRESSURE: 7 mm Hg @ 165°C

NAME: **NITROPROPANES**

SYNONYMS: 1-nitropropane; 2-nitropropane;2-sec-nitropropane

FORMULA: $C_3H_7NO_2$

NFPA 30/OSHA CLASSIFICATION: IC

DOT CLASS: Class 3, Flammable and combustible liquid

SHIPPING LABEL: FLAMMABLE LIQUID

ID NO.: UN 2608

CAS NO.: 108-03-2 (1-nitropropane) 79-46-9 (2-nitropropane)

MOL. WT.: 89.1

STATEMENT OF HAZARDS: Flammable liquid. Products of combustion may be more hazardous than the material itself. May decompose explosively. Slight health hazard.

EMERGENCY RESPONSE PERSONAL PROTECTIVE EQUIPMENT: Wear full protective clothing and positive pressure self-contained breathing apparatus.

SPILL OR LEAK PROCEDURES: Eliminate all ignition sources. Stop or control the leak, if this can be done without undue risk. Use water spray to cool and disperse vapors and protect personnel.

FIRE FIGHTING PROCEDURES: Use water spray, dry chemical foam, or carbon dioxide. Use water spray to keep fire-exposed containers cool. Fight fire from protected location or maximum possible distance.

HEALTH HAZARDS: Slight health hazard. May be harmful if absorbed through skin or inhaled. Irritating to skin, eyes, and respiratory system. Symptoms of overexposure include headache, nausea, vomiting, diarrhea, and anoxia.

FIRE AND EXPLOSION HAZARDS: Flammable liquid. Vapors are heavier than air and may travel to a source of ignition and flash back. Combustion may produce oxides of nitrogen and other irritants and toxic gases. May decompose explosively under fire conditions. Closed containers may rupture violently when heated.

FLASH POINT: 75 – 93°F (24 – 34°C)

AUTOIGNITION TEMPERATURE: 789 – 802°F (421 – 428°C)

FLAMMABLE LIMITS: LOWER: 2.2% UPPER: not determined

INSTABILITY AND REACTIVITY HAZARDS: Material becomes sensitive and decomposes with heat or in combination with other chemicals.

STORAGE RECOMMENDATIONS: Store in a cool, dry, well-ventilated location. Separate from amines, acids, alkalies, oxidizing materials, metal oxides, and combustibles. Outside or detached storage is preferred.

USUAL SHIPPING CONTAINERS: Bottles packed in insulating material. Metal cans, pails, drums.

PHYSICAL PROPERTIES: Colorless liquid. Mild fruity odor.

MELTING POINT: – 162 to – 135°F (– 108 to – 93°C)

BOILING POINT: 249 to 269°F (120 to 132°C)

SPECIFIC GRAVITY: 0.98 to 1.00

SOLUBILITY IN WATER: not soluble

VAPOR PRESSURE: 13 mm Hg @ 20°C

ELECTRICAL EQUIPMENT: Class I, Group C

NAME: **NITROTOLUENES, liquid o-, m- p-NITROTOLUENES, solid o-, m-, p-**

SYNONYMS: methylnitrobenzene; 2-nitrotoluene; 3-nitrotoluene; 4-nitrotoluene; nitrotoluol

FORMULA: $NO_2(C_6H_4)CH_3$

NFPA 30/OSHA CLASSIFICATION: IIIB

DOT CLASS: Class 6.1, Poisonous material

SHIPPING LABEL: POISON

ID NO.: UN 1664

CAS NO.: o: 88-72-2

m: 99-08-1

p: 99-99-0

MOL. WT.: 137.1

STATEMENT OF HAZARDS: Serious health hazard. Combustible liquid or solid. Combustion by-products may include oxides of nitrogen.

EMERGENCY RESPONSE PERSONAL PROTECTIVE EQUIPMENT: Wear special protective clothing and positive pressure self-contained breathing apparatus.

SPILL OR LEAK PROCEDURES: For solids: Shovel into suitable dry container. For liquids: Stop or control the leak, if this can be done without undue risk. Cover in noncombustible material for proper disposal.

FIRE FIGHTING PROCEDURES: Use dry chemical, carbon dioxide, or water spray. Water streams or foam may cause frothing. Use water spray to keep fire-exposed containers cool. Approach fire from upwind to avoid hazardous vapors and toxic decomposition products. Extinguish fire using agent suitable for surrounding fire.

HEALTH HAZARDS: Serious health hazard. May be harmful if absorbed through skin or inhaled. Irritating to skin, eyes, and respiratory system. Symptoms of overexposure include anoxia, cyanosis, headache, weakness, dizziness, nausea, and vomiting.

FIRE AND EXPLOSION HAZARDS: Combustible liquid or solid. Combustion by-products include oxides of nitrogen and other irritants and toxic gases.

FLASH POINT: o: 223°F (106°C)

m: 214°F (101°C)

p: 223°F (106°C)

AUTOIGNITION TEMPERATURE: o: 581°F (305°C) p: 734°F (390°C)

FLAMMABLE LIMITS: LOWER: o: 2.2% UPPER: not determined

FLAMMABLE LIMITS: LOWER: m: 1.6% UPPER: not determined

FLAMMABLE LIMITS: LOWER: p: 1.6% UPPER: not determined

STORAGE RECOMMENDATIONS: Store in a cool, dry, well-ventilated location. Separate from acids, alkalies, oxidizing materials, and reducing agents.

USUAL SHIPPING CONTAINERS: Bottles, metal cans, pails, drums. Para form may be shipped in fiber drums.

PHYSICAL PROPERTIES: Yellow liquid or crystals. Aromatic odor.

MELTING POINT: o: 15°F (– 9°C)

m: 61°F (16°C)

p: 130°F (54°C)

BOILING POINT: o: 432°F (222°C) m: 451°F (233°C) p: 460°F (238°C)

SPECIFIC GRAVITY: 1.16

SOLUBILITY IN WATER: not soluble

NAME: **OXALIC ACID (as dihydrate)**

SYNONYMS: ethanedioic acid

FORMULA: HOOCCOOH: $2(H_2O)$

NFPA 30/OSHA CLASSIFICATION:

DOT CLASS: N/A

ID NO.: N/A

CAS NO.: 144-62-7

MOL. WT.: 90.0/ 126.1 hydrate

STATEMENT OF HAZARDS: Corrosive and combustible solid.

EMERGENCY RESPONSE PERSONAL PROTECTIVE EQUIPMENT: Wear special protective clothing and positive pressure self-contained breathing apparatus.

SPILL OR LEAK PROCEDURES: Shovel into suitable dry container. Clean up and drum any spilled solid.

FIRE FIGHTING PROCEDURES: Use water spray, dry chemical, "alcohol resistant" foam, or carbon dioxide. Dust may be reduced with water spray. Aqueous solutions must be contained for disposal. Use water spray to keep fire-exposed containers cool. Water may cause foaming of molten material.

HEALTH HAZARDS: Corrosive. Causes severe eye and skin burns. May be harmful if absorbed through skin or inhaled. Irritating to skin, eyes, and respiratory system. Renal damage can occur as result of formation of excessive calcium oxalate.

FIRE AND EXPLOSION HAZARDS: Combustible solid. Combustion may produce irritants and toxic gases, including formic acid.

INSTABILITY AND REACTIVITY HAZARDS: Reacts with strong alkalies, strong oxidizing materials, chlorites, and hypochlorites. Forms highly insoluble calcium oxalate.

STORAGE RECOMMENDATIONS: Store in a cool, dry, well-ventilated location.

USUAL SHIPPING CONTAINERS: Bottles, boxes, pails, drums, and paper bags.

PHYSICAL PROPERTIES: Colorless, odorless crystals or white powder that sink and mix with water.

MELTING POINT: 372°F (189°C)

SPECIFIC GRAVITY: 1.65 SUBLIMES AT: 315°F (157°C)

SOLUBILITY IN WATER: partly soluble

NAME: **OXYGEN, refrigerated liquid**

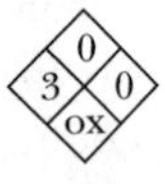

SYNONYMS: LOX; oxygen

FORMULA: O_2

NFPA 30/OSHA CLASSIFICATION:

DOT CLASS: Class 2.2, Nonflammable compressed gas

SHIPPING LABEL: NONFLAMMABLE GAS and OXIDIZER

ID NO.: UN 1073 refrigerated liquid

CAS NO.: 7782-44-7

MOL. WT.: 32.0

STATEMENT OF HAZARDS: Strong oxidizer. Contact with liquid will cause frostbite. May initiate fire/explosion in combustible materials.

EMERGENCY RESPONSE PERSONAL PROTECTIVE EQUIPMENT: Wear special protective clothing and positive pressure self-contained breathing apparatus.

SPILL OR LEAK PROCEDURES: A leak of liquid oxygen onto combustible material represents a severe explosion potential. Eliminate all ignition sources. Stop or control the leak, if this can be done without undue risk. Use water spray to disperse vapors and protect personnel.

FIRE FIGHTING PROCEDURES: Extinguish fire using agent suitable for surrounding fire. Use water spray to keep fire-exposed containers cool.

HEALTH HAZARDS: Contact with liquid will cause frostbite.

FIRE AND EXPLOSION HAZARDS: Not combustible but readily supports combustion/explosion of organic matter and other oxidizable materials. Clothing that becomes saturated with oxygen becomes a severe fire hazard.

INSTABILITY AND REACTIVITY HAZARDS: Readily oxidizes many materials, some violently.

STORAGE RECOMMENDATIONS: Store in an open area. Separate from combustible materials. See also NFPA 430, Code for the Storage of Liquid and Solid Oxidizers.

USUAL SHIPPING CONTAINERS: Cryogenic containers.

PHYSICAL PROPERTIES: Colorless to pale blue, cryogenic liquid or colorless gas. Odorless.

MELTING POINT: −361°F (−218°C)

BOILING POINT: −297°F (−183°C)

SPECIFIC GRAVITY: 1.14

SOLUBILITY IN WATER: not soluble

VAPOR DENSITY: 1.10

NAME: **PARAFORMALDEHYDE**

SYNONYMS: paraform; polyoxymethylene

FORMULA: $[CH_2O]_x$

NFPA 30/OSHA CLASSIFICATION: IIIA

DOT CLASS: Class 4.1, Flammable solid

SHIPPING LABEL: FLAMMABLE SOLID

ID NO.: UN 2213

CAS NO.: 30525-89-4

MOL. WT.: approx. 600

STATEMENT OF HAZARDS: Moderate health hazard. Combustible solid. Combustion by-products may include flammable formaldehyde gas.

EMERGENCY RESPONSE PERSONAL PROTECTIVE EQUIPMENT: Wear full protective clothing and positive pressure self-contained breathing apparatus.

SPILL OR LEAK PROCEDURES: Approach release from upwind. Prompt cleanup and removal necessary. Shovel into suitable dry container. Control runoff and isolate discharged material for proper disposal.

FIRE FIGHTING PROCEDURES: Use flooding quantities of water as fog or spray, dry chemical, "alcohol resistant" foam, or carbon dioxide. Use water spray to keep fire-exposed containers cool.

HEALTH HAZARDS: Moderate health hazard. May be harmful if absorbed through skin or inhaled. Irritating to skin, eyes, and respiratory system. When heated, evolves formaldehyde vapor.

FIRE AND EXPLOSION HAZARDS: Combustible solid. When exposed to heat material vaporizes, producing flammable formaldehyde gas.

FLASH POINT: 160°F (71°C)

AUTOIGNITION TEMPERATURE: 572°F (300°C)

FLAMMABLE LIMITS: LOWER: 7.0% UPPER: 73.0%

INSTABILITY AND REACTIVITY HAZARDS: Reacts with oxidizing materials, acids, alkalies.

STORAGE RECOMMENDATIONS: Store in a cool, dry, well-ventilated location. Store away from heat, oxidizers, and sunlight. Separate from combustibles, acids, alkalies, oxidizing materials.

USUAL SHIPPING CONTAINERS: Glass bottles, fiber drums, multiwall paper bags.

PHYSICAL PROPERTIES: White crystalline powder or prills with odor of formaldehyde.

MELTING POINT: 313°F (156°C)

SPECIFIC GRAVITY: 1.46

SOLUBILITY IN WATER: slowly dissolves

VAPOR DENSITY: 1.03

VAPOR PRESSURE: 1.2 mm Hg @ 25°C

NAME: **PARALDEHYDE**

SYNONYMS: p-acetaldehyde; paracetaldehyde; 2,4,6-trimethyl-1,3,5-trioxone

FORMULA: $(CH_3CHO)_3$

NFPA 30/OSHA CLASSIFICATION: IC

DOT CLASS: Class 3, Flammable and combustible liquid

SHIPPING LABEL: FLAMMABLE LIQUID

ID NO.: UN 1264

CAS NO.: 123-63-7

MOL. WT.: 132.2

STATEMENT OF HAZARDS: Flammable liquid. Moderate health hazard. Narcotic vapors.

EMERGENCY RESPONSE PERSONAL PROTECTIVE EQUIPMENT: Wear full protective clothing and positive pressure self-contained breathing apparatus.

SPILL OR LEAK PROCEDURES: Eliminate all ignition sources. Stop or control the leak, if this can be done without undue risk. Use water spray to cool and disperse vapors, protect personnel, and dilute spills to form nonflammable mixtures. Absorb in noncombustible material for proper disposal.

FIRE FIGHTING PROCEDURES: Use water spray, dry chemical, "alcohol resistant" foam, or carbon dioxide. Water may be ineffective. Use water spray to keep fire-exposed containers cool. Approach fire from upwind to avoid hazardous vapors and toxic decomposition products.

HEALTH HAZARDS: Moderate health hazard. May be harmful if inhaled. Irritating to skin, eyes, and respiratory system. Symptoms of overexposure include headache, central nervous system depression, bronchitis, and pulmonary edema.

FIRE AND EXPLOSION HAZARDS: Flammable liquid. Vapors are heavier than air and may travel to a source of ignition and flash back. Combustion may produce irritants and toxic gases.

FLASH POINT: 96°F (36°C) (oc)

AUTOIGNITION TEMPERATURE: 460°F (238°C)

FLAMMABLE LIMITS: LOWER: 1.3% UPPER: not determined

STORAGE RECOMMENDATIONS: Store in a cool, dry, well-ventilated location. Separate from alkalies, acids, iodides, oxidizing materials, rubber, and plastic. Inside storage should be in a standard flammable liquids storage warehouse, room, or cabinet.

USUAL SHIPPING CONTAINERS: Bottles packed in insulating material. Metal cans, pails, drums.

PHYSICAL PROPERTIES: Colorless liquid. Characteristic aromatic odor. Warm, disagreeable taste.

MELTING POINT: 55°F (13°C)

BOILING POINT: 255°F (124°C)

SPECIFIC GRAVITY: 0.99

SOLUBILITY IN WATER: partly soluble

NAME: **PENTABORANE**

SYNONYMS: dihydropentaborane; pentaborane(9); pentaboron nonahydride; pentaboron undecahydride

FORMULA: B_5H_9

NFPA 30/OSHA CLASSIFICATION: IC

DOT CLASS: Class 4.2, Spontaneously combustible material

SHIPPING LABEL: SPONTANEOUSLY COMBUSTIBLE and POISON

ID NO.: UN 1380

CAS NO.: 19624-22-7

MOL. WT.: 63.2

STATEMENT OF HAZARDS: Pyrophoric. Flammable liquid. Low ignition energy. Severe health hazard. Thermally unstable. Decomposes at elevated temperatures. Vapors may accumulate in air and explode without a source of ignition.

EMERGENCY RESPONSE PERSONAL PROTECTIVE EQUIPMENT: Wear special protective clothing and positive pressure self-contained breathing apparatus.

SPILL OR LEAK PROCEDURES: Releases may require isolation or evacuation. Stop or control the leak, if this can be done without undue risk. Spills may autoignite.

FIRE FIGHTING PROCEDURES: Fire situations may require evacuation. Use fine spray or fog to control fire by preventing its spread and absorbing some of its heat. Do not use halocarbons. Use water spray to keep fire-exposed containers cool. Explosive decomposition may occur under fire conditions. Fight fire from protected location or maximum possible distance. Approach fire from upwind to avoid hazardous vapors and toxic decomposition products.

HEALTH HAZARDS: Severe health hazard. May be fatal if absorbed through skin or inhaled. Irritating to skin, eyes, and respiratory system. Symptoms of overexposure include dizziness, headache, drowsiness, incoherence, tremor, and convulsions.

FIRE AND EXPLOSION HAZARDS: Flammable liquid. Pyrophoric; may ignite spontaneously on exposure to air. Fires may reignite. Combustion by-products include boron fumes, irritants, and other toxic gases. Closed containers may rupture violently when heated.

FLASH POINT: 86°F (30°C)

AUTOIGNITION TEMPERATURE: 95°F (35°C)

FLAMMABLE LIMITS: LOWER: 0.42% UPPER: 98%

INSTABILITY AND REACTIVITY HAZARDS: Thermally unstable. Decomposes above 300°F (149°C) if it is not already ignited.

STORAGE RECOMMENDATIONS: Store in a cool, dry, well-ventilated location. Store away from heat, oxidizing materials, and sunlight. Separate from rubber, grease, oils, halogens, and oxidizing materials.

USUAL SHIPPING CONTAINERS: Steel or nickel cylinders in wooden box.

PHYSICAL PROPERTIES: Colorless liquid. Strong, pungent odor of sour milk.

MELTING POINT: −189°F to −53°F (−123°C to −47°C)

BOILING POINT: 140°F to 145°F (60 to 63°C)

SPECIFIC GRAVITY: 0.61 to 0.66

SOLUBILITY IN WATER: not soluble (decomposes)

VAPOR PRESSURE: 66 mm Hg @ 0°C 171 mm Hg @ 20°C

NAME: **PENTACHLOROPHENOL**

SYNONYMS: PCP; penta; pentachlorol

FORMULA: C_6Cl_5OH

NFPA 30/OSHA CLASSIFICATION:

DOT CLASS: N/A

ID NO.: N/A

CAS NO.: 87-86-5

MOL. WT.: 266.4

STATEMENT OF HAZARDS: Serious health hazard.

EMERGENCY RESPONSE PERSONAL PROTECTIVE EQUIPMENT: Wear special protective clothing and positive pressure self-contained breathing apparatus.

SPILL OR LEAK PROCEDURES: Shovel into suitable dry container.

FIRE FIGHTING PROCEDURES: Extinguish surrounding fire using suitable agent. Approach fire from upwind to avoid hazardous vapors and toxic decomposition products. Use water spray to keep fire-exposed containers cool.

HEALTH HAZARDS: Serious health hazard. May be harmful if absorbed through skin or inhaled. Symptoms of overexposure include an increase followed by a decrease in respiration, blood pressure, and urinary output; fever; increase in bowel action; motor weakness; and collapse with convulsions and death. Irritating to skin, eyes, and respiratory system. May cause chloracne.

FIRE AND EXPLOSION HAZARDS: Not combustible but if involved in a fire decomposes to produce hydrogen chloride and other irritants and toxic gases. May be in hydrocarbon solution.

INSTABILITY AND REACTIVITY HAZARDS: Reacts with acids, alkalies, oxidizing materials, and other organic materials.

STORAGE RECOMMENDATIONS: Store in a cool, dry, well-ventilated location. Separate from acids, alkalies, oxidizing materials, and other organic materials.

USUAL SHIPPING CONTAINERS: Lined fiber bags or drums. Bulk packaging in trucks and rail cars and bulk in tank barges.

PHYSICAL PROPERTIES: Light brown crystals. Pungent odor.

MELTING POINT: 374 to 376°F (190 to 191°C)

BOILING POINT: 590°F (310°C) (decomposes)

SPECIFIC GRAVITY: 1.98

SOLUBILITY IN WATER: not soluble

VAPOR PRESSURE: <1 mm Hg @ 20°C

NAME: **PERACETIC ACID (less than 40%)**

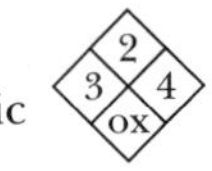

SYNONYMS: acetyl hydroperoxide; ethaneperoxoic acid; peroxyacetic acid

FORMULA: CH_3COOOH

NFPA 30/OSHA CLASSIFICATION: II

DOT CLASS: N/A

ID NO.: N/A

CAS NO.: 79-21-0

MOL. WT.: 76.1

STATEMENT OF HAZARDS: Corrosive. Strong oxidizer. Thermally unstable. Decomposes explosively at elevated temperatures. Combustible liquid.

EMERGENCY RESPONSE PERSONAL PROTECTIVE EQUIPMENT: Wear special protective clothing and positive pressure self-contained breathing apparatus.

SPILL OR LEAK PROCEDURES: Use water spray to cool and disperse vapors, protect personnel, and dilute spills to form nonflammable mixtures. Absorb in noncombustible material for proper disposal.

FIRE FIGHTING PROCEDURES: Use flooding quantities of water. Use water spray to keep fire-exposed containers cool. Fight fire from protected location or maximum possible distance. Approach fire from upwind to avoid hazardous vapors and toxic decomposition products.

HEALTH HAZARDS: Corrosive. Causes severe eye and skin burns. May be fatal if absorbed through skin or inhaled. Irritating to skin, eyes, and respiratory system.

FIRE AND EXPLOSION HAZARDS: Combustible liquid. Thermally unstable. May decompose explosively. May explode if material exceeds 56% of carrier due to evaporation. Concentrated material may be shock and friction sensitive. Closed containers may rupture violently when heated. Combustion may produce irritants and toxic gases. Properties depend on concentration and carrier used. For 40% by weight in acetic acid.

FLASH POINT: 105°F (41°C)

AUTOIGNITION TEMPERATURE: 392°F (200°C)

INSTABILITY AND REACTIVITY HAZARDS: Shock- and friction-sensitive when concentrated above 56%. Forms corrosive solutions with water. Reacts violently with a broad range of materials. Vapor may deflagrate.

STORAGE RECOMMENDATIONS: Store in a cool, dry, well-ventilated location. Separate from acids, alkalies, organic materials, heavy metals. Normally kept refrigerated. Outside or detached storage is preferred. See also NFPA 430, Code for the Storage of Liquid and Solid Oxidizers.

USUAL SHIPPING CONTAINERS: Bottles packed in insulating material. Polyethylene-lined cans or drums. Usual shipping strength is about 35% by weight.

PHYSICAL PROPERTIES: Colorless liquid. Acrid odor.

MELTING POINT: 32°F (0°C)

BOILING POINT: 221°F (105°C)

SPECIFIC GRAVITY: 1.23

SOLUBILITY IN WATER: soluble

ELECTRICAL EQUIPMENT: Class I, Group D

NAME: **PERCHLORIC ACID (>50% <72%)**

SYNONYMS: dioxonium perchlorate; per-chloriate solution; perchloric acid solution

FORMULA: $HClO_4$

NFPA 30/OSHA CLASSIFICATION:

DOT CLASS: Class 5.1, Oxidizer Class 8, Corrosive material

SHIPPING LABEL: OXIDIZER and CORROSIVE (UN 1873) CORROSIVE and OXIDIZER (UN 1802)

ID NO.: UN 1873 Class 5.1 UN 1802 (<50%) Class 8

CAS NO.: 7601-90-3

MOL. WT.: 100.5

STATEMENT OF HAZARDS: Corrosive. Strong oxidizer.

EMERGENCY RESPONSE PERSONAL PROTECTIVE EQUIPMENT: Wear special protective clothing and positive pressure self-contained breathing apparatus.

SPILL OR LEAK PROCEDURES: Stop or control the leak, if this can be done without undue risk. Absorb in noncombustible material for proper disposal. Prompt cleanup and removal are necessary.

FIRE FIGHTING PROCEDURES: Extinguish fire using agent suitable for surrounding fire. Use flooding quantities of water as spray. Explosive decomposition may occur under fire conditions. Fight fire from protected location or maximum possible distance. Use water spray to keep fire-exposed containers cool.

HEALTH HAZARDS: Corrosive. Causes severe eye skin burns. May be harmful if inhaled. Irritating to skin, eyes, and respiratory system. Causes burning sensation, coughing, and vomiting.

FIRE AND EXPLOSION HAZARDS: May decompose explosively when heated. Not combustible, but if involved in a fire decomposes to produce irritants and toxic gases. Closed containers may rupture violently when heated.

INSTABILITY AND REACTIVITY HAZARDS: If distilled, dried, or reacted with dehydrating agents or any oxidizable materials, the mixture may spontaneously explode. Reacts violently with a broad range of materials.

STORAGE RECOMMENDATIONS: Store in a cool, dry, well-ventilated location. Separate from alkalies, organic materials, oxidizing materials, and reducing agents. Protect from freezing. See also NFPA 430, Code for the Storage of Liquid and Solid Oxidizers.

USUAL SHIPPING CONTAINERS: Glass or polyethylene bottles, carboys, polyethylene-lined drums. Bulk packaging in trucks and rail cars and bulk in tank barges.

PHYSICAL PROPERTIES: Colorless, volatile, fuming liquid.

MELTING POINT: 25°F (−4°C) (solution)

−170°F (−112°C) (anhydrous)

BOILING POINT: 66°F (19°C) (decomposes)

SPECIFIC GRAVITY: 1.77

SOLUBILITY IN WATER: soluble

VAPOR DENSITY: 3.46

NAME: **PHENOL**
solid PHENOL
molten PHENOL solutions

SYNONYMS: carbolic acid; hydroxybenzene

FORMULA: C_6H_5OH

NFPA 30/OSHA CLASSIFICATION: IIIA

DOT CLASS: Class 6.1, Poisonous material

SHIPPING LABEL: POISON

ID NO.: UN 1671 solid UN 2312 molten UN 2821 solutions

CAS NO.: 108-95-2

MOL. WT.: 94.1

STATEMENT OF HAZARDS: Severe health hazard. Corrosive and combustible solid.

EMERGENCY RESPONSE PERSONAL PROTECTIVE EQUIPMENT: Wear special protective clothing and positive pressure self-contained breathing apparatus.

SPILL OR LEAK PROCEDURES: Control runoff and isolate discharged material for proper disposal. Approach release from upwind.

FIRE FIGHTING PROCEDURES: Use water spray, dry chemical, "alcohol resistant" foam, or carbon dioxide. Use water spray to keep fire-exposed containers cool.

HEALTH HAZARDS: Severe health hazard. May be fatal if absorbed through skin or inhaled. Corrosive. Causes severe eye and skin burns. Rapidly absorbed through skin. Irritating to skin, eyes, and respiratory system. Symptoms included severe tearing, conjunctivitis, and corneal edema. Nose, throat, and respiratory irritant.

FIRE AND EXPLOSION HAZARDS: Combustible solid.

FLASH POINT: 175°F (79°C)

AUTOIGNITION TEMPERATURE: 1319°F (715°C)

FLAMMABLE LIMITS: LOWER: 1.3% UPPER: 8.6%

INSTABILITY AND REACTIVITY HAZARDS: Hot phenol reacts with metals and oxidizers.

STORAGE RECOMMENDATIONS: Store in a cool, dry, well-ventilated location. Separate from oxidizers and acute fire hazards.

USUAL SHIPPING CONTAINERS: Bottles, drums, and bulk packaging in trucks or rail cars.

PHYSICAL PROPERTIES: Colorless/white crystals or light pink watery liquid if wet.

MELTING POINT: 106°F (41°C)

BOILING POINT: 358°F (182°C)

SPECIFIC GRAVITY: 1.07

SOLUBILITY IN WATER: soluble

VAPOR DENSITY: 3.24

VAPOR PRESSURE: 0.357 mm Hg @ 20°C 1 mm Hg @ 40°C

NAME: **PHENYLMERCURIC ACETATE**

DRY

ORGANIC SOLUTION

SYNONYMS: phenylmercury acetate; PMA; PMAC; PMAS

FORMULA: $(C_6H_5)HgCOOCH_3$

NFPA 30/OSHA CLASSIFICATION: II

DOT CLASS: Class 6.1, Poisonous material

SHIPPING LABEL: POISON

ID NO.: UN 1674

CAS NO.: 62-38-4

MOL. WT.: 336.8

STATEMENT OF HAZARDS: Serious health hazard. Combustible solid.

EMERGENCY RESPONSE PERSONAL PROTECTIVE EQUIPMENT: Wear special protective clothing and positive pressure self-contained breathing apparatus.

SPILL OR LEAK PROCEDURES: Solid material: Control release and place material and disposal equipment into appropriate containers. Solvent-based material: Control runoff. In all cases, avoid contact with material. Keep material from entering the environment to the fullest extent practicable.

FIRE FIGHTING PROCEDURES: If material is in solution with organic solvent, treat fire according to the solvent characteristics, in addition to the mercuric hazard. Unless otherwise indicated, use water spray, dry chemical, "alcohol resistant" foam, or carbon dioxide. Water may be ineffective.

HEALTH HAZARDS: Serious health hazard. May be harmful if absorbed through skin or inhaled. Inhalation may result in nausea, vomiting, diarrhea, and severe nervous system symptoms such as confusion, loss of sensation, emotional instability, hallucination, death. Irritating to skin, eyes, and respiratory system. Causes blistering of skin.

FIRE AND EXPLOSION HAZARDS: Combustible solid. If in solution, fire characteristics may depend on solvent. Combustion by-products include mercuric vapors and fumes.

FLASH POINT: >100°F (>38°C)

STORAGE RECOMMENDATIONS: Store in a cool, dry, well-ventilated, noncombustible location. Separate from oxidizing materials, halides.

USUAL SHIPPING CONTAINERS: Small bottles as a solid or dissolved in combustible solvent in drums.

PHYSICAL PROPERTIES: White crystalline powder. Odorless.

MELTING POINT: 300°F (149°C)

SOLUBILITY IN WATER: soluble

VAPOR PRESSURE: <1 mm Hg @ 35°C

NAME: **PHOSGENE**

SYNONYMS: carbon oxychloride; carbonyl chloride; chloroformyl chloride

FORMULA: $COCl_2$

NFPA 30/OSHA CLASSIFICATION:

DOT CLASS: Class 2.3, Poisonous gas

SHIPPING LABEL: POISON GAS and CORROSIVE

ID NO.: UN 1076

CAS NO.: 75-44-5

MOL. WT.: 98.9

STATEMENT OF HAZARDS: Severe health hazard. Corrosive gas.

EMERGENCY RESPONSE PERSONAL PROTECTIVE EQUIPMENT: Wear special protective clothing and positive pressure self-contained breathing apparatus.

SPILL OR LEAK PROCEDURES: Approach release from upwind. Releases may require isolation or evacuation. Stop or control the leak, if this can be done without undue risk. Water will increase evaporation of spilled material. Control runoff and isolate discharged material for proper disposal.

FIRE FIGHTING PROCEDURES: Use remote equipment wherever possible. Use water spray to keep fire-exposed containers cool. Extinguish fire using agent suitable for surrounding fire.

HEALTH HAZARDS: Severe health hazard. May be fatal if inhaled. Pulmonary edema may be delayed up to 24 hours. Exposure to lethal concentrations may not produce immediately noticeable irritation. Corrosive. Causes severe eye and skin burns.

FIRE AND EXPLOSION HAZARDS: Noncombustible gas.

INSTABILITY AND REACTIVITY HAZARDS: Reacts with alkalies, ammonia, alcohols, active metals, and many other materials.

STORAGE RECOMMENDATIONS: Store in a cool, dry, well-ventilated location. Outside or detached storage is preferred. Must be stored in a dry location.

USUAL SHIPPING CONTAINERS: Steel cylinders, special tank cars, and tank trucks.

PHYSICAL PROPERTIES: Low boiling liquid with smell ranging from musty hay at low concentrations to sharp and pungent odor at high concentrations.

MELTING POINT: −180°F (−118°C)

BOILING POINT: 46°F (8°C)

SPECIFIC GRAVITY: 1.38

SOLUBILITY IN WATER: partly soluble

VAPOR DENSITY: 3.41

VAPOR PRESSURE: 568 mm Hg @ 0°C 1215 mm Hg @ 20°C

NAME: **PHOSPHINE**

SYNONYMS: hydrogen phosphide; phosphorated hydrogen; phosphorous hydride

FORMULA: PH_3

NFPA 30/OSHA CLASSIFICATION:

DOT CLASS: Class 2.3, Poisonous gas

SHIPPING LABEL: POISON GAS and FLAMMABLE GAS

ID NO.: UN 2199

CAS NO.: 7803-51-2

MOL. WT.: 34.0

STATEMENT OF HAZARDS: Pyrophoric. Flammable gas. Severe health hazard. Low ignition energy.

EMERGENCY RESPONSE PERSONAL PROTECTIVE EQUIPMENT: Wear special protective clothing and positive pressure self-contained breathing apparatus.

SPILL OR LEAK PROCEDURES: Stop or control the leak, if this can be done without undue risk. Use water spray to cool and disperse vapors and protect personnel. Approach release from upwind.

FIRE FIGHTING PROCEDURES: Approach fire from upwind to avoid hazardous vapors and toxic decomposition products. Explosive decomposition may occur under fire conditions. Fight fire from protected location or maximum possible distance. Stop flow of gas before extinguishing fire. Use flooding quantities of water as spray. DO NOT use halogenated extinguishing agents. Use water spray to keep fire-exposed containers cool.

HEALTH HAZARDS: Severe health hazard. May be fatal if inhaled. Irritating to skin, eyes, and respiratory system. Symptoms of overexposure include pain in region of the diaphragm, feeling of convulsions, weakness, vertigo, dyspnea, bronchitis, pulmonary edema, lung damage, and convulsions.

FIRE AND EXPLOSION HAZARDS: Flammable gas. Pyrophoric; may ignite spontaneously in air or accumulate and explode in air without source of ignition. Evolves hydrogen and ignites on contact with many materials. Vapors are heavier than air and may travel to a source of ignition and flash back. Closed containers may rupture violently when heated.

FLAMMABLE LIMITS: LOWER: 1.6% UPPER: 98% (estimated)

INSTABILITY AND REACTIVITY HAZARDS: Reacts violently with a broad range of materials, including air and halogens.

STORAGE RECOMMENDATIONS: Store in a cool, dry, well-ventilated location. Separate from acids, alkalies, and halogenated compounds. Outside or detached storage is preferred.

USUAL SHIPPING CONTAINERS: Steel cylinders.

PHYSICAL PROPERTIES: Colorless gas. Odor of rotten fish.

MELTING POINT: −207°F (−133°C)

BOILING POINT: −126°F (−88°C)

SPECIFIC GRAVITY: 0.76 (liquid)

SOLUBILITY IN WATER: not soluble

VAPOR DENSITY: 1.17

VAPOR PRESSURE: >760 mm Hg @ 20°C

NAME: **PHOSPHORIC ACID**

DOT SHIPPING NAME: **PHOSPHORIC ACID, aqueous**

SYNONYMS: orthophosphoric acid; white phosphoric acid

FORMULA: H_3PO_4

NFPA 30/OSHA CLASSIFICATION:

DOT CLASS: Class 8, Corrosive material

SHIPPING LABEL: CORROSIVE

ID NO.: UN 1805

CAS NO.: 7664-38-2

MOL. WT.: 98.0 (50-85% in water)

STATEMENT OF HAZARDS: Corrosive.

EMERGENCY RESPONSE PERSONAL PROTECTIVE EQUIPMENT: Wear special protective clothing and positive pressure self-contained breathing apparatus.

SPILL OR LEAK PROCEDURES: Stop or control the leak, if this can be done without undue risk. Control runoff and isolate discharged material for proper disposal.

FIRE FIGHTING PROCEDURES: Use water spray to keep fire-exposed containers cool. Extinguish fire using agent suitable for surrounding fire.

HEALTH HAZARDS: Corrosive. Causes severe eye and skin burns. May be harmful if inhaled. Irritating to skin, eyes, and respiratory system. Inhalation of mist can cause damage to respiratory system.

FIRE AND EXPLOSION HAZARDS: Not combustible. Evolves hydrogen on contact with most metals. Combustion by-products include oxides of phosphorus.

INSTABILITY AND REACTIVITY HAZARDS: Reacts with strong alkalies and most metals.

STORAGE RECOMMENDATIONS: Store in a cool, dry, well-ventilated location. Separate from alkalies and most metals.

USUAL SHIPPING CONTAINERS: Glass bottles, carboys, fiber glass, plastic or polyethylene-lined drums, special SS drums.

PHYSICAL PROPERTIES: Clear syrupy liquid. Dehydrates to pyrophosphoric acid above 392°F (200°C).

MELTING POINT: 108°F (42°C)

BOILING POINT: 415°F (213°C)

SPECIFIC GRAVITY: 1.89

SOLUBILITY IN WATER: soluble

VAPOR PRESSURE: 0.03 mm Hg @ 20°C

NAME: **PHOSPHORUS, amorphous**

SYNONYMS: Hittorf's phosphorus; red phosphorus

FORMULA: P_4

NFPA 30/OSHA CLASSIFICATION:

DOT CLASS: Class 4.1, Flammable solid

SHIPPING LABEL: FLAMMABLE SOLID

ID NO.: UN 1338

CAS NO.: 7723-14-0

MOL. WT.: 123.9

STATEMENT OF HAZARDS: Combustible solid. Under fire situations the more hazardous white phosphorus may be formed. Slight health hazard.

EMERGENCY RESPONSE PERSONAL PROTECTIVE EQUIPMENT: Wear full protective clothing and positive pressure self-contained breathing apparatus.

SPILL OR LEAK PROCEDURES: Blanket release with wet sand, clay, or ground limestone. Shovel into suitable dry container.

FIRE FIGHTING PROCEDURES: Flood with water to control flames, then smother with wet sand, clay, ground limestone. Approach fire from upwind to avoid hazardous vapors and toxic decomposition products.

HEALTH HAZARDS: Slight health hazard. White phosphorus may be present as a contaminant or formed in fire situations. Fumes from phosphorus fires are highly irritating to lungs, skin, eyes.

FIRE AND EXPLOSION HAZARDS: Combustible solid. Ignites in presence of air at 500°F (260°C). May decompose at 554°F (290°C) into more hazardous white (yellow) phosphorus. May ignite with friction or contact with oxidizers. Combustion by-products include oxides of phosphorus, phosphine, phosphoric acid if water is present.

AUTOIGNITION TEMPERATURE: 500°F (260°C)

INSTABILITY AND REACTIVITY HAZARDS: Reacts with halogens, halides, sulfur, oxidizing materials. Reacts with strong alkali to form highly toxic phosphine gas.

STORAGE RECOMMENDATIONS: Store in a cool, dry, well-ventilated location. Separate from oxidizing materials. Always keep container closed.

USUAL SHIPPING CONTAINERS: Hermetically sealed cans in wooden box, metal drums, tank barges.

PHYSICAL PROPERTIES: Reddish-brown amorphous solid or powder.

MELTING POINT: 781°F (416°C) (sublimes)

SPECIFIC GRAVITY: 2.34

SOLUBILITY IN WATER: not soluble

NAME: **PHOSPHORUS, white, molten**

SYNONYMS: WP; yellow phosphorus

FORMULA: P_4

NFPA 30/OSHA CLASSIFICATION:

DOT CLASS: Class 4.2, Spontaneously combustible material

SHIPPING LABEL: SPONTANEOUSLY COMBUSTIBLE and POISON

ID NO.: UN 2447

CAS NO.: 7723-14-0

MOL. WT.: 123.9

STATEMENT OF HAZARDS: Pyrophoric. Severe health hazard. Combustion by-products may include oxides of phosphorus, phosphine, and phosphoric acid if water is present.

EMERGENCY RESPONSE PERSONAL PROTECTIVE EQUIPMENT: Wear special protective clothing and positive pressure self-contained breathing apparatus.

SPILL OR LEAK PROCEDURES: Prompt cleanup and removal are necessary. Shovel into suitable dry container. Control runoff and isolate discharged material for proper disposal.

FIRE FIGHTING PROCEDURES: Flood with water to control flames, then smother with wet sand, clay, ground limestone. Approach fire from upwind to avoid hazardous vapors and toxic decomposition products. Where access to the area is strictly controlled, it may be best to allow the release to burn itself out. Fire situations may require evacuation. Fight fire from protected location or maximum possible distance.

HEALTH HAZARDS: Severe health hazard. May be fatal if inhaled. Corrosive. Causes severe eye and skin burns. Inhalation may cause severe internal irritation, collapse, and convulsions. Fumes from phosphorus fires are highly irritating to lungs, skin, eyes.

FIRE AND EXPLOSION HAZARDS: Pyrophoric. Flammable solid. Ignites in presence of air above 86°F (30°C). May explode on contact with oxidizing materials. Combustion by-products include oxides of phosphorus, phosphine, phosphoric acid if water is present.

AUTOIGNITION TEMPERATURE: 86°F (30°C)

INSTABILITY AND REACTIVITY HAZARDS: Reacts with air, halogens, halides, sulfur, oxidizing materials. Reacts with alkali hydroxides to form phosphine gas. Reacts with metals to form highly reactive phosphides.

STORAGE RECOMMENDATIONS: Separate from air, oxidizing materials, combustibles. Always keep container closed, with material under water or inert gas.

USUAL SHIPPING CONTAINERS: Hermetically sealed cans in wooden box; metal drums; tanks on trucks, rail cars, barges. Always kept under water or inert gas.

PHYSICAL PROPERTIES: Colorless, white, or yellowish wax-like solid. Darkens on exposure to light. Produces acrid fumes in air.

MELTING POINT: 111°F (44°C)

BOILING POINT: 536°F (280°C)

SPECIFIC GRAVITY: 1.82 @ 68°F (20°C)

SOLUBILITY IN WATER: not soluble

VAPOR PRESSURE: <1 mm Hg @ 0°C

NAME: **PHOSPHORUS OXYCHLORIDE**

SYNONYMS: phosphorus oxytrichloride; phosphoryl chloride

FORMULA: $POCl_3$

NFPA 30/OSHA CLASSIFICATION:

DOT CLASS: Class 8, Corrosive material

SHIPPING LABEL: CORROSIVE and POISON

ID NO.: UN 1810

CAS NO.: 10025-87-3

MOL. WT.: 153.3

STATEMENT OF HAZARDS: Severe health hazard. Corrosive. Water reactive.

EMERGENCY RESPONSE PERSONAL PROTECTIVE EQUIPMENT: Wear special protective clothing and positive pressure self-contained breathing apparatus.

SPILL OR LEAK PROCEDURES: Releases may require isolation or evacuation. Use water spray to cool and disperse vapors and protect personnel.

FIRE FIGHTING PROCEDURES: Use appropriate extinguishing agents on nearby combustible fires. Use water spray to knock down acid vapors.

HEALTH HAZARDS: Severe health hazard. May be fatal if inhaled. Inhalation may cause pulmonary edema. Irritating to eyes, skin, and respiratory system. Corrosive. Causes severe eye and skin burns. Fumes from fires are irritating to respiratory passages, eyes, skin, and may contain phosphine, phosphoric acid, hydrogen chloride.

FIRE AND EXPLOSION HAZARDS: Not combustible, but if involved in a fire may react to produce hydrogen chloride and phosphoric acid.

INSTABILITY AND REACTIVITY HAZARDS: Reacts violently with water, acids, alkalies, alkali metals, alcohols.

STORAGE RECOMMENDATIONS: Store in a cool, dry, well-ventilated location. Separate from acids, alkalies, alkali metals, alcohols.

USUAL SHIPPING CONTAINERS: Bottles, cans, drums, tanks on trucks, rail cars, barges.

PHYSICAL PROPERTIES: Colorless liquid. Pungent or musty odor. Fumes in moist air.

MELTING POINT: 36°F (2°C)

BOILING POINT: 223°F (105°C)

SPECIFIC GRAVITY: 1.68 @ 16°C

SOLUBILITY IN WATER: decomposes

VAPOR PRESSURE: 28 mm Hg @ 20°C 104 mm Hg @ 50°C

NAME: **PHOSPHORUS PENTACHLORIDE**

SYNONYMS: phosphoric chloride; phosphorus perchloride

FORMULA: PCl_5

NFPA 30/OSHA CLASSIFICATION:

DOT CLASS: Class 8, Corrosive material

SHIPPING LABEL: CORROSIVE

ID NO.: UN 1806

CAS NO.: 10026-13-8

MOL. WT.: 208.3

STATEMENT OF HAZARDS: Corrosive. Water reactive.

EMERGENCY RESPONSE PERSONAL PROTECTIVE EQUIPMENT: Wear special protective clothing and positive pressure self-contained breathing apparatus.

SPILL OR LEAK PROCEDURES: Use water spray to cool and disperse vapors and protect personnel.

FIRE FIGHTING PROCEDURES: Use appropriate extinguishing agents on nearby combustible fires. Dry chemical or carbon dioxide preferred. Use water spray to knock down acid vapors.

HEALTH HAZARDS: Serious health hazard. May be harmful if inhaled. Inhalation may cause pulmonary edema. Irritating to eyes, skin, and respiratory system. Corrosive. Causes severe eye and skin burns. Fumes from fires are irritating to respiratory passages, eyes, skin, and may contain phosphine, phosphoric acid, hydrogen chloride.

FIRE AND EXPLOSION HAZARDS: Not combustible, but if involved in a fire decomposes to produce hydrogen chloride, phosphoric acid, phosphine.

INSTABILITY AND REACTIVITY HAZARDS: Reacts violently with water, acids, alkalies, alkali metals, alcohols, amines, organic acids.

STORAGE RECOMMENDATIONS: Store in a cool, dry, well-ventilated location. Separate from acids, alkalies, alkali metals, organic compounds. Store under nitrogen.

USUAL SHIPPING CONTAINERS: Bottles, cans, drums, tanks on trucks, rail cars, barges.

PHYSICAL PROPERTIES: White to pale yellow crystalline solid. Acrid odor. Fumes in moist air.

MELTING POINT: 212°F (100°C) (normal pressure, sublimes) 298°F (148°C) (under pressure, decomposes)

BOILING POINT: 320°F (160°C) (sublimes)

SPECIFIC GRAVITY: 1.60

SOLUBILITY IN WATER: decomposes

VAPOR PRESSURE: 1 mm Hg @ 56°C

NAME: **PHOSPHORUS PENTASULFIDE**

SYNONYMS: phosphoric sulfide; phosphorus persulfide; thiophosphoric anhydride

FORMULA: P_2S_5 or P_4S_{10}

NFPA 30/OSHA CLASSIFICATION:

DOT CLASS: Class 4.3, Dangerous when wet material

SHIPPING LABEL: DANGEROUS WHEN WET

ID NO.: UN 1340

CAS NO.: 1314-80-3

MOL. WT.: 222.2 or 444.5

STATEMENT OF HAZARDS: Moderate health hazard. Combustible solid. Water reactive.

EMERGENCY RESPONSE PERSONAL PROTECTIVE EQUIPMENT: Wear full protective clothing and positive pressure self-contained breathing apparatus.

SPILL OR LEAK PROCEDURES: Keep water away from release. Blanket release with dry sand, clay, or ground limestone. Shovel into suitable dry container.

FIRE FIGHTING PROCEDURES: Use dry chemical, carbon dioxide, sodium chloride based Class D extinguishers. DO

NOT use water. Fire or explosion may result. Carefully use water spray to knock down acid vapors.

HEALTH HAZARDS: Moderate health hazard. May be harmful if inhaled. Irritating to skin, eyes, and respiratory system. Fumes from fires are irritating to respiratory passages, eyes, skin, and may contain hydrogen sulfide, phosphine, sulfur dioxide, phosphorus pentoxide, phosphoric acid.

FIRE AND EXPLOSION HAZARDS: Combustible solid. Evolves hydrogen sulfide and may ignite on contact with water, acids. Combustion produces irritants and toxic gases. May heat and ignite spontaneously.

AUTOIGNITION TEMPERATURE: 287°F (142°C)

INSTABILITY AND REACTIVITY HAZARDS: Reacts violently with water, acids to produce phosphoric acid, hydrogen sulfide. Reacts with alkalies, alcohols, amines, organic acids.

STORAGE RECOMMENDATIONS: Store in a cool, dry, well-ventilated location. Separate from acids, alkalies, organic compounds. Always keep container closed.

USUAL SHIPPING CONTAINERS: Bottles, cans, drums.

PHYSICAL PROPERTIES: Pale yellow to greenish-yellow crystalline solid. Odor of rotten eggs. Fumes in moist air.

MELTING POINT: 527°F (287°C)

BOILING POINT: 995°F (514°C)

SPECIFIC GRAVITY: 2.09

SOLUBILITY IN WATER: decomposes

VAPOR PRESSURE: 1 mm Hg @ 287°C

NAME: **PHOSPHORUS TRIBROMIDE**

SYNONYMS: phosphorus bromide; tribromophosphine

FORMULA: PBr_3

NFPA 30/OSHA CLASSIFICATION:

DOT CLASS: Class 8, Corrosive material

SHIPPING LABEL: CORROSIVE

ID NO.: UN 1808

CAS NO.: 7789-60-8

MOL. WT.: 270.7

STATEMENT OF HAZARDS: Corrosive. Water reactive.

EMERGENCY RESPONSE PERSONAL PROTECTIVE EQUIPMENT: Wear special protective clothing and positive pressure self-contained breathing apparatus.

SPILL OR LEAK PROCEDURES: Isolate the area until the release is under full control. Use water spray to cool and disperse vapors and protect personnel.

FIRE FIGHTING PROCEDURES: Use appropriate extinguishing agents on nearby combustible fires. Use water spray to knock down acid vapors.

HEALTH HAZARDS: Serious health hazard. May be harmful if inhaled. Irritating eyes, skin, and respiratory system. Corrosive. Causes severe eye and skin burns. Fumes from fires are irritating to respiratory passages, eyes, skin, and may contain phosphine, phosphoric acid, hydrogen bromide.

FIRE AND EXPLOSION HAZARDS: Not combustible, but if involved in a fire decomposes to produce hydrogen bromide, phosphoric acid, phosphine.

INSTABILITY AND REACTIVITY HAZARDS: Reacts violently with water, acids, alkalies, alcohols, oxidizing materials, alkali metals.

STORAGE RECOMMENDATIONS: Store in a cool, dry, well-ventilated location. Separate from acids, alkalies, organics, alkali metals.

USUAL SHIPPING CONTAINERS: Bottles, cans, drums, tanks on trucks, rail cars, barges.

PHYSICAL PROPERTIES: Colorless liquid. Sharp, penetrating odor. Fumes in moist air.

MELTING POINT: −40°F (−40°C)

BOILING POINT: 343°F (173°C)

SPECIFIC GRAVITY: 2.85 @ 21°C

SOLUBILITY IN WATER: decomposes

VAPOR PRESSURE: 10 mm Hg @ 48°C

NAME: **PHOSPHORUS TRICHLORIDE**

SYNONYMS: chloride of phosphorus; phosphorus chloride

FORMULA: PCl_3

NFPA 30/OSHA CLASSIFICATION:

DOT CLASS: Class 8, Corrosive material

SHIPPING LABEL: CORROSIVE and POISON

ID NO.: UN 1809

CAS NO.: 7719-12-2

MOL. WT.: 137.3

STATEMENT OF HAZARDS: Corrosive. Water reactive.

EMERGENCY RESPONSE PERSONAL PROTECTIVE EQUIPMENT: Wear special protective clothing and positive pressure self-contained breathing apparatus.

SPILL OR LEAK PROCEDURES: Releases may require isolation or evacuation. Use water spray to cool and disperse vapors and protect personnel.

FIRE FIGHTING PROCEDURES: Use appropriate extinguishing agents on nearby combustible fires. Use water spray to knock down acid vapors.

HEALTH HAZARDS: Severe health hazard. May be fatal if inhaled. Irritating to eyes, skin, and respiratory system. Corrosive. Causes severe eye and skin burns. Fumes from fires are irritating to respiratory passages, eyes, skin, and may contain phosphine, phosphoric acid, hydrogen chloride.

FIRE AND EXPLOSION HAZARDS: Not combustible, but if involved in a fire decomposes to produce hydrogen chloride, phosphoric acid, phosphine.

INSTABILITY AND REACTIVITY HAZARDS: Reacts violently with water, acids, alkalies, alcohols, oxidizing materials, alkali metals.

STORAGE RECOMMENDATIONS: Store in a cool, dry, well-ventilated location. Separate from acids, alkalies, organics, alkali metals.

USUAL SHIPPING CONTAINERS: Bottles, cans, drums, tanks on trucks, rail cars, barges.

PHYSICAL PROPERTIES: Colorless liquid. Sharp, irritating odor. Fumes in moist air.

MELTING POINT: −169°F (−112°C)

BOILING POINT: 168°F (76°C)

SPECIFIC GRAVITY: 1.57 @ 21°C

SOLUBILITY IN WATER: decomposes

VAPOR PRESSURE: 100 mm Hg @ 21°C 385 mm Hg @ 55°C

NAME: **PHTHALIC ANHYDRIDE**

SYNONYMS: 1,3-dioxophthalan; 1,3-isobenzofurandione; PAN; phthalandione

FORMULA: $C_6H_4(CO)_2O$

NFPA 30/OSHA CLASSIFICATION: IIIB

DOT CLASS: Class 8, Corrosive material

SHIPPING LABEL: CORROSIVE

ID NO.: UN 2214

CAS NO.: 85-44-9

MOL. WT.: 148.1

STATEMENT OF HAZARDS: Corrosive. Combustible solid.

EMERGENCY RESPONSE PERSONAL PROTECTIVE EQUIPMENT: Wear special protective clothing and positive pressure self-contained breathing apparatus.

SPILL OR LEAK PROCEDURES: Keep water away from release. Prompt cleanup and removal are necessary. Shovel into suitable dry container.

FIRE FIGHTING PROCEDURES: Use dry chemical, foam, carbon dioxide, or water spray. Water or foam may cause frothing. Approach fire from upwind to avoid hazardous vapors and toxic decomposition products.

HEALTH HAZARDS: Corrosive. Causes severe eye and skin burns. May be armful if inhaled. Symptoms of overexposure include ulcer bleeding, upper respiratory irritation, bronchitis, asthma, and dermatitis.

FIRE AND EXPLOSION HAZARDS: Combustible solid. Dust may form explosive mixtures with air.

FLASH POINT: 305°F (152°C)

AUTOIGNITION TEMPERATURE: 1058°F (570°C)

FLAMMABLE LIMITS: LOWER: 1.7% UPPER: 10.4%

STORAGE RECOMMENDATIONS: Store in a cool, dry, well-ventilated location. Separate from acids, alkalies, oxidizing materials, reducing agents, and moisture.

USUAL SHIPPING CONTAINERS: Lined fiber bags. As molten material in heated tanks on trucks, rail cars, barges.

PHYSICAL PROPERTIES: White, lustrous needles. Characteristic choking odor.

MELTING POINT: 268°F (131°C)

BOILING POINT: 544°F (285°C)

SPECIFIC GRAVITY: 1.53

SOLUBILITY IN WATER: not soluble

VAPOR PRESSURE: 1 mm Hg @ 96°C

ELECTRICAL EQUIPMENT: Class II, Group G

NAME: **PICRIC ACID, wet, with not less than 10% water**

SYNONYMS: carbazotic acid; nitroxanthic acid; picro-nitric acid; 2,4,6-trinitrophenol

FORMULA: $(NO_2)_3(C_6H_2)OH$

NFPA 30/OSHA CLASSIFICATION: IIIB

DOT CLASS: Class 4.1, Flammable solid

SHIPPING LABEL: FLAMMABLE SOLID

ID NO.: NA 1344

CAS NO.: 88-89-1

MOL. WT.: 229.1

STATEMENT OF HAZARDS: Flammable solid. Air or oxygen is not required for decomposition or oxidation. Serious health hazard. Strong sensitizer. May cause severe allergic reaction and dermatitis.

EMERGENCY RESPONSE PERSONAL PROTECTIVE EQUIPMENT: Wear special protective clothing and positive pressure self-contained breathing apparatus.

SPILL OR LEAK PROCEDURES: Prompt cleanup and removal are necessary. During cleanup, avoid shock, friction, or heat. With extreme caution, shovel into suitable dry container.

FIRE FIGHTING PROCEDURES: Explosive decomposition may occur under fire conditions. Fight fire from protected location or maximum possible distance. Use flooding quantities of water as spray. DO NOT use carbon dioxide or halogenated extinguishing agents. Approach fire from upwind to avoid hazardous vapors and toxic decomposition products.

HEALTH HAZARDS: Serious health hazard. May be harmful if absorbed through skin or inhaled. Irritating to skin, eyes, and respiratory system. Sensitizer. May cause severe allergic reaction and dermatitis.

FIRE AND EXPLOSION HAZARDS: Flammable solid. Explodes above 572°F (300°C) with release of oxides of nitrogen. Closed containers may rupture violently when heated.

FLASH POINT: 302°F (150°C)

AUTOIGNITION TEMPERATURE: 572°F (300°C)

INSTABILITY AND REACTIVITY HAZARDS: Anhydrous material is shock-, friction-, and heat-sensitive. Highly unstable in crystalline form.

STORAGE RECOMMENDATIONS: Store in a cool, dry, well-ventilated detached location. Do not allow material to become dry. Isolate from organic materials; transition and heavy metals.

USUAL SHIPPING CONTAINERS: Normally in solution with 10-20% water. 1 or 5 lb bottles, 25 lb boxes, 100 lb kegs, 300 lb barrels.

PHYSICAL PROPERTIES: Pale yellow crystals. Odorless. Intensely bitter taste.

MELTING POINT: 252°F (122°C)

BOILING POINT: explodes

SPECIFIC GRAVITY: 1.76

SOLUBILITY IN WATER: not soluble

VAPOR PRESSURE: <1 mm Hg @ 20°C

NAME: **PIPERIDINE**

SYNONYMS: azacyclohexane; cyclopentimine; cypentil; hexahydropyridine; hexazane; pentamethyleneamine

FORMULA: $C_5H_{11}N$

NFPA 30/OSHA CLASSIFICATION: IB

DOT CLASS: Class 3, Flammable and combustible liquid

SHIPPING LABEL: FLAMMABLE LIQUID

ID NO.: UN 2401

CAS NO.: 110-89-4

MOL. WT.: 85.2

STATEMENT OF HAZARDS: Serious health hazard. Corrosive and flammable liquid.

EMERGENCY RESPONSE PERSONAL PROTECTIVE EQUIPMENT: Wear special protective clothing and positive pressure self-contained breathing apparatus.

SPILL OR LEAK PROCEDURES: Use water spray to cool and disperse vapors, protect personnel, and dilute spills to form nonflammable mixtures. Control runoff and isolate discharged material for proper disposal.

FIRE FIGHTING PROCEDURES: Use water spray, dry chemical, "alcohol resistant" foam, or carbon dioxide. Use water spray to keep fire-exposed containers cool.

HEALTH HAZARDS: Serious health hazard. May be harmful if absorbed through skin or inhaled. Causes severe eye and skin burns. Irritating to eyes, skin, and respiratory system.

FIRE AND EXPLOSION HAZARDS: Flammable liquid. Combustion may produce irritants and toxic gases, inlcuding nitrogen oxides.

FLASH POINT: 61°F (16°C)

INSTABILITY AND REACTIVITY HAZARDS: Reacts vigorously with oxidizing materials. Explodes on contact with N-nitrosoacetanilide, 1-perchloryl-piperidine, and dicyanofurazan.

STORAGE RECOMMENDATIONS: Store in a cool, dry, well-ventilated location. Outside or detached storage is preferred. Store away from heat and oxidizing materials.

PHYSICAL PROPERTIES: Clear, colorless liquid with heavy, sweet, floral, animal odor. It has a burning, peppery taste.

MELTING POINT: 19°F (−7°C)

BOILING POINT: 223°F (106°C)

SPECIFIC GRAVITY: 0.86

SOLUBILITY IN WATER: soluble

VAPOR PRESSURE: 40 mm Hg @ 29°C

NAME: **POLYCHLORINATED BIPHENYLS**

SYNONYMS: chlorinated biphenyls; chlorobiphenyls; PCBs

FORMULA: $C_{12}H_{10}$-nCl_n (n = 3,4,5)

NFPA 30/OSHA CLASSIFICATION: IIIB

DOT CLASS: Class 9, Miscellaneous hazardous material

SHIPPING LABEL: Class 9, MISCELLANEOUS HAZARDOUS MATERIAL

ID NO.: UN 2315

CAS NO.: 1336-36-3

MOL. WT.: 257.6 – 326.4

STATEMENT OF HAZARDS: Toxic. Harmful if absorbed through skin or inhaled. Eye and skin irritant. Combustible liquid. Products of combustion may be more hazardous than the material itself.

EMERGENCY RESPONSE PERSONAL PROTECTIVE EQUIPMENT: Wear full protective clothing and positive pressure self-contained breathing apparatus.

SPILL OR LEAK PROCEDURES: Stop or control the leak, if this can be done without undue risk. Absorb in noncombustible material for proper disposal.

FIRE FIGHTING PROCEDURES: Extinguish fire using agent suitable for surrounding fire. Use dry chemical, foam, carbon dioxide, or water spray. Use water spray to keep fire-exposed containers or transformers cool. Approach fire from upwind to avoid hazardous vapors and toxic decomposition products.

HEALTH HAZARDS: Toxic. Harmful if absorbed through skin or inhaled. Eye and skin irritant. Symptoms of overexposure include contact dermatitis, chloracne, excessive eye discharge, and swelling. In the range of 1112 to 1202°F (600 to 650°C) highly toxic derivatives, polychlorinated dibenzo-para-dioxins (PCDDs) and polychlorinated dibenzofurans (PCDFs) can be formed, which may be a greater health risk than PCBs. Symptoms include chloracne, liver damage, thymic atrophy, hemorrhage, lymphoid depletion.

FIRE AND EXPLOSION HAZARDS: Combustible liquid. Products of combustion may be more hazardous than the material itself. By-products include hydrogen chloride, polychlorinated dibenzodioxins and furans (PCDD, PCDF), and other irritants and toxic gases.

FLASH POINT: 286 to 385°F (141 to 196°C) (oc) Flash points shown are a range for various PCBs. Some forms do not exhibit flash points.

STORAGE RECOMMENDATIONS: PCBs are no longer commercially produced in the U.S. Drums, transformers, and other containers should be frequently inspected for leakage. Store in a cool, dry, well-ventilated location. Detached storage must be used.

USUAL SHIPPING CONTAINERS: Metal cans, pails, drums. Tanks on trucks, rail cars, barges. Transformers, capacitors, and oil switches manufactured prior to 1979.

PHYSICAL PROPERTIES: Generally colorless to yellow oily liquid, white to yellow crystals, or yellow to black resin. Mild, distinctive odor.

BOILING POINT: 527 to 788°F (275 to 420°C)

SPECIFIC GRAVITY: 1.20 to 1.56

SOLUBILITY IN WATER: not soluble

VAPOR PRESSURE: <1 mm Hg @ 38°C

NAME: **POTASSIUM**

SYNONYMS: kalium

FORMULA: K

NFPA 30/OSHA CLASSIFICATION:

DOT CLASS: Class 4.3, Dangerous when wet material

SHIPPING LABEL: DANGEROUS WHEN WET

ID NO.: UN 2257

CAS NO.: 7440-09-7

MOL. WT.: 39.1

STATEMENT OF HAZARDS: Combustible solid. Corrosive. Water reactive.

EMERGENCY RESPONSE PERSONAL PROTECTIVE EQUIPMENT: Wear special protective clothing and positive pressure self-contained breathing apparatus.

SPILL OR LEAK PROCEDURES: Keep water away from release. Shovel into suitable dry container.

FIRE FIGHTING PROCEDURES: Use approved Class D extinguishers or smother with dry sand, dry clay, or dry ground limestone. DO NOT use carbon dioxide or halogenated extinguishing agents. DO NOT use water. Violent reaction may result.

HEALTH HAZARDS: Corrosive. Causes severe eye and skin burns.

FIRE AND EXPLOSION HAZARDS: Combustible solid. Evolves hydrogen and ignites on contact with water. May ignite spontaneously on exposure to air. Combustion may produce irritants and toxic gases. If damp, burns readily in combination with combustibles.

INSTABILITY AND REACTIVITY HAZARDS: Reacts violently with a broad range of materials, including water and air.

STORAGE RECOMMENDATIONS: Store in a cool, dry, well-ventilated location. Separate from water, acids, halogens, silicates, sulfates, nitrates, carbonates, phosphates, oxides and hydroxides of heavy metals, organics, and Teflon.

USUAL SHIPPING CONTAINERS: Hermetically sealed can inside wooden box. Metal cans, pails, drums, and tanks. Tanks on trucks, rail cars, barges. Packaged under inert gas or mineral oil.

PHYSICAL PROPERTIES: Soft, silvery-white metal. Tarnishes on exposure to air.

MELTING POINT: 146°F (63°C)

BOILING POINT: 1410°F (766°C)

SPECIFIC GRAVITY: 0.86

SOLUBILITY IN WATER: soluble (decomposes)

NAME: **POTASSIUM CYANIDE**

FORMULA: KCN

NFPA 30/OSHA CLASSIFICATION:

DOT CLASS: Class 6.1, Poisonous material

SHIPPING LABEL: POISON

ID NO.: UN 1680

CAS NO.: 151-50-8

MOL. WT.: 65.1

STATEMENT OF HAZARDS: Serious health hazard. Corrosive. Reacts with water or any acid releasing hydrogen cyanide.

EMERGENCY RESPONSE PERSONAL PROTECTIVE EQUIPMENT: Wear special protective clothing and positive pressure self-contained breathing apparatus.

SPILL OR LEAK PROCEDURES: Keep water away from release. Flush spill area with hypochlorite solution. Cover in noncombustible material for proper disposal. Shovel into suitable dry container. Control runoff and isolate discharged material for proper disposal.

FIRE FIGHTING PROCEDURES: Do not use carbon dioxide extinguisher. Extinguish fire using agent suitable for surrounding fire. Water may be used on nearby fires not involving potassium cyanide. Use water spray to keep fire-exposed containers cool. Use alkali dry chemical.

HEALTH HAZARDS: Corrosive. Causes severe eye and skin burns. May be harmful if absorbed through skin or inhaled. May cause cyanosis.

FIRE AND EXPLOSION HAZARDS: Not combustible. Reaction with acids releases flammable hydrogen cyanide gas.

INSTABILITY AND REACTIVITY HAZARDS: Reacts with acids to produce hydrogen cyanide.

STORAGE RECOMMENDATIONS: Store in a cool, dry, well-ventilated location. Separate from water, acids, and carbon dioxide. Outside or detached storage is preferred.

USUAL SHIPPING CONTAINERS: Glass bottles, special metal containers, and steel drums.

PHYSICAL PROPERTIES: White lumps or crystals (deliquescent) with faint odor of bitter almonds.

MELTING POINT: 1174°F (634°C)

BOILING POINT: 2957°F (1625°C)

SPECIFIC GRAVITY: 1.52

SOLUBILITY IN WATER: soluble

NAME: **POTASSIUM DICHLORO-S-TRIAZINETRIONE**

DOT SHIPPING NAME: **DICHLOROISOCYANURIC ACID**

dry DICHLOROISOCYANURIC ACID SALTS

SYNONYMS: potassium dichloroisocyanurate; troclosene potassium

FORMULA: $KCl_2(NOC)_3$

NFPA 30/OSHA CLASSIFICATION:

DOT CLASS: Class 5.1, Oxidizer

SHIPPING LABEL: OXIDIZER

ID NO.: UN 2465

CAS NO.: 2244-21-5

MOL. WT.: 236.1

STATEMENT OF HAZARDS: Serious health hazard. Oxidizer. Reacts with water, releasing chlorine gas. Thermally unstable. Decomposes at 464°F (240°C).

EMERGENCY RESPONSE PERSONAL PROTECTIVE EQUIPMENT: Wear special protective clothing and positive pressure self-contained breathing apparatus.

SPILL OR LEAK PROCEDURES: Keep water away from release. Approach release from upwind. Isolate leaking containers, if this can be done without undue risk. Prompt cleanup and removal are necessary. Shovel into suitable dry container. Control runoff and isolate discharged material for proper disposal.

FIRE FIGHTING PROCEDURES: Approach fire from upwind to avoid hazardous vapors and toxic decomposition products. Fight fire from protected location or maximum possible distance. Use remote equipment whenever possible. Use flooding quantities of water on fire-involved containers. If necessary use water spray to keep fire-exposed containers cool.

HEALTH HAZARDS: Serious health hazard. May be harmful if inhaled. May cause pulmonary edema. Effects may be delayed. Irritating to skin, eyes, and respiratory system. Reacts with water to release toxic chlorine gas and nitrogen trichloride liquid.

FIRE AND EXPLOSION HAZARDS: Contact with foreign materials, organic matter, or easily chlorinated or oxidized materials may result in fire. Mixture with ammonium salts or similar nitrogen containing compounds may result in exothermic reactions, causing fire or explosion. Reacts with water to release chlorine gas and nitrogen trichloride and in confined spaces increases temperature and pressure to dangerous levels. Closed containers may rupture violently when heated. Thermally unstable. Decomposes at fire temperature and is self-sustaining even if heat source is removed.

INSTABILITY AND REACTIVITY HAZARDS: Reacts with water to produce chlorine. Reacts explosively with solutions of ammonia, amines, or calcium hypochlorite. Reacts with most reducing agents.

STORAGE RECOMMENDATIONS: Store in a cool, dry, well-ventilated location. Outside or detached storage is preferred. Must be stored in a dry location on pallets arranged according to NFPA 430, Code for Storage of Liquid and Solid Oxidizers. Separate from combustibles, oxidizing materials, ammonia, sodium carbonate (soda ash), calcium hypochlorite, hydrogen peroxide.

USUAL SHIPPING CONTAINERS: Moisture-excluding fiber drums with polyethylene bag liner, and lined pails. Smaller quantities in glass or polyethylene bottles and in special laminated packets.

PHYSICAL PROPERTIES: White crystalline solid with strong chlorine odor. Thermally unstable. Decomposes at 464°F (240°C).

SPECIFIC GRAVITY: 0.96

SOLUBILITY IN WATER: slowly reacts

NAME: **POTASSIUM HYDROXIDE, solid**
POTASSIUM HYDROXIDE, solution

SYNONYMS: caustic potash; potash lye

FORMULA: KOH

NFPA 30/OSHA CLASSIFICATION:

DOT CLASS: Class 8, Corrosive material

SHIPPING LABEL: CORROSIVE

ID NO.: UN 1813 for solid UN 1814 for solution

CAS NO.: 1310-58-3

MOL. WT.: 56.1

STATEMENT OF HAZARDS: Corrosive. Serious health hazard. Either solid or concentrated solution.

EMERGENCY RESPONSE PERSONAL PROTECTIVE EQUIPMENT: Wear special protective clothing and positive pressure self-contained breathing apparatus.

SPILL OR LEAK PROCEDURES: Keep water away from release. Prompt cleanup and removal are necessary. Control runoff and isolate discharged material for proper disposal.

FIRE FIGHTING PROCEDURES: Extinguish fire using agent suitable for type of surrounding fire. Use water spray to keep fire-exposed containers cool. Use flooding quantities of water.

HEALTH HAZARDS: Corrosive. Causes severe eye and skin burns. Irritating to skin, eyes, and respiratory system. May be harmful if inhaled.

FIRE AND EXPLOSION HAZARDS: Not combustible. Dissolves in water, releasing heat. If moist, reacts with many common metals to form hydrogen gas.

INSTABILITY AND REACTIVITY HAZARDS: Soluble in water, releasing heat sufficient to ignite combustibles. Reacts with acids, giving off heat. When moist, reacts with many metals such as aluminum, lead, tin, and zinc to form hydrogen gas.

STORAGE RECOMMENDATIONS: Store in a cool, dry, well-ventilated location. Separate from water, acids, and metals.

USUAL SHIPPING CONTAINERS: Bottles, drums, and tank cars.

PHYSICAL PROPERTIES: White deliquescent crystals, lumps, rods, or pellets. May be in concentrated water solution.

MELTING POINT: 680°F (360°C)

BOILING POINT: 2408°F (1320°C)

SPECIFIC GRAVITY: 2.04

SOLUBILITY IN WATER: soluble

NAME: **POTASSIUM PEROXIDE**

SYNONYMS: potassium superoxide

FORMULA: K_2O_2

NFPA 30/OSHA CLASSIFICATION:

DOT CLASS: Class 5.1, Oxidizer

SHIPPING LABEL: OXIDIZER

ID NO.: UN 1491

CAS NO.: 17014-71-0

MOL. WT.: 110.2

STATEMENT OF HAZARDS: Corrosive. Strong oxidizer.

EMERGENCY RESPONSE PERSONAL PROTECTIVE EQUIPMENT: Wear special protective clothing and positive pressure self-contained breathing apparatus.

SPILL OR LEAK PROCEDURES: Use flooding quantities of water to dilute spills to form nonreactive mixtures, protect personnel.

FIRE FIGHTING PROCEDURES: Extinguish fire using agent suitable for surrounding fire. Use flooding quantities of water as spray.

HEALTH HAZARDS: Corrosive. Causes severe eye and skin burns. May be harmful if absorbed through skin or inhaled.

FIRE AND EXPLOSION HAZARDS: Strong oxidizer. Enhances combustion in combination with combustibles. Not combustible. Mixtures with combustibles may ignite spontaneously.

INSTABILITY AND REACTIVITY HAZARDS: Reacts vigorously with strong acids, metals, and organics. Reacts with water.

STORAGE RECOMMENDATIONS: Store in a cool, dry, well-ventilated location. Separate from organic and oxidizing materials. Immediately remove and properly dispose of any spilled material. See also NFPA 430, Code for the Storage of Solid and Liquid Oxidizers.

USUAL SHIPPING CONTAINERS: Glass bottles, fiber bags or boxes, metal cans, drums.

PHYSICAL PROPERTIES: White to yellowish odorless powder.

MELTING POINT: 914°F (490°C)

BOILING POINT: decomposes

SOLUBILITY IN WATER: soluble

NAME: **POTASSIUM-SODIUM ALLOYS**

FORMULA: Na_xK_y

NFPA 30/OSHA CLASSIFICATION:

DOT CLASS: Class 4.3, Dangerous when wet material

SHIPPING LABEL: DANGEROUS WHEN WET

ID NO.: UN 1422

CAS NO.: 11135-81-2

MOL. WT.: 23.0 - 39.1

STATEMENT OF HAZARDS: Corrosive. Combustible liquid metal. Water reactive. May ignite spontaneously on exposure to moist air.

EMERGENCY RESPONSE PERSONAL PROTECTIVE EQUIPMENT: Wear special protective clothing and positive pressure self-contained breathing apparatus.

SPILL OR LEAK PROCEDURES: Keep water away from release. Absorb in noncombustible material for proper disposal. Shovel into suitable dry container.

FIRE FIGHTING PROCEDURES: Use approved Class D extinguishers or smother with dry sand, dry clay, or dry ground limestone. DO NOT use carbon dioxide or halogenated extinguishing agents. DO NOT use water. Violent reaction may result.

HEALTH HAZARDS: Corrosive. Causes severe eye and skin burns.

FIRE AND EXPLOSION HAZARDS: Combustible liquid metal. Evolves hydrogen and ignites on contact with water. May ignite spontaneously on exposure to moist air. Combustion may produce irritants and toxic gases.

INSTABILITY AND REACTIVITY HAZARDS: Reacts violently with a broad range of materials, including water and moist air.

STORAGE RECOMMENDATIONS: Store in a cool, dry, well-ventilated location. Separate from Teflon, halogens, chlorinated solvents, acids, alcohols, organic materials, carbon dioxide, oxidizing materials, and water.

USUAL SHIPPING CONTAINERS: DOT 4BW240 carbon steel cylinders, glass ampules. Packaged under inert gas.

PHYSICAL PROPERTIES: Liquid, silvery metal. Commercial mixtures are 40 to 90% potassium.

MELTING POINT: 12°F

SOLUBILITY IN WATER: decomposes

VAPOR DENSITY: 1.02-1.29

NAME: **POTASSIUM SULFIDE, anhydrous**

SYNONYMS: potassium monosulfide

FORMULA: K_2S

NFPA 30/OSHA CLASSIFICATION:

DOT CLASS: Class 4.2, Spontaneously combustible material

SHIPPING LABEL: SPONTANEOUSLY COMBUSTIBLE

ID NO.: UN 1382

CAS NO.: 1312-73-8

MOL. WT.: 110.3

STATEMENT OF HAZARDS: Corrosive. Combustible solid.

EMERGENCY RESPONSE PERSONAL PROTECTIVE EQUIPMENT: Wear special protective clothing and positive pressure self-contained breathing apparatus.

SPILL OR LEAK PROCEDURES: Prompt cleanup and removal are necessary. Cover in noncombustible material for proper disposal. Keep water away from release.

FIRE FIGHTING PROCEDURES: Use flooding quantities of water as spray. Approach fire from upwind to avoid hazardous vapors and toxic decomposition products.

HEALTH HAZARDS: Corrosive. Causes severe eye and skin burns. May be harmful if inhaled. Releases hydrogen sulfide on contact with water and under fire conditions.

FIRE AND EXPLOSION HAZARDS: Combustible solid. Fire conditions may produce hydrogen sulfide. Finely divided potassium sulfide may explode in air at room temperature. May act as an oxidizer.

INSTABILITY AND REACTIVITY HAZARDS: Reacts violently with acids, oxidizing materials, halogens.

STORAGE RECOMMENDATIONS: Store in a cool, dry, well-ventilated location. Separate from acids, oxidizing materials, halogens.

USUAL SHIPPING CONTAINERS: Glass bottles, metal cans, pails, drums.

PHYSICAL PROPERTIES: White to yellowish to brownish-red crystalline solid. Rotten egg odor.

MELTING POINT: 1674°F (912°C) Decomposes at 1562°F (850°C)

SPECIFIC GRAVITY: 1.74

SOLUBILITY IN WATER: soluble

ELECTRICAL EQUIPMENT: Class II, Group Undesignated

NAME: **PROPARGYL ALCOHOL**

SYNONYMS: ethynylcarbinol; ethynylmethanol; 2-propyn-1-ol; 1-propyne-3-ol; 3-propynol

FORMULA: HC ≡ CCH_2OH

NFPA 30/OSHA CLASSIFICATION: IC

DOT CLASS: Class 3, Flammable and combustible liquid

SHIPPING LABEL: FLAMMABLE LIQUID and POISON

ID NO.: NA 1986

CAS NO.: 107-19-7

MOL. WT.: 56.1

STATEMENT OF HAZARDS: Severe health hazard. Flammable liquid. May polymerize or decompose explosively.

EMERGENCY RESPONSE PERSONAL PROTECTIVE EQUIPMENT: Wear special protective clothing and positive pressure self-contained breathing apparatus.

SPILL OR LEAK PROCEDURES: Eliminate all ignition sources. Stop or control the leak if this can be done without undue risk. Use water spray to cool and disperse vapors, protect personnel, and dilute spills to form nonflammable mixtures. Absorb in noncombustible material for proper disposal.

FIRE FIGHTING PROCEDURES: Use water spray, dry chemical, "alcohol resistant" foam, or carbon dioxide. Use water spray to keep fire-exposed containers cool. Fight fire from protected location or maximum possible distance.

HEALTH HAZARDS: Severe health hazard. May be fatal if absorbed through skin or inhaled. Irritating to skin, eyes, and respiratory system.

FIRE AND EXPLOSION HAZARDS: Flammable liquid. Vapors are heavier than air and may travel to a source of ignition and flash back. Closed containers may rupture violently when heated.

FLASH POINT: 97°F (33°C) (oc)

INSTABILITY AND REACTIVITY HAZARDS: May polymerize explosively. Polymerization may be caused by elevated temperature, oxidizers, peroxides, caustic solutions, or sunlight. Uninhibited monomer vapor may form polymer in vents and other confined spaces.

STORAGE RECOMMENDATIONS: Store in a cool, dry, well-ventilated location. Store away from heat, oxidizing materials, acids, alkalies, and sunlight.

USUAL SHIPPING CONTAINERS: Metal cans, pails, drums.

PHYSICAL PROPERTIES: Colorless liquid. Mild geranium odor.

MELTING POINT: −61 to −54°F (−52 to −48°C)

BOILING POINT: 237 to 239°F (114 to 115°C)

SPECIFIC GRAVITY: 0.95

SOLUBILITY IN WATER: soluble

VAPOR PRESSURE: 11.6 mm Hg @ 20°C

ELECTRICAL EQUIPMENT: Class I, Group Undesignated

NAME: **PROPIONALDEHYDE**

SYNONYMS: propanal; propionic aldehyde; propyl-aldehyde

FORMULA: CH_3CH_2CHO

NFPA 30/OSHA CLASSIFICATION: IB

DOT CLASS: Class 3, Flammable and combustible liquid

SHIPPING LABEL: FLAMMABLE LIQUID

ID NO.: UN 1275

CAS NO.: 123-38-6

MOL. WT.: 58.1

STATEMENT OF HAZARDS: Flammable liquid. May form explosive peroxides if exposed to air. Moderate health hazard.

EMERGENCY RESPONSE PERSONAL PROTECTIVE EQUIPMENT: Wear full protective clothing and positive pressure self-contained breathing apparatus.

SPILL OR LEAK PROCEDURES: Eliminate all ignition sources. Stop or control the leak, if this can be done without undue risk. Use water spray to cool and disperse vapors, protect personnel, and dilute spills to form nonflammable mixtures. Control runoff and isolate discharged material for proper disposal.

FIRE FIGHTING PROCEDURES: Fight fire from protected location or maximum possible distance. Use water spray to keep fire-exposed containers cool. Use water spray, dry chemical, "alcohol resistant" foam, or carbon dioxide. Water may be ineffective.

HEALTH HAZARDS: Moderate health hazard. May be harmful if inhaled. Irritating to skin, eyes, and respiratory system. Narcosis, nausea, and loss of consciousness may result from exposure to high concentrations of vapor.

FIRE AND EXPLOSION HAZARDS: Flammable liquid. Combustion may produce irritants and toxic gases. Vapors are heavier than air and may travel to a source of ignition and flash back. Closed containers may rupture violently when heated.

FLASH POINT: 16°F (−9°C)

AUTOIGNITION TEMPERATURE: 405°F (207°C)

FLAMMABLE LIMITS: LOWER: 2.9% UPPER: 17.0%

INSTABILITY AND REACTIVITY HAZARDS: Reacts with oxidizing materials, amines, strong alkalies, and acids. Hazardous polymerization may occur.

STORAGE RECOMMENDATIONS: Store in a cool, dry, well-ventilated location. Store away from heat and oxidizers. Outside or detached storage is preferred. Inside storage should be in a standard flammable liquids storage warehouse, room, or cabinet. Separate from oxidizing materials and other reactive hazards.

USUAL SHIPPING CONTAINERS: Vapor-tight glass bottles, drums, and tanks.

PHYSICAL PROPERTIES: Colorless liquid with suffocating fruity odor.

MELTING POINT: −114°F (−81°C)

BOILING POINT: 120°F (49°C)

SPECIFIC GRAVITY: 0.81

SOLUBILITY IN WATER: partly soluble

VAPOR PRESSURE: 300 mm Hg @ 20°C

ELECTRICAL EQUIPMENT: Class I, Group C

NAME: **PROPIONIC ACID**

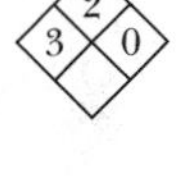

SYNONYMS: methylacetic acid; propanoic acid

FORMULA: CH_3CH_2COOH

NFPA 30/OSHA CLASSIFICATION: II

DOT CLASS: Class 8, Corrosive material

SHIPPING LABEL: CORROSIVE

ID NO.: UN 1848

CAS NO.: 79-09-4

MOL. WT.: 74.1

STATEMENT OF HAZARDS: Corrosive and combustible liquid.

EMERGENCY RESPONSE PERSONAL PROTECTIVE EQUIPMENT: Wear special protective clothing and positive pressure self-contained breathing apparatus.

SPILL OR LEAK PROCEDURES: Use water spray to cool and disperse vapors, protect personnel, and dilute spills to form nonflammable mixtures. Control runoff and isolate discharged material for proper disposal.

FIRE FIGHTING PROCEDURES: Use water spray, dry chemical, "alcohol resistant" foam, or carbon dioxide. Use water spray to keep fire-exposed containers cool.

HEALTH HAZARDS: Corrosive. Causes severe eye and skin burns. Irritating to skin, eyes, and respiratory system. May be harmful if inhaled.

FIRE AND EXPLOSION HAZARDS: Combustible liquid.

FLASH POINT: 126°F (52°C)

AUTOIGNITION TEMPERATURE: 955°F (513°C)

FLAMMABLE LIMITS: LOWER: 2.9% UPPER: 12.1%

INSTABILITY AND REACTIVITY HAZARDS: Reacts with oxidizing materials and caustic substances. Products of combustion include carbon dioxide and carbon monoxide as well as irritating fumes.

STORAGE RECOMMENDATIONS: Outside or detached storage is preferred. Store in a cool, dry, well-ventilated location.

USUAL SHIPPING CONTAINERS: Glass bottles, carboys, lined drums and tank trucks and tank cars.

PHYSICAL PROPERTIES: Colorless, oily liquid with pungent, disagreeable, rancid odor.

MELTING POINT: −6°F (−21°C)

BOILING POINT: 286°F (141°C)

SPECIFIC GRAVITY: 1.00

SOLUBILITY IN WATER: soluble

VAPOR PRESSURE: 2 mm Hg @ 20°C

ELECTRICAL EQUIPMENT: Class I, Group D

NAME: **PROPIONIC ANHYDRIDE**

SYNONYMS: methylacetic acid anhydride; propionyl-oxide; propanoic anhydride

FORMULA: $(CH_3CH_2CO)_2O$

NFPA 30/OSHA CLASSIFICATION: IIIA

DOT CLASS: Class 8, Corrosive material

SHIPPING LABEL: CORROSIVE

ID NO.: UN 2496

CAS NO.: 123-62-6

MOL. WT.: 130.1

STATEMENT OF HAZARDS: Corrosive and combustible liquid.

EMERGENCY RESPONSE PERSONAL PROTECTIVE EQUIPMENT: Wear special protective clothing and positive pressure self-contained breathing apparatus.

SPILL OR LEAK PROCEDURES: Use water spray to cool and disperse vapors, protect personnel, and dilute spills to form nonflammable mixtures. Control runoff and isolate discharged material for proper disposal. Neutralize spill and washings with soda ash or lime.

FIRE FIGHTING PROCEDURES: Use water spray, dry chemical, "alcohol resistant" foam, or carbon dioxide. Use water spray to keep fire-exposed containers cool. Hazardous reactions may be avoided by using large quantities of water to solubilize the anhydride and fully absorb the heat of reaction.

HEALTH HAZARDS: Corrosive. Causes severe eye and skin burns. May be harmful if inhaled. Irritating to skin, eyes, and respiratory system.

FIRE AND EXPLOSION HAZARDS: Combustible liquid. Contact with oxidizers should be avoided. Material reacts with water producing heat. Combustion may produce irritants and toxic gases.

FLASH POINT: 145°F (63°C)

AUTOIGNITION TEMPERATURE: 540°F (285°C)

FLAMMABLE LIMITS: LOWER: 1.5% @ 165°F (74°C) UPPER: 11.9% @ 261°F (127°C)

INSTABILITY AND REACTIVITY HAZARDS: Reacts with oxidizing materials, water, alcohols, and alkalies. Products of combustion include carbon dioxide and carbon monoxide as well as irritating fumes.

STORAGE RECOMMENDATIONS: Outside or detached storage is preferred. Separate from heat and oxidizing materials. Exclude moisture from vapor space in storage tank.

USUAL SHIPPING CONTAINERS: Glass bottles, carboys, lined drums, and tank trucks or tank cars.

PHYSICAL PROPERTIES: Colorless liquid with pungent odor. Slowly dissolves in water to form propionic acid.

MELTING POINT: −49°F (−45°C)

BOILING POINT: 333°F (167°C)

SPECIFIC GRAVITY: 1.01

SOLUBILITY IN WATER: slowly reacts

VAPOR PRESSURE: 10 mm Hg @ 58°C

ELECTRICAL EQUIPMENT: Class I, Group D

NAME: **PROPYLAMINE**

SYNONYMS: 1-aminopropane, 1-propanamine; n-propylamine

FORMULA: $CH_3CH_2CH_2NH_2$

NFPA 30/OSHA CLASSIFICATION: IB

DOT CLASS: Class 3, Flammable and combustible liquid

SHIPPING LABEL: FLAMMABLE LIQUID and CORROSIVE

ID NO.: UN 1277

CAS NO.: 107-10-8

MOL. WT.: 59.1

STATEMENT OF HAZARDS: Corrosive. Flammable liquid.

EMERGENCY RESPONSE PERSONAL PROTECTIVE EQUIPMENT: Wear special protective clothing and positive pressure self-contained breathing apparatus.

SPILL OR LEAK PROCEDURES: Stop or control the leak, if this can be done without undue risk. Eliminate all ignition sources. Use water spray to cool and disperse vapors, protect personnel, and dilute spills to form nonflammable mixtures. Approach release from upwind. Absorb in noncombustible material for proper disposal.

FIRE FIGHTING PROCEDURES: Use water spray, dry chemical, "alcohol resistant" foam, or carbon dioxide. Use water spray to keep fire-exposed containers cool. Solid streams of water may be ineffective and spread material.

HEALTH HAZARDS: Corrosive. Causes severe eye and skin burns. May be harmful if inhaled. Vapors cause extreme irritation of eyes with lachrymation, conjunctivitis, and corneal edema. Irritating to skin, eyes, and respiratory system. Inhalation may cause difficulties ranging from coughing and nausea to pulmonary edema. Skin sensitizer. May cause severe allergic reaction.

FIRE AND EXPLOSION HAZARDS: Flammable liquid. Vapors are heavier than air and may travel to a source of ignition and flash back.

FLASH POINT: −35°F (−37°C)

AUTOIGNITION TEMPERATURE: 604°F (318°C)

FLAMMABLE LIMITS: LOWER: 2.0% UPPER: 10.4%

INSTABILITY AND REACTIVITY HAZARDS: Avoid contact with acids, oxidizing materials, chlorine, hypochlorite, halogenated compounds, and reactive organic compounds. Products of decomposition include carbon monoxide, carbon dioxide, hydrocarbons, and toxic oxides of nitrogen as well as toxic amine vapors. Ammonia vapors are liberated upon decomposition.

STORAGE RECOMMENDATIONS: Outside or detached storage is preferred. Avoid oxidizing materials, acids, and sources of halogen. Store in a cool, dry, well-ventilated location.

USUAL SHIPPING CONTAINERS: Glass bottles, cans, drums, and tank cars.

PHYSICAL PROPERTIES: Colorless liquid with strong odor or ammonia. Soluble in water.

MELTING POINT: −117°F (−83°C)

BOILING POINT: 120°F (48°C)

SPECIFIC GRAVITY: 0.72

SOLUBILITY IN WATER: soluble

VAPOR PRESSURE: 248 mm Hg @ 20°C

ELECTRICAL EQUIPMENT: Class I, Group D

NAME: **PROPYLENE DICHLORIDE**

SYNONYMS: 1,2-dichloropropane

FORMULA: $CH_3CHClCH_2Cl$

NFPA 30/OSHA CLASSIFICATION: IB

DOT CLASS: Class 3, Flammable and combustible liquid

SHIPPING LABEL: FLAMMABLE LIQUID

ID NO.: UN 1279

CAS NO.: 78-87-5

MOL. WT.: 113.0

STATEMENT OF HAZARDS: Flammable liquid. Combustion by-products may include hydrogen chloride. Moderate health hazard.

EMERGENCY RESPONSE PERSONAL PROTECTIVE EQUIPMENT: Wear full protective clothing and positive pressure self-contained breathing apparatus.

SPILL OR LEAK PROCEDURES: Eliminate all ignition sources. Approach release from upwind. Stop or control the leak, if this can be done without undue risk. Control runoff and isolate discharged material for proper disposal.

FIRE FIGHTING PROCEDURES: Approach fire from upwind to avoid hazardous vapors and toxic decomposition products. Use water spray, dry chemical, foam, or carbon dioxide. Use water spray to keep fire-exposed containers cool.

HEALTH HAZARDS: Moderate health hazard. May be harmful if inhaled. Irritating to eye, skin, and respiratory system. Combustion by-products may include hydrogen chloride.

FIRE AND EXPLOSION HAZARDS: Flammable liquid. Vapors are heavier than air and may travel to a source of ignition and flash back. Combustion may produce irritants and toxic gases, including hydrogen chloride.

FLASH POINT: 60°F (16°C)

AUTOIGNITION TEMPERATURE: 1035°F (557°C)

FLAMMABLE LIMITS: LOWER: 3.2% UPPER: 14.5%

INSTABILITY AND REACTIVITY HAZARDS: Reacts with oxidizing materials, alkalies, and alkali metals, such as aluminum.

STORAGE RECOMMENDATIONS: Outside or detached storage is preferred. Inside storage should be in a standard flammable liquids storage warehouse, room, or cabinet. Separate from oxidizing materials and active metals.

USUAL SHIPPING CONTAINERS: Glass bottles, drums; tanks on trucks, rail cars, barges.

PHYSICAL PROPERTIES: Colorless liquid with odor like chloroform.

MELTING POINT: −148°F (−100°C)

BOILING POINT: 205°F (96°C)

SPECIFIC GRAVITY: 1.16

SOLUBILITY IN WATER: not soluble

VAPOR DENSITY: 3.90

VAPOR PRESSURE: 40 mm Hg @ 20°C

ELECTRICAL EQUIPMENT: Class I, Group D

NAME: **PROPYLENE OXIDE**

SYNONYMS: 1,2-epoxypropane; methyloxirane; propene oxide

FORMULA: $CH_3\overbrace{HC—CH_2}^{O}$

NFPA 30/OSHA CLASSIFICATION: IA

DOT CLASS: Class 3, Flammable and combustible liquid

SHIPPING LABEL: FLAMMABLE LIQUID

ID NO.: UN 1280

CAS NO.: 75-56-9

MOL. WT.: 58.1

STATEMENT OF HAZARDS: Flammable liquid. Corrosive. Low ignition energy.

EMERGENCY RESPONSE PERSONAL PROTECTIVE EQUIPMENT: Wear special protective clothing and positive pressure self-contained breathing apparatus.

SPILL OR LEAK PROCEDURES: Eliminate all ignition sources. Approach release from upwind. Stop or control the leak, if this can be done without undue risk. Use water spray to cool and disperse vapors, protect personnel, and dilute spills to form nonflammable mixtures. Do not use clay-based absorbents. Control runoff and isolate discharged material for proper disposal.

FIRE FIGHTING PROCEDURES: Use flooding quantities of water as fog. May use water spray, dry chemical, "alcohol resistant" foam, or carbon dioxide. Use water spray to keep fire-exposed containers cool. Fight fire from protected location or maximum possible distance.

HEALTH HAZARDS: Corrosive. Causes severe eye and skin burns. May be harmful if inhaled. Pulmonary edema may result. Irritating to skin, eyes, and respiratory system.

FIRE AND EXPLOSION HAZARDS: Flammable liquid. Vapors are heavier than air and may travel to a source of ignition and flash back. Closed containers may rupture violently when heated.

FLASH POINT: −35°F (−37°C)

AUTOIGNITION TEMPERATURE: 869°F (465°C)

FLAMMABLE LIMITS: LOWER: 2.1% UPPER: 37.0%

INSTABILITY AND REACTIVITY HAZARDS: Hazardous polymerization may occur when in contact with highly active catalytic surfaces, acids, and bases. Reacts with acids, alkalies, salts, combustible materials, clay based absorbents. Reaction with water may lead to a runaway reaction.

STORAGE RECOMMENDATIONS: Store in a cool, dry, well-ventilated location. Outside or detached storage is preferred. Separate from acids, alkalies, salts, combustible materials, clay-based absorbents.

USUAL SHIPPING CONTAINERS: Steel cylinders; tanks on trucks, rail cars, barges. Nitrogen cover required.

PHYSICAL PROPERTIES: Colorless liquid with sweet ether-like odor.

MELTING POINT: −170°F (−112°C)

BOILING POINT: 94°F (34°C)

SPECIFIC GRAVITY: 0.86

SOLUBILITY IN WATER: soluble

VAPOR DENSITY: 2.00

VAPOR PRESSURE: 442 mm Hg @ 20°C

ELECTRICAL EQUIPMENT: Class I, Group B (C)

NAME: **n-PROPYL NITRATE**

SYNONYMS: nitric acid propyl ester

FORMULA: $CH_3(CH_2)_2ONO_2$

NFPA 30/OSHA CLASSIFICATION: IB

DOT CLASS: Class 3, Flammable and combustible liquid

SHIPPING LABEL: FLAMMABLE LIQUID

ID NO.: UN 1865

CAS NO.: 627-13-4

MOL. WT.: 105.1

STATEMENT OF HAZARDS: Flammable liquid. Thermally unstable. Strong oxidizer. Moderate health hazard. Combustion by-products may include oxides of nitrogen.

EMERGENCY RESPONSE PERSONAL PROTECTIVE EQUIPMENT: Wear full protective clothing and positive pressure self-contained breathing apparatus.

SPILL OR LEAK PROCEDURES: Eliminate all ignition sources. Stop or control the leak, if this can be done without undue risk. Use appropriate foam to blanket release and suppress vapors. Absorb in noncombustible material for proper disposal.

FIRE FIGHTING PROCEDURES: Use dry chemical, foam, carbon dioxide, or water spray. Water may be ineffective. Use water spray to keep fire-exposed containers cool. Fight fire from protected location or maximum possible distance.

HEALTH HAZARDS: Moderate health hazard. May be harmful if inhaled. Irritating to skin, eyes, and respiratory system. Combustion by-products may include oxides of nitrogen.

FIRE AND EXPLOSION HAZARDS: Flammable liquid. Explodes when heated. Vapors are heavier than air and may travel to a source of ignition and flash back. Closed containers may rupture violently when heated. Combustion may produce irritants and toxic gases.

FLASH POINT: 68°F (20°C)

AUTOIGNITION TEMPERATURE: 347°F (175°C)

FLAMMABLE LIMITS: LOWER: 2% UPPER: 100%

INSTABILITY AND REACTIVITY HAZARDS: Thermally unstable. Decomposes at 347°F (175°C). Shock-sensitive. Reacts with oxidizing materials and forms explosive mixtures with combustible materials.

STORAGE RECOMMENDATIONS: Store in a cool, dry, well-ventilated location. Separate from oxidizing materials and combustibles. Outside or detached storage is preferred. Immediately remove and properly dispose of any spilled material. See also NFPA 430, Code for the Storage of Liquid and Solid Oxidizers.

USUAL SHIPPING CONTAINERS: Bottles packed in insulating material. Metal cans, pails, drums.

PHYSICAL PROPERTIES: Pale yellow liquid. Sickly, sweet odor.

MELTING POINT: <−150°F (<−101°C)

BOILING POINT: 230°F (110°C)

SPECIFIC GRAVITY: 1.05

SOLUBILITY IN WATER: not soluble

VAPOR PRESSURE: 18 mm Hg @ 20°C

ELECTRICAL EQUIPMENT: Class I, Group B

NAME: **PROPYLTRICHLOROSILANE**

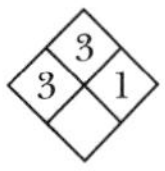

SYNONYMS: trichloropropylsilane

FORMULA: $C_3H_7SiCl_3$

NFPA 30/OSHA CLASSIFICATION: II

DOT CLASS: Class 8, Corrosive material

SHIPPING LABEL: CORROSIVE

ID NO.: UN 1816

CAS NO.: 141-57-1

MOL. WT.: 177.5

STATEMENT OF HAZARDS: Corrosive and flammable liquid.

EMERGENCY RESPONSE PERSONAL PROTECTIVE EQUIPMENT: Wear special protective clothing and positive pressure self-contained breathing apparatus.

SPILL OR LEAK PROCEDURES: Eliminate all ignition sources. Stop or control the leak, if this can be done without undue risk. Use water spray to cool and disperse vapors and protect personnel. Spills can be neutralized by flushing with large quantities of water followed by treatment with sodium bicarbonate. Control runoff and isolate discharged material for proper disposal.

FIRE FIGHTING PROCEDURES: Use dry chemical, foam, carbon dioxide, or water spray. Use water spray to keep fire-exposed containers cool. Approach fire from upwind to avoid hazardous vapors and toxic decomposition products.

HEALTH HAZARDS: Corrosive. Causes severe eye and skin burns. May be harmful if absorbed through skin or inhaled. Irritating to skin, eyes, and respiratory system.

FIRE AND EXPLOSION HAZARDS: Flammable liquid. Combustion by-products include hydrogen chloride, other chlorine compounds, and other irritants and toxic gases.

FLASH POINT: 100°F (38°C)

INSTABILITY AND REACTIVITY HAZARDS: Reacts with water to produce hydrogen chloride.

STORAGE RECOMMENDATIONS: Store in a cool, dry, well-ventilated location. Separate from acids, alkalies, oxidizing materials, and water. Outside or detached storage is preferred.

USUAL SHIPPING CONTAINERS: Glass bottle inside wooden box. Metal cans, pails, drums. Packaged under nitrogen gas.

PHYSICAL PROPERTIES: Colorless liquid. Acrid odor.

BOILING POINT: 252°F (122°C)

SPECIFIC GRAVITY: 1.19

SOLUBILITY IN WATER: not soluble (decomposes)

ELECTRICAL EQUIPMENT: Class I, Group D

NAME: **PYRIDINE**

SYNONYMS: azabenzene; azine

FORMULA: C_5H_5N

NFPA 30/OSHA CLASSIFICATION: IB

DOT CLASS: Class 3, Flammable and combustible liquid

SHIPPING LABEL: FLAMMABLE LIQUID and POISON

ID NO.: UN 1282

CAS NO.: 110-86-1

MOL. WT.: 79.1

STATEMENT OF HAZARDS: Serious health hazard. Flammable liquid.

EMERGENCY RESPONSE PERSONAL PROTECTIVE EQUIPMENT: Wear special protective clothing and positive pressure self-contained breathing apparatus.

SPILL OR LEAK PROCEDURES: Eliminate all ignition sources. Stop or control the leak, if this can be done without undue risk. Use water spray to cool and disperse vapors, protect personnel, and dilute spills to form nonflammable mixtures. Control runoff and isolate discharged material for proper disposal.

FIRE FIGHTING PROCEDURES: Use water spray, dry chemical, "alcohol resistant" foam, or carbon dioxide. Solid streams of water may be ineffective. Use water spray to keep fire-exposed containers cool.

HEALTH HAZARDS: Serious health hazard. May be harmful if absorbed through skin or inhaled. Corrosive. Causes severe eye and skin burns. Irritating to skin, eyes, and respiratory system. Overexposure causes nausea, headache, and nervous symptoms.

FIRE AND EXPLOSION HAZARDS: Flammable liquid. Vapors are heavier than air and may travel to a source of ignition and flash back. Products of combustion include carbon monoxide, carbon dioxide, and oxides of nitrogen.

FLASH POINT: 68°F (20°C)

AUTOIGNITION TEMPERATURE: 900°F (482°C)

FLAMMABLE LIMITS: LOWER: 1.8% UPPER: 12.4%

INSTABILITY AND REACTIVITY HAZARDS: Reacts with many acids and oxidizers.

STORAGE RECOMMENDATIONS: Outside or detached storage is preferred. Isolate from oxidizing materials and acids.

USUAL SHIPPING CONTAINERS: Bottles, drums, and tank cars.

PHYSICAL PROPERTIES: Clear, colorless to light yellow liquid with penetrating and nauseating odor.

MELTING POINT: −44°F (−42°C)

BOILING POINT: 240°F (115°C)

SPECIFIC GRAVITY: 0.98

SOLUBILITY IN WATER: soluble

VAPOR PRESSURE: 18 mm Hg @ 20°C

ELECTRICAL EQUIPMENT: Class I, Group D

NAME: **SILANE**

SYNONYMS: monosilane; silicane; silicon tetrahydride

FORMULA: SiH_4

NFPA 30/OSHA CLASSIFICATION:

DOT CLASS: Class 2.1, Flammable gas

SHIPPING LABEL: FLAMMABLE GAS

ID NO.: UN 2203

CAS NO.: 7803-62-5

MOL. WT.: 32.1

STATEMENT OF HAZARDS: Pyrophoric. Flammable gas. Low ignition energy. Slight health hazard.

EMERGENCY RESPONSE PERSONAL PROTECTIVE EQUIPMENT: Wear full protective clothing and positive pressure self-contained breathing apparatus.

SPILL OR LEAK PROCEDURES: Stop or control the leak, if this can be done without undue risk. Use water spray to cool and disperse vapors and protect personnel. Releases may ignite spontaneously.

FIRE FIGHTING PROCEDURES: Use fine spray or fog to control fire by preventing its spread and absorbing some of its heat. Stop flow of gas before extinguishing fire. Use water spray to keep fire-exposed containers cool. Do not use halocarbons. Explosive decomposition may occur under fire conditions. Fight fire from protected location or maximum possible distance. Approach fire from upwind to avoid hazardous vapors and toxic decomposition products.

HEALTH HAZARDS: Slight health hazard. Irritating to skin, eyes, and respiratory system.

FIRE AND EXPLOSION HAZARDS: Flammable gas. Pyrophoric; may ignite spontaneously on exposure to air. Decomposes at 752°F (400°C) with release of silicon fumes and hydrogen. Closed containers may rupture violently when heated.

FLAMMABLE LIMITS: LOWER: 1.4% UPPER: 96% (estimated)

INSTABILITY AND REACTIVITY HAZARDS: May explode with halocarbons when ignited.

STORAGE RECOMMENDATIONS: Store in a cool, dry, well-ventilated location. Separate from alkalies, oxidizing materials, halogens, and air. Outside or detached storage is preferred.

USUAL SHIPPING CONTAINERS: Cylinders or tanks.

PHYSICAL PROPERTIES: Colorless gas. Repulsive odor.

MELTING POINT: −301°F (−185°C)

BOILING POINT: −170°F (−112°C)

SPECIFIC GRAVITY: 0.68 @ (−185°C)

SOLUBILITY IN WATER: not soluble (slowly decomposes)

VAPOR DENSITY: 1.11

NAME: **SILANE, (4-AMINOBUTYL)-DIETHOXYMETHYL**

SYNONYMS: (4-aminobutyl)diethoxymethyl-silane; aminobutylmethyl diethoxysilane

FORMULA: $C_9H_{23}NO_2Si$

NFPA 30/OSHA CLASSIFICATION:

DOT CLASS: N/A

ID NO.: N/A

CAS NO.: 3037-72-7

MOL. WT.: 205.4

STATEMENT OF HAZARDS: Corrosive and combustible liquid.

EMERGENCY RESPONSE PERSONAL PROTECTIVE EQUIPMENT: Wear special protective clothing and positive pressure self-contained breathing apparatus.

SPILL OR LEAK PROCEDURES: Stop or control the leak, if this can be done without undue risk. Use water spray to cool and disperse vapors and protect personnel. Control runoff and isolate discharged material for proper disposal.

FIRE FIGHTING PROCEDURES: Use dry chemical, foam, carbon dioxide, or water spray. Approach fire from upwind to avoid hazardous vapors and toxic decomposition products.

HEALTH HAZARDS: Corrosive. Causes severe eye and skin burns. May be harmful if absorbed through skin or inhaled.

FIRE AND EXPLOSION HAZARDS: Combustible liquid. Combustion may produce irritants and toxic gases.

INSTABILITY AND REACTIVITY HAZARDS: May attack glass. Hydrolyzes in water.

STORAGE RECOMMENDATIONS: Store in a cool, dry, well-ventilated location. Separate from glass, water, oxidizing materials.

PHYSICAL PROPERTIES: Liquid.

SOLUBILITY IN WATER: not soluble (decomposes)

NAME: **SILICON TETRACHLORIDE**

SYNONYMS: silicon chloride; tetrachlorosilane

FORMULA: $SiCl_4$

NFPA 30/OSHA CLASSIFICATION:

DOT CLASS: Class 8, Corrosive material

SHIPPING LABEL: CORROSIVE

ID NO.: UN 1818

CAS NO.: 10026-04-7

MOL. WT.: 169.9

STATEMENT OF HAZARDS: Corrosive. Water reactive.

EMERGENCY RESPONSE PERSONAL PROTECTIVE EQUIPMENT: Wear special protective clothing and positive pressure self-contained breathing apparatus.

SPILL OR LEAK PROCEDURES: Keep water away from release. Stop or control the leak, if this can be done without undue risk. Use appropriate foam to blanket release and suppress vapors. Approach release from upwind. Adsorb in noncombustible material for proper disposal.

FIRE FIGHTING PROCEDURES: Extinguish fire using agent suitable for surrounding fire. Use water spray to keep fire-exposed containers cool. Approach fire from upwind to avoid hazardous vapors and toxic decomposition products.

HEALTH HAZARDS: Corrosive. Causes severe eye and skin burns. Irritating to skin, eyes, and respiratory system. Symptoms of overexposure include coughing, choking, dermatitis, intense thirst and pain if swallowed, nausea, vomiting, diarrhea, and collapse.

FIRE AND EXPLOSION HAZARDS: Not combustible, but if involved in a fire may produce irritants and toxic gases. Forms dense clouds in moist air.

INSTABILITY AND REACTIVITY HAZARDS: Reacts with water to produce silicic acid and hydrogen chloride.

STORAGE RECOMMENDATIONS: Store in a cool, dry, well-ventilated location. Separate from acids, alkalies, oxidizing materials, glass, alcohols, and metals.

USUAL SHIPPING CONTAINERS: Glass bottle inside wooden box. Packaged under nitrogen gas.

PHYSICAL PROPERTIES: Colorless, mobile, fuming liquid. Suffocating odor.

MELTING POINT: −57°F (−70°C)

BOILING POINT: 138°F (59°C)

SPECIFIC GRAVITY: 1.48

SOLUBILITY IN WATER: not soluble (decomposes)

VAPOR PRESSURE: 194 mm Hg @ 20°C

NAME: **SILICON TETRAFLUORIDE**

SYNONYMS: silicon fluoride; tetrafluorosilane

FORMULA: SiF_4

NFPA 30/OSHA CLASSIFICATION:

DOT CLASS: Class 2.3, Poisonous gas

SHIPPING LABEL: POISON GAS and CORROSIVE

ID NO.: UN 1859

CAS NO.: 7783-61-1

MOL. WT.: 104.1

STATEMENT OF HAZARDS: Corrosive. Water reactive.

EMERGENCY RESPONSE PERSONAL PROTECTIVE EQUIPMENT: Wear special protective clothing and positive pressure self-contained breathing apparatus.

SPILL OR LEAK PROCEDURES: Stop or control the leak, if this can be done without undue risk. Use appropriate foam to blanket release and suppress vapors. Approach release from upwind.

FIRE FIGHTING PROCEDURES: Extinguish fire using agent suitable for surrounding fire. Use water spray to keep fire-exposed containers cool. Approach fire from upwind to avoid hazardous vapors and toxic decomposition products.

HEALTH HAZARDS: Corrosive. Causes severe eye and skin burns. May be harmful if absorbed through skin or inhaled. Irritating to skin, eyes, and respiratory system.

FIRE AND EXPLOSION HAZARDS: Not combustible, but if involved in a fire may produce irritants and toxic gases. Forms dense clouds in moist air.

INSTABILITY AND REACTIVITY HAZARDS: Reacts with water, producing silicic acid and hydrogen fluoride.

STORAGE RECOMMENDATIONS: Store in a cool, dry, well-ventilated location. Separate from acids, alkalies, glass, alcohol, and alkali metals.

USUAL SHIPPING CONTAINERS: Steel cylinders.

PHYSICAL PROPERTIES: Colorless gas. Pungent, acrid odor.

MELTING POINT: −130°F (−90°C)

BOILING POINT: −123°F (−65°C)

SPECIFIC GRAVITY: 1.59

SOLUBILITY IN WATER: not soluble (decomposes)

VAPOR DENSITY: 4.67

NAME: **SODIUM**

SYNONYMS: natrium

FORMULA: Na

NFPA 30/OSHA CLASSIFICATION:

DOT CLASS: Class 4.3, Dangerous when wet material

SHIPPING LABEL: DANGEROUS WHEN WET

ID NO.: UN 1428

CAS NO.: 7440-23-5

MOL. WT.: 22.9

STATEMENT OF HAZARDS: Corrosive. Combustible solid. May ignite spontaneously on exposure to moist air. Water reactive.

EMERGENCY RESPONSE PERSONAL PROTECTIVE EQUIPMENT: Wear special protective clothing and positive pressure self-contained breathing apparatus.

SPILL OR LEAK PROCEDURES: Keep water away from release. Do not create dust. Shovel into suitable dry container.

FIRE FIGHTING PROCEDURES: Use approved Class D extinguishers or smother with dry sand, dry clay, or dry ground limestone. DO NOT use carbon dioxide or halogenated extinguishing agents. DO NOT use water. Violent reaction may result.

HEALTH HAZARDS: Corrosive. Causes severe eye and skin burns.

FIRE AND EXPLOSION HAZARDS: Combustible solid. Evolves hydrogen and ignites on contact with water. Combustion may produce irritants and toxic gases.

AUTOIGNITION TEMPERATURE: 250°F (121°C)

INSTABILITY AND REACTIVITY HAZARDS: Reacts violently with a broad range of materials, including water.

STORAGE RECOMMENDATIONS: Store in a cool, dry, well-ventilated location. Separate from water.

USUAL SHIPPING CONTAINERS: Hermetically sealed can inside wooden box. Metal cans, pails, drums, tanks, and stainless steel tubes. Tanks on trucks, rail cars, barges. Packaged under inert gas or mineral oil.

PHYSICAL PROPERTIES: Light, silvery-white metal. Soft solid. Odorless.

MELTING POINT: 208°F (98°C)

BOILING POINT: 1619°F (881°C)

SPECIFIC GRAVITY: 0.97

SOLUBILITY IN WATER: decomposes

VAPOR PRESSURE: 1 mm Hg @ 440°C

NAME: **SODIUM CHLORITE**

FORMULA: $NaClO_2$

NFPA 30/OSHA CLASSIFICATION:

DOT CLASS: Class 5.1, Oxidizer

SHIPPING LABEL: OXIDIZER

ID NO.: UN 1496

CAS NO.: 7758-19-2

MOL. WT.: 90.4

STATEMENT OF HAZARDS: Strong oxidizer. Thermally unstable. Decomposes above 356°F (180°C) releasing heat. Reacts with ammonia and amines to form explosive compounds. Slight health hazard.

EMERGENCY RESPONSE PERSONAL PROTECTIVE EQUIPMENT: Wear full protective clothing and positive pressure self-contained breathing apparatus.

SPILL OR LEAK PROCEDURES: Prompt cleanup and removal are necessary. Shovel into suitable dry container. Control runoff and isolate discharged material for proper disposal.

FIRE FIGHTING PROCEDURES: Approach fire from upwind to avoid hazardous vapors and toxic decomposition products. Use flooding quantities of water as fog or spray. Use water spray to keep fire-exposed containers cool. Extinguish fire using agent suitable for surrounding fire.

HEALTH HAZARDS: Slight health hazard. Irritating to skin, eyes, and respiratory system.

FIRE AND EXPLOSION HAZARDS: Strong oxidizer. Not combustible. Contact with combustible materials will increase fire hazard. Thermally unstable. Decomposes above 356°F (180°C) releasing heat.

INSTABILITY AND REACTIVITY HAZARDS: Strong oxidizer. Shock- and friction-sensitive when mixed with organic materials. Acid causes release of explosive chlorine dioxide. Reacts with ammonia and amines to form explosive compounds.

STORAGE RECOMMENDATIONS: Store in a cool, dry, well-ventilated location. Separate from oxidizing materials, combustibles, acids, ammonia, and amines. Immediately remove and properly dispose of any spilled material. See also NFPA 430, Code for the Storage of Liquid and Solid Oxidizers.

USUAL SHIPPING CONTAINERS: Metal can inside wooden box. Glass bottle inside wooden box.

PHYSICAL PROPERTIES: White crystals.

MELTING POINT: 356 - 392°F and (180 - 200°C)

SOLUBILITY IN WATER: soluble

NAME: **SODIUM CYANIDE**

SYNONYMS: cyanide of sodium; prussiate of soda

FORMULA: NaCN

NFPA 30/OSHA CLASSIFICATION:

DOT CLASS: Class 6.1, Poisonous material

SHIPPING LABEL: POISON

ID NO.: UN 1689

CAS NO.: 143-33-9

MOL. WT.: 49.0

STATEMENT OF HAZARDS: Corrosive. Reacts with acid to release hydrogen cyanide gas.

EMERGENCY RESPONSE PERSONAL PROTECTIVE EQUIPMENT: Wear special protective clothing and positive pressure self-contained breathing apparatus.

SPILL OR LEAK PROCEDURES: Keep water away from release. Avoid contact with dust, mist, or solution. Do not create dust. Prompt cleanup and removal are necessary. Shovel into suitable dry container. Control runoff and isolate discharged material for proper disposal.

FIRE FIGHTING PROCEDURES: Avoid carbon dioxide extinguishers. Extinguish fire using agent suitable for surrounding fire. Use water spray to keep fire-exposed containers cool.

HEALTH HAZARDS: Corrosive. Causes severe eye and skin burns. May be harmful if absorbed through skin or inhaled. Irritating to skin, eyes, and respiratory system. May cause cyanosis

FIRE AND EXPLOSION HAZARDS: Not combustible, but if involved in a fire decomposes to produce hydrogen cyanide and oxides of nitrogen.

INSTABILITY AND REACTIVITY HAZARDS: Reacts with acids or carbon dioxide to release hydrogen cyanide.

STORAGE RECOMMENDATIONS: Store in a cool, dry, well-ventilated location. Separate from water, acids, carbon dioxide.

USUAL SHIPPING CONTAINERS: Glass bottles, special metal containers, and steel drums. Solutions may be shipped in tanks on trucks and rail cars.

PHYSICAL PROPERTIES: White solid granules, flakes, or lumps. Almond odor.

MELTING POINT: 1047°F (564°C)

BOILING POINT: 2725°F (1496°C)

SPECIFIC GRAVITY: 1.60

SOLUBILITY IN WATER: soluble

NAME: **SODIUM DICHLORO-s-TRIAZINETRIONE DIHYDRATE**

MOL. WT. 219.9

MOL. WT. 255.9

SYNONYMS: sodium dichloroisocyanurate

FORMULA: $NaCl_2(NCO)_3$; $NaCl_2(NCO)_3\ 2H_2O$

NFPA 30/OSHA CLASSIFICATION:

DOT CLASS: N/A

ID NO.: N/A

CAS NO.: 2893-78-9

MOL. WT.: 219.9 and 255.9

STATEMENT OF HAZARDS: Moderate health hazard. Oxidizer. Reacts with water, releasing chlorine gas. Thermally unstable. Decomposes at 464°F (240°C). Thermal decomposition continues even after removal of heat source.

EMERGENCY RESPONSE PERSONAL PROTECTIVE EQUIPMENT: Wear special protective clothing and positive pressure self-contained breathing apparatus.

SPILL OR LEAK PROCEDURES: Keep water away from release of dry material. Approach release from upwind. Isolate leaking containers, if this can be done without undue risk. Prompt cleanup and removal are necessary. Shovel into suitable dry container. Control runoff and isolate discharged material for proper disposal. Do not return spill material to original containers.

FIRE FIGHTING PROCEDURES: Approach fire from upwind to avoid hazardous vapors and toxic decomposition products. Use flooding quantities of water on fire-involved containers. If necessary use water spray to keep fire-exposed containers cool. Avoid use of water on non-involved material wherever possible. Do not use dry chemical extinguishers containing ammonium compounds.

HEALTH HAZARDS: Moderate health hazard. May be harmful if inhaled. Irritating to skin, eyes, and respiratory system. Reaction with water releases chlorine gas and nitrogen trichloride liquid.

FIRE AND EXPLOSION HAZARDS: Oxidizer. Not combustible. Reaction with combustible materials, ammonium salts, or foreign substances may increase the fire hazard. Thermally unstable. Decomposes at fire temperature and is self-sustaining even if heat source is removed. Closed containers may rupture violently when heated.

INSTABILITY AND REACTIVITY HAZARDS: Reacts explosively with calcium hypochlorite in the presence of water. Reacts with ammonia or amines producing nitrogen trichloride. Reacts with most reducing agents. Decomposes exothermically at 464°F (240°C). Anhydrous material has a significantly lower decomposition temperature.

STORAGE RECOMMENDATIONS: Store in a cool, dry, well-ventilated location. Outside or detached storage is preferred. Must be stored in a dry location on pallets arranged according to NFPA 430, Code for Storage of Liquid and Solid Oxidizers. Separate from combustibles, oxidizables, ammonia, sodium carbonate (soda ash), calcium hypochlorite, hydrogen peroxide.

USUAL SHIPPING CONTAINERS: Moisture-excluding fiber drums with polyethylene bag liner and lined pails. Smaller quantities in glass or polyethylene bottles and in special laminated packets. Commercial materials are packaged in supersacks and metal tote bins.

PHYSICAL PROPERTIES: White crystalline solid with strong chlorine odor. Thermally unstable. Decomposes at 464°F (240°C).

SPECIFIC GRAVITY: 0.96

SOLUBILITY IN WATER: soluble

NAME: **SODIUM FLUORIDE**

SYNONYMS: roach salt; villiaumite

FORMULA: NaF

NFPA 30/OSHA CLASSIFICATION:

DOT CLASS: Class 6.1, Poisonous material

SHIPPING LABEL: KEEP AWAY FROM FOOD

ID NO.: UN 1690

CAS NO.: 7681-49-4

MOL. WT.: 42.0

STATEMENT OF HAZARDS: Serious health hazard.

EMERGENCY RESPONSE PERSONAL PROTECTIVE EQUIPMENT: Wear special protective clothing and positive pressure self-contained breathing apparatus.

SPILL OR LEAK PROCEDURES: Shovel into suitable dry container. Control runoff and isolate discharged material for proper disposal.

FIRE FIGHTING PROCEDURES: Extinguish fire using agent suitable for surrounding fire.

HEALTH HAZARDS: Serious health hazard. May be harmful if absorbed through skin or inhaled. Irritating to skin, eyes, and respiratory system.

FIRE AND EXPLOSION HAZARDS: Not combustible.

INSTABILITY AND REACTIVITY HAZARDS: Reacts with acids to form hydrogen fluoride.

STORAGE RECOMMENDATIONS: Store in a cool, dry, well-ventilated location. Separate from acids and alkalies.

USUAL SHIPPING CONTAINERS: Drums and multiwall bags.

PHYSICAL PROPERTIES: White powder. Insecticide grade is tinted blue.

MELTING POINT: 1819°F (993°C)

BOILING POINT: 3083°F (1695°C)

SPECIFIC GRAVITY: 2.56

SOLUBILITY IN WATER: not soluble

NAME: **SODIUM HYDRIDE**

SYNONYMS: NaH 80

FORMULA: NaH

NFPA 30/OSHA CLASSIFICATION:

DOT CLASS: Class 4.3, Dangerous when wet material

SHIPPING LABEL: DANGEROUS WHEN WET

ID NO.: UN 1427

CAS NO.: 7646-69-7

MOL. WT.: 24.0

STATEMENT OF HAZARDS: Flammable solid. May ignite spontaneously on exposure to moist air. Water reactive. Corrosive.

EMERGENCY RESPONSE PERSONAL PROTECTIVE EQUIPMENT: Wear special protective clothing and positive pressure self-contained breathing apparatus.

SPILL OR LEAK PROCEDURES: Keep water away from release. Shovel into suitable dry container. Immediately remove and properly dispose of any spilled material.

FIRE FIGHTING PROCEDURES: Use approved Class D extinguishers or smother with dry sand, dry clay, or dry ground limestone. DO NOT use carbon dioxide or halogenated extinguishing agents. DO NOT use water. Violent reaction may result.

HEALTH HAZARDS: Corrosive. Causes severe eye and skin burns. May be harmful if inhaled. Irritating to skin, eyes, and respiratory system.

FIRE AND EXPLOSION HAZARDS: Flammable solid. May ignite spontaneously on exposure to moist air. Evolves hydrogen and ignites on contact with water. Combustion may produce irritants and toxic gases.

INSTABILITY AND REACTIVITY HAZARDS: Reacts violently with a broad range of materials, including water.

STORAGE RECOMMENDATIONS: Store in a cool, dry, well-ventilated location.

USUAL SHIPPING CONTAINERS: Metal can inside wooden box or other container. Packaged under argon or nitrogen gas.

PHYSICAL PROPERTIES: Silvery needles or gray-white powder with odor of kerosene.

MELTING POINT: 1472°F (800°C) (decomposes)

BOILING POINT: decomposes

SPECIFIC GRAVITY: 0.92

SOLUBILITY IN WATER: decomposes

NAME: **SODIUM HYDROSULFITE**

DOT SHIPPING NAME: **SODIUM DITHIONITE**

SYNONYMS: sodium hyposulfite; sodium sulfoxylate

FORMULA: $Na_2S_2O_4$

NFPA 30/OSHA CLASSIFICATION:

DOT CLASS: Class 4.2, Spontaneously combustible material

SHIPPING LABEL: SPONTANEOUSLY COMBUSTIBLE

ID NO.: UN 1384

CAS NO.: 7775-14-6

MOL. WT.: 174.1

STATEMENT OF HAZARDS: Moderate health hazard. Combustible solid.

EMERGENCY RESPONSE PERSONAL PROTECTIVE EQUIPMENT: Wear full protective clothing and positive pressure self-contained breathing apparatus.

SPILL OR LEAK PROCEDURES: Keep water away from release. Prompt cleanup and removal are necessary. Control runoff and isolate discharged material for proper disposal.

FIRE FIGHTING PROCEDURES: Use only flooding quantities of water. Monitor temperature of containers exposed to fire for at least 48 hours to verify decomposition has not begun in the sealed container.

HEALTH HAZARDS: Moderate health hazard. May be harmful if inhaled. Irritating to skin, eyes, and respiratory system. Combustion by-products may include sulfur dioxide.

FIRE AND EXPLOSION HAZARDS: Combustible solid. Easily oxidized. Combustion by-products include toxic sulfur dioxide. Heats spontaneously in contact with moisture and air, and may ignite surrounding combustible materials. Closed containers may rupture violently when heated.

INSTABILITY AND REACTIVITY HAZARDS: Reacts with oxidizing agents, acidic materials, moisture. Exposure to moisture either from humid air or from small amounts of water can result in spontaneous chemical reactions which may generate sufficient heat to initiate thermal decomposition. Heat above 50°C can also initiate thermal decomposition.

STORAGE RECOMMENDATIONS: Store in a cool, dry, well-ventilated location. Outside or detached storage is preferred. Separate from combustibles and oxidizing materials. Immediately remove and properly dispose of any spilled material.

USUAL SHIPPING CONTAINERS: Glass bottle inside wooden box. Specially constructed drums.

PHYSICAL PROPERTIES: White or grayish-white crystalline powder possibly with faint sulfurous odor.

MELTING POINT: 158° to 266°F (70° to 130°C) decomposes

SPECIFIC GRAVITY: 1.4

SOLUBILITY IN WATER: soluble (decomposes)

NAME: **SODIUM HYDROXIDE, solid SODIUM HYDROXIDE SOLUTION**

SYNONYMS: caustic soda; lye

FORMULA: NaOH

NFPA 30/OSHA CLASSIFICATION:

DOT CLASS: Class 8, Corrosive material

SHIPPING LABEL: CORROSIVE

ID NO.: UN 1823 solid UN 1824 solution

CAS NO.: 1310-73-2

MOL. WT.: 40.0

STATEMENT OF HAZARDS: Corrosive. Either solid or concentrated solution.

EMERGENCY RESPONSE PERSONAL PROTECTIVE EQUIPMENT: Wear special protective clothing and positive pressure self-contained breathing apparatus.

SPILL OR LEAK PROCEDURES: Keep water away from release. Stop or control the leak, if this can be done without undue risk. Prompt cleanup and removal are necessary. Shovel into suitable dry container. Control runoff and isolate discharged material for proper disposal.

FIRE FIGHTING PROCEDURES: Extinguish fire using agent suitable for surrounding fire. Use water spray to keep fire-exposed containers cool.

HEALTH HAZARDS: Corrosive. Causes severe eye and skin burns. Irritating to skin, eyes, and respiratory system.

FIRE AND EXPLOSION HAZARDS: Not combustible.

INSTABILITY AND REACTIVITY HAZARDS: Strong alkali. Dissolves in water releasing heat. Reacts with metals, such as aluminum, tin, and zinc, and may cause formation of hydrogen gas.

STORAGE RECOMMENDATIONS: Store in a cool, dry, well-ventilated location. Separate from acids, water, metals. Immediately remove and properly dispose of any spilled material.

USUAL SHIPPING CONTAINERS: Bottles, cans, drums; tanks on trucks, rail cars, barges.

PHYSICAL PROPERTIES: White pellets, flakes, sticks, or solid cast. Deliquescent. May be shipped as water solution.

MELTING POINT: 604°F (318°C)

BOILING POINT: 2534°F (1390°C)

SPECIFIC GRAVITY: 2.13

SOLUBILITY IN WATER: soluble

NAME: **SODIUM PEROXIDE**

SYNONYMS: sodium superoxide

FORMULA: Na_2O_2

NFPA 30/OSHA CLASSIFICATION:

DOT CLASS: Class 5.1, Oxidizer

SHIPPING LABEL: OXIDIZER

ID NO.: UN 1504

CAS NO.: 1313-60-6

MOL. WT.: 78.0

STATEMENT OF HAZARDS: Corrosive. Strong oxidizer.

EMERGENCY RESPONSE PERSONAL PROTECTIVE EQUIPMENT: Wear special protective clothing and positive pressure self-contained breathing apparatus.

SPILL OR LEAK PROCEDURES: Use only flooding quantities of water to decompose spills to form nonreactive mixtures and protect personnel.

FIRE FIGHTING PROCEDURES: Use only flooding quantities of water as spray. DO NOT use halogenated extinguishing agents. Use carbon dioxide or suitable dry chemical extinguisher.

HEALTH HAZARDS: Corrosive. Causes severe eye and skin burns. May be harmful if absorbed through skin or inhaled.

FIRE AND EXPLOSION HAZARDS: Strong oxidizer. Not combustible, but will increase fire hazard if in contact with combustibles. May explode in combination with combustibles.

INSTABILITY AND REACTIVITY HAZARDS: Reacts vigorously with water. Forms self-igniting mixtures with organic materials, metals.

STORAGE RECOMMENDATIONS: Store in a cool, dry, well-ventilated location. Separate from organic and oxidizing materials, acids, metal powders. Immediately remove and properly dispose of any spilled material. See also NFPA 430, Code for the Storage of Liquid and Solid Oxidizers.

USUAL SHIPPING CONTAINERS: Glass bottles, fiber bags or boxes, metal cans, drums.

PHYSICAL PROPERTIES: White to yellowish odorless powder.

MELTING POINT: DECOMPOSES: 860°F (460°C)

BOILING POINT: (decomposes)

SPECIFIC GRAVITY: 2.80

SOLUBILITY IN WATER: reacts

NAME: **SODIUM SULFIDE, anhydrous**

SYNONYMS: sodium monosulfide; sodium sulfuret; sodium sulphide

FORMULA: Na_2S

NFPA 30/OSHA CLASSIFICATION:

DOT CLASS: Class 4.2, Spontaneously combustible material

SHIPPING LABEL: SPONTANEOUSLY COMBUSTIBLE

ID NO.: UN 1385

CAS NO.: 1313-82-2

MOL. WT.: 78.0

STATEMENT OF HAZARDS: Corrosive and combustible solid.

EMERGENCY RESPONSE PERSONAL PROTECTIVE EQUIPMENT: Wear special protective clothing and positive pressure self-contained breathing apparatus.

SPILL OR LEAK PROCEDURES: Approach release from upwind. Keep water away from release. Prompt cleanup and removal are necessary. Shovel dry material into suitable dry container. Control runoff and isolate discharged material for proper disposal.

FIRE FIGHTING PROCEDURES: Approach fire from upwind to avoid hazardous vapors and toxic decomposition products. Use flooding quantities of water. Do not use carbon dioxide.

HEALTH HAZARDS: Corrosive. Causes severe eye and skin burns. May be harmful if inhaled. Releases hydrogen sulfide on contact with water and under fire conditions.

FIRE AND EXPLOSION HAZARDS: Combustible solid. Finely divided material may explode in air. Reaction with water or acid produces hydrogen sulfide. Combustion may produce irritants and toxic gases.

INSTABILITY AND REACTIVITY HAZARDS: Reacts with water to form strong solutions and hydrogen sulfide. Reacts with acid more vigorously, producing corrosive solutions and hydrogen sulfide. Decomposes in air at 920° – 950°C, forming sulfur dioxide and sodium oxide.

STORAGE RECOMMENDATIONS: Store in a cool, dry, well-ventilated location. Separate from water, acids, and carbon dioxide. Outside or detached storage is preferred. Immediately remove and properly dispose of any spilled material.

USUAL SHIPPING CONTAINERS: Glass bottles, cans, and steel drums.

PHYSICAL PROPERTIES: Yellow to red solid flakes. Hygroscopic. Odor of rotten eggs.

MELTING POINT: 2156°F (1180°C) (in vacuum). 1688 to 1742°F (920 to 950°C) (in air)

SPECIFIC GRAVITY: 1.86

SOLUBILITY IN WATER: partly soluble (reacts)

ELECTRICAL EQUIPMENT: Class II, Group G

NAME: **STANNIC CHLORIDE, anhydrous**

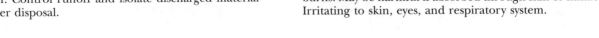

SYNONYMS: fuming spirit of Libavius; tin (IV) chloride; tin perchloride; tin tetrachloride

FORMULA: $SnCl_4$

NFPA 30/OSHA CLASSIFICATION:

DOT CLASS: Class 8, Corrosive material

SHIPPING LABEL: CORROSIVE

ID NO.: UN 1827

CAS NO.: 7646-78-8

MOL. WT.: 260.5

STATEMENT OF HAZARDS: Corrosive.

EMERGENCY RESPONSE PERSONAL PROTECTIVE EQUIPMENT: Wear special protective clothing and positive pressure self-contained breathing apparatus.

SPILL OR LEAK PROCEDURES: Use water spray to cool and disperse vapors, protect personnel, and carefully dilute spills to form nonreactive mixtures.

FIRE FIGHTING PROCEDURES: Use appropriate extinguishing agents on nearby combustible fires. Do not use water-based extinguishers on fires where this material has been released. Use water spray to keep fire-exposed containers cool. Visibility can be reduced by the solid tin oxide fumes produced when reacted with moisture.

HEALTH HAZARDS: Corrosive. Causes severe eye and skin burns. May be harmful if absorbed through skin or inhaled. Irritating to skin, eyes, and respiratory system.

FIRE AND EXPLOSION HAZARDS: Not combustible, but if involved in a fire decomposes to produce hydrogen chloride, and fumes of tin and tin oxides.

INSTABILITY AND REACTIVITY HAZARDS: Reacts violently with bases, oxidizing materials, organic matter. Reacts vigorously with water and moisture to form hydrogen chloride, tin oxide fume, and heat.

STORAGE RECOMMENDATIONS: Store in a cool, dry, well-ventilated location. Outside or detached storage is preferred.

USUAL SHIPPING CONTAINERS: Glass bottles and carboys, steel drums, tank cars.

PHYSICAL PROPERTIES: Colorless, caustic liquid. Fumes in moist air.

MELTING POINT: −27°F (−33°C)

BOILING POINT: 237°F (114°C)

SPECIFIC GRAVITY: 2.23

SOLUBILITY IN WATER: reacts

VAPOR PRESSURE: 20 mm Hg @ 22°C

NAME: **STIBINE**

SYNONYMS: antimony hydride; hydrogen antimonide

FORMULA: SbH_3

NFPA 30/OSHA CLASSIFICATION:

DOT CLASS: Class 2.3, Poisonous gas

SHIPPING LABEL: POISON GAS and FLAMMABLE GAS

ID NO.: UN 2676

CAS NO.: 7803-52-3

MOL. WT.: 124.8

STATEMENT OF HAZARDS: Severe health hazard. Flammable gas. Low ignition energy.

EMERGENCY RESPONSE PERSONAL PROTECTIVE EQUIPMENT: Wear special protective clothing and positive pressure self-contained breathing apparatus.

SPILL OR LEAK PROCEDURES: Approach release from upwind. Eliminate all ignition sources. Stop or control the leak, if this can be done without undue risk.

FIRE FIGHTING PROCEDURES: Stop flow of gas before extinguishing fire. Approach fire from upwind to avoid hazardous vapors and toxic decomposition products. Fight fire from protected location or maximum possible distance. Explosive decomposition may occur under fire conditions. Use flooding quantities of water as spray. DO NOT use halogenated extinguishing agents. Use water spray to keep fire-exposed containers cool.

HEALTH HAZARDS: Severe health hazard. May be fatal if absorbed through skin or inhaled. Strong sensitizer. May cause severe allergic respiratory reaction. Symptoms of overexposure include headache, weakness, nausea, abdominal pain, lumbar pain, jaundice, and lung irritation.

FIRE AND EXPLOSION HAZARDS: Flammable gas. Rapid decomposition begins at 392°F (200°C). Vapors are heavier than air and may travel to a source of ignition and flash back. Closed containers may rupture violently when heated. Evolves hydrogen and ignites on contact with many materials. Combustion by-products include antimony fumes.

INSTABILITY AND REACTIVITY HAZARDS: Thermally unstable. Decomposes above 392°F (200°C). Decomposes in air.

STORAGE RECOMMENDATIONS: Store in a cool, dry, well-ventilated location. Separate from acids, alkalies, halogenated compounds, oxidizing materials, and water. Outside or detached storage is preferred.

USUAL SHIPPING CONTAINERS: Steel cylinders.

PHYSICAL PROPERTIES: Colorless gas. Disagreeable odor.

MELTING POINT: −126°F (−88°C)

BOILING POINT: −1°F (−17°C)

SPECIFIC GRAVITY: 2.20 (liquid)

SOLUBILITY IN WATER: not soluble

VAPOR DENSITY: 4.36

VAPOR PRESSURE: >760 mm Hg @ 20°C

ELECTRICAL EQUIPMENT: Class I, Group C

NAME: **STYRENE monomer, inhibited**

SYNONYMS: cinnamene; phenylethylene; styrol; vinyl-benzene

FORMULA: $C_6H_5CH{=}CH_2$

NFPA 30/OSHA CLASSIFICATION: IC

DOT CLASS: Class 3, Flammable and combustible liquid

SHIPPING LABEL: FLAMMABLE LIQUID

ID NO.: UN 2055

CAS NO.: 100-42-5

MOL. WT.: 104.2

STATEMENT OF HAZARDS: Flammable liquid. May accumulate static electricity. Moderate health hazard.

EMERGENCY RESPONSE PERSONAL PROTECTIVE EQUIPMENT: Wear full protective clothing and positive pressure self-contained breathing apparatus.

SPILL OR LEAK PROCEDURES: Absorb in noncombustible material for proper disposal. Stop or control the leak, if this can be done without undue risk. Use water spray to cool and disperse vapors and protect personnel. Control runoff and isolate discharged material for proper disposal.

FIRE FIGHTING PROCEDURES: Use water spray, dry chemical, foam, or carbon dioxide. Fight fire from protected location or maximum possible distance. Use water spray to keep fire-exposed containers cool.

HEALTH HAZARDS: Moderate health hazard. May be harmful if inhaled or absorbed through the skin. Irritating to skin, eyes, and respiratory system. Signs and symptoms of excessive exposure may be anesthetic or narcotic effects. Liquid may cause corneal injury.

FIRE AND EXPLOSION HAZARDS: Flammable liquid. Vapors are heavier than air and may travel to a source of ignition and flash back. Liquid floats on water and may travel to a source of ignition and spread fire. Hazardous polymerization may occur under fire conditions. Closed containers may rupture violently when heated.

FLASH POINT: 88°F (31°C)

AUTOIGNITION TEMPERATURE: 914°F (490°C)

FLAMMABLE LIMITS: LOWER: 1.1% UPPER: 7.0%

INSTABILITY AND REACTIVITY HAZARDS: Hazardous polymerization may occur. Avoid heat, flame, and spark. Avoid acids, oxidizing materials, peroxides, metal salts such as iron chloride or aluminum chloride, and polymer initiators. Usually contains inhibitors to prevent polymerization. Polymerization may be caused by elevated temperature, oxidizers, peroxides, or sunlight. Uninhibited monomer vapor may form polymer in vents and other confined spaces.

STORAGE RECOMMENDATIONS: Store in a cool, dry, well-ventilated place. Separate from oxidizing materials, peroxides, and metal salts.

USUAL SHIPPING CONTAINERS: Drums, tank cars, tank trucks, and tank barges.

PHYSICAL PROPERTIES: Colorless to light yellow liquid with sweet aromatic odor at low concentrations and sharp penetrating disagreeable odor at higher concentrations.

MELTING POINT: −23°F (−31°C)

BOILING POINT: 293°F (145°C)

SPECIFIC GRAVITY: 0.91

SOLUBILITY IN WATER: not soluble

VAPOR PRESSURE: 5 mm Hg @ 20°C

ELECTRICAL EQUIPMENT: Class I, Group D

NAME: **SULFUR, molten**

SYNONYMS: brimstone; sulphur

FORMULA: S_8

NFPA 30/OSHA CLASSIFICATION: IIIB

DOT CLASS: Class 4.1, Flammable solid

SHIPPING LABEL: FLAMMABLE SOLID

ID NO.: UN 2448 molten

CAS NO.: 7704-34-9

MOL. WT.: 256.5

STATEMENT OF HAZARDS: Moderate health hazard. Combustible liquid. Combustion by-products may include sulfur dioxide gas. Reacts with oxidizing agents.

EMERGENCY RESPONSE PERSONAL PROTECTIVE EQUIPMENT: Wear full protective clothing and positive pressure self-contained breathing apparatus.

SPILL OR LEAK PROCEDURES: Allow molten sulfur to solidify before removal. Shovel into suitable dry container.

FIRE FIGHTING PROCEDURES: Approach fire from upwind to avoid hazardous vapors and toxic decomposition products. Use fine spray or fog to control fire by preventing its spread and absorbing some of its heat. Water may cause frothing of molten sulfur.

HEALTH HAZARDS: Moderate health hazard. May be harmful if inhaled. Molten sulfur can cause thermal burns. Irritating to skin, eyes, and respiratory system. Combustion by-products may include sulfur dioxide gas.

FIRE AND EXPLOSION HAZARDS: Combustible liquid. Combustion by-products include sulfur dioxide gas. Hydrogen sulfide is released from molten sulfur.

FLASH POINT: 405°F (207°C)

AUTOIGNITION TEMPERATURE: 450°F (232°C)

FLAMMABLE LIMITS: LOWER: 3.3% UPPER: 46.0% for hydrogen sulfide

INSTABILITY AND REACTIVITY HAZARDS: Reacts with strong oxidizing materials.

STORAGE RECOMMENDATIONS: Store in a cool, dry, well-ventilated location. Separate from chlorates, nitrates, other oxidizing materials, and hydrocarbons.

USUAL SHIPPING CONTAINERS: Tank trucks, rail cars, and barges.

PHYSICAL PROPERTIES: Amber liquid.

MELTING POINT: 239°F (115°C)

BOILING POINT: 833°F (445°C)

SPECIFIC GRAVITY: 2.08

SOLUBILITY IN WATER: not soluble

ELECTRICAL EQUIPMENT: Class II, Group G

NAME: **SULFUR CHLORIDES**

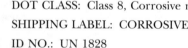

SYNONYMS: disulfur dichloride; sulfur monochloride; sulfur subchloride

FORMULA: S_2Cl_2

NFPA 30/OSHA CLASSIFICATION: IIIB

DOT CLASS: Class 8, Corrosive material

SHIPPING LABEL: CORROSIVE

ID NO.: UN 1828

CAS NO.: 10025-67-9

MOL. WT.: 135.0

STATEMENT OF HAZARDS: Corrosive. Combustible liquid. Water reactive.

EMERGENCY RESPONSE PERSONAL PROTECTIVE EQUIPMENT: Wear special protective clothing and positive pressure self-contained breathing apparatus.

SPILL OR LEAK PROCEDURES: Keep water away from release. Absorb in noncombustible material for proper disposal. Shovel into suitable dry container.

FIRE FIGHTING PROCEDURES: Use dry chemical or carbon dioxide. Use water spray to keep fire-exposed containers cool. Approach fire from upwind to avoid hazardous vapors and toxic decomposition products.

HEALTH HAZARDS: Corrosive. Causes severe eye and skin burns. May be harmful if absorbed through skin or inhaled. Irritating to skin, eyes, and respiratory system.

FIRE AND EXPLOSION HAZARDS: Combustible liquid. Combustion may produce irritants and toxic gases.

FLASH POINT: 245°F (118°C)

AUTOIGNITION TEMPERATURE: 453°F (234°C)

INSTABILITY AND REACTIVITY HAZARDS: Forms highly corrosive liquids on contact with water. Decomposes on contact with water to produce heat and toxic and corrosive fumes. Reacts with alcohols.

STORAGE RECOMMENDATIONS: Store in a cool, dry, well-ventilated location. Isolate from water and oxidizing materials.

USUAL SHIPPING CONTAINERS: Glass bottle inside wooden box. Metal cans, pails, drums. Tanks on trucks, rail cars, barges.

PHYSICAL PROPERTIES: Amber to yellow-red, fuming liquid. Penetrating odor.

MELTING POINT: −107°F (−77°C)

BOILING POINT: 280°F (138°C)

SPECIFIC GRAVITY: 1.67

SOLUBILITY IN WATER: reacts

NAME: **SULFUR DIOXIDE, liquefied**

SYNONYMS: sulfurous acid anhydride; sulfurous anhydride; sulfurous oxide

FORMULA: SO_2

NFPA 30/OSHA CLASSIFICATION:

DOT CLASS: Class 2.3 , Poisonous gas

SHIPPING LABEL: POISON GAS

ID NO.: UN 1079

CAS NO.: 7446-09-5

MOL. WT.: 64.1

STATEMENT OF HAZARDS: Serious health hazard. Gas usually shipped as a liquid.

EMERGENCY RESPONSE PERSONAL PROTECTIVE EQUIPMENT: Wear special protective clothing and positive pressure self-contained breathing apparatus.

SPILL OR LEAK PROCEDURES: Approach release from upwind. Stop or control the leak, if this can be done without undue risk. Use water spray to disperse vapors and protect personnel. Control runoff and isolate discharged material for proper disposal. Releases may require isolation or evacuation.

FIRE FIGHTING PROCEDURES: Use water spray to keep fire-exposed containers cool. Extinguish fire using agent suitable for surrounding fire.

HEALTH HAZARDS: Serious health hazard. May be harmful if inhaled. Irritating to skin, eyes, and respiratory system. Corrosive when dissolved in water as sulfurous acid.

FIRE AND EXPLOSION HAZARDS: Not combustible.

INSTABILITY AND REACTIVITY HAZARDS: Reacts with alkaline materials. Reacts with some active metals like aluminum.

STORAGE RECOMMENDATIONS: Store in a cool, dry, well-ventilated location. Outside or detached storage is preferred. Isolate from oxidizing materials and alkalies.

USUAL SHIPPING CONTAINERS: Steel cylinders; pressurized tanks on trucks, rail cars, barges.

PHYSICAL PROPERTIES: Colorless gas with irritating, suffocating sulfurous odor. May be shipped as a liquid under pressure.

MELTING POINT: −104°F (−76°C)

BOILING POINT: 14°F (−10°C)

SPECIFIC GRAVITY: 1.46 @ −10°C

SOLUBILITY IN WATER: partly soluble; dissolves to form sulfurous acid

VAPOR DENSITY: 2.21

NAME: **SULFURIC ACID**

SYNONYMS: battery acid; chamber acid; fertilizer acid; oil of vitriol

FORMULA: H_2SO_4

NFPA 30/OSHA CLASSIFICATION:

DOT CLASS: Class 8, Corrosive material

SHIPPING LABEL: CORROSIVE

ID NO.: UN 1830

CAS NO.: 7664-93-9

MOL. WT.: 98.1 SO_3 dissolves in H_2SO_4 in all proportions to give oleum or fuming sulfuric acid. Equimolar amounts of each yield pyrosulfuric acid. OLEUM is NA 1831.

STATEMENT OF HAZARDS: Corrosive. Water reactive. Oleum is extremely reactive with water. Reaction with metals may produce hydrogen gas.

EMERGENCY RESPONSE PERSONAL PROTECTIVE EQUIPMENT: Wear special protective clothing and positive pressure self-contained breathing apparatus.

SPILL OR LEAK PROCEDURES: Keep water away from release. Stop or control the leak, if this can be done without undue risk. Control runoff and isolate discharged material for proper disposal.

FIRE FIGHTING PROCEDURES: Extinguish fire using agents suitable for nearby fires. Use water spray only to keep fire-exposed containers cool.

HEALTH HAZARDS: Corrosive. Causes severe eye and skin burns. May be harmful if inhaled.

FIRE AND EXPLOSION HAZARDS: Not combustible. Strong dehydrating agent, which may cause ignition of finely divided materials on contact. Reaction with metals may produce hydrogen gas. Oxides of sulfur may be produced in fire.

INSTABILITY AND REACTIVITY HAZARDS: Water reactive. Reacts with alkalies, releasing heat. Reacts with metals, releasing hydrogen gas. Reacts with picrates, chlorates, nitrates, and many other materials.

STORAGE RECOMMENDATIONS: Store in cool, dry, well-ventilated location. Separate from combustibles and other reactive materials. Separate from carbides, chlorates, fulminates, nitrates, picrates, and powdered metals.

USUAL SHIPPING CONTAINERS: Glass bottles and carboys, special drums, tank trucks, tank cars, and tank barges.

PHYSICAL PROPERTIES: Colorless to brown, odorless, oily liquid.

MELTING POINT: 50°F (10°C)

BOILING POINT: 626°F (330°C)

SPECIFIC GRAVITY: 1.84

SOLUBILITY IN WATER: soluble

NAME: **SULFURYL CHLORIDE**

SYNONYMS: sulfonyl chloride; sulfuric oxy-chloride

FORMULA: SO_2Cl_2

NFPA 30/OSHA CLASSIFICATION:

DOT CLASS: Class 8, Corrosive material

SHIPPING LABEL: CORROSIVE and POISON

ID NO.: UN 1834

CAS NO.: 7791-25-5

MOL. WT.: 135.0

STATEMENT OF HAZARDS: Corrosive. Water reactive.

EMERGENCY RESPONSE PERSONAL PROTECTIVE EQUIPMENT: Wear special protective clothing and positive pressure self-contained breathing apparatus.

SPILL OR LEAK PROCEDURES: Stop or control the leak, if this can be done without undue risk. Approach release from upwind. Absorb in noncombustible material for proper disposal.

FIRE FIGHTING PROCEDURES: Extinguish fire using agent suitable for surrounding fire. Do not use water if the sulfuryl chloride has been released.

HEALTH HAZARDS: Corrosive. Causes severe eye and skin burns. May be harmful if absorbed through skin or inhaled. Symptoms of overexposure include burning, coughing, wheezing, headache, nausea, vomiting, respiratory inflammation, spasm, pulmonary edema, death.

FIRE AND EXPLOSION HAZARDS: Not combustible, but if involved in a fire decomposes to produce chlorine, hydrogen chloride, oxides of sulfur, and other irritants.

INSTABILITY AND REACTIVITY HAZARDS: Reacts with water.

STORAGE RECOMMENDATIONS: Store in a cool, dry, well-ventilated location. Separate from acids, alkalies, alcohols, amines, peroxides, metals, and water.

USUAL SHIPPING CONTAINERS: Glass bottle inside wooden box, glass carboys, multiple bottles in steel drum overpacks. Packaged under nitrogen gas.

PHYSICAL PROPERTIES: Colorless to pale yellow mobile liquid. Pungent odor.

MELTING POINT: −65°F (−54°C)

BOILING POINT: 156°F (69°C)

SPECIFIC GRAVITY: 1.67

SOLUBILITY IN WATER: decomposes

VAPOR PRESSURE: 105 mm Hg @ 20°C

NAME: **TETRABROMOETHANE**

SYNONYMS: acetylene tetrabromide; Muthmann's liquid; TBE; 1,1,2,2-tetrabromoethane,

FORMULA: $Br_2(CH)_2Br_2$

NFPA 30/OSHA CLASSIFICATION:

DOT CLASS: Class 6.1, Poisonous material

SHIPPING LABEL: KEEP AWAY FROM FOOD

ID NO.: UN 2504

CAS NO.: 79-27-6

MOL. WT.: 345.7

STATEMENT OF HAZARDS: Serious health hazard. Reacts with oxidizing materials and alkalies.

EMERGENCY RESPONSE PERSONAL PROTECTIVE EQUIPMENT: Wear special protective clothing and positive pressure self-contained breathing apparatus.

SPILL OR LEAK PROCEDURES: Stop or control the leak, if this can be done without undue risk. Use appropriate foam to blanket release and suppress vapors. Approach release from upwind. Absorb in noncombustible material for proper disposal. Control runoff and isolate discharged material for proper disposal.

FIRE FIGHTING PROCEDURES: Extinguish fire using agent suitable for surrounding fire. Use water spray to cool fire-exposed containers.

HEALTH HAZARDS: Serious health hazard. May be harmful if absorbed through skin or inhaled. Irritating to skin, eyes, and respiratory system. Symptoms of overexposure include nausea, dizziness, and headache. May cause abdominal pain and jaundice.

FIRE AND EXPLOSION HAZARDS: Not combustible, but decomposes at 374°F (190°C) to liberate flammable and highly toxic vapors.

INSTABILITY AND REACTIVITY HAZARDS: Reacts with oxidizing materials and alkalies.

STORAGE RECOMMENDATIONS: Store in a cool, dry, well-ventilated location. Separate from oxidizing materials and alkalies.

USUAL SHIPPING CONTAINERS: Glass bottles; metal cans, pails, drums; tanks on trucks, rail cars, tank barges.

PHYSICAL PROPERTIES: Heavy, colorless to yellow liquid with odor of camphor and iodoform (sweet, medicinal).

MELTING POINT: 32°F (0°C)

BOILING POINT: 462°F (239°C)

SPECIFIC GRAVITY: 2.96

SOLUBILITY IN WATER: not soluble

NAME: **TETRACHLOROETHYLENE**

SYNONYMS: ethylene tetrachloride; perchloroethylene; Tetracap

FORMULA: $Cl_2C=CCl_2$

NFPA 30/OSHA CLASSIFICATION:

DOT CLASS: Class 6.1, Poisonous material

SHIPPING LABEL: KEEP AWAY FROM FOOD

ID NO.: UN 1897

CAS NO.: 127-18-4

MOL. WT.: 165.8

STATEMENT OF HAZARDS: Moderate health hazard. Combustion by-products may include hydrogen chloride and phosgene.

EMERGENCY RESPONSE PERSONAL PROTECTIVE EQUIPMENT: Wear full protective clothing and positive pressure self-contained breathing apparatus.

SPILL OR LEAK PROCEDURES: Approach release from upwind. Stop or control the leak, if this can be done without undue risk. Control runoff and isolate discharged material for proper disposal.

FIRE FIGHTING PROCEDURES: Approach fire from upwind to avoid hazardous vapors and toxic decomposition products. Use water spray to keep fire-exposed containers cool. Use flooding quantities of water as fog or spray. Extinguish fire using agent suitable for surrounding fire.

HEALTH HAZARDS: Moderate health hazard. May be harmful if inhaled. Irritating to skin, eyes, and respiratory system. Narcotic. Combustion by-products may include hydrogen chloride and phosgene.

FIRE AND EXPLOSION HAZARDS: No flash point in conventional closed tester. Not combustible, but if involved in a fire decomposes to produce hydrogen chloride and phosgene.

INSTABILITY AND REACTIVITY HAZARDS: Open flames may produce hydrogen chloride and phosgene. Reacts with active metals.

STORAGE RECOMMENDATIONS: Store in a cool, dry, well-ventilated location. Separate from active metals. Isolate from open flames, and combustibles.

USUAL SHIPPING CONTAINERS: Bottles, cans, drums; tanks on trucks, rail cars, barges.

PHYSICAL PROPERTIES: Colorless liquid with ethereal odor like chloroform.

MELTING POINT: −8°F (−22°C)

BOILING POINT: 250°F (121°C)

SPECIFIC GRAVITY: 1.62

SOLUBILITY IN WATER: not soluble

VAPOR PRESSURE: 13 mm Hg @ 20°C

NAME: **TETRAFLUOROETHYLENE, inhibited**

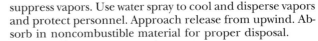

SYNONYMS: tetrafluoroethene

FORMULA: $F_2C=CF_2$

NFPA 30/OSHA CLASSIFICATION: IA

DOT CLASS: Class 2.1, Flammable gas

SHIPPING LABEL: FLAMMABLE GAS

ID NO.: UN 1081

CAS NO.: 116-14-3

MOL. WT.: 100.0

STATEMENT OF HAZARDS: Flammable gas. May polymerize explosively. Thermally unstable. Moderate health hazard. Combustion by-products may include hydrogen fluoride and carbonyl fluoride (similar to phosgene).

EMERGENCY RESPONSE PERSONAL PROTECTIVE EQUIPMENT: Wear full protective clothing and positive pressure self-contained breathing apparatus.

SPILL OR LEAK PROCEDURES: Eliminate all ignition sources. Stop or control the leak, if this can be done without undue risk. Use appropriate foam to blanket release and suppress vapors. Use water spray to cool and disperse vapors and protect personnel. Approach release from upwind. Absorb in noncombustible material for proper disposal.

FIRE FIGHTING PROCEDURES: Use dry chemical, foam, carbon dioxide, or water spray. Stop flow of gas before extinguishing fire. Use water spray to keep fire-exposed containers cool. Fight fire from protected location or maximum possible distance. Approach fire from upwind to avoid hazardous vapors and toxic decomposition products.

HEALTH HAZARDS: Moderate health hazard. May be harmful if absorbed through skin or inhaled. Irritating to skin, eyes, and respiratory system. Combustion by-products may include hydrogen fluoride and carbonyl fluoride (similar to phosgene).

FIRE AND EXPLOSION HAZARDS: Flammable gas. Vapors are heavier than air and may travel to a source of ignition and flash back. Explodes when heated. Decomposes explosively under pressures greater than 2025 mm Hg (2.66 atm). Combustion by-products include hydrogen fluoride, carbonyl fluoride, and other toxic and irritating gases. Closed containers may rupture violently when heated.

FLASH POINT: <32°F (<0°C)

AUTOIGNITION TEMPERATURE: 370°F (188°C)

FLAMMABLE LIMITS: LOWER: 11% UPPER: 60%

INSTABILITY AND REACTIVITY HAZARDS: Hazardous polymerization may occur. Usually contains inhibitors to prevent polymerization. Reacts violently with oxidizing materials. Inhibited monomer can decompose explosively when exposed to materials with which it can react exothermically or when exposed to fire conditions.

STORAGE RECOMMENDATIONS: Store in a cool, dry, well-ventilated location. Separate from oxidizing materials, air, sulfur trioxide, halogen compounds. Outside or detached storage is preferred.

USUAL SHIPPING CONTAINERS: Steel cylinders; pressurized tanks on trucks, rail cars, barges. This material has specialized packaging requirements due to its tendency to explode under pressure.

PHYSICAL PROPERTIES: Colorless gas with strong, sweet odor.

MELTING POINT: −224°F (−142°C)

BOILING POINT: −108°F (−78°C)

SOLUBILITY IN WATER: not soluble

VAPOR DENSITY: 3.45

ELECTRICAL EQUIPMENT: Cannot be classified in conventional Groups A, B, C, or D owing to the exceptional flammable properties

NAME: **TETRAHYDROFURAN**

SYNONYMS: diethylene oxide; tetramethylene oxide, THF

FORMULA: $CH_2CH_2CH_2CH_2O$

NFPA 30/OSHA CLASSIFICATION: IB

DOT CLASS: Class 3, Flammable and combustible liquid

SHIPPING LABEL: FLAMMABLE LIQUID

ID NO.: UN 2056

CAS NO.: 109-99-9

MOL. WT.: 72.1

STATEMENT OF HAZARDS: Flammable liquid. Forms explosive peroxides with air when standing. Closed containers may rupture violently when heated. Moderate health hazard.

EMERGENCY RESPONSE PERSONAL PROTECTIVE EQUIPMENT: Wear full protective clothing and positive pressure self-contained breathing apparatus.

SPILL OR LEAK PROCEDURES: Eliminate all ignition sources. Approach release from upwind. Stop or control the leak, if this can be done without undue risk. Use water spray to cool and disperse vapors, protect personnel, and dilute spills to form nonflammable mixtures. Control runoff and isolate discharged material for proper disposal.

FIRE FIGHTING PROCEDURES: Approach fire from upwind to avoid hazardous vapors and toxic decomposition products. Use water spray, dry chemical, "alcohol resistant" foam, or carbon dioxide. Use water spray to keep fire-exposed containers cool.

HEALTH HAZARDS: Moderate health hazard. May be harmful if inhaled. Irritating to skin, eyes, and respiratory system. Inhalation may cause narcosis.

FIRE AND EXPLOSION HAZARDS: Flammable liquid. Vapors are heavier than air and may travel to a source of ignition and flash back.

FLASH POINT: 6°F (−14°C)

AUTOIGNITION TEMPERATURE: 610°F (321°C)

FLAMMABLE LIMITS: LOWER: 2.0% UPPER: 11.8%

INSTABILITY AND REACTIVITY HAZARDS: Forms thermally explosive peroxides in absence of inhibitors. Peroxide formation may occur in containers that have been opened and remain in storage. Peroxides can be detonated by friction, impact, or heating. Reacts with oxidizing materials. Hazardous polymerization may occur.

STORAGE RECOMMENDATIONS: Store in a cool, dry, well-ventilated location. Store away from heat, oxidizing materials, and sunlight. Outside or detached storage is preferred. Inside storage should be in a standard flammable liquids storage warehouse, room, or cabinet.

USUAL SHIPPING CONTAINERS: Cans, drums; tanks on trucks, rail cars, barges.

PHYSICAL PROPERTIES: Colorless liquid with ethereal odor.

MELTING POINT: −163°F (−108°C)

BOILING POINT: 151°F (66°C)

SPECIFIC GRAVITY: 0.89

SOLUBILITY IN WATER: soluble

VAPOR PRESSURE: 145 mm Hg @ 20°C

ELECTRICAL EQUIPMENT: Class I, Group C

NAME: **TETRAMETHOXYSILANE**

DOT SHIPPING NAME: **METHYL ORTHO SILICATE**

SYNONYMS: tetramethyl orthosilicate

FORMULA: $Si(CH_3O)_4$

NFPA 30/OSHA CLASSIFICATION: IB

DOT CLASS: Class 3, Flammable and combustible liquid

SHIPPING LABEL: FLAMMABLE LIQUID and POISON

ID NO.: UN 2606

CAS NO.: 681-84-5

MOL. WT.: 152.2

STATEMENT OF HAZARDS: Corrosive and flammable liquid.

EMERGENCY RESPONSE PERSONAL PROTECTIVE EQUIPMENT: Wear special protective clothing and positive pressure self-contained breathing apparatus.

SPILL OR LEAK PROCEDURES: Releases may require isolation or evacuation. Eliminate all ignition sources. Use water spray to cool and disperse vapors and protect personnel. Control runoff and isolate discharged material for proper disposal.

FIRE FIGHTING PROCEDURES: Use dry chemical, foam, or carbon dioxide. Use water spray to keep fire-exposed containers cool. Approach fire from upwind to avoid hazardous vapors and toxic decomposition products.

HEALTH HAZARDS: Corrosive. Causes severe eye and skin burns. Exposure may result in blindness. May be harmful if absorbed through skin or inhaled.

FIRE AND EXPLOSION HAZARDS: Flammable liquid. Vapors are heavier than air and may travel to a source of ignition and flash back. Combustion may produce irritants and toxic gases.

FLASH POINT: 69°F (20°C)

INSTABILITY AND REACTIVITY HAZARDS: Reacts with water, forming corrosive solution. Undergoes hydrolysis readily, producing methanol.

STORAGE RECOMMENDATIONS: Store in a cool, dry, well-ventilated location. Separate from acids, oxidizing materials, and water. Outside or detached storage is preferred.

PHYSICAL PROPERTIES: Liquid.

MELTING POINT: 25°F (−4°C)

BOILING POINT: 250°F (121°C)

SPECIFIC GRAVITY: 1.02

SOLUBILITY IN WATER: not soluble (decomposes)

ELECTRICAL EQUIPMENT: Class I, Group D

NAME: **THIONYL CHLORIDE**

SYNONYMS: sulfinyl chloride; sulfurous oxychloride; thionyl dichloride

FORMULA: $SOCl_2$

NFPA 30/OSHA CLASSIFICATION:

DOT CLASS: Class 8, Corrosive material

SHIPPING LABEL: CORROSIVE and POISON

ID NO.: UN 1836

CAS NO.: 7719-09-7

MOL. WT.: 119.0

STATEMENT OF HAZARDS: Severe health hazard. Corrosive. Water reactive.

EMERGENCY RESPONSE PERSONAL PROTECTIVE EQUIPMENT: Wear special protective clothing and positive pressure self-contained breathing apparatus.

SPILL OR LEAK PROCEDURES: Do not use water if material has been released. Use water to keep fire-exposed containers cool. Stop or control the leak, if this can be done without undue risk. Approach release from upwind. Absorb in noncombustible material for proper disposal.

FIRE FIGHTING PROCEDURES: Extinguish fire using agent suitable for surrounding fire. DO NOT use water. Violent reaction may result. Fight fire from protected location or maximum possible distance.

HEALTH HAZARDS: Severe health hazard. May be fatal if absorbed through skin or inhaled. Corrosive. Causes severe eye and skin burns. Causes severe tearing. Inhalation may result in pulmonary edema, inflammation, and spasms.

FIRE AND EXPLOSION HAZARDS: Not combustible, but closed containers may rupture violently when heated. Decomposition begins at 284°F (140°C). Decomposition byproducts include chlorine, hydrogen chloride, oxides of sulfur, and other irritants.

INSTABILITY AND REACTIVITY HAZARDS: Reacts violently with water.

STORAGE RECOMMENDATIONS: Store in a cool, dry, well-ventilated location. Separate from acids, alkalies, alcohols, amines, metals, water.

USUAL SHIPPING CONTAINERS: Glass bottles, carboys; nickel cylinders, drums; tanks on trucks, rail cars, barges.

PHYSICAL PROPERTIES: Colorless to pale yellow to reddish fuming liquid. Acrid, suffocating odor.

MELTING POINT: −192°F (−125°C)

BOILING POINT: 169°F (76°C)

SPECIFIC GRAVITY: 1.64

SOLUBILITY IN WATER: decomposes

VAPOR PRESSURE: 100 mm Hg @ 21°C

NAME: **TITANIUM TETRACHLORIDE**

SYNONYMS: titanic chloride; titanium (IV) chloride

FORMULA: $TiCl_4$

NFPA 30/OSHA CLASSIFICATION:

DOT CLASS: Class 8, Corrosive material

SHIPPING LABEL: CORROSIVE and POISON

ID NO.: UN 1838

CAS NO.: 7550-45-0

MOL. WT.: 189.7

STATEMENT OF HAZARDS: Corrosive.

EMERGENCY RESPONSE PERSONAL PROTECTIVE EQUIPMENT: Wear special protective clothing and positive pressure self-contained breathing apparatus.

SPILL OR LEAK PROCEDURES: Release may require isolation or evacuation. Approach release from upwind. Use water spray to cool and disperse vapors, protect personnel, and carefully dilute spills to form nonreactive mixtures. Report any release in excess of 1 lb.

FIRE FIGHTING PROCEDURES: Use appropriate extinguishing agents on nearby combustible fires. DO NOT use water-based extinguishers on fires where this material has been released. Use water spray to keep fire-exposed containers cool. Visibility can be reduced by the solid titanium oxide fumes produced from the reaction with water.

HEALTH HAZARDS: Corrosive. Causes severe eye and skin burns. May be harmful if inhaled. Irritating to skin, eyes, and respiratory system.

FIRE AND EXPLOSION HAZARDS: Not combustible, but if involved in a fire decomposes to produce hydrogen chloride, and fumes of titanium and titanium oxides.

INSTABILITY AND REACTIVITY HAZARDS: Reacts violently with water, producing heat, hydrogen chloride, dense white clouds.

STORAGE RECOMMENDATIONS: Store in a cool, dry, well-ventilated, noncombustible location. Always keep container closed.

USUAL SHIPPING CONTAINERS: Glass bottles and carboys, lead sleeves in wooden boxes, steel drums, tank cars.

PHYSICAL PROPERTIES: Colorless to pale yellow caustic liquid. Irritating odor. Produces dense white clouds in moist air.

MELTING POINT: −11°F (−24°C)

BOILING POINT: 278°F (136°C)

SPECIFIC GRAVITY: 2.23

SOLUBILITY IN WATER: reacts

VAPOR PRESSURE: 9.6 mm Hg @ 22°C

NAME: **TOLUENE**

SYNONYMS: methylbenzene; phenylmethane; toluol

FORMULA: $C_6H_5CH_3$

NFPA 30/OSHA CLASSIFICATION: IB

DOT CLASS: Class 3, Flammable and combustible liquid

SHIPPING LABEL: FLAMMABLE LIQUID

ID NO.: UN 1294

CAS NO.: 108-88-3

MOL. WT.: 92.1

STATEMENT OF HAZARDS: Flammable liquid. May accumulate static electricity. Moderate health hazard.

EMERGENCY RESPONSE PERSONAL PROTECTIVE EQUIPMENT: Wear full protective clothing and positive pressure self-contained breathing apparatus.

SPILL OR LEAK PROCEDURES: Eliminate all ignition sources. Stop or control the leak, if this can be done without undue risk. Use water spray to cool and disperse vapors and protect personnel. Absorb in noncombustible material for proper disposal. Control runoff and isolate discharged material for proper disposal.

FIRE FIGHTING PROCEDURES: Approach fire from upwind to avoid hazardous vapors and toxic decomposition products. Use water spray, dry chemical, foam, or carbon dioxide. Use water spray to keep fire-exposed containers cool.

HEALTH HAZARDS: Moderate health hazard. May be harmful if inhaled. Irritating to skin, eyes, and respiratory system.

FIRE AND EXPLOSION HAZARDS: Flammable liquid. Vapors are heavier than air and may travel to a source of ignition and flash back. Liquid floats on water and may travel to a source of ignition and spread fire.

FLASH POINT: 40°F (4°C)

AUTOIGNITION TEMPERATURE: 896°F (480°C)

FLAMMABLE LIMITS: LOWER: 1.2% UPPER: 7.1%

INSTABILITY AND REACTIVITY HAZARDS: Reacts with oxidizing materials.

STORAGE RECOMMENDATIONS: Outside or detached storage is preferred. Inside storage should be in a standard flammable liquids storage warehouse, room, or cabinet. Separate from oxidizing materials.

USUAL SHIPPING CONTAINERS: Glass bottles, cans, drums, and tanks on trucks, rail cars, barges.

PHYSICAL PROPERTIES: Colorless liquid with aromatic odor like benzene.

MELTING POINT: −139°F (−95°C)

BOILING POINT: 232°F (111°C)

SPECIFIC GRAVITY: 0.87

SOLUBILITY IN WATER: not soluble

VAPOR PRESSURE: 22 mm Hg @ 20°C

ELECTRICAL EQUIPMENT: Class I, Group D

NAME: **TOLUENE DIISOCYANATE**

SYNONYMS: 2,4-diisocyanatotoluene; TDI; 2,4-tolylene diisocyanate

FORMULA: $(OC{=}N)_2(C_6H_3)CH_3$

NFPA 30/OSHA CLASSIFICATION: IIIB

DOT CLASS: Class 6.1, Poisonous material

SHIPPING LABEL: POISON

ID NO.: UN 2078

CAS NO.: 584-84-9

MOL. WT.: 174.2

STATEMENT OF HAZARDS: Serious health hazard. Combustible liquid. Hazardous polymerization and/or hazardous decomposition may occur on contact with water or on exposure to heat.

EMERGENCY RESPONSE PERSONAL PROTECTIVE EQUIPMENT: Wear special protective clothing and positive pressure self-contained breathing apparatus.

SPILL OR LEAK PROCEDURES: Stop or control the leak, if this can be done without undue risk. Use water spray to cool and disperse vapors and protect personnel. Approach release from upwind. Absorb in noncombustible material for proper disposal.

FIRE FIGHTING PROCEDURES: Use dry chemical or carbon dioxide. Use water spray to keep fire-exposed containers cool. Approach fire from upwind to avoid hazardous vapors and toxic decomposition products. Fight fire from protected location or maximum possible distance.

HEALTH HAZARDS: Serious health hazard. May be harmful if absorbed through skin or inhaled. Strong sensitizer. May cause severe allergic respiratory reaction and skin sensitizer. Irritating to skin, eyes, and respiratory system. Symptoms of overexposure include choking sensation, bronchial asthma, nausea, pulmonary edema, asthma, and dermatitis.

FIRE AND EXPLOSION HAZARDS: Combustible liquid. Combustion by-products include oxides of nitrogen, hydrogen cyanide, and other irritants and toxic gases. Closed containers may rupture violently when heated.

FLASH POINT: 260°F (127°C)

FLAMMABLE LIMITS: LOWER: 0.9% UPPER: 9.5%

INSTABILITY AND REACTIVITY HAZARDS: Hazardous polymerization may occur. Hazardous decomposition may occur on contact with water. Reacts violently with bases, amines, organometallic compounds, alcohols, organic acids. Reacts with water. Self-reacts at elevated temperatures to form dimers, trimers, and polymers giving off carbon dioxide and heat.

STORAGE RECOMMENDATIONS: Store in a cool, dry, well-ventilated location. Separate from acids, alkalies, oxidizing materials, amines, and water. Immediately remove and properly dispose of any spilled material.

USUAL SHIPPING CONTAINERS: Cylinders and metal or polyethylene cans, pails, or drums. Tanks on trucks, rail cars, tank barges. Sometimes packaged under dry nitrogen.

PHYSICAL PROPERTIES: Colorless to faint yellow liquid.

MELTING POINT: 67 to 71°F (20 to 22°C)

BOILING POINT: 484°F (251°C)

SPECIFIC GRAVITY: 1.22

SOLUBILITY IN WATER: decomposes

VAPOR PRESSURE: 0.01 mm Hg @ 20°C

NAME: **o-TOLUIDINE**

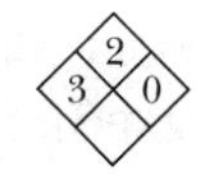

DOT SHIPPING NAME: **TOLUIDINES, liquid**

SYNONYMS: 2-aminotoluene; ortho-methylaniline; 2-methylaniline; 1,2-toluidine

FORMULA: $CH_3C_6H_4NH_2$

NFPA 30/OSHA CLASSIFICATION: IIIA

DOT CLASS: Class 6.1, Poisonous material

SHIPPING LABEL: POISON

ID NO.: UN 1708

CAS NO.: 95-53-4

MOL. WT.: 107.2

STATEMENT OF HAZARDS: Serious health hazard. Combustible liquid.

EMERGENCY RESPONSE PERSONAL PROTECTIVE EQUIPMENT: Wear special protective clothing and positive pressure self-contained breathing apparatus.

SPILL OR LEAK PROCEDURES: Approach release from upwind. Stop or control the leak, if this can be done without undue risk. Use water spray to cool and disperse vapors and protect personnel. Absorb in noncombustible material for proper disposal. Control runoff and isolate discharged material for proper disposal.

FIRE FIGHTING PROCEDURES: Use water spray, dry chemical, foam, or carbon dioxide. Use water spray to keep fire-exposed containers cool.

HEALTH HAZARDS: Serious health hazard. May be harmful if absorbed through skin or inhaled. Irritating to skin, eyes, and respiratory system. May cause cyanosis.

FIRE AND EXPLOSION HAZARDS: Combustible liquid.

FLASH POINT: 185°F (85°C)

AUTOIGNITION TEMPERATURE: 900°F (482°C)

FLAMMABLE LIMITS: LOWER: 1.5% UPPER: not determined

INSTABILITY AND REACTIVITY HAZARDS: Reacts with oxidizing materials, acids, and bases.

STORAGE RECOMMENDATIONS: Separate from oxidizing materials. Store in cool, dry, well-ventilated location. Store away from heat and sunlight.

USUAL SHIPPING CONTAINERS: Bottles, cans, drums, and tank trucks or tank cars.

PHYSICAL PROPERTIES: Colorless to yellow liquid with amine odor. May darken to a reddish brown.

MELTING POINT: −3°F (−16°C)

BOILING POINT: 391°F (200°C)

SPECIFIC GRAVITY: 1.00

SOLUBILITY IN WATER: not soluble

VAPOR PRESSURE: <1 mm Hg @ 20°C

ELECTRICAL EQUIPMENT: Class I, Group D

NAME: **p-TOLUIDINE**

DOT SHIPPING NAME: **TOLUIDINES, solid**

SYNONYMS: 4-aminotoluene; para-methylaniline; 4-methylaniline

FORMULA: $CH_3C_6H_4NH_2$

NFPA 30/OSHA CLASSIFICATION: IIIA

DOT CLASS: Class 6.1, Poisonous material

SHIPPING LABEL: POISON

ID NO.: UN 1708

CAS NO.: 106-49-0

MOL. WT.: 107.2

STATEMENT OF HAZARDS: Serious health hazard. Combustible solid.

EMERGENCY RESPONSE PERSONAL PROTECTIVE EQUIPMENT: Wear special protective clothing and positive pressure self-contained breathing apparatus.

SPILL OR LEAK PROCEDURES: Approach release from upwind. Stop or control the leak, if this can be done without undue risk. Use water spray to cool and disperse vapors and protect personnel. Control runoff and isolate discharged material for proper disposal.

FIRE FIGHTING PROCEDURES: Use fine spray or fog to control fire by preventing its spread and absorbing some of its heat. Use water spray, dry chemical, foam, or carbon dioxide. Use water spray to keep fire-exposed containers cool.

HEALTH HAZARDS: Serious health hazard. May be harmful if absorbed through skin or inhaled. Irritating to skin, eyes, and respiratory system. May cause cyanosis.

FIRE AND EXPLOSION HAZARDS: Combustible solid.

FLASH POINT: 190°F (88°C)

AUTOIGNITION TEMPERATURE: 900°F (482°C)

INSTABILITY AND REACTIVITY HAZARDS: Avoid contact with oxidizers, acids, and bases.

STORAGE RECOMMENDATIONS: Store in cool, dry, well-ventilated location. Store away from heat, oxidizers, and sunlight.

USUAL SHIPPING CONTAINERS: Bottles, cans, or fiber drums.

PHYSICAL PROPERTIES: Lustrous white solid.

MELTING POINT: 111°F (44°C)

BOILING POINT: 391°F (201°C)

SPECIFIC GRAVITY: 1.05

SOLUBILITY IN WATER: not soluble

VAPOR PRESSURE: <1 mm Hg @ 20°C

ELECTRICAL EQUIPMENT: Class I, Group D

NAME: **TRIBUTYLAMINE**

SYNONYMS: tri-n-butylamine

FORMULA: $(C_4H_9)_3N$

NFPA 30/OSHA CLASSIFICATION: IIIA

DOT CLASS: Class 8, Corrosive material

SHIPPING LABEL: CORROSIVE

ID NO.: UN 2542

CAS NO.: 102-82-9

MOL. WT.: 185.4

STATEMENT OF HAZARDS: Corrosive and combustible liquid.

EMERGENCY RESPONSE PERSONAL PROTECTIVE EQUIPMENT: Wear special protective clothing and positive pressure self-contained breathing apparatus.

SPILL OR LEAK PROCEDURES: Use water spray to cool and disperse vapors and protect personnel. Approach release from upwind. Sand, clay, earth, or other absorbent material may be used to contain liquid.

FIRE FIGHTING PROCEDURES: Use water spray, dry chemical, foam, or carbon dioxide. Use water spray to keep fire-exposed containers cool.

HEALTH HAZARDS: Corrosive. Causes severe eye and skin burns. May be harmful if absorbed through skin or inhaled. Irritating to skin, eyes, and respiratory system. May cause severe tearing, conjunctivitis, and corneal edema. Inhalation may cause difficulties ranging from coughing and nausea to pulmonary edema.

FIRE AND EXPLOSION HAZARDS: Combustible liquid. Combustion may produce irritants and toxic gases.

FLASH POINT: 145°F (63°C)

INSTABILITY AND REACTIVITY HAZARDS: Reacts with acids, oxidizing materials, chlorine, hypochlorite, halogenated compounds, and reactive organic compounds.

STORAGE RECOMMENDATIONS: Outside or detached storage is preferred. Separate from oxidizing materials, acids, and sources of halogen. Store in a cool, dry, well-ventilated location.

USUAL SHIPPING CONTAINERS: Glass bottles, cans, drums, and tank cars.

PHYSICAL PROPERTIES: Hygroscopic liquid with characteristic odor of ammonia.

MELTING POINT: −94°F (−70°C)

BOILING POINT: 417°F (214°C)

SPECIFIC GRAVITY: 0.78

SOLUBILITY IN WATER: not soluble

VAPOR PRESSURE: <1 mm Hg @ 20°C

ELECTRICAL EQUIPMENT: Class I, Group D

NAME: **1,1,1-TRICHLOROETHANE**

SYNONYMS: chloroethane; methylchloroform

FORMULA: CH_3CCl_3

NFPA 30/OSHA CLASSIFICATION:

DOT CLASS: Class 6.1, Poisonous material

SHIPPING LABEL: KEEP AWAY FROM FOOD

ID NO.: UN 2831

CAS NO.: 71-55-6

MOL. WT.: 133.4

STATEMENT OF HAZARDS: Moderate health hazard. Combustion by-products may include hydrogen chloride and phosgene.

EMERGENCY RESPONSE PERSONAL PROTECTIVE EQUIPMENT: Wear full protective clothing and positive pressure self-contained breathing apparatus.

SPILL OR LEAK PROCEDURES: Approach release from upwind. Stop or control the leak, if this can be done without undue risk. Control runoff and isolate discharged material for proper disposal.

FIRE FIGHTING PROCEDURES: Approach fire from upwind to avoid hazardous vapors and toxic decomposition products. Use water spray to keep fire-exposed containers cool. Extinguish fire using agent suitable for surrounding fire.

HEALTH HAZARDS: Moderate health hazard. May be harmful if inhaled. Irritating to skin, eyes, and respiratory system. Narcotic. Combustion by-products may include hydrogen chloride and phosgene.

FIRE AND EXPLOSION HAZARDS: No flash point in conventional closed tester; however, vapors in containers can explode if subjected to high energy source. Combustion may produce irritants and toxic gases including hydrogen chloride.

AUTOIGNITION TEMPERATURE: 932°F (500°C)

FLAMMABLE LIMITS: LOWER: 7.0% UPPER: 16.0%

INSTABILITY AND REACTIVITY HAZARDS: Exposure to open flames and arc welding may produce hydrogen chloride and phosgene. Reacts with oxidizing materials, alkalies, and active metals, such as aluminum.

STORAGE RECOMMENDATIONS: Store in a cool, dry, well-ventilated location. Separate from oxidizing materials, ammonia, and active metals, such as aluminum. Isolate from open flames, arc welding, and combustibles.

USUAL SHIPPING CONTAINERS: Bottles, cans, drums; tanks on trucks, rail cars, barges.

PHYSICAL PROPERTIES: Colorless liquid with mild odor like chloroform.

MELTING POINT: −22°F (−30°C)

BOILING POINT: 165°F (74°C)

SPECIFIC GRAVITY: 1.34

SOLUBILITY IN WATER: not soluble

VAPOR PRESSURE: 100 mm Hg @ 20°C

NAME: **1,1,2-TRICHLOROETHANE**

SYNONYMS: ethane trichloride; 1,2,2-trichloroethane

FORMULA: $ClCH_2CHCl_2$

NFPA 30/OSHA CLASSIFICATION:

DOT CLASS: N/A

ID NO.: N/A

CAS NO.: 79-00-5

MOL. WT.: 133.4

STATEMENT OF HAZARDS: Moderate health hazard. Combustion by-products may include hydrogen chloride and phosgene.

EMERGENCY RESPONSE PERSONAL PROTECTIVE EQUIPMENT: Wear special protective clothing and positive pressure self-contained breathing apparatus.

SPILL OR LEAK PROCEDURES: Use appropriate foam to blanket release and suppress vapors. Absorb in noncombustible material for proper disposal. Report any release in excess of 1 lb.

FIRE FIGHTING PROCEDURES: Extinguish fire using suitable agent for surrounding fire. Use water spray to keep fire-exposed containers cool. Approach fire from upwind to avoid hazardous vapors and toxic decomposition products.

HEALTH HAZARDS: Moderate health hazard. May be harmful if absorbed through skin or inhaled. Irritating to skin, eyes, and respiratory system. Symptoms of overexposure include dizziness, narcosis, abdominal cramps, central nervous system depression, liver and kidney damage. Combustion by-products may include hydrogen chloride and phosgene.

FIRE AND EXPLOSION HAZARDS: No flash point in conventional closed tester; however, vapors in containers can explode if subjected to a high energy source. Combustion by-products include hydrogen chloride.

FLAMMABLE LIMITS: LOWER: 6% UPPER: 15.5%

INSTABILITY AND REACTIVITY HAZARDS: Reacts with oxidizing materials, alkalies, aluminum.

STORAGE RECOMMENDATIONS: Store in a cool, dry, well-ventilated location. Separate from oxidizing materials, aluminum, ammonia.

USUAL SHIPPING CONTAINERS: Metal cans, pails, drums; tanks on trucks, rail cars, barges.

PHYSICAL PROPERTIES: Colorless, heavy liquid. Odor similar to chloroform (sweet, pleasant).

MELTING POINT: −34°F (−36°C)

BOILING POINT: 235°F (113°C)

SPECIFIC GRAVITY: 1.44

SOLUBILITY IN WATER: not soluble

VAPOR PRESSURE: 19 mm Hg @ 20°C 40 mm Hg @ 35°C

NAME: **TRICHLOROETHYLENE**

SYNONYMS: ethylene trichloride; trichlor

FORMULA: $ClCH=CCl_2$

NFPA 30/OSHA CLASSIFICATION:

DOT CLASS: Class 6.1, Poisonous material

SHIPPING LABEL: KEEP AWAY FROM FOOD

ID NO.: UN 1710

CAS NO.: 79-01-6

MOL. WT.: 131.4

STATEMENT OF HAZARDS: Moderate health hazard. Combustion by-products may include hydrogen chloride and phosgene.

EMERGENCY RESPONSE PERSONAL PROTECTIVE EQUIPMENT: Wear full protective clothing and positive pressure self-contained breathing apparatus.

SPILL OR LEAK PROCEDURES: Approach release from upwind. Stop or control the leak, if this can be done without undue risk. Control runoff and isolate discharged material for proper disposal.

FIRE FIGHTING PROCEDURES: Approach fire from upwind to avoid hazardous vapors and toxic decomposition products. Use water spray to keep fire-exposed containers cool. Extinguish fire using agent suitable for surrounding fire.

HEALTH HAZARDS: Moderate health hazard. May be harmful if inhaled. Irritating to skin, eyes, and respiratory system. Symptoms of exposure include dizziness and loss of consciousness. Combustion by-products may include hydrogen chloride and phosgene.

FIRE AND EXPLOSION HAZARDS: No flash point in conventional closed tester; however, vapors in containers can explode if subjected to a high energy source. Combustion may produce irritants and toxic gases including hydrogen chloride.

AUTOIGNITION TEMPERATURE: 788°F (420°C)

FLAMMABLE LIMITS: LOWER: 8% UPPER: 10.5%

INSTABILITY AND REACTIVITY HAZARDS: Reacts with active metals.

STORAGE RECOMMENDATIONS: Store in a cool, dry, well-ventilated location. Separate from active metals. Isolate from open flames and combustibles.

USUAL SHIPPING CONTAINERS: Bottles, cans, drums; tanks on trucks, rail cars, barges.

PHYSICAL PROPERTIES: Colorless liquid with mild odor like chloroform.

MELTING POINT: −121°F (−85°C)

BOILING POINT: 189°F (87°C)

SPECIFIC GRAVITY: 1.46

SOLUBILITY IN WATER: not soluble

VAPOR PRESSURE: 58 mm Hg @ 20°C

NAME: **TRICHLOROISOCYANURIC ACID, dry**

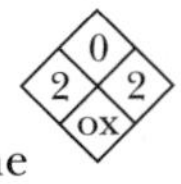

SYNONYMS: TCCA; trichloro; tri-chloroimino-cyanuric acid; trichloro-s-triazinetrione; symclosene

FORMULA: $C_3Cl_3N_3O_3$

NFPA 30/OSHA CLASSIFICATION:

DOT CLASS: Class 5.1, Oxidizer

SHIPPING LABEL: OXIDIZER

ID NO.: UN 2468

CAS NO.: 87-90-1

MOL. WT.: 232.4

STATEMENT OF HAZARDS: Moderate health hazard. Oxidizer. Reacts with combustible materials or ammonium salts resulting in fire. Reacts with small amounts of water, releasing chlorine gas and nitrogen trichloride, which is a highly explosive compound when concentrated. Thermally unstable. Decomposes at 437°F (225°C).

EMERGENCY RESPONSE PERSONAL PROTECTIVE EQUIPMENT: Wear special protective clothing and positive pressure self-contained breathing apparatus.

SPILL OR LEAK PROCEDURES: Keep water away from release. Approach release from upwind. Isolate leaking containers, if this can be done without undue risk. Prompt cleanup and removal is necessary. Shovel into suitable dry container. Control runoff and isolate discharged material for proper disposal.

FIRE FIGHTING PROCEDURES: Approach fire from upwind to avoid hazardous vapors and toxic decomposition products. Fight fire from protected location or maximum possible distance. Use flooding quantities of water on fire-involved containers. If necessary use water spray to keep fire-exposed containers cool. Avoid use of water on non-involved material wherever possible.

HEALTH HAZARDS: Moderate health hazard. May be harmful if or inhaled. Irritating to skin, eyes, and respiratory system. Water reactive. Releases chlorine gas and nitrogen chloride on contact with water.

FIRE AND EXPLOSION HAZARDS: Not combustible. Reacts with combustible materials, ammonium salts, or foreign substances, resulting in fire. Closed containers may rupture violently when heated. Thermally unstable. Decomposes at 437°F (225°C).

INSTABILITY AND REACTIVITY HAZARDS: Water reactive. Reacts with small amounts of water, releasing chlorine gas and nitrogen trichloride, which is a highly explosive compound when concentrated. Reaction with ammonia or amines produces nitrogen trichloride. Reacts with most reducing agents. Reacts explosively with calcium hypochlorite and water.

STORAGE RECOMMENDATIONS: Store in a cool, dry, well-ventilated location. Outside or detached storage is preferred. Must be stored in a dry location on pallets arranged according to NFPA 430, Code for Storage of Liquid and Solid Oxidizers. Separate from combustibles, oxidizables, ammonia, sodium carbonate (soda ash), calcium hypochlorite, hydrogen peroxide.

USUAL SHIPPING CONTAINERS: Moisture-excluding fiber drums with polyethylene bag liners and lined pails. Unlined 25 pound plastic pails. Smaller quantities in glass or polyethylene bottles and in special laminated packets.

PHYSICAL PROPERTIES: White crystalline solid with strong chlorine odor. Thermally unstable. Decomposes at 437°F (225°C).

SPECIFIC GRAVITY: 1.2

SOLUBILITY IN WATER: reacts very slowly

NAME: **TRICHLOROSILANE**

SYNONYMS: silicochloroform; trichloromonosilane

FORMULA: $HSiCl_3$

NFPA 30/OSHA CLASSIFICATION: IA

DOT CLASS: Class 4.3, Dangerous when wet material

SHIPPING LABEL: DANGEROUS WHEN WET and FLAMMABLE LIQUID and CORROSIVE

ID NO.: UN 1295

CAS NO.: 10025-78-2

MOL. WT.: 135.5

STATEMENT OF HAZARDS: Flammable liquid. Corrosive. Low ignition energy. May accumulate static electricity. Water reactive.

EMERGENCY RESPONSE PERSONAL PROTECTIVE EQUIPMENT: Wear special protective clothing and positive pressure self-contained breathing apparatus.

SPILL OR LEAK PROCEDURES: Eliminate all ignition sources. Approach release from upwind. Keep water away from release. Stop or control the leak, if this can be done without undue risk. Prompt cleanup and removal are necessary. May ignite spontaneously in insulating materials (absorbent materials) depending on size of piles. Control runoff and isolate discharged material for proper disposal.

FIRE FIGHTING PROCEDURES: Do not use halocarbons. Dry powders and carbon dioxide may be ineffective. Approach fire from upwind to avoid hazardous vapors and toxic decomposition products. Material is reactive with water but can be extinguished with a 6% solution in water of medium expansion foam. Use water spray to keep fire-exposed containers cool. For small fires use copious quantities of water as spray to react with chlorosilane.

HEALTH HAZARDS: Corrosive. Causes severe eye and skin burns. Serious health hazard. May be harmful if absorbed through skin or inhaled. Combustion by-products include hydrogen chloride and chlorine. Water reactive. Hydrochloric acid is released.

FIRE AND EXPLOSION HAZARDS: Flammable liquid. Forms explosive mixtures over a wide range. Vapors are heavier than air and may travel to a source of ignition and flash back. Combustion may produce irritants and toxic gases.

FLASH POINT: −18°F (−28°C)

AUTOIGNITION TEMPERATURE: 360°F (182°C)

FLAMMABLE LIMITS: LOWER: 7.0% UPPER: 83% @ 40°C

INSTABILITY AND REACTIVITY HAZARDS: Reacts violently with water and aqueous solutions, alcohols, organic acids, peroxides, amines, and oxidizing materials. Products of combustion include hydrogen chloride and other chlorosilanes.

STORAGE RECOMMENDATIONS: Separate from water, alcohols, organic acids, peroxides, amines, and oxidizing materials. Outside or detached storage is preferred. Store away from heat, oxidizing materials, and sunlight. Must be stored in a dry location. Inside storage should be in a standard flammable liquids storage warehouse, room, or cabinet.

USUAL SHIPPING CONTAINERS: Glass bottles and drums.

PHYSICAL PROPERTIES: Colorless liquid. Volatile and mobile. Fumes in air. Odor of hydrochloric acid.

MELTING POINT: −196°F (−127°C)

BOILING POINT: 90°F (32°C)

SPECIFIC GRAVITY: 1.34

SOLUBILITY IN WATER: reacts violently

VAPOR DENSITY: 4.67

VAPOR PRESSURE: 500 mm Hg @ 20°C

ELECTRICAL EQUIPMENT: Class I, Group D

NAME: **TRIETHYLALUMINUM**

SYNONYMS: aluminum triethyl

FORMULA: $(C_2H_5)_3Al$

NFPA 30/OSHA CLASSIFICATION:

DOT CLASS: N/A

ID NO.: N/A

CAS NO.: 97-93-8

MOL. WT.: 114.2

STATEMENT OF HAZARDS: Pyrophoric. Corrosive. Flammable liquid. Water reactive.

EMERGENCY RESPONSE PERSONAL PROTECTIVE EQUIPMENT: Wear special protective clothing and positive pressure self-contained breathing apparatus.

SPILL OR LEAK PROCEDURES: Approach release from upwind. Keep water away from release. Do not use foam to blanket release and suppress vapors. Stop or control the leak, if this can be done without undue risk. Spills may ignite spontaneously if solvent evaporates. Control runoff and isolate discharged material for proper disposal.

FIRE FIGHTING PROCEDURES: Stop flow of liquid before extinguishing fire. Fight fire from protected location or maximum possible distance. DO NOT use water as straight stream directly on spilled material. Violent reaction may result. Water fog can be used to control fires. Use graphite powder, soda ash, or powdered sodium chloride to extinguish fire. On solvent-based materials use dry chemical or carbon dioxide. Use water spray cautiously to keep fire-exposed containers cool.

HEALTH HAZARDS: Corrosive. Causes severe eye and skin burns. May be harmful if absorbed through skin or inhaled. Irritating to skin, eyes, and respiratory system. "Metal fume fever" may result from inhalation of fumes.

FIRE AND EXPLOSION HAZARDS: Pyrophoric material in flammable solvent. Water reactive. Flammable hydrocarbons are produced. Combustion may produce irritants and toxic gases. Material is flammable in air at all temperatures. Closed containers may rupture violently when heated.

INSTABILITY AND REACTIVITY HAZARDS: Reacts violently with air and water. Reacts with oxidizing materials, acids, and alcohols.

STORAGE RECOMMENDATIONS: Separate from oxidizing materials, acids, alcohols, air, and water. Store in a cool, dry, well-ventilated location. Must be stored in a dry location. Outside or detached storage is preferred. Inside storage should be in a standard flammable liquids storage warehouse, room, or cabinet.

USUAL SHIPPING CONTAINERS: Bottles, cylinders, tank trucks, and tank cars containing a blanket of nitrogen gas.

PHYSICAL PROPERTIES: Clear colorless liquid. Aluminum alkyls are generally supplied as 20% solutions in selected solvents so as to be less reactive. Properties may depend on solvent.

MELTING POINT: −51°F (−46°C)

BOILING POINT: 365°F (185°C)

SPECIFIC GRAVITY: 0.83

SOLUBILITY IN WATER: reacts violently

NAME: **TRIETHYLAMINE**

SYNONYMS: TEA; TEN

FORMULA: $(C_2H_5)_3N$

NFPA 30/OSHA CLASSIFICATION: IB

DOT CLASS: Class 3, Flammable and combustible liquid

SHIPPING LABEL: FLAMMABLE LIQUID

ID NO.: UN 1296

CAS NO.: 121-44-8

MOL. WT.: 101.2

STATEMENT OF HAZARDS: Corrosive. Flammable liquid.

EMERGENCY RESPONSE PERSONAL PROTECTIVE EQUIPMENT: Wear special protective clothing and positive pressure self-contained breathing apparatus.

SPILL OR LEAK PROCEDURES: Eliminate all ignition sources. Approach release from upwind. Use water spray to cool and disperse vapors and protect personnel. Absorb in noncombustible material for proper disposal. Control runoff and isolate discharged material for proper disposal.

FIRE FIGHTING PROCEDURES: Use water spray to keep fire-exposed containers cool. Use water spray, dry chemical, "alcohol resistant" foam, or carbon dioxide.

HEALTH HAZARDS: Corrosive. Causes severe eye and skin burns. May be harmful if absorbed through skin or inhaled. Irritating to skin, eyes, and respiratory system. May cause irritation, conjunctivitis, and corneal damage. Inhalation may cause coughing, nausea, and pulmonary edema.

FIRE AND EXPLOSION HAZARDS: Flammable liquid. Vapors are heavier than air and may travel to a source of ignition and flash back.

FLASH POINT: 16°F (−9°C)

AUTOIGNITION TEMPERATURE: 480°F (249°C)

FLAMMABLE LIMITS: LOWER: 1.2% UPPER: 8.0%

INSTABILITY AND REACTIVITY HAZARDS: May react with acids, oxidizing materials, chlorine, hypochlorite, halogenated compounds, reactive organic compounds, and some metals. Products of decomposition include carbon monoxide, carbon dioxide, hydrocarbons, and oxides of nitrogen, as well as amine vapors.

STORAGE RECOMMENDATIONS: Avoid oxidizing materials, acids, and sources of halogens. Store in cool, dry, well-ventilated location.

USUAL SHIPPING CONTAINERS: Glass bottles, cans, drums, and tank cars.

PHYSICAL PROPERTIES: Colorless liquid with strong ammonia-like odor.

MELTING POINT: −175°F (−115°C)

BOILING POINT: 193°F (89°C)

SPECIFIC GRAVITY: 0.73

SOLUBILITY IN WATER: not soluble

VAPOR PRESSURE: 54 mm Hg @ 20°C

ELECTRICAL EQUIPMENT: Class I, Group C

NAME: **TRIETHYLENETETRAMINE**

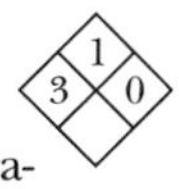

SYNONYMS: N,N'-bis(2-aminotheyl) 1,2-ethanediamine; 3,6-diazaoctane-1,8-diamine; 1,4,7,10-tetra-azadecane

FORMULA: $C_6H_{18}N_4$

NFPA 30/OSHA CLASSIFICATION: IIIB

DOT CLASS: Class 8, Corrosive material

SHIPPING LABEL: CORROSIVE

ID NO.: UN 2259

CAS NO.: 112-24-3

MOL. WT.: 146.3

STATEMENT OF HAZARDS: Corrosive and combustible liquid.

EMERGENCY RESPONSE PERSONAL PROTECTIVE EQUIPMENT: Wear special protective clothing and positive pressure self-contained breathing apparatus.

SPILL OR LEAK PROCEDURES: Use water spray to cool and disperse vapors, and protect personnel. Control runoff and isolate discharged material for proper disposal.

FIRE FIGHTING PROCEDURES: Use dry chemical, foam, carbon dioxide, or water spray. Use water spray to keep fire-exposed containers cool. Approach fire from upwind to avoid hazardous vapors and toxic decomposition products.

HEALTH HAZARDS: Corrosive. Causes severe eye and skin burns. May be harmful if absorbed through skin or inhaled.

May cause skin sensitization. Irritating to skin, eyes, and respiratory system. May cause pulmonary edema.

FIRE AND EXPLOSION HAZARDS: Combustible liquid. Combustion may produce irritants and toxic gases, including oxides of nitrogen.

FLASH POINT: 275°F (135°C)

AUTOIGNITION TEMPERATURE: 640°F (338°C)

INSTABILITY AND REACTIVITY HAZARDS: May react with oxidizing materials.

STORAGE RECOMMENDATIONS: Separate from oxidizing materials. Store in a cool, dry, well-ventilated location.

PHYSICAL PROPERTIES: Moderately viscous yellowish liquid.

MELTING POINT: 54°F (12°C)

BOILING POINT: 511°F (266°C)

SPECIFIC GRAVITY: 0.98

SOLUBILITY IN WATER: soluble

VAPOR PRESSURE: <0.01 mm Hg @ 20°C

NAME: **TRIISOBUTYLALUMINUM**

SYNONYMS: aluminum, tris (2-methylpropyl); tri-isobutylalane

FORMULA: (iso-$C_4H_9)_3Al$

NFPA 30/OSHA CLASSIFICATION:

DOT CLASS: N/A

ID NO.: N/A

CAS NO.: 100-99-2

MOL. WT.: 198.3

STATEMENT OF HAZARDS: Pyrophoric. Flammable liquid. Corrosive. Water reactive.

EMERGENCY RESPONSE PERSONAL PROTECTIVE EQUIPMENT: Wear special protective clothing and positive pressure self-contained breathing apparatus.

SPILL OR LEAK PROCEDURES: Approach release from upwind. Keep water away from release. Do not use foam to blanket release and suppress vapors. Stop or control the leak, if this can be done without undue risk. Control runoff and isolate discharged material for proper disposal.

FIRE FIGHTING PROCEDURES: Fight fire from protected location or maximum possible distance. DO NOT use water as straight stream directly on spilled material. Violent reaction may result. Water fog may be used to control fires. Use graphite powder, soda ash, or powdered sodium chloride to extinguish fire. On solvent-based materials use dry chemical, foam, or carbon dioxide. Use water spray cautiously to keep fire-exposed containers cool. Extinguish fire using agent suitable for surrounding fire.

HEALTH HAZARDS: Corrosive. Causes severe eye and skin burns. May be harmful if absorbed through skin or inhaled. Irritating to skin, eyes, and respiratory system. "Metal fume fever" may result from inhalation of fumes.

FIRE AND EXPLOSION HAZARDS: Flammable liquid. Pyrophoric; may ignite spontaneously on exposure to air. Water reactive. Combustion may produce irritants and toxic gases. Material is flammable in air at all temperatures. Closed containers may rupture violently when heated.

INSTABILITY AND REACTIVITY HAZARDS: Reacts violently with air and water. Reacts with oxidizers, acids, and alcohols.

STORAGE RECOMMENDATIONS: Store in a cool, dry, well-ventilated location. Must be stored in a dry location. Outside or detached storage is preferred. Inside storage should be in a standard flammable liquids storage warehouse, room, or cabinet.

USUAL SHIPPING CONTAINERS: Bottles, cylinders, tank trucks, and tank cars containing a blanket of nitrogen gas.

PHYSICAL PROPERTIES: Clear, colorless liquid. Aluminum alkyls are generally supplied as 20% solutions in selected solvents so as to be less reactive. Properties may depend on solvent. Solvent may evaporate during spill or exposure.

MELTING POINT: 34°F (11°C)

BOILING POINT: 414°F (212°C)

SPECIFIC GRAVITY: 0.79

SOLUBILITY IN WATER: reacts violently

NAME: **TRIMETHOXYSILANE**

FORMULA: $HSi(OCH_3)_3$

NFPA 30/OSHA CLASSIFICATION: IB

DOT CLASS: Class 6.1, Poisonous material

SHIPPING LABEL: POISON and FLAMMABLE LIQUID

ID NO.: NA 9269

CAS NO.: 2487-90-3

MOL. WT.: 122.2

STATEMENT OF HAZARDS: Severe health hazard. Corrosive and flammable liquid. May accumulate static electricity. Hazardous polymerization may occur.

EMERGENCY RESPONSE PERSONAL PROTECTIVE EQUIPMENT: Wear special protective clothing and positive pressure self-contained breathing apparatus.

SPILL OR LEAK PROCEDURES: Releases may require isolation or evacuation. Eliminate all ignition sources. Use water spray to cool and disperse vapors and protect personnel. Control runoff and isolate discharged material for proper disposal.

FIRE FIGHTING PROCEDURES: Use dry chemical, aqueous foam, or carbon dioxide. Use water spray to keep fire-exposed containers cool. Fight fire from protected location or maximum possible distance. Approach fire from upwind to avoid hazardous vapors and toxic decomposition products.

HEALTH HAZARDS: Severe health hazard. May be fatal if absorbed through skin or inhaled. Corrosive to tissues when wet. Irritating to skin, eyes, and respiratory system.

FIRE AND EXPLOSION HAZARDS: Flammable liquid. Vapors are heavier than air and may travel to a source of ignition and flash back. Combustion may produce irritants and toxic gases. Closed containers may rupture violently when heated.

FLASH POINT: 45°F (7°C)

FLAMMABLE LIMITS: LOWER: 43% @ 34°C UPPER: 40.1% @ 62°C

INSTABILITY AND REACTIVITY HAZARDS: Reacts with water, forming corrosive solution. Reacts with a broad range of materials. Hazardous polymerization may occur when exposed to heat or other catalysts.

STORAGE RECOMMENDATIONS: Store in a cool, dry, well-ventilated location. Separate from acids, oxidizing materials, and water. Outside or detached storage is preferred.

USUAL SHIPPING CONTAINERS: Unknown.

PHYSICAL PROPERTIES: Clear, low colored liquid; ester odor.

MELTING POINT: −175°F (−115°C)

BOILING POINT: 178°F (81°C)

SPECIFIC GRAVITY: 0.96

SOLUBILITY IN WATER: not soluble (decomposes)

VAPOR PRESSURE: < 57 mm Hg @ 20°C

ELECTRICAL EQUIPMENT: Class I, Group C

NAME: **TRIMETHYLAMINE, anhydrous**

SYNONYMS: TMA

FORMULA: $(CH_3)_3N$

NFPA 30/OSHA CLASSIFICATION:

DOT CLASS: Class 2.1, Flammable gas

SHIPPING LABEL: FLAMMABLE GAS

ID NO.: UN 1083

CAS NO.: 75-50-3

MOL. WT.: 59.1

STATEMENT OF HAZARDS: Flammable gas. Cylinders and tanks may rocket under fire conditions. Gas and aqueous solutions are corrosive.

EMERGENCY RESPONSE PERSONAL PROTECTIVE EQUIPMENT: Wear special protective clothing and positive pressure self-contained breathing apparatus.

SPILL OR LEAK PROCEDURES: Releases may require isolation or evacuation. Eliminate all ignition sources. Approach release from upwind. Use water spray to absorb vapors, protect personnel, and dilute spills to form nonflammable mixtures. Five percent sulfuric acid may be used to neutralize diluted pools. Absorb in noncombustible material for proper disposal. Control runoff and isolate discharged material for proper disposal.

FIRE FIGHTING PROCEDURES: Stop flow of gas before extinguishing fire. Use water spray to keep fire-exposed containers cool. Use water spray, dry chemical, or "alcohol resistant" foam. Aqueous solutions will burn unless diluted thoroughly with spray.

HEALTH HAZARDS: Corrosive. Causes severe eye and skin burns. May be harmful if absorbed through skin or inhaled. Irritating to skin, eyes, and respiratory system. May cause irritation, conjunctivitis, and corneal damage. Inhalation may cause coughing, nausea, and pulmonary edema.

FIRE AND EXPLOSION HAZARDS: Flammable gas. Vapors are heavier than air and may travel to a source of ignition and flash back. Aqueous solutions are flammable unless diluted extensively.

AUTOIGNITION TEMPERATURE: 374°F (190°C)

FLAMMABLE LIMITS: LOWER: 2.0% UPPER: 11.6%

INSTABILITY AND REACTIVITY HAZARDS: May react with acids, oxidizing materials, chlorine, hypochlorite, halogenated compounds, reactive organic compounds and some metals, and mercury and nitrosating compounds. Products of decomposition include carbon monoxide, carbon dioxide, hydrocarbons, and toxic oxides of nitrogen as well as toxic amine vapors.

STORAGE RECOMMENDATIONS: Avoid oxidizing materials, acids, and sources of halogens. Store in cool, dry, well-ventilated location.

USUAL SHIPPING CONTAINERS: Glass bottles, cans, drums, tank cars, and tank trailers.

PHYSICAL PROPERTIES: Flammable gas. Very soluble in water, forming very strong alkaline solutions. May be in water solution as shipped or used. Anhydrous material floats and boils on water as it mixes.

MELTING POINT: −179°F (−118°C)

BOILING POINT: 37°F (3°C)

SPECIFIC GRAVITY: liquid 0.66 @ −5°C

SOLUBILITY IN WATER: soluble

VAPOR DENSITY: 2.04

VAPOR PRESSURE: 1650 mm Hg @ 25°C Aqueous solutions will boil 65 to 85°F (40 to 50°C) higher and freeze at proportionately higher temperatures. Vapor pressure of aqueous solutions range from 215 to 500 mm Hg. Specific gravity values for aqueous solutions are 0.83 to 0.93.

ELECTRICAL EQUIPMENT: Class I, Group C

NAME: **TRIPENTYLAMINE**

SYNONYMS: triamylamine

FORMULA: $(C_5H_{11})_3N$

NFPA 30/OSHA CLASSIFICATION: IIIB

DOT CLASS: N/A

ID NO.: N/A

CAS NO.: 621-77-2

MOL. WT.: 227.4

STATEMENT OF HAZARDS: Corrosive. Combustible liquid.

EMERGENCY RESPONSE PERSONAL PROTECTIVE EQUIPMENT: Wear special protective clothing and positive pressure self-contained breathing apparatus.

SPILL OR LEAK PROCEDURES: Stop or control the leak, if this can be done without undue risk. Use water spray or foam to cool and disperse vapors and protect personnel. Approach release from upwind. Absorb in noncombustible material for proper disposal.

FIRE FIGHTING PROCEDURES: Use water spray, dry chemical, foam, or carbon dioxide. Use water spray to keep fire-exposed containers cool.

HEALTH HAZARDS: Corrosive. Causes severe eye and skin burns. May be harmful if absorbed through skin or inhaled. Irritating to skin, eyes, and respiratory system. May cause irritation, conjunctivitis, and corneal damage. Inhalation may cause coughing, nausea, and pulmonary edema.

FIRE AND EXPLOSION HAZARDS: Combustible liquid. Combustion by-products include oxides of nitrogen.

FLASH POINT: 215°F (102°C) (oc)

INSTABILITY AND REACTIVITY HAZARDS: Strong alkali.

STORAGE RECOMMENDATIONS: Store in a cool, dry, well-ventilated location. Separate from acids and oxidizing materials.

USUAL SHIPPING CONTAINERS: Metal cans, pails, drums. Tanks on trucks, rail cars, barges.

PHYSICAL PROPERTIES: Colorless to yellow liquid. Odor of amines (ammonia).

BOILING POINT: 453°F (234°C)

SPECIFIC GRAVITY: 0.79

SOLUBILITY IN WATER: not soluble

NAME: **VANADIUM TETRACHLORIDE**

SYNONYMS: vanadium (IV) chloride

FORMULA: VCl_4

NFPA 30/OSHA CLASSIFICATION:

DOT CLASS: Class 8, Corrosive material

SHIPPING LABEL: CORROSIVE

ID NO.: UN 2444

CAS NO.: 7632-51-1

MOL. WT.: 192.7

STATEMENT OF HAZARDS: Corrosive. Water reactive.

EMERGENCY RESPONSE PERSONAL PROTECTIVE EQUIPMENT: Wear special protective clothing and positive pressure self-contained breathing apparatus.

SPILL OR LEAK PROCEDURES: Keep water away from release. Use water spray to cool and disperse vapors and protect personnel. Use appropriate foam to blanket release and suppress vapors.

FIRE FIGHTING PROCEDURES: Use appropriate extinguishing agents on nearby combustible fires. Dry chemical or carbon dioxide preferred. DO NOT use water. Violent reaction may result.

HEALTH HAZARDS: Corrosive. Causes severe eye and skin burns. May be harmful if inhaled. Irritating to skin, eyes, and respiratory system. Material decomposes to release hydrogen chloride.

FIRE AND EXPLOSION HAZARDS: Not combustible, but if involved in a fire decomposes to produce hydrogen chloride and fumes of vanadium and vanadium oxides.

INSTABILITY AND REACTIVITY HAZARDS: Reacts violently with water, producing heat, hydrogen chloride, vanadium trichloride, vanadium oxydichloride.

STORAGE RECOMMENDATIONS: Store in a cool, dry, well-ventilated location. Keep cylinders restrained.

USUAL SHIPPING CONTAINERS: Steel cylinders or tanks.

PHYSICAL PROPERTIES: Reddish-brown liquid. Irritating odor. Fumes in moist air.

MELTING POINT: −18°F (−28°C)

BOILING POINT: 299°F (148°C)

SPECIFIC GRAVITY: 1.82 @ 30°C

SOLUBILITY IN WATER: decomposes

NAME: **VINYL ACETATE, inhibited**

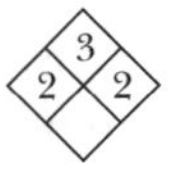

SYNONYMS: VAM; vinyl A monomer; VyAc

FORMULA: $CH_3CO_2CH{=}CH_2$

NFPA 30/OSHA CLASSIFICATION: IB

DOT CLASS: Class 3, Flammable and combustible liquid

SHIPPING LABEL: FLAMMABLE LIQUID

ID NO.: UN 1301

CAS NO.: 108-05-4

MOL. WT.: 86.1

STATEMENT OF HAZARDS: Flammable liquid. Moderate health hazard.

EMERGENCY RESPONSE PERSONAL PROTECTIVE EQUIPMENT: Wear full protective clothing and positive pressure self-contained breathing apparatus.

SPILL OR LEAK PROCEDURES: Eliminate all ignition sources. Stop or control the leak, if this can be done without undue risk. Use water spray to cool and disperse vapors, protect personnel, and dilute spills to form nonflammable mixtures. Control runoff and isolate discharged material for proper disposal.

FIRE FIGHTING PROCEDURES: Fight fire from protected location or maximum possible distance. Use water spray, dry chemical, foam, or carbon dioxide. Water may be ineffective. Use water only in flooding quantities as fog. Use water spray to keep fire-exposed containers cool.

HEALTH HAZARDS: Moderate health hazard. May be harmful if inhaled. Irritating to skin, eyes, and respiratory system.

FIRE AND EXPLOSION HAZARDS: Flammable liquid. Vapors are heavier than air and may travel to a source of ignition and flash back. Combustion may produce irritants and toxic gases. Closed containers may rupture violently when heated. Liquid floats on water and may spread fire.

FLASH POINT: 18°F (−6°C)

AUTOIGNITION TEMPERATURE: 756°F (402°C)

FLAMMABLE LIMITS: LOWER: 2.6% UPPER: 13.4%

INSTABILITY AND REACTIVITY HAZARDS: Hazardous polymerization may occur. Usually contains an inhibitor to prevent self-polymerization. Polymerization may be caused by elevated temperature, oxidizing materials, peroxides. Uninhibited monomer vapor may form polymer in vents and other confined spaces.

STORAGE RECOMMENDATIONS: Store in cool, dry, well-ventilated location. Separate from oxidizing materials, peroxides. Outside or detached storage is preferred. Inside storage should be in a standard flammable liquids storage warehouse, room, or cabinet.

USUAL SHIPPING CONTAINERS: Cans, drums, tank cars, tank trucks, and tank barges.

PHYSICAL PROPERTIES: Colorless, watery liquid. Pleasant, fruity odor.

MELTING POINT: $-135°F$ ($-93°C$)

BOILING POINT: 163°F (73°C)

SPECIFIC GRAVITY: 0.93

SOLUBILITY IN WATER: not soluble

VAPOR PRESSURE: 88 mm Hg @ 20°C

ELECTRICAL EQUIPMENT: Class I, Group D

NAME: **VINYL ACETYLENE**

SYNONYMS: 1-buten-3-yne

FORMULA: $H_2C=CHC=CH$

NFPA 30/OSHA CLASSIFICATION:

DOT CLASS: N/A

ID NO.: N/A

CAS NO.: 689-97-4

MOL. WT.: 52.1

STATEMENT OF HAZARDS: Flammable gas. May decompose explosively. Low ignition energy. Forms peroxides in absence of inhibitors. Moderate health hazard.

EMERGENCY RESPONSE PERSONAL PROTECTIVE EQUIPMENT: Wear full protective clothing and positive pressure self-contained breathing apparatus.

SPILL OR LEAK PROCEDURES: Eliminate all ignition sources. Stop or control the leak, if this can be done without undue risk. Use water spray or foam to reduce possibility of ignition or peroxide formation. Approach release from upwind.

FIRE FIGHTING PROCEDURES: Stop flow of gas before extinguishing fire. Use dry chemical, foam, carbon dioxide, or flooding quantities of water as spray. Water may be ineffective. Use water spray to keep fire-exposed containers cool. Explosive decomposition may occur under fire conditions. Fight fire from protected location or maximum possible distance.

HEALTH HAZARDS: Moderate health hazard. May be harmful if absorbed through skin or inhaled.

FIRE AND EXPLOSION HAZARDS: Flammable gas. Explodes when heated. Vapors are heavier than air and may travel to a source of ignition and flash back. Closed containers may rupture violently when heated. Combustion may produce irritants and toxic gases.

INSTABILITY AND REACTIVITY HAZARDS: May polymerize or decompose explosively. Polymerization may be caused by elevated temperature, oxygen, air, oxidizing materials, peroxides, or sunlight. May form explosive peroxides and acetylides. Polymer may also form peroxides.

STORAGE RECOMMENDATIONS: Store in a cool, dry, well-ventilated location. Store away from heat, oxidizing materials, and sunlight. Outside or detached storage is preferred. Separate from oxygen, air, oxidizing materials, silver, mercury, copper and its alloys.

USUAL SHIPPING CONTAINERS: Steel cylinders.

PHYSICAL PROPERTIES: Colorless gas.

BOILING POINT: 41°F (5°C)

SPECIFIC GRAVITY: 0.71 (liquid)

SOLUBILITY IN WATER: not soluble

VAPOR DENSITY: 1.80

ELECTRICAL EQUIPMENT: Class I, Group A

NAME: **VINYL CHLORIDE, inhibited**

SYNONYMS: chloroethene; chloroethylene; VCM

FORMULA: $CH_2=CHCl$

NFPA 30/OSHA CLASSIFICATION: IA

DOT CLASS: Class 2.1, Flammable gas

SHIPPING LABEL: FLAMMABLE GAS

ID NO.: UN 1086

CAS NO.: 75-01-4

MOL. WT.: 62.5

STATEMENT OF HAZARDS: Flammable gas. Hazardous polymerization may occur. Moderate health hazard.

EMERGENCY RESPONSE PERSONAL PROTECTIVE EQUIPMENT: Wear full protective clothing and positive pressure self-contained breathing apparatus.

SPILL OR LEAK PROCEDURES: Eliminate all ignition sources. Stop or control the leak, if this can be done without undue risk. Use water spray to disperse vapors and protect personnel. Control runoff and isolate discharged material for proper disposal.

FIRE FIGHTING PROCEDURES: Stop flow of gas before extinguishing fire. Fight fire from protected location or maximum possible distance. Use water spray, dry chemical, foam, or carbon dioxide. Use water spray to keep fire-exposed containers cool. Use flooding quantities of water as fog.

HEALTH HAZARDS: Moderate health hazard. May be harmful if inhaled. Symptoms of exposure include anesthesia, narcosis, CNS depression, and loss of consciousness. Rapid evaporation of liquid causes frostbite damage to eyes and skin.

FIRE AND EXPLOSION HAZARDS: Flammable gas. Vapors are heavier than air and may travel to a source of ignition and flash back. Combustion may produce irritants and toxic gases, including hydrogen chloride, carbon monoxide. Closed containers may rupture violently when heated.

FLASH POINT: $-108°F$ ($-78°C$) (oc)

AUTOIGNITION TEMPERATURE: 882°F (472°C)

FLAMMABLE LIMITS: LOWER: 3.6% UPPER: 33.0%

INSTABILITY AND REACTIVITY HAZARDS: Hazardous polymerization may occur. Polymerization may be caused by elevated temperature, oxidizing materials, peroxides. Reacts with aluminum, aluminum alloys, or copper.

STORAGE RECOMMENDATIONS: Store in cool, dry, well-ventilated location. Separate from oxidizing materials.

USUAL SHIPPING CONTAINERS: Pressure cylinders, tank cars, and tank barges.

PHYSICAL PROPERTIES: Colorless, sweet smelling gas. Liquid below 7°F ($-14°C$).

MELTING POINT: $-245°F$ ($-154°C$)

BOILING POINT: 7°F ($-14°C$)

SPECIFIC GRAVITY: 0.91

SOLUBILITY IN WATER: not soluble

VAPOR DENSITY: 2.16

VAPOR PRESSURE: 2524 mm Hg @ 20°C

ELECTRICAL EQUIPMENT: Class I, Group D

NAME: **VINYL ETHER**

DOT SHIPPING NAME: **DIVINYL ETHER, inhibited**

SYNONYMS: divinyl oxide; ethenyloxyethene; 1,1-oxy-bis-ethene

FORMULA: $(CH_2{=}CH)_2O$

NFPA 30/OSHA CLASSIFICATION: IA

DOT CLASS: Class 3, Flammable and combustible liquid

SHIPPING LABEL: FLAMMABLE LIQUID

ID NO.: UN 1167

CAS NO.: 109-93-3

MOL. WT.: 70.1

STATEMENT OF HAZARDS: Flammable liquid. May accumulate static electricity. Low ignition energy. Moderate health hazard. Forms peroxides in absence of inhibitors. May polymerize explosively.

EMERGENCY RESPONSE PERSONAL PROTECTIVE EQUIPMENT: Wear full protective clothing and positive pressure self-contained breathing apparatus.

SPILL OR LEAK PROCEDURES: Eliminate all ignition sources. Stop or control the leak, if this can be done without undue risk. Use water spray to cool and disperse vapors and protect personnel.

FIRE FIGHTING PROCEDURES: Use dry chemical, foam, carbon dioxide, or water spray. Water may be ineffective. Use water spray to keep fire-exposed containers cool. Fight fire from protected location or maximum possible distance.

HEALTH HAZARDS: Moderate health hazard. May be harmful if inhaled. Irritating to skin, eyes, and respiratory system. Symptoms of exposure include anesthesia, narcosis, and loss of consciousness.

FIRE AND EXPLOSION HAZARDS: Flammable liquid. Vapors are heavier than air and may travel to a source of ignition and flash back. Liquid floats on water and may travel to a source of ignition and spread fire. Closed containers may rupture violently when heated. Combustion may produce irritants and toxic gases.

FLASH POINT: <-22°F (<-30°C)

AUTOIGNITION TEMPERATURE: 680°F (360°C)

FLAMMABLE LIMITS: LOWER: 1.7% UPPER: 27.0%

INSTABILITY AND REACTIVITY HAZARDS: Usually contains inhibitors to prevent polymerization. May polymerize explosively with evolution of highly flammable acetylene gas. Uninhibited monomer vapor may form polymer in vents and other confined spaces.

STORAGE RECOMMENDATIONS: Store in a cool, dry, well-ventilated location. Store away from heat, oxidizing materials, and sunlight. Separate from oxidizing materials. Outside or detached storage is preferred.

USUAL SHIPPING CONTAINERS: Amber glass bottles, steel drums, and tanks on trucks, rail cars, and tank barges.

PHYSICAL PROPERTIES: Colorless, mobile liquid. Characteristic odor.

MELTING POINT: -150°F (-101°C)

BOILING POINT: 83°F (28°C)

SPECIFIC GRAVITY: 0.77

SOLUBILITY IN WATER: not soluble

VAPOR DENSITY: 2.41

ELECTRICAL EQUIPMENT: Class I, Group C

NAME: **VINYLIDENE CHLORIDE, inhibited**

SYNONYMS: 1,1-dichloroethene; vinylidene chloride; 1,1-dichloroethylene; asym-dichloroethylene

FORMULA: $CH_2{=}CCl_2$

NFPA 30/OSHA CLASSIFICATION: IA

DOT CLASS: Class 3, Flammable and combustible liquid

SHIPPING LABEL: FLAMMABLE LIQUID

ID NO.: UN 1303

CAS NO.: 75-35-4

MOL. WT.: 96.9

STATEMENT OF HAZARDS: Flammable liquid. Moderate health hazard. Combustion by-products may include hydrogen chloride and phosgene.

EMERGENCY RESPONSE PERSONAL PROTECTIVE EQUIPMENT: Wear full protective clothing and positive pressure self-contained breathing apparatus.

SPILL OR LEAK PROCEDURES: Eliminate all ignition sources. Stop or control the leak, if this can be done without undue risk. Use appropriate foam to blanket release and suppress vapors. Absorb in noncombustible material for proper disposal.

FIRE FIGHTING PROCEDURES: Use dry chemical, foam, carbon dioxide, or water spray. Use water spray to keep fire-exposed containers cool. Use flooding quantities of water. Fight fire from protected location or maximum possible distance.

HEALTH HAZARDS: Moderate health hazard. May be harmful if inhaled. Inhalation may cause irritation or narcosis. Irritating to skin, eyes, and respiratory system. Combustion by-products may include hydrogen chloride and phosgene.

FIRE AND EXPLOSION HAZARDS: Flammable liquid. Vapors are heavier than air and may travel to a source of ignition and flash back. Combustion by-products may include hydrogen chloride, phosgene. Closed containers may rupture violently when heated.

FLASH POINT: 0°F (-18°C)

AUTOIGNITION TEMPERATURE: 1058°F (570°C)

FLAMMABLE LIMITS: LOWER: 7.3% UPPER: 16.0%

INSTABILITY AND REACTIVITY HAZARDS: Hazardous polymerization may occur. Usually contains inhibitors to prevent polymerization. Polymerization may be caused by elevated temperature, oxidizers, peroxides, or air. Uninhibited monomer vapor may form polymer in vents and other confined spaces. May form organic peroxides following prolonged contact with air. May react with aluminum and its alloys.

STORAGE RECOMMENDATIONS: Store in a cool, dry, well-ventilated location. Do not store in aluminum. Separate from air, light, heat, strong oxidizing materials. Outside or detached storage is preferred. Inside storage should be in a standard flammable liquids storage warehouse, room, or cabinet.

USUAL SHIPPING CONTAINERS: Metal cans, pails, drums; tanks on trucks, rail cars, barges.

PHYSICAL PROPERTIES: Colorless liquid with chloroform (mild, sweet) odor.

MELTING POINT: −189°F (−122°C)

BOILING POINT: 89°F (32°C)

SPECIFIC GRAVITY: 1.22

SOLUBILITY IN WATER: not soluble

VAPOR DENSITY: 3.34

VAPOR PRESSURE: 400 mm Hg @ 15°C

ELECTRICAL EQUIPMENT: Class I, Group D

NAME: **VINYL TOLUENE, inhibited mixed isomers**

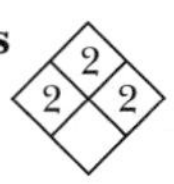

SYNONYMS: methyl styrene

FORMULA: $CH_2{=}CHC_6H_4CH_3$

NFPA 30/OSHA CLASSIFICATION: II

DOT CLASS: Class 3, Flammable and combustible liquid

SHIPPING LABEL: FLAMMABLE LIQUID

ID NO.: UN 2618

CAS NO.: 25013-15-4

MOL. WT.: 118.2

STATEMENT OF HAZARDS: Combustible liquid. May accumulate static electricity. Hazardous polymerization may occur. Moderate health hazard.

EMERGENCY RESPONSE PERSONAL PROTECTIVE EQUIPMENT: Wear full protective clothing and positive pressure self-contained breathing apparatus.

SPILL OR LEAK PROCEDURES: Absorb in noncombustible material for proper disposal (e.g., sand). Stop or control the leak, if this can be done without undue risk. Use water spray to disperse vapors and protect personnel.

FIRE FIGHTING PROCEDURES: Use water spray, dry chemical, foam, or carbon dioxide. Use water spray to keep fire-exposed containers cool. Fight fire from protected location or maximum possible distance.

HEALTH HAZARDS: Moderate health hazard. May be harmful if inhaled. Irritating to skin, eyes, and respiratory system. Symptoms of overexposure may include dizziness, weakness, nausea, fatigue, unconsciousness, and CNS depression.

FIRE AND EXPLOSION HAZARDS: Combustible liquid. Closed containers may rupture violently when heated.

FLASH POINT: 125°F (51.7°C)

AUTOIGNITION TEMPERATURE: 921°F (494°C)

FLAMMABLE LIMITS: LOWER: 0.1% @ 185°F (85°C) UPPER: 11.0% @ 248°F (120°C)

INSTABILITY AND REACTIVITY HAZARDS: Hazardous polymerization may occur. Reacts with acids, oxidizing materials, peroxides, metal salts such as iron chloride or aluminum chloride, or polymer initiators. Usually contains inhibitors to prevent polymerization. Pure vapor will be uninhibited and may polymerize in vents or other confined spaces.

STORAGE RECOMMENDATIONS: Outside or detached storage is preferred. Store in a cool, dry, well-ventilated location. Store away from heat, oxidizing materials, and sunlight. Separate from acids, oxidizing materials, peroxides, and metal salts.

USUAL SHIPPING CONTAINERS: Drums and tank cars.

PHYSICAL PROPERTIES: Colorless liquid with a strong disagreeable odor.

MELTING POINT: −107°F (−77°C)

BOILING POINT: 334°F (168°C)

SPECIFIC GRAVITY: 0.92

SOLUBILITY IN WATER: not soluble

VAPOR PRESSURE: 1.1 mm Hg @ 20°C

ELECTRICAL EQUIPMENT: Class I, Group D

NAME: **XYLENES**

SYNONYMS: 1,2-dimethylbenzene; 1,3-dimethylbenzene; 1,4-dimethylbenzene; dimethyl benzene; xylol

FORMULA: $C_6H_4(CH_3)_2$

NFPA 30/OSHA CLASSIFICATION: o: IB; m: IC; p: IC

DOT CLASS: Class 3, Flammable and combustible liquid

SHIPPING LABEL: FLAMMABLE LIQUID

ID NO.: UN 1307

CAS NO.: o: 95-47-6
m: 108-38-3
p: 106-42-3
mixed xylenes: 1330-20-7

MOL. WT.: 106.2

STATEMENT OF HAZARDS: Flammable liquid. May accumulate static electricity. Moderate health hazard.

EMERGENCY RESPONSE PERSONAL PROTECTIVE EQUIPMENT: Wear full protective clothing and positive pressure self-contained breathing apparatus.

SPILL OR LEAK PROCEDURES: Eliminate all ignition sources. Stop or control the leak, if this can be done without undue risk. Use appropriate foam to blanket release and suppress vapors. Control runoff and isolate discharged material for proper disposal.

FIRE FIGHTING PROCEDURES: Use dry chemical, foam, carbon dioxide, or water spray. Water may be ineffective. Use water spray to keep fire-exposed containers cool.

HEALTH HAZARDS: Moderate health hazard. May be harmful if absorbed through skin or inhaled. Irritating to skin, eyes, and respiratory system. Narcotic in high concentrations. Symptoms of overexposure include dizziness, excitement, drowsiness, staggering gait, nausea, vomiting, and dermatitis.

FIRE AND EXPLOSION HAZARDS: Flammable liquid. Vapors are heavier than air and may travel to a source of ignition and flash back. Liquid floats on water and may travel to a source of ignition and spread fire. Combustion may produce irritants and toxic gases.

FLASH POINT	LEL	UEL	AIT
m: 77°F (25°C)	1.1	7.0	982°F (527°C)
o: 63°F (17°C)	0.9	6.7	867°F (463°C)
p: 77°F (25°C)	1.1	7.0	984°F (528°C)

INSTABILITY AND REACTIVITY HAZARDS: Reacts with strong acids and oxidizing materials.

STORAGE RECOMMENDATIONS: Store in a cool, dry, well-ventilated location. Separate from acetic acid, nitric acid, and strong oxidizing materials. Inside storage should be in a standard flammable liquids storage warehouse, room, or cabinet.

USUAL SHIPPING CONTAINERS: Bottles packed in insulating material. Metal cans, pails, drums. Tanks on trucks, rail cars, barges.

PHYSICAL PROPERTIES: Colorless liquid. Sweet, aromatic odor.

MELTING POINT: o: −13°F (−25°C) m: −54°F (−48°C) p: 55°F (13°C)

BOILING POINT: o: 291°F (144°C) m: 282°F (139°C) p: 279°F (137°C)

SPECIFIC GRAVITY: 0.87

SOLUBILITY IN WATER: not soluble

ELECTRICAL EQUIPMENT: Class I, Group D

NAME: **XYLIDINES, solid** or **solution**

SYNONYMS: 2,3-dimethylaniline; 2,3-dimethylbenzenamine; 2,3-xylylamine

FORMULA: $(CH_3)_2C_6H_3NH_2$

NFPA 30/OSHA CLASSIFICATION: IIIB

DOT CLASS: Class 6.1, Poisonous material

SHIPPING LABEL: POISON

ID NO.: UN 1711

CAS NO.: 87-59-2

MOL. WT.: 121.2

STATEMENT OF HAZARDS: Serious health hazard. Combustible liquid.

EMERGENCY RESPONSE PERSONAL PROTECTIVE EQUIPMENT: Wear special protective clothing and positive pressure self-contained breathing apparatus.

SPILL OR LEAK PROCEDURES: Stop or control the leak, if this can be done without undue risk. Use appropriate foam to blanket release and suppress vapors. Approach release from upwind. Absorb in noncombustible material for proper disposal. Control runoff and isolate discharged material for proper disposal.

FIRE FIGHTING PROCEDURES: Use dry chemical, foam, carbon dioxide, or water spray. Water may be ineffective. Water or foam may cause frothing. Approach fire from upwind to avoid hazardous vapors and toxic decomposition products.

HEALTH HAZARDS: Serious health hazard. May be harmful if absorbed through skin or inhaled. Irritating to skin, eyes, and respiratory system. Health hazards similar to aniline but with fewer warning properties and greater toxicity. Symptoms may include anoxia; cyanosis; injury to kidneys, liver, and blood.

FIRE AND EXPLOSION HAZARDS: Combustible liquid. Combustion by-products include oxides of nitrogen and other irritants and toxic gases.

FLASH POINT: 205°F (96°C)

INSTABILITY AND REACTIVITY HAZARDS: Forms chloroamines on contact with hypochlorite salts or solutions. Reacts with oxidizing materials.

STORAGE RECOMMENDATIONS: Store in a cool, dry, well-ventilated location. Separate from acids, oxidizing materials, and hypochlorite mixtures. Outside or detached storage is preferred.

USUAL SHIPPING CONTAINERS: Glass bottles; metal cans, pails, drums. Tanks on trucks, rail cars, barges.

PHYSICAL PROPERTIES: Pale yellow to brown liquid.

MELTING POINT: 36°F (2°C)

BOILING POINT: 430°F (221°C)

SPECIFIC GRAVITY: 0.99

SOLUBILITY IN WATER: not soluble

NAME: **ZINC CYANIDE**

FORMULA: $Zn(CN)_2$

NFPA 30/OSHA CLASSIFICATION:

DOT CLASS: Class 6.1, Poisonous material

SHIPPING LABEL: POISON

ID NO.: UN 1713

CAS NO.: 557-21-1

MOL. WT.: 117.4

STATEMENT OF HAZARDS: Corrosive. Reacts with acids to release hydrogen cyanide gas.

EMERGENCY RESPONSE PERSONAL PROTECTIVE EQUIPMENT: Wear special protective clothing and positive pressure self-contained breathing apparatus.

SPILL OR LEAK PROCEDURES: Adsorb in noncombustible material for proper disposal; shovel into suitable dry container.

FIRE FIGHTING PROCEDURES: Extinguish fire using agent suitable for surrounding fire.

HEALTH HAZARDS: Corrosive. Causes severe eye and skin burns. May be harmful if absorbed through skin or inhaled. Irritating to skin, eyes, and respiratory system. May cause cyanosis.

FIRE AND EXPLOSION HAZARDS: Not combustible. Combustion may produce irritants and toxic gases, including flammable and toxic hydrogen cyanide.

INSTABILITY AND REACTIVITY HAZARDS: Contact with acids or acid salts releases poisonous gas.

STORAGE RECOMMENDATIONS: Store in a cool, dry, well-ventilated location. Outside or detached storage is preferred. Store away from acids or acid salts.

PHYSICAL PROPERTIES: White powder.

SPECIFIC GRAVITY: 1.85

SOLUBILITY IN WATER: not soluble

NAME: **ZINC PHOSPHIDE**

FORMULA: Zn_3P_2

NFPA 30/OSHA CLASSIFICATION:

DOT CLASS: Class 4.3, Dangerous when wet material

SHIPPING LABEL: DANGEROUS WHEN WET and POISON

ID NO.: UN 1714

CAS NO.: 1314-84-7

MOL. WT.: 258.1

STATEMENT OF HAZARDS: Serious health hazard. Combustible solid.

EMERGENCY RESPONSE PERSONAL PROTECTIVE EQUIPMENT: Wear special protective clothing and positive pressure self-contained breathing apparatus.

SPILL OR LEAK PROCEDURES: Prompt cleanup and removal is necessary. Shovel into suitable dry container.

FIRE FIGHTING PROCEDURES: Use approved Class D extinguishers or smother with dry sand, dry clay, or dry ground limestone. DO NOT use carbon dioxide or halogenated extinguishing agents. Approach fire from upwind to avoid hazardous vapors and toxic decomposition products.

HEALTH HAZARDS: Serious health hazard. May be harmful if absorbed through skin or inhaled. Zinc fumes may be released in fire situations and cause "metal fume fever."

FIRE AND EXPLOSION HAZARDS: Combustible solid. Combustion may produce irritants, toxic gases, zinc oxides, metal fumes.

INSTABILITY AND REACTIVITY HAZARDS: Reacts with common acids.

STORAGE RECOMMENDATIONS: Store in a cool, dry, well-ventilated location. Isolate from water, acids, and oxidizing materials. Outside or detached storage is preferred.

USUAL SHIPPING CONTAINERS: Lined fiber bags. Metal cans, pails, drums.

PHYSICAL PROPERTIES: Dark gray crystals or lustrous or dull powder.

MELTING POINT: 788°F (420°C)

BOILING POINT: 2012°F (1100°C)

SPECIFIC GRAVITY: 4.55

SOLUBILITY IN WATER: not soluble

NAME: **ZIRCONIUM TETRACHLORIDE**

SYNONYMS: zirconium chloride

FORMULA: $ZrCl_4$

NFPA 30/OSHA CLASSIFICATION:

DOT CLASS: Class 8, Corrosive material

SHIPPING LABEL: CORROSIVE

ID NO.: UN 2503

CAS NO.: 10026-11-6

MOL. WT.: 233.0

STATEMENT OF HAZARDS: Corrosive. Water reactive

EMERGENCY RESPONSE PERSONAL PROTECTIVE EQUIPMENT: Wear special protective clothing and positive pressure self-contained breathing apparatus.

SPILL OR LEAK PROCEDURES: Use water spray to cool and disperse vapors and protect personnel.

FIRE FIGHTING PROCEDURES: Use appropriate extinguishing agents on nearby combustible fires. Dry chemical, "alcohol resistant" foam, or carbon dioxide preferred. Water may cause violent reaction.

HEALTH HAZARDS: Corrosive. Causes severe eye and skin burns. May be harmful if inhaled. Irritating to skin, eyes, and respiratory system. Material releases hydrogen chloride on contact with water.

FIRE AND EXPLOSION HAZARDS: Not combustible but if involved in a fire decomposes to produce hydrogen chloride fumes of zirconium, and zirconium oxides.

INSTABILITY AND REACTIVITY HAZARDS: Reacts with water, producing heat, hydrogen chloride, dense white clouds.

STORAGE RECOMMENDATIONS: Store in a cool, dry, well-ventilated location. Always keep container closed.

USUAL SHIPPING CONTAINERS: Glass bottles, steel drums.

PHYSICAL PROPERTIES: White lustrous crystals. Produces dense white clouds in moist air.

MELTING POINT: 572°F (300°C) (sublimes)

SPECIFIC GRAVITY: 2.80

SOLUBILITY IN WATER: reacts

Chapter 6 Referenced Publications

6.1 The following documents or portions thereof are referenced within this document and should be considered part of the recommendations of this document. The edition indicated for each reference is the current edition as of the date of the NFPA issuance of this document.

6.1.1 NFPA Publications. National Fire Protection Association, 1 Batterymarch Park, P.O. Box 9101, Quincy, MA 02269-9101.

NFPA 30, Flammable and Combustible Liquids Code, 2000 edition.

NFPA 70, National Electrical Code®, 2002 edition.

NFPA 77, Recommended Practice on Static Electricity, 2000 edition.

NFPA 86, Standard for Ovens and Furnaces, 1999 edition.

NFPA 321, Standard on Basic Classification of Flammable and Combustible Liquids, 1991 edition.

NFPA 325, Fire Hazard Properties of Flammable Liquids, Gases, and Volatile Solids, 1994 edition.

NFPA 430, Code for the Storage of Liquid and Solid Oxidizers, 2000 edition.

NFPA 432, Code for the Storage of Organic Peroxide Formulations, 1997 edition.

NFPA 490, Code for the Storage of Ammonium Nitrate, 1998 edition.

NFPA 491M, Manual of Hazardous Chemical Reactions, 1991 edition.

NFPA 495, Explosive Materials Code, 2001 edition.

NFPA 496, Standard for Purged and Pressurized Enclosures for Electrical Equipment, 1998 edition.

NFPA 497, Recommended Practice for Classification of Flammable Liquids, Gases, or Vapors and of Hazardous (Classified) Locations for Electrical Installations in Chemical Process Areas, 1997 edition.

NFPA 497M, Manual for Classification of Gases, Vapors, and Dusts for Electrical Equipment in Hazardous (Classified) Locations, 1991 edition.

NFPA 704, Standard System for the Identification of the Hazards of Materials for Emergency Response, 2001 edition.

NFPA 1991, Standard on Vapor-Protective Ensembles for Hazardous Materials Emergencies, 2000 edition.

NFPA 1992, Standard on Liquid Splash-Protective Ensembles and Clothing for Hazardous Materials Emergencies, 2000 edition.

6.1.2 Other Publications.

6.1.2.1 U.S. Government Publication. U.S. Government Printing Office, Superintendent of Documents, Washington, DC 20402.

Code of Federal Regulations, Title 49, Part 172.01.

6.1.2.2 ANSI Publication. American National Standards Institute, Inc., 11 West 42nd Street, New York, NY 10036.

ANSI Z129.1-1988, American National Standard for Hazardous Industrial Chemicals = mPrecautionary Labeling.

6.1.2.3 ASTM Publications. American Society for Testing and Materials, 100 Barr Harbor Drive, West Conshohocken, PA 19428-2959.

ASTM D 56-87, Standard Method of Test for Flash Point by the Tag Closed Cup Tester.

ASTM D 92-90, Cleveland Open Cup Test Method.

ASTM D 93-90, Standard Method of Test for Flash Point by the Pensky-Martens Closed Tester.

ASTM D 1310-86, Standard Method of Test for Flash Point and Fire Points of Liquids by Tag Open Cup Apparatus.

ASTM D 2883-87, Test Method for Reaction Threshold Temperature of Liquid and Solid Materials.

ASTM D 3278-89, Standard Method of Tests for Flash Point of Liquids by Setaflash Closed Cup Apparatus.

ASTM E 659-78, Standard Test Method for Autoignition Temperatures of Liquid Chemicals.

ASTM E 681-85, Standard Test Methods for Limits of Flammability of Chemicals.

ASTM E 789-89, Standard Test Method for Pressure and Rate of Pressure Rise for Dust Explosions in a 1.2 liter Closed Cylindrical Vessel.

ASTM E 1226-88, Standard Test Method for Pressure and Rate of Pressure Rise for Combustible Dusts.

6.1.2.4 NMAB Documents. National Materials Advisory Board of the National Research Council, 2101 Constitution Avenue, NW, Washington, DC 20418.

NMAB 353-4, Classification of Dusts Relative to Electrical Equipment in Class II Hazardous Locations.

NMAB 353-5, Classification of Gases, Liquids, and Volatile Solids Relative to Explosion-Proof Electrical Equipment.

Appendix A

This Appendix is not a part of the recommendations of this NFPA document, but is included for informational purposes only.

Explanation of Information Provided in this Standand.

1. Identity and Arrangement of Listing.

Names and Synonyms. Chemicals are listed alphabetically according to their proper shipping name, as given by the U.S. Department of Transportation in the Hazardous Materials Table, Part 172.101 of Title 49, Transportation, of the Code of Federal Regulations (49 CFR 172). Any commonly used synonyms are listed and cross-referenced to the proper entry. The Hazard Class to which the chemical is assigned by DOT is listed, along with the ID number. (See additional information below.)

NFPA 704 Hazard Ratings. The NFPA 704 hazard ratings are given in the square-on-point. These ratings are based on the criteria described in NFPA 704, *Standard System for the Identification of the Hazards of Materials for Emergency Response,* included in this Guide.

Formula. The chemical's structural line formula is given, according to the protocol of the International Union of Pure and Applied Chemistry. Double and triple bonds are indicated by double and triple horizontal lines. Ringed structures are shown only where necessary for a clear understanding of the arrangement of the molecule.

DOT Hazard Class and ID Numbers. The U.S. Department of Transportation has established criteria for the classification of packaged hazardous materials. Any chemical deemed to come under DOT's hazardous materials regulations, Title 49 CFR, is assigned to one or more of the following hazard classes:

Class, Division	Name of class or division
1.1	Explosives (with a mass explosion hazard)
1.2	Explosives (with a projection hazard)
1.3	Explosives (with predominantly a fire hazard)
1.4	Explosives (with no significant blast hazard)
1.5	Very insensitive explosives; blasting agents
1.6	Extremely insensitive detonating substances
2.1	Flammable gas
2.2	Nonflammable compressed gas
2.3	Poisonous gas
3	Flammable and combustible liquid
4.1	Flammable solid
4.2	Spontaneously combustible material
4.3	Dangerous when wet material
5.1	Oxidizer
5.2	Organic peroxide
6.1	Poisonous material
6.2	Infectious substance (etiologic agent)
7	Radioactive material
8	Corrosive material
9	Miscellaneous hazardous material
None	Other regulated material; ORM-D

Where a hazardous material possesses properties meeting the definition of more than one hazard class or division, the material is assigned to a class/division according to the precedence of hazards among classes and divisions as set forth in Title 49 CFR 173.2a. The subsidiary hazard properties of such a material, which are not indicated by the class to which the material is assigned, are typically identified through the requirement for additional labels that communicate the subsidiary hazards.

ID Number. The identification number (either UN or NA) is a four-digit number that is specific to the chemical's entry in the Hazardous Materials Table in the DOT regulations. This four-digit number must appear on the shipping papers and as a marking on the packages, freight containers, portable tanks, tank vessels, etc. The number is also cross-referenced to recommended emergency action procedures in DOT's Emergency Response Guide. As they appear in the Hazardous Materials Tables, the numbers are preceded by "UN" or "NA." UN numbers are recognized for international shipments. NA numbers are only recognized in the U.S. and Canada.

CAS Number. The number under which the chemical is registered by the Chemical Abstracts Service of the American Chemical Society is listed. The CAS number used is that which appears in the current Toxic Substances Control Act (TSCA) Chemical Substances Inventory, Volumes II and III: Substance Name Index. The user is cautioned that more than one CAS number may exist for certain chemicals.

Molecular Weight. The molecular weight of the chemical is given. The molecular weight is used for many chemical calculations, but its importance here is for the calculation of the volume of air required to dilute a flammable atmosphere to a safe level. Information on the calculation method may be found in NFPA 86, *Standard for Ovens and Furnaces,* and in *Industrial Ventilation= mA Manual of Recommended Practice.*

2. Statement of Hazards. The key words used to describe the principal hazards are those established by ANSI Z129.1, American National Standard for Hazardous Industrial Chemicals = mPrecautionary Labeling. The technical committee agreed to use the ANSI Z129.1 terminology because it provides a logical hierarchy of succinct descriptors of the major hazards that NFPA 49 addresses. For those chemicals that present more than one hazard, the key words are given in order of descending severity of hazard. Where multiple hazards are of equal severity, the key words are listed in the order of health, flammability, instability. Appendix C lists the key words used by NFPA 49.

3. Emergency Response Personal Protective Equipment. This section describes the preferred personal protective equipment that should be worn by emergency response personnel. As used in NFPA 49, "full protective clothing" means protection to prevent direct contact of gases, vapors, liquids, and solids with the skin.

Full protective clothing, as used in NFPA 49, includes helmet, self-contained breathing apparatus (SCBA), coat and pants customarily worn by fire fighters (turnout or bunker coat and pants), rubber boots, and gloves. It also includes bands around the legs, arms, and waist and covering for the neck, ears, and other parts of the body not otherwise protected.

"Special protective clothing," as used in NFPA 49, means clothing that is specially designed to protect the wearer against a specific hazard (often referred to as chemical-protective clothing). Special protective clothing is recommended for any chemical whose Health Hazard Rating is 3 or 4.

SCBA is used in addition to full or special protective clothing. See:

(a) NFPA 1991, *Standard on Vapor-Protective Ensembles for Hazardous Materials Emergencies.*

(b) NFPA 1992, *Standard on Liquid Splash-Protective Ensembles and Clothing for Hazardous Materials Emergencies.*

(c) "Guidelines for the Selection of Chemical Protective Clothing" (American Conference of Governmental Industrial Hygienists).

Breathing Equipment. Breathing equipment for use in toxic or oxygen-deficient atmospheres is of two types: self-contained breathing apparatus (SCBA) and supplied air with auxiliary escape SCBA. With the latter, air is supplied in the positive pressure mode to the user by means of a hose connected to a supply, either a compressor or a bank of high pressure cylinders. The auxiliary SCBA should be sized to permit escape if the air supply is interrupted. Self-contained apparatus provides a supply of clean air from a source worn by the user and independent of the surrounding atmosphere, usually from a supply tank. All self-contained breathing apparatus should operate in the positive pressure mode (i.e., air is constantly being bled into the face piece so that the pressure within the face piece is slightly greater than the surrounding atmosphere, thus preventing leaks of any hazardous gas into the face piece), should have a full face piece with adequate eye protection, and should be approved by the National Institute for Occupational Safety and Health (NIOSH).

Contamination. Contamination of clothing may occur during fire fighting or emergency response operations. Many chemicals are capable of being absorbed through the skin, causing burns, poisoning, or death. For this reason, any protective clothing that has been even slightly contaminated must be removed promptly and carefully and must be thoroughly decontaminated. As a guide, any clothing that may contain residues from contact with a chemical having an NFPA 704 Health Hazard Rating of 3 or 4 should be decontaminated. As a minimum, a thorough washing with a strong detergent and rinsing with copious quantities of clean water is necessary. Clothing that cannot be satisfactorily decontaminated should be discarded.

4. Spill and Leak Procedures. Spilled or accidentally released chemicals may present special problems in emergency situations, causing damage to health, property, and the environment. As a general rule, complete control of spilled or released chemicals is imperative to prevent the release from continuing, to prevent further environmental damage, to minimize or prevent property damage or danger to the general public, and to minimize exposure to emergency personnel.

The spill and leak procedures recommended in this document attempt to address both large and small spills. Any spill or release that exceeds the reportable quantity must be reported to local, state, and federal emergency response agencies. For the purposes of this document, emphasis is on preplanning and cleanup procedures.

The following procedures may apply to both large and small spills:

(a) Isolate the area until the spill or release is under full control.

(b) Dike the area to contain the spill. Provisions should be made to pump spilled materials into tanks or other holding containers to minimize the potential for soil or ground water contamination if such action will not create reaction hazards from the contaminated materials.

(c) Keep all obvious ignition sources away from the spill.

(d) Stop or control the leak, if this can be done without undue risk.

(e) If the spilled material is not water reactive, use water spray to reduce vapors or to sweep vapors away from the area of the spill. Also, where practical, use a foam blanket to hold down the release of vapors from pools of spilled material.

(f) Avoid direct contact with spilled material. All emergency personnel in the area of the spill should wear appropriate protective clothing.

(g) Do not allow water to enter containers of the spilled material.

For small spills, it may be appropriate to absorb the spilled material using sand, clay, or other inert absorbent material. The contaminated absorbent can then be put into appropriate containers for later disposal.

For control and disposal of a large spill, the following must be taken into consideration:

(a) Compatibility of the spilled material with water or other fire fighting agents must be determined before fire suppression efforts begin.

(b) In situations where it is decided to use water to disperse, dissolve, or neutralize a leak or spill, there must be enough water available to complete the process.

(c) Dike the area completely around the spill.

(d) Where access to the area is strictly controlled, it may be best to allow the spill to evaporate or otherwise disperse.

5. Fire Fighting Procedures. The information in this section indicates the preferred method of attacking a fire involving the chemical. All recommendations pertain to manual fire fighting. In most cases, water is the agent of choice, because of its cooling capability and because it is usually readily available in large quantities. However, the choice of application method should be made with care. The method and rate of application of the extinguishing agent in relation to the size and type of fire must be carefully considered, particularly where large-scale application may be involved. The physical and chemical properties of the material involved may also have an impact on the choice of the proper agent.

Under one or more of the following conditions it may be prudent to allow the fire to continue to burn:

(a) Continued burning reduces the hazards to personnel.

(b) Continued burning reduces the environmental impact of the incident.

(c) Fire fighting hazards outweigh the benefits of extinguishment.

(d) Lack of available resources.

(e) Minimal downwind hazard.

Use of Water to Cool Fire-Exposed Containers. In cases where they are exposed by the heat or flames of a fire, tanks or containers should be cooled by application of hose streams. Application should begin as soon as possible and should concentrate on any unwetted portions of the containers. Experience has shown that large tanks, such as tank trailers or railroad tank cars, that are directly exposed to intense heat or flame may rupture in as little as five minutes. It is imperative that cooling streams be applied within the first several minutes of exposure. If this is not possible, it may be more prudent to set up unmanned monitor nozzles and immediately evacuate the area. Evacuation is also the proper tactic if cooling efforts are hampered by inadequate water supplies or if cooling streams cannot be directed at all exposed surfaces of the tank.

Use of Water on Flammable Liquids. Water may be ineffective for fighting fires involving liquids whose flash points are less than 100°F (38°C). Water can be applied as a fine spray to absorb the heat of the fire and to cool exposed containers or material and, if properly applied, is capable of extinguishing the fire by sweeping the flames off the surface of the burning liquid. However, the advice for most such liquids will include the phrase, "Water may be ineffective" to indicate that extinguishment will only occur under favorable conditions and when hose streams are applied by experienced fire fighters. In general, fire fighting foams are the most effective agents for fires involving low flash point liquids.

Use of Water on Water-Soluble Liquids. Water is capable of extinguishing fires involving water-soluble liquids by diluting the liquid to the point where it is no longer flammable.

Use of Water on High Density Liquids. Water may be used to blanket the surface of any liquid that has a specific gravity greater than about 1.1, water itself being 1.0, and that is not water-soluble. Application method is important: the water must be applied gently to the surface of the liquid to prevent splashing and aerating the liquid.

Precautions when Using Water. Water and fire fighting foams that are water-based may cause frothing when applied on fires involving viscous flammable liquids. Where applicable, this is stated in NFPA 49 as a precaution and does not indicate that water should not be used at all. It is recognized that frothing may be violent and is capable of endangering personnel close to the fire. On the other hand, a carefully applied water spray can be used to extinguish such a fire, because the froth actually blankets the surface of the liquid and excludes oxygen. (Note:- Frothing is not to be confused with a boil-over.)

Water will not be recommended for fighting fires involving any chemical that reacts violently with water. A "W" with a line through its center (W̶) alerts fire fighting personnel to the possible hazard of use of water. A "W̶" will be used when the reaction with water has the potential to cause one or more of the following:

(a) Rapid energy release on contact with water that could result in explosion.

(b) Ignition of nonpyrophoric chemical on contact with water.

(c) Rapid, copious release of toxic gas on contact (without net benefit as a control measure).

Water reactivity (as denoted by the W symbol) does not in all cases exclude the case of aqueous foams for vapor suppression or fire fighting. When aqueous foams may be appropriate, this is noted on specific chemical data sheets.

However, sprinkler protection is appropriate and should be provided in chemical storage facilities. The purpose of such systems is to provide automatic protection for the entire facility, where a variety of flammables and combustibles may be present. Chemicals that are reactive with water are normally in waterproof containers. Sprinkler protection will help prevent rupture of containers.

Use of Fire Fighting Foams. As indicated above, fire fighting foams are the agent of choice for most flammable liquid fires. It is important to remember that certain liquids, notably alcohols and amines, are water-soluble and will break down the common foams.

Foam is recommended for most nonsoluble or slightly soluble nonpolar flammable liquids. Good judgment must be exercised if there is no or little success in extinguishing the fire. The other extinguishing systems such as other foams, dry chemicals, etc., must be considered.

Special "alcohol resistant" foams must be used with any polar flammable liquid that is slightly or completely soluble in water. Certain high molecular weight alcohols and amines will also break down alcohol resistant foams, even when applied at very high delivery rates.

"Alcohol resistant" foams have been developed for use on both polar and nonpolar flammable liquids. These foams are suitable for use on nearly all flammable liquids (except those that are water reactive) and are preferred for flammable liquid fire emergencies since they greatly minimize problems of foam selection.

The foam suppliers should be consulted for recommendations regarding foam types, delivery rates for specific applications and specific limitations.

Stop Flow of Gas. Rather than extinguishing the fire, stopping the flow of gas is usually the best procedure to follow when escaping gas is burning. It may be dangerous to extinguish the flame and allow the gas to continue to flow, as an explosive mixture may be formed with air and, if ignited, may cause far greater damage than if the original fire had been allowed to burn. Extinguishing the flame by carbon dioxide or dry chemical may be desirable where necessary to permit immediate access to valves to shut off the supply. In many cases, however, it is preferable to allow the flame to continue, keeping the surroundings cool with water spray to prevent ignition of other combustible materials.

Dry Chemical Extinguishing Agents. The term "dry chemical" refers to those powdered extinguishing agents that are suitable for use with flammable gases, flammable and combustible liquids, and combustible solids. The term "dry powder" refers to those powdered agents specifically formulated for use in extinguishing fires involving combustible metals. The two types of agents are not the same and cannot be used interchangeably.

Multipurpose dry chemical material is composed of small particles of mostly ammonium phosphate and other materials such as sodium bicarbonate, potassium bicarbonate, and potassium chloride. When discharged, it extinguishes primarily by interruption of the combustion chain through either of various chemical reactions, reducing flammable liquid evaporation rates by reduction in flame radiation at the liquid-vapor interface, and by inerting that reduces the ambient oxygen concentration at the flame areas. There is some heat absorption, some cooling by the chemical formation of water from the ongoing pyrolysis and some carbon dioxide formation from the ongoing pyrolysis; these are minor secondary effects.

Protection from Explosions. Where there is a possibility of violent thermal polymerization or explosive decomposition or detonations under fire conditions, personnel are advised to fight a fire from a "protected location." A protected location is defined as an area separated from the fire by distance or a barricade or both so that the blast effects of an explosion present a minimal hazard to emergency personnel. The protected location can be an area behind a substantial manmade or natural barricade. Such locations may include an area behind a building, an intervening earthen berm or slope, or a reinforced concrete wall. The barricade must be located some distance from the source of the explosion, the actual distance required being a matter of judgment and depending on the type and quantity of materials involved and the severity and type of potential explosion. The objective is to protect personnel from shrapnel, missiles, blast effect, and the radiant energy of an expanding fireball.

To use the statement "protected location or maximum possible distance" the following criteria are applied:

(a) Thermally polmerizes violently under fire conditions, or

(b) Decomposes violently under fire conditions.

Almost all liquidtight metal containers can rupture violently due to a pressure buildup when exposed to fire for a prolonged period. Drums containing volatile liquids may "rocket," cylinders of compressed gas not having fusible plugs may burst at high pressure, and tank trailers or railroad tank cars may Boiling Liquid Evaporating Vapor Explosion (BLEVE) under fire conditions. These precautions have been removed from the data sheets for normally thermally stable chemicals. The statement "Closed containers may rupture violently when heated" is given only to chemicals that are thermally unstable as indicated by an instability rating of 2 or greater.

6. Health Hazards. The statements on health hazards are intended to clearly describe the effects of acute (short-term, high level) exposure to each chemical by physical contact, eye and skin absorption, or inhalation. Because the scope of NFPA 49 is primarily directed at emergency situations, the effects of ingestion and chronic (long-term, low level) exposure, such as routine occupational exposure, are not addressed. Likewise, no information is given on chronic health effects such as carcinogenicity, mutagenicity, etc. Also, no information is given on biological hazards.

If acute exposure can produce delayed or permanent effects, these effects are described, except as previously noted [see Section 2-2(f)]. In all cases, the user is encouraged to obtain more in-depth information from suitable industrial health and hygiene references.

The statements used to describe health effects are based on those recommended by ANSI Z129.1 and are included in Appendix C.

7. Fire and Explosion Hazards. The first part of this section describes in general terms the basic combustion hazards presented by the material. If the material ignites on contact with air or water, this is stated. If the material is capable of spontaneous ignition, deflagration, or detonation, this is also stated. Any explosive behavior due to chemical instability or reactivity including mixture with other substances is addressed in the section on chemical hazards.

Combustion, Deflagration, and Detonation. Combustion is a chemical process of oxidation that occurs at a rate fast enough to produce heat and usually light (either as a glow or flame). In the case of glowing combustion, the reaction is a surface phenomenon and can only occur in solid fuels. In the case of flaming combustion, the reaction is usually a gas-phase phenomenon, although it may involve fuel that is initially in the solid, liquid, or gaseous state. Liquids must be vaporized before they will actually burn. Some solids (such as titanium, silicon, boron) have boiling points higher than their oxides, and in such cases the combustion zone is located almost on or near the surface.

When a cloud of combustible gas or vapor is ignited, the burning proceeds quite rapidly and may produce a significant pressure effect. Such an occurrence is called a combustion explosion and may be further defined as either a deflagration or a detonation. In a deflagration, the flame front proceeds through the unburned fuel mixture at a rate that is less than the speed of sound, as measured in the unburned fuel. In a detonation, the flame front proceeds through the unburned fuel at the speed of sound or greater, as measured in the unburned fuel. The pressure effect associated with a deflagration is a pushing, tearing, or stretching effect. In contrast, the pressure effect associated with a detonation is a distinct shattering effect.

Flame Propagation. Propagation of flame is the spread of flame outward from the source of ignition (spark or pilot flame) through the air/fuel mixture. A gas or vapor mixed with air in proportions below the lower flammable limit may burn at the source of ignition, i.e., in the immediate area of the source, but flame will not spread outward away from the source. If the mixture is within the flammable range, however, propagation of the flame will occur throughout the mixture.

Flash Point. Flash point is the minimum temperature at which a liquid gives off sufficient vapor to form an ignitible mixture with air near the surface of the liquid or within the test vessel used. By "ignitible mixture" is meant a mixture that is within the flammable range (see discussion below) and that is capable of propagation of flame away from the ignition source. Although vapors are evolved at temperatures below the flash point, the concentration is not sufficient for ignition to occur. Although flash point is defined as a characteristic of liquids, there are certain solids, such as camphor and naphthalene, that sublime or slowly evaporate at ordinary ambient temperatures and will exhibit a flash point while in the solid state. The same is true of liquids, such as benzene, that can freeze at ambient temperatures.

The flash points listed in NFPA 49 are those determined by closed cup test methods, unless otherwise stated, in which case the flash point will be followed by the symbol "oc" (open cup). Broadly speaking, closed cup test methods are representative of conditions in closed tanks, while open cup methods are more indicative of conditions in open-top tanks or of spill situations. For most liquids, the numerical value of the closed cup flash point, in °F, is some 10 to 20 degrees lower than that of the open cup flash point. Larger differences are observed at higher temperatures or if a small amount of contaminant with lower flash point is present.

Flash point is determined by several different test procedures. The Tag Closed Tester (ASTM D56) is used to test liquids that have a viscosity less than 45 Saybolt Universal Seconds (SUS) at 100°F (38°C) and are expected to have a flash point below 200°F (93°C). The Pensky-Martens Closed Tester (ASTM D93) is used to test liquids that have a viscosity of 45 SUS or higher at 100°F (38°C) and are expected to have a flash point of 200°F (93°C) or higher. The Setaflash Closed Tester (ASTM D3278) has been accepted as an alternate to both the Tag Closed Tester and the Pensky-Martens Closed Tester. Two other flash point testers are still in use: the Cleveland Open Cup Tester (ASTM D92) is sometimes used for high flash point liquids and the Tag Open Cup Tester (ASTM D1310) is sometimes used for low flash point liquids when it is desirable to have test data that is representative of liquid behavior in open tanks or for labeling purposes.

Static Electricity. For the purposes of NFPA 49, liquids that may have electrical conductivities less than 50 picoSiemens/meter (pS/m) are given the hazard statement of "may accumulate static electricity" to indicate low conductivity. If a gas or liquid vapor has a minimum ignition energy less than 0.2 mJ the statement "low ignition energy" is given.

NFPA 77, *Recommended Practice on Static Electricity,* provides practical guidance to assist in reducing the fire hazard of static electricity. Included is a discussion of the nature and origin of static charges, methods for mitigation, and recommendation for charge dissipation in certain specific operations.

Autoignition Temperature. The autoignition temperature is the minimum temperature required to initiate self-sustained combustion in a substance without any apparent source of ignition. The substance may be solid, liquid, or gaseous. Autoignition temperatures given in NFPA 49 are the lowest values reported in the literature, consistent with standard methods of test. Since autoignition temperatures vary significantly depending on test method and test apparatus, they should be considered as approximations only. Some of the variables known to affect autoignition are composition and pressure of the fuel/air mixture, shape and size of the test vessel, rate of heating, duration of heating, and even the material of construction of the test vessel. The autoignition temperature of a solid substance is further influenced by the physical size of the test specimen and the rate of airflow (if any) in the test vessel. With small test specimens, it has been shown that as the airflow or the rate of heating increases, the autoignition temperature decreases to a minimum value, then increases.

The majority of the data reported in NFPA 49 have been obtained using one of two test methods: ASTM D286 and ASTM D2155. Both of these test methods have been withdrawn. ASTM D2155 has been replaced by ASTM E659, *Standard Test Method for Autoignition Temperatures of Liquid Chemicals.* An earlier test method, ASTM D2883, *Test Method for Reaction Threshold Temperature of Liquid and Solid Materials,* provides for testing at reduced and elevated pressures.

The earlier ASTM test procedures provided for visual detection of ignition only. As a result, the autoignition temperatures obtained were the minimum values for hot-flame ignition. Current test methods use thermoelectric flame detectors that are capable of detecting nonluminous or barely luminous reactions (called cool flames) that are difficult or impossible to detect visually.

Flammable Limits. For any mixture of gas or vapor and air, there is a minimum concentration of the fuel below which flame propagation cannot take place. There is also a maximum concentration above which combustion cannot take place. These limits are known as the lower flammable limit (LFL) and upper flammable limit (UFL), respectively, and the concentration between the two limits is called the flammable range. The limits are always expressed as percent by volume of gas or vapor in air. In popular terms, a mixture that is below the lower flammable limit is "too lean" to burn, while a mixture that is above the upper flammable limit is "too rich" to burn.

The flammable limits reported in NFPA 49 are those determined at 77°F (25°C) and 760 mm Hg, unless otherwise indicated. The flammable limits vary considerably with changes in temperature and pressure. Generally, an increase in temperature or pressure results in a decrease in the LFL and an increase in the UFL, i.e., the flammable range widens. A decrease in temperature or pressure tends to have the reverse effect. The currently accepted test method for determining flammable limits is ASTM E681, *Standard Test Method for Concentration Limits of Flammability of Chemicals,* although some of the data presented in NFPA 49 may have been obtained by previously used methods. Research has shown that the flammability limits are not fundamental combustion properties, but are dependent on many variables, including the surface-to-volume ratio of the test vessel and the conditions of test.

For combustible dusts, there exists a similar lower concentration limit known as the minimum explosive concentration (MEC). This is the lowest concentration of a combustible dust in suspension in air that can be ignited. The MEC is determined by procedures (ASTM E789 and ASTM E1226) that are very dependent on the nature of the dust, its particle size, moisture content, and how well the dust is mixed with the air. Although there exists a maximum explosive concentration analogous to the UFL, it is very difficult to determine by test, and such test data frequently is not reproducible, so is not reported.

8. Instability and Reactivity Hazards. This section provides information on chemical hazards such as thermal instability, potential hazardous reactions with air, water, or other classes of chemicals, or friction or shock sensitivity. It is important to note that absence of information does not infer that the material is without any such hazards, only that no such hazards have been reported. Also, materials that ignite on contact with air or water are reported in Section 7, Fire and Explosion Hazards.

Thermal Instability. Materials that are thermally unstable will, at some specific temperature, undergo some type of potentially hazardous reaction (decomposition, polymerization, rearrangement, etc.), with consequent release of energy. In general, the temperature at which such a reaction begins is reported. If known, the "self-accelerating decomposition temperature" is also reported. The self-accelerating decomposition temperature is discussed in the following paragraph. Also reported here are any hazardous reactions with other classes of chemicals, such as oxidizers and reducing agents, and violent neutralization reactions. NFPA 49 does not attempt to describe such reactions in detail. The user is referred to NFPA 491M, *Manual of Hazardous Chemical Reactions,* for information on reactions with specific chemicals.

Self-Accelerating Decomposition Temperature. Certain compounds, such as organic peroxides and swimming pool chemicals, when held at moderate ambient temperatures for an extended period of time, may undergo an exothermic reaction that accelerates with increase in temperature. If the heat liberated by this reaction is not lost to the environment, the bulk material increases in temperature, which leads to an increase in the rate of decomposition. Unchecked, the temperature grows exponentially to a point at which the decomposition cannot be stopped or slowed. The minimum temperature at which this exponential growth occurs in a material packed in its largest standard shipping container is defined as the self-accelerating decomposition temperature. Self-accelerating decomposition temperature is a measure of the ease in which decomposition occurs under normal storage conditions. It is not an indicator of the violence of any decomposition reaction under conditions of fire exposure or contact with incompatible materials.

Organic peroxides have combined oxidizing and combustible properties. They may in some cases undergo accelerating self-reaction, which may be violent. Specific recommendations are given in NFPA 432, *Code for the Storage of Organic Peroxide Formulations.*

Oxidizers. Oxidizers are solids, liquids, or gases that yield oxygen or other oxidizing gas during the course of a chemical reaction or that readily react to oxidize combustible materials. The rates of reaction vary considerably and may be rapid enough to be quite violent. The hazard greatly increases with increasing temperature, and explosive deflagrations are possible under fire exposure conditions. Further, combustible materials that are contaminated or mixed with oxidizers may become sensitive to heat, shock, friction, or impact. Oxidizers include: chlorates, perchlorates, bromates, peroxides, nitrates, nitrites, nitric acid, and permanganates. The halogens (fluorine, chlorine, bromine, and iodine) react similarly to oxygen under certain conditions and are, therefore, classed as oxidizers.

Because most inorganic oxidizers are not themselves combustible, their flammability hazard is zero, according to NFPA 704. However, they will greatly intensify a fire in which they become involved. Because the oxidation reaction involves another chemical, NFPA 704 does not indicate the hazard or its degree. NFPA 704 identifies oxidizers by means of the symbol "OX" in the bottom quadrant. Additional information on the storage of oxidizers may be found in NFPA 430, *Code for the Storage of Liquid and Solid Oxidizers.* As stated in the scope of NFPA 49, chemicals whose only hazard is mild oxidizing ability will not be addressed.

Polymerization. Some chemicals present a hazard due to their ability to undergo a self-sustaining exothermic polymerization reaction. The reaction is usually exothermic and sometimes produces significant quantities of gas or heat that are capable of producing overpressures and possible container rupture. Generally, this reaction can be controlled or prevented by adding certain chemicals called inhibitors or by controlling the bulk temperature of the material. However, contamination of materials subject to polymerization, as well as external heating from fire exposure, can overwhelm these safeguards. For these reasons, fires involving chemicals that are capable of polymerization must be approached carefully.

9. Storage Recommendations. Storage Recommendations. This section will provide basic information on safe storage practices for the specific chemical. In general, the information provided will be limited to identifying incompatible materials with which the chemical should not be stored. The user should seek the advice of the supplier for detailed recommendations. Where applicable, the reader is referred to pertinent NFPA standards or to standards of other organizations such as the Compressed Gas Association.

In this document, "isolate" and "separate" are terms used to describe storage procedures intended to prevent incompatible materials from coming into direct contact with each other due to spill or release from their containers. The degree of isolation or separation will depend on the quantities of the materials, the chemical and physical properties of the materials, and the packaging systems employed. "Isolate" means to store in a different area from incompatible materials, such as in a different room, in a different fire area, in a different building, or in a separate outside storage area. "Separate" means to store in the same area or room, but with intervening distance or intervening storage of mutually compatible material.

10. Usual Shipping Containers. The containers listed are those in which the materials are usually shipped or stored in commercial practice.

11. Physical Properties. The information provided in this section attempts to give the user as much physical property data as practical for accurate identification of the specific material in the form in which it is most typically encountered. Information provided includes: physical state (i.e., solid, liquid, or gas); appearance (i.e., crystalline, powdery, amorphous, etc.); odor; color; and clarity. This list is not intended to be all-inclusive. Where desirable or necessary, additional information will be presented.

Melting and Boiling Points. The melting and boiling points are the temperatures at which the substance undergoes a phase change (e.g., solid to liquid or liquid to gas) and are determined at normal atmospheric pressure of 14.7 psi (760 mm Hg) (absolute). They are given in both degrees Fahrenheit and degrees Celsius. The user is cautioned that both melting point and boiling point decrease with increasing altitude, so the data given here may not be accurate in some locales.

Specific Gravity. The specific gravity of a liquid or solid substance is the ratio of the weight of a unit volume of the substance (i.e., its density) to the weight of an equal volume of a standard reference substance, usually water at 68°F (20°C). A substance whose specific gravity is greater than 1.0 will tend to sink in water, while one whose specific gravity is less than 1.0 will tend to float.

Water Solubility. Water solubility is described in qualitative terms only, i.e., "soluble," "partly soluble," "not soluble." Information on water solubility is useful in determining which fire extinguishing agents are most effective. For example, "alcohol resistant" fire fighting foams are most suitable for use with water-soluble materials and polar solvents. Water-soluble flammable liquids may be extinguished by dilution with water, but this method is not often used because of the amount of water normally required.

The reasons that the Technical Committee declined to provide quantitative data on water solubility were the lack of uniformity of the manner in which solubility data are reported in the literature and the conflicting data that occasionally appear. For those substances for which reliable data exist, the designation "not soluble" indicates less than 10 grams solubility in 100 ml of water, "partly soluble" indicates 10 to 24 grams per 100 ml, and "soluble" indicates 25 grams or more solubility per 100 ml. In those cases where there is doubt about water solubility or about its effect on extinguishment, appropriate tests should be conducted.

Vapor Density. Vapor density is the ratio of the weight of a unit volume of a pure gas to the weight of an equal volume of dry air, both being at the same temperature and pressure. It is easily determined, however, by calculating the ratio of the molecular weight of the gas to the average molecular weight of dry air, 29. A vapor density of less than 1.0 indicates that the gas is less dense than air and will tend to rise in a relatively calm atmosphere, thus readily dissipating. A vapor density of greater than 1.0 indicates that the gas is denser than air and will tend to sink to ground level and not dissipate as readily. Vapors of flammable liquids generally are denser than air at ambient temperature and may travel at ground level for considerable distances to a source of ignition (vapors of combustible liquids, on the other hand, unless heated, are not considered likely to flash back). It should be noted, however, that ambient air is seldom calm and that mixing of the vapors with the air will occur.

NFPA 49 reports vapor density values for gases and for liquids with boiling points below 100°F (38°C).

Examples of Vapor Densities

Typical Industrial Gases	Molecular Weight	Vapor Density (MW/29)	Compared to Air (1.0)
Air	29 (avg.)	1.00	Standard
Carbon Dioxide	44	1.52	Heavier
Hydrogen	2	0.07	Much Lighter
Methane	16	0.55	Lighter
Propane	44	1.52	Heavier

Vapor Pressure. Vapor pressure is a measure of the force exerted by molecules evaporating (passing from the liquid to the vapor state) from the surface of a liquid. Vapor pressure is a direct indicator of the volatility of a liquid. The more volatile a liquid, the lower its boiling point. Combustible liquids with similar combustion properties (e.g., petroleum fractions) have flash points that vary approximately inversely with their vapor pressures. This is because the molecules are more easily able to pass from the liquid to the vapor state, thus forming an ignitible vapor/air mixture. The temperature at which the vapor pressure equals the surrounding atmospheric pressure is the boiling point. Vapor pressure is expressed as millimeters of mercury at a specified temperature.

12. Electrical Equipment Group Classification. The handling of a hazardous chemical in storage and processing operations may release significant quantities of the chemical into the air. When the chemical is flammable or combustible, an ignitible concentration of the material in air may be formed. Ordinary electrical equipment is considered a potential source of ignition for such concentrations because of arcing contacts, hot surfaces, and sparks generated by normal or abnormal operation. For this reason, it is often necessary to specify and use special electrical equipment, wiring, and installation that will not cause ignition.

Appendix D discusses three classes of electrical installations in accordance with the requirements of NFPA 70, *National Electrical Code,* Article 500, "Hazardous (Classified) Locations."

The Group classifications of a more extensive list of flammable gases and liquids, combustible liquids, and combustible dusts are available in NFPA 497M, *Manual for the Classification of Gases, Vapors, and Dusts for Electrical Equipment in Hazardous (Classified) Locations.*

In accordance with NFPA 30, *Flammable and Combustible Liquids Code,* special electrical equipment is required for combustible liquids only where the materials are stored or handled above their flash points. NFPA 49 lists Electrical Group Classifications only for NFPA 321 defined Class I Flammable Liquids and Class II Combustible Liquids.

Where a flammable or combustible liquid or flammable gas is not listed in NFPA 497M, NFPA 49 shows the Group as "undesignated," e.g., Class I, Group D. The NFPA 497M Committee is always adding to its Group listings, and a user of NFPA 49 may sometimes get a Group designation for a particular chemical from the NFPA Technical Committee on Electrical Equipment in Chemical Atmospheres or, failing this, may submit a sample to Underwriters Laboratories for testing and determination of the proper group.

The same is true of the combustible dusts. NFPA 49 shows the group as "undesignated" when NFPA 497M has no specific listing for the material, and the NFPA 497M Committee or Underwriters Laboratories may be able to provide the proper group.

Information on the extent of hazardous locations and on the type of electrical equipment and installations used in such areas is included in Appendix D.

Appendix B Guide for the Preparation of Hazardous Chemicals Data Sheets for NFPA 49

This Appendix is not a part of the recommendations of this NFPA document, but is included for informational purposes only.

Purpose. The purpose of this guide is to give interested persons the information needed to assemble a preliminary data sheet on a specific chemical for proposed inclusion in NFPA 49. This guide sets out the selection protocol by which the user of this guide can determine whether a chemical should be included in NFPA 49, then provides detailed instructions on completing a data sheet. A blank data sheet form and a completed sample form are included with this guide.

Selection Protocol. Since it is not possible for NFPA 49 to address all of the acutely hazardous chemicals in commerce, the Committee has established a list of criteria. A chemical that does not meet at least one of the criteria set forth below will not be included in NFPA 49. Further, the chemical must be of commercial significance. To be considered commercially significant, a chemical must be available in containers of 5-gallon (18.9 liters) size or larger or in pallet-load quantities, or must otherwise be considered commercially significant. Mild oxidizers, commercial explosives and blasting agents, mutagens, carcinogens, teratogens, oncogens, and etiological agents will not be included. Commercial formulations of organic peroxides will also not be included due to the numerous different peroxide formulations currently being produced.

To be included in NFPA 49, a chemical must meet one of the criteria listed below. (NFPA 704, Standard System for the Identification of Hazards of Materials for Emergency Response, is used to identify the relative hazards of materials. For your convenience, the definitions of the NFPA 704 hazard ratings are included in Appendix B.)

Chemicals having an NFPA 704 Health Hazard Rating, by short-term inhalation or physical contact, of 2 or higher.

Chemicals having an NFPA 704 Instability Rating of 1 or higher, but not including chemicals whose major hazard is mild oxidizing ability.

Chemicals that present unusual spill control or fire fighting problems.

Chemicals that present unusual storage problems.

NOTE: Chemicals that have only a fire hazard rating will not be covered. NFPA 49 will include an index listing the commonly used names and synonyms of the chemicals covered.

Format. The data sheets provide the following information (refer to the sample data sheet):

1. Identity. Name and synonyms (according to the U.S. Department of Transportation); DOT Hazard Class; UN (or NA) number; Chemical Abstracts Service (CAS) registry number; chemical formula; molecular weight; NFPA 704 Hazard Ratings.
2. Statement of Hazards. Key words describing the major health, fire, and instability hazards, using standard terminology established by ANSI Z129.1, American National Standard for Hazardous Industrial Chemicals = mPrecautionary Labeling.
3. Emergency Response Personal Protective Equipment. Protective clothing and equipment for use by emergency response personnel.
4. Spill or Leak Procedures. Appropriate procedures to minimize hazards of spills or leaks; quantities for which spills or leaks must be reported to the Environmental Protection Agency.
5. Fire Fighting Procedures. Appropriate tactics and extinguishing agents suitable for small and large fires.
6. Health Hazards. Effects that may result from short-term exposure.
7. Fire and Explosion Hazards. Any unusual fire or explosion hazards, such as pyrophoricity; flash point; autoignition temperature; flammable limits.
8. Instability and Reactivity Hazards. Thermal instability; reactivity with air, water, or other classes of chemicals; other chemical hazards such as shock, impact, and friction sensitivity.
9. Storage Recommendations. Appropriate storage guidelines and recommendations for separation.
10. Usual Shipping Containers.
11. Physical Properties. Appearance, color, odor, and physical state; melting and boiling points; specific gravity; water solubility; vapor density and vapor pressure.
12. Electrical Equipment Group Classification (if applicable).
13. References. List of sources of data used to fill out the sheet.

Specific Instructions for Completing the Data Sheet.

NOTE: In any case where information for a specific entry is not available, not determined, or otherwise not known, use the term "UNK," for unknown.

1. Identity. The name used for the chemical will be its proper shipping name, as specified by the U.S. Department of Transportation. Commonly used synonyms should also be given. The DOT hazard class and four-digit UN (or NA) number are to be given. These may be found in the Code of Federal Regulations, Title 49, Part 172, Tables 172.101 and 172.102. The Chemical Abstracts Service (CAS) registry number is to be given. (A convenient source of the latter is the TOSCA Chemical Substances Inventory, Volumes II and III: Substance Name Index.)

   The structural line formula should follow the protocol of the International Union of Pure and Applied Chemistry. In most cases, the formula found in standard chemistry references, such as the CRC Handbook of Chemistry and Physics, will meet this requirement. Double and triple bonds are to be shown by horizontal lines. The molecular weight of the chemical is to be listed.

   The NFPA 704 hazard ratings are to be given in the diamond-shaped boxes provided. The ratings for many chemicals may be found in the 1975 edition of NFPA 49, Hazardous Chemicals Data, or in NFPA 325M, Fire Hazard Properties of Flammable Liquids, Gases, and Volatile Solids. For new candidates, the ratings will have to be chosen according to criteria established by NFPA 704, Standard System for the Identification of the Hazards of Materials for Emergency Response. (See Appendix B for further information.)
2. Statement of Hazards. The key words used to describe the principal hazards are those defined in the current edition of ANSI Z129.1-1988, American National Standard for Hazardous Industrial Chemicals Precautionary Labeling. For chemicals having multiple hazards, the key words should be listed in order of descending severity. If the multiple hazards are equally severe, then the key words are to be listed in the following order: health, flammability, instability. Appropriate key words are described in NFPA 704, *Standard System for the Identification of the Hazards of Materials for Emergency Response,* included in this guide.
3. Emergency Response Personal Protective Equipment. In this section report the preferred personal protective equipment to be worn by any emergency response personnel involved in rescue, fire fighting, or incident mitigation. This section is to include information on required breathing apparatus.

   If breathing apparatus is recommended, simply state this. NFPA 49 will describe the type of breathing apparatus that is acceptable for use in emergency situations. This will almost always be self-contained breathing apparatus, operating in the positive pressure mode and equipped with full eye protection and a full face piece.

   Describe the type of protective clothing appropriate for the hazard. As used in NFPA 49, "full protective clothing" means protection to prevent hazardous materials from contacting the skin of the emergency responder. The term includes helmet, breathing apparatus, coat and pants customarily worn by fire fighters, rubber boots, gloves, and covering for the neck, ears, and any parts of the head not protected by the helmet, breathing apparatus, or face piece. "Special protective clothing" refers to clothing that is specifically designed to protect the wearer from a specific hazard or the effects of a specific chemical. Special protective clothing will be further defined in NFPA 49. Special protective clothing is recommended for those materials having an NFPA 704 Health Hazard Rating of 3 or 4 and for those materials that present such an extreme fire hazard that full encapsulation, high temperature proximity suits may be required.

4. Spill or Leak Procedures. This section is to be used to describe appropriate procedures for controlling or stabilizing a spill or leak. Guidance should only be directed at stopping a leak, preventing runoff, and avoiding hazardous reactions due to unintended contact or mixing with incompatible materials. This section is NOT intended to prescribe detailed cleanup or disposal instructions.

5. Fire Fighting Procedures. This section is to recommend appropriate suppression tactics to control or extinguish a fire involving the chemical. Where possible, specify different tactics for small versus large fires. List appropriate extinguishing agents and any agents that are not recommended due to possible hazardous reactions. Describe any special precautions that need to be taken. Keep in mind that the most readily available suppression agent is water and that it must be applied differently depending on the nature of the chemical. If the chemical is water-soluble, then water must be applied in large, flooding quantities to dilute the burning material. If the chemical is not water-soluble, then the water must be applied as a fine spray or fog to control the fire, to prevent its spread, and to absorb some of the heat generated by the fire. For solid chemicals that are not water reactive, flooding quantities of water are appropriate.

   In specifying fire fighting foam, remember that water-soluble liquids will require that "alcohol resistant" foams be specified.

   For solids that are water reactive, it may be best to simply smother with dry sand or clay or crushed limestone. In the case of combustible metals, use only dry sand or the special dry powder agents specifically approved for combustible metals. NEVER specify water, carbon dioxide, or halogenated agents for use on fires involving combustible metals.

   For flammable gases, it should be stated that the flow of gas must be stopped before extinguishment can be attempted.

   Where appropriate, point out that uninvolved containers will require hose streams for immediate cooling. Also, materials subject to violent decomposition or containers subject to violent rupture will require that fire fighting be conducted from a safe distance or from a protected location.

6. Health Hazards. The statement of health hazard ("life hazard" in past editions of NFPA 49) should clearly state the effects of acute (i.e., short-term, high level) exposure to the chemical by physical contact, eye and skin absorption, or inhalation. Since NFPA 49 is primarily intended to give emergency information, ingestion or chronic (long-term, low level) exposure will not be considered, nor will any carcinogenic, mutagenic, oncogenic, or teratogenic effects. If acute exposure can result in delayed or permanent effects, these effects should be described.

   ANSI Z129.1-1988 is to be used as a guide for health hazard statements.

7. Fire and Explosion Hazards. If the chemical displays any unusual fire or explosion hazards, such as pyrophoric behavior or susceptibility to detonation, note this information on the first line. Such behavior may include spontaneous ignition on contact with air or moisture or reaction with water to produce hydrogen gas.

   The flash point temperature is to be based on a closed cup test method, if at all possible. If the flash point temperature is based on a calculated value, such as is sometimes done for gases, indicate "(calc.)." Any flash point based on the Tag Open Tester (ASTM D1310) or the Cleveland Open Cup Tester (ASTM D92) is to be identified by "oc" after the temperature. Additional discussion on flash point materials is in NFPA 704, *Standard System for the Identification of the Hazards of Materials for Emergency Response,* included in this guide

   The autoignition temperature (AIT), as determined by the Standard Test Method for Autoignition Temperatures of Liquid Chemicals (ASTM E659), is to be listed. Existing data, which may have been determined using earlier, no longer recognized test procedures may still be used.

   The lower flammability limit (LFL) and upper flammability limit (UFL), in percent volume in air, are to be listed. It will be assumed that the flammable limits given were determined at standard temperature and pressure [77°F (25°C), 760 mm Hg]. Flammable limits determined at other conditions should include the reference temperature and/or pressure.

8. Instability and Reactivity Hazards. In this section, report information on thermal instability, and hazardous reactivity with air, water, or other classes of chemicals, in this order. Please note, that ignition on contact with air or water should be reported in the section on Fire and Explosion Hazards. In reporting thermal instability, report the temperature at which the material will undergo decomposition, polymerization, or other hazardous reaction. If the "self-accelerating decomposition temperature" (SADT) is known, report it here. Also report here the maximum temperature at which the material is considered thermally stable. If the material does not exhibit thermal instability, report it as "Stable."

   Report any hazardous reactions with other classes of chemicals, such as reactions with oxidizers or reducing agents, or violent neutralization reactions. Also report here any violent reactions with water that do not result in ignition and any reactions that may produce a poisonous gas or otherwise dangerous gas or vapor.

   On the line marked Other Hazards, report any unusual sensitivity to shock, friction, or pressure. Also report here any significant corrosive properties. For example, some materials may be prone to violent decomposition when subjected to high pressures.

9. Storage Recommendations. In this section, specify any necessary recommendations for safe storage. Specify if exhaust ventilation is necessary to reduce hazardous concentrations of the chemical in air or if the chemical must be maintained at a specific temperature range. Guidance should be given for separation from incompatible materials. Where possible, refer to specific standards such as those

available from the National Fire Protection Association or the Compressed Gas Association.

10. Usual Shipping Containers.
11. Physical Properties. The chemical's physical state (e.g., solid, liquid, gas), appearance (e.g., crystalline, powdery), odor (e.g., sweet, pungent), and color (e.g., colorless, water-white, brown, clear, turbid) is to be listed.

    List the chemical's melting and boiling points at standard pressure, and its specific gravity at the reported reference temperature. If water solubility data is available, fill in the appropriate section using the words "soluble," "partly soluble," or "not soluble," whichever is most correct. For the purposes of this Guide, "soluble" means 25 grams or more in 100 ml of water, "partly soluble" means 10 to 24 grams per 100 ml, and "not soluble" means less than 10 grams per 100 ml. The chemical's vapor density and vapor pressure (along with the reference temperature) should be given.
12. Electrical Equipment Group Classification. For flammable gases and liquids and for combustible dusts, it is often necessary to specify explosion-proof or dust ignition-proof electrical equipment. To properly specify such equipment, the correct group classification for the chemical should be circled. Sources of this information include: NFPA 497, *Recommended Practice for the Classification of Flammable Liquids, Gases, or Vapors and of Hazardous (Classified) Locations for Electrical Installations in Chemical Process Areas;* NMAB 353-4, *Classification of Dusts Relative to Electrical Equipment in Class II Hazardous Locations;* NMAB 353-5, *Classification of Gases, Liquids, and Volatile Solids Relative to Explosion-Proof Electrical Equipment.*

    If hazardous location electrical equipment is not required, circle "None."
13. References Used. List in this section any appropriate references used to prepare the data sheet. This information is solely for the use of the Committee during preparation of NFPA 49.
14. Preparer's Identification. The preparer of the data sheet should date the sheet and provide his or her name, address, and telephone number. This information is solely for the use of the Committee during preparation of NFPA 49. It will not be published in the final edition.

Suggested Terminology from ANSI Z12 9.1, American National Standard for Hazardous Industrial Chemicals—Precautionary Labeling

Key Words for Statements of Hazard

Hazard	Suggested Statements
TOXICITY	Highly toxic. May be fatal if absorbed through skin. Highly toxic. May be fatal if inhaled. Toxic. Harmful if absorbed through skin. Toxic. Harmful if inhaled.
IRRITATION	Strong sensitizer. May cause severe allergic respiratory reaction. Respiratory irritant. Causes respiratory tract irritation. Eye irritant. Causes eye irritation.
OXYGEN DEPLETION	Inert gas (vapor). Reduces oxygen available for breathing.
CORROSIVITY	Corrosive. Causes severe eye (skin) burns.
FLAMMABILITY	Pyrophoric. Extremely flammable. Catches fire if exposed to air. Flammable gas. May cause flash fire. (Extremely) flammable liq uid and vapor. Vapor may cause flash fire. Flammable solid. Eas ily ignited. Combustible liquid and vapor.
REACTIVITY	Strong oxidizer. Contact with combustible material may cause fire. Water reactive. Contact with water or moist air may cause fire (hazardous reaction). Thermally unstable. Decomposes at ______°F. Thermally unstable. Polymerizes at ______°F. Shock- (friction-) sensitive.

SAMPLE DATA SHEET

NAME: ____________________

SYNONYMS: ____________________

FORMULA: ____________________

DOT CLASS: ____________________

ID NO.: ____________________

CAS NO.: ____________________

MOL. WT.: ____________________

STATEMENT OF HAZARDS: ____________________

EMERGENCY RESPONSE PERSONAL PROTECTIVE EQUIPMENT: ____________________

SPILL OR LEAK PROCEDURES: ____________________

FIRE FIGHTING PROCEDURES: ____________________

HEALTH HAZARDS: ____________________

FIRE AND EXPLOSION HAZARDS: ____________________

FLASH POINT: ____________________

AUTOIGNITION TEMPERATURE: ____________________

FLAMMABLE LIMITS: ____________________

INSTABILITY AND REACTIVITY HAZARDS: ____________________

STORAGE RECOMMENDATIONS: ____________________

USUAL SHIPPING CONTAINERS: ____________________

PHYSICAL PROPERTIES: ____________________

MELTING POINT: ____________________

BOILING POINT: ____________________

SPECIFIC GRAVITY: ____________________

SOLUBILITY IN WATER: ____________________

VAPOR DENSITY: ____________________

VAPOR PRESSURE: ____________________

ELECTRICAL EQUIPMENT: ____________________

SAMPLE DATA SHEET

NAME: ____________________

SYNONYMS: ____________________

FORMULA: ____________________

DOT CLASS: ____________________

ID NO.: ____________________

CAS NO.: ____________________

MOL. WT.: ____________________

STATEMENT OF HAZARDS: ____________________

EMERGENCY RESPONSE PERSONAL PROTECTIVE EQUIPMENT: ____________________

SPILL OR LEAK PROCEDURES: ____________________

FIRE FIGHTING PROCEDURES: ____________________

HEALTH HAZARDS: ____________________

FIRE AND EXPLOSION HAZARDS: ____________________

FLASH POINT: ____________________

AUTOIGNITION TEMPERATURE: ____________________

FLAMMABLE LIMITS: ____________________

INSTABILITY AND REACTIVITY HAZARDS: ____________________

STORAGE RECOMMENDATIONS: ____________________

USUAL SHIPPING CONTAINERS: ____________________

PHYSICAL PROPERTIES: ____________________

MELTING POINT: ____________________

BOILING POINT: ____________________

SPECIFIC GRAVITY: ____________________

SOLUBILITY IN WATER: ____________________

VAPOR DENSITY: ____________________

VAPOR PRESSURE: ____________________

ELECTRICAL EQUIPMENT: ____________________

Suggested Health Hazard Statements.

Do not get in eyes, on skin, or on clothing. Wash thoroughly after handling.

Do not breathe (dust/vapor/gas).

Suggested Fire Hazard Statements.
Keep away from sources of ignition.
Keep away from heat, sparks, and flame.
In case of fire, flood with water.
In case of fire, use water, dry chemical, carbon dioxide, or ("alcohol resistant") foam.
In case of fire, use water spray.
In case of fire, soak with water.
In case of fire, smother with dry sand, dry clay, dry ground limestone, or use approved Class D extinguishers. DO NOT use carbon dioxide or halogenated extinguishing agents. DO NOT use water.
In case of fire, do not attempt to extinguish until flow of gas is shut off.
Apply cooling streams of water from a safe distance or from a protected location.

Appendix C Electrical Requirements for Hazardous Locations

This Appendix is not a part of the recommendations of this NFPA document, but is included for informational purposes only.

Article 500 - "Hazardous (Classified) Locations" of the National Electrical Code provides specific requirements for electrical installations in locations where fire or explosion hazards exist due to flammable gases or vapors, flammable liquids, combustible dusts, or ignitible fibers or flyings. Hazardous locations are divided into three classes:

Class I locations are those in which flammable gases or vapors are present in air in quantities sufficient to produce explosive or ignitible mixtures.

Class II locations are those that are hazardous because of the presence of combustible dust.

Class III locations are those that are hazardous because of easily ignitible fibers and flyings. This class is not of interest as far as NFPA 49 is concerned.

Further, the NEC divides Class I and Class II hazardous locations into Division 1 and Division 2 locations. A Division 1 location is one in which an ignitible atmosphere is assumed to be present most or part of the time. A good example is the area around an open top tank blending operation. The rationale here is that an ignitible atmosphere is present during normal operation, repair or maintenance and that only a malfunction of the electrical system is necessary for ignition to occur. A Division 2 location is one in which an ignitible concentration is not normally present but can result due to an abnormal condition in the processing or storage equipment. A good example is an outside, totally contained, processing plant which may on occasion release ignitible vapors due to a leak or other malfunction. The rationale here is that two abnormal conditions=mfailure of the electrical system and abnormal operation of process equipment=mmust occur more or less simultaneously for an ignition to take place. There is also a Division 2 transition area around almost every Division 1 area since a Division 1 area and an unclassified area cannot adjoin each other.

An electrical installation that is satisfactory for a Class I location is not usually satisfactory for a Class II location and vice versa. Further, electrical equipment that is satisfactory for one vapor or gas is not necessarily satisfactory for another vapor or gas. The same is true for Class II locations=mthe electrical equipment for one dust is not necessarily satisfactory for another dust. To assure the specification of proper electrical equipment for the hazard inherent in the material, the classes are further subdivided into groups as follows:

Class I
Group A. Atmospheres containing acetylene.
Group B. Atmospheres containing hydrogen or other gases of equivalent hazard.
Group C. Atmospheres containing cyclopropane, ethylene, ethyl ether, or gases or vapors of equivalent hazard.
Group D. Atmospheres containing acetone, ethanol, gasoline, methane, propane, or gases or vapors of equivalent hazard.

Class II
Group E. Atmospheres containing combustible metal dusts, including aluminum, magnesium, and their alloys, or other combustible dusts whose particle size, abrasiveness, and conductivity present similar hazards in the use of electrical equipment.
Group F. Atmospheres containing combustible carbonaceous dusts that have more than 8 percent total entrapped volatiles or that have been sensitized by other materials so that they present an explosion hazard.
Group G. Atmospheres containing other combustible dusts including flour, grain, wood flour, plastic, and chemicals.

Special electrical equipment for Class I, Division 1 locations is known as explosion-proof equipment. All electrical equipment tends to breathe despite tight, gasketed joints and close fitting flanges. This can allow ignitible gases and vapors from the surrounding atmosphere to penetrate to the inside of the equipment. Explosion-proof electrical equipment is designed with the strength to contain the expected explosion pressure and with joints tight enough to prevent the propagation of flame from within the equipment to the outside atmosphere. Such equipment is approved for one or more of the classified Groups of gases or vapors. Special electrical equipment for Class I, Division 2 locations is less stringent and is generally described as non-sparking. Assured ventilation in an area, either from being in an outside location or from having interlocked ventilating fans, can reduce the classification of areas from Vision 1 to Division 2. Also, since the lower flammable limit of almost all hazardous chemicals is considerably higher than the threshold limit value that must be maintained for health reasons, there are very few true, large, Vision 1 locations i.e., an ignitible atmosphere is present most or all of the time. Table 5-3.5.3 Electrical Area Classifications in NFPA 30, Flammable and Combustible Liquids Code specifies the extents of the Class I, Division 1 and 2 areas in various flammable liquid storing and handling operations.

Special electrical equipment for Class II, Division 1 locations is known as dust ignition-proof and the equipment for Class II, Division 2 locations is described as dust-tight. Since gaskets and seals are effective in preventing ignitible dusts from penetrating into the electrical equipment and coming into contact with sparking parts, the design problem in Class II electrical equipment, is preventing ignition due to high surface temperatures or tracking.

The problem of preventing ignition of either Class I or Class II flammable atmospheres by electrical equipment can also be handled by providing purged and pressurized electrical equipment. Here enclosures with ordinary electrical equipment is provided with purge air at a pressure high enough to sweep out existing ignitible mixtures and prevent the reentry of ignitible mixtures into the equipment, while it is electrically alive. See NFPA 496, Standard for Purged and Pressurized Enclosures for Electrical Equipment.

Also suitable for use in hazardous locations is intrinsically safe electrical equipment. Here the energy of any spark that may be generated during malfunction of the approved electrical equipment is incapable of igniting the flammable atmosphere. See UL 913, Intrinsically Safe Apparatus and Associated Apparatus for Use in Class I, II, and III, Division 1, Hazardous (Classified) Locations.

For a definitive discussion of area classification and for recommendations of how far away from a vapor or dust source a hazardous location should extend, the reader should consult NFPA 497 *Recommended Practice for the Classification of Flammable Liquids, Gases, or Vapors and of Hazardous (Classified) Locations for Electrical Installations in Chemical Process Areas.*

NFPA 325

1994 Edition

Fire Hazard Properties of

Flammable Liquids, Gases, and Volatile Solids

NFPA 325

Guide to

Fire Hazard Properties of Flammable Liquids, Gases, and Volatile Solids

1994 Edition, Amended 2001

This edition of NFPA 325, *Guide to Fire Hazard Properties of Flammable Liquids, Gases, and Volatile Solids,* was revised by NFPA Staff and the Technical Committee on Classification and Properties of Hazardous Chemical Data. At the NFPA Fall Meeting held November 15–18, 1998 in Atlanta, GA, the document was withdrawn from the *National Fire Codes®*, along with NFPA 49 and later NFPA 491. Many of the recent revisions to NFPA 49, 325, and 491 were generated by the Committee with the prompting of staff, since few if any public proposals or comments were received. The Committee wished to note that these reasons, coupled with concern of the speed in updating the data (which was not possible in a 3 to 5 year cycle), were the sole reasons the documents were withdrawn.

Origin and Development of NFPA 325

The first edition of NFPA 325, 325M, was presented to the Association in 1930. Successively revised and enlarged editions were published in 1935, 1941, 1945, 1947, 1951, 1954, 1960, 1965, 1969, 1977, 1984, 1991, and 1994.

This 2001 edition is an amended version of the 1994 edition. Many of the chemicals were re-rated in accordance with the 1990 and 1996 editions of NFPA 704, *Standard System for the Identification of the Fire Hazards of Materials,* which contained more quantitative criteria for the ratings. Up-to-date chemical data were used to rate the chemicals, which are easily and more readily available in this age of electronic databases. New data included in this edition of the *Guide* are NFPA 30/OSHA flammable and combustible liquid classifications and Chemical Abstracts Service (CAS) numbers.

NFPA 325 summarizes in table format data the fire hazard properties of about 1,500 substances. In addition, the chemical names, synonyms, and CAS numbers cross-referenced to the appropriate document are listed in three matrixes at the beginning of the *Guide.*

This document is a compilation of basic fire protection properties of various materials, prefaced by an explanation of the properties covered. The data contained have been collected from numerous authoritative sources, including the U.S. Bureau of Mines, Factory Mutual Research Corporation, and Underwriters Laboratories Inc., as well as from the manufacturers of the materials. The originating source of the data is on file at NFPA headquarters and may be obtained upon request.

The values for any given property are representative and deemed suitable for general use. Where differences exist in reference sources, the value selected for inclusion in this compilation is conservative. Slight differences are to be expected between data sources due to differences in the purity of test samples, minor differences in test apparatus, and minor differences in technique and observation. In almost all cases, these minor variations have little practical significance. Where there is difference of opinion as to the actual value of a property of a given material or where the validity of the data presented is questioned, further tests should then be conducted on representative samples of the specific material in question by a qualified testing laboratory.

Technical Committee on Classification and Properties of Hazardous Chemical Data

Gary Robinson, *Chair*
LMG Property Engineering, IL [I]
Rep. The Alliance of American Insurers

Robert A. Michaels, *Secretary*
RAM TRAC Corporation, NY [SE]

Laurence G. Britton, Union Carbide Corporation, WV [M]
Lance "Skip" Edwards, National Paint & Coatings Association, DC [M]
Richard Gowland, Dow Chemical, Great Britain [M]
Ronald Keefer, Menlo Park Fire Protection District, CA [E]
Ron A. Kirsch, OHS Associates, Inc., TN [SE]
Arthur A. Krawetz, Phoenix Chemical Laboratory, Inc., IL [RT]
F. Owen Kubias, Rocky River, OH [SE]
Roland J. Land, Risk Control Consultants, LLC, NJ [SE]
Jennifer L. Nelson, AT&T — EH&S, NY [U]
Rep. NFPA Industrial Fire Protection Section
Curtis G. Payne, U.S. Coast Guard, DC [U]
David F. Peterson, Madison, WI Fire Department, WI [E]
Thomas A. Salamone, Health Care & Life Safety Concepts, NY [I]
William J. Satterfield, III, RODE & Associates, LLC, RI [I]

Nonvoting

Whitney Fay Long, c/o CDR Long SACLANTCEN, APO AE
Ira Wainless, U.S. Department of Labor/OSHA, DC

Amy B. Spencer, NFPA Staff Liaison

Committee Scope: This Committee shall have primary responsibility for documents on the classification of the relative hazards of all chemical solids, liquids, and gases and to compile data on the hazard properties of these hazardous chemicals.

This list represents the membership at the time the Committee was balloted on the text of this edition. Since that time, changes in the membership may have occurred.

NOTE: Membership on a Committee shall not in and of itself constitute an endorsement of the Association or any document developed by the Committee on which the member serves.

Contents

NFPA 325

Guide to

Fire Hazard Properties of Flammable Liquids, Gases, and Volatile Solids

1994 Edition, Amended 2001

Chapter 1 General

1-1 Scope. This guide applies to flammable liquids, flammable gases, and volatile flammable solids.

1-2 Purpose. The purpose of this guide is to provide the user with basic fire hazard information on the materials covered by the scope.

1-3 Definitions of Fire Hazard Properties.

1-3.1 No single fire hazard property, such as flash point or ignition temperature, should be used to describe or appraise the fire hazard or fire risk of a material, product, assembly, or system under actual fire conditions. The fire hazard properties given in this guide have been determined under controlled laboratory conditions and may properly be used to measure or describe the response of materials, products, assemblies, or systems under these conditions. Properties measured under these conditions may be used as elements of a fire risk assessment only when such assessment takes into account all of the factors that are pertinent to the evaluation of the fire hazard of a given situation.

1-3.2 The pertinent literature seldom mentions the degree of purity of the material being tested; even boiling point or melting point data are frequently missing. These data, if available, would permit judging the purity of the material and, hence, the reliance to be placed on the values reported, particularly with respect to flash point and flammable range. Finally, it must be remembered that there is little industrial use of high purity materials. As a consequence of these considerations, no values of purity are given in this compilation. The melting points and boiling points should be regarded as approximations.

1-3.3 Flash Point. The flash point of a liquid is the minimum temperature at which the liquid gives off sufficient vapor to form an ignitible mixture with air near the surface of the liquid or within the test vessel used. By "ignitible mixture" it is meant a mixture that is within the flammable range (between the upper and lower limits) and, thus, is capable of propagation of flame away from the source of ignition. Some evaporation takes place below the flash point, but not in quantities sufficient to form an ignitible mixture. Flash point applies mostly to flammable and combustible liquids, although certain solids, such as camphor and naphthalene, that slowly volatilize at ordinary room temperature, or certain liquids, such as benzene, that freeze at relatively high temperatures, will exhibit a flash point in the solid state.

The flash points given in this manual are, for the most part, closed cup flash points. Where the only available data are based on open cup tests, this is designated by the initials "oc" after the entry. In the case of some of the older data in this manual, it could not be determined whether a closed cup or open cup procedure had been used. In these cases, it has been assumed that the data are based on closed cup tests. For further information on the acceptable flash point test procedures, see NFPA 704, *Standard System for the Identification of the Hazards of Materials for Emergency Response.*

1-3.4 Ignition Temperature. The ignition temperature of a substance, whether solid, liquid, or gas, is the minimum temperature required to cause self-sustained combustion, independently of the heating or heated element. Ignition temperatures observed under one set of conditions may differ markedly from those observed under another set of conditions. For this reason, ignition temperatures should be regarded as approximations. Some of the variables known to affect ignition temperature are the percentage of the gas or vapor in the mixture, the shape and size of the test vessel, the rate and duration of heating, the kind and temperature of the ignition source, and catalytic or other effects of materials that may be present. As there are many differences in ignition temperature test methods, such as the size and shape of the test vessel, the material of construction of the test vessel, method and rate of heating, residence time, and method of flame detection, it is not surprising that reported ignition temperatures may differ for the same material.

The majority of the data reported in this manual have been obtained by one of two methods: ASTM D286 and ASTM D2155. Both have been withdrawn by the American Society for Testing and Materials. ASTM D2155 has been replaced by ASTM E659, *Standard Test Method for Autoignition Temperatures of Liquid Chemicals.* An earlier test method, ASTM D2883, *Test Method for Reaction Threshold Temperature of Liquid and Solid Materials,* provides for the study of autoignition phenomena at reduced and elevated pressures. Federal Test Method Standard 791B, Method 5050, is another current test method that provides for the measurement of autoignition properties in the same terms used by the ASTM procedures.

Previous test methods relied only on visual detection of flame. Consequently, the ignition temperatures obtained by these procedures were the minimum temperatures at which hot-flame ignition occurred. The current test methods employ thermoelectric flame detection, thus permitting the detection of nonluminous or barely luminous reactions that were difficult or impossible to detect by the older procedures. As a result, the following terms have come into use:

Hot-Flame Ignition. A rapid, self-sustaining, sometimes audible gas-phase reaction of the sample or its decomposition products with an oxidant. A readily visible yellow or blue flame usually accompanies the reaction.

Cool-Flame Ignition. A relatively slow, self-sustaining, barely luminous gas-phase reaction of the sample or its decomposition products with an oxidant. Cool flames are visible only in a darkened area.

Pre-Flame Reaction. A slow, nonluminous gas-phase reaction of the sample or its decomposition products with an oxidant.

Catalytic Reaction. A relatively fast, self-sustaining, energetic, sometimes luminous, sometimes audible reaction that occurs as a result of the catalytic action of any substance on the sample or its decomposition products, in admixture with an oxidant.

Non-Combustive Reaction. A reaction other than combustion or thermal degradation that is undergone by certain substances when they are exposed to heat. Thermal polymerization is an example of this type of reaction.

Reaction Threshold. The lowest temperature at which any reaction of the sample or its decomposition products occurs, for any sample/oxidant ratio.

Autoignition Temperature (AIT). The currently accepted term for the Hot-Flame Ignition Temperature.

Cool-Flame Reaction Threshold (CFT). The lowest temperature at which cool-flame ignitions are observed for a particular system. Previously undefined.

Preflame-Reaction Threshold (RTT). The lowest temperature at which exothermic gas-phase reactions are observed for a particular system. Previously undefined.

Previously, reported ignition temperatures, including those given in this manual, have corresponded roughly to the autoignition temperature (AIT), provided that proper allowances were made for empirical differences in the measurement technique. In the future, it is expected that CFT and RTT will routinely be reported. Both are lower than AIT and are significant factors to be evaluated in the assessment of the overall ignition risk of a given system. Cool flames are self-sustaining, exothermic ignition reactions that, under proper circumstances, may act as the initiator of more energetic hot-flame reactions. Pre-flame reactions have the capacity, under adiabatic or near-adiabatic conditions, to elevate the temperature of a fuel/air mixture to the point where cool- or hot-flame ignition may occur.

As an illustration of the effects of test methods, the ignition temperature of hexane, as determined by three different methods, are 437°F (225°C), 637°F (336°C), and 950°F (510°C). The effect of percentage composition is shown by the following ignition temperatures for pentane: 1018.4°F (548.4°C) at 1.5 percent, 935.6°F (502.4°C) at 3.75 percent, and 888.8°F (476.3°C) at 7.65 percent. The following ignition temperatures for carbon disulfide demonstrate the effect of the size of the test vessel: 248°F (120°C) in a 200 ml flask, 230°F (110°C) in a 1 liter flask, and 205°F (96°C) in a 10 liter flask. The effect of the material of construction of the test vessel is shown by the following ignition temperatures for benzene: 1060°F (572°C) in a quartz vessel and 1252°F (678°C) in an iron vessel.

The ignition temperature of a combustible solid is influenced by the rate of air flow, rate of heating, and size of the sample. Small sample tests have shown that, as the rate of air flow or the rate of heating is increased, the ignition temperature decreases to a minimum value, then increases.

1-3.5 Flammable (Explosive) Limits. In the case of gases or vapors that form flammable mixtures with air, oxygen, or other oxidizers, such as chlorine and nitrous oxide, there is a minimum concentration of the material below which propagation of flame does not occur. Similarly, there is a maximum concentration above which propagation of flame does not occur. These boundary mixtures, which, if ignited, will just propagate flame, are known as the "lower and upper flammable or explosive limits" and are usually expressed as percent by volume of the material in air (or other oxidant). In popular terms, a mixture below the lower flammable limit (LFL) is too "lean" to burn, while a mixture above the upper flammable limit (UFL) is too "rich" to burn.

The values for the flammable limits given in this manual are based on atmospheric temperatures and pressures, unless otherwise indicated. There will be considerable variation in flammable limits at temperatures and pressures above or below ambient. The general effect of an increase in temperature or pressure is to decrease the lower limit and to increase the upper limit, i.e., broaden the range between the two limits. A decrease in the temperature or pressure has the opposite effect. In most cases, the values given in this manual represent the concentration limits over which hot-flame ignitions have been observed. If cool-flame ignitions are considered, wider flammable ranges are observed.

Research has shown that flammability limits are not a fundamental combustion property, but depend on many variables, including the surface-to-volume ratio of the test vessel, the direction of air flow, and the velocity of air flow. In some experiments conducted at laminar flow velocities, the upper limit increased with increasing flow velocity, reached a maximum that was independent of the diameter of the test vessel, then decreased as flow became turbulent. The lower limit has been unaffected by air flow rate.

ASTM E681 is the current test method for determining flammable limits. However, much of the data were obtained in small diameter tubes with ignition at the bottom so that flame propagation was upward. For most hydrocarbons, this method is appropriate. However, for highly oxygenated, aminated, or halogenated materials, larger diameter equipment is required to avoid quenching of the flame. Larger diameter test equipment or more energetic ignition sources may better reflect real world burning conditions.

The terms "flammable limits" and "explosive limits" are interchangeable.

The range of concentration between the lower flammable limit and the upper flammable limit is known as the "flammable range," also referred to and synonymous with "explosive range." All concentrations of a gas or vapor in air that lie between the flammable limits are ignitible.

1-3.6 Specific Gravity (Relative Density). The specific gravity of a substance is the ratio of the weight of that substance to the weight of an equal volume of another substance. In this manual, the other substance is water. The values given in this manual for specific gravity are rounded to the nearest tenth. For materials whose specific gravity is from 0.95 to 1.0, the value is shown as 1.0 –. For materials whose specific gravity is from 1.0 to 1.05, the value is given as 1.0+. In a few cases, such as fuel oils, where the percentage composition of the substance varies, specific gravity is given as less than (<) or greater than (>) 1.

1-3.7 Vapor Density. The vapor density of a substance is the ratio of the weight of a volume of pure vapor or gas (no air present) to an equal volume of dry air at the same temperature and pressure. It is calculated as the ratio of the molecular weight of the substance to the molecular weight of air, 29. A vapor density of less than 1 indicates that the substance is lighter than air and will tend to rise in a relatively calm atmosphere. A vapor density of greater than 1 indicates that the substance is heavier than air and may travel along grade level for a considerable distance to a source of ignition and flash back, assuming the gas or vapor is flammable.

1-3.8 Boiling Point. The boiling point of each liquid is given at a pressure of 14.7 psia (760 mm Hg). Where an accurate boiling point is not available for a specific entry or where a specific entry is actually a mixture of components and does not have a constant boiling point, the boiling point given is the 10 percent distillation point as determined by ASTM D86, *Standard Method of Test for Distillation of Petroleum Products.*

1-3.9 Melting Point. Melting points are reported in this manual for most materials that melt at 70°F (21°C) or higher.

However, the melting point is not available for some of these materials.

1-3.10 Water Solubility. Water solubility data are reported only for those materials for which reliable information is available, because of the lack of uniformity with which water solubility data are reported in the literature and because of the conflicting statements that sometimes accompany these data. Where such data is reported in this manual, "No" indicates that the material's solubility is less than 10 grams per 100 milliliters (ml) of water; "Slight" indicates solubility is between 10 and 24 grams per 100 ml of water; "Yes" indicates solubility of 25 or more grams per 100 ml of water.

"No," "Very Slight," "Slight," and "Yes" are sometimes used without definition in the literature to describe water solubility. In those cases where doubt exists as to a material's solubility in water, tests should be conducted.

Information on the degree to which a material is soluble in water is useful in determining effective extinguishing methods and agents. For example, alcohol-resistant fire fighting foams are usually recommended for water-soluble flammable and combustible liquids. Also, fires involving water-soluble liquids can be extinguished by dilution with water, although this method is not commonly used because of the amount of water needed to dilute most flammable liquids to the point of noncombustibility and because of the danger of frothing if the liquid is heated to the boiling point of water, 212°F (100°C).

1-4 Extinguishing Methods.

1-4.1 General. The extinguishing methods commonly used for fires involving flammable liquids are suitable for use on fires involving most of the materials listed in this manual. Carbon dioxide, dry chemical, foam, and vaporizing liquid extinguishing agents have all been found to be suitable for use on flammable liquid fires of moderate size, such as in dip tanks or small spills of no appreciable depth. The following comments apply to other extinguishing methods that have been found effective for the control or extinguishment of some flammable liquids fires.

Water spray or fog can be particularly effective on fires involving flammable liquids and volatile solids whose flash points exceed 100°F (37.8°C). However, with liquids whose flash points exceed 212°F (100°C), frothing may occur. For information on the installation of water spray protection for flammable and combustible liquids, see NFPA 15, *Standard for Water Spray Fixed Systems for Fire Protection.*

Automatic sprinklers are similar to water spray systems in extinguishing effectiveness. Their principal value is in absorbing the heat from the fire and keeping the surroundings cool until the flammable liquids fire either burns out or is extinguished by other means. Automatic sprinklers have a good record of fire control in garages, in paint and oil rooms, and in storage areas where liquids are kept in closed containers. In some industries that use water-soluble liquids, such as the distilled spirits industry, sprinkler systems have been used to achieve protection and extinguishment with excellent results. Where automatic sprinklers are used to protect open tanks, overflow drains are necessary to prevent sprinkler discharge from overflowing the tank and spreading burning liquid to other parts of the property. For further information on automatic sprinklers, see NFPA 13, *Standard for the Installation of Sprinkler Systems.*

Hose streams, both solid and straight streams, are frequently used to cool tanks, containers, and equipment from the heat of an exposing fire. They are also used for washing burning spills away from areas where the burning liquid could ignite other material. However, hose streams may also spread and extend the spill fire, if improperly used. Also, hose streams applied to open containers of burning liquid will only serve to spread the fire, either by splashing the burning liquid out of the container or by causing frothing of the liquid.

Use of automatic-closing covers on open tanks or equipment containing flammable or combustible liquid is also effective in fire control and extinguishment. The covers should be operated by a fusible link, with a manual override. Such covers are suitable for any size tank except where objects being dipped or conveyor systems may prevent tight closing of the cover.

1-4.2 Selecting an Extinguishing Method. The selection of the extinguishing method used should be made with some degree of caution. Flowing fires, such as may be caused by a leaking overhead pipe, with burning liquid on the ground, are always difficult to extinguish. The amount of extinguishing agent and its rate and method of application must be carefully chosen in relation to the size and type of fire anticipated and may call for special engineering judgment. The use of approved extinguishing equipment is also a major consideration.

The chemical and physical properties of the material involved will also affect the choice of extinguishing method and agent. Standard fire fighting foam cannot be used on fires involving water-soluble flammable liquids; the liquid destroys the foam blanket. Those properties that affect extinguishment were taken into consideration when selecting the methods given for each material in the column headed "Extinguishing Methods." The following information describes the properties of the material that dictate the numerically designated entries in this column.

1. *Water May Be Ineffective.* This precaution applies to materials that have a flash point below 100°F (37.8°C). Obviously, the lower the flash point, the less effective the water will be. However, water can be used on low-flash point liquids when applied as a spray to absorb heat and to protect exposed material of structures. Much of the effectiveness of using water spray, particularly from hose lines, will depend on the method of application. With proper selection of nozzles, even gasoline spill fires can be extinguished when several coordinated hose streams are used to sweep the flames from the surface of the burning liquid. Water has also been used to extinguish fires involving water-soluble flammable liquids by cooling and diluting the liquid. The distilled spirits industry has been especially successful in using water to control and extinguish fires of this type.

Thus, the phrase "water may be ineffective" indicates that, although water can be used to cool and protect exposed material, water may not be capable of extinguishing the fire unless used under favorable conditions by experienced fire fighters trained in fighting all types of flammable liquids fires.

2. *Water or Foam May Cause Frothing.* This statement applies to liquids having flash points above 212°F (100°C) and is included only as a precaution. It does not indicate that water or fire fighting foam should not be used. The frothing may be violent and could endanger any fire fighters located too close to the burning liquid, particularly when solid streams of water are directed onto the hot, burning liquid. On the other hand, a carefully applied water spray has frequently been used to achieve extinguishment by deliberately causing frothing only on the surface of the liquid; the foaming action

blankets the surface of the liquid and extinguishes the fire by excluding oxygen. This tactic is especially successful with high viscosity liquids. For example, certain asphalts have a low-flash point solvent added for fluidity, but because of the relatively high viscosity, frothing action is able to achieve fire control and extinguishment.

3. *Water May Be Used to Blanket Fire.* This statement is applicable to those liquids that have a specific gravity of 1.1 or greater and are not water-soluble. However, the water must be gently applied to the surface of the liquid, preferably with a fine spray or fog nozzle.

4. *Water May Be Ineffective, Except as a Blanket.* This statement is used as a warning for liquids whose flash points are below 100°F (37.8°C) and applies only to those liquids that have a specific gravity of 1.1 or greater and are not water-soluble. Here again, the water must be gently applied to the surface of the liquid.

5. *Alcohol Foam.* Alcohol-resistant fire fighting foam is recommended for use on all water-soluble liquids or polar solvent-type liquids, except for those that are only "very slightly" soluble. Certain judgment factors are introduced, however, since ordinary fire fighting foam may be used on some liquids that are only "slightly" soluble, particularly if the foam is applied at higher-than-normal application rates. Conversely, some flammable liquids, such as the higher molecular weight alcohols and amines, will destroy alcohol-resistant foams, even when applied at very high rates. Foams should not be used on water-reactive materials.

Some recently developed alcohol-resistant foams have been listed for use on both polar and nonpolar liquids. These "multipurpose" foams are suitable for use on nearly all flammable liquids (except those that are water-reactive) and are preferred for flammable liquid fires because they greatly minimize the problems of foam selection. Fire fighting foam suppliers should be consulted for recommendations regarding types of foam and application rates.

6. *Stop Flow of Gas.* For fires involving flammable gases, the best procedure is to stop the flow of the gas before attempting extinguishment of the fire. To extinguish the fire while allowing continued flow of the gas is extremely dangerous; an explosive cloud of gas/air mixture may be created that, if ignited, may cause far more damage than the original fire. Extinguishing the flame using carbon dioxide or dry chemical may be desirable to allow immediate access to valves to shut off the flow of gas, but this must be done carefully. In many cases, it will be preferable to allow continued burning, while protecting exposures with water spray, until the flow of gas can be stopped.

1-5 Suggested Hazard Identification.

1-5.1 The increased use of chemicals, many of which introduced hazards other than flammability, led to the need for a simple hazard identification system that could be immediately recognized by emergency response personnel. This need led to the development of the NFPA 704 Hazard Identification System, otherwise known as the NFPA 704 diamond. This system is completely described in NFPA 704, *Standard System for the Identification of the Hazards of Materials for Emergency Response.* The system provides simple, readily recognized, and easily understood markings that give, at a glance, a general idea of the inherent hazards of the material and the order of severity of these hazards, as they relate to fire protection, exposure, and control. The system's objectives are to provide an appropriate alert signal and on-the-spot information to safeguard the lives of both public and private emergency response personnel. The system also assists in planning for effective fire fighting operations and may be used by plant design engineers and plant protection and safety personnel.

The system identifies the hazards of a material in terms of three categories: "Health," "Flammability," and "Instability." It indicates the order of severity of these hazards by means of a numerical rating of 0, indicating no special hazard, to 4, indicating extreme hazard. The three hazard categories were selected after studying about 35 inherent and environmental hazards of materials that could affect fire fighting operations. The five degrees of hazard were decided upon as necessary to give the required information. Finally, the system had to be relatively simple and readily understood.

While the system is basically simple in application, the hazard evaluation required for the use of the system in a specific location must be made by experienced, technically competent persons. Their judgment must be based on factors that encompass a knowledge of the inherent hazards of different materials, including the extent of change in behavior to be anticipated under conditions of fire exposure and control.

1-5.2 Degrees of Hazard. The columns under "Suggested Hazard Identification" in this manual give the NFPA 704 severity ratings for each of the hazard categories for which information was available. Blank spaces indicate that sufficient information was not available for a severity rating to be assigned. It should be understood that the assignment of the ratings is based on judgment and that extenuating circumstances in plants and processes may dictate a change in any individual rating.

The following commentary on the degrees of hazard are an interpretation of the information contained in NFPA 704, *Standard System for the Identification of the Hazards of Materials for Emergency Response,* and are specifically related to fire fighting. See NFPA 704, contained in this Guide, for more detailed information.

Note: All materials contained in this guide have not yet been rated using the new definitions appearing in the 2000 edition of NFPA 704.

1-5.3 Health Hazard Rating. In general, the health hazard in fire fighting is that of a single exposure that may vary from a few seconds to as much as an hour. The physical exertion demanded in fire fighting operations or other emergencies may be expected to intensify the effects of any exposure. Only hazards arising out of the inherent properties of the material are considered. The following information is a brief summary based on the information in NFPA 704 and relates to the protective equipment normally available to fire fighters.

4 Materials that, on very short exposure, could cause death or major residual injury, including those that are too dangerous to be approached without specialized protective equipment. A few whiffs of the vapor or gas can cause death, or contact with the vapor or liquid may be fatal, if it penetrates the fire fighter's normal protective gear. The normal full protective clothing and breathing apparatus available to the typical fire fighter will not provide adequate protection against inhalation or skin contact with these materials.

3 Materials that, on short exposure, could cause serious temporary or residual injury, including those requiring protection from all bodily contact. Fire fighters may enter the area only if they are protected from all contact with the

material. Full protective clothing, including self-contained breathing apparatus, coat, pants, gloves, boots, and bands around legs, arms, and waist, should be provided. No skin surface should be exposed.

2 Materials that, on intense or continued (but not chronic) exposure, could cause temporary incapacitation or possible residual injury, including those requiring the use of respiratory protective equipment that has an independent air supply. These materials are hazardous to health, but areas may be entered freely if personnel are provided with full-face mask self-contained breathing apparatus that provides complete eye protection.

1 Materials that, on exposure, would cause significant irritation, but only minor residual injury, including those requiring the use of an approved air-purifying respirator. These materials are only slightly hazardous to health and only breathing protection is needed.

0 Materials that, on exposure under fire conditions, offer no hazard beyond that of ordinary combustible material.

1-5.4 Flammability Hazard Rating. Susceptibility to ignition and burning is the basis for assigning the degree of hazard within this category. The method of attacking the fire is influenced by this susceptibility factor. For further information, refer to Section 1-4, Extinguishing Methods. The following information is a brief summary based on the definitions of Flammability Hazard Rating contained in NFPA 704, *Standard System for the Identification of the Hazards of Materials for Emergency Response.*

4 This degree includes flammable gases, flammable cryogenic materials, pyrophoric liquids, and Class IA flammable liquids. The preferred method of fire attack is to stop the flow of material or to protect exposures while allowing the fire to burn itself out.

3 This degree includes Class IB and IC flammable liquids and materials that can be easily ignited under almost all normal temperature conditions. Water may be ineffective in controlling or extinguishing fires in such materials.

2 This degree includes materials that must be moderately heated before ignition will occur and includes Class II and IIIA combustible liquids and solids and semi-solids that readily give off ignitible vapors. Water spray may be used to extinguish fires in these materials because the materials can be cooled below their flash points.

1 This degree includes materials that must be preheated before ignition will occur, such as Class IIIB combustible liquids and solids and semi-solids whose flash point exceeds 200°F (93.4°C), as well as most ordinary combustible materials. Water may cause frothing if it sinks below the surface of the burning liquid and turns to steam. However, a water fog that is gently applied to the surface of the liquid will cause frothing that will extinguish the fire.

0 This degree includes any material that will not burn under typical fire conditions.

1-5.5 Instability Hazard Rating. The assignment of the degree of instability hazard is based on the potential of the material to release energy either by itself or when in contact with water. In assigning this rating, fire exposure was considered, along with exposure to shock and pressure. The following information is a brief summary based on the definitions of Instability Hazard Rating contained in NFPA 704, *Standard System for the Identification of the Hazards of Materials for Emergency Response.*

4 This degree includes those materials that, in themselves, are readily capable of detonation, explosive decomposition, or explosive reaction at normal temperatures and pressures. This includes materials that are sensitive to localized mechanical or thermal shock. If a material having this Instability Hazard Rating is involved in an advanced or massive fire, the area should be immediately evacuated.

3 This degree includes materials that, in themselves, are capable of detonation, explosive decomposition, or explosive reaction, but require a strong initiating source or heating under confinement. This includes materials that are sensitive to thermal and mechanical shock at elevated temperatures and pressures and materials that react explosively with water. Fires involving these materials should be fought from a protected location.

2 Materials that can undergo violent chemical changes at elevated temperatures and pressures. This also includes materials that may react violently with water or that may form potentially explosive mixtures with water. In advanced or massive fires involving these materials, fire fighting should be done from a safe distance or from a protected location.

1 This degree includes materials that are normally stable, but that may become unstable at elevated temperatures and pressures and materials. Fires involving these materials should be approached with caution.

0 This degree includes materials that are normally stable, even under fire exposure conditions, and that do not react with water. Normal fire fighting procedures may be used.

1-5.6 Additional Markings. The fourth space in the NFPA 704 rating is reserved for the use of two special symbols: OX, to denote materials that are oxidizing agents, and W̶, to denote materials that are water-reactive.

1-6 Additional Information.

1-6.1 Mixtures with Oxygen. Unless otherwise indicated, all values in this manual are based on tests conducted in normal air. For mixtures involving enriched oxygen atmospheres, the values may differ and an increase in hazard is probable.

1-6.2 Mixtures of Materials. Mixtures of two or more materials may have different fire hazard properties than any of the components. Although it is common practice to base the fire hazard of a mixture on that of the most hazardous component, consideration should be given to testing the mixture itself.

1-6.3 Mists and Froths. In finely divided form, such as a mist or spray, liquids can be ignited at temperatures considerably below their flash points. As in the case of vapors, the droplets of mist or spray must be present at a minimum concentration. Similarly, froths may be ignited at temperatures below the flash point.

1-7 Alphabetical Listing of Chemicals.

1-7.1 The materials in this manual are listed alphabetically by the name considered to be the most common. Other names and synonyms are indexed to this common name.

1-7.2 The following prefixes are considered to be a part of the name of the material. As such, they are generally not hyphenated and are used to alphabetically index the material when they appear at the beginning of the name.

Bis	Iso	Tetra
Di	Mono	Tri
Hexa	Penta	Tris

1-7.3 The prefix "mono" is often omitted. Thus, monochlorobenzene is frequently referred to as chlorobenzene. This manual uses the more common form. The alternate form is not given, unless it is also frequently used.

1-7.4 The following prefixes are not considered to be part of the name of the material. As such, they are hyphenated, but they are not used to alphabetically index the material.

o- (ortho)	d- (dextro)
m- (meta)	l- (levulo)
p- (para)	N- (nitro)
n- (normal)	α- (alpha)
sec- (secondary)	β- (beta)
tert- (tertiary)	γ- (gamma)

These prefixes may be written out in full, as in paradichlorobenzene. In this manual, they are usually abbreviated. Thus, paradichlorobenzene appears in this manual as p-dichlorobenzene and is indexed under D. In accordance with custom, the prefix n-, for "normal," is omitted, unless it appears in the middle of a name.

1-7.5 The prefixes "cis" and "trans" may be placed either at the beginning or the end of a name. In this manual, they are always listed at the end.

Fire Hazard Properties of Flammable Liquids, Gases, and Volatile Solids Table

Chemical Name Formula (Synonym) CAS No.	NFPA 30/ OSHA Class	Flash Point °F(°C)	Ignition Temp. °F(°C)	Flammable Limits Percent by Vol. Lower	Upper	Sp.Gr. (Water =1)	Vapor Density (Air =1)	Boiling Point °F(°C)	Water Soluble	Extinguishing Methods	Hazard Identification Health	Flammability	Instability
Abalyn	See Methyl Abietate.												
Acetal $CH_3CH(OC_2H_5)_2$ (Acetaldehydediethylacetal) **105-57-7**	IB	−5 (−21)	446 (230)	1.6	10.4	0.8	4.1	215 (102)	Slight	1 5	1	3	0
Acetaldehyde CH_3CHO (Acetic Aldehyde) (Ethanal) **75-07-0**	IA Note: Polymerizes. See NFPA 49 contained in this guide.	−38 (−39)	347 (175)	4.0	60	0.8	1.5	70 (21)	Yes	1 5	2	4	2
Acetaldehyde-diethylacetal	See Acetal.												
Acetaldol	See Aldol.												
Acetanilide $CH_3CONHC_6H_5$ **103-84-4**	Note: Melting point 237 (114).	337 (169) (oc)	985 ± 10 (530)			1.21	4.65	582 (306)		2	1	1	0
Acetic Acid, Glacial CH_3COOH **64-19-7**	II See NFPA 49 contained in this guide.	103 (39)	867 (463)	4.0	19.9	1.0+	2.1	245 (118)	Yes	5	3	2	0
Acetic Acid, Water Solutions (Ethanoic Acid)	Note: Ordinary acetic acid is the same as glacial acetic acid with water. The properties of ordinary acetic acid depend upon the strength of the solution. In concentrated form its properties approach those of glacial acetic acid. In dilute solution it is nonhazardous.								Yes				
Acetic Acid, Isopropyl Ester	See Isopropyl Acetate.												
Acetic Acid, Methyl Ester	See Methyl Acetate.												
Acetic Acid, n-Propyl Ester	See Propyl Acetate.												
Acetic Aldehyde	See Acetaldehyde.												
Acetic Anhydride $(CH_3CO)_2O$ (Ethanoic Anhydride) **108-24-7**	II See NFPA 49 contained in this guide.	120 (49)	600 (316)	2.7	10.3	1.1	3.5	284 (140)	Yes	5	3	2	1
Acetic Ester	See Ethyl Acetate.												

Chemical Name Formula (Synonym) CAS No.	NFPA 30/ OSHA Class	Flash Point °F(°C)	Ignition Temp. °F(°C)	Flammable Limits Percent by Vol. Lower	 Upper	Sp.Gr. (Water =1)	Vapor Density (Air =1)	Boiling Point °F(°C)	Water Soluble	Extin- guishing Methods	Hazard Identification Health	 Flamma- bility	 Insta- bility
Acetic Ether	See Ethyl Acetate.												
Acetoacetanilide $CH_3COCH_2CONHC_6H_5$ **102-01-2**		365 (185) (oc)				1.1 @ melting point			Slight	5 2	1	1	0
	Note: Melting point 185 (85).												
o-Acetoacet Anisidide CH_3COCH_2CONH- $C_6H_4OCH_3$ **92-15-9**		325 (168) (oc)				1.1 @ melting point	7.0		No	2	1	1	0
	Note: Melting point 187.9 (87).												
Acetoacet-para-Phenetide CH_3COCH_2CONH- $C_6H_4OCH_2CH_3$ **122-82-7**	IIIB	325 (163)				1.0+		Decomposes		2	2	1	0
	Note: Melting point 210–219 (99–104).												
Acetoacet-ortho-Toluidide CH_3COCH_2- $CONHC_6H_4CH_3$ (o-acetoacetotoluidide) **93-68-5**	IIIB	320 (160)						Decomposes		2	2	1	0
	Note: Melting point 214 (101).												
m-Acetoacet Xylidide CH_3COCH_2- $CONHC_6H_3(CH_3)_2$ **97-36-9**		340 (171) (oc)				1.2			Slight	5 2			
	Note: Melting point 197 (92).												
Acetoacetic Acid, Ethyl Ester	See Ethyl Acetoacetate.												
Acetoethylamide	See N-Ethylacetamide.												
Acetone CH_3COCH_3 (Dimethyl Ketone)- (2-Propanone) **67-64-1**	IB	−4 (−20)	869 (465)	2.5	12.8	0.8	2.0	133 (56)	Yes	1 5	1	3	0
Acetone Cyanohydrin $(CH_3)_2C(OH)CN$ (2-Hydroxy-2-Methyl Propionitrile) **75-86-5**	IIIA	165 (74)	1270 (688)	2.2	12.0	0.9	2.9	248 (120) Decomposes	Yes	5	4	2	2
	See NFPA 49 contained in this guide.												
Acetonitrile CH_3CN (Methyl Cyanide) **75-05-8**		42 (6) (oc)	975 (524)	3.0	16.0	0.8	1.4	179 (82)	Yes	1 5	2	3	0
	See NFPA 49 contained in this guide.												
Acetonyl Acetone $(CH_2COCH_3)_2$ (2,5-Hexanedione) **110-13-4**	IIIA	174 (79)	920 (499)			1.0−	3.9	378 (192)	Yes	5	1	2	0
Acetophenone $C_6H_5COCH_3$ (Phenyl Methyl Ketone) **98-86-2**	IIIA	170 (77)	1058 (570)	1.1	6.7	1.0+	4.1	396 (202)	No		2	2	0
p-Acetotoluidide $CH_3CONHC_6H_4CH_3$ **103-89-9**	IIIB	334 (168)				1.2	5.4	583 (306)	No	2	2	1	
Acetyl Acetone	See 2,4-Pentanedione.												
Acetyl Chloride CH_3COCl (Ethanoyl Chloride) **75-36-5**	IB	40 (4)	734 (390)	5.0		1.1	2.7	124 (51)	Violent de- composi- tion.	Do not use water or foam.	3	3	2 W
	See NFPA 49 contained in this guide.												
Acetylene CH:CH (Ethine) (Ethyne) **74-86-2**		Gas	581 (305)	2.5	100		0.9	−118 (−83)	No	6	0	4	3
	Note: Low pressure. Acetylene dissolved in acetone in closed cylinders can carry a 2 instability. See NFPA 49 contained in this guide.												

Chemical Name Formula (Synonym) CAS No.	NFPA 30/ OSHA Class	Flash Point °F(°C)	Ignition Temp. °F(°C)	Flammable Limits Percent by Vol.		Sp.Gr. (Water = 1)	Vapor Density (Air = 1)	Boiling Point °F(°C)	Water Soluble	Extinguishing Methods	Hazard Identification		
				Lower	Upper						Health	Flammability	Instability
Acetylene Dichloride-cis	See Dichloroethylene-cis.												
Acetylene Dichloride-trans	See Dichloroethylene-trans.												
N-Acetyl Ethanolamine $CH_3C{:}ONHCH_2CH_2OH$ [N-(2-Hydroxyethyl)-acetamide] **142-24-7**		355 (179) (oc)	860 (460)			1.1		304–308 (151–153) @ 10 mm Decomposes	Yes	5 2	2	1	1
N-Acetyl Morpholine $CH_3CONCH_2CH_2OCH_2CH_2$ **1696-20-4**	IIIB	235 (113)				1.1		Decomposes	Yes	5 2	2	1	1
Acetyl Oxide	See Acetic Anhydride.												
Acetyl Peroxide $(CH_3CO)_2O_2$ **110-22-5**		113 (45) (oc)				1.2	4.1	Explodes on heating	Slight		3	2	4
Acetylphenol	See Phenyl Acetate.												
Acrolein $CH_2{:}CHCHO$ (Acrylic Aldehyde) **107-02-8**	IB	−15 (−26)	428 (220) Unstable	2.8	31	0.8	1.9	125 (52)	Yes	1 5	4	3	3
	Note: May polymerize explosively. See NFPA 49 contained in this guide.												
Acrolein Dimer $(CH_2{:}CHCHO)_2$ **100-73-2**		118 (48) (oc)				1.1		304 (151)	Yes	5	2	2	1
Acrylic Acid, Glacial $H_2C{:}CHCOOH$ **79-10-7**		122 (50) (oc)	820 (438)	2.4	8.0	1.1	2.5	287 (142)	Yes	5	3	2	2
	Note: Polymerizes. See NFPA 49 contained in this guide.												
Acrylic Aldehyde	See Acrolein.												
Acrylonitrile $CH_2{:}CHCN$ (Vinyl Cyanide) (Propenenitrile) **107-13-1**		32 (0) (oc)	898 (481)	3.0	17	0.8	1.8	171 (77)	Yes	1 5	4	3	2
	Note: Polymerizes. See NFPA 49 contained in this guide.												
Adipic Acid $HOOC(CH_2)_4$ COOH **124-04-9**	IIIB	385 (196)	788 (420)			1.37	5.04	509 (265)@ 100 mm	No	2	1	1	0
	Note: Melting point 304 (151).												
Adipic Ketone	See Cyclopentanone.												
Adiponitrile $NC(CH_2)_4CN$ (Adipyldinitrile) (adipic acid dinitrile) **111-69-3**		200 (93) (oc)	1022 (550)	1.0		1.0–		563 (295)	Slight	5	3	2	1
	See NFPA 49 contained in this guide.												
Adipoyl Chloride $(\text{-}CH_2CH_2COCl)_2$ (Adipyl Chloride) **110-50-2**	IIIA	162 (72)						257–262 (125–128) @ 11 mm		5	3	2	0
Alcohol	See Ethyl Alcohol, Methyl Alcohol, Denatured Alcohol, etc.												
Aldol $CH_3CH(OH)CH_2CHO$ (3-Hydroxybutanal) (β-Hydroxybuteraldehyde) **107-89-1**		150 (66) (oc)	482 (250)			1.1	3.0	174–176 (79–80)@ 12 mm Decomposes @ 176 (80)	Yes	5	3	2	1
Allyl Acetate $CH_3COCH_2CH{:}CH_2$ **591-87-7**		72 (22) (oc)	705 (374)			0.9	3.45	219 (104)	No	5 1	3	3	0

Chemical Name Formula (Synonym) CAS No.	NFPA 30/ OSHA Class	Flash Point °F(°C)	Ignition Temp. °F(°C)	Flammable Limits Percent by Vol.		Sp.Gr. (Water = 1)	Vapor Density (Air = 1)	Boiling Point °F(°C)	Water Soluble	Extin-guishing Methods	Hazard Identification		
				Lower	Upper						Health	Flamma-bility	Insta-bility
Allyl Alcohol CH_2:$CHCH_2OH$ **107-18-6**	IB See NFPA 49 contained in this guide.	70 (21)	713 (378)	2.5	18.0	0.9	2.0	206 (97)	Yes	1 5	4	3	1
Allylamine CH_2:$CHCH_2NH_2$ (2-Propenylamine) **107-11-9**	IB See NFPA 49 contained in this guide.	−20 (−29)	705 (374)	2.2	22	0.8	2.0	128 (53)	Yes	1 5	4	3	1
Allyl Bromide CH_2:$CHCH_2Br$ (3-Bromopropene) **106-95-6**	IB See NFPA 49 contained in this guide.	30 (−1)	563 (295)	4.4	7.3	1.4	4.2	160 (71)	No	5 4	3	3	1
Allyl Caproate $CH_3(CH_2)_4COOCH_2$- CH:CH_2 (Allyl Hexanoate) (2-Propenyl Hexanoate) **123-68-2**	IIIA	150 (66)				0.9		367–370 (186–188)	No	5	2	2	0
Allyl Chloride CH_2:$CHCH_2Cl$ (3-Chloropropene) **107-05-1**	IB See NFPA 49 contained in this guide.	−25 (−32)	737 (485)	2.9	11.1	0.9	2.6	113 (45)	No	5	3	3	1
Allyl Chlorocarbonate	See Allyl Chloroformate.												
Allyl Chloroformate CH_2:$CHCH_2COOCl$ (Allyl Chlorocarbonate) **2937-50-0**	IC See NFPA 49 contained in this guide.	88 (31)				1.1	4.2	223–237 (106–114)	No	5 4	4	3	1
Allyl Diglycol Carbon-ate	See Diethylene Glycol Bis (Allylcarbonate).												
Allylene	See Propyne.												
Allyl Ether $(CH_2$:$CHCH_2)_2O$ (Diallyl Ether) **557-40-4**		20 (−7) (oc)				0.8	3.4	203 (95)	Slight	5 1	2	3	1
Allylidene Diacetate CH_2:$CHCH(OCOCH_3)_2$ **869-29-4**		180 (82) (oc)				1.1		225 (107)@ 50 mm	No	3	2	2	1
Allyl Isothiocyanate	See Mustard Oil.												
Allylpropenyl	See 1,4-Hexadiene.												
Allyl Trichloride	See 1,2,3-Trichloropropane.												
Allyl Trichlorosilane CH_2:$CHCH_2SiCl_3$ **107-37-9**		95 (35) (oc)				1.2	6.05	243 (117.5)		1	3	3	2 ₩
Allyl Vinyl Ether	See Vinyl Allyl Ether.												
Alpha Methyl Pyridine	See 2-Picoline.												
Aminobenzene	See Aniline.												
2-Aminobiphenyl	See 2-Biphenylamine.												
1-Aminobutane	See Butylamine.												
2-Amino-1-Butanol $CH_3CH_2CHNH_2CH_2OH$ **96-20-8**		165 (74) (oc)				0.9	3.1	352 (178)	Yes	5	2	2	0
Aminocyclohexane	See Cyclohexylamine.												
1-Aminodecane	See Decylamine.												
Amino Ethane	See Ethylamine.												

Chemical Name Formula (Synonym) CAS No.	NFPA 30/ OSHA Class	Flash Point °F(°C)	Ignition Temp. °F(°C)	Flammable Limits Percent by Vol. Lower	Upper	Sp.Gr. (Water =1)	Vapor Density (Air =1)	Boiling Point °F(°C)	Water Soluble	Extin-guishing Methods	Hazard Identification Health	Flamma-bility	Insta-bility
2-Aminoethanol	See Ethanolamine.												
1-Amino-4-Ethoxybenzene	See p-Phenetidine.												
β-Aminoethyl Alcohol	See Ethanolamine.												
2-Aminoethyl-ethanolamine $NH_2C_2H_4NHC_2H_4OH$ [N-(2-hydroxyethyl)-ethylenediamine] (Aminoethylethanol-amine) **111-41-1**	IIIB	270 (132)	695 (368)	1 (calc.)	8 (calc.)	1.0+		470 (243)	Yes	5 2	3	1	0
4-(2-Aminoethyl)-Morpholine $C_2H_4OC_2H_4NC_2H_4NH_2$ **2038-03-1**						1.0	4.5	396 (203)	Yes	5	2	2	0
1-(2-Aminoethyl)-Piperazine $H_2NC_2H_4NCH_2CH_2$- $NHCH_2CH_2$ (N-Aminoethylpipera-zine) **140-31-8**		200 (93) (oc)				1.0−	4.4	432 (222)	Yes	5	2	2	0
1-Aminoheptane	See Heptylamine.												
α-Aminoisopropyl Alcohol	See 1-Amino-2-Propanol.												
2-Amino-4-Methylpentane	See 1,3-Dimethylbutylamine.												
2-Amino-2-Methyl-1-Propanol $(CH_3)_2C(NH_2)CH_2OH$ **124-68-5**	IIIA	153 (67)				0.9	3.0	329 (165)	Yes	5	2	2	0
1-Aminooctane	See Octylamine.												
2-Aminopentane	See sec-Amylamine.												
p-Aminophenetole	See p-Phenetidine.												
(m-Aminophenyl) Methyl Carbinol $NH_2C_6H_4[CH(OH)CH_3]$ (m-Amino-α-Methylbenzyl Alcohol) **7568-93-6**		315 (157) (oc)				1.1		423 (217)@ 100 mm	Yes	5 2	2	1	0
3-Aminopropanol $H_2N(CH_2)_3OH$ (n-Propanolamine) **156-87-6**		175 (80) (oc)				<1.0		363–367 (184–186)	Yes	5	3	2	0
1-Amino-2-Propanol $NH_2CH_2CHOHCH_3$ (α-Aminoisopropyl Alcohol) (Isopropanolamine) **78-96-6**	IIIA	171 (77)	705 (374)	2.2 (calc.)	12 (est.)	1.0−	2.6	320 (160)	Yes	5	3	2	0
N-(3-Aminopropyl) Cyclohexylamine $C_6H_{11}NHC_3H_6NH_2$ **3312-60-5**		175 (79) (oc)				0.9	5.4		Yes	5	2	2	0
N-(3-Aminopropyl) Morpholine $C_2H_4OC_2H_4N$- $(CH_2)_3NH_2$ **123-00-2**		220 (104) (oc)				1.0−		438 (226)	Yes	5 2	2	1	0

Chemical Name Formula (Synonym) CAS No.	NFPA 30/ OSHA Class	Flash Point °F(°C)	Ignition Temp. °F(°C)	Flammable Limits Percent by Vol.		Sp.Gr. (Water =1)	Vapor Density (Air =1)	Boiling Point °F(°C)	Water Soluble	Extin-guishing Methods	Hazard Identification		
				Lower	Upper						Health	Flamma-bility	Insta-bility
Ammonia, anhydrous NH_3 **7664-41-7**		Gas	1204 (651)	15	28	0.7@ −33°C	0.6 @ 32(0)	−28 (−33)	Yes	6	3	1*	0
	See NFPA 49 contained in this guide. *This gas is '1' instead of '4' because it is hard to burn.												
Amoxybenzene	See Amyl Phenyl Ether.												
Amyl Acetate $CH_3COOC_5H_{11}$ (1-Pentanol Acetate) Comm. **628-63-7**	IB	60 (16) 70 (21)	680 (360)	1.1	7.5	0.9	4.5	300 (149)	Slight	1 5	1	3	0
sec-Amyl Acetate $CH_3COOCH(CH_3)$- $(CH_2)_2CH_3$ (2-Pentanol Acetate) **626-38-0**	IC	89 (32)	680–714 (360–379)	1.0	7.5	0.9	4.5	249 (121)	Slight	1 5	1	3	0
Amyl Alcohol $CH_3(CH_2)_3CH_2OH$ (1-Pentanol) **71-41-0**	IC	91 (33)	572 (300)	1.2	10.0 @ 212 (100)	0.8	3.0	280 (138)	Slight	5 1	1	3	0
sec-Amyl Alcohol $CH_3CH_2CH_2CH(OH)$- CH_3 (Diethyl Carbinol) (Methyl Propyl Carbinol) (2-Pentanol) **6032-29-7**	IC	91 (33)	650 (343)	1.2	9.0	0.8	3.0	245 (118)	Slight	1 5	1	3	0
Amylamine $C_5H_{11}NH_2$ (Pentylamine) **110-58-7**	IB	30 (−1)		2.2	22	0.8	3.0	210 (99)	Yes	1 5	3	3	0
	See NFPA 49 contained in this guide.												
sec-Amylamine $CH_3(CH_2)_2CH(CH_3)$- NH_2 (2-Aminopentane) (Methylpropylcarbinylam-ine) **625-30-9**	IB	20 (−7)				0.7	3.0	198 (92)	Yes	5 1	2	3	0
	See NFPA 49 contained in this guide.												
p-tert-Amylaniline $(C_2H_5)(CH_3)_2CC_6H_4NH_2$ **2049-92-5**	IIIB	215 (102)				0.9		498–504 (259–262)	No	2	3	1	0
Amylbenzene $C_6H_5C_5H_{11}$ (Phenylpentane) **538-68-1**		150 (66) (oc)				0.8–0.9	5.1	365 (185)	No		1	2	0
Amyl Bromide $CH_3CH_2CH_2CH_2CH_2Br$ (1-Bromopentane) **110-53-2**	IC	90 (32)				1.2		128–129 (53–54)@ 746 mm	No	4	1	3	0
Amyl Butyrate $C_5H_{11}OOCC_3H_7$ **540-18-1**	II	135 (57)				0.9	5.46	365 (185)	No	5	0	2	0
Amyl Carbinol	See Hexyl Alcohol.												
Amyl Chloride $CH_3(CH_2)_3CH_2Cl$ (1-Chloropentane) **543-59-9**		55 (13) (oc)	500 (260)	1.6	8.6	0.9	3.7	223 (106)	No	1	1	3	0
tert-Amyl Chloride $CH_3CH_2CCl(CH_3)CH_3$ (2-Chloro-2-methylbutane) **594-36-5**		15 (−9)	653 (345)	1.5	7.4	0.9	3.7	187 (86)	No	3	1	3	0
Amyl Chlorides (Mixed) $C_5H_{11}Cl$		38 (3) (oc)				0.9		185–228 (85–109)	No	1	1	3	0

Chemical Name Formula (Synonym) CAS No.	NFPA 30/ OSHA Class	Flash Point °F(°C)	Ignition Temp. °F(°C)	Flammable Limits Percent by Vol.		Sp.Gr. (Water =1)	Vapor Density (Air =1)	Boiling Point °F(°C)	Water Soluble	Extin-guishing Methods	Hazard Identification		
				Lower	Upper						Health	Flamma-bility	Insta-bility
Amylcyclohexane $C_5H_{11}C_6H_{11}$ **4292-92-6**			462 (239)			0.8		395 (202)			1		0
Amylene	See 1-Pentene.												
β-Amylene-cis $C_2H_5CH{:}CHCH_3$ (2-Pentene-cis) **627-20-3**	IA	< −4 (< −20)				0.66	2.42	99 (37)		1	1	4	0
β-Amylene-trans $C_2H_5CH{:}CHCH_3$ (2-Pentene-trans) **646-04-8**	IA	< −4 (< −20)				0.67	2.42	97 (36)		1	1	4	1
Amylene Chloride	See 1,5-Dichloropentane.												
Amyl Ether $C_5H_{11}OC_5H_{11}$ (Diamyl Ether) (Pentyloxypentane) **693-65-2**		135 (57) (oc)	338 (170)			0.8–0.9	5.5	374 (190)	No	5	1	2	0
Amyl Formate $HCOCC_5H_{11}$ **638-49-3**	IC	79 (26)				0.9	4.0	267 (131)	No	1	1	3	0
Amyl Lactate $C_2H_5OCOOCH_2$- $CH(CH_3)C_2H_5$	IIIA	175 (79)				1.0−	5.5	237–239 (114–115) @ 36 mm	Very slight		1	2	0
Amyl Laurate $C_{11}H_{23}COOC_5H_{11}$ **5350-03-8**	IIIB	300 (149)				0.9		554–626 (290–330)	No	2	0	1	0
Amyl Maleate $(CHCOOC_5H_{11})_2$	IIIB	270 (132)				1.0−		518–599 (270–315)	No	2	0	1	0
n-Amyl Mercaptan $C_5H_{11}SH$ (1-Pentanethiol) **110-66-7**	See NFPA 49 contained in this guide.	65 (18) (oc)				0.8	3.59	260 (127)	No	1	2	3	0
Amyl Mercaptans (Mixed) $CH_3(CH_2)_4SH$	See NFPA 49 contained in this guide.	65 (18) (oc)				0.8		176–257 (80–125)	No	1	2	3	0
Amyl Naphthalene $C_{10}H_7C_5H_{11}$		255 (124) (oc)				1.0−		550 (288)	No	2	0	1	0
Amyl Nitrate $CH_3(CH_2)_4NO_3$ (n-amyl nitrate) **1002-16-0**		118 (48) (oc)				1.0−		306–315 (153–157)	No		0	2	OX
Amyl Oleate $C_{17}H_{33}COOC_5H_{11}$	IIIB	366 (186)				0.9		392–464 (200–240) @ 20 mm	No	2	0	1	0
Amyl Oxalate $(COOC_5H_{11})_2$ (Diamyl Oxalate)	IIIB	245 (118)				1.0−		464–523 (240–273)	No	2	0	1	0
o-Amyl Phenol $C_5H_{11}C_6H_4OH$ **136-81-2**		219 (104) (oc)				1.0−		455–482 (235–250)	Slight	5 2	2	1	0
p-tert-Amyl Phenol	See Pentaphen.												
p-sec-Amylphenol $C_5H_{11}C_6H_4OH$ **25735-67-5**	IIIB	270 (132)				1.0−		482–516 (250–269)	No	2	1	1	0

Chemical Name Formula (Synonym) CAS No.	NFPA 30/ OSHA Class	Flash Point °F(°C)	Ignition Temp. °F(°C)	Flammable Limits Percent by Vol. Lower	Upper	Sp.Gr. (Water =1)	Vapor Density (Air =1)	Boiling Point °F(°C)	Water Soluble	Extin-guishing Methods	Hazard Identification Health	Flamma-bility	Insta-bility
2-(p-tert-Amylphenoxy)-ethanol $C_5H_{11}C_6H_4OCH_2CH_2OH$ **6382-07-6**	IIIB	280 (138)				1.0+		567–590 (297–310)	No	2	1	1	0
2-(p-tert-Amylphenoxy) ethyl Laurate $C_{11}H_{23}COO(CH_2)_2$-$OC_6H_4C_5H_{11}$	IIIB	410 (210)				0.9		464–500 (240–260) @ 6 mm		2	0	1	0
p-tert-Amylphenyl Acetate $CH_3COOC_6H_4C_5H_{11}$	IIIB	240 (116)				1.0−		507–511 (264–266)		2	0	1	0
p-tert-Amylphenyl Butyl Ether $C_5H_{11}C_6H_4OC_4H_9$	IIIB	275 (135)				0.9		540–550 (282–288)	No	2	0	1	0
Amyl Phenyl Ether $CH_3(CH_2)_4OC_6H_5$ (Amoxybenzene)	IIIA	185 (85)				0.9	5.7	421–444 (216–229)	No		0	2	0
p-tert-Amylphenyl Methyl Ether $C_5H_{11}C_6H_4OCH_3$	IIIB	210 (99)				0.9		462–469 (239–243)			0	1	0
Amyl Phthalate	See Diamyl Phthalate.												
Amyl Propionate $C_2H_5COO(CH_2)_4CH_3$ (Pentyl Propionate) **624-54-4**		106 (41) (oc)	712 (378)			0.9		275–347 (135–175)	No		1	3	0
Amyl Salicylate $HOC_6H_4COOC_5H_{11}$ **2050-08-0**	IIIB	270 (132)				1.1		512 (267)	No	2	0	1	0
Amyl Stearate $CH_3(CH_2)_{16}COOC_5H_{11}$ **6382-13-4**		365 (185) (oc)				0.9		680 (360)	No	2	0	1	0
Amyl Sulfides (Mixed) $C_5H_{11}S$ **872-10-6**		185 (85) (oc)				0.9		338–356 (170–180)	No		2	2	0
Amyl Toluene $C_5H_{11}C_6H_4CH_3$ **1320-01-0**		180 (82) (oc)				0.9		400–415 (204–213)	No		2	2	0
Amyl Trichlorosilane $C_5H_{11}SiCl_3$ **107-72-2**		145 (63) (oc)				1.1	7.1	334 (168)			3	2	2 ₩
Amyl Xylyl Ether $C_5H_{11}OC_6H_3(CH_3)_2$ **1320-21-4**		205 (96) (oc)				0.9		480–500 (249–260)	No		2	1	0
Aniline $C_6H_5NH_2$ (Aminobenzene) (Phenylamine) **62-53-3**	IIIA	158 (70) See NFPA 49 contained in this guide.	1139 (615)	1.3	11	1.0+	3.2	364 (184)	Slight	5	2	2	0
Aniline Hydrochloride $C_6H_5NH_2HCl$ **142-04-1**	Note: Melting point 389 (198).	380 (193) (oc)				1.22	4.46	473 (245)		2	1	1	0
2-Anilinoethanol	See N-Phenylethanolamine.												
β-Anilinoethanol Ethoxyaniline	See 2-Anilinoethanol.												
o-Anisaldehyde	See o-Methoxy Benzaldehyde.												
o-Anisidine $H_2NC_6H_4OCH_3$ (2-Methoxyaniline) **29191-52-4**		244 (118) (oc)				1.1		435 (224)	No	5 2	2	1	0

Chemical Name Formula (Synonym) CAS No.	NFPA 30/ OSHA Class	Flash Point °F(°C)	Ignition Temp. °F(°C)	Flammable Limits Percent by Vol.		Sp.Gr. (Water =1)	Vapor Density (Air =1)	Boiling Point °F(°C)	Water Soluble	Extin-guishing Methods	Hazard Identification		
				Lower	Upper						Health	Flamma-bility	Insta-bility
Anisole $C_6H_5OCH_3$ (Methoxybenzene) (Methyl Phenyl Ether) **100-66-3**		125 (52) (oc)	887 (475)			1.0−	3.7	309 (154)	No		1	2	0
Anol	See Cyclohexanol.												
Anthracene $(C_6H_4CH)_2$ **120-12-7**	IIIB	250 (121)	1004 (540)	0.6		1.24	6.15	644 (340)	No	2	1	1	0
	Note: Melting point 423 (217).												
Anthraquinone $C_6H_4(CO)_2C_6H_4$ **84-65-1**	IIIB	365 (185)				1.44	7.16	716 (380)	No	2	2	1	0
	Note: Melting point 354 (179).												
Artificial Almond Oil	See Benzaldehyde.												
Asphalt (Cutback)		<50 (<10)							No	2	0	3	0
Asphalt, Liquid-Medium Curing Grades MC-30 and MC-70; Grades MC-250; MC-800; and MC-3000		100 (38) (oc) 150 (66) (oc)							No	2	0	2	0
Asphalt, Liquid-Rapid Curing Grades RC-250; RC-800; and RC-3000		80 (27) (oc)							No	2	0	3	0
Asphalt, Liquid-Slow Curing (Grade SC-70)		150+ (66) (oc)							No	2	0	2	0
	See also Asphalt, Liquid-Slow Curing (Grade SC-250, Grade SC-800, and Grade SC-3000).												
Asphalt, Liquid-Slow Curing (Grade SC-250)		175+ (79) (oc)	Grade SC-250								0	2	0
	Note: See also Asphalt, Liquid-Slow Curing (Grade SC-70, Grade SC-800, and Grade SC-3000).												
Asphalt, Liquid-Slow Curing (Grade SC-800)		200+ (93) (oc)	Grade SC-800								0	1	0
	Note: See also Asphalt, Liquid-Slow Curing (Grade SC-70, Grade SC-250, and Grade SC-3000).												
Asphalt, Liquid-Slow Curing (Grade SC-3000)		225+ (107) (oc)	Grade SC-3000								0	1	0
	Note: See also Asphalt, Liquid-Slow Curing (Grade SC-70, Grade SC-250, and Grade SC-800).												
Asphalt (Typical) (Petroleum Pitch) **8052-42-4**	IIIB	400+ (204+)	905 (485)			1.0–1.1		>700 (>371)	No	2	0	1	0
Aziridine	See Ethyleneimine.												
Azobisisobutyronitrile $N{:}CC(CH_3)_2$- $N{:}NC(CH_3)_2C{:}N$ **78-67-1**			147 (64)					Decomposes	No		3	3	3
	Note: Melting point 221 (105).												
Azole	See Pyrrole.												
Banana Oil	See Isoamyl Acetate.												
Benzaldehyde C_6H_5CHO (Artificial Almond Oil) (Benzenecarbonal) **100-52-7**	IIIA	145 (63)	377 (192)	1.4		1.1	3.7	355 (179)	No	3	1	2	0
	See NFPA 49 contained in this guide.												
Benzedrine $C_6H_5CH_2CH(CH_3)NH_2$ (1-Phenyl Isopropyl Amine) **300-62-9**		<212 (<100)				0.93	4.67	392 (200)			3	1	0

Chemical Name Formula (Synonym) CAS No.	NFPA 30/ OSHA Class	Flash Point °F(°C)	Ignition Temp. °F(°C)	Flammable Limits Percent by Vol.		Sp.Gr. (Water =1)	Vapor Density (Air =1)	Boiling Point °F(°C)	Water Soluble	Extin-guishing Methods	Hazard Identification		
				Lower	Upper						Health	Flamma-bility	Insta-bility
Benzene C_6H_6 (Benzol) **71-43-2**	IB	12 (−11)	928 (498)	1.2	7.8	0.9	2.8	176 (80)	No	1	1	3	0
	See NFPA 49 contained in this guide.												
Benzenecarbonal	See Benzaldehyde.												
Benzene Carbonyl Chloride	See Benzoyl Chloride.												
Benzine	See Petroleum Ether.												
Benzocyclobutene	IC	95 (35)	477 (247)			0.96		306 (152)		1		3	0
Benzoic Acid C_6H_5COOH **65-85-0**	IIIB	250 (121)	1058 (570)			1.27	4.21	482 (250)	Slight	2	1	1	0
	Note: Melting point 252 (122).												
Benzol	See Benzene.												
Benzol Diluent	IB	−25 (−32)	450 (232)	1.0	7.0	<1		140–210 (60–99)	No	1			
	Note: Flash point and ignition temperature will vary depending on the manufacturer.												
p-Benzoquinone $C_6H_4O_2$ (Quinone) **106-51-4**		100–200 (38–93)	1040 (560)			1.3	3.7	Sublimes	No		3	2	0
	Note: Melting point 234–237 (112–114).												
Benzotrichloride $C_6H_5CCl_3$ (Toluene, α, α,-α-Trichloro) (Phenyl Chloroform) **98-07-7**	IIIB	260 (127)	412 (211)			1.4		429 (221)	No	2	4	1	0
Benzotrifluoride $C_6H_5CF_3$ **98-08-8**	IB	54 (12)	1148 (620)			1.2	5	216 (102)	No	4	3	3	1
	See NFPA 49 contained in this guide.												
Benzoyl Chloride C_6H_5COCl (Benzene Carbonyl Chloride) **98-88-4**		162 (72) (oc)		1.2	4.9	1.2	4.9	387 (197)	Decom-poses		3	2	2 ~~W~~
	See NFPA 49 contained in this guide.												
Benzyl Acetate $CH_3COOCH_2C_6H_5$ **140-11-4**	IIIA	195 (90)	860 (460)			1.1	5.2	417 (214)	Slight	5 2	1	2	0
Benzyl Alcohol $C_6H_5CH_2OH$ (Phenyl Carbinol) **100-51-6**	IIIB	200 (93)	817 (436)			1.0+	3.72	403 (206)	Slight	5 2	1	1	0
Benzyl Benzoate $C_6H_5COOCH_2C_6H_5$ **120-51-4**	IIIB	298 (148)	896 (480)			1.1		614 (323)	No	2	1	1	0
Benzyl Butyl Phthalate $C_4H_9COOC_6H_4COOCH_2$-C_6H_5 (Butyl Benzyl Phthalate) **85-68-7**	IIIB	390 (199)				1.1		698 (370)	No	2	1	1	0
Benzyl Carbinol	See Phenethyl Alcohol.												
Benzyl Chloride $C_6H_5CH_2Cl$ (α-Chlorotoluene) **100-44-7**	IIIA	153 (67)	1085 (585)	1.1	7.1	1.1	4.4	354 (179)	No	3	3	2	1
	See NFPA 49 contained in this guide.												
Benzyl Cyanide $C_6H_5CH_2CN$ (Phenyl Acetonitrile) (α-Tolunitrile) **140-29-4**		235 (113) (oc)				1.0+		452 (233.5)	No	5 2	3	1	0

Chemical Name Formula (Synonym) CAS No.	NFPA 30/ OSHA Class	Flash Point °F(°C)	Ignition Temp. °F(°C)	Flammable Limits Percent by Vol.		Sp.Gr. (Water =1)	Vapor Density (Air =1)	Boiling Point °F(°C)	Water Soluble	Extin-guishing Methods	Hazard Identification		
				Lower	Upper						Health	Flamma-bility	Insta-bility
N-Benzyldiethylamine $C_6H_5CH_2N(C_2H_5)_2$ **772-54-3**		170 (77) (oc)				0.9		405–420 (207–216)			2	2	0
Benzyl Ether	See Dibenzyl Ether.												
Benzyl Mercaptan $C_6H_5CH_2SH$ (α-Toluenethiol) **100-53-8**	IIIA	158 (70)				1.06	4.28	383 (195)			2	2	0
Benzyl Salicilate $OHC_6H_4COOCH_2C_6H_5$ (Salycilic Acid Benzyl Ester) (Benzyl Salicylate) **118-58-1**	IIIB	>212 (>100)				1.2		406 (208)	No	5 2	0	1	0
Bicyclohexyl $[CH_2(CH_2)_4CH]_2$ (Dicyclohexyl) **92-51-3**	IIIA	165 (74)	473 (245)	0.7 @ 212 (100)	5.1 @ 302 (150)	0.9	5.7	462 (239)	Slight	5	1	2	0
Biphenyl $C_6H_5C_6H_5$ (Diphenyl) (Phenylbenzene) **92-52-4**	IIIB Note: Melting point 158 (70).	235 (113)	1004 (540)	0.6 @ 232 (111)	5.8 @ 311 (155)	1.2		489 (254)	No	2	1	1	0
2-Biphenylamine $NH_2C_6H_4C_6H_5$ (2-Aminobiphenyl) **90-41-5**	Note: Melting point 121 (49).	>230 (>110)	842 (450)				5.8	570 (299)	No	2	1	1	0
Bis(p-tert-Butylphenyl)phenyl Phosphate $(C_4H_9C_6H_4O)_2POOC_6H_5$ **115-87-7**	IIIB	482 (250)				1.1		500–527 (260–275) @ 5 mm	No	2	2	1	0
Bis[2-(2-Chloroethoxy)ethyl] Ether $(CH_2ClCH_2OCH_2CH_2)_2O$ (Tetraglycol Dichloride) (Tetraethylene Glycol Dichloride) **638-56-2**	IIIB	>250 (>121)				1.2		237 (114)	Slight	5 2	2	1	0
Bis(2-Chloroethyl) Ether $(CH_2ClCH_2)_2O$ (Chlorex) (2,2′-Dichloroethyl Ether) **111-44-4**	II	131 (55)	696 (369)	2.7		1.2	4.9	353 (178)	Very slight		2	2	0
Bis(2-Chloroethyl) Formal $CH_2(OCH_2CH_2Cl)_2$ [Di-(2-Chloroethyl) Formal] (2,2-Dichloroethyl Formal) **111-91-1**		230 (110) (oc)				1.2		425 (218)	Very slight	5 2	2	1	0
Bis(β-Chloroisopropyl) Ether	See Dichloroisopropyl Ether.												
Bis-Diethylene Glycol Ethyl Ether Phthalate $C_6H_4(COOC_2H_4OC_2H_4OC_2H_5)_2$	IIIB	405 (207)				1.1		500 (260)		5 2	1	1	0
Bis(2,4-Dimethylbutyl) Maleate $[(CH_3)_2CHCH_2CH(CH_3)OCOCH:]_2$ [Di(Methylamyl) Maleate]		290 (143) (oc)				0.9		394 (201)@ 50 mm	No	2	1	1	0

Chemical Name Formula (Synonym) CAS No.	NFPA 30/ OSHA Class	Flash Point °F(°C)	Ignition Temp. °F(°C)	Flammable Limits Percent by Vol.		Sp.Gr. (Water =1)	Vapor Density (Air =1)	Boiling Point °F(°C)	Water Soluble	Extin-guishing Methods	Hazard Identification		
				Lower	Upper						Health	Flamma-bility	Insta-bility
N,N′-Bis-(1,4-Dimethylpentyl) p-Phenylenediamine $C_6H_4[NHCH(CH_3)CH_2-CH_2CH(CH_3)_2]_2$ **3081-14-9**		347 (175) (oc)	770 (410)			0.9				5 2	2	1	0
1,3-Bis(Ethylamino) Butane	See N,N-Diethyl-1,3-Butanediamine.												
Bis(2-Ethylhexyl) Amine $[C_4H_9CH(C_2H_5)-CH_2]_2NH$ (Diethylhexylamine) (Dioctylamine) **106-20-7**		270 (132) (oc)				0.8		537 (281)	Slight	5 2	2	1	0
Bis(2-Ethylhexyl) Ethanolamine $[C_4H_9CH(C_2H_5)CH_2]_2-NC_2H_4OH$ (Diethylhexylethanol-amine)	IIIB	280 (138)				0.9		421 (216)@ 50 mm	Slight	5 2	1	1	0
Bis(2-Ethylhexyl) Maleate $C_8H_{17}OCOCH{:}CH-COOC_8H_{17}$ Di(2-Ethylhexyl) Maleate **142-16-5**	IIIB	365 (185)				0.9		408 (209) @ 10 mm	No	5 2	1	1	0
Bis(2-Ethylhexyl) Phosphoric Acid $[C_4H_9CH(C_2H_5)CH]_2-HPO_4$ [Di(2-Ethylhexyl) Phos-phoric Acid] **298-07-7 and 2915-57-3**		385 (196) (oc)				1.0 –		Decomposes	No	5 2	2	1	0
Bis(2-Ethylhexyl) Succinate $(C_{10}H_{19}O_2)_2$ [Di(2-Ethylhexyl) Succi-nate] **2915-57-3**	IIIB	315 (157)				0.9		495 (257) @ 50 mm	Slight	5 2	0	1	0
N,N-Bis(1-Methylheptyl)-Ethylenediamine $HC(CH_3)(C_6H_{13})NHCH_2-CH_2NHCH(CH_3)-(C_6H_{13})$	IIIB	>400 (>204)				0.8		424 (218) @ 43 mm	No	2	0	1	0
Bis(β-Methylpropyl) Amine	See Diisobutylamine.												
Bis(2,2,4-Trimethylpentane-diolisobutyrate) Diglycolate $C_{28}H_{27}O_9$		383 (195) (oc)				1.1		639 (337)		2	0	1	0
Blast-furnace Gas	See Gas.												
Borneo Camphor	See Borneol.												
Borneol $C_{10}H_{17}OH$ (Borneo Camphor) (L-Borneol) (D-Borneol) **464-45-9 (L-Borneol)** **507-70-0 (D-Borneol)**	IIIA	150 (60)				1.0+		413 (212) Sublimes	No		2	2	0
Boron Trifluoride Etherate $CH_3CH_2O(BF_3)CH_2CH_3$ **109-63-7**		147 (64) (oc)				1.1		259 (126)	Decom-poses		3	2	2 ₩
Brandy	See Ethyl Alcohol and Water.												

Chemical Name Formula (Synonym) CAS No.	NFPA 30/ OSHA Class	Flash Point °F(°C)	Ignition Temp. °F(°C)	Flammable Limits Percent by Vol.		Sp.Gr. (Water =1)	Vapor Density (Air =1)	Boiling Point °F(°C)	Water Soluble	Extin- guishing Methods	Hazard Identification		
				Lower	Upper						Health	Flamma- bility	Insta- bility
Brazil Wax	See Carnauba Wax.												
Bromobenzene C_6H_5Br (Phenyl Bromide) **108-86-1**	II	124 (51)	1049 (565)			1.5	5.4	313 (156)	No	3	1	2	0
1-Bromobutane	See Butyl Bromide.												
4-Bromodiphenyl $C_6H_5C_6H_4Br$ **92-66-0**	IIIB	291 (144)						592 (311)	No	2	1	1	0
Bromoethane	See Ethyl Bromide.												
Bromomethane	See Methyl Bromide.												
1-Bromopentane	See Amyl Bromide.												
3-Bromopropene	See Allyl Bromide.												
3-Bromopropyne $HC{:}CCH_2Br$ (Propargyl Bromide) **106-96-7**	IB See NFPA 49 contained in this guide.	50 (10)	615 (324)	3.0		1.57	4.10	192 (89)	No	4	3	3	4
o-Bromotoluene $BrC_6H_4CH_3$ **95-46-5**	IIIA	174 (79)				1.4	5.9	359 (182)	No	3	1	2	0
p-Bromotoluene $BrC_6H_4CH_3$ **106-38-7**	IIIA	185 (85)				1.4	5.9	363 (184)	No	3	2	2	0
1,3-Butadiene $CH_2{:}CHCH{:}CH_2$ (Erythrene) **106-99-0**	Note: Polymerizes. See NFPA 49 contained in this guide.	Gas	788 (420)	2.0	12.0		1.9	24 (−4)	No	6	2	4	2
Butadiene Monoxide $CH_2{:}CHCHOCH_2$ (Vinylethylene Oxide) **930-22-3**	IB	<−58 (<−50)				0.9	2.4	151 (66)		1		3	2
Butanal	See Butyraldehyde.												
Butanal Oxime	See Butyraldoxime.												
Butane $CH_3CH_2CH_2CH_3$ **106-97-8**	IA	Gas [−76 (−60)]	550 (287)	1.9	8.5		2.0	31 (−1)	No	6	1	4	0
1,3-Butanediamine $NH_2CH_2CH_2CHNH_2CH_3$ (1,3-Diaminobutane) **590-88-5**		125 (52) (oc)				0.9	3.0	289–302 (143–150)	Yes	5	3	2	0
1,2-Butanediol $CH_3CH_2CHOHCH_2OH$ (1,2-Dihydroxybutane) (Ethylethylene Glycol) **584-03-2**	II	104 (40)				1.0	3.1	381 (194)	Slight	5	1	2	0
1,3-Butanediol	See β-Butylene Glycol.												
1,4-Butanediol $HOCH_2CH_2CH_2CH_2OH$ (Tetramethylene Glycol) **110-63-4**	Note: Melting point 64–66 (18–19).	250 (121) (oc)	662 (350)	1.95	18.3	1.0+	3.1	442 (228)	Yes	2 5	1	1	0
2,3-Butanediol $CH_3CHOHCHOHCH_3$ **513-85-9**	Note: Melting point 77 (25).	185 (85)	756 (402)			1.0+		363 (184)	Yes	5	1	1	0
2,3-Butanedione $CH_3COCOCH_3$ (Diacetyl) **431-03-8**	IC	80 (27)				1.0−	3.0	190 (88)	Yes	5 1	2	3	0

Chemical Name Formula (Synonym) CAS No.	NFPA 30/ OSHA Class	Flash Point °F(°C)	Ignition Temp. °F(°C)	Flammable Limits Percent by Vol.		Sp.Gr. (Water =1)	Vapor Density (Air =1)	Boiling Point °F(°C)	Water Soluble	Extin- guishing Methods	Hazard Identification		
				Lower	Upper						Health	Flamma- bility	Insta- bility
1-Butanethiol $CH_3CH_2CH_2CH_2SH$ (Butyl Mercaptan) **109-79-5**	IB	35 (2)				0.8	3.1	208 (98)	Slight	5 1	1	3	0
2-Butanethiol C_4H_9SH (sec-Butyl Mercaptan) **513-53-1**	IB	−10 (−23)				0.8	3.11	185 (85)	No	5 1	2	3	0
1-Butanol	See Butyl Alcohol.												
2-Butanol	See sec-Butyl Alcohol.												
2-Butanone	See Methyl Ethyl Ketone.												
2-Butenal	See Crotonaldehyde.												
1-Butene $CH_3CH_2CH{:}CH_2$ (α-Butylene) **106-98-9**		Gas	725 (385)	1.6	10.0		1.9	21 (−6)	No	6	1	4	0
2-Butene-cis $CH_3CH{:}CHCH_3$ **590-18-1**		Gas	617 (325)	1.7	9.0	0.6	1.9	38.7 (4)		6	1	4	0
2-Butene-trans $CH_3CH{:}CHCH_3$ (β-Butylene) **624-64-6**		Gas	615 (324)	1.8	9.7		1.9	−34 (1)	No	6	2	4	1
Butenediol $HOCH_2CH{:}CHCH_2OH$ (2-Butene-1,4-Diol) **110-64-5**	Note: Melting point 45 (7).	263 (128) (oc)				1.1	3.0	286–300 (141–149) @ 20 mm	Yes	2 5		1	0
2-Butene-1,4-Diol	See Butenediol.												
2-Butene Nitrile	See Crotononitrile.												
Butoxybenzene	See Butyl Phenyl Ether.												
1-Butoxybutane	See Dibutyl Ether.												
2,β-Butoxyethoxy-ethyl Chloride $C_4H_9CH_2CH_2$- OCH_2CH_2Cl	IIIA	190 (88)				1.0	6.1	392–437 (200–225)			2	2	0
1-(Butoxyethoxy)-2-Propanol $CH_3CH(OH)CH_2O$- $C_2H_4OC_2H_4C_2H_5$ **124-16-3**		250 (121) (oc)	509 (265)			0.9		445 (229)	Yes	5 2	2	1	0
Butoxyethyl Diglycol Carbonate	See Diethylene Glycol Bis (2-Butoxyethyl Carbonate).												
β-Butoxyethyl Salicylate $OCH_6H_4COOCH_2$- $CH_2OC_4H_9$	IIIB	315 (157)				1.0+		367–378 (186–192)	No	2	0	1	0
Butoxyl	See 3-Methoxybutyl Acetate.												
N-Butyl Acetamide $CH_3CONHC_4H_9$ **1119-49-9**	IIIB	240 (116)				0.9		455–464 (235–240)		2		1	0
N-Butylacetanilide $CH_3(CH_2)_3N(C_6H_5)$- $COCH_3$ **91-49-6**	IIIB	286 (141)				1.0−		531–538 (277–281)	No	2		1	0

Chemical Name Formula (Synonym) CAS No.	NFPA 30/ OSHA Class	Flash Point °F(°C)	Ignition Temp. °F(°C)	Flammable Limits Percent by Vol.		Sp.Gr. (Water =1)	Vapor Density (Air =1)	Boiling Point °F(°C)	Water Soluble	Extin-guishing Methods	Hazard Identification		
				Lower	Upper						Health	Flamma-bility	Insta-bility
Butyl Acetate $CH_3COOC_4H_9$ (Butylethanoate) (n-Butyl acetate) **123-86-4**	IB	72 (22)	797 (425)	1.3	7.6	0.9	4.0	260 (127)	Slight	1 5	2	3	0
sec-Butyl Acetate $CH_3COOCH(CH_3)C_2H_5$ **105-46-4**		88 (31) (oc)		1.7	9.8	0.9	4.0	234 (112)	Slight	1 5	1	3	0
Butyl Acetoacetate CH_3COCH_2- $COO(CH_2)_3CH_3$ **591-60-6**		185 (85) (oc)				1.0–	5.5	417 (214)	Slight	5	1	2	0
Butyl Acetyl Ricinoleate $C_{17}H_{32}(OCOCH_3)$- $(COOC_4H_9)$ **140-04-5**	IIIB	230 (110)	725 (385)			0.9		428 (220)	No	2	0	1	0
Butyl Acrylate CH_2:$CHCOOC_4H_9$ **141-32-2**	IC See NFPA 49 contained in this guide.	84 (29)	559 (292)	1.7	9.9	0.9	4.4	260 (127) Polymerizes	No	1	3	2	2
Butyl Alcohol $CH_3(CH_2)_2CH_2OH$ (1-Butanol) (Propyl Carbinol) (Propyl Methanol) **71-36-3**	IC	98 (37)	650 (343)	1.4	11.2	0.8	2.6	243 (117)	No	1 5	2	3	0
sec-Butyl Alcohol $CH_3CH_2CHOHCH_3$ (2-Butanol) (Methyl Ethyl Carbinol) **78-92-2**	IC	75 (24)	761 (405)	1.7 @ 212 (100)	9.8 @ 212 (100)	0.8	2.6	201 (94)	Slight	1 5	2	3	0
tert-Butyl Alcohol $(CH_3)_2COHCH_3$ (2-Methyl-2-Propanol) (Trimethyl Carbinol) **75-65-0**	IB	52 (11)	892 (478)	2.4	8.0	0.8	2.6	181 (83)	Yes	1 5	2	3	0
Butylamine $C_4H_9NH_2$ (1-Amino Butane) **109-73-9**	IB See NFPA 49 contained in this guide.	10 (−12)	594 (312)	1.7	9.8	0.8	2.5	172 (78)	Yes	1 5	3	3	0
sec-Butylamine $CH_3CH_2CH(NH_2)CH_3$ **13952-84-6**	IB	−3 (−19)	712 (378)			0.72	2.52	145 (63)		1	3	3	0
tert-Butylamine $(CH_3)_3C$:NH_2 **75-64-9**	IB	16 (−8)	716 (380)	1.7 @ 212 (100)	8.9 @ 212 (100)	0.7	2.5	113 (45)	Yes	5	3	3	0
Butylamine Oleate $C_{17}H_{33}COONH_3C_4H_9$ **26094-13-3**		150 (66) (oc)				0.9			Yes	5	3	2	0
tert-Butylaminoethyl Methacrylate $(CH_3)_3CNHC_2H_4$- $OOCC(CH_3)$:CH_2 **3775-90-4**	Note: May polymerize.	205 (96) (oc)				0.9	5.5	200–221 (93–105)	No		3	2	0
N-Butylaniline $C_6H_5NHC_4H_9$ **1126-78-9**		225 (107) (oc)				0.9		465 (241)	Slight	5 2	2	1	0
Butylbenzene $C_6H_5C_4H_9$ **104-51-8**		160 (71) (oc)	770 (410)	0.8	5.8	0.9	4.6	356 (180)	No		1	2	0
sec-Butylbenzene $C_6H_5CH(CH_3)C_2H_5$ **135-98-8**	II	126 (52)	784 (418)	0.8	6.9	0.9	4.6	344 (173)	No		1	2	0

Chemical Name Formula (Synonym) CAS No.	NFPA 30/ OSHA Class	Flash Point °F(°C)	Ignition Temp. °F(°C)	Flammable Limits Percent by Vol.		Sp.Gr. (Water =1)	Vapor Density (Air =1)	Boiling Point °F(°C)	Water Soluble	Extin-guishing Methods	Hazard Identification		
				Lower	Upper						Health	Flamma-bility	Insta-bility
tert-Butylbenzene $C_6H_5C(CH_3)_3$ **98-06-6**		140 (60) (oc)	842 (450)	0.7 @ 212 (100)	5.7 @ 212 (100)	0.9	4.6	336 (169)	No		1	3	0
Butyl Benzoate $C_6H_5COOC_4H_9$ **136-60-7**		225 (107) (oc)				1.0		482 (250)	No	2	2	1	0
Butyl Benzyl Phthalate	See Benzyl Butyl Phthalate.												
2-Butylbiphenyl $C_6H_5.C_6H_4.C_4H_9$	IIIB	>212 (>100)	806 (430)				7.26	~554 (~290)		2	0	1	
Butyl Bromide $CH_3(CH_2)_2CH_2Br$ (1-Bromo Butane) **109-65-9**	IB	65 (18)	509 (265)	2.6 @ 212 (100)	6.6 @ 212 (100)	1.3	4.7	215 (102)	No	4	1	3	0
Butyl Butyrate $CH_3(CH_2)_2COOC_4H_9$ **109-21-7**		128 (53) (oc)				0.9	5.0	305 (152)	Slight	5	1	2	0
Butylcarbamic Acid, Ethyl Ester	See N-Butylurethane.												
tert-Butyl Carbinol $(CH_3)_3CCH_2OH$ (2,2-Dimethyl-1-Propanol) **75-84-3**	IC	98 (37)				0.8	3.0	237 (114)	Slight	1 5	1	3	0
Butyl Carbitol	See Diethylene Glycol Butyl Ether.												
4-tert-Butyl Catechol $(OH)_2C_6H_3C(CH_3)_3$ **98-29-3**	IIIB	266 (130)				1.0+		545 (285)	No	2	3	1	0
Butyl Chloride C_4H_9Cl (1-Chlorobutane) **109-69-3**	IB	15 (−9)	464 (240)	1.8	10.1	0.9	3.2	170 (77)	No	1	1	3	0
sec-Butyl Chloride $CH_3CHClC_2H_5$ (2-Chlorobutane) **78-86-4**	IB	<32 (<0)				0.87	3.20	155 (68)		1	1	3	0
tert-Butyl Chloride $(CH_3)_3CCl$ (2-Chloro-2-Methyl-Propane) **507-20-0**	IB	<32 (<0)				0.87	3.20	124 (51)		1	1	3	0
4-tert-Butyl-2-Chlorophenol $ClC_6H_3(OH)C(CH_3)_3$ **98-28-2**	IIIB	225 (107)				1.1		453–484 (234–251)	No	2	2	1	0
tert-Butyl-m-Cresol $C_6H_3(C_4H_9)(CH_3)OH$ **1333-13-7**	II	116 (47)				1.0−		451–469 (233–243)	No		2	2	0
p-tert-Butyl-o-Cresol $(OH)C_6H_3CH_3C(CH_3)_3$ **98-27-1**	IIIB	244 (118)				1.0−		278–280 (137–138)	No	2	2	1	0
Butylcyclohexane $C_4H_9C_6H_{11}$ (1-Cyclohexylbutane) **1678-93-9**		106 (41)	475 (246)			0.8		352–356 (178–180)				1	0
sec-Butylcyclohexane $CH_3CH_2CH(CH_3)C_6H_{11}$ (2-Cyclohexylbutane)			531 (277)			0.8		351 (177)				2	0
tert-Butylcyclohexane $(CH_3)_3CC_6H_{11}$ **3178-22-1**		108 (42)	648 (342)			0.8		333–336 (167–169)			0		0

Chemical Name Formula (Synonym) CAS No.	NFPA 30/ OSHA Class	Flash Point °F(°C)	Ignition Temp. °F(°C)	Flammable Limits Percent by Vol. Lower	Upper	Sp.Gr. (Water =1)	Vapor Density (Air =1)	Boiling Point °F(°C)	Water Soluble	Extin-guishing Methods	Hazard Identification Health	Flamma-bility	Insta-bility
N-Butylcyclo-hexylamine $C_6H_{11}NH(C_4H_9)$ **10108-56-2**		200 (93) (oc)				0.8		409 (209)	Slight	5	2	1	0
Butylcyclopentane $C_4H_9C_5H_9$			480 (250)			0.8		314 (157)				1	0
Butyldecalin $C_4H_9C_{10}H_{17}$	IIIB	500 (260)								2	1	1	0
tert-Butyldecalin $C_4H_9C_{10}H_{17}$	IIIB	640 (338)								2	1	1	0
N-Butyldiethanolamine $C_4H_9N(C_2H_4OH)_2$ **102-79-4**		245 (118) (oc)				1.0–		504 (262)	Yes	5 2	2	1	0
tert-Butyldiethano-lamine $C_8H_{10}NO_2$ [2,2-(tert-Butylimino) Diethanol] **2160-93-2**	Note: Melting point 117 (47).	285 (141) (oc)				1.0–		329–338 (165–170) @ 33 mm	Yes	2 5	2	1	0
Butyl Diglycol Carbonate	See Diethylene Glycol Bis (Butyl Carbonate).												
α-Butylene	See 1-Butene.												
β-Butylene	See 2-Butene-trans.												
γ-Butylene	See 2-Methylpropene.												
α-Butylene Glycol $C_2H_5CHOHCH_2OH$ (1,2-Butanediol) **584-03-2**	IIIA	194 (90)				1.01	3.10	377 (192)			1	2	0
β-Butylene Glycol $CH_3CH(OH)CH_2CH_2OH$ (1,3-Butanediol) **107-88-0**	IIIB	250 (121)	743 (395)			1.0		399 (204)	Yes	5 2	1	1	0
2,3-Butylene Oxide $CH_3HCOCHCH_3$ **21490-63-1**	IB	5 (–15)	822 (439)	1.5	18.3	0.83	2.49	149 (65)	Slight	1	1	3	1
1,2-Butylene Oxide $H_2COCHCH_2CH_3$ **106-88-7**	IB See NFPA 49 contained in this guide.	–7 (–22)	822 (439)	1.7	19	0.8	2.2	145 (63)	Yes	5 1	3	3	2 ~~W~~
Butyl Ethanedioate	See Butyl Oxalate.												
N-Butyl Ethanolamine $CH_3(CH_2)_3NHCH_2$-CH_2OH **111-75-1**		170 (77) (oc)				0.9	4.0	377 (192)	Yes	5	3	2	0
Butyl Ether	See Dibutyl Ether.												
Butylethylacetalde-hyde	See 2-Ethylhexanal.												
Butyl Ethylene	See 1-Hexene.												
Butyl Ethyl Ether	See Ethyl Butyl Ether.												
Butyl Formate $HCOOC_4H_9$ (Butyl Methanoate) (Formic Acid, Butyl Ester) **592-84-7**	IB	64 (18)	612 (322)	1.7	8.2	0.9	3.5	225 (107)	Yes	1 5	2	3	0
Butyl Glycolate $CH_2OHCOOC_4H_9$ **7397-62-8**	IIIA	142 (61)				1.01	4.45	~356 (~180)			0	2	0

Chemical Name Formula (Synonym) CAS No.	NFPA 30/ OSHA Class	Flash Point °F(°C)	Ignition Temp. °F(°C)	Flammable Limits Percent by Vol.		Sp.Gr. (Water =1)	Vapor Density (Air =1)	Boiling Point °F(°C)	Water Soluble	Extin-guishing Methods	Hazard Identification		
				Lower	Upper						Health	Flamma-bility	Insta-bility
tert-Butyl Hydroperoxide $(CH_3)_3COOH$ **75-91-2**	Note: May explode.	<80 (<27)				0.9		Decomposes @ 200 (93)	Slight	5 1	4	4	4 OX
2,2-(Butylimino)-diethanol	See tert-Butyldiethanolamine.												
n-Butyl Isocyanate $CH_3(CH_2)_3NCO$ (Butyl Isocyanate) **111-36-4**	IB	66 (19)				0.9	3.00	235 (113)	Reacts	5 1	3	3	2 ~~W~~
Butyl Isovalerate $C_4H_9OOCCH_2CH(CH_3)_2$ **109-19-3**	II	127 (53)				0.87	5.45	302 (150)			0	2	0
Butyl Lactate $CH_3CH(OH)COOC_4H_9$ **138-22-7**		160 (71) (oc)	720 (382)			1.0−	5.0	320 (160)	Slight	5	1	2	0
Butyl Mercaptan	See 1-Butanethiol.												
tert-Butyl Mercaptan	See 2-Methyl-2-Propanethiol.												
Butyl Methacrylate $CH_2{:}C(CH_3)COO-(CH_2)_3CH_3$ **97-88-1**		126 (52) (oc)				0.9	4.9	325 (163)	No		1	2	2
Butyl Methanoate	See Butyl Formate.												
Butyl Naphthalene $C_4H_9C_{10}H_7$	IIIB	680 (360)							No	2		1	0
Butyl Nitrate $CH_3(CH_2)_3ONO_2$ **928-45-0**	IC	97 (36)				1.0+	4.1	277 (136)	No	1	2	3	3
2-Butyloctanol $C_6H_{13}CH(C_4H_9)CH_2OH$ **3913-02-8**	IIIB	230 (110)				0.8		486 (252)	No	2	1	1	0
Butyl Oleate $C_{17}H_{33}COOC_4H_9$ **142-77-8**		356 (180) (oc)				0.9		440.6–442.4 (227–228) @ 15 mm	No	2	1	1	0
Butyl Oxalate $(COOC_4H_9)_2$ (Butyl Ethanedioate)		265 (129) (oc)				1.0−		472 (244)	No	2		1	0
tert-Butyl Peracetate $CH_3CO(O_2)C(CH_3)_3$ **107-71-1**	Note: Rapid decomposition at 200 (93).	<80 (<27)						Explodes on heating.	No	1	3	3	3
tert-Butyl Perbenzoate $C_6H_5COOOC(CH_3)_3$ **614-45-9**		>190 (>88) (oc)				1.0+		Explodes on heating.	No		2	3	3 OX
tert-Butyl Peroxypiva-late $(CH_3)_3COOCOC(CH_3)_3$ **927-07-1**	Note: Rapid decomposition at 90 (32).	>155 (>68) (oc)						Explodes on heating.	No		3	3	3 OX
β-(p-tert-Butyl Phenoxy) Ethanol $(CH_3)_3CC_6H_4OCH_2.CH_2OH$		248 (120) (oc)				1.0+		293–313 (145–156)	No	2	0	1	0
β-(p-tert-Butylphenoxy) Ethyl Acetate $(CH_3)_3CC_6H_4OCH_2CH_2O-COCH_3$		324 (162) (oc)				1.0+		579–585 (304–307)	No	2	0	1	0
Butyl Phenyl Ether $CH_3(CH_2)_3OC_6H_5$ (Butoxybenzene) **1126-79-0**		180 (82) (oc)				0.9	5.2	410 (210)	No			2	0

Chemical Name Formula (Synonym) CAS No.	NFPA 30/ OSHA Class	Flash Point °F(°C)	Ignition Temp. °F(°C)	Flammable Limits Percent by Vol. Lower	Upper	Sp.Gr. (Water =1)	Vapor Density (Air =1)	Boiling Point °F(°C)	Water Soluble	Extin-guishing Methods	Hazard Identification Health	Flamma-bility	Insta-bility
4-tert-Butyl-2-Phenylphenol $C_6H_5C_6H_3OHC(CH_3)_3$ **577-92-4**	IIIB	320 (160)				1.0+		385–388 (196–198)	No	2	1	1	0
Butyl Phosphate	See Tributyl Phosphate.												
Butyl Phthalyl Butyl Glycolate $C_6H_4(COO)_2(C_4H_9)CH_2$-$COOC_4H_9$ **85-70-1**		390 (199) (oc)				1.1		653 (345)	No	2	1	1	0
Butyl Propionate $C_2H_5COOC_4H_9$ **590-01-2**	IC	90 (32)	799 (426)			0.9	4.5	295 (146)	No	1	2	3	0
Butyl Ricinoleate $C_{18}H_{33}O_3C_4H_9$ **151-13-3**	IIIB	230 (110)				0.9		790 (421)	No	2	1	1	0
Butyl Sebacate	See Dibutyl Sebacate.												
Butyl Stearate $C_{17}H_{35}COOC_4H_9$ **123-95-5**	IIIB	320 (160)	671 (355)			0.9		650 (343)	No	2	0	1	0
tert-Butylstyrene	IIIA	177 (81)TCC		1	2.7	0.9		426 (219)	No		1	2	2
tert-Butyl Tetralin $C_4H_9C_{10}H_{11}$ **73090-68-3**	IIIB	680 (360)								2	2	1	0
Butyl Trichlorosilane $CH_3(CH_2)_3SiCl_3$ **7521-80-4**		130 (54) (oc)				1.2	6.5	300 (149)	No	3		2	0
N-Butylurethane $CH_3(CH_2)_3NHCOOC_2H_5$ (Butylcarbamic Acid, Ethyl Ester) (Ethyl Butylcarbamate) **591-62-8**	IIIA	197 (92)				0.9	5.0	396–397 (202–203)	No			2	0
Butyl Vinyl Ether	See Vinyl Butyl Ether.												
2-Butyne $CH_3C{:}CCH_3$ (Crotonylene) **503-17-3**	IA	−4 (<−20)		1.4		0.69	1.86	81 (27)		1	1	4	3
Butyraldehyde $CH_3(CH_2)_2CHO$ (Butanal) (Butyric Aldehyde) **123-72-8**	IB	−8 (−22)	425 (218)	1.9	12.5	0.8	2.5	169 (76)	No	1	3	3	0
	See NFPA 49 contained in this guide.												
Butyraldol $C_8H_{16}O_2$ **496-03-7**		165 (74) (oc)				0.9		280 (138)@ 50 mm	Slight	5	2	2	0
Butyraldoxime C_4H_8NOH (Butanal Oxime) **110-69-0**	II	136 (58)				0.9	3.0	306 (152)	Slight	5	1	2	0
Butyric Acid $CH_3(CH_2)_2COOH$ **107-92-6**	IIIA	161 (72)	830 (443)	2.0	10.0	1.0−	3	327 (164)	Yes	5	3	2	0
	See NFPA 49 contained in this guide.												
Butyric Acid, Ethyl Ester	See Ethyl Butyrate.												
Butyric Aldehyde	See Butyraldehyde.												
Butyric Anhydride $[CH_3(CH_2)_2CO]_2O$ **106-31-0**	IIIA	180 (54)	535 (279)	0.9	5.8	1.0−	5.4	388 (196)	Decom-poses	5	3	2	1

Chemical Name Formula (Synonym) CAS No.	NFPA 30/ OSHA Class	Flash Point °F(°C)	Ignition Temp. °F(°C)	Flammable Limits Percent by Vol.		Sp.Gr. (Water = 1)	Vapor Density (Air = 1)	Boiling Point °F(°C)	Water Soluble	Extin-guishing Methods	Hazard Identification		
				Lower	Upper						Health	Flamma-bility	Insta-bility
Butyric Ester	See Ethyl Butyrate.												
Butyrolactone $CH_2CH_2CH_2COO$ (ring) **96-48-0**		209 (98) (oc)				1.1		399 (204)	Yes	5	1	2	0
Butyrone	See 4-Heptanone.												
Butyronitrile $CH_3CH_2CH_2CN$ **109-74-0**	See NFPA 49 contained in this guide.	76 (24) (oc)	935 (501)	1.65		0.8	2.4	243 (117)	Slight	5 1	3	3	0
Camphor $C_{10}H_{16}O$ (Gum Camphor) **76-22-2**	IIIA	150 (66)	871 (466)	0.6	3.5	1.0−	5.24	399 (204)	No		2	2	0
Camphor Oil (Liquid Camphor) **8008-51-3**	II	117 (47)				0.9		347–392 (175–200)	No		2	2	0
Caproaldehyde	See Hexanal.												
Caproic Acid $(CH_3)(CH_2)_4COOH$ (Hexanoic Acid) **142-62-1**		215 (102) (oc)	716 (380)	1.3	9.3	0.9		400 (204)	No	2	3	1	0
Caprylaldehyde $CH_3(CH_2)_6CHO$ (Caprylic Aldehyde) (Octanal) **124-13-0**	II	125 (52)				0.8	4.4	335 (168)	Very slight			2	0
Caprylic Aldehyde	See Caprylaldehyde.												
Caprylyl Chloride $CH_3(CH_2)_6COCl$ **111-64-8**	IIIA	180 (82)				1.0−	5.6	384 (196)	Decom-poses	5	3	2	1
Carbitol	See Diethylene Glycol Ethyl Ether.												
Carbolic Acid	See Phenol.												
Carbon Bisulfide	See Carbon Disulfide.												
Carbon Disulfide CS_2 (Carbon Bisulfide) **75-15-0**	IB See NFPA 49 contained in this guide.	−22 (−30)	194 (90)	1.3	50.0	1.3	2.6	115 (46)	No	4	3	4	0
Carbon Monoxide CO **630-08-0**	See NFPA 49 contained in this guide.	Gas	1128 (609)	12.5	74		1.0	−314 (−192)	Slight or very slight, 2 or 3 ml per 100 ml.	6	2	4	0
Carbon Oxysulfide COS (Carbonyl Sulfide) **463-58-1**		Gas		12	29		2.1	−58 (−50)		6	3	4	1
Carbonyl Sulfide	See Carbon Oxysulfide.												
Carnauba Wax (Brazil Wax) **8015-86-9**	IIIB Note: Melting point 185 (85).	540 (282)				1.0−			No	2	1	1	0
Castor Oil (Ricinus Oil) **8001-79-4**	IIIB	445 (229)	840 (449)			1.0−		595 (313)	No	2	1	1	0
Castor Oil (Hydrogenated) $(C_{18}H_{35}O_3)_3C_3H_5$ **8001-78-3**	IIIB	401 (205)							No	2	1	1	0
Cellulose Nitrate Wet with Alcohol	See Nitrocellulose.												

Chemical Name Formula (Synonym) CAS No.	NFPA 30/ OSHA Class	Flash Point °F(°C)	Ignition Temp. °F(°C)	Flammable Limits Percent by Vol.		Sp.Gr. (Water =1)	Vapor Density (Air =1)	Boiling Point °F(°C)	Water Soluble	Extin-guishing Methods	Hazard Identification		
				Lower	Upper						Health	Flamma-bility	Insta-bility
Cetane	See Hexadecane.												
China Wood Oil	See Tung Oil.												
Chlorex	See Bis(2-Chloroethyl) Ether.												
Chlorine Monoxide Cl_2O **7791-21-1**		Gas		23.5	100			Explodes @ 39 (4)	Yes	6	3	4	3
Chloroacetic Acid $CH_2ClCOOH$ **79-11-8**	IIIB	259 (126)	>932 (>500)	8.0		1.58	3.26	372 (189)	Yes	2	4	1	0
	Note: Melting point 142–145 (61–63). See NFPA 49 contained in this guide.												
Chloroacetophenone $C_6H_5COCH_2Cl$ (Phenacyl Chloride) **532-27-4**	IIIB	244 (118)				1.32	5.32	477 (247)	No	2	3	1	0
Chloro-4-tert-Amylphenol $C_5H_{11}C_6H_3ClOH$ **73090-69-4**	IIIB	225 (107)				1.1		487–509 (253–265)		2	2	1	0
2-Chloro-4,6-Di-tert-Amylphenol $(C_5H_{11})_2C_6H_2ClOH$ **42350-99-2**	IIIB	250 (121)				1.0+		320–354 (160–179)@ 22 mm		2	2	1	0
2-Chloro-4-tert-Amylphenyl Methyl Ether $C_5H_{11}C_6H_3ClOCH_3$	IIIB	230 (110)				1.1	7.3	518–529 (270–276)		2	1	1	0
p-Chlorobenzaldehyde ClC_6H_4CHO **104-88-1**	IIIA	190 (88)				1.2		417 (214)	Slight	5	1	2	0
	Note: Melting point 114 (46).												
Chlorobenzene C_6H_5Cl (Chlorobenzol) (Monochlorobenzene) (Phenyl Chloride) **108-90-7**	IC	82 (28)	1099 (593)	1.3	9.6	1.1	3.9	270 (132)	No	4	3	3	0
	See NFPA 49 contained in this guide.												
Chlorobenzol	See Chlorobenzene.												
Chlorobenzotrifluoride $ClC_6H_4CF_3$ **98-15-7**	II	117 (47)				1.35	6.24	282 (139)				2	0
o-Chlorobenzotri-fluoride $ClC_6H_4CF_3$ (o-Chloro-α,α,α-trifluorotoluene) **88-16-4**	II	138 (59)				1.4	6.2	306 (152)			1	2	1
Chlorobutadiene	See 2-Chloro-1,3-Butadiene.												
2-Chloro-1,3-Butadiene $CH_2:CCl:CH:CH_2$ (Chlorobutadiene) (Chloroprene) **126-99-8**	IB	−4 (−20)		1.9	11.3	1.0	3.0	138 (59)	Slight	1 5	2	3	1
1-Chlorobutane	See Butyl Chloride.												
2-Chlorobutene-2 $CH_3CCl:CHCH_3$ **4461-41-0**	IB	−3 (−19)		2.3	9.3	0.9	3.1	143–159 (62–71)	Very slight	1	2	3	0
Chlorodiethylaluminum	See Diethylaluminum Chloride.												
Chlorodinitrobenzene	See Dinitrochlorobenzene.												

Chemical Name Formula (Synonym) CAS No.	NFPA 30/ OSHA Class	Flash Point °F(°C)	Ignition Temp. °F(°C)	Flammable Limits Percent by Vol.		Sp.Gr. (Water =1)	Vapor Density (Air =1)	Boiling Point °F(°C)	Water Soluble	Extin-guishing Methods	Hazard Identification		
				Lower	Upper						Health	Flamma-bility	Insta-bility
Chloroethane	See Ethyl Chloride.												
2-Chloroethanol CH_2ClCH_2OH (Ethylene Chlorohydrin) (2-Chloroethyl Alcohol) **107-07-3**	IIIA See NFPA 49 contained in this guide.	140 (60)	797 (425)	4.9	15.9	1.2	2.8	264–266 (129–130)	Yes	5	4	2	0
Chloroethyl Acetate $C_2H_4ClOOCCH_3$	II	129 (54)				1.2	4.2	293 (145)	No	3		2	0
2-Chloroethyl Acetate $CH_3COOCH_2CH_2Cl$ **542-58-5**	IIIA	151 (66)				1.2	4.2	291 (144)	No	3	3	2	0
2-Chloroethyl Alcohol	See 2-Chloroethanol.												
Chloro-4-Ethylbenzene $C_2H_5C_6H_4Cl$	IIIA	147 (64)				1.0+	4.9	364 (184)	No		1	2	0
Chloroethylene	See Vinyl Chloride.												
2-Chloroethyl Vinyl Ether	See Vinyl 2-Chloroethyl Ether.												
2-Chloroethyl-2-Xenyl Ether $C_6H_5C_6H_4OCH_2CH_2Cl$	IIIB	320 (160)				1.1		613 (323)	Slight	2 5			
1-Chlorohexane $CH_3(CH_2)_4CH_2Cl$ (Hexyl Chloride) **544-10-5**	IC	95 (35)				0.9	4.2	270 (132)	No	1	1	3	0
Chloroisopropyl Alcohol	See 1-Chloro-2-Propanol.												
Chloromethane	See Methyl Chloride.												
1-Chloro-2-Methyl Propane	See Isobutyl Chloride.												
1-Chloronaphthalene $C_{10}H_7Cl$ **90-13-1**	IIIB	250 (121)	>1036 (>558)			1.2	5.6	505 (263)	No	2	2	1	0
2-Chloro-5-Nitrobenzotrifluoride $C_6H_3CF_3(2\text{-}Cl, 5\text{-}NO_2)$ (2-Chloro-α,α,α-Trifluoro-5-Nitrotoluene) **777-37-7**	IIIB	275 (135)				1.6		446 (230)		2	1	1	0
1-Chloro-1-Nitroethane $C_2H_4NO_2Cl$ **598-92-5**		133 (56) (oc)				1.3	3.8	344 (173)	Slight	5	1	2	3
1-Chloro-1-Nitropropane $CHNO_2ClC_2H_5$ **600-25-9**		144 (62) (oc)				1.2	4.3	285 (141)	Slight	5	3	2	3
2-Chloro-2-Nitropropane $CH_3CNO_2ClCH_3$ **594-71-8**	 Note: Explodes on heating.	135 (57) (oc)				1.2	4.3	273 (134)	Slight			2	3
1-Chloropentane	See Amyl Chloride.												
β-Chlorophenetole $C_6H_5OCH_2CH_2CL$ (β-Phenoxyethyl Chloride) **622-86-6**	IIIB	225 (107)				1.1		306–311 (152–155)	Slight	5 2		1	0
o-Chlorophenol ClC_6H_4OH **95-57-8**	IIIA See NFPA 49 contained in this guide.	147 (64)				1.3	4.4	347 (175)	No	5	2	2	0

Chemical Name Formula (Synonym) CAS No.	NFPA 30/ OSHA Class	Flash Point °F(°C)	Ignition Temp. °F(°C)	Flammable Limits Percent by Vol. Lower	Upper	Sp.Gr. (Water =1)	Vapor Density (Air =1)	Boiling Point °F(°C)	Water Soluble	Extin-guishing Methods	Hazard Identification Health	Flamma-bility	Insta-bility
p-Chlorophenol C_6H_4OHCl **106-48-9**	IIIB	250 (121)				1.31	4.43	428 (220)	No	2	4	1	0
	Note: Melting point 109 (43). See NFPA 49 contained in this guide.												
2-Chloro-4-Phenylphenol $C_6H_5C_6H_3ClOH$ **92-04-6**	IIIB	345 (174)				<1		613 (323)	Slight	2 5	2	1	0
	Note: Melting point 172–176 (78–80).												
Chloroprene	See 2-Chloro-1,3-Butadiene.												
1-Chloropropane **540-54-5**	See Propyl Chloride.												
2-Chloropropane	See Isopropyl Chloride.												
1-Chloro-2-Propanol $CH_2ClCHOHCH_3$ (Chloroisopropyl Alcohol) (sec-Propylene Chlorohydrin) **127-00-4**		125 (52) (oc)				1.1	3.3	261 (127)	Yes	5	3	2	0
2-Chloro-1-Propanol $CH_3CHClCH_2OH$ (β-Chloropropyl Alcohol) (Propylene Chlorohydrin) **78-89-7**	II	125 (52)				1.1	3.3	271–273 (133–134)	Yes	5	2	2	0
1-Chloro-1-Propene	See 1-Chloropropylene.												
3-Chloropropene	See Allyl Chloride.												
α-Chloropropionic Acid $CH_3CHClCOOH$ (2-Chloropropionic Acid) **598-78-7**	IIIB	225 (107)	932 (500)			1.3		352–374 (178–190)	Yes	5 2	3	1	0
3-Chloropropionitrile $ClCH_2CH_2CN$ **542-76-7**	IIIA	168 (76)				1.1	3.0	348.8 (176) Decomposes	Yes	5	2	2	1
2-Chloropropionyl Chloride	IC	88 (31)				1.3	0.12	230 (110)	Reacts			3	
β-Chloropropyl Alcohol	See 2-Chloro-1-Propanol.												
1-Chloropropylene $CH_3CH{:}CHCl$ (1-Chloro-1-Propene) **590-21-6**	IA	<21 (<−6)		4.5	16	0.9		95–97 (35–36)		1	1	4	1
2-Chloropropylene $CH_3CCl{:}CH_2$ (β-Chloropropylene) (2-Chloropropene) **557-98-2**	IA	<4 (<−20)		4.5	16	0.93	2.63	73 (23)		1	2	4	1
3-Chloropropylene Oxide	See Epichlorohydrin.												
γ-Chloropropylene Oxide	See Epichlorohydrin.												
Chlorotoluene $C_6H_4ClCH_3$ (Tolyl Chloride) **25168-05-2**	II	126 (52) (oc)				1.06	4.37	324 (162)			2	2	1
α-Chlorotoluene	See Benzyl Chloride.												
Chlorotrifluoroethylene	See Trifluorochloroethylene.												
2-Chloro-α,α,α-Trifluoro-5-Nitrotoluene	See 2-Chloro-5-Nitrobenzotrifluoride.												

Chemical Name Formula (Synonym) CAS No.	NFPA 30/ OSHA Class	Flash Point °F(°C)	Ignition Temp. °F(°C)	Flammable Limits Percent by Vol.		Sp.Gr. (Water = 1)	Vapor Density (Air = 1)	Boiling Point °F(°C)	Water Soluble	Extin-guishing Methods	Hazard Identification		
				Lower	Upper						Health	Flamma-bility	Insta-bility
o-Chloro-α,α,α-Trifluorotoluene	See o-Chlorobenzotrifluoride.												
Cimene	See Dipentene.												
Cinnamene	See Styrene.												
Citral $(CH_3)_2C:CH(CH_2)_2C-(CH_3):CHCHO$ (3,7-Dimethyl-2,6-Octadienal) (Geranial) **5392-40-5**	IIIA	195 (91)				0.9		197–199 (92–93)	No	5	2	1	0
Citronellel $(CH_3)_2C:CH(CH_2)_2-CH(CH_3)CH_2CHO$ (3,7-Dimethyl-6-Octenal) (Rhodinal) **106-23-0**	IIIA	165 (74)				0.9		117 (47)	No	5		2	
Citronellol $(CH_3)_2C:CH(CH_2)_2CH-(CH_3)(CH_2)_2OH$ (3,7-Dimethyl-6-Octen-1-ol) **106-22-9**	IIIB	205 (96)				0.85		227 (108.4)	No	5	2	2	0
Cleaning Solvent	See Stoddard Solvent. See Perchloroethylene.												
Coal Gas	See Gas.												
Coal Oil	See Fuel Oil No. 1.												
Coal Tar Light Oil (Upper Coal Tar Distil-late) **65996-91-0**		<80 (<27)				<1			No	1	2	3	0
Coal Tar Pitch **8007-45-2**	IIIB	405 (207)				>1			No	2	1	3	0
Cobalt Naphtha (Cobalt Naphthenate) **61789-51-3**	II	121 (49)	529 (276)			0.9			No		1	2	0
Cobalt Naphthenate	See Cobalt Naphtha.												
Cocoanut Oil Refined Crude **8001-31-8**	IIIB	420 (216) 548 (287) 420 (216) Note: Melting point 72 (22).				0.9			No	2	1	1	0
Cod Liver Oil **8001-69-2**	IIIB	412 (211)				0.9			No	2	0	1	0
Collodion $C_{12}H_{16}O_6(NO_3)_4$-$C_{13}H_{17}O_7(NO_3)_3$ Solution of Nitrated Cel-lulose in Ether-Alcohol **9004-70-0**	IA See Nitrocellulose and Pyroxylin Solution.	<0 (< −18)	338 (170)	1.9	48	0.8	2.6	95 (35)		1 5	2	4	0
Cologne Spirits	See Ethyl Alcohol.												
Columbian Spirits	See Methyl Alcohol.												
Colza Oil	See Rapeseed Oil.												
Corn Oil Cooking **8001-30-7**		490 (254) 610 (321) (oc)	740 (393)			0.9 <1			No	2	0	1	0
Cottonseed Oil Cooking **8001-29-4**		486 (252) 610 (321) (oc)	650 (343)			0.9 <1			No	2	0	1	0
Creosote Oil **8001-58-9**	IIIA	165 (74)	637 (336)			>1		382–752 (194–400)	No	3	2	2	0

Chemical Name Formula (Synonym) CAS No.	NFPA 30/ OSHA Class	Flash Point °F(°C)	Ignition Temp. °F(°C)	Flammable Limits Percent by Vol.		Sp.Gr. (Water =1)	Vapor Density (Air =1)	Boiling Point °F(°C)	Water Soluble	Extin-guishing Methods	Hazard Identification		
				Lower	Upper						Health	Flamma-bility	Insta-bility
o-Cresol $CH_3C_6H_4OH$ (o-Hydroxytoluene) (o-Methyl Phenol) **95-48-7**	IIIA	178 (81)	1110 (599)	1.4 @ 300 (149)		1.1	3.7	376 (191)	No	3	3	2	0
	Note: Melting point 88 (31). See NFPA 49 contained in this guide.												
m- or p-Cresol $CH_3C_6H_4OH$ **108-39-4** **(m-Cresol)** **106-44-5** **(p-Cresol)**	IIIA	187 (86)	1038 (558)	1.1 @302 (150)		1.0		395 (201)	No		3	2	0
	Note: Melting point of meta: 53.6 (12); of para: 94.6 (35). See NFPA 49 contained in this guide.												
p-Cresyl Acetate $CH_3C_6H_4OCOCH_3$ (p-Tolyl Acetate) **140-39-6**	IIIA	195 (91)				1.1				5	1	2	0
Cresyl Diphenyl Phosphate $(C_6H_5O)_2[(CH_3)_2\text{-}C_6H_4O]PO_4$ **26444-49-5**	IIIB	450 (232)				1.2		734 (390)		2	1	1	0
Crotonaldehyde $CH_3CH{:}CHCHO$ (2-Butenal) (Crotonic Aldehyde) (Propylene Aldehyde) **4170-30-3**	IB	55 (13)	450 (232)	2.1	15.5	0.9	2.4	216 (102)	Slight	1 5	4	3	2
	See NFPA 49 contained in this guide.												
Crotonic Acid $CH_3CH{:}CHCOOH$ **3724-65-0**		190 (88) (oc)	745 (396)			1.0– @ 176(80)	3.0	372 (189)	Yes	5	3	2	0
	Note: Melting point 162 (72). See NFPA 49 contained in this guide.												
Crotonic Aldehyde	See Crotonaldehyde.												
Crotononitrile $CH_3CH{:}CHCN$ (2-Butenenitrile) **4786-20-3**	IB	68 (20)				0.8	2.3	230–240.8 (110–116)	No	1	3	3	1
Crotonyl Alcohol $CH_3CH{:}CHCH_2OH$ (2-Buten-1-ol) (Crotyl Alcohol) **6117-91-5**	IC	81 (27)	660 (349)	4.2	35.3	0.85	2.49	250 (121)	To 16%		2	3	0
1-Crotyl Bromide $CH_3CH{:}CHCH_2Br$ (1-Bromo-2-Butene) **4784-77-4**		52 (11)		4.6	12.0	1.3	4.66	207–210 (97–99)			2	3	2
1-Crotyl Chloride $CH_3CH{:}CHCH_2Cl$ (1-Chloro-2-Butene) **591-97-9**		23 (–5)		4.2	19.0	0.9	3.13	183–185 (84–85)			2	3	1
Cumene $C_6H_5CH(CH_3)_2$ (Cumol) (2-Phenyl Propane) (Isopropyl Benzene) **98-82-8**	IC	96 (36)	795 (424)	0.9	6.5	0.9	4.1	306 (152)	No	1	2	3	1
	See NFPA 49 contained in this guide.												
Cumene Hydroperoxide $C_6H_5C(CH_3)_2OOH$ **80-15-9**	IIIA	175 (79)		0.9	6.5	1.0+ @ 25°C		Explodes on heating.	Slight		1	2	4 OX
	Note: Decomposes violently above 300 (149).												
Cumol	See Cumene.												
Cyanamide NH_2CN **156-62-7**	IIIB	286 (141)				1.07	1.45	500 (260) Decomposes		2		3	1 ₩
	Note: Melting point 111 (44).												
2-Cyanoethyl Acrylate $CH_2CHCOOCH_2CH_2CN$ **7085-85-0**		255 (124) (oc)				1.1	4.3	Polymerizes	No	2	2	2	2

Chemical Name Formula (Synonym) CAS No.	NFPA 30/ OSHA Class	Flash Point °F(°C)	Ignition Temp. °F(°C)	Flammable Limits Percent by Vol.		Sp.Gr. (Water =1)	Vapor Density (Air =1)	Boiling Point °F(°C)	Water Soluble	Extin-guishing Methods	Hazard Identification		
				Lower	Upper						Health	Flamma-bility	Insta-bility
N-(2-Cyanoethyl) Cyclohexylamine $C_6H_{11}NHC_2H_4CN$ **702-03-4**		255 (124) (oc)				0.9	5.2		No	2	2	1	0
Cyanogen $(CN)_2$ **460-19-5**	See NFPA 49 contained in this guide.	Gas		6.6	32	0.95	1.8	−6 (−21)	Yes	6	4	4	1
Cyclamen Aldehyde $(CH_3)_2CHC_6H_4CH(CH_3)$-CH_2CHO [α-Methyl-4-(1-methylethyl) benzenepropanol] (α-Methyl-p-isopropylphenylpropyl-aldehyde) **103-95-7**	IIIA	190 (88)				1.0−				5	1	2	0
Cyclobutane C_4H_8 (Tetramethylene) **287-23-0**		Gas		1.8			1.9	55 (13)	No	6	1	4	0
1,5,9-Cyclododecatriene $C_{12}H_{18}$ **4904-61-4**	IIIA	160 (71)				0.9		448 (231)	No		2	2	1
Cycloheptane $CH_2(CH_2)_5CH_2$ (ring) **291-64-5**	IB	<70 (<21)		1.1	6.7	0.81	3.39	246 (119)		1	0	3	0
Cyclohexane C_6H_{12} (Hexahydrobenzene) (Hexamethylene) **110-82-7**	IB	−4 (−20)	473 (245)	1.3	8	0.8	2.9	179 (82)	No	1	1	3	0
1,4-Cyclohexane Dimethanol $C_8H_{16}O_2$ (CHDM) **105-08-8**	IIIB	332 (167)	600 (316)			1.0−		525 (274)	Yes	5 2	1	1	0
Cyclohexanethiol $C_6H_{11}SH$ (Cyclohexylmercaptan) **1569-69-3**	II	110 (43)				0.95	4.00	315–319 (157–159)	No	5	2	2	0
Cyclohexanol $C_6H_{11}OH$ (Anol) (Hexalin) (Hydralin) **108-93-0**	IIIA Note: Melting point 75 (24).	154 (68)	572 (300)			1.0−	3.5	322 (161)	Slight	5	1	2	0
Cyclohexanone $C_6H_{10}O$ (Pimelic Ketone) **108-94-1**	II	111 (44)	788 (420)	1.1 @212 (100)	9.4	0.9	3.4	313 (156)	Slight	5	1	2	0
Cyclohexene $CH_2CH_2CH_2CH_2CH{:}CH$ (ring) **110-83-8**	IB	<20 (<−7)	471 (244)			0.8	2.8	181 (83)	No	1	1	3	0
3-Cyclohexene-1-Carboxaldehyde	See 1,2,3,6-Tetrahydrobenzaldehyde.												
Cyclohexenone Δ C_6H_8O **930-68-7**	IC	93 (34)					3.3	313 (156)		1	1	3	0
Cyclohexyl Acetate $CH_3CO_2C_6H_{11}$ (Hexalin Acetate) **622-45-7**	II	136 (58)	635 (335)			1.0−	4.9	350 (177)	No		1	2	0

Chemical Name Formula (Synonym) CAS No.	NFPA 30/ OSHA Class	Flash Point °F(°C)	Ignition Temp. °F(°C)	Flammable Limits Percent by Vol.		Sp.Gr. (Water =1)	Vapor Density (Air =1)	Boiling Point °F(°C)	Water Soluble	Extin-guishing Methods	Hazard Identification		
				Lower	Upper						Health	Flamma-bility	Insta-bility
Cyclohexylamine $C_6H_{11}NH_2$ (Amino Cyclohexane) (Hexahydroaniline) **108-91-8**	IC See NFPA 49 contained in this guide.	88 (31)	560 (293)	1.5	9.4	0.9	3.4	274 (134)	Yes	1 5	3	3	0
Cyclohexylbenzene $C_6H_5C_6H_{11}$ (Phenylcyclohexane) **827-52-1**		210 (99) (oc)				0.9		459 (237)	No		2	1	0
Cyclohexyl Chloride $CH_2(CH_2)_4CHCl$ (Chlorocyclohexane) **542-18-7**	IC	90 (32)				0.99	4.08	288 (142)		1	1	3	0
Cyclohexylcyclohexa-nol $C_6H_{11}C_6H_{10}OH$ **6531-86-8**	IIIB	270 (132)				1.0−		304–313 (151–156)	No	2	1	1	0
Cyclohexyl Formate $CH_2(CH_2)_4HCOOCH$	II	124 (51)				1.01	4.42	324 (162)				2	0
Cyclohexylmethane	See Methylcyclohexane.												
o-Cyclohexylphenol $C_6H_{11}C_6H_4OH$ **119-42-6**	IIIB Note: Melting point 116 (47).	273 (134)				1.0+		298 (148)@ 10 mm	Slight	5 2	2	1	0
Cyclohexyltrichlorosi-lane $C_6H_{11}SiCl_3$ **98-12-4**		196 (91) (oc)				1.2	7.5	406 (208)	No	3	3	2	1
1,5-Cyclooctadiene C_8H_{10} **111-78-4**	IC	95 (35)				0.9	3.66	304 (151)	No	1	2	3	0
Cyclopentane C_5H_{10} **287-92-3**	IB	<20 (<−7)	682 (361)	1.5		0.7	2.4	121 (49)	No	1	1	3	0
Cyclopentanol $CH_2(CH_2)_3CHOH$ **96-41-3**	II	124 (51)				0.95	2.97	286 (141)			1	2	0
Cyclopentanone $OCCH_2CH_2CH_2CH_2$ (Adipic Ketone) **120-92-3**	IC	79 (26)				0.9	2.3	267 (131)	Slight	1 5	2	3	0
Cyclopentene $CH{:}CHCH_2CH_2CH_2$ **142-29-0**	IB	−20 (−29)	743 (395)			0.8	2.35	111 (44)		1	1	3	1
Cyclopropane $(CH_2)_3$ (Trimethylene) **75-19-4**		Gas	928 (498)	2.4	10.4		1.5	−29 (−34)	No	6	1	4	0
p-Cymene $CH_3C_6H_4CH(CH_3)_2$ Tech.(4-Isopropyl-1-Methyl Benzene) **99-87-6**	II	117 (47) 127 (53)	817 (436) 833 (445)	0.7 @ 212 (100)	5.6 5.6	0.9	4.6	349 (176)	No		1	2	0
DDS	See Dimethyldichlorosilane.												
Decaborane $B_{10}H_{14}$ **17702-41-9**	IIIA Note: Melting point 211.5 (100). See NFPA 49 contained in this guide.	176 (80)	300 (149)			0.9		416 (213)	Slight		3	2	2 W̶

Chemical Name Formula (Synonym) CAS No.	NFPA 30/ OSHA Class	Flash Point °F(°C)	Ignition Temp. °F(°C)	Flammable Limits Percent by Vol.		Sp.Gr. (Water =1)	Vapor Density (Air =1)	Boiling Point °F(°C)	Water Soluble	Extin-guishing Methods	Hazard Identification		
				Lower	Upper						Health	Flamma-bility	Insta-bility
Decahydronaphthalene $C_{10}H_{18}$ (Decalin) **91-17-8**	II	136 (58)	482 (250)	0.7 @ 212 (100)	4.9 @ 212 100)	0.9	4.8	382 (194)	No		2	2	0
Decahydronaphtha-lene-trans $C_{10}H_{18}$ **493-02-7**	II	129 (54)	491 (255)	0.7	5.4	0.87	4.77	369 (187)			1	2	0
Decalin	See Decahydronaphthalene.												
Decane $CH_3(CH_2)_8CH_3$ **124-18-5**	II	115 (46)	410 (210)	0.8	5.4	0.7	4.9	345 (174)	No		1	2	0
Decanol $CH_3(CH_2)_8CH_2OH$ (Decyl Alcohol) **112-30-1**		180 (82) (oc)	550 (288)			0.8	5.5	444.2 (229)	No		2	2	0
1-Decene $CH_3(CH_2)_7CH{:}CH_2$ **872-05-9**	II	<131 (<55)	455 (235)	0.5	5.4	0.74	4.84	342 (172)	No		0	2	0
Decyl Acrylate $CH_3(CN_2)_9OCOCH{:}CH_2$ **2156-96-9**		441 (227) (oc)				0.9		316 (158)@ 50 mm	Very slight	2	2	1	2
Decyl Alcohol	See Decanol.												
Decylamine $CH_3(CH_2)_9NH_2$ (1-Aminodecane) **2016-57-1**	IIIB	210 (99)				0.8		429 (221)	Slight	5	3	1	0
Decylbenzene $C_{10}H_{21}C_6H_5$ **104-72-3**	IIIB	225 (107)				0.9		491–536 (255–280)	No	2	1	1	0
tert-Decylmercaptan $C_{10}H_{21}SH$ **30174-58-4**	IIIA	190 (88)				0.9	6.0	410–424 (210–218)			2	2	0
Decylnaphthalene $C_{10}H_{21}C_{10}H_7$	IIIB	350 (177)				0.9		635–680 (335–360)	No	2	1	1	0
Decyl Nitrate $CH_3(CH_2)_9ONO_2$		235 (113) (oc)				1.0 –		261 (127)@ 11 mm	No	2		1	0
Dehydroacetic Acid $CH_3C{:}CHC(O)CH$- $(COCH_3)C(O)O$ (DHA) (Methylacetopyranone) **520-45-6**		315 (157) (oc)	690 (366)					518 (270)	No	2	2	1	0
	Note: Melting point 228–232 (109–111).												
Denatured Alcohol	IB	60 (16)	750 (399)			0.8	1.6	175 (79)	Yes	1 5	0	3	0
	See also Denatured Alcohol Government Formula.												
Denatured Alcohol	IB	60 (16)	750 (399)			0.8	1.6	175 (79)	Yes	1 5	0	3	0
Government Formula (CD-5)		60–62 (16–17)											
(CD-5A)		60–61 (15.5–16)											
(CD-10)		49–59 (9–15)											
(SD-1)		57 (14)											
(SD-2B)		56 (13)											
(SD-3A)		59 (15)											
(SD-13A)		<19 (< –7)											
(SD-17)		60 (16)											
(SD-23A)		35 (2)											
(SD-30)		59 (15)											
(SD-39B)		60 (16)											
(SD-39C)		59 (15)											
(SD-40M)		59 (15)											

Chemical Name Formula (Synonym) CAS No.	NFPA 30/ OSHA Class	Flash Point °F(°C)	Ignition Temp. °F(°C)	Flammable Limits Percent by Vol. Lower	Upper	Sp.Gr. (Water =1)	Vapor Density (Air =1)	Boiling Point °F(°C)	Water Soluble	Extin-guishing Methods	Hazard Identification Health	Flamma-bility	Insta-bility
Deuterium D_2 (Heavy Hydrogen) **7782-39-0**		Gas		5	75			−417.1 (−249.5)		6	0	4	0
Diacetone	See Diacetone Alcohol.												
Diacetone Alcohol $CH_3COCH_2C(CH_3)_2OH$ Acetone-free Commercial (Diacetone) (4-Hydroxy-4-Methyl-2-Pentanone) **123-42-2**	IIIA	148 (64) 136 (58) 148 (64)	1118 (603) 1190 (643) 1118 (603)	1.8	6.9	0.9	4.0	328 (164)	Yes	5	1	2	0
Diacetyl	See 2,3-Butanedione.												
Diallyl Ether	See Allyl Ether.												
Diallyl Phthalate $C_6H_4(CO_2C_3H_5)_2$ **131-17-9**	IIIB	330 (166)				1.1		554 (290)	No	2	1	1	1
1,3-Diaminobutane	See 1,3-Butanediamine.												
1,3-Diaminopropane	See 1,3-Propanediamine.												
1,3-Diamino-2-Propanol $NH_2CH_2CHOHCH_2NH_2$ **616-29-5**	IIIB	270 (132)				1.1		266 (130)	Yes	2 5	2	1	0
Diamylamine $(C_5H_{11})_2NH$ **2050-92-2**	II See NFPA 49 contained in this guide.	124 (51)				0.8	5.4	356 (180)	Slight	5	3	2	0
Diamylbenzene $(C_5H_{11})_2C_6H_4$		225 (107) (oc)				0.9		491–536 (255–280)	No	2	0	1	0
Diamylbiphenyl $C_5H_{11}(C_6H_4)_2C_5H_{11}$ (Diaminodiphenyl)	IIIB	340 (171)				1.0−		687–759 (364–404)	No	2	0	1	0
Di-tert-Amylcyclohexanol $(C_5H_{11})_2C_6H_9OH$	IIIB	270 (132)				0.9		554–572 (290–300)	No	2	0	1	0
Diamyldiphenyl	See Diamylbiphenyl.												
Diamylene $C_{10}H_{20}$		118 (48) (oc)				0.8		302 (150)			0	2	0
Diamyl Ether	See Amyl Ether.												
Diamyl Maleate $(CHCOOC_5H_{11})_2$ **10099-71-5**	IIIB	270 (132)				1.0−		505–572 (263–300)	No	2	0	1	0
Diamyl Naphthalene $C_{10}H_6(C_5H_{11})_2$		315 (159) (oc)				0.9		624 (329)	No	2	0	1	0
2,4-Diamylphenol $(C_5H_{11})_2C_6H_3OH$		260 (127) (oc)				0.9		527 (275)	No	2	2	1	0
Di-tert-Amylphenoxy Ethanol $C_6H_3(C_5H_{11})_2OC_2H_4OH$		300 (149) (oc)				1.0−		615 (324)	No	2	0	1	0
Diamyl Phthalate $C_6H_4(COOC_5H_{11})_2$ (Amyl Phthalate) **131-18-0**	IIIB	245 (118)				1.0		475–490 (246–254) @ 50 mm	No	2	1	1	0
Diamyl Sulfide $(C_5H_{11})_2S$ **872-10-6**		185 (85) (oc)				0.9		338–356 (170–180)	No		2	2	0

Chemical Name Formula (Synonym) CAS No.	NFPA 30/ OSHA Class	Flash Point °F(°C)	Ignition Temp. °F(°C)	Flammable Limits Percent by Vol.		Sp.Gr. (Water =1)	Vapor Density (Air =1)	Boiling Point °F(°C)	Water Soluble	Extin-guishing Methods	Hazard Identification		
				Lower	Upper						Health	Flamma-bility	Insta-bility
o-Dianisidine $[NH_2(OCH_3)C_6H_3]_2$ (o-Dimethoxybenzidine) (3,3′-Dimethoxybenzidine) **119-90-4**	IIIB	403 (206)					8.43			2	1	1	0
	Note: Melting point 297 (147).												
Dibenzyl Ether $(C_6H_5CH_2)_2O$ (Benzyl Ether) **103-50-4**	IIIB	275 (135)				1.0		568 (298)	No	2	1	1	0
Diborane B_2H_6 **19287-45-7**		Gas	100–125 (38–52)	0.8	88		1.0−	−135 (−93)	No	6	4	4	3
	Note: Ignites spontaneously in moist air. See NFPA 49 contained in this guide.												
Dibutoxy Ethyl Phthalate $C_6H_4(COOC_2H_4OC_4H_9)_2$ **117-83-9**		407 (208) (oc)				1.1		437 (225)	No	5 2	1	1	0
Dibutoxymethane $CH_2(OC_4H_9)_2$ **2568-90-3**	IIIA	140 (60)				0.8		330–370 (166–188)	No		0	2	0
	Note: Melting point 140 (60).												
Dibutoxy Tetraglycol $(C_4H_9OC_2H_4OC_2H_4)_2O$ (Tetraethylene Glycol Dibutyl Ether) **112-98-1**		305 (152) (oc)				0.9		635 (335)	Slight	2 5	2	1	0
N,N-Dibutylacetamide $CH_3CON(C_4H_9)_2$ **1563-90-2**	IIIB	225 (107)				0.9		469–482 (243–250)		2	0	1	0
Dibutylamine $(C_4H_9)_2NH$ **111-92-2**	II	117 (47)		1.1		0.8	4.5	322 (161)	Slight	5	3	2	0
	See NFPA 49 contained in this guide.												
Di-sec-Butylamine $[C_2H_5(CH_3)CH]_2NH$ **626-23-3**		75 (24) (oc)				0.8	4.5	270–275 (132–135)	Yes	5 1	3	3	0
Dibutylaminoethanol $(C_4H_9)_2NC_2H_4OH$ **102-81-8**		200 (93) (oc)				0.9		432 (222)	No		3	2	0
1-Dibutylamino-2-Propanol	See Dibutylisopropanolamine.												
N,N-Dibutylaniline $C_6H_5N(CH_2CH_2CH_2CH_3)_2$ **613-29-6**	IIIB	230 (110)				0.9		505–527 (263–275)	No	2	3	1	0
Di-tert-Butyl-p-Cresol $C_6H_2(C_4H_9)_2(CH_3)OH$ **128-37-0**	IIIB	261 (127)						495–511 (257–266)	No	2	2	1	0
	Note: Melting point 154.4 (68).												
Dibutyl Ether $(C_4H_9)_2O$ (1-Butoxybutane) (Butyl Ether) **142-96-1**	IC	77 (25)	382 (194)	1.5	7.6	0.8	4.5	286 (141)	No	1 5	1	3	1
	See NFPA 49 contained in this guide.												
2,5-Di-tert-Butylhydroquinone $[C(CH_3)_3]_2C_6H_2(OH)_2$ (DTBHQ)		420 (216) (oc)	790 (421)						No	2	1	1	0
	Note: Melting point 410 (210).												
Dibutyl Isophthalate $C_6H_4(CO_2C_4H_9)_2$ **3126-90-7**	IIIB	322 (161)							No	2	0	1	0
N,N′-Di-sec-Butyl-p-Phenylenediamine $C_6H_4[\text{-}NHCH(CH_3)CH_2CH_3]_2$ **101-96-2**	IIIB	270 (132)	625 (329)	0.6 @ 329		0.9				5 2	2	2	0

Chemical Name Formula (Synonym) CAS No.	NFPA 30/ OSHA Class	Flash Point °F(°C)	Ignition Temp. °F(°C)	Flammable Limits Percent by Vol. Lower	Upper	Sp.Gr. (Water =1)	Vapor Density (Air =1)	Boiling Point °F(°C)	Water Soluble	Extin-guishing Methods	Hazard Identification Health	Flamma-bility	Insta-bility
Dibutylisopropanol-amine $CH_3CHOHCH_2N(C_4H_9)_2$ **2109-64-0**		205 (96) (oc)				0.8		444 (229)	Slight	5	2	1	0
Dibutyl Maleate $(\text{-}CHCO_2C_4H_9)_2$ **105-76-0**		285 (141) (oc)				1.0–		Decomposes		2	1	1	0
Dibutyl Oxalate $C_4H_9OOCCOOC_4H_9$ **2050-60-4**	IIIB	220 (104)				1.0+		472 (244)	No	2	0	1	0
Di-tert-Butyl Peroxide $(CH_3)_3COOC(CH_3)_3$ **110-05-4**		65 (18) (oc)				0.8		231 (111)	Slight	1	3	2	4 OX
Dibutyl Phosphate $(C_4H_9O)_2P(O)H$ **109-47-7**	II	120 (49)				1.0–		239 (115)	No		3	2	0
Dibutyl Phthalate $C_6H_4(CO_2C_4H_9)_2$ (Dibutyl-o-Phthalate) **84-74-2**	IIIB	315 (157)	757 (402)	0.5 @ 456 (235)		1.0+		644 (340)	No	2	2	1	0
Dibutyl Sebacate $[(CH_2)_4COOC_4H_9]_2$ (Decanedioic Dibutyl Ester) (Butyl Sebacate) **109-43-3**		353 (178) (oc)	690 (365)	0.44 @ 469 (243)		1.0–		650 (343)	No	2	2	1	0
N,N-Dibutyl Stearamide $C_{17}H_{35}CON(C_4H_9)_2$	IIIB	420 (216)				0.9		343–347 (173–175) @ 0.4 mm	No	2	0	1	0
n-Dibutyl Tartrate $(COOC_4H_9)_2(CHOH)_2$ (Dibutyl-d-2,3-Dihydroxy-butanedioate) **87-92-3**	IIIA	195 (91)	544 (284)			1.1		650 (343)	No	5	0	2	0
N,N′-Dibutyltoluene-sulfonamide $CH_3C_6H_4SO_3N(C_4H_9)_2$	IIIB	330 (166)				1.1		392 (200)@ 10 mm		2	0	1	0
Dicaproate	See Triethylene Glycol.												
Dicapryl Phthalate $C_6H_4[COOCH(CH_3)\text{-}C_6H_{13}]_2$ **131-15-7**	IIIB	395 (202)				1.0–	9.8	441–453 (227–234) @ 4.5 mm	No	2	1	1	0
Dichloroacetyl Chlo-ride $CHCl_2COCl$ (Dichloroethanoyl Chloride) **79-36-7**	IIIA See NFPA 49 contained in this guide.	151 (66)				1.5	5.1	225–226 (107–108)	Decom-poses	5	3	2	2 ~~W~~
3,4-Dichloroaniline $NH_2C_6H_3Cl_2$ **95-76-1**	Note: Melting point 161 (72). See NFPA 49 contained in this guide.	331 (166) (oc)	509 (265)	2.8	7.2			522 (272)	No	2	2	1	0
o-Dichlorobenzene $C_6H_4Cl_2$ (o-Dichlorobenzol) **95-50-1**	IIIA See NFPA 49 contained in this guide.	151 (66)	1198 (648)	2.2	9.2	1.3	5.1	356 (180)	No	3	2	2	0
p-Dichlorobenzene $C_6H_4Cl_2$ **106-46-7**	IIIA Note: Melting point 127(53).	150 (66)				1.5	5.1	345 (174)	No	3	2	2	0
o-Dichlorobenzol	See o-Dichlorobenzene.												

Chemical Name Formula (Synonym) CAS No.	NFPA 30/ OSHA Class	Flash Point °F(°C)	Ignition Temp. °F(°C)	Flammable Limits Percent by Vol.		Sp.Gr. (Water =1)	Vapor Density (Air =1)	Boiling Point °F(°C)	Water Soluble	Extin-guishing Methods	Hazard Identification		
				Lower	Upper						Health	Flamma-bility	Insta-bility
2,3-Dichlorobutadiene-1,3 $CH_2:C(Cl)C(Cl):CH_2$ **1653-19-6**	IB	50 (10)	694 (368)	1.0	12.0	1.2	4.24	212 (100)	No	1	3	3	2
1,2-Dichlorobutane $CH_3CH_2CHClCH_2Cl$			527 (275)				4.38				2	2	0
1,4-Dichlorobutane $CH_2ClCH_2CH_2CH_2Cl$ **110-56-5**	II See NFPA 49 contained in this guide.	126 (52)		1.5	4.0	1.1	4.4	311 (155)	No	3	1	2	0
2,3-Dichlorobutane $CH_3CHClCHClCH_3$ **7581-97-7**		194 (90) (oc)				1.1	4.4	241–253 (116–123)			2	2	0
1,3-Dichloro-2-Butene $CH_2ClCH:CClCH_3$ **926-57-8**	IC	80 (27)				1.2	4.31	262 (128)	No	1	3	3	2
3,4-Dichlorobutene-1 $CH_2ClCHClCHCH_2$ **64037-54-3**	II	113 (45)				1.1	4.31	316 (158)			3	2	1
Dichlorodimethylsilane	See Dimethyldichlorosilane.												
1,1-Dichloroethane	See Ethylidene Dichloride.												
1,2-Dichloroethane	See Ethylene Dichloride.												
Dichloroethanoyl Chloride	See Dichloroacetyl Chloride.												
1,1-Dichloroethylene	See Vinylidene Chloride.												
1,2-Dichloroethylene $ClCH:CHCl$ (sym-Dichloroethylene) **540-59-0**	IB Note: Exists as cis and trans isomers.	36 (2)	860 (460)	5.6	12.8	1.3	3.4	119 (48)	No	4	1	3	2
2,2′-Dichloroethyl Ether $ClCH_2CH_2OCH_2CH_2Cl$ (Dichlorodiethyl ether) **111-44-4**	II See NFPA 49 contained in this guide.	131 (55)	696 (369)	2.7		1.2	4.93	352 (178)	No	5	3	2	1
2,2-Dichloroethyl Formal	See Bis(2-Chloroethyl) Formal.												
Di-(2-Chloroethyl) Formal	See Bis(2-Chloroethyl) Formal.												
1,3-Dichloro-2,4-Hexadiene $CH_2ClCH:CClCH:$- $CHCH_3$	IIIA	168 (76)										2	0
Dichloroisopropyl Ether $ClCH_2CH(CH_3)$- $OCH(CH_3)CH_2Cl$ [Bis(β-Chloroisopropyl) Ether] [Bis(2-Chloro-1-Methylethyl) Ether] **108-60-1**		185 (85) (oc)				1.1	6.0	369 (187)	No	3	3	2	0
Dichloromethane	See Methylene Chloride.												
1,1-Dichloro-1-Nitroethane $CH_3CCl_2NO_2$ **594-72-9**		168 (76) (oc)				1.4	5.0	255 (124)	No	3	3	2	3
1,1-Dichloro-1-Nitropropane $C_2H_5CCl_2NO_2$		151 (66) (oc)				1.3	5.5	289 (143)	Slight	5	2	2	3

Chemical Name Formula (Synonym) CAS No.	NFPA 30/ OSHA Class	Flash Point °F(°C)	Ignition Temp. °F(°C)	Flammable Limits Percent by Vol.		Sp.Gr. (Water =1)	Vapor Density (Air =1)	Boiling Point °F(°C)	Water Soluble	Extin- guishing Methods	Hazard Identification		
				Lower	Upper						Health	Flamma- bility	Insta- bility
Dichloropentanes (Mixed) $C_5H_{10}Cl_2$ **30586-10-8**		106 (41) (oc)				1.0+	4.8	266 (130)	No		2	2	0
1,5-Dichloropentane $CH_2Cl(CH_2)_3CH_2Cl$ (Amylene Chloride) (Pentamethylene Dichloride) **628-76-2**		>80 (>27) (oc)				1.1	4.9	352–358 (178–181)	No	4			
2,4-Dichlorophenol $Cl_2C_6H_3OH$ **120-83-2**	Note: Melting point 113 (45).	237 (114) (oc)				1.4 @ 140(60)	5.6	410 (210)	Slight	5 2	3	1	0
1,2-Dichloropropane	See Propylene Dichloride.												
1,3-Dichloro-2-Propanol $CH_2ClCHOHCH_2Cl$ **96-23-1**		165 (74) (oc)				1.4	4.4	346 (174)	Slight	5	3	2	0
2,3-Dichloro-1-propanol $CH_2ClCHClCH_2OH$ (α,β-Glycerin Dichlorohydrin) **616-23-9**	IIIB	200 (93)				1.4		360 (182)	Yes	5	2	1	0
1,3-Dichloropropene $CHCl{:}CHCH_2Cl$ **542-75-6**	IC See NFPA 49 contained in this guide.	95 (35)		5.3	14.5	1.2	3.8	219 (104)	No	4	2	3	0
2,3-Dichloropropene CH_2CClCH_2Cl **78-88-6**	IB	59 (15) (TCC)		2.6	7.8	1.2	3.8	201 (94)	Slight		3	3	0
Dichlorosilane H_2SiCl_2 **4109-96-0**	IA See NFPA 49 contained in this guide.	Gas [−35 (−37)]	136 (36)	4.1	99	1.2	3.5	47 (8)	Reacts	Do not use halocarbons	4	4	2 ₩
2,6-Dichlorostyrene $C_6H_3CCl{:}CHCl$ **28469-92-3**		160 (71)				1.27		190–194 (88–90) @ 8 mm Hg	No	2	1	2	0
Dichlorvos $(CH_3O)_2P(O)OCH{:}CCl_2$ (DDVP) (Dimethyl-o,o-Dichlorovinyl-2,2-Phosphate) (Phosphoric acid, 2,2-dichlorovinyl dimethyl ester) **62-73-7**		350 (177) (oc)						248 (120)@ 14 mm	Slight	5 2	3	1	
Dicyclohexyl	See Bicyclohexyl.												
Dicyclohexylamine $(C_6H_{11})_2NH$ **101-83-7**	See NFPA 49 contained in this guide.	>210 (>99) (oc)				0.9		496 (258)	Slight	5	3	1	0
Dicyclopentadiene $C_{10}H_{12}$ **77-73-6**	Note: Melting point 91 (33).	90 (32) (oc)	937 (503)	0.8	6.3	1.0−		342 (172)	No	1	3	3	1
Didecyl Ether $(C_{10}H_{21})_2O$ (Decyl Ether) **2456-28-2**			419 (215)				10.3				0	1	0
Diesel Fuel Oil No. 1-D **68334-30-5**	II	100 (38) Min. or Legal							No		1	2	0
Diesel Fuel Oil No. 2-D **68476-34-6**	II	125 (52) Min. or Legal							No		1	2	0
Diesel Fuel Oil No. 4-D	II	130 (54) Min. or Legal							No		1	2	0

Chemical Name Formula (Synonym) CAS No.	NFPA 30/ OSHA Class	Flash Point °F(°C)	Ignition Temp. °F(°C)	Flammable Limits Percent by Vol.		Sp.Gr. (Water =1)	Vapor Density (Air =1)	Boiling Point °F(°C)	Water Soluble	Extin-guishing Methods	Hazard Identification		
				Lower	Upper						Health	Flamma-bility	Insta-bility
Diethanolamine $(HOCH_2CH_2)_2NH$ **111-42-2**		342 (172) (oc)	1224 (662)	1.6 (calc.)	9.8 (est.)	1.1		514 (268)	Yes	5 2	3	1	0
	Note: Melting point 82 (28).												
1,2-Diethoxyethane	See Diethyl Glycol.												
Diethylacetaldehyde	See 2-Ethylbutyraldehyde.												
Diethylacetic Acid	See 2-Ethylbutyric Acid.												
N,N-Diethylaceto-acetamide $CH_3COCH_2CON(C_2H_5)_2$ **2235-46-3**		250 (121) (oc)				1.0–	5.4	Decomposes	Yes	2 5	0	1	0
Diethyl Acetoacetate $CH_3COC(C_2H_5)_2$- $COOC_2H_5$	IIIA	170 (77)				1.0–	6.4	412–424 (211–218) Decomposes	Very slight		2	2	0
Diethylaluminum Chloride $(C_2H_5)_2AlCl$ (Chlorodiethylaluminum) **96-10-6**						0.97		417 (214)	Violent re-action		3	4	3 ~~W~~
	Note: Ignites spontaneously in air. See NFPA 49 contained in this guide.												
Diethylaluminum Hydride $(C_2H_5)_2AlH$ **871-27-2**												3	3 ~~W~~
	Note: Ignites spontaneously in air. Do not use water, foam, or halogenated extinguishing agents.												
Diethylamine $(C_2H_5)_2NH$ **109-89-7**	IB	–9 (–23)	594 (312)	1.8	10.1	0.7	2.5	134 (57)	Yes	5 1	3	3	0
	See NFPA 49 contained in this guide.												
2-Diethylaminoethanol	See N,N-Diethylethanolamine.												
2-(Diethylamino)ethyl Acrylate CH_2:$CHCOOCH_2$- $CH_2HN(CH_3CH_2)_2$ **2426-54-2**		195 (91) (oc)				0.9	5.9	Decomposes	Decom-poses		3	2	2
3-(Diethylamino)-propylamine $(C_2H_5)_2NCH_2$- $CH_2CH_2NH_2$ (N,N-Diethyl-1,3-Propanediamine) **104-78-9**		138 (59) (oc)				0.8	4.5	337 (169)	Yes	5	2	2	0
N,N-Diethylaniline $C_6H_5N(C_2H_5)_2$ (Phenyldiethylamine) **91-66-7**	IIIA	185 (85)	1166 (630)			1.0–	5.0	421 (216)	Slight	5	2	2	0
o-Diethylbenzene $C_6H_4(C_2H_5)_2$ **135-01-3**	II	135 (57)	743 (395)			0.9	4.6	362 (183)	No		2	2	0
m-Diethylbenzene $C_6H_4(C_2H_5)_2$ **141-93-5**	II	133 (56)	842 (450)			0.9	4.6	358 (181)	No		2	2	0
p-Diethylbenzene $C_6H_4(C_2H_5)_2$ **105-05-5**	II	132 (55)	806 (430)	0.7	6.0	0.9	4.6	358 (181)	No		2	2	0
N,N-Diethyl-1,3-Butanediamine $C_2H_5NHCH_2CH_2CHN$- $(C_2H_5)CH_3$ [1,3-Bis(ethylamino) Bu-tane] **32280-46-9**		115 (46) (oc)				0.8	5.0	354–365 (179–185)	Yes	5	2	2	0
Di-2-Ethylbutyl Phthalate $C_6H_4[COOCH_2CH$- $(C_2H_5)_2]_2$		381 (194) (oc)				1.0+		662 (350)	No	5 2	0	1	0

Chemical Name Formula (Synonym) CAS No.	NFPA 30/ OSHA Class	Flash Point °F(°C)	Ignition Temp. °F(°C)	Flammable Limits Percent by Vol. Lower	Upper	Sp.Gr. (Water =1)	Vapor Density (Air =1)	Boiling Point °F(°C)	Water Soluble	Extin-guishing Methods	Hazard Identification Health	Flamma-bility	Insta-bility
Diethyl Carbamyl Chloride $(C_2H_5)_2NCOCl$ **88-10-8**		325–342 (163–172) (oc)						369–374 (187–190)	Yes	5 2	1	2	2 ₩
Diethyl Carbinol	See sec-Amyl Alcohol.												
Diethyl Carbonate $(C_2H_5)_2CO_3$ (Ethyl Carbonate) **105-58-8**	IC	77 (25)				1.0−	4.1	259 (126)	No	1	1	3	1
Diethylcyclohexane $C_{10}H_{20}$	II	120 (49)	464 (240)	0.8 @ 140 (60)	6.0 @ 230 (110)	0.8		344 (173)			2	2	0
1,3-Diethyl-1,3-Diphenyl Urea $[(C_2H_5)(C_6H_5)N]_2CO$ **85-98-3**	IIIB Note: Melting point 160 (71).	302 (150)				1.1		620 (327)		2	0	1	3
Diethylene Diamine	IIIA	144 (62)						299 (150)	Yes				
Diethylene Dioxide	See p-Dioxane.												
Diethylene Glycol $O(CH_2CH_2OH)_2$ (2,2-Dihydroxyethyl Ether) **111-46-6**	IIIB	255 (124)	435 (224)	1.6	10.8	1.1		472 (244)	Yes	5 2 1	1	1	0
Diethylene Glycol Bis(Allylcarbonate) $(CH_2{:}CHCH_2OCOOCH_2CH_2)_2O$ (Allyl Diglycol Carbonate) **142-22-3**		378 (192) (oc)				1.1		320 (160) @ 2 mm	No	2	3	1	1
Diethylene Glycol Bis(2-Butyoxyethyl Carbonate) $[CH_3(CH_2)_3O(CH_2)_2OOCOCH_2CH_2]_2O$ (Butoxyethyl Diglycol Carbonate)	IIIB	379 (193)				1.1		392–403 (200–206) @ 2 mm	Slight	5 2	1	1	1
Diethylene Glycol Bis-(Butyl Carbonate) $[CH_3(CH_2)_3OOCOCH_2CH_2]_2O$ (Butyl Diglycol Carbonate)	IIIB	372 (189)				1.1		327 (164) @ 2 mm	Slight	5 2	1	1	1
Diethylene Glycol Bis-(Phenylcarbonate) $(C_6H_5OOCOCH_2CH_2)_2O$ (Phenyl Diglycol Carbonate)	IIIB	460 (238)				1.2		437–444 (225–229) @ 2 mm	No	2	0	1	1
Diethylene Glycol n-Butyl Ether	See Diethylene Glycol Monobutyl Ether.												
Diethylene Glycol Butyl Ether Acetate $CH_3COO(C_2H_4O)_2C_4H_9$ (Diethylene Glycol Monobutyl Ether Acetate) **124-17-4**		241 (116) (oc)	563 (295)	0.76	5.0	0.98	7.05	475 (246)	Slight	5 2	1	1	0
Diethylene Glycol Diacetate $(CH_3COOC_2H_4)_2O$ **628-68-2**		275 (135) (oc)				1.1		482 (250)	Yes	5 2	1	1	0
Diethylene Glycol Dibenzoate $(C_6H_5COOCH_2CH_2)_2O$ **120-55-8**	IIIB	450 (232)				1.2 @ 68 (20)		457 (236) @ 5 mm	Yes	5 2	1	1	0

Chemical Name Formula (Synonym) CAS No.	NFPA 30/ OSHA Class	Flash Point °F(°C)	Ignition Temp. °F(°C)	Flammable Limits Percent by Vol.		Sp.Gr. (Water = 1)	Vapor Density (Air = 1)	Boiling Point °F(°C)	Water Soluble	Extin-guishing Methods	Hazard Identification		
				Lower	Upper						Health	Flamma-bility	Insta-bility
Diethylene Glycol Dibutyl Ether $C_4H_9O(C_2H_4O)_2C_4H_9$ (Dibutoxy Diethylene Glycol) **112-73-2**	IIIB	245 (118)	590 (310)			0.9		493 (256)	Slight	5 2	1	1	0
Diethylene Glycol Diethyl Ether $CH_3(CH_2OCH_2)_3CH_3$ **112-36-7**		180 (82) (oc)				0.9	5.6	372 (189)	Yes	5	1	2	1
Diethylene Glycol Diethyl Levulinate $(CH_3COC_2H_4COO$- $C_2H_4)_2O$	IIIB	340 (171)				1.14	10.4			2	0	1	0
Diethylene Glycol Dimethyl Ether $CH_3OCH_2CH_2OCH_2$- CH_2OCH_3 **111-96-6**	IIIA	153 (67)				0.95		324 (162)	Yes	5	1	2	1
Diethylene Glycol Dipropionate $(C_2H_5COOC_2H_4)_2O$	IIIB	260 (127)				1.1		491–529 (255–276)	Slight	5 2	1	1	0
Diethylene Glycol Ethyl Ether $C_2H_5OC_2H_4OC_2H_4OH$ (Diethylene Glycol Monoethyl Ether) (Carbitol) **111-90-0**	IIIA	196 (91)	400 (204)	1.2	23.5 @ 360F (182C)	1.0	4.65	396 (202)	Yes	5	2	2	0
Diethylene Glycol Ethyl Ether Phthalate $C_6H_4[COO$- $(C_2H_4O)_2C_2H_5]_2$ (Bis[2-(Ethoxyethoxy)-Ethyl] Phthalate) (Carbitol Phthalate)	IIIB	406 (208)				1.12	13.7	>500 (>260)		2	0	1	0
Diethylene Glycol Methyl Ether $CH_3OC_2H_4OC_2H_4OH$ [2-(2-Methoxyethoxy)Ethanol] (Diethylene Glycol Monomethyl Ether) **111-77-3**		205 (96) (oc)	465 (240)	1.38	22.7	1.04	4.14	379 (193)	Yes		1	2	0
Diethylene Glycol Methyl Ether Acetate $CH_3COOC_2H_4O$- $C_2H_4OCH_3$		180 (82) (oc)				1.04	5.59	410 (210)			0	2	0
Diethylene Glycol Monobutyl Ether $C_4H_9OCH_2CH_2OCH_2$- CH_2OH (Diethylene Glycol N-Butyl Ether) (Butoxy Diethylene Glycol) **112-34-5**	IIIA	172 (78)	400 (204)	0.85	24.6	1.0−	5.6	448 (231)	Yes	5 2	1	2	1
Diethylene Glycol Monobutyl Ether Acetate	See Diethylene Glycol Butyl Ether Acetate.												
Diethylene Glycol Monoethyl Ether	See Diethylene Glycol Ethyl Ether.												
Diethylene Glycol Monoethyl Ether Acetate $C_2H_5O(CH_2)_2O$- $(CH_2)_2OOCCH_3$ **112-15-2**		225 (107) (oc)	680 (360)	1.0 @ 275 (135)	19.4 @ 365 (185)	1.0+		424 (218)	Yes	5 2	2	1	0
Diethylene Glycol Monoisobutyl Ether $(CH_3)_2CHCH_2O(CH_2)_2O$- $(CH_2)_2OH$	IIIB	222 (106)	452–485 (233–252)	0.98	10.7	1.0−		422–437 (217–225)	Yes	5 2	1	1	0

Chemical Name Formula (Synonym) CAS No.	NFPA 30/ OSHA Class	Flash Point °F(°C)	Ignition Temp. °F(°C)	Flammable Limits Percent by Vol. Lower	Upper	Sp.Gr. (Water =1)	Vapor Density (Air =1)	Boiling Point °F(°C)	Water Soluble	Extin-guishing Methods	Hazard Identification Health	Flamma-bility	Insta-bility
Diethylene Glycol Methyl Ether Formal $CH_2(CH_3OCH_2\text{-}CH_2OCH_2CH_2O)_2$		310 (154) (oc)				1.0+		581 (305)	Yes	5 2	1	1	0
Diethylene Glycol Monomethyl Ether	See Diethylene Glycol Methyl Ether.												
Diethylene Glycol Phthalate $C_6H_4[COO(CH_2)_2OC_2H_5]_2$ **2202-98-4**	IIIB	343 (173)				1.1			Yes	5 2	0	1	0
Diethylene Oxide	See Tetrahydrofuran.												
Diethylenetriamine $NH_2CH_2CH_2NHCH_2\text{-}CH_2NH_2$ **111-40-0**	See NFPA 49 contained in this guide.	208 (98) (oc)	676 (358)	2	6.7	1.0−	3.56	404 (207)	Yes	5 2	3	1	0
N,N-Diethylethanolamine $(C_2H_5)_2NC_2H_4OH$ [2-(Diethylamino) Ethanol] **100-37-8**	See NFPA 49 contained in this guide.	140 (60) (oc)	608 (320)	6.7	11.7	0.9	4.0	324 (162)	Yes	5	3	2	0
Diethyl Ether	See Ethyl Ether.												
N,N-Diethylethylene-diamine $(C_2H_5)_2NC_2H_4NH_2$ **111-74-0**		115 (46) (oc)				0.8	4.0	293 (145)	Yes	5	3	3	0
Diethyl Fumarate $C_2H_5OCOCH{:}CH\text{-}COOC_2H_5$ **623-91-6**	IIIB	220 (104)				1.0+ @ 68(20)		442 (217)	Slight	5 2	3	2	0
Diethyl Glycol $(C_2H_5OCH_2)_2$ (1,2-Diethoxyethane)	IC	95 (35)	401 (205)			0.84	4.07	252 (122)	Slight			3	0
Di-2-Ethylhexyl Adipate $C_4H_8[COOCH_2CH\text{-}(C_2H_5)C_4H_9]_2$ (Dioctyl Adipate) (DOA) **103-23-1**	IIIB	385 (196)				0.9		783 (417)	No	5 2	0	1	0
Diethylhexylamine	See Bis (2-Ethylhexyl) Amine.												
Diethylhexylethanolamine	See Bis (2-Ethylhexyl) Ethanolamine.												
Di(2-Ethylhexyl) Maleate	See Bis (2-Ethylhexyl) Maleate.												
Di(2-Ethylhexyl) Phosphoric Acid	See Bis (2-Ethylhexyl) Phosphoric Acid.												
Di(2-Ethylhexyl) Succinate	See Bis (2-Ethylhexyl) Succinate.												
Diethyl Ketone $C_2H_5COC_2H_5$ (3-Pentanone) **96-22-0**		55 (13) (oc)	842 (450)	1.6	6.4	0.8	3.0	217 (103)	Slight	1 5	1	3	0
N,N-Diethyllauramide $C_{11}H_{23}CON(C_2H_5)_2$ **3352-87-2**		>150 (>66) (oc)				0.9	8.8	331–351 (166–177) @ 2 mm	No			2	0
Diethyl Maleate $(\text{-}CHCO_2C_2H_5)_2$ **141-05-9**		250 (121) (oc)	662 (350)			1.1		438 (226)	No	2	1	1	0

Chemical Name Formula (Synonym) CAS No.	NFPA 30/ OSHA Class	Flash Point °F(°C)	Ignition Temp. °F(°C)	Flammable Limits Percent by Vol. Lower	Upper	Sp.Gr. (Water =1)	Vapor Density (Air =1)	Boiling Point °F(°C)	Water Soluble	Extin-guishing Methods	Hazard Identification Health	Flamma-bility	Insta-bility
Diethyl Malonate $CH_2(COOC_2H_5)_2$ (Ethyl Malonate) **105-53-3**		200 (93) (oc)				1.1		390 (199)	No	3	1	2	0
Diethyl Oxide	See Ethyl Ether.												
3,3-Diethylpentane $CH_3CH_2C(C_2H_5)_2CH_2CH_3$			554 (290)	0.7	5.7	0.8	4.4	295 (146)	No		0	3	0
Diethyl Peroxide $C_2H_5OOC_2H_5$ **628-37-5**			Explodes on heat-ing.	2.3		0.8	7.7	Explodes on heating.				4	4
Diethyl Phthalate $C_6H_4(COOC_2H_5)_2$ **84-66-2**		322 (161) (oc)	855 (457)	0.7 @ 368 (186)		1.1		565 (296)	No	2	1	1	0
p-Diethyl Phthalate	See Diethyl Terephthalate.												
N,N-Diethyl-1,3-Propanediamine	See 3-(Diethylamino)propylamine.												
2,2-Diethyl-1,3-Propanediol $HOCH_2C(C_2H_5)_2CH_2OH$ **115-76-4**		215 (102) (oc)				0.9 @ 142(61)		320 (160) @ 50 mm	Yes	5 2		1	0
	Note: Melting point 142 (61).												
Diethyl Selenide $(C_2H_5)_2Se$ **627-53-2**				2.5		1.2	4.7	226 (108)	No		2	2	0
N,N-Diethylstearamide $C_{17}H_{35}CON(C_2H_5)_2$	IIIB	375 (191)				0.9		246–401 (119–205) @ 1 mm	No	2	0	1	0
Diethyl Succinate $(CH_2COOCH_2CH_3)_2$ **123-25-1**	IIIA	195 (90)				1.0+		421 (216)	Slight	5 2	1	2	0
Diethyl Sulfate $(C_2H_5)_2SO_4$ (Ethyl Sulfate) **64-67-5**	IIIB	220 (104)	817 (436)			1.2		Decomposes, giving Ethyl Ether	No, slight decomposi-tion	5 2	3	1	1
	See NFPA 49 contained in this guide.												
Diethyl Tartrate $CHOHCOO(C_2H_5)_2$ **87-91-2**	IIIB	200 (93)				1.2		536 (280)	Yes	5	1	2	0
Diethyl Terephthalate $C_6H_4(COOC_2H_5)_2$ (p-Diethyl Phthalate) **636-09-9**	IIIB	243 (117)				1.1		576 (302)	No	2	0	1	0
	Note: Melting point 112 (44).												
3,9-Diethyl-6-Tridecanol	See Heptadecanol.												
Diethylzinc $(C_2H_5)_2Zn$ (Zinc Diethyl) **557-20-0**						1.2		243 (117)	Reacts		3	4	3 W
	Note: Ignites spontaneously in air. Decomposes explosively at 248 (120). See NFPA 49 contained in this guide.												
Difluoro-1-Chloroethane CF_2ClCH_3 (R-142B) (1-Chloro-1,1-Difluoroethane) **75-68-3**		Gas		6.2	17.9			4 (−16)		6	2	4	0
Diglycol Chlorformate $O:(CH_2CH_2OCOCl)_2$		295 (146) (oc)						256–261 (124–127) @ 5 mm		2	0	1	0
Diglycol Chlorohydrin $HOCH_2CH_2OCH_2CH_2Cl$ **628-89-7**		225 (107) (oc)				1.2		387 (197)	Yes	5 2	2	1	0

Chemical Name Formula (Synonym) CAS No.	NFPA 30/ OSHA Class	Flash Point °F(°C)	Ignition Temp. °F(°C)	Flammable Limits Percent by Vol. Lower	Upper	Sp.Gr. (Water =1)	Vapor Density (Air =1)	Boiling Point °F(°C)	Water Soluble	Extin- guishing Methods	Hazard Identification Health	Flamma- bility	Insta- bility
Diglycol Diacetate $(CH_3COOCH_2CH_2)_2$:O	IIIB	255 (124)				1.1	6.5	482 (250)	Yes	2 5	0	1	0
Diglycol Dilevulinate $[CH_2CH_2OOC(CH_2)_2CO$-$CH_3]_2$:O	IIIB	340 (171)				1.1			Yes	2 5	0	1	
Diglycol Laurate $C_{16}H_{32}O_4$ **141-20-8**	IIIB	290 (143)				1.0−		559–617 (293–325)		2	0	1	0
Dihexyl	See Dodecane.												
Dihexylamine $[CH_3(CH_2)_5]_2NH$ **143-16-8**		220 (104) (oc)				0.8		451–469 (233–243)	No	2	3	3	0
Dihexyl Ether	See Hexyl Ether.												
Dihydropyran $CH_2CH_2CH_2$:CHCHO (ring) **110-87-2**	IB	0 (−18)				0.9	2.9	186 (86)	Slight	5	1	3	1
o-Dihydroxybenzene $C_6H_4(OH)_2$ (Pyrocatechol) (Catechol) **120-80-9**	IIIB Note: Melting point 220 (104).	260 (127)				1.34	3.79	473 (245)	Slight	2	3	1	0
p-Dihydroxybenzene	See Hydroquinone.												
1,2-Dihydroxybutane	See 1,2-Butanediol.												
2,2-Dihydroxyethyl Ether	See Diethylene Glycol.												
2,5-Dihydroxyhexane	See 2,5-Hexanediol.												
Diisobutylaluminum Hydride $[(CH_3)_2CHCH_2]_2AlH$ **1191-15-7**	Note: Ignites spontaneously in air.									Do not use water, foam, or halogenated extinguishing agents.	3	4	3 ₩
Diisobutylamine $[(CH_3)_2CHCH_2]_2NH$ [Bis(β-Methylpropyl) Amine] **110-96-3**	IC	85 (29)	554 (290)			0.7	4.46	273–286 (134–141)	No	5 1	3	3	0
Diisobutyl Carbinol $[(CH_3)_2CHCH_2]_2CHOH$ (Nonyl Alcohol) **143-08-8**	IIIA	165 (74)		0.8 @ 212 (100)	6.1 @ 212 (100)	0.8	5.0	353 (178)	No	5	2	2	0
Diisobutylene $(CH_3)_3CCH_2C(CH_3)$:CH_2 **25167-70-8**	IB	23 (−5)	736 (391)	0.8	4.8	0.7	3.87	214 (101)		1	1	3	0
Diisobutyl Ketone $[(CH_3)_2CHCH_2]_2CO$ (2,6-Dimethyl-4-Heptanone) (Isovalerone) **108-83-8**	II	120 (49)	745 (396)	0.8 @ 200 (93)	7.1 @ 200 (93)	0.8	4.9	335 (168)	No		1	2	0
Diisobutyl Phthalate $C_6H_4[COOCH_2CH$-$(CH_3)_2]_2$ **84-69-5**		365 (185) (oc)	810 (432)	0.4 @ 448		1.0+		621 (327)	No	5 2	1	1	0
Diisodecyl Adipate $C_{10}H_{21}O_2C(CH_2)_4$-$CO_2C_{10}H_{21}$ **27178-16-1**		225 (107) (oc)				0.9		660 (349)		2	1	1	0

Chemical Name Formula (Synonym) CAS No.	NFPA 30/ OSHA Class	Flash Point °F(°C)	Ignition Temp. °F(°C)	Flammable Limits Percent by Vol.		Sp.Gr. (Water = 1)	Vapor Density (Air = 1)	Boiling Point °F(°C)	Water Soluble	Extin-guishing Methods	Hazard Identification		
				Lower	Upper						Health	Flamma-bility	Insta-bility
Diisodecyl Phthalate $C_6H_4(COOC_{10}H_{21})_2$ **26761-40-0**		450 (232) (oc)	755 (402)	0.3 @ 508 (264)		1.0–		482 (250)	No	5 2	0	1	0
Diisooctyl Phthalate $(C_8H_{17}COO)_2C_6H_4$ **27554-26-3**	IIIB	450 (232)				1.0–		698 (370)	No	2	1	1	0
Diisopropanolamine $[CH_3CH(OH)CH_2]_2NH$ **110-97-4**		260 (127) (oc)	705 (374)	1.1 (calc.)	5.4 (est.)	1.0–		480 (249)	Yes	5 2	3	1	0
	Note: Melting point 111 (44).												
Diisopropyl	See 2,3-Dimethylbutane.												
Diisopropylamine $[(CH_3)_2CH]_2NH$ **108-18-9**		30 (–1) (oc)	600 (316)	1.1	7.1	0.7	3.5	183 (84)	Yes	1 5	3	3	0
	See NFPA 49 contained in this guide.												
Diisopropylbenzene $[(CH_3)_2CH]_2C_6H_4$ **25321-09-9**		170 (77) (oc)	840 (449)			0.9	5.6	401 (205)	No		1	2	0
N,N-Diisopropyl-ethanolamine $[(CH_3)_2CH]_2NC_2H_4OH$ **96-80-0**		175 (79) (oc)				0.9	5.0	376 (191)	No		3	2	0
Diisopropyl Ether	See Isopropyl Ether.												
Diisopropyl Maleate $(CH_3)_2CHOCOCH$:- $CHCOOCH(CH_3)_2$ **10099-70-4**		220 (104) (oc)				1.0+		444 (229)	Slight	5 2	1	1	0
Diisopropylmethanol	See 2,4-Dimethyl-3-Pentanol.												
Diisopropyl Peroxydicarbonate $(CH_3)_2CHOCOO$- $COOCH(CH_3)_2$ **105-64-6**								Explodes on heating.	No		3	4	4 OX
	Note: Rapid decomposition at 53 (12). Melting point 46–50 (8–10).												
Diketene $CH_2:CCH_2C(O)O$ (Vinylaceto-β-Lactone) **674-82-8**	IC	93 (34)				1.1	2.9	261 (127)	Decom-poses	5	3	3	2
	See NFPA 49 contained in this guide.												
2,5-Dimethoxyaniline $NH_2C_6H_3(OCH_3)_2$ **102-56-7**		302 (150) (oc)	735 (391)					518 (270)	Yes	2		1	0
	Note: Melting point 156–163 (69–73).												
2,5-Dimethoxychloro-benzene $C_8H_9ClO_2$ **2100-42-7**	IIIB	243 (117)					5.9	460–467 (238–242)	Slight	2 5	2	1	0
1,2-Dimethoxyethane	See Ethylene Glycol Dimethyl Ether.												
Dimethoxyethyl Phthalate $C_6H_4(COOCH_2$- $CH_2OCH_3)_2$ [Bis(2-methoxyethyl) Phthalate]		410 (210) (oc)	750 (399)	0.7 @ 440 (227)		1.2		644 (340)	No	5 2	0	1	0
Dimethoxymethane	See Methylal.												
Dimethoxy Tetraglycol $CH_3OCH_2(CH_2OCH_2)_3$- CH_2OCH_3 (Tetraethylene Glycol Dimethyl Ether) **143-24-8**		285 (141) (oc)				1.0+		528 (276)	Yes	2 5	2	1	1
Dimethylacetamide $(CH_3)_2NC:OCH_3$ (DMAC) **127-19-5**		158 (70) (oc)	914 (490)	1.8 @ 212 (100)	11.5 @ 320 (160)	1.0		330 (165)	Yes	5	2	2	0

Chemical Name Formula (Synonym) CAS No.	NFPA 30/ OSHA Class	Flash Point °F(°C)	Ignition Temp. °F(°C)	Flammable Limits Percent by Vol. Lower	Upper	Sp.Gr. (Water =1)	Vapor Density (Air =1)	Boiling Point °F(°C)	Water Soluble	Extin-guishing Methods	Hazard Identification Health	Flamma-bility	Insta-bility
Dimethylamine $(CH_3)_2NH$ **124-40-3**	See NFPA 49 contained in this guide.	Gas	752 (400)	2.8	14.4	1.38 @ 15	1.6	45 (7)	Yes	6	3	4	0
2-(Dimethylamino)-ethanol $(CH_3)_2NCH_2CH_2OH$ (Dimethylethanolamine) **108-01-0**		105 (41) (oc)	563 (295)	1.6	11.9	0.9	3.1	272 (133)	Yes	1 5	3	2	0
2-(Dimethylamino)-ethyl Methacrylate $C_8H_{15}NO_2$ **2867-47-2**	Note: Polymerizes.	165 (74) (oc)				0.9	5.4	207 (97) @ 40 mm	Yes	5	2	2	1
3-(Dimethylamino) propionitrile $(CH_3)_2NC_2H_4CN$		149 (65) (oc)				0.86	3.35	338 (170)				2	1
3-(Dimethylamino) propylamine $(CH_3)_2N(CH_2)_3NH_2$ **109-55-7**		100 (38) (oc)				0.8	3.5	278 (137)	Yes	5	3	3	0
N,N-Dimethylaniline $C_6N_5N(CH_3)_2$ C.P. **121-69-7**	IIIA	145 (63) 165 (74)	700 (371)			1.0–	4.2	379 (193)	Slight	5	3	2	0
o-Dimethylaniline	See o-Xylidine.												
Dimethyl Anthranilate $CH_3OOCC_6H_4NHCH_3$ (N-Methyl Methyl Anthranilate)	IIIA	195 (91)				1.1					1	2	0
1,2-Dimethylbenzene	See o-Xylene.												
1,3-Dimethylbenzene	See m-Xylene.												
1,4-Dimethylbenzene	See p-Xylene.												
Dimethylbenzyl-carbinyl Acetate $C_6H_5CH_2C(CH_3)_2$-$OOCCH_3$ (α, α-Dimethylphenethyl Acetate) **151-05-3**	IIIB Note: Melting point 84–86 (29–30).	205 (96)				1.0–					1	1	0
2,2-Dimethylbutane $(CH_3)_3CCH_2CH_3$ (Neohexane) **75-83-2**	IB	–54 (–48)	761 (405)	1.2	7.0	0.6	3.0	122 (50)	No	1	2	3	0
2,3-Dimethylbutane $(CH_3)_2CHCH(CH_3)_2$ (Diisopropyl) **79-29-8**	IB	–20 (–29)	761 (405)	1.2	7.0	0.7	3.0	136 (58)	No	1	1	3	0
1,3-Dimethylbutanol	See Methyl Isobutyl Carbinol.												
2,3-Dimethyl-1-Butene $CH_3CH(CH_3)C(CH_3):CH_2$	IB	<–4 (<–20)	680 (360)			0.68	2.91	133 (56)		1	0	3	0
2,3-Dimethyl-2-Butene $CH_3C(CH_3):C(CH_3)_2$ (Tetramethylethylene) **563-79-1**	IB	<–4 (<–20)	753 (401)			0.71	2.91	163 (73)		1	1	3	1
1,3-Dimethylbutyl Acetate	See 4-Methyl-2-Pentanol Acetate.												
1,3-Dimethylbutylamine $CH_3CHNH_2(CH_2)$-$CH(CH_3)_2$ (2-Amino-4-Methylpentane) **108-09-8**		55 (13) (oc)				0.7	3.5	223–228 (106–109)	No	1	2	3	0

Chemical Name Formula (Synonym) CAS No.	NFPA 30/ OSHA Class	Flash Point °F(°C)	Ignition Temp. °F(°C)	Flammable Limits Percent by Vol.		Sp.Gr. (Water =1)	Vapor Density (Air =1)	Boiling Point °F(°C)	Water Soluble	Extin-guishing Methods	Hazard Identification		
				Lower	Upper						Health	Flamma-bility	Insta-bility
Dimethyl Carbinol	See Isopropyl Alcohol.												
Dimethyl Carbonate	See Methyl Carbonate.												
Dimethyl Chloracetal $ClCH_2CH(OCH_3)_2$ **97-97-2**	II	111 (44)	450 (232)			1.0+		259–270 (126–132)				2	0
Dimethylcyanamide $(CH_3)_2NCN$ **1467-79-4**	IIIA	160 (71)				0.88	2.42	320 (160)			3	2	1
1,2-Dimethyl-cyclohexane $(CH_3)_2C_6H_{10}$			579 (304)			0.8	3.87	260 (127)	No		0		0
1,3-Dimethyl-cyclohexane $(CH_3)_2C_6H_{10}$ (Hexahydroxylene)	IB	~50 (10)	583 (306)			0.8	3.87	~256 (124)	No	1	0	3	0
1,4-Dimethyl-cyclohexane $(CH_3)_2C_6H_{10}$ (Hexahydroxylol) **589-90-2**	IB	52 (11)	579 (304)			0.8	3.9	248 (120)	No	1	2	3	0
1,4-Dimethyl-cyclohexane-cis $C_6H_{10}(CH_3)_2$ **624-29-3**	IB	61 (16)						255 (124)			2	3	0
1,4-Dimethyl-cyclohexane-trans $C_6H_{10}(CH_3)_2$ **589-90-2**	IB	51 (11)						246 (119)			2	3	0
Dimethyl Decalin $C_{10}H_{16}(CH_2)_2$	IIIA	184 (84)	455 (235)	0.7 @ 200 (93)	5.3 @ 300 (149)	1.0		455 (235)					
Dimethyldichlorosilane $(CH_3)_2SiCl_2$ (Dichlorodimethylsilane) **75-78-5**	IB See NFPA 49 contained in this guide.	<70 (<21)	>750 (>399)	3.4	>9.5	1.1	4.4	158 (70)	Decom-poses		3	3	1 ~~W~~
Dimethyldioxane $CH_3CHCH_2OCH_2(CH_3)$- CHO (ring) **25136-55-4**		75 (24) (oc)				0.9	4.0	243 (117)	Slight	1 5		3	0
1,3-Dimethyl-1,3-Diphenylcyclobu-tane $(C_6H_5CCH_3)_2(CH_2)_2$	IIIB Note: Melting point 120 (49).	289 (143)				1.0− @ 122 (50)		585–588 (307–309)	No	2	0	1	0
Dimethylene Oxide	See Ethylene Oxide.												
N,N-Dimethylethano-lamine	See 2-(Dimethylamino)ethanol.												
Dimethyl Ether	See Methyl Ether.												
Dimethyl Ethyl Carbinol	See 2-Methyl-2-Butanol.												
2,4-Dimethyl-3-Ethylpentane $CH_3CH(CH_3)CH(CH_2H_5)$- $CH(CH_3)_2$ (3-Ethyl-2,4-Dimethylpentane)	IIIB	734 (390)				0.74	4.43	279 (137)		2	0	3	0
N,N-Dimethyl-formamide $HCON(CH_3)_2$ **68-12-2**	II	136 (58)	833 (445)	2.2 @ 212 (100)	15.2	0.9	2.5	307 (153)	Yes	5	2	2	0

Chemical Name Formula (Synonym) CAS No.	NFPA 30/ OSHA Class	Flash Point °F(°C)	Ignition Temp. °F(°C)	Flammable Limits Percent by Vol. Lower	 Upper	Sp.Gr. (Water =1)	Vapor Density (Air =1)	Boiling Point °F(°C)	Water Soluble	Extin- guishing Methods	Hazard Identification Health	 Flamma- bility	 Insta- bility
2,5-Dimethylfuran $OC(CH_3){:}CHCH{:}C(CH_3)$ **625-86-5**		45 (7) (oc)				0.9	3.3	200 (93)	Slight	1 5	3	3	0
Dimethyl Glycol Phthalate $C_6H_4[COO(CH_2)_2OCH_3]_2$ **117-82-8**	IIIB	369 (187)				1.8		446 (230)		2	2	1	0
3,3-Dimethylheptane $CH_3(CH_2)_3C(CH_3)_2$- CH_2CH_3			617 (325)			0.73	4.43	279 (137)			0	3	0
2,6-Dimethyl-4-Heptanone	See Diisobutyl Ketone.												
2,3-Dimethylhexane $CH_3CH(CH_3)CH(CH_3)$- $C_2H_5CH_3$		45 (7) (oc)	820 (438)			0.7	3.9	237 (114)	No	1	0	3	0
2,4-Dimethylhexane $CH_3CH(CH_3)CH(CH_3)$- $C_2H_5CH_3$		50 (10) (oc)				0.7	3.9	229 (109)	No	1	0	3	0
Dimethyl Hexynol $C_4H_9CCH_3(OH)C{:}CH$ (3,5-Dimethyl-1-Hexyn-3-ol)		135 (57) (oc)				0.85	4.35	302 (150)			0	2	0
1,1-Dimethylhydrazine $(CH_3)_2NNH_2$ (Dimethylhydrazine, Unsymmetrical) **57-14-7**	IB See NFPA 49 contained in this guide.	5 (−15)	480 (249)	2	95	0.8	2.0	145 (63)	Yes	5 1	4	3	1
Dimethylhydrazine, Unsymmetrical	See 1,1-Dimethylhydrazine.												
Dimethylisophthalate $CH_3OOCC_6H_4COOCH_3$ **1459-93-4**	IIIB Note: Melting point 153–154 (67–68).	280 (138)							No	2	1	1	0
N,N-Dimethylisopropanolamine $(CH_3)_2NCH_2CH(OH)CH_3$ **108-16-7**		95 (35) (oc)				0.9	3.6	257 (125)	Yes	1 5	3	3	0
Dimethyl Ketone	See Acetone.												
Dimethyl Maleate $(\text{-}CHCOOCH_3)_2$ **624-48-6**		235 (113) (oc)				1.2		393 (201)	No	2	2	2	0
2,6-Dimethylmorpholine $CH(CH_3)CH_2OCH_2CH$- $(CH_3)NH$ **141-91-3**		112 (44) (oc)				0.9	4.0	296 (147)	Yes	5	2	2	0
2,3-Dimethyloctane $CH_3(CH_2)_4CH(CH_3)$- $CH(CH_3)CH_3$		<131 (<55)	437 (225)			0.74	4.91	327 (164)			0	2	0
3,4-Dimethyloctane $C_3H_7CH(CH_3)CH(CH_3)$- C_3H_7		<131 (<55)				0.75	4.91	324 (162)			0	2	0
2,3-Dimethylpentaldehyde $CH_3CH_2CH(CH_3)CH$- $(CH_3)CHO$ **32749-94-3**		94 (34) (oc)				0.8	3.9	293 (145)		1		3	0
2,3-Dimethylpentane $CH_3CH(CH_3)CH(CH_3)$- CH_2CH_3 **565-59-3**	IB	<20 (<−7)	635 (335)	1.1	6.7	0.7	3.5	194 (90)	No	1	2	3	0

Chemical Name Formula (Synonym) CAS No.	NFPA 30/ OSHA Class	Flash Point °F(°C)	Ignition Temp. °F(°C)	Flammable Limits Percent by Vol.		Sp.Gr. (Water =1)	Vapor Density (Air =1)	Boiling Point °F(°C)	Water Soluble	Extin-guishing Methods	Hazard Identification		
				Lower	Upper						Health	Flamma-bility	Insta-bility
2,4-Dimethylpentane $(CH_3)_2CHCH_2CH(CH_3)_2$ **108-08-7**	IB	10 (−12)				0.7	3.5	177 (81)	No	1	2	3	0
2,4-Dimethyl-3-Pentanol $(CH_3)_2CHCHOHCH(CH_3)_2$ (Diisopropylmethanol) **600-36-2**	II	120 (49)				0.8	4.0	284 (140)	Very slight		0	2	0
Dimethyl Phthalate $C_6H_4(COOCH_3)_2$ **131-11-3**	IIIB	295 (146)	915 (490)	0.9 @ 358 (180)		1.2	6.69	540 (282)	No	2	1	1	0
Dimethylpiperazine-cis $C_6H_{14}N_2$		155 (68) (oc)				0.92	3.94	329 (165)				2	0
2,2-Dimethylpropane $(CH_3)_4C$ (Neopentane) **463-82-1**		Gas	842 (450)	1.4	7.5		2.5	49 (9)	No	6	2	4	0
2,2-Dimethyl-1-Propanol	See tert-Butyl Carbinol.												
2,5-Dimethylpyrazine $CH_3C{:}CHN{:}C(CH_3)CH{:}N$ **123-32-0**		147 (64) (oc)				0.99	3.72	311 (155)	Yes			2	0
Dimethyl Sebacate $[\text{-}(CH_2)_4COOCH_3]_2$ (Methyl Sebacate) **106-79-6**		293 (145) (oc)				1.0–		565 (296)		2	1	1	0
	Note: Melting point 76 (24).												
Dimethyl Sulfate $(CH_3)_2SO_4$ (Methyl Sulfate) **77-78-1**		182 (83) (oc)	370 (188)			1.3	4.4	370 (188) Decomposition	Very slight	3	4	2	1
	See NFPA 49 contained in this guide.												
Dimethyl Sulfide $(CH_3)_2S$ **75-18-3**	IA	<0 (<−18)	403 (206)	2.2	19.7	0.8	2.1	99 (37)	Slight	1	2	4	0
	See NFPA 49 contained in this guide.												
Dimethyl Sulfoxide $(CH_3)_2SO$ (DMSO) **67-68-5**		203 (95) (oc)	419 (215)	2.6	42	1.1		372 (189)	Yes	5	2	2	0
	Note: Melting point 65 (18).												
Dimethyl Terephthalate $C_6H_4(COOCH_3)_2$ (Dimethyl-1,4-Benzenedicarboxylate) (DMT) **120-61-6**		308 (153) (oc)	965 (518)					543 (284)	No	5 2	1	1	0
2,4-Dinitroaniline $(NO_2)_2C_6H_3NH_2$ **97-02-9**	IIIB	435 (224)				1.6			No	2	2	1	3
	Note: Melting point 370 (188).												
o-Dinitrobenzene $C_6H_4(NO_2)_2$ (1,2-Dinitrobenzol) **528-29-0**	IIIB	302 (150)				1.57	5.79	604 (318)		2	3	1	4
	Note: Melting point 244 (118).												
Dinitrochlorobenzene $C_6H_3Cl(NO_2)_2$ (Chlorodinitrobenzene) **97-00-7**	IIIB	382 (194)		2.0	22	1.7		599 (315)	No	2	3	1	4
	Note: Melting point 109 (43). See NFPA 49 contained in this guide.												
2,4-Dinitrotoluene $(NO_2)_2C_6H_3CH_3$ **121-14-2**	IIIB	404 (207)				1.52	6.27	572 (300)	No		3	1	3
	Note: Melting point 158 (70).												

Chemical Name Formula (Synonym) CAS No.	NFPA 30/ OSHA Class	Flash Point °F(°C)	Ignition Temp. °F(°C)	Flammable Limits Percent by Vol. Lower	 Upper	Sp.Gr. (Water =1)	Vapor Density (Air =1)	Boiling Point °F(°C)	Water Soluble	Extin-guishing Methods	Hazard Identification Health	 Flamma-bility	 Insta-bility
Dioctyl Adipate $[(CH_2)_2COOCH_2CH$- $(C_2H_5)C_4H_9]_2$ [Bis(2-Ethylhexyl) Adipate] [Di(2-Ethylhexyl) Adipate] **103-23-1**		402 (206) (oc)	710 (377)	0.4 @ 467 (242)		0.9		680 (360)	No	5 2	1	1	0
Dioctylamine	See Bis (2-Ethylhexyl) Amine.												
Dioctyl Azelate $(CH_2)_7[COOCH_2CH$- $(C_2H_5)C_4H_9]_2$ [Bis(2-Ethylhexyl) Azelate] [Di(2-Ethylhexyl) Azelate] **103-24-2**		440 (227) (oc)	705 (374)	0.3 @ 510 (266)		0.9		709 (376)	No	5 2	1	1	0
Dioctyl Ether $(C_8H_{17})_2O$ (Octyl Ether) **629-82-3**	IIIB	>212 (>100)	401 (205)			0.82	8.36	558 (292)		2			
Dioctyl Phthalate $C_6H_4[CO_2CH_2CH$- $(C_2H_5)C_4H_9]_2$ [Di(2-Ethylhexyl) Phthalate] [Bis(2-Ethylhexyl) Phthalate] (DOP) **117-84-0**		420 (215) (oc)	735 (390)	0.3 @ 474 (245)		1.0−		723 (384)	No	2	1	1	0
p-Dioxane $OCH_2CH_2OCH_2CH_2$ (Diethylene Dioxide) **123-91-1**	IB See NFPA 49 contained in this guide.	54 (12)	356 (180)	2.0	22	1.0+	3.0	214 (101)	Yes	1 5	2	3	1
Dioxolane $OCH_2CH_2OCH_2$ **100-79-8** **646-06-0**		35 (2) (oc)				1.1	2.6	165 (74)	Yes	1 5	1	3	2
Dipentene $C_{10}H_{16}$ (Cinene) (Limonene) **138-86-3**	II	113 (45)	458 (237)	0.7 @ 302 (150)	6.1 @ 302 (150)	0.9	4.7	339 (170)	No		2	2	0
Diphenyl	See Biphenyl.												
Diphenylamine $(C_6H_5)_2NH$ (Phenylaniline) **122-39-4**	IIIB Note: Melting point 127 (53).	307 (153)	1173 (634)			1.2		575 (302)	No	2	2	1	0
1,1-Diphenylbutane $(C_6H_5)_2CHC_3H_7$ **719-79-9**	IIIB	>212 (>100)	851 (455)			0.98	7.26	561 (294)		2	0	1	0
1,3-Diphenyl-2-buten-1-one	See Dypnone.												
Diphenyldichlorosilane $(C_6H_5)_2SiCl_2$ **80-10-4**	IIIB	288 (142)				1.2		581 (305)	Reacts	2	3	1	2 ~~W~~
Diphenyldodecyl Phosphite $(C_6H_5O)_2POC_{10}H_{21}$	Note: Melting point 64(18).	425 (218) (oc)				1.0+			No	2	0	1	0
1,1-Diphenylethane (uns) $(C_6H_5)_2CHCH_3$ **612-00-0**	IIIB	>212 (>100)	824 (440)			1.0	6.29	546 (286)		2	2	1	0
1,2-Diphenylethane (sym) $C_6H_5CH_2CH_2C_6H_5$ **103-29-7**	IIIB	264 (129)	896 (480)			1.0	6.29	544 (284)		2	0	1	0

Chemical Name Formula (Synonym) CAS No.	NFPA 30/ OSHA Class	Flash Point °F(°C)	Ignition Temp. °F(°C)	Flammable Limits Percent by Vol.		Sp.Gr. (Water =1)	Vapor Density (Air =1)	Boiling Point °F(°C)	Water Soluble	Extin-guishing Methods	Hazard Identification		
				Lower	Upper						Health	Flamma-bility	Insta-bility
Diphenyl Ether	See Diphenyl Oxide.												
Diphenylmethane $(C_6H_5)_2CH_2$ (Ditane) **101-81-5**	IIIB	266 (130)	905 (485)			1.0		508 (264)	No	2	1	1	0
	Note: Melting point 79 (26).												
Diphenyl (o-Xenyl) Phosphate $(C_6H_5O)_2PO(OC_6H_4C_6H_5)$ **132-29-6**	IIIB	437 (225)				1.2		482–545 (250–285) @ 5 mm		2	0	1	0
Diphenyl Oxide $(C_6H_5)_2O$ (Diphenyl Ether) **101-84-8**	IIIB	239 (115)	1144 (618)	0.7	6.0	1.1		496 (258)	No	2	1	1	0
	Note: Melting point 81 (27).												
1,1-Diphenylpentane $(C_6H_5)_2CHC_4H_9$	IIIB	>212 (>100)	824 (440)			0.97	7.74	586 (308)		2	0	1	0
Diphenyl Phthalate $C_6H_4(COOC_6H_5)_2$ **84-62-8**	IIIB	435 (224)				1.3		761 (405)	No	2	1	1	0
	Note: Melting point 158 (70).												
1,1-Diphenylpropane $CH_3CH_2CH(C_6H_5)_2$	IIIB	>212 (>100)	860 (460)			0.97	6.77	541 (283)		2	0	1	0
Dipropylaluminum Hydride $(C_3H_7)_2AlH$												3	3 ~~W~~
	Note: Ignites spontaneously in air. Do not use water, foam, or halogenated extinguishing agents.												
Dipropylamine $(C_3H_7)_2NH$ **142-84-7**		63 (17) (oc)	570 (299)			0.7	3.5	229 (109)	No	1	3	3	0
Dipropylene Glycol $[CH_3CHOHCH_2]_2O$ **110-98-5**		250 (121) (oc)		2.2		1.0+	4.63	449 (232)	Yes	2 5	1	1	0
Dipropylene Glycol Methyl Ether $CH_3OC_3H_6OC_3H_6OH$ **34590-94-8**	IIIA	186 (86)		1.1 @ 200°C	3.0	1.0	5.11	408 (209)	Partly		2	2	0
Dipropyl Ether	See n-Propyl Ether.												
Dipropyl Ketone	See 4-Heptanone.												
Ditane	See Diphenylmethane.												
Ditridecyl Phthalate $C_6H_4(COOC_{13}H_{27})_2$ **119-06-2**		470 (243) (oc)				1.0–		547 (286) @ 5 mm		2	1	1	0
Divinyl Acetylene $(\vdots CCH{:}CH_2)_2$ (1,5-Hexadien-3-yne) **821-08-9**	IB	<–4 (<–20)					2.69	183 (84)				3	4
Divinylbenzene $C_6H_4(CH{:}CH_2)_2$ **1321-74-0**		169 (76) (oc)	878 (470)	0.7	6.2	0.9	4.5	392 (200)	No		1	2	2
	See NFPA 49 contained in this guide.												
Divinyl Ether $(CH_2{:}CH)_2O$ (Ethenyloxyethene) (Vinyl Ether) **109-93-3**	IA	<–22 (<–30)	680 (360)	1.7	27	0.8	2.4	83 (28)	No	1	0	4	2
	See NFPA 49 contained in this guide.												
Di(o-Xenyl) Phenyl Phosphate $(C_6H_5C_6H_4)_2PO(OC_6H_5)$	IIIB	482 (250)				1.2		545–626 (285–330) @ 5 mm		2	0	1	0
Dodecane $CH_3(CH_2)_{10}CH_3$ (Dihexyl) **112-40-3**	IIIA	165 (74)	397 (203)	0.6		0.8	5.9	421 (216)	No		1	2	0

Chemical Name Formula (Synonym) CAS No.	NFPA 30/ OSHA Class	Flash Point °F(°C)	Ignition Temp. °F(°C)	Flammable Limits Percent by Vol.		Sp.Gr. (Water =1)	Vapor Density (Air =1)	Boiling Point °F(°C)	Water Soluble	Extin-guishing Methods	Hazard Identification		
				Lower	Upper						Health	Flamma-bility	Insta-bility
1-Dodecanethiol $CH_3(CH_2)_{11}SH$ (Dodecyl Mercaptan) (Lauryl Mercaptan) **112-55-0**		262 (128) (oc)				0.8		289 (143)@ 15 mm	No	5 2	2	1	0
1-Dodecanol $CH_3(CH_2)_{11}OH$ (Lauryl Alcohol) **112-53-8**	IIIB Note: Melting point 75 (24).	260 (127)	527 (275)			0.8		491 (255)	No	2	3	1	0
Dodecyl Benzene $C_6H_5C_{12}H_{25}$ (Alkane) (Detergent Alkylate) **123-01-3**	IIIB	285 (141)				0.9		554–770 (290–410)	No	2	1	1	0
Dodecyl Bromide	See Lauryl Bromide.												
α-Dodecylene $C_{10}H_{21}CH{:}CH_2$ (1-Dodecane)	IIIB	<212 (<100)	491 (255)			0.76	5.81	406 (208)					
Dodecyl Mercaptan	See 1-Dodecanethiol.												
tert-Dodecyl Mercaptan $C_{12}H_{25}SH$ **25103-58-6**		205 (96) (oc)				0.9	>3	428–451 (220–233)	No		2	1	0
4-Dodecyloxy-2-Hydroxy-Benzophenone $C_{25}H_{34}O_3$	IIIB Note: Melting point 109 (43).	498 (254)	715 (379)						No	2		1	0
Dodecyl Phenol $C_{12}H_{25}C_6H_4OH$ **27193-86-8**		325 (163) (oc)				0.9	9.0	597–633 (314–334)	No	2	0	1	0
Dypnone $C_6H_5COCH{:}C(CH_3)C_6H_5$ (1,3-Diphenyl-2-Buten-1-one)		350 (177) (oc)				1.1		475 (246)@ 50 mm	Slight	2 5		1	0
Eicosane $C_{20}H_{42}$ **112-95-8**	IIIB	>212 (>100)	450 (232)			0.79	9.75	651 (344)		2	0	1	0
Epichlorohydrin CH_2CHOCH_2Cl (3-Chloropropylene Oxide) (γ-Chloropropylene Oxide) (Chloromethyloxirane) **106-89-8**	IC See NFPA 49 contained in this guide.	88 (31)	772 (411)	3.8	21.0	1.2	3.2	239 (115)	No	5 4	4	3	2
1,2-Epoxyethane	See Ethylene Oxide.												
Erythrene	See 1,3-Butadiene.												
Ethanal	See Acetaldehyde.												
Ethane CH_3CH_3 **74-84-0**		Gas	882 (472)	3.0	12.5		1.0	−128 (−89)	No	6	1	4	0
1,2-Ethanediol	See Ethylene Glycol.												
1,2-Ethanediol Diformate $HCOOCH_2CH_2OOCH$ (Ethylene Formate) (Ethylene Glycol Diformate) (Glycol Diformate) **629-15-2**	Note: Decomposes in water.	200 (93) (oc)				1.2		345 (174)	Decom-poses		1	2	0
Ethanethiol	See Ethyl Mercaptan.												

Chemical Name Formula (Synonym) CAS No.	NFPA 30/ OSHA Class	Flash Point °F(°C)	Ignition Temp. °F(°C)	Flammable Limits Percent by Vol.		Sp.Gr. (Water =1)	Vapor Density (Air =1)	Boiling Point °F(°C)	Water Soluble	Extin-guishing Methods	Hazard Identification		
				Lower	Upper						Health	Flamma-bility	Insta-bility
Ethanoic Acid	See Acetic Acid.												
Ethanoic Anhydride	See Acetic Anhydride.												
Ethanol	See Ethyl Alcohol.												
Ethanolamine $NH_2CH_2CH_2OH$ (2-Aminoethanol) (β-Aminoethyl Alcohol) **141-43-5** See NFPA 49 contained in this guide.	IIIA	186 (86)	770 (410)	3.0	23.5 @ 140°C	1.0+	2.1	342 (172)	Yes	5	3	2	0
Ethanoyl Chloride	See Acetyl Chloride.												
Ethene	See Ethylene.												
Ethenyl Ethanoate	See Vinyl Acetate.												
Ethenyloxyethene	See Divinyl Ether.												
Ether	See Ethyl Ether.												
Ethine	See Acetylene.												
Ethoxyacetylene $C_2H_5OC{:}CH$ **927-80-0**	IB	<20 (< −7)				0.8	2.4	124 (51)	No	1		3	3
Ethoxybenzene $C_6H_5OC_2H_5$ (Ethyl Phenyl Ether) (Phenetole)	IIIA	145 (63)				1.0−	4.2	342 (172)	No			2	0
2-Ethoxy-3,4-Dihydro-2-Pyran $C_7H_{12}O_2$ **103-75-3**		111 (44) (oc)				1.0−		289 (143)	Very slight		1	2	1
2-Ethoxy Ethanol	See Ethylene Glycol Ethyl Ether.												
2-Ethoxyethyl Acetate $CH_3COOCH_2CH_2OC_2H_5$ (Ethyl Glycol Acetate) (Ethylene Glycol Monoethyl Ether Acetate) (Cellosolve Acetate) **111-15-9**	II	117 (47)	716 (380)	1.7	10	1.0−	4.6	313 (156)	Yes	5	2	2	0
3-Ethoxypropanal $C_2H_5OC_2H_4CHO$ (3-Ethoxypropionaldehyde) **2806-85-1**	II	100 (38)				0.98	3.52	275 (135)	Yes	5	2	3	0
1-Ethoxypropane	See Ethyl Propyl Ether.												
3-Ethoxypropionaldehyde	See 3-Ethoxypropanal.												
3-Ethoxypropionic Acid $C_2H_5OCH_2CH_2COOH$ **4324-38-3** **1331-11-9**	IIIB	225 (107)				1.0+		426 (219)	Yes	5 2	2	1	0
Ethoxytriglycol $C_2H_5O(C_2H_4O)_3H$ (Triethylene Glycol Ethyl Ether) **112-50-5**		275 (135) (oc)				1.0+		492 (256)	Yes	2 5	1	1	0
Ethyl Abietate $C_{19}H_{29}COOC_2H_5$ **629-15-2**		352 (178) (oc)				1.0+		662 (350)	No	2			
N-Ethylacetamide $CH_3CONHC_2H_5$ (Acetoethylamide) **625-50-3**	IIIB	230 (110)				0.9		401 (205)	Yes	5 2	0	1	0

Chemical Name Formula (Synonym) CAS No.	NFPA 30/ OSHA Class	Flash Point °F(°C)	Ignition Temp. °F(°C)	Flammable Limits Percent by Vol. Lower	Upper	Sp.Gr. (Water =1)	Vapor Density (Air =1)	Boiling Point °F(°C)	Water Soluble	Extin-guishing Methods	Hazard Identification Health	Flamma-bility	Insta-bility
N-Ethyl Acetanilide $CH_3CON(C_2H_5)(C_6H_5)$	II	126 (52)				0.9	5.6	400 (204)	No		0	2	0
Ethyl Acetate $CH_3COOC_2H_5$ (Acetic Ester) (Acetic Ether) (Ethyl Ethanoate) **141-78-6**	IB	24 (−4)	800 (426)	2.0	11.5	0.9	3.0	171 (77)	Slight	1 5	1	3	0
Ethyl Acetoacetate $C_2H_5CO_2CH_2COCH_3$ (Acetoacetic Acid, Ethyl Ester) (Ethyl 3-Oxobutanoate) **141-97-9**	II	135 (57)	563 (295)	1.4 @ 200 (93)	95 @ 350 (176)	1.0+	4.5	356 (180)	Slight	5	1	2	0
Ethyl Acetyl Glycolate $CH_3COOCH_2COOC_2H_5$ (Ethyl Glycolate Acetate)	IIIA	180 (82)				1.09	5.04	~365 (~185)	No		0	2	0
Ethyl Acrylate $CH_2{:}CHCOOC_2H_5$ **140-88-5** Note: Polymerizes. See NFPA 49 contained in this guide.		50 (10) (oc)	702 (372)	1.4	14	0.9	3.5	211 (99)	Slight	1 5	3	3	2
Ethyl Alcohol C_2H_5OH (Grain Alcohol, Cologne Spirits, Ethanol) **64-17-5** See also Ethyl Alcohol and Water.	IB	55 (13)	685 (363)	3.3	19	0.8	1.6	173 (78)	Yes	1 5	2	3	0
Ethyl Alcohol and Water (96 vol %) C_2H_5OH	IB	62 (17)							Yes	1 5	2	3	0
Ethyl Alcohol and Water (95 vol %) C_2H_5OH	IB	63 (17)							Yes	1 5	2	3	0
Ethyl Alcohol and Water (80 vol %) C_2H_5OH	IB	68 (20)							Yes	1 5	2	3	0
Ethyl Alcohol and Water (70 vol %) C_2H_5OH	IB	70 (21)							Yes	1 5	2	3	0
Ethyl Alcohol and Water (60 vol %) C_2H_5OH	IB	72 (22)							Yes	1 5	2	3	0
Ethyl Alcohol and Water (50 vol %) C_2H_5OH	IC	75 (24)							Yes	1 5	2	3	0
Ethyl Alcohol and Water (40 vol %) C_2H_5OH	IC	79 (26)							Yes	1 5	1	3	0
Ethyl Alcohol and Water (30 vol %) C_2H_5OH	IC	85 (29)							Yes	1 5	1	3	0
Ethyl Alcohol and Water (20 vol %) C_2H_5OH	IC	97 (36)							Yes	1 5	1	3	0
Ethyl Alcohol and Water (10 vol %) C_2H_5OH	II	120 (49)							Yes	1 5	1	2	0
Ethyl Alcohol and Water (5 vol %) C_2H_5OH	IIIA	144 (62)							Yes	1 5	1	2	0

Chemical Name Formula (Synonym) CAS No.	NFPA 30/ OSHA Class	Flash Point °F(°C)	Ignition Temp. °F(°C)	Flammable Limits Percent by Vol.		Sp.Gr. (Water =1)	Vapor Density (Air =1)	Boiling Point °F(°C)	Water Soluble	Extin-guishing Methods	Hazard Identification		
				Lower	Upper						Health	Flamma-bility	Insta-bility
Ethylaluminum Dichloride $C_2H_5AlCl_2$ (Dichloroethylaluminum) **563-43-9**		−1 (−18)				1.2		239 (115) @ 50 mm	Reacts violently			4	3
	Notes: Fumes vigorously in air. May ignite spontaneously. Melting point 90 (32).												
Ethylaluminum Sesquichloride $(C_2H_5)_3Al_2Cl_3$ **12075-68-2**	IB	−4 (−20)				1.1		297 (147)	Reacts violently		3	3	3 ~~W~~
	Note: Ignites spontaneously in air.												
Ethylamine, 70% $C_2H_5NH_2$ (Aminoethane) **75-04-7**	IA	<0 (<−18)	725 (385)	3.5	14.0	0.8	1.6	62 (17)	Yes	1 5	3	4	0
	See NFPA 49 contained in this guide.												
Ethylaminoethanol	See N-Ethylethanolamine.												
O-Ethylaniline $C_2H_5NH(C_6H_5)$ **578-54-1**		185 (85) (oc)				1.0−	4.2	401 (205)	No		1	2	0
	See NFPA 49 contained in this guide.												
Ethylbenzene $C_2H_5C_6H_5$ (Ethylbenzol) (Phenylethane) **100-41-4**	IB	70 (21)	810 (432)	0.8	6.7	0.9	3.7	277 (136)	No	1	2	3	0
	See NFPA 49 contained in this guide.												
Ethyl Benzoate $C_6H_5COOC_2H_5$ **93-89-0**	IIIA	190 (88)	914 (490)			1.0+		414 (212)	No		1	1	0
Ethylbenzol	See Ethylbenzene.												
Ethyl Benzoylacetate $C_6H_5COCH_2COOC_2H_5$ **94-02-0**		285 (141) (oc)				1.1		291–298 (144–148)	No	2	0	2	0
Ethylbenzylaniline $C_6H_5N(C_2H_5)CH_2C_6H_5$ **92-59-1**		284 (140) (oc)	<932 (500)			1.0+		594 (312) Slight decomp.	No	5 2	1	1	0
Ethyl Borate $(C_2H_5)_3BO_3$	IB	52 (11)				0.9	5.0	233 (112)	Decomposes		2	3	0
Ethyl Bromide C_2H_5Br (Bromoethane) **74-96-4**		−4 (−20)	952 (511)	6.8	8.0	1.4	3.8	100 (38)	Slight	1	3	3	0
Ethyl Bromoacetate $BrCH_2COOC_2H_5$ **105-36-2**	II	118 (48)				1.5		318 (159)	No	3	3	2	1
2-Ethylbutanal	See 2-Ethylbutyraldehyde.												
Ethyl Butanoate	See Ethyl Butyrate.												
2-Ethyl-1-Butanol	See 2-Ethylbutyl Alcohol.												
2-Ethyl-1-Butene $(C_2H_5)_2C{:}CH_2$ **760-21-4**	IB	<−4 (<−20)	599 (315)			0.69	2.90	144 (62)			1	3	0
3-(2-Ethylbutoxy) Propionic Acid $CH_3CH_2CH(C_2H_5)CH_2$- OCH_2CH_2COOH		280 (138) (oc)				1.0−		392 (200) @ 100 mm	No	2	2	1	0
2-Ethylbutyl Acetate $CH_3COOCH_2CH(C_2H_5)_2$ **10031-87-5**		130 (54) (oc)				0.9	5.0	324 (162)	No			2	0
2-Ethylbutyl Acrylate $CH_2{:}CHCOOCH_2CH$- $(C_2H_5)C_2H_5$		125 (52) (oc)				0.9		180 (82) @ 10 mm	No		1	2	0

Chemical Name Formula (Synonym) CAS No.	NFPA 30/ OSHA Class	Flash Point °F(°C)	Ignition Temp. °F(°C)	Flammable Limits Percent by Vol. Lower	Upper	Sp.Gr. (Water =1)	Vapor Density (Air =1)	Boiling Point °F(°C)	Water Soluble	Extin-guishing Methods	Hazard Identification Health	Flamma-bility	Insta-bility
2-Ethylbutyl Alcohol $(C_2H_5)_2CHCH_2OH$ (2-Ethyl-1-Butanol) **97-95-0**		135 (57) (oc)	580 (304) (est.)	1.9	8.8	0.8	3.5	301 (149)	No		3	2	0
Ethylbutylamine $CH_3CH_2CH_2CH_2$- $NHCH_3CH_2$ **13360-63-9**		64 (18) (oc)				0.7	3.5	232 (111)	No	1	3	3	0
Ethyl Butylcarbamate	See N-Butylurethane.												
Ethyl Butyl Carbonate $(C_2H_5)(C_4H_9)CO_3$	II	122 (50)				0.9	5.0	275 (135)			2	2	1
Ethyl Butyl Ether $C_2H_5OC_4H_9$ (Butyl Ethyl Ether) **628-81-9**	IB	40 (4)				0.8	3.7	198 (92)	Slight	1 5	2	3	1
2-Ethyl Butyl Glycol $(C_2H_5)_2CHCH_2OC_2H_4OH$ [2-(2-Ethylbutoxy)ethanol]		180 (82) (oc)				0.90	5.05	386 (197)			0	2	0
Ethyl Butyl Ketone $C_2H_5CO(CH_2)_3CH_3$ (3-Heptanone) **106-35-4**		115 (46) (oc)		1.4	8.8	0.8	4.0	299 (148)	No		2	2	0
2-Ethyl-2-Butyl-1,3-Propanediol $HOCH_2C(C_2H_5)(C_4H_9)$- CH_2OH	Note: Melting point 107 (42).	280 (138) (oc)				0.9 @122°F (50°C)		352 (178)@ 50 mm	Yes	2 5	2	1	0
2-Ethylbutyraldehyde $(C_2H_5)_2CHCHO$ (Diethyl Acetaldehyde) (2-Ethylbutanal) **97-96-1**		70 (21) (oc)		1.2	7.7	0.8	3.5	242 (117)	No	1 5	2	3	0
Ethyl Butyrate $CH_3CH_2CH_2COOC_2H_5$ (Butyric Acid, Ethyl Ester) (Butyric Ester) (Ethyl Butanoate) **105-54-4**	IC	75 (24)	865 (463)			0.9	4.0	248 (120)	No	1 5	1	3	0
2-Ethylbutyric Acid $(C_2H_5)_2CHCOOH$ (Diethyl Acetic Acid) **88-09-5**		210 (99) (oc)	752 (400)			0.9		380 (193)	Slight	5	3	1	0
2-Ethylcaproaldehyde	See 2-Ethylhexanal.												
Ethyl Caproate $C_5H_{11}COOC_2H_5$ (Ethyl Hexoate) (Ethyl Hexanoate) **123-66-0**	II	120 (49)				0.9	4.97	333 (167)	No	5	1	2	0
Ethyl Caprylate $CH_3(CH_2)_6COOC_2H_5$ (Ethyl Octoate) (Ethyl Octanoate) **106-32-1**	IIIA	175 (79)				0.9		405–408 (207–209)	No	5	1	2	0
Ethyl Carbonate	See Diethyl Carbonate.												
Ethyl Chloride C_2H_5Cl (Chloroethane) (Hydrochloric Ether) (Muriatic Ether) **75-00-3**	IA	−58 (−50)	966 (519)	3.8	15.4	0.9	2.2	54 (12)	Slight	1	2	4	0
Ethyl Chloroacetate $ClCH_2COOC_2H_5$ **105-39-5** **541-41-3**	See NFPA 49 contained in this guide.	147 (64) (oc)				1.2	4.3	295 (146)	No	3	3	2	0

Chemical Name Formula (Synonym) CAS No.	NFPA 30/ OSHA Class	Flash Point °F(°C)	Ignition Temp. °F(°C)	Flammable Limits Percent by Vol.		Sp.Gr. (Water =1)	Vapor Density (Air =1)	Boiling Point °F(°C)	Water Soluble	Extin-guishing Methods	Hazard Identification		
				Lower	Upper						Health	Flamma-bility	Insta-bility
Ethyl Chlorocarbonate	See Ethyl Chloroformate.												
Ethyl Chloroformate $ClCOOC_2H_5$ (Ethyl Chlorocarbonate) (Ethyl Chloromethanoate) **541-41-3**	IB	61 (16)	932 (500)			1.1	3.7	201 (94)	Decom-poses	1	4	3	1
Ethyl Chloromethanoate	See Ethyl Chloroformate.												
Ethyl Crotonate $CH_3CH{:}CHCOOC_2H_5$ **623-70-1** **10544-63-5**	IB	36 (2)		1.5		0.9	3.9	282 (139)	No	1	2	3	0
Ethyl Cyanoacetate $CH_2CNCOOC_2H_5$ **105-56-6**	IIIB	230 (110)				1.1		401–408 (205–209)		2	1	1	1
Ethylcyclobutane $C_2H_5C_4H_7$ **4806-61-5**	IB	<4 (<−16)	410 (210)	1.2	7.7		2.9	160 (71)	No			3	0
Ethylcyclohexane $C_2H_5C_6H_{11}$ **1678-91-7**	IC	95 (35)	460 (238)	0.9	6.6	0.8	3.9	269 (132)	No		1	3	0
N-Ethylcyclohexyl-amine $C_6H_{11}NHC_2H_5$ **5459-93-8**		86 (30) (oc)				0.8	4.4	329 (165)	Slight	1 5	3	3	0
Ethylcyclopentane $C_2H_5C_5H_9$ **1640-89-7**	IB	<70 (<21)	500 (260)	1.1	6.7	0.8	3.4	218 (103)				3	0
Ethyl Decanoate $C_9H_{19}COOC_2H_5$ (Ethyl Caprate) **110-38-3**	IIIB	>212 (>100)				0.9		469 (243)	No	5 2	0	1	0
Ethyl Dichlorosilane $C_2H_5SiHCl_2$ **1789-58-8**	IB	30 (−1)		2.9		1.1	4.45	168 (75.5)	Yes	1	3	3	2 ₩
N-Ethyldiethanolamine $C_2H_5N(C_2H_4OH)_2$ **139-87-7**		280 (138) (oc)				1.0+		487 (253)	Yes	2 5	2	1	0
Ethyl Dimethyl Meth-ane	See Isopentane.												
Ethylene $H_2C{:}CH_2$ (Ethene) **74-85-1**		Gas	842 (450)	2.7	36.0	1.26 @ 0°C	1.0	−155 (−104)	No	6	2	4	2
	See NFPA 49 contained in this guide.												
Ethylene Acetate	See Glycol Diacetate.												
Ethylene Carbonate OCH_2CH_2OCO (ring) **96-49-1**		290 (143) (oc)						351 (177)@ 100 mm	Yes	2 5	2	1	1
	Note: Melting point 96 (36).												
Ethylene Chlorohydrin	See 2-Chloroethanol.												
Ethylene Cyanohydrin $CH_2(OH)CH_2CN$ (Hydracrylonitrile) **109-78-4**		265 (129) (oc)	922 (494)	2.3	12.1	1.1		445 (229) Decomposes	Yes	2 5	1	1	2
	See NFPA 49 contained in this guide.												
Ethylenediamine $H_2NCH_2CH_2NH_2$ Anhydrous 76% **107-15-3**		104 (40) 150 (66) (oc)	725 (385)	2.5 @ 100°C	12	0.9 1.0−	2.1	241 (116) 239–252 (115–122)	Yes	5	3	2	0
	See NFPA 49 contained in this guide.												

Chemical Name Formula (Synonym) CAS No.	NFPA 30/ OSHA Class	Flash Point °F(°C)	Ignition Temp. °F(°C)	Flammable Limits Percent by Vol. Lower	Upper	Sp.Gr. (Water =1)	Vapor Density (Air =1)	Boiling Point °F(°C)	Water Soluble	Extin-guishing Methods	Hazard Identification Health	Flamma-bility	Insta-bility
Ethylene Dichloride CH_2ClCH_2Cl (1,2-Dichloroethane) (Glycol Dichloride) **107-06-2**	IB	56 (13)	775 (413)	6.2	16	1.3	3.4	183 (84)	No	4	2	3	0
	See NFPA 49 contained in this guide.												
Ethylene Dicyanide	See Succinonitrile.												
2,2-Ethylenedioxy-diethanol	See Triethylene Glycol.												
Ethylene Formate	See 1,2-Ethanediol Diformate.												
Ethylene Glycol HOC_2H_4OH (1,2-Ethanediol) (Glycol) **107-21-1**	IIIB	232 (111)	748 (398)	3.2		1.1		387 (197)	Yes	5 2	2	1	0
Ethylene Glycol Acetate $CH_2OHCH_2OOCCH_3$ (Glycol Monoacetate) **542-59-6**		215 (102) (oc)				1.1		357 (181)	Yes	5 2	2	1	0
Ethylene Glycol n-Butyl Ether (Ethylene Glycol Mono-butyl Ether) (2-Butoxyethanol) (Butyl Cellosolve) **111-76-2**	IIIA	143 (62)	460 (238)	1.1 @ 200 (93)	12.7 @ 275 (135)	0.9	4.1	340 (171)	Yes	5	3	2	0
Ethylene Glycol Diacetate	See Glycol Diacetate.												
Ethylene Glycol Dibutyl Ether $C_4H_9OC_2H_4OC_4H_9$ **112-48-1**	IIIA	185 (85)				0.8		399 (204)	No	5	1	2	0
Ethylene Glycol Diethyl Ether $C_2H_5OCH_2CH_2OC_2H_5$ **629-14-1**		95 (35) (oc)	406 (208)			0.8	4.07	251 (122)	Slight	5 1	2	3	0
Ethylene Glycol Diformate	See 1,2-Ethanediol Diformate.												
Ethylene Glycol Dimethyl Ether $CH_3O(CH_2)_2OCH_3$ (1,2-Dimethoxyethane) **110-71-4**	IB	29 (−2)	395 (202)			0.9	3.1	185 (85)	Slight	5	1	3	0
Ethylene Glycol Ethylbutyl Ether $(C_2H_5)_2CHCH_2OCH_2CH_2OH$		180 (85) (oc)				0.9		386 (197)	No	5	1	2	0
Ethylene Glycol Ethylhexyl Ether $C_4H_9CH(C_2H_5)CH_2OCH_2CH_2OH$ **1559-35-9**		230 (110) (oc)				0.9		442 (228)	No	5 2	3	2	0
Ethylene Glycol Isopropyl Ether $(CH_3)_2CHOCH_2CH_2OH$ **109-59-1**		92 (33) (oc)				0.9	3.58	289 (143)	Yes	5 1	3	2	1
Ethylene Glycol Monoacrylate	See 2-Hydroxyethyl Acrylate.												
Ethylene Glycol Monobenzyl Ether $C_6H_5CH_2OCH_2CH_2OH$ **622-08-2**		265 (129) (oc)	665 (352)			1.1		493 (256)	No	5 2	2	1	0

Chemical Name Formula (Synonym) CAS No.	NFPA 30/ OSHA Class	Flash Point °F(°C)	Ignition Temp. °F(°C)	Flammable Limits Percent by Vol.		Sp.Gr. (Water =1)	Vapor Density (Air =1)	Boiling Point °F(°C)	Water Soluble	Extin-guishing Methods	Hazard Identification		
				Lower	Upper						Health	Flamma-bility	Insta-bility
Ethylene Glycol Mono-butyl Ether $C_4H_9O(CH_2)_2OH$ (2-Butoxyethanol) (Ethylene Glycol n-Butyl Ether) (Butyl Cellosolve) **111-76-2**	IIIA	143 (62)	460 (238)	1.1 @ 200(93)	12.7 @ 275 (135)	0.9	4.1	340 (171)	Yes	5	3	2	0
Ethylene Glycol Mono-butyl Ether Acetate $C_4H_9O(CH_2)_2OOCCH_3$ **112-07-2**	IIIA	160 (71)	645 (340)	0.88 @ 200(93)	8.54 @ 275 (135)	0.9		377 (192)	No	5	1	2	0
Ethylene Glycol Ethyl Ether $HOCH_2CH_2OC_2H_5$ (2-Ethoxyethanol) **110-80-5**	II	110 (43)	455 (235)	1.7 @ 200(93)	15.6 @ 200(93)	0.9	3.0	275 (135)	Yes	5	1	2	0
Ethylene Glycol Mo-noethyl Ether Ace-tate	See 2-Ethoxyethyl Acetate.												
Ethylene Glycol Mono-isobutyl Ether $(CH_3)_2CHCH_2OCH_2CH_2OH$ **4439-24-1**	II	136 (58)	540 (282)	1.2 @ 200(93)	9.4 @ 275 (135)	0.9	4.1	316–323 (158–162)	Yes	5	2	2	
Ethylene Glycol Methyl Ether $CH_3OCH_2CH_2OH$ (2-Methoxyethanol) **109-86-4**	II	102 (39)	545 (285)	1.8 @STP	14 @STP	1.0–	2.6	255 (124)	Yes	5	1	2	1
Ethylene Glycol Methyl Ether Acetal $CH_3CH(OCH_2CH_2OCH_3)_2$		200 (93) (oc)				1.0–		405 (207)	Yes	5	1	2	
Ethylene Glycol Methyl Ether Acetate $CH_3O(CH_2)_2OOCCH_3$ (Methyl Cellosolve Ace-tate) (2-Methoxyethyl Acetate) **110-49-6**	II	120 (49)	740 (392)	1.5 @ 200(93)	12.3 @ 200(93)	1.0+	4.1	293 (145)	Yes	5	2	2	0
Ethylene Glycol Methyl Ether Formal $CH_2(OCH_2CH_2OCH_3)_2$		155 (68) (oc)				1.0–	5.65	394 (201)	Yes	5	1	2	
Ethylene Glycol Phenyl Ether $C_6H_5OC_2H_4OH$ (2-Phenoxyethanol) **122-99-6**	IIIB	260 (127)				1.1	4.8	473 (245)	No	2	3	1	0
Ethylene Oxide CH_2OCH_2 (ring) (Dimethylene Oxide) (1,2-Epoxyethane) (Oxirane) (EO) **75-21-8**	IA	–20 (–29)	804 (429)	3.0	100	0.9	1.5	51 (11)	Yes	1	3	4	3
	Note: Vapors explosive. See NFPA 49 contained in this guide.												
Ethylenimine $NHCH_2CH_2$ (ring) (Aziridine) **151-56-4**	IB	12 (–11)	608 (320)	3.3	54.8	0.8	1.5	132 (56)	Yes	5	4	3	3
	See NFPA 49 contained in this guide.												
Ethyl Ethanoate	See Ethyl Acetate.												
N-Ethylethanolamine $C_2H_5NHC_2H_4OH$ (Ethylaminoethanol) [2-(Ethylamino) ethanol] **110-73-6**		160 (71) (oc)				0.9	3.0	322 (161)	Yes	5	3	2	0

Chemical Name Formula (Synonym) CAS No.	NFPA 30/ OSHA Class	Flash Point °F(°C)	Ignition Temp. °F(°C)	Flammable Limits Percent by Vol.		Sp.Gr. (Water =1)	Vapor Density (Air =1)	Boiling Point °F(°C)	Water Soluble	Extin- guishing Methods	Hazard Identification		
				Lower	Upper						Health	Flamma- bility	Insta- bility
Ethyl Ether $C_2H_5OC_2H_5$ (Diethyl Ether) (Diethyl Oxide) (Ether) (Ethyl Oxide) **60-29-7**	IA See NFPA 49 contained in this guide.	−49 (−45)	356 (180)	1.9	36.0	0.7	2.6	95 (35)	Slight	1 5	1	4	1
Ethylethylene Glycol	See 1,2-Butanediol.												
Ethyl Fluoride C_2H_5F (1-Fluoroethane) **353-36-6**				5	10	0.72 @ 7.2 atm	1.66	−36 (−38)	Yes		2	4	0
Ethyl Formate $HCO_2C_2H_5$ (Ethyl Methanoate) (Formic Acid, Ethyl Ester) **109-94-4**	IB	−4 (−20)	851 (455)	2.8	16.0	0.9	2.6	130 (54)	No	1 5	2	3	0
o-Ethyl Formate $(C_2H_5O)_3CH$ (Triethyl Orthoformate) **109-94-4**	IC	86 (30)				0.90	5.11	291 (144)			2	3	0
Ethyl Glycol Acetate	See 2-Ethoxyethyl Acetate.												
2-Ethylhexaldehyde	See 2-Ethylhexanal.												
2-Ethylhexanal $C_4H_9CH(C_2H_5)CHO$ (Butylethylacetaldehyde) (2-Ethylcaproaldehyde) (2-Ethylhexaldehyde) **123-05-7**	II	112 (44)	375 (190)	0.85 @ 200(93)	7.2 @ 275 (135)	0.8	4.4	325 (163)	Very slight		2	2	1
2-Ethyl-1,3-Hexanediol $C_3H_7CH(OH)CH(C_2H_5)$- CH_2OH (Octylene Glycol) **94-96-2**		260 (127) (oc)	680 (360)			0.9	5.03	472 (244)	Slight	2 5	2	1	0
2-Ethylhexanoic Acid $C_4H_9CH(C_2H_5)COOH$ (2-Ethyl Hexoic Acid)		245 (118) (oc)	700 (371)	0.8	6.0	0.9	5.0	440 (227)	No	2	1	1	0
2-Ethylhexanol $C_4H_9CH(C_2H_5)CH_2OH$ (2-Ethylhexyl Alcohol) (Octyl Alcohol) **104-76-7**	IIIA	164 (73)	448 (231)	0.88	9.7	0.8	4.5	359 (182)	Slight	5	2	2	0
2-Ethylhexenyl	See 2-Ethyl-3-Propylacrolein.												
2-Ethylhexoic Acid	See 2-Ethylhexanoic Acid.												
2-Ethylhexyl Acetate $CH_3COOCH_2CH(C_2H_5)$- C_4H_9 (Octyl Acetate) **103-09-3**	IIIA	160 (71)	515 (268)	0.76	8.14	0.9	5.9	390 (199)	No		1	2	0
2-Ethylhexyl Acrylate CH_2:$CHCOOCH_2CH$- $(C_2H_5)C_4H_9$ **103-11-7**	 See NFPA 49 contained in this guide.	180 (82) (oc)	485 (252)	0.7	8.2	0.9		266 (130) @ 50 mm	No		1	2	1
2-Ethylhexylamine $C_4H_9CH(C_2H_5)CH_2NH_2$ **104-75-6**		140 (60) (oc)	563 (295)			0.8	4.5	337 (169)	Yes	5	2	2	0
N-2-(Ethylhexyl) Ani- line $C_6H_5NHCH_2CH$- $(C_2H_5)C_4H_9$		325 (163) (oc)				0.9		379 (193) @ 50 mm	No	2		1	0
2-Ethylhexyl Chloride $C_4H_9CH(C_2H_5)CH_2Cl$ **123-04-6**		140 (60) (oc)				0.9	5.1	343 (173)	No			2	0

Chemical Name Formula (Synonym) CAS No.	NFPA 30/ OSHA Class	Flash Point °F(°C)	Ignition Temp. °F(°C)	Flammable Limits Percent by Vol.		Sp.Gr. (Water = 1)	Vapor Density (Air = 1)	Boiling Point °F(°C)	Water Soluble	Extin-guishing Methods	Hazard Identification		
				Lower	Upper						Health	Flamma-bility	Insta-bility
N-(2-Ethylhexyl)-cyclohexylamine $C_6H_{11}NH[CH_2CH(C_2H_5)C_4H_9]$		265 (129) (oc)				0.8		342 (172) @ 50 mm	No	2	2	1	0
2-Ethylhexyl Ether $[C_4H_9CH(C_2H_5)CH_2]_2O$	IIIB	235 (113)				0.8		517 (269)	No	2	1	1	0
2-Ethylhexyl Vinyl Ether	See Vinyl-2-Ethylhexyl Ether.												
1,1-Ethylidene Dichloride CH_3CHCl_2 (1,1-Dichloroethane) **75-34-3**	IB	2 (−17)	856 (458)	5.4	11.4	1.2	3.42	135–138 (57–59)	Slight	4 5	1	3	0
1,2-Ethylidene Dichloride $ClCH_2CH_2Cl$ **107-06-2**	IB	55 (13)	824 (440)	6.2	16	1.25	3.42	183 (84)			1	3	0
Ethyl Isobutyrate $(CH_3)_2CHCOOC_2H_5$ **97-62-1**	IB	<70 (<21)				0.87	4.0	230 (110)			3	2	0
2-Ethylisohexanol $(CH_3)_2CHCH_2CH(C_2H_5)CH_2OH$ (2-Ethyl Isohexyl Alcohol) (2-Ethyl-4-Methyl Pentanol) **100-67-2**	IIIA	158 (70)	600 (316)			0.8		343–358 (173–181)			1	2	
Ethyl Lactate $CH_3CHOHCOOC_2H_5$ Tech. **97-64-3**	II	115 (46) 131 (55)	752 (400)	1.5 @ 212 (100)		1.0+	4.1	309 (154)	Yes	5	3	2	0
Ethyl Malonate	See Diethyl Malonate.												
Ethyl Mercaptan C_2H_5SH (Ethanethiol) (Ethyl Sulfhydrate) **75-08-1**	IA	<0 (<−18)	572 (300)	2.8	18.0	0.8	2.1	95 (35)	No	1	2	4	1
Ethyl Methacrylate $CH_2{:}C(CH_3)COOC_2H_5$ (Ethyl Methyl Acrylate) **97-63-2**		68 (20) (oc)	740 (393)	1.8		0.9	3.9	239–248 (115–120)	No	1	2	3	2
Ethyl Methanoate	See Ethyl Formate.												
Ethyl Methyl Acrylate	See Ethyl Methacrylate.												
Ethyl Methyl Ether	See Methyl Ethyl Ether.												
7-Ethyl-2-Methyl-4-Hendecanol $C_4H_9CH(C_2H_5)C_2H_4CHOHCH_2CH(CH_3)_2$		285 (141) (oc)				0.8		507 (264)	Very slight	2	0	1	0
Ethyl Methyl Ketone	See Methyl Ethyl Ketone.												
4-Ethylmorpholine $CH_2CH_2OC_2H_4NCH_2CH_3$ **100-74-3**		90 (32) (oc)				0.9	4.0	280 (138)	Yes	1 5	2	3	0
1-Ethylnaphthalene $C_{10}H_7C_2H_5$			896 (480)			1.02	5.39	496 (258)			0	1	0
Ethyl Nitrate $CH_3CH_2ONO_2$ (Nitric Ether) **625-58-1**	IB	50 (10)		4.0		1.1	3.1	190 (88)	No	4	2	3	4

Chemical Name Formula (Synonym) CAS No.	NFPA 30/ OSHA Class	Flash Point °F(°C)	Ignition Temp. °F(°C)	Flammable Limits Percent by Vol.		Sp.Gr. (Water =1)	Vapor Density (Air =1)	Boiling Point °F(°C)	Water Soluble	Extin-guishing Methods	Hazard Identification		
				Lower	Upper						Health	Flamma-bility	Insta-bility
Ethyl Nitrite C_2H_5ONO (Nitrous Ether) **109-95-5**	IA	−31 (−35)	194 (90)	4.0	50.0	0.9	2.6	63 (17)	No	1	4	4	4
	Note: Decomposes explosively at 194 (90). See NFPA 49 contained in this guide.												
3-Ethyloctane $C_5H_{11}CH(C_2H_5)C_2H_5$ **5881-17-4**			446 (230)			0.74	4.91	333 (167)			0	2	0
4-Ethyloctane $C_4H_9CH(C_2H_5)C_3H_7$ **15869-86-0**			445 (229)			0.74	4.91	328 (164)			0	2	0
Ethyl Orthosilicate	See Ethyl Silicate.												
Ethyl Oxalate $(COOC_2H_5)_2$ (Oxalic Ether) (Diethyl Oxalate) **95-92-1**	IIIA	168 (76)				1.1	5.0	367 (186)	Slight grad-ual decom-position		1	2	1
Ethyl Oxide	See Ethyl Ether.												
Ethyl 3-Oxobutanoate	See Ethyl Acetoacetate.												
p-Ethylphenol $HOC_6H_4C_2H_5$ (4-Ethylphenol) **123-07-9**	IIIB	219 (104)				1.0− @ 140°F (60°C)	4.2	426 (219)	Slight	5 2	2	1	0
	Note: Melting point 115 (46).												
Ethyl Phenylacetate $C_6H_5CH_2COOC_2H_5$ **101-97-3**	IIIB	210 (99)				1.0+		529 (276)	No		1	1	
Ethyl Phenyl Ether	See Ethoxybenzene.												
Ethyl Phenyl Ketone $C_2H_5COC_6H_5$ (Propiophenone) **93-55-0**		210 (99) (oc)				1.01	4.63	425 (218)			1	1	0
	Note: Melting point 70 (21).												
Ethyl Phosphate	See Triethyl Phosphate.												
Ethyl Phthalyl Ethyl Glycolate $C_2H_5OCOC_6H_4OCO$- $CH_2OCOC_2H_5$	IIIB	365 (185)				1.2		608 (320)	Yes	2 5	0	1	0
Ethyl Propenyl Ether $CH_3CH{:}CHOCH_2CH_3$ **557-31-3**		>19 (> −7) (oc)				0.8		158 (70)		1	2	3	1
Ethyl Propionate $C_2H_5COOC_2H_5$ **105-37-3**	IB	54 (12)	824 (440)	1.9	11	0.9	3.5	210 (99)	No	1	1	3	0
2-Ethyl-3-Propylacrolein $C_3H_7CH{:}C(C_2H_5)CHO$ (2-Ethylhexenal) **645-62-5**		155 (68) (oc)				0.9	4.4	347 (175)	No	5		2	1
2-Ethyl-3-Propylacrylic Acid $C_3H_7CH{:}C(C_2H_5)COOH$		330 (166) (oc)				0.9		450 (232)	Slight	2 5	2	1	1
Ethyl Propyl Ether $C_2H_5OC_3H_7$ (1-Ethoxypropane) **628-32-0**		<−4 (<−20)		1.7	9.0	0.8		147 (64)	Yes	5	1	3	0
Ethyl Silicate $(C_2H_5)_4SiO_4$ (Ethyl Orthosilicate) (Tetraethyl Orthosilicate) **78-10-4**		125 (52) (oc)		1.3	23	0.9	7.2	334 (168)	Decom-poses		2	3	1
Ethyl Sulfate	See Diethyl Sulfate.												

Chemical Name Formula (Synonym) CAS No.	NFPA 30/ OSHA Class	Flash Point °F(°C)	Ignition Temp. °F(°C)	Flammable Limits Percent by Vol. Lower	Upper	Sp.Gr. (Water =1)	Vapor Density (Air =1)	Boiling Point °F(°C)	Water Soluble	Extin-guishing Methods	Hazard Identification Health	Flamma-bility	Insta-bility
Ethyl Sulfhydrate	See Ethyl Mercaptan.												
m-Ethyltoluene $CH_3C_6H_4C_2H_5$ (1-Methyl-3-Ethylbenzene) (3-Ethyltoluene) **620-14-4**		86 (30)	896 (480)			0.86	4.15	322 (161)			1	3	0
o-Ethyltoluene $CH_3C_6H_4C_2H_5$ (1-Methyl-2-Ethylbenzene) (2-Ethyltoluene) **611-14-3**		103 (39)	824 (440)			0.88	4.15	329 (165)			2	2	0
p-Ethyltoluene $CH_3C_6H_4C_2H_5$ (1-Methyl-4-Ethylbenzene) (4-Ethyltoluene) **622-96-8**		98 (36)	887 (475)			0.86	4.15	324 (162)	No		1	3	0
Ethyl p-Toluene Sulfon-amide $C_7H_7SO_2NHC_2H_5$ **80-39-7**	IIIB	260 (127)				1.3		208 (98) @ 745 mm		2		1	0
Ethyl p-Toluene Sulfo-nate $C_7H_7SO_3C_2H_5$ **80-40-0**	IIIB	316 (158)				1.2		345 (174)	No	2	1	1	0
Ethyltrichlorosilane $CH_3CH_2SiCl_3$ **115-21-9**	See NFPA 49 contained in this guide.	72 (22) (oc)				1.2	1.4 @ 100 (38)	208 (98) @ 745 mm	Reacts	1	3	3	2 ~~W~~
Ethyl Vinyl Ether	See Vinyl Ethyl Ether.												
Ethyne	See Acetylene.												
Fish Oil (bisulfated mix) **68187-82-6**	IIIB	420 (216)							No	2	1	1	0
Fluorobenzene C_6H_5F **462-06-6**	IB	5 (−15)				1.03	3.31	185 (85)	No	1	1	3	0
Formal	See Methylal.												
Formaldehyde 37%, 15% Methanol HCHO (Formalin) (Methylene Oxide)	II See also Formaldehyde and Formaldehyde 37% Methanol-free. See NFPA 49 contained in this guide.	122 (50)									3	2	0
Formaldehyde 37% Methanol-free HCHO	IIIA See also Formaldehyde and Formaldehyde 37%, 15% Methanol. See NFPA 49 contained in this guide.	[Gas 185 (85)]						214 (101)		5	3	2	0
Formamide $HCONH_2$ **75-12-7**		310 (154) (oc)				1.1		410 (210) Decomposes	Yes	2	2	1	0
Formic Acid HCOOH 90% Solution **64-18-6**	IIIA See NFPA 49 contained in this guide.	156 (69) 122 (50)	1004 (539) 813 (434)	18	57	1.2	1.6	213 (101)	Yes	5	3	2	0
Formic Acid, Butyl Ester	See Butyl Formate.												

Chemical Name Formula (Synonym) CAS No.	NFPA 30/ OSHA Class	Flash Point °F(°C)	Ignition Temp. °F(°C)	Flammable Limits Percent by Vol. Lower	Flammable Limits Percent by Vol. Upper	Sp.Gr. (Water =1)	Vapor Density (Air =1)	Boiling Point °F(°C)	Water Soluble	Extin-guishing Methods	Hazard Identification Health	Hazard Identification Flamma-bility	Hazard Identification Insta-bility
Formic Acid, Ethyl Ester	See Ethyl Formate.												
Formic Acid, Methyl Ester	See Methyl Formate.												
Fuel Oil No. 1 (Jet Fuel A) (Kerosene) (Range Oil) **8008-20-6**		100–162 (38–72)	410 (210)	0.7	5	<1		304–574 (151–301)	No		2	2	0
Fuel Oil No. 2 **68476-30-2**		126–204 (52–96)	494 (257)			<1			No		1	2	0
Fuel Oil No. 4 **68476-31-3**		142–240 (61–116)	505 (263)			<1			No		1	2	0
Fuel Oil No. 5 Light Heavy **70892-11-4**		156–336 (69–169)				<1			No		1	2	0
Fuel Oil No. 6 (Bunker Oil) (Bunker C) **68553-00-4**		150–270 (66–132)	765 (407)			1±			No		1	2	0
2-Furaldehyde	See Furfural.												
Furan CH:CHCH:CHO (Furfuran) **110-00-9**	IA	<32 (<0)		2.3	14.3	0.9	2.3	88 (31)	No	1	2	4	1
Furfural OCH:CHCH:CHCHO (2-Furaldehyde) (Furfuraldehyde) (Furol) **98-01-1**	IIIA See NFPA 49 contained in this guide.	140 (60)	600 (316)	2.1	19.3	1.2	3.3	322 (161)	Slight	5	3	2	1
Furfuraldehyde	See Furfural.												
Furfuran	See Furan.												
Furfuryl Acetate OCH:CHCH:C- CH_2OOCCH_3 **623-17-6**	IIIA	185 (85)				1.1	4.8	356–367 (180–186)	No	3	1	2	1
Furfuryl Alcohol OCH:CHCH:CCH_2OH **98-00-0**		167 (75) (oc)	915 (491)	1.8	16.3	1.1	3.4	340 (171)	Yes	5	3	2	1
Furfurylamine $C_4H_3OCH_2NH_2$ **617-89-0**		99 (37) (oc)				1.05	3.35	295 (146)		1	2	3	0
Furol	See Furfural.												
Fusel Oil	See Isoamyl Alcohol.												
Gas, Blast Furnace **65996-68-1**				35	74					6	2	4	0
Gas, Coal Gas				5.3	32					6	2	4	0
Gas, Coke-Oven **65996-81-8**				4.4	34					6	2	4	0
Gas, Natural (Natural Gas) **8006-14-2**			900–1170 (482–632)	3.8–6.5	13–17					6	1	4	0
Gas, Oil Gas **68476-26-6**				4.8	32.5					6	2	4	0

Chemical Name Formula (Synonym) CAS No.	NFPA 30/ OSHA Class	Flash Point °F(°C)	Ignition Temp. °F(°C)	Flammable Limits Percent by Vol.		Sp.Gr. (Water =1)	Vapor Density (Air =1)	Boiling Point °F(°C)	Water Soluble	Extin- guishing Methods	Hazard Identification		
				Lower	Upper						Health	Flamma- bility	Insta- bility
Gas, Producer **8006-20-0**				20–30	70–80					6	2	4	0
Gas, Water				7.0	72					6	2	4	0
Gas, Water (Carbu- reted)				5.6	46.2					6	2	4	0
Gas Oil **64741-44-2**	IIIA	150+ (66+)	640 (338)	0.5	5.0	<1		500–700 (260–371)	No		0	2	0
Gasoline C_5H_{12} to C_9H_{20} 56–60 Octane 73 Octane 92 Octane 100 Octane **8006-61-9**	IB	−45 (−43) −45 (−43) −36 (−38)	536 (280) 853 (456)	1.4	7.6	0.8	3.0–4.0	100–400 (38–204)	No	1	1	3	0
	Note: Values may vary considerably for different grades of gasoline.												
Gasoline 100–130 (Aviation Grade) **8006-61-9**		−50 (−46) (approx.)	824 (440)	1.3	7.1					1	1	3	0
Gasoline 115–145 (Aviation Grade) **8006-61-9**		−50 (−46) (approx.)	880 (471)	1.2	7.1					1	1	3	0
Gasoline, Casinghead (Gasoline, Natural) **68425-31-0**	IB	0 (−18) or less		1.4	7.6	0.8	3.0–4.0	100–399 (38–204)	No	1	1	3	0
Geraniol $(CH_3)_2C{:}CH(CH_2)_2C$- $(CH_3){:}CHCH_2OH$ (trans-3,7-Dimethyl-2,6- Octadien-1-ol) **106-24-1**	IIIB	>212 (>100)				0.9		446 (230)	No	5 2	2	1	0
Geranyl Acetate $(CH_3)COOC_{10}H_{17}$ (Geraniol Acetate) **105-87-3**	IIIB	>212 (>100)				0.9		468–473 (242–245)	No	5 2	1	1	0
Geranyl Butyrate $C_3H_7COOC_{10}H_{17}$ (Geraniol Butyrate) **106-29-6**	IIIB	>212 (>100)				0.9		304 (151)	No	5 2	1	1	0
Geranyl Formate $HCOOC_{10}H_{17}$ (Geraniol Formate) **105-86-2**	IIIA	185 (85)				0.9		235 (113)	No	5	1	2	0
Geranyl Propionate $C_2H_5COOC_{10}H_{17}$ (Geraniol Propionate) **105-90-8**	IIIB	>212 (>100)				0.9				5 2	1	1	0
Gin	See Ethyl Alcohol and Water.												
Glucose Pentapropio- nate $C_6H_7O_6(COC_2H_5)_5$ (Pentapropionyl Glucose) (Tetrapropionyl Glucosyl Propionate)	IIIB	509 (265)				1.2		401 (205) @ 2 mm	No	2	1	1	0
Glycerine $HOCH_2CHOHCH_2OH$ (Glycerol) **56-81-5**	IIIB	390 (199)	698 (370)			1.3	3.1	340 (171)	Yes	2 5	1	1	0
Glycerol	See Glycerine.												
Glyceryl Triacetate $(C_3H_5)(OOCCH_3)_3$ (Triacetin) **102-76-1**	IIIB	280 (138)	812 (433)	1.0 @ 373 (189)		1.2		496 (258)	Slight	2 5	0	1	0

Chemical Name Formula (Synonym) CAS No.	NFPA 30/ OSHA Class	Flash Point °F(°C)	Ignition Temp. °F(°C)	Flammable Limits Percent by Vol. Lower	 Upper	Sp.Gr. (Water =1)	Vapor Density (Air =1)	Boiling Point °F(°C)	Water Soluble	Extin- guishing Methods	Hazard Identification Health	 Flamma- bility	 Insta- bility
Glyceryl Tributyrate $C_3H_5(OOCC_3H_7)_3$ (Tributyrin) (Butyrin) (Glycerol Tributyrate) **60-01-5**		356 (180) (oc)	765 (407)	0.5 @ 406 (208)		1.0+		597 (314)	No	5 2	0	1	0
Glyceryl Trichlorohy-drin	See 1,2,3-Trichloropropane.												
Glyceryl Trinitrate	See Nitroglycerine.												
Glyceryl Tripropionate $(C_2H_5COO)_3C_3H_5$ (Tripropionin) **139-45-7**		332 (167) (oc)	790 (421)	0.8 @ 367		1.1		540 (282)	No	5 2			
Glycidyl Acrylate CH_2:$CHCOOCH_2CH$- CH_2O (ring) **106-90-1**		141 (61) (oc)	779 (415)			1.1	4.4	135 (57) @ 2 mm	No		2	2	2
Glycol	See Ethylene Glycol.												
Glycol Benzyl Ether $C_6H_5CH_2OCH_2CH_2OH$ (2-Benzyloxyethanol) **622-08-2**		264 (129) (oc)	662 (350)			1.07	5.20	493 (256)	No	2	0	1	0
Glycol Diacetate $(CH_2OOCCH_3)_2$ (Ethylene Acetate) (Ethylene Glycol Diaceate) **111-55-7**	IIIA	191 (88)	900 (482)	1.6	8.4	1.1		375 (191)	Slight	5	1	2	0
Glycol Dichloride	See Ethylene Dichloride.												
Glycol Diformate	See 1,2-Ethanediol Diformate.												
Glycol Dimercaptoace-tate $(HSCH_2C{:}OOCH_2\text{-})_2$ (GDMA) **123-81-9**	IIIB	396 (202)				1.3		280 (138) @ 1.2 mm	No	5 2	2	1	0
Glycol Monoacetate	See Ethylene Glycol Monoacetate.												
Grain Alcohol	See Ethyl Alcohol.												
Heavy Hydrogen	See Deuterium.												
Hendecane $CH_3(CH_2)_9CH_3$ (Undecane) **1120-21-4**		149 (65) (oc)				0.7	5.4	384 (196)	No	1	1	2	0
Heptadecanol $C_4H_9CH(C_2H_5)$- $C_2H_4CH(OH)C_2H_4CH$- $(C_2H_5)_2$ (3,9-Diethyl-6-Tridecanol) **2541-75-5**	Note: Melting point 130 (54).	310 (154) (oc)				0.8		588 (309)	No	2	1	1	0
Heptane $CH_3(CH_2)_5CH_3$ **142-82-5**	IB	25 (−4)	399 (204)	1.05	6.7	0.7	3.5	209 (98)	No	1	1	3	
2-Heptanol $CH_3(CH_2)_4CH(OH)CH_3$ **543-49-7**	IIIA	160 (71)				0.8	4.0	320 (160)	No		0	2	0
3-Heptanol $CH_3CH_2CH(OH)C_4H_9$ **589-82-2**	IIIA	140 (60)				0.8	4.0	313 (156)	Slight	5	0	2	0
3-Heptanone	See Ethyl Butyl Ketone.												

Chemical Name Formula (Synonym) CAS No.	NFPA 30/ OSHA Class	Flash Point °F(°C)	Ignition Temp. °F(°C)	Flammable Limits Percent by Vol.		Sp.Gr. (Water = 1)	Vapor Density (Air = 1)	Boiling Point °F(°C)	Water Soluble	Extin-guishing Methods	Hazard Identification		
				Lower	Upper						Health	Flamma-bility	Insta-bility
4-Heptanone $(C_3H_7)_2CO$ (Butyrone) (Dipropyl Ketone) **123-19-3**	II	120 (49)				0.8	3.9	290 (143)	No		1	2	0
1-Heptene	See Heptylene.												
3-Heptene (mixed cis and trans) $C_3H_7CH{:}CHC_2C_5$ (3-Heptylene)	IB	21 (−6)				0.7	3.39	203 (95)	No	1	0	3	0
Heptylamine $CH_3(CH_2)_6NH_2$ (1-Aminoheptane) **111-68-2**		130 (54) (oc)				0.8	4.0	311 (155)	Slight	5	2	2	0
Heptylene $C_5H_{11}CH{:}CH_2$ (1-Heptene) **25339-56-4**	IB	<32 (<0)	500 (260)	1.0		0.7	3.39	201 (94)	No	1	1	3	0
Heptylene-2-trans $C_4H_9CH{:}CHCH_3$ (2-Heptene-trans) **31242-93-0**	IB	<32 (<0)				0.7	3.34	208 (98)		1	2	3	0
Hexachlorobutadiene $Cl_2C{:}CClCCl{:}CCl_2$ **87-68-3**			1130 (610)			1.7	8.99	410–428 (210–220)	No		3	1	0
Hexachlorodiphenyl Oxide $(C_6H_2Cl_3)_2O$ [Bis(Trichlorophenyl) Ether] **142-83-6**			1148 (620)				13.0				1	1	1
Hexadecane $CH_3(CH_2)_{14}CH_3$ (Cetane) **544-76-3**	IIIB Note: Melting point 68 (20).	>212 (>100)	396 (202)			0.8 @ 68 (20)	7.8	549 (287)	No	2	1	1	0
tert-Hexadecanethiol $C_{16}H_{33}SH$ (Hexadecyl-tert-Mercaptan) **2917-26-2**		265 (129) (oc)				0.9		298–307 (148–153) @ 11 mm	No	2	0	1	0
1-Hexadecene $CH_3(CH_2)_{13}CH{:}CH_2$ (Hexadecylene-1) **26952-14-7**	IIIB	>212 (>100)	464 (240)			0.78	7.72	525 (274)	No	2	1	1	0
Hexadecyl-tert-Mercaptan	See tert-Hexadecanethiol.												
Hexadecyltrichlorosilane $C_{16}H_{33}SiCl_3$ **5894-60-0**	IIIB	295 (146)				1.0−		516 (269)	Yes	2	3	1	1
2,4-Hexadienal $CH_3CH{:}CHCH{:}CHC(O)H$ **142-83-6**		154 (68) (oc)		1.3	8.1	0.9		339 (171)	Very slight		2	2	0
1,4-Hexadiene $CH_3CH{:}CHCH_2CH{:}CH_2$ (Allylpropenyl) **592-45-0**	IB	−6 (−21)		2.0	6.1	0.7	2.8	151 (66)	No	1	1	3	0
Hexahydroaniline	See Cyclohexylamine.												
Hexahydrobenzene	See Cyclohexane.												
Hexahydropyridine	See Piperidine.												

Chemical Name Formula (Synonym) CAS No.	NFPA 30/ OSHA Class	Flash Point °F(°C)	Ignition Temp. °F(°C)	Flammable Limits Percent by Vol. Lower	Upper	Sp.Gr. (Water =1)	Vapor Density (Air =1)	Boiling Point °F(°C)	Water Soluble	Extin-guishing Methods	Hazard Identification Health	Flamma-bility	Insta-bility
Hexahydrotoluene	See Methylcyclohexane.												
Hexahydroxylol	See 1,4-Dimethylcyclohexane.												
Hexaldehyde	See Hexanal.												
Hexalin	See Cyclohexanol.												
Hexalin Acetate	See Cyclohexyl Acetate.												
Hexamethylene	See Cyclohexane.												
Hexanal $CH_3(CH_2)_4CHO$ (Caproaldehyde) (Hexaldehyde) **66-25-1**		90 (32) (oc)				0.8	3.6	268 (131)	No	1	2	3	1
Hexane $CH_3(CH_2)_4CH_3$ (Hexyl Hydride) **110-54-3**	IB	−7 (−22)	437 (225)	1.1	7.5	0.7	3.0	156 (69)	No	1		3	0
1,2-Hexanediol	See Hexylene Glycol.												
2,5-Hexanediol $CH_3CH(OH)CH_2CH_2$- $CH(OH)CH_3$ (2,5-Dihydroxyhexane) **2935-44-6**	IIIB	230 (110)				1.0−		429 (221)	Yes	2 5	2	1	0
2,5-Hexanedione	See Acetonyl Acetone.												
1,2,6-Hexanetriol $HOCH_2CH(OH)(CH_2)_3$- CH_2OH **106-69-4**		375 (191) (oc)				1.1		352 (178) @ 5 mm	Yes	2 5	1	1	0
Hexanoic Acid	See Caproic Acid.												
1-Hexanol	See Hexyl Alcohol.												
2-Hexanone	See Methyl Butyl Ketone.												
3-Hexanone $C_2H_5COC_3H_7$ (Ethyl n-Propyl Ketone) **589-38-8**		95 (35) (oc)		~1	~8	0.82	3.46	253 (123)		1	1	3	0
1-Hexene $CH_2{:}CH(CH_2)_3CH_3$ (Butyl Ethylene) **592-41-6**	IB	<20 (<−7)	487 (253)	1.2 (est.)		0.7	3.0	146 (63)	No	1	1	3	0
2-Hexene $CH_3CH{:}CH(CH_2)_2CH_3$ **4050-45-7 (trans)**	IB	<20 (<−7)	473 (245)			0.7	3.0	155 (68)	No	1	1	3	0
2-Hexene-cis $C_3H_7CH{:}CHCH_3$ **7688-21-3**	IB	<−4 (<−20)				0.69	2.90	156 (69)		1	0	3	0
3-Hexenol-cis CH_3CH_2CH:- $CHCH_2CH_2OH$ (3-Hexen-l-ol) (Leaf Alcohol) **928-96-1**	II	130 (54)				0.85	3.45	313 (156)	Slight	5	1	2	0
Hexone	See Methyl Isobutyl Ketone.												
Hexyl Acetate $(CH_3)_2CH(CH_2)_3OOCCH_3$ (Methylamyl Acetate) **142-92-7**	II	113 (45)				0.9	5.0	285 (141)	No	5	1	2	0

Chemical Name Formula (Synonym) CAS No.	NFPA 30/ OSHA Class	Flash Point °F(°C)	Ignition Temp. °F(°C)	Flammable Limits Percent by Vol.		Sp.Gr. (Water = 1)	Vapor Density (Air = 1)	Boiling Point °F(°C)	Water Soluble	Extin-guishing Methods	Hazard Identification		
				Lower	Upper						Health	Flamma-bility	Insta-bility
Hexyl Alcohol $CH_3(CH_2)_4CH_2OH$ (Amyl Carbinol) (1-Hexanol) **111-27-3**	IIIA	145 (63)	580 (304) (est.)	1.2 (calc.)	7.7 (calc.)	0.8	3.5	311 (155)	Slight	5	3	2	0
sec-Hexyl Alcohol $C_4H_9CH(OH)CH_3$ (2-Hexanol)	II	136 (58)				0.81	3.53	284 (140)			0	2	0
Hexylamine $CH_3(CH_2)_5NH_2$ **111-26-2**		85 (29) (oc)				0.8	3.5	269 (132)	Slight	1 5	3	3	0
Hexyl Chloride	See 1-Chlorohexane.												
Hexyl Cinnamic Alde-hyde $C_6H_{13}C(CHO):CHC_6H_5$ (Hexyl Cinnamaldehyde) **101-86-0**	IIIB	>212 (>100)				1.0–		486 (252)		5 2	2	1	0
Hexylene Glycol $CH_2OHCHOH(CH_2)_3CH_3$ (1,2-Hexanediol) (2-Methyl-2,4-Pentanediol) **6920-22-5**		205 (96) (oc)	583 (306) (calc.)	1.2	8.1 (calc.)	0.92	4.07	385 (196)	Yes		2	1	0
Hexyl Ether $C_6H_{13}OC_6H_{13}$ (Dihexyl Ether) **112-58-3**		170 (77) (oc)	365 (185)			0.8	6.4	440 (227)	No			2	0
Hexyl Hydride	See Hexane.												
Hexyl Methacrylate $C_6H_{13}OOCC(CH_3):CH_2$ **142-09-6**		180 (82) (oc)				0.9	5.9	388–464 (198–240)			0	2	0
Hexyl Methyl Ketone	See Methyl Hexyl Ketone.												
Hydracrylonitrile	See Ethylene Cyanohydrin.												
Hydralin	See Cyclohexanol.												
Hydrazine (anhydrous) H_2NNH_2 **302-01-2**	II		100 (38)	2.9	98	1.0+	1.1	236 (113)	Yes		4	4	3
	Note: Vapors explosive. Ignition temperatures vary widely in contact with iron rust 74 (23); black iron 270 (132); stainless steel 313 (156); glass 518 (270). See NFPA 49 contained in this guide.												
Hydrochloric Ether	See Ethyl Chloride.												
Hydrocyanic Acid, 96% HCN (Prussic Acid) (Hydrogen Cyanide) **74-90-8**	IA	0 (–18)	1000 (538)	5.6	40.0	0.7	0.9	79 (26)	Yes	1	4	4	1
	Note: Vapors extremely toxic. See NFPA 49 contained in this guide.												
Hydrogen H_2 **1333-74-0**		Gas	932 (500)	4.0	75		0.1	–422 (–252)	Slight	6	0	4	0
	See NFPA 49 contained in this guide.												
Hydrogen Cyanide	See Hydrocyanic Acid.												
Hydrogen Sulfide H_2S **7783-06-4**		Gas	500 (260)	4.0	44.0		1.2	–76 (–60)	Yes	6	4	4	0
	See NFPA 49 contained in this guide.												
Hydroquinone $C_6H_4(OH)_2$ (HQ) (Quinol) (Hydroquinol) (p-Dihydroxybenzene) **123-31-9**	IIIB	329 (165)	960 (516)			1.3	3.81	547 (286)	No	5 2	2	1	0
	Note: Melting point is 338 (170).												
Hydroquinone Di-(β-Hydroxyethyl) Ether $C_6H_4(\text{-}OCH_2CH_2OH)_2$ **104-38-1**	IIIB	435 (224)	875 (468)					365–392 (185–200) @ 0.3 mm	Slight	2		1	0
	Note: Melting point 201–205 (94–96).												

Chemical Name Formula (Synonym) CAS No.	NFPA 30/ OSHA Class	Flash Point °F(°C)	Ignition Temp. °F(°C)	Flammable Limits Percent by Vol. Lower	Upper	Sp.Gr. (Water =1)	Vapor Density (Air =1)	Boiling Point °F(°C)	Water Soluble	Extin-guishing Methods	Hazard Identification Health	Flamma-bility	Insta-bility
Hydroquinone Monomethyl Ether $CH_3OC_6H_4OH$ (HQMME) (4-Methoxy Phenol) (Para-Hydroxyanisole) **150-76-5**		270 (132) (oc)	790 (421)			1.5		475 (246)	No	2	2	1	0
	Note: Melting point 126 (52).												
o-Hydroxybenzaldehyde	See Salicylaldehyde.												
3-Hydroxybutanal	See Aldol.												
β-Hydroxybutyraldehyde	See Aldol.												
Hydroxycitronellal $(CH_3)_2C(OH)(CH_2)_3CH(CH_3)CH_2CHO$ (Citronellal Hydrate) (3,7-Dimethyl-7-Hydroxyoctanal) **107-75-5**	IIIB	>212 (>100)				0.9		201–205 (94–96) @ 1 mm	Slight	5 2	1	1	0
N-(2-Hydroxyethyl)-acetamide	See N-Acetyl Ethanolamine.												
2-Hydroxyethyl Acrylate (HEA), Ethylene Glycol Monoacrylate **818-61-1**	IIIB	214 (101)		1.8 @ 100°C		1.1		410 (210)	Yes	2	3	1	2
β-Hydroxyethylaniline	See 2-Anilinoethanol.												
N-(2-Hydroxyethyl) Cyclohexylamine $C_6H_{11}NHC_2H_4OH$ **2842-38-8**		249 (121) (oc)							Yes	2 5	3	1	0
	Note: Melting point 97–102 (36–39).												
(2-Hydroxyethyl)-Ethylenediamine	See (2-Aminoethyl) Ethanolamine.												
4-(2-Hydroxyethyl) Morpholine $C_2H_4OC_2H_4NC_2H_4OH$ **622-40-2**		210 (99) (oc)				1.1		437 (225)	Yes	5	2	1	0
1-(2-Hydroxyethyl) Piperazine $HOCH_2CH_2NCH_2$- $CH_2NHCH_2CH_2$ **103-76-4**		255 (124) (oc)				1.1	4.5	475 (246)	Yes	2 5	0	1	0
n-(2-Hydroxyethyl) Propylenediamine $CH_3CH(NHC_2H_4OH)$- CH_2NH_2		260 (127) (oc)				1.0–		465 (241)	Yes	2 5	2	1	0
Hydroxylamine NH_2OH (Oxammonium) **7803-49-8**		Ex- plodes@ 265 (129)				1.2	1.1 (calc.)	158 (70)	Yes		2		
	Note: Melting point 92 (33). See NFPA 49 contained in this guide.												
4-Hydroxy-4-Methyl-2-Pentanone	See Diacetone Alcohol.												
2-Hydroxy-2-methylpropionitrile	See Acetone Cyanohydrin.												
Hydroxypropyl Acrylate	See Propylene Glycol Monoacrylate.												
o-Hydroxytoluene	See o-Cresol.												
Indan C_9H_{16} (Hexahydroindane) (Octahydroindene) (Hydrindene) **496-11-7**			565 (296)			0.9		318 (159)		5	1	2	0

Chemical Name Formula (Synonym) CAS No.	NFPA 30/ OSHA Class	Flash Point °F(°C)	Ignition Temp. °F(°C)	Flammable Limits Percent by Vol. Lower	Upper	Sp.Gr. (Water =1)	Vapor Density (Air =1)	Boiling Point °F(°C)	Water Soluble	Extin-guishing Methods	Hazard Identification Health	Flamma-bility	Insta-bility
α-Ionone $C(CH_3)_2CH_2CH_2$- $CH{:}C(CH_3)CHCH$:- $CHC(CH_3){:}O$ (α-Cyclocitry-lideneacetone) [4-(2,6,6-Trimethyl-2-Cyclohexen-1-yl)-3-Buten-2-one]	IIIB	>212 (>100)				0.9		259–262 (126–128) @ 12 mm	Slight	5 2		1	0
β-Ionone $C(CH_3)_2CH_2CH_2CH_2C$- $(CH_3){:}CCHCHC$- $(CH_3){:}O$ (β-Cyclocitry-lideneacetone) [4-(2,6,6-Trimethyl-1-Cyclohexen-1-yl)-3-Buten-2-one] **14901-07-6**	IIIB	>212 (>100)				0.9		284 (140) @ 18 mm	No	5 2		1	0
Iron Carbonyl $Fe(CO)_5$ **13463-40-6**	IB	5 (−15)				1.45	6.74	221 (105)			1	3	1
Isano Oil Note: Exothermic reaction above 502 (261); may become explosive.						1.0–						1	3
Isoamyl Acetate $CH_3COOCH_2CH_2CH$- $(CH_3)_2$ (Banana Oil) (3-Methyl-1-Butanol Acetate) (2-Methyl Butyl Ethanoate) **123-92-2**	IC	77 (25)	680 (360)	1.0 @ 212 (100)	7.5	0.9	4.5	290 (143)	Slight	5 1	1	3	0
Isoamyl Alcohol $(CH_3)_2CHCH_2CH_2OH$ (Isobutyl Carbinol) (Fusel Oil) (3-Methyl-1-Butanol) **123-51-3**	II	109 (43)	662 (350)	1.2	9.0 @ 212 (100)	0.8	3.0	270 (132)	Slight	5	1	2	0
tert-Isoamyl Alcohol	See 2-Methyl-2-Butanol.												
Isoamyl Butyrate $C_3H_7CO_2(CH_2)_2CH(CH_3)_2$ (Isopentyl Butyrate) **106-27-4**	II	138 (59)				0.88	5.45	352 (178)			1	2	0
Isoamyl Chloride $(CH_3)_2CHCH_2CH_2Cl$ (1-Chloro-3-Methylbutane) **107-84-6**	IB	<70 (<21)		1.5	7.4	0.89	3.67	212 (100)		1		3	
Isoamyl Nitrite $CH_3(CH_2)_4NO_2$ (Amyl nitrite) **110-46-3**	IB	50 (10)	410 (210)			0.9	4.0	220 (104)	Slight	5	2	3	2
Isobornyl Acetate $C_{10}H_{17}OOCCH_3$ **125-12-2**	IIIA	190 (88)				1.0–		428–435 (220–224)	No	5	1	2	0
Isobutane $(CH_3)_3CH$ (2-Methylpropane) **75-28-5**		Gas	860 (460)	1.8	8.4		2.0	11 (−12)	No	6	0	4	0
Isobutyl Acetate $CH_3COOCH_2CH(CH_3)_2$ (β-Methyl Propyl Ethanoate) **110-19-0**	IB	64 (18)	790 (421)	1.3	10.5	0.9	4.0	244 (118)	No	5 1	1	3	0

Chemical Name Formula (Synonym) CAS No.	NFPA 30/ OSHA Class	Flash Point °F(°C)	Ignition Temp. °F(°C)	Flammable Limits Percent by Vol.		Sp.Gr. (Water =1)	Vapor Density (Air =1)	Boiling Point °F(°C)	Water Soluble	Extin-guishing Methods	Hazard Identification		
				Lower	Upper						Health	Flamma-bility	Insta-bility
Isobutyl Acrylate $(CH_3)_2CHCH_2$- $OOCCH:CH_2$ **106-63-8**		86 (30) (oc)	800 (427)			0.9	4.42	142–145 (61–63) @ 15 mm	No	5 1	2	3	2
Isobutyl Alcohol $(CH_3)_2CHCH_2OH$ (Isopropyl Carbinol) (2-Methyl-1-Propanol) **78-83-1**	IC	82 (28)	780 (415)	1.7 @ 123(51)	10.6@ 202(94)	0.8	2.6	225 (107)	Yes	5 1	2	3	0
Isobutylamine $(CH_3)_2CHCH_2NH_2$ **78-81-9**	IB	15 (−9)	712 (378)	3.4	9	0.7	2.5	150 (66)	Yes	5 1	3	3	0
Isobutylbenzene $(CH_3)_2CHCH_2C_6H_5$ **538-93-2**	II	131 (55)	802 (427)	0.8	6.0	0.9	4.6	343 (173)	No		1	2	0
Isobutyl Butyrate $C_3H_7CO_2CH_2CH(CH_3)_2$ **539-90-2**	II	122 (50)				0.87	5.0	315 (157)			1	2	
Isobutyl Carbinol	See Isoamyl Alcohol.												
Isobutyl Chloride $(CH_3)_2CHCH_2Cl$ (1-Chloro-3- Methylpropane) **513-36-0**	IB	<70 (<21)		2.0	8.8	0.9	3.2	156 (69)			1	3	0
Isobutylcyclohexane $(CH_3)_2CHCH_2C_6H_{11}$			525 (274)			0.8		336 (169)			0		0
Isobutylene	See 2-Methylpropene.												
Isobutyl Formate $HCOOCH_2CH(CH_3)_2$ **542-55-2**	IB	<70 (<21)	608 (320)	~1.7	~8	0.88	3.52	208 (98)			2	3	0
Isobutyl Heptyl Ketone $(CH_3)_2CHCH_2COCH_2CH$- $(CH_3)CH_2CH(CH_3)_2$ (2,6,8-Trimethyl-4- Nonanone) **19594-40-2**		195 (91) (oc)	770 (410)			0.8		412–426 (211–219)	No	5	2	2	0
Isobutyl Isobutyrate $(CH_3)_2CHCOOCH_2CH$- $(CH_3)_2$ **97-85-8**	II	101 (38)	810 (432)	0.96	7.59	0.9	4.97	291–304 (144–151)	No	5	0	3	0
Isobutyl Phenylacetate $(CH_3)_2CHCH_2$- $OOCCH_2C_6H_5$ **120-13-6**	IIIB	>212 (>100)				1.0		477 (247)		5 2	0	1	0
Isobutyl Phosphate $PO_4(CH_2CH(CH_3)_2)_3$ (Triisobutyl Phosphate) **126-71-6**		275 (135) (oc)				0.98	9.12	302 (150) @ 20 mm		2	1	1	0
Isobutyl Vinyl Ether	See Vinyl Isobutyl Ether.												
Isobutyraldehyde $(CH_3)_2CHCHO$ (2-Methylpropanal) **78-84-2**	IB	−1 (−18)	385 (196)	1.6	10.6	0.8	2.5	142 (61)	Slight	5 1	2	3	1
Isobutyric Acid $(CH_3)_2CHCOOH$ **79-31-2**	II	132 (56)	900 (481)	2.0	9.2	1.0–	3	306 (152)	Yes	5	3	2	0
Isobutyric Anhydride $[(CH_3)_2CHCO]_2O$ **97-72-3**	II	139 (59)	625 (329)	1.0	6.2	1.0–	5.5	360 (182)	Decom- poses	5	3	2	1

Chemical Name Formula (Synonym) CAS No.	NFPA 30/ OSHA Class	Flash Point °F(°C)	Ignition Temp. °F(°C)	Flammable Limits Percent by Vol.		Sp.Gr. (Water =1)	Vapor Density (Air =1)	Boiling Point °F(°C)	Water Soluble	Extin-guishing Methods	Hazard Identification		
				Lower	Upper						Health	Flamma-bility	Insta-bility
Isobutyronitrile $(CH_3)_2CHCN$ (2-Methylpropanenitrile) (Isopropylcyanide) **78-82-0**	IB	47 (8)	900 (482)			0.8	2.38	214–216 (101–102)	Slight	5 1	3	3	0
Isodecaldehyde $C_9H_{19}CO$		185 (85) (oc)				0.8	5.4	387 (197)	No		0	2	0
Isodecanes, Mixed $C_7H_{15}CH(CH_3)_2$ (2-Methylnonane)			410 (210)			0.73	4.91	333 (167)			1	2	0
Isodecanoic Acid $C_9H_{19}COOH$ **26403-17-8**		300 (149) (oc)				0.9	5.9	489 (254)	No	2	0	1	0
Isodecanol $C_{10}H_{21}OH$		220 (104) (oc)				0.8	5.5	428 (220)	No	2	0	1	0
Isoeugenol $(CH_3CHCH)C_6H_3O$- $HOCH_3$ (1-Hydroxy-2-Methoxy- 4-Propenylbenzene) **97-53-0 and 97-54-1**	IIIB	>212 (>100)				1.1		514 (268)	No	5 2	2	2	0
Isoheptane $(CH_3)_2CHC_4H_9$ (Ethylisobutylmethane) (2-Methylhexane) **591-76-4**	IB	<0 (−18)	536 (280)	1.0	6.0	0.7	3.45	194 (90)	No	1	1	3	0
Isoheptane, Mixed Isomers	IB	<0 (<−18)	428 (220)	1.0	6.0	0.7		176–195 (80–91)	No	1	1	3	0
Isohexane (Mixture of Hexane Isomers) **107-83-5** **73513-42-5**	IB	<−20 (<−29)	507 (264)	1.0	7.0	0.7		134–142 (57–61)	No	1	1	3	0
tert-Isohexyl Alcohol $C_2H_5(CH_3)C(OH)C_2H_5$ (3-Methyl-3-Pentanol)	II	115 (46)				0.77	3.53	252 (122)				2	0
Isooctane $(CH_3)_2CHCH_2C(CH_3)_3$ (2,2,4-Trimethylpentane) **592-27-8**		40 (4.5) (oc)	784 (418)			0.7	3.94	210 (99)	No	1	1	3	0
Isooctanoic Acid $C_6H_{15}COOH$ **25103-52-0**		270 (132) (oc)	738 (392)			0.9	5.0	428 (220) Decomposes	No	2	1	1	0
Isooctenes C_8H_{16} **11071-47-9**	IB	<20 (−7)				0.7	3.87	190–200 (88–93)		1	1	3	0
Isooctyl Alcohol $C_7H_{15}CH_2OH$ (Isooctanol) **26952-21-6**		180 (82) (oc)	530 (277) (est.)	0.9		0.8		83–91 (182–195)	No	5	3	2	0
Isooctyl Nitrate $C_8H_{17}NO_3$		205 (96) (oc)				1.0 –		106–109 (41–43) @ 1 mm	No			1	
Isooctyl Vinyl Ether	See Vinyl Isooctyl Ether.												
Isopentaldehyde $(CH_3)_2CHCH_2CHO$ (Isovaleraldehyde) **590-86-3**		48 (9) (oc)	464 (240)	1.7	6.8	0.8	2.97	194 (90)	Slight	5 1	1	3	0
Isopentane $(CH_3)_2CHCH_2CH_3$ (2-Methylbutane) (Ethyl Dimethyl Methane) **78-78-4**	IA	<−60 (<−51)	788 (420)	1.4	7.6	0.6	2.5	82 (28)	No	1	1	4	0

Chemical Name Formula (Synonym) CAS No.	NFPA 30/ OSHA Class	Flash Point °F(°C)	Ignition Temp. °F(°C)	Flammable Limits Percent by Vol. Lower	Upper	Sp.Gr. (Water =1)	Vapor Density (Air =1)	Boiling Point °F(°C)	Water Soluble	Extin-guishing Methods	Hazard Identification Health	Flamma-bility	Insta-bility
Isopentanoic Acid $(CH_3)_2CHCH_2COOH$ (Isovaleric Acid) **503-74-2**			781 (416)			0.9		361 (183)	No		3	2	0
Isophorone $COCHC(CH_3)CH_2C$- $(CH_3)_2CH_2$	IIIA	184 (84)	860 (460)	0.8	3.8	0.9	4.75	419 (215)	Slight		2	2	1
78-59-1	See NFPA 49 contained in this guide.												
Isophthaloyl Chloride $C_6H_4(COCl)_2$ (m-Phthalyl Dichloride)		356 (180) (oc)				1.4	6.9	529 (276)	No	2	2	1	1
99-63-8	Note: Melting point 109.9 (43).												
Isoprene $CH_2{:}C(CH_3)CH{:}CH_2$ (2-Methyl-1,3-Butadiene)	IA	−65 (−54)	743 (395)	1.5	8.9	0.7	2.4	93 (34)	No	1	1	4	2
78-79-5	See NFPA 49 contained in this guide.												
Isopropanol	See Isopropyl Alcohol.												
Isopropanolamine	See 1-Amino-2-Propanol.												
Isopropenyl Acetate $CH_3COOC(CH_3){:}CH_2$ (1-Methylvinyl Acetate) **108-22-5**	IB	60 (16)	808 (431)			0.9	3.5	207 (97)	Slight	5 1	1	3	1
Isopropenyl Acetylene $CH_2{:}C(CH_3)C{:}CH$ **78-80-8**		<19 (<−7) (oc)				0.7	2.3	92 (33)	Slight	1 5	1	4	2
2-Isopropoxypropane	See Isopropyl Ether.												
3-Isopropoxypropio-nitrile $(CH_3)_2CHOCH_2CH_2CN$ **110-47-4**	IIIA	155 (68)				0.9	3.9	149 (65)@ 10 mm	Slight	5	1	2	1
Isopropyl Acetate $(CH_3)_2CHOOCCH_3$ **108-21-4**	IB	35 (2)	860 (460)	1.8 @100 (38)	8	0.9	3.5	194 (90)	Slight	5 1	2	3	0
Isopropyl Alcohol, 88% $(CH_3)_2CHOH$ (Isopropanol) (Dimethyl Carbinol) (2-Propanol) **67-63-0**	IB	53 (12) 57 (14)	750 (399)	2.0	12.7 @ 200(93)	0.8	2.1	181 (83)	Yes	5 1	1	3	0
Isopropylamine $(CH_3)_2CHNH_2$		−35 (−37) (oc)	756 (402)	2.0	10.4	0.7	2.0	89 (32)	Yes	5 1	3	4	0
75-31-0	See NFPA 49 contained in this guide.												
Isopropylbenzene	See Cumene.												
Isopropyl Benzoate $C_6H_5COOCH(CH_3)_2$ **939-48-0**	IIIB	210 (99)				1.0+		426 (219)	No		1	1	0
Isopropyl Bicyclohexyl $C_{15}H_{28}$	IIIB	255 (124)	446 (230)	0.5 @302 (150)	4.1 @400 (204)	0.9		530–541 (277–283)		2	0	1	0
2-Isopropylbiphenyl $C_{15}H_{16}$ **25640-78-2**	IIIB	285 (141)	815 (435)	0.5 @347 (175)	3.2 @392 (200)	1.0−		518 (270)		2	0	1	0
Isopropyl Carbinol	See Isobutyl Alcohol.												
Isopropyl Chloride $(CH_3)_2CHCl$ (2-Chloropropane) **75-29-6**	IA	−26 (−32)	1100 (593)	2.8	10.7	0.9	2.7	95 (35)	Very slight	1	2	4	0

Chemical Name Formula (Synonym) CAS No.	NFPA 30/ OSHA Class	Flash Point °F(°C)	Ignition Temp. °F(°C)	Flammable Limits Percent by Vol. Lower	Flammable Limits Percent by Vol. Upper	Sp.Gr. (Water =1)	Vapor Density (Air =1)	Boiling Point °F(°C)	Water Soluble	Extin-guishing Methods	Hazard Identification Health	Hazard Identification Flamma-bility	Hazard Identification Insta-bility
Isopropylcyclohexane $(CH_3)_2CHC_6H_{11}$ (Hexahydrocumene) (Normanthane) **696-29-7**		96 (35)	541 (283)			0.8		310 (154.5)			1		0
Isopropylcyclohexy-lamine $C_6H_{11}NHCHC_2H_6$ **1195-42-2**		93 (34) (oc)				0.8	4.9	140–149 (60–65) @ 12 mm	No	1	3	3	0
Isopropyl Ether $(CH_3)_2CHOCH(CH_3)_2$ (2-Isopropoxypropane) (Diisopropyl Ether) **108-20-3**	IB	−18 (−28)	830 (443)	1.4	7.9	0.7	3.5	156 (69)	Very slight	5 1	2	3	1
	See NFPA 49 contained in this guide.												
Isopropylethylene	See 3-Methyl-1-Butene.												
Isopropyl Formate $HCOOCH(CH_3)_2$ (Isopropyl Methanoate) **625-55-8**	IB	22 (−6)	905 (485)			0.9	3.0	153 (67)	Slight	1	1	3	0
	See NFPA 49 contained in this guide.												
4-Isopropylheptane $C_3H_7CH(C_3H_7)C_3H_7$ (m-Dihydroxybenzene)			491 (255)			0.87	3.04	155 (68)			0	2	0
Isopropyl-2-Hydroxypropanoate	See Isopropyl Lactate.												
Isopropyl Lactate $CH_3CHOHCOCH(CH_3)_2$ (Isopropyl-2-Hydroxypropionate) **617-51-6**		130 (54) (oc)				1.0 –	4.2	331–334 (166– 168)	Yes	5	2	2	0
Isopropyl Methanoate	See Isopropyl Formate.												
4-Isopropyl-1-Methyl Benzene	See p-Cymene.												
Isopropyl Vinyl Ether	See Vinyl Isopropyl Ether.												
Isovalerone	See Diisobutyl Ketone.												
Jet Fuels Jet A and Jet A-1		110–150 (43–66)						400–550 (204–288)			0	2	0
Jet Fuels Jet B		−10 to +30 (−23 to −1)								1	1	3	0
Jet Fuels JP-4	IB	−10 to +30 (−23 to −1)	464 (240)	1.3	8.0	0.75-0.18		140–518 (60–270)	No	1	3	3	0
Jet Fuels JP-5		95–145 (35–63)	475 (246) (approx.)								2	2	0
Jet Fuels JP-6		100 (38) (oc)	446 (230)	0.6	3.7	0.8	<1	250 (121)	No				
Katchung Oil	See Peanut Oil (cooking).												
Kerosene	See Fuel Oil No. 1.												
Kerosene, Deodorized (Ultrasene) **8008-20-6**	IIIA	175 (79)							No		1	2	0
Lactonitrile $CH_3CH(OH)CN$ **78-97-3**	IIIA	171 (77)				0.98	2.45	361 (183)	Yes		4	2	0

Chemical Name Formula (Synonym) CAS No.	NFPA 30/ OSHA Class	Flash Point °F(°C)	Ignition Temp. °F(°C)	Flammable Limits Percent by Vol. Lower	Upper	Sp.Gr. (Water =1)	Vapor Density (Air =1)	Boiling Point °F(°C)	Water Soluble	Extin-guishing Methods	Hazard Identification Health	Flamma-bility	Insta-bility
Lanolin (Wool Grease) **8006-54-0**	IIIB	460 (238)	833 (445)			<1			No	2	1	1	0
Lard Oil (Commercial or Animal) No. 1 **8016-28-2**	IIIB	395 (202) 440 (227)	833 (445)			<1			No	2	1	1	0
Lard Oil (Pure) No. 2, Mineral	IIIB	500 (260) 419 (215) 404 (207)				0.9			No	2	1	1	0
Lauryl Alcohol	See 1-Dodecanol.												
Lauryl Bromide $CH_3(CH_2)_{10}CH_2Br$ (Dodecyl Bromide) **143-15-7**	IIIB	291 (144)				1.0+		356 (180) @ 45 mm	No	2	1	1	0
Lauryl Mercaptan	See 1-Dodecanethiol.												
Linalool, Synthetic $(CH_3)_2C{:}CHCH_2CH_2C$-(CH_3)OHCA:CH_2 (3,7-Dimethyl-1,6-Octadiene-3,1) (Linalol) (Linalyl Alcohol) **78-70-6**	IIIA	160 (71)	455 (235)	0.9	5.2	0.9		383–390 (195–199)	No	5	1	2	0
Linseed Oil, Raw Boiled **8001-26-1**	IIIB	432 (222) 403 (206)	650 (343)			0.9		600+ (316+)	No	2	1	1	0
Liquid Camphor	See Camphor Oil (light).												
Lubricating Oil, Mineral (C20-C50) (Paraffin Oil, includes Motor Oil) **72623-85-9**	IIIB	300–450 (149–232)	500-700 (260-371)			<1		576–1099 (302–593)	No	2	1	1	0
Lubricating Oil, Spindle (Spindle Oil)	IIIA	169 (76)	478 (248)			<1			No		0	2	0
Lubricating Oil, Turbine (Turbine Oil)		400 (204) (oc)	700 (371)			<1			No	2	0	1	0
Lynalyl Acetate, Synthetic $(CH_3)_2C{:}CHCH_2CH_2C$-(-OOCCH_3)CH:CH_2 (Bergamol) **115-95-7**	IIIA	185 (85)				0.9		226–230 (108–110)	No	5	2	2	0
Maleic Anhydride $(COCH)_2O$ **108-31-6**	IIIB	215 (102)	890 (477)	1.4	7.1	0.9		396 (202)	Slight	5 2	3	1	1
	Note: Melting point 127 (53). See NFPA 49 contained in this guide.												
Marsh Gas	See Methane.												
Menhaden Oil (Pogy Oil) **8002-50-4** **68605-68-5**	IIIB	435 (224)	828 (442)			0.9			No	2	0	1	0
2-Mercaptoethanol $HSCH_2CH_2OH$ **60-24-2**		165 (74) (oc)				1.1	2.7	315 (157)	Yes	5	3	2	1
Mesitylene	See 1,3,5-Trimethylbenzene.												
Mesityl Oxide $(CH_3)_2C{:}CHCOCH_3$ **141-79-7**	IC	87 (31)	652 (344)	1.4	7.2	0.9	3.4	266 (130)	Slight	1 5	3	3	1
	See NFPA 49 contained in this guide.												

Chemical Name Formula (Synonym) CAS No.	NFPA 30/ OSHA Class	Flash Point °F(°C)	Ignition Temp. °F(°C)	Flammable Limits Percent by Vol. Lower	Upper	Sp.Gr. (Water =1)	Vapor Density (Air =1)	Boiling Point °F(°C)	Water Soluble	Extin-guishing Methods	Hazard Identification Health	Flamma-bility	Insta-bility
Metaldehyde $(C_2H_4O)_4$ **108-62-3**	IC	97 (36)						Sublimes @ 233–240 (112–116)	No	1	3	3	1
α-Methacrolein	See 2-Methylpropenal.												
Methacrylic Acid CH_2:$C(CH_3)COOH$ **79-41-4**	IIIA	153 (67)	752 (400)	1.6	8.8	1.0+	2.97	316 (158)	Yes	5	3	2	2
	Note: Polymerizes. Melting point 61 (16). See NFPA 49 contained in this guide.												
Methacrylonitrile C_4H_5N **126-98-7**	IB	34 (1.1) (TCC)		2	6.8	0.8	2.3	194 (90)	Slight	1	4	3	2
Methallyl Alcohol $CH_2C(CH_3)CH_2OH$ **513-42-8**	IC	92 (33)				0.9	2.5	237 (114)	Slight	1 5	2	3	0
Methallyl Chloride $CH_2C(CH_3)CH_2Cl$ **563-47-3**	IB	11 (−12)		3.2	8.1	0.9	3.1	162 (72)	No	1 5	1	3	1
Methane CH_4 (Marsh Gas) **74-82-8**		Gas	999 (537)	5.0	15.0		0.6	–259 (–162)	No	6	2	4	0
Methanol	See Methyl Alcohol.												
Methanethiol	See Methyl Mercaptan.												
Methox	See Methoxyethyl Phthalate.												
o-Methoxy-benzaldehyde $CH_3OC_6H_4CHO$ (o-Anisaldehyde) **135-02-4**	IIIB	243 (117)				1.1		457–471 (236–244)	No	2	1	1	0
	Note: Melting point 95–100 (35–38)												
Methoxybenzene	See Anisole.												
3-Methoxybutanol $CH_3CH(OCH_3)CH_2$-CH_2OH **2517-43-3**		165 (74) (oc)				0.9	3.6	322 (161)	Yes	5	2	2	0
3-Methoxybutyl Acetate $CH_3OCH(CH_3)CH_2$-CH_2OOCCH_3 (Butoxyl) **4435-53-4**	IIIA	170 (77)				1.0−	5.0	275–343 (135–173)	Slight	5	1	2	1
3-Methoxy-butyraldehyde $CH_3CH(OCH_3)CH_2CHO$ (Aldol Ether)	IIIA	140 (60)				0.94	3.52	262 (128)			0	2	0
2-Methoxyethanol	See Ethylene Glycol Methyl Ether.												
2-Methoxyethyl Acrylate $C_2H_3COOC_2H_4OCH_3$ **3121-61-7**		180 (82) (oc)				1.01	4.49	142 (61) @ 17 mm			3	2	2
Methoxyethyl Phthalate (Methox) **117-82-8**	IIIB	275 (135)				1.2		376–412 (191–211)		2	1	1	0
3-Methoxypropionitrile $CH_3OC_2H_4CN$ **110-67-8**		149 (65) (oc)				0.92	2.94	320 (160)			3	2	1
3-Methoxypropylamine $CH_3OC_3H_6NH_2$ **5332-73-0**	IC	90 (32)				0.86	3.07	241 (116)		1	3	3	0

Chemical Name Formula (Synonym) CAS No.	NFPA 30/ OSHA Class	Flash Point °F(°C)	Ignition Temp. °F(°C)	Flammable Limits Percent by Vol.		Sp.Gr. (Water =1)	Vapor Density (Air =1)	Boiling Point °F(°C)	Water Soluble	Extin-guishing Methods	Hazard Identification		
				Lower	Upper						Health	Flamma-bility	Insta-bility
Methoxy Triglycol $CH_3O(C_2H_4O)_3H$ (Triethylene Glycol Methyl Ether) **112-35-6**		245 (118) (oc)				1.0+		480 (249)	Yes	5 2	1	1	0
Methoxytriglycol Acetate $CH_3COO(C_2H_4O)_3CH_3$ **3610-27-3**		260 (127) (oc)				1.1		266 (130)	Yes	2 5	0	1	0
Methyl Abietate $C_{19}H_{29}COOCH_3$ (Abalyn) **127-25-3**		356 (180) (oc)				1.0+		680–689 (360–365) Decomposes	No	2	2	1	0
Methyl Acetate CH_3COOCH_3 (Acetic Acid Methyl Ester) (Methyl Acetic Ester) **79-20-9**	IB	14 (−10)	850 (454)	3.1	16	0.9	2.8	140 (60)	Yes	1 5	2	3	0
Methyl Acetic Ester	See Methyl Acetate.												
Methyl Acetoacetate $CH_3CO_2CH_2COCH_3$ **105-45-3**	IIIA	170 (77)	536 (280)	3.1	16	1.1	4.0	338 (170)	Yes	5	2	2	0
p-Methyl Acetophe-none $CH_3C_6H_4COCH_3$ (Methyl para-Tolyl Ketone) (p-Acetotoluene) **122-00-9**	IIIB	205 (96)				1.0−		439 (226)	No	5	1	1	0
Methylacetylene	See Propyne.												
α-Methylacrolein	See 2-Methylpropenal.												
Methyl Acrylate $CH_2{:}CHCOOCH_3$ **96-33-3**		27 (−3) (oc)	875 (468)	2.8	25	1.0−	3.0	176 (80)	Very slight	1	3	3	2
	Note: Polymerizes. See NFPA 49 contained in this guide.												
Methylal $CH_3OCH_2OCH_3$ (Dimethoxymethane) (Formal) **109-87-5**		−26 (−32) (oc)	459 (237)	2.2	13.8	0.9	2.6	111 (44)	Yes	1 5	1	3	1
Methyl Alcohol CH_3OH (Methanol) (Wood Alcohol) (Columbian Spirits) **67-56-1**	IB	52 (11)	867 (464)	6.0	36	0.8	1.1	147 (64)	Yes	1 5	1	3	0
Methylaluminum Sesquibromide $(CH_3)_3Al_2Br_3$ **12263-85-3**	Note: Ignites spontaneously in air.										3	4	3 ₩
Methylaluminum Sesquichloride $(CH_3)_3Al_2Cl_3$ **12542-85-7**	Note: Ignites spontaneously in air.										3	4	3 ₩
Methylamine CH_3NH_2 **74-89-5**		Gas	806 (430)	4.9	20.7		1.0	21 (−6)	Yes	6	3	4	0
	See NFPA 49 contained in this guide.												
2-(Methylamino) Ethanol	See N-Methylethanolamine.												
Methylamyl Acetate	See Hexyl Acetate.												
Methylamyl Alcohol	See 2-Methyl-1-Pentanol.												

Chemical Name Formula (Synonym) CAS No.	NFPA 30/ OSHA Class	Flash Point °F(°C)	Ignition Temp. °F(°C)	Flammable Limits Percent by Vol.		Sp.Gr. (Water =1)	Vapor Density (Air =1)	Boiling Point °F(°C)	Water Soluble	Extin- guishing Methods	Hazard Identification		
				Lower	Upper						Health	Flamma- bility	Insta- bility
Methyl Amyl Ketone $CH_3CO(CH_2)_4CH_3$ 2-Heptanone **110-43-0**	II	102 (39)	740 (393)	1.1 @ 151(66)	7.9 @ 250 (121)	0.8	3.9	302 (150)	Slight	5	1	2	0
2-Methylaniline	See o-Toluidine.												
4-Methylaniline	See p-Toluidine.												
Methyl Anthranilate $H_2NC_6H_4CO_2CH_3$ (Methyl-o-Amino Benzo-ate) (Nevoli Oil, Artificial) **134-20-3**	IIIB	>212 (>100)				1.2		275 @ 15 mm (135)	Slight	5 2	1	1	0
Methylbenzene	See Toluol.												
Methyl Benzoate $C_6H_5COOCH_3$ (Niobe Oil) **93-58-3**	IIIA	181 (83)				1.1	4.7	302 (150)	No	3	1	2	0
α-Methylbenzyl Alcohol	See Phenyl Methyl Carbinol.												
α-Methylbenzylamine $C_6H_5CH(CH_3)NH_2$ **98-89-0**		175 (79) (oc)				1.0−	4.2	371 (188)	Slight	5	2	2	0
α-Methylbenzyl Dimethyl Amine $C_6H_5CH(CH_3)N(CH_3)_2$ **2449-49-2**		175 (79) (oc)				0.9	5.2	384 (196)	Slight	5	2	2	0
α-Methylbenzyl Ether $C_6H_5CH(CH_3)OCH(CH_3)C_6H_5$ **93-96-9** **538-86-3**		275 (135) (oc)				1.0		548 (287)	No	2 5	2	1	0
2-Methylbiphenyl $C_6H_5C_6H_4CH_3$ **28682-72-4**		280 (137) (oc)	936 (502)			1.0+		492 (255)		2	2		0
Methyl Borate $B(OCH_3)_3$ (Trimethyl Borate) **121-43-7**		<80 (<27)				0.9	3.6	156 (69)	Decom- poses	1	1	3	1
Methyl Bromide CH_3Br (Bromomethane) **74-83-9**	See NFPA 49 contained in this guide.	Practically nonflamm- able	999 (537)	10	16.0	1.7	3.3	38.4 (4)	No		3	1	0
2-Methyl-1,3-Butadiene	See Isoprene.												
2-Methylbutane	See Isopentane.												
3-Methyl-2-Butanethiol $C_5H_{11}SH$ (sec-Isoamyl Mercaptan) **2084-18-6**		37 (3) (oc)				0.85	3.59	230 (110)	No	5 1	2	3	0
2-Methyl-1-Butanol $CH_3CH_2CH(CH_3)CH_2OH$ **137-32-6**		122 (50) (oc)	725 (385)			0.8	3.0	262 (128)	Slight	5	3	2	0
2-Methyl-2-Butanol $CH_3CH_2(CH_3)_2COH$ (tert-Isoamyl Alcohol) (Dimethyl Ethyl Carbinol) **75-85-4**	IB	67 (19)	819 (437)	1.2	9.0	0.8	3.0	215 (102)	Slight	5 1	1	3	0
3-Methyl-1-Butanol	See Isoamyl Alcohol.												
3-Methyl-1-Butanol Acetate	See Isoamyl Acetate.												

Chemical Name Formula (Synonym) CAS No.	NFPA 30/ OSHA Class	Flash Point °F(°C)	Ignition Temp. °F(°C)	Flammable Limits Percent by Vol.		Sp.Gr. (Water =1)	Vapor Density (Air =1)	Boiling Point °F(°C)	Water Soluble	Extin-guishing Methods	Hazard Identification		
				Lower	Upper						Health	Flamma-bility	Insta-bility
2-Methyl-1-Butene (Technical Grade) CH_2:C(CH_3)CH_2CH_3 **563-46-2**	IA	<20 (< −7)				0.7	2.4	88 (31)	No	1	1	4	1
2-Methyl-2-Butene $(CH_3)_2$C:CCHCH_3 (Trimethylethylene) **513-35-9**	IB	<20 (< −7)				0.7	2.4	101 (38)	Slight	1 5	1	3	0
3-Methyl-1-Butene $(CH_3)_2$CHCH:CH_2 (Isopropylethylene) **563-45-1**	IA	<20 (< −7)	689 (365)	1.5	9.1	0.6	2.4	68 (20)	No	1	1	4	0
N-Methylbutylamine $CH_3CH_2CH_2CH_2NHCH_3$ **110-68-9**		55 (13) (oc)				0.7	3.0	196 (91)	Yes	1 5	3	3	0
2-Methyl Butyl Ethanoate	See Isoamyl Acetate.												
Methyl Butyl Ketone $CH_3CO(CH_2)_3CH_3$ (2-Hexanone) **591-78-6**	IC	77 (25)	795 (423)	1.2	8	0.8	3.5	262 (128)	Slight	1 5	2	3	0
3-Methyl Butynol $(CH_3)_2$C(OH)C:CH **115-19-5**		77 (25) (oc)				0.9	2.9	218 (103)	Yes	1 5	1	3	1
2-Methylbutyraldehyde $CH_3CH_2CH(CH_3)CHO$ **96-17-3**	See NFPA 49 contained in this guide.	49 (9) (oc)				0.8	2.97	198–199 (92–93)	No	5 1	2	3	0
Methyl Butyrate $CH_3OOCCH_2CH_2CH_3$ **623-42-7**	IB	57 (14)		0.9	3.5	0.9	3.5	215 (102)	Slight	1 5	1	3	0
Methyl Carbonate $CO(OCH_3)_2$ (Dimethyl Carbonate) **616-38-6**	See NFPA 49 contained in this guide.	66 (19) (oc)				1.1	3.1	192 (89)	Slight	1 5	1	3	1
Methyl Cellosolve Acetate **110-49-6**	See Ethylene Glycol Methyl Ether Acetate.												
Methyl Chloride CH_3Cl (Chloromethane) **74-87-3**	IA	−50	1170 (632)	8.1	17.4		1.8	−11 (−24)	Slight	6	2	4	0
Methylchloroacetate $CH_2ClCOOCH_3$ (Methyl Chloroethanoate) **96-34-4**		135 (57) (oc)	869 (465)	7.5	18.5	1.2	3.8	266 (130)	Very slight		2	2	1
Methyl Chloroethanoate	See Methyl Chloroacetate.												
Methyl p-Cresol $CH_3C_6H_4OCH_3$ (p-Methylanisole) (p-Cresyl Methyl Ether, p-Methoxy Toluene) (4-Methylanisole) **104-93-8**	IIIA	140 (60)				1.0−	4.21	325 (163)		5	1	2	0
Methyl Cyanide	See Acetonitrile.												
Methylcyclohexane $CH_2(CH_2)_4CHCH_3$ (Cyclohexylmethane) (Hexahydroxytoluene) **108-87-2**	IB	25 (−4)	482 (250)	1.2	6.7	0.8	3.4	214 (101)	No	1	1	3	0
2-Methylcyclohexanol $C_7H_{13}OH$ **583-59-5**	IIIA	149 (65)	565 (296)			0.9	3.9	329 (165)	Slight	5	2	2	0

Chemical Name Formula (Synonym) CAS No.	NFPA 30/ OSHA Class	Flash Point °F(°C)	Ignition Temp. °F(°C)	Flammable Limits Percent by Vol.		Sp.Gr. (Water =1)	Vapor Density (Air =1)	Boiling Point °F(°C)	Water Soluble	Extin- guishing Methods	Hazard Identification		
				Lower	Upper						Health	Flamma- bility	Insta- bility
3-Methylcyclohexanol $CH_3C_6H_{10}OH$ **591-23-1**	IIIA	~158 (~70)	563 (295)								2	2	0
4-Methylcyclohexanol $CH_3C_6H_{10}OH$ **589-91-3**	IIIA	158 (70)	563 (295)			0.9	3.9	343 (173)	Slight	5		2	0
Methylcyclohexanone $C_7H_{12}O$ **583-60-8**	II	118 (48)				0.9	3.9	325 (163)	No		2	2	0
4-Methylcyclohexene $CH:CHCH_2CH(CH_3)$- CH_2CH_2 **591-47-9**		30 (−1) (oc)				0.8	3.3	217 (103)	No	1	1	3	0
Methylcyclohexyl Acetate $C_9H_{16}O_2$ **30232-11-2**	IIIA	147 (64)				0.9		351–381 (177–194)			1	2	0
Methyl Cyclopentadiene C_6H_8	II	120 (49)	833 (445)	1.3 @ 212 (100)	7.6 @ 212 (100)	0.9		163 (73)			1	2	1
Methylcyclopentane $(C_5H_9)CH_3$ **96-37-7**	IB See NFPA 49 contained in this guide.	<20 (< −7)	496 (258)	1.0	8.35	0.8	2.9	161 (72)	No	1	1	3	0
2-Methyldecane $CH_3(CH_2)_7CH(CH_3)_2$			437 (225)			0.74	5.39	374 (190)			0	2	0
Methyldichlorosilane CH_3HSiCl_2 **75-54-7**	IB See NFPA 49 contained in this guide.	15 (−9)	>600 (316)	6.0	55	1.1	3.97	106 (41)	Yes	1	4	3	2 ~~W~~
N-Methyldiethanolamine $CH_3N(C_2H_4OH)_2$ **105-59-9**		260 (127) (oc)				1.04		464 (240)	Yes	2 5	1	1	0
1-Methyl-3,5-Diethylbenzene $(CH_3)C_6H_3(C_2H_5)_2$ (3,5-Diethyltoluene) **2050-24-0**			851 (455)			0.86	5.12	394 (201)			0	2	0
Methyl Dihydroabietate $C_{19}H_{31}COOCH_3$	IIIB	361 (183)				1.0+		689–698 (365–370)		2	1	1	0
Methylene Chloride CH_2Cl_2 (Dichloromethane) **75-09-2**	See NFPA 49 contained in this guide.	None	1033 (556)	13	23	1.3	2.9	104 (40)	Slight		2	1	0
Methylenedianiline $H_2NC_6H_4CH_2C_6H_4NH_2$ (MDA) (p,p′-Diaminodi-Phenylmethane) **101-77-9**	IIIB Note: Melting point 198–199 (92–93).	428 (220)				1.1		748–750 (398–399) @ 78 mm	Slight	2	2	1	0
Methylene Oxide	See Formaldehyde.												
N-Methylethanolamine $CH_3NHCH_2CH_2OH$ [2-(Methylamino) Ethanol] **109-83-1**		165 (74) (oc)				0.9	2.6	319 (159)	Yes	5	3	2	0
Methyl Ether $(CH_3)_2O$ (Dimethyl Ether) (Methyl Oxide) **115-10-6**	See NFPA 49 contained in this guide.	Gas	662 (350)	3.4	27.0		1.6	−11 (−24)	Yes	6	2	4	1
Methyl Ethyl Carbinol	See sec-Butyl Alcohol.												

Chemical Name Formula (Synonym) CAS No.	NFPA 30/ OSHA Class	Flash Point °F(°C)	Ignition Temp. °F(°C)	Flammable Limits Percent by Vol.		Sp.Gr. (Water =1)	Vapor Density (Air =1)	Boiling Point °F(°C)	Water Soluble	Extin-guishing Methods	Hazard Identification		
				Lower	Upper						Health	Flamma-bility	Insta-bility
2-Methyl-2-Ethyl-1,3-Dioxolane $(CH_3)(C_2H_5)COCH_2CH_2O$ **126-39-6**		74 (23) (oc)				0.9	4.0	244 (118)	No	1	1	3	0
Methyl Ethylene Glycol	See Propylene Glycol.												
Methyl Ethyl Ether $CH_3OC_2H_5$ (Ethyl Methyl Ether) **540-67-0**	IA See NFPA 49 contained in this guide.	−35 (−37)	374 (190)	2.0	10.1	0.7	2.1	51 (11)	Yes	1 5	1	4	1
2-Methyl-4-Ethylhexane $(CH_3)_2CHCH_2CH(C_2H_5)_2$ (4-Ethyl-2-Methylhexane)	IB	<70 (<21)	536 (280)	~0.7		0.72	4.43	273 (134)		1	0	3	0
3-Methyl-4-Ethylhexane $C_2H_5CH(CH_3)CH(C_2H_5)_2$ (3-Ethyl-4-Methylhexane)	IC	75 (24)				0.72	4.43	284 (140)		1	0	3	0
Methyl Ethyl Ketone $C_2H_5COCH_3$ (2-Butanone) (Ethyl Methyl Ketone) **78-93-3**	IB	16 (−9)	759 (404)	1.4 @ 200(93)	11.4 @ 200(93)	0.8	2.5	176 (80)	Yes	1 5	1	3	0
Methyl Ethyl Ketoxime $CH_3C(C_2H_5):NOH$ **96-29-7**	IIIA	156–170 (69–77)				0.9	3.0	306–307 (152–153)	Slight	5	2	2	1
2-Methyl-3-Ethylpentane $(CH_3)_2CHCH(C_2H_5)_2$ (3-Ethyl-2-Methylpentane)	IB	<70 (<21)	860 (460)			0.72	3.94	241 (116)		1	0	3	0
2-Methyl-5-Ethylpiperidine $NHCH(CH_3)CH_2CH_2CH$- $(C_2H_5)CH_2$		126 (52) (oc)				0.8	4.4	326 (163)	Slight	5	2	2	0
2-Methyl-5-Ethylpyridine $N:C(CH_3)CH:CHC$- $(C_2H_5):CH$ (Aldehydine) **104-90-5**	See NFPA 49 contained in this guide.	155 (68) (oc)	939 (504)	1.1	6.6	0.9	4.2	353 (178)	Slight	5	3	2	0
Methyl Eugenol $(CH_3O)_2C_6H_3CH_2CH:CH_2$ (4-Allyl-1,2-Dimethoxybenzene) (4-Allyl Veratrole) (1,2-Dimethoxy-4-Allylbenzene) (Eugenyl Methyl Ether) **93-15-2**	IIIB	210 (99)				1.0+		196–203 (91–95)	No	5	0	1	0
Methyl Formate CH_3OOCH (Formic Acid, Methyl Ester) (Methyl Methanoate) **107-31-3**	IA See NFPA 49 contained in this guide.	−2 (−19)	840 (449)	4.5	23	1.0−	2.1	90 (32)	Yes	1 5	2	4	0
2-Methylfuran $C_4H_3OCH_3$ (Sylvan) **534-22-5**	IB	−22 (−30)				0.9		144–147 (62–64)	No	1	4	3	1
Methyl Heptadecyl Ketone $C_{17}H_{35}COCH_3$	IIIB Note: Melting point 127 (53)	255 (124)						329 (165) @ 3 mm	No	2	0	1	0

Chemical Name Formula (Synonym) CAS No.	NFPA 30/ OSHA Class	Flash Point °F(°C)	Ignition Temp. °F(°C)	Flammable Limits Percent by Vol. Lower	Flammable Limits Percent by Vol. Upper	Sp.Gr. (Water =1)	Vapor Density (Air =1)	Boiling Point °F(°C)	Water Soluble	Extin- guishing Methods	Hazard Identification Health	Hazard Identification Flamma- bility	Hazard Identification Insta- bility
Methylheptenone $(CH_3)_2C{:}CH(CH_2)_2$- $COCH_3$ (6-Methyl-5-Hepten-2-one) **111-12-6**	II	135 (57)				0.9	4.35	343–345 (173–174)	No	5	1	2	0
Methyl Heptine Carbonate $CH_3(CH_2)_4C{:}CCOOCH_3$ (Methyl 2-Octynoate) **111-12-6**	IIIA	190 (88)				0.9				5		2	0
Methyl Heptyl Ketone $C_7H_{15}COCH_3$ (5-Methyl-2-Octanone) **821-55-6**	IIIA	140 (60)	680 (360)	0.9 @ 180(82)	5.9 @ 313 (156)	0.8 @ 86(30)	4.9	361–383 (183–195)	No		0	2	0
2-Methylhexane	See Isoheptane.												
3-Methylhexane $CH_3CH_2CH(CH_3)$- $CH_2CH_2CH_3$ **589-34-4**	IB	25 (−4)	536 (280)			0.69	3.46	198 (92)		1	1	3	0
Methyl Hexyl Ketone $CH_3COC_6H_{13}$ (2-Octanone) (Octanone) **111-13-7**	II	125 (52)				0.8	4.41	344 (173.5)	No	5	1	2	0
Methylhydrazine CH_3NHNH_2 **60-34-4**	IB See NFPA 49 contained in this guide.	17 (−8)	382 (194)	2.5	92	0.9	1.6	190 (88)	Slight	1 5	4	3	2
Methyl-3-Hydroxybutyrate $CH_3CHOHCH_2COOCH_3$		180 (82) (oc)				1.1	4.1	347 (175)	Yes	5	1	2	0
Methyl Ionone $C_{14}H_{22}O$ (Irone)	IIIB	>212 (>100)				0.9		291 (144) @ 16 mm	No	5 2	0	1	0
Methyl Isoamyl Ketone $CH_3COCH_2CH_2CH(CH_3)_2$ **110-12-3**	IC	96 (36)	375 (191)	1.0 @ 200(93)	8.2 @ 200(93)	0.8	3.9	294 (146)	No	1	1	3	0
Methylisobutylcarbinol Acetate	See 4-Methyl-2-Pentanol Acetate.												
Methyl Isobutyl Ketone $CH_3COCH_2CH(CH_3)_2$ (Hexone) (4-Methyl-2-Pentanone) **108-10-1**	IB See NFPA 49 contained in this guide.	64 (18)	840 (448)	1.2 @ 200(93)	8.0 @ 200(93)	0.8	3.5	244 (118)	Slight	5 1	1	3	0
Methyl Isocyanate $CH_3N{:}CO$ (Methyl Carbonimide) **624-83-9**	IB Note: Polymerization may occur. See NFPA 49 contained in this guide.	19 (−7)	994 (534)	5.3	26	1.0−	1.97	102 (39)	Yes Reacts vig- orously	5	4	3	2 ₩
Methyl Isoeugenol $CH_3CH{:}CHC_6H_3(OCH_3)_2$ (Propenyl Guaiacol) **93-16-3**	IIIB	>212 (>100)				1.1		504–507 (262–264)	No	5 2	0	1	0
Methyl Isopropenyl Ketone $CH_3COC{:}CH_2(CH_3)$ **814-78-8**		52 (11)		1.8	9.0	0.85	2.9	208 (98)		1	4	3	1
Methyl Lactate $CH_3CHOHCOOCH_3$ **547-64-8**	II	121 (49)	725 (385)	2.2 @ 212 (100)		1.1	3.6	293 (145)	Yes Decom- poses		1	2	0
Methyl Mercaptan CH_3SH (Methanethiol) **74-93-1**	See NFPA 49 contained in this guide.	Gas		3.9	21.8	0.9	1.7	42.4 (6)	Yes	5 6	4	4	1

Chemical Name Formula (Synonym) CAS No.	NFPA 30/ OSHA Class	Flash Point °F(°C)	Ignition Temp. °F(°C)	Flammable Limits Percent by Vol.		Sp.Gr. (Water =1)	Vapor Density (Air =1)	Boiling Point °F(°C)	Water Soluble	Extin-guishing Methods	Hazard Identification		
				Lower	Upper						Health	Flamma-bility	Insta-bility
β-Methyl Mercaptopropional-dehyde $CH_3SC_2H_4CHO$ [3-(Methylthio) Propion-aldehyde] **3268-49-3**	IIIA	142 (61)	491 (255)			1.03	3.6	~329 (~165)				2	0
Methyl Methacrylate $CH_2{:}C(CH_3)COOCH_3$ **80-62-6**		50 (10) (oc)	815 (435)	1.7	8.2	0.9	3.6	212 (100)	Very slight	1	2	3	2
	Note: Polymerizes. See NFPA 49 contained in this guide.												
Methyl Methanoate	See Methyl Formate.												
4-Methylmorpholine $C_2H_4OC_2H_4NCH_3$ **109-02-4**	IC	75 (24)				0.9	3.5	239 (115)	Yes	1 5	3	3	0
1-Methylnaphthalene $C_{10}H_7CH_3$ **90-12-0**		180 (82)	984 (529)			1.0+		472 (244)	No		1	1	0
Methyl Nonyl Ketone $C_9H_{19}COCH_3$ **112-12-9**	IIIA	192 (89)				0.8 @ 86(30)	5.9	433 (223)	No		1	2	0
Methyl Oxide	See Methyl Ether.												
Methyl Pentadecyl Ke-tone $C_{15}H_{31}COCH_3$	IIIB	248 (120)						313 (156) @ 3 mm	No	2	0	1	0
2-Methyl-1,3-Pentadiene $CH_2{:}C(CH_3)CH{:}CHCH_3$ **1118-58-7**	IB	< −4 (< −20)				0.72	2.83	169 (76)			2	3	1
4-Methyl-1,3-Pentadiene $CH_2{:}CHCH_2{:}C(CH_3)_2$ **926-56-7**	IB	−30 (−34)				0.7		168 (76)	No	1	1	3	1
Methylpentaldehyde $CH_3CH_2CH_2$-$C(CH_3)HCHO$ (Methyl Pentanal) (2-Methylvaleraldehyde) **123-15-9**		68 (20) (oc)				0.8	3.5	243 (117)	Very slight	1	2	3	1 ~~W~~
Methyl Pentanal	See Methylpentaldehyde.												
2-Methylpentane $(CH_3)_2CH(CH_2)_2CH_3$ (Isohexane) **107-83-5**	IB	<20 (< −7)	583 (306)	1.2	7.0	0.7	3.0	140 (60)	No	1	1	3	0
3-Methylpentane $CH_3CH_2CH(CH_3)CH_2CH_3$ **96-14-0**	IB	<20 (< −7)	532 (278)	1.2	7.0	0.7	3.0	146 (63)	No	1	1	3	0
2-Methyl-1,3-Pentanediol $CH_3CH_2CH(OH)CH(CH_3)$-CH_2OH **149-31-5**	IIIB	230 (110)				1.0−		419 (215)		2		1	0
2-Methyl-2,4-Pentanediol **107-41-5**	See Hexylene Glycol.												
2-Methylpentanoic Acid $C_3H_7CH(CH_3)COOH$ **97-61-0**		225 (107) (oc)	712 (378)			0.9	4.0	381 (194)	No	2	0	1	0

Chemical Name Formula (Synonym) CAS No.	NFPA 30/ OSHA Class	Flash Point °F(°C)	Ignition Temp. °F(°C)	Flammable Limits Percent by Vol. Lower	Upper	Sp.Gr. (Water =1)	Vapor Density (Air =1)	Boiling Point °F(°C)	Water Soluble	Extin-guishing Methods	Hazard Identification Health	Flamma-bility	Insta-bility
2-Methyl-1-Pentanol $CH_3(CH_2)_2CH$-$(CH_3)CH_2OH$ (Isohexyl Alcohol) (Methylamyl Alcohol) (Methyl Isobutyl Carbinol) **105-30-6**	II	129 (54)	590 (310)	1.1	9.65	0.8	3.5	298 (148)	No		2	2	0
4-Methyl-2-Pentanol Acetate $CH_3COOCH(CH_3)CH_2$-$CH(CH_3)_2$ (Methylisobutylcarbinol Acetate) (1,3-Dimethylbutyl Acetate) **108-84-9**	II	113 (45)	660 (349)	0.9 @ 212 (100)	5.83 @ 212 (100)	0.9	5.0	295 (146)	Very slight	5	1	2	0
4-Methyl-2-Pentanone	See Methyl Isobutyl Ketone.												
2-Methyl-2-Pentene $(CH_3)_2C{:}CHCH_2CH_3$	IB	<20 (< −7)				0.7	2.9	153 (67)		1	1	3	0
2-Methyl-1-Pentene $CH_2{:}C(CH_3)CH_2CH_2CH_3$ **763-29-1**	IB	<20 (< −7)	572 (300)	1.2		0.7	2.9	143 (62)	No	1	1	3	0
4-Methyl-1-Pentene $CH_2{:}CHCH_2CH(CH_3)_2$ **691-37-2**	IB	<20 (< −7)	572 (300)	1.2		0.7	2.9	129 (54)		1	1	3	1
4-Methyl-2-Pentene $CH_3CH{:}CHCH(CH_3)_2$	IB	<20 (< −7)				0.7		133–137 (56–58)		1	1	3	0
4-Methyl-2-Pentanol $CH_3CHOHCH_2$-$CHCH_3CH_3$ (1,3-Dimethylbutanol) (4-Methyl-2-Pentanol) (Methylamyl Alcohol) (Methyl Isobutyl Carbinol) **108-11-2**	II	106 (41)		1.0	5.5	0.8		266–271 (130–133)	Slight	5	2	2	0
3-Methyl-1-Pentynol $(C_2H_5)(CH_3)C(OH)C{:}CH$ **77-75-8**		101 (38) (oc)				0.9	3.4	250 (121)	Yes	5	1	2	0
o-Methyl Phenol	See o-Cresol.												
Methyl Phenylacetate $C_6H_5CH_2COOCH_3$ **140-39-6**	IIIA	195 (91)				1.1		424 (218)	No	5	0	2	0
Methylphenyl carbinol $C_6H_5CH(CH_3)OH$ (α-Methylbenzyl Alcohol) (Styralyl Alcohol) (sec-Phenethyl Alcohol) **98-85-1**	IIIB	200 (93)				1.0+		399 (204)	Slight	5	2	2	0
Methyl Phenyl Carbinyl Acetate $C_6H_5CH(CH_3)COOCH_3$ (α-Methyl-Benzyl Acetate) (Styralyl Acetate) (sec-Phenylethyl Acetate) (Phenyl Methylcarbinyl Acetate) **93-92-5**	IIIA	195 (91)				1.0+			No	5	0	2	0
Methyl Phenyl Ether	See Anisole.												
Methyl Phthalyl Ethyl Glycolate $CH_3COOC_6H_4COOCH_2$-$COOC_2H_5$		380 (193) (oc)				1.2		590 (310)	No	2	2	1	0

Chemical Name Formula (Synonym) CAS No.	NFPA 30/ OSHA Class	Flash Point °F(°C)	Ignition Temp. °F(°C)	Flammable Limits Percent by Vol.		Sp.Gr. (Water =1)	Vapor Density (Air =1)	Boiling Point °F(°C)	Water Soluble	Extin-guishing Methods	Hazard Identification		
				Lower	Upper						Health	Flamma-bility	Insta-bility
1-Methyl Piperazine $CH_3NCH_2CH_2NHCH_2CH_2$ **109-01-3**		108 (42) (oc)				0.9	3.5	280 (138)	Yes	5	3	2	0
2-Methylpropanal	See Isobutyraldehyde.												
2-Methylpropane	See Isobutane.												
2-Methyl-2-Propanethiol $(CH_3)_3CSH$ (tert-Butyl Mercaptan) **75-66-1**	IB	< −20 (< −29)				0.8	3.1	149–153 (65–67)	No	1	1	3	0
2-Methyl Propanol-1	See Isobutyl Alcohol.												
2-Methyl-2-Propanol	See tert-Butyl Alcohol.												
2-Methylpropenal CH_2:$C(CH_3)CHO$ (Methacrolein) (α-Methyl Acrolein) **78-85-3**		35 (2) (oc)				0.8	2.4	154 (68)	Yes	1 5	3	3	2
2-Methylpropene CH_2:$C(CH_3)CH_3$ (γ-Butylene) (Isobutylene) (Isobutene) **115-11-7**		Gas	869 (465)	1.8	9.6		1.9	20 (−7)	No	6	2	4	1
Methyl Propionate $CH_3COOCH_2CH_3$ **554-12-1**	IB	28 (−2)	876 (469)	2.5	13	0.9	3.0	176 (80)	No	1	1	3	0
Methyl Propyl Acetylene $CH_3C_2H_4C$:CCH_3 (2-Hexyne)	IB	<14 (< −10)				0.73	2.83	185 (85)		1		3	
Methylpropylcarbinol	See sec-Amyl Alcohol.												
Methylpropylcarbiny-lamine	See sec-Amylamine.												
Methyl n-Propyl Ether $CH_3OC_3H_7$	IB	< −4 (< −20)				0.91	2.56	102 (39)		1	0	3	0
Methyl Propyl Ketone $CH_3COC_3H_7$ (2-Pentanone) **107-87-9**	IB	45 (7)	846 (452)	1.5	8.2	0.8	3.0	216 (102)	Slight	1 5	2	3	0
2-Methylpyrazine N:C(CH₃)CH:NCH:CH **109-08-0**		122 (50) (oc)				1.02	3.25	275 (135) @ 761 mm			1	2	0
2-Methyl Pyridine	See 2-Picoline.												
Methylpyrrole $N(CH_3)CH$:$CHCH$:CH **96-54-8**	IB	61 (16)				0.9	2.8	234 (112)	No	1	2	3	1
Methylpyrrolidine $CH_3NC_4H_8$ **120-94-5**	IB	7 (−14)				0.8	2.9	180 (82)	Slight	5 1	2	3	1
1-Methyl-2-Pyrrolidinone $CH_3NCOCH_2CH_2CH_2$ (n-Methyl-2-Pyrrolidone) **872-50-4**		204 (96) (oc)	655 (346)			1.0+	3.4	396 (202)	Yes	5	2	2	0
Methyl Salicylate $HOC_6H_4COOCH_3$ (Oil of Wintergreen) (Gaultheria Oil) (Betula Oil) (Sweet-Birch Oil) **119-36-8**	IIIB	205 (96)	850 (454)			1.2	5.25	432 (222)	No	2	2	1	0

Chemical Name Formula (Synonym) CAS No.	NFPA 30/ OSHA Class	Flash Point °F(°C)	Ignition Temp. °F(°C)	Flammable Limits Percent by Vol.		Sp.Gr. (Water =1)	Vapor Density (Air =1)	Boiling Point °F(°C)	Water Soluble	Extin- guishing Methods	Hazard Identification		
				Lower	Upper						Health	Flamma- bility	Insta- bility
Methyl Stearate $C_{17}H_{35}COOCH_3$ **112-61-8**	IIIB	307 (153)				0.9		421 (216)	No	2	1	1	0
α-Methylstyrene (1-Methylethenyl-Benzine) (1-Methyl-1-phenylethene)	II	129 (54)	1066 (574)	1.9	6.1	0.9		329–331 (165–166)	No		1	2	1
Methylstyrene	See Vinyl Toluene.												
Methyl Sulfate	See Dimethyl Sulfate.												
2-Methyltetra-hydrofuran $C_4H_7OCH_3$ **96-47-9**	IB	12 (−11)				0.9	3.0	176 (80)	Slight	1 5	1	3	1
Methyl Toluene Sulfonate $CH_3C_6H_4SO_3CH_3$ **80-48-8**		306 (152) (oc)						315 (157) @ 8 mm	No	2	2	1	1
	Note: Melting point 75 (24).												
Methyltrichlorosilane CH_3SiCl_3 (Methyl Silico Chloroform) (Trichloromethylsilane) **75-79-6**	IB	15 (−9)	>760 (>404)	7.6	11.9	1.29	5.16	151 (66)	Reacts		4	3	2 ₩
	See NFPA 49 contained in this guide.												
Methyl Undecyl Ketone $C_{11}H_{23}COCH_3$ (2-Tridecanone) **593-08-8**	IIIB	225 (107)				0.8		248 (120)	No	2	1	1	0
2-Methylvaleraldehyde **123-15-9**	See Methylpentaldehyde.												
1-Methylvinyl Acetate	See Isopropenyl Acetate.												
Methyl Vinyl Ether	See Vinyl Methyl Ether.												
Methyl Vinyl Ketone $CH_3COCH:CH_2$ **78-94-4**	IB	20 (−7)	915 (491)	2.1	15.6	0.86	2.4	177 (81)	Yes	1	4	3	2
	See NFPA 49 contained in this guide.												
Mineral Oil **8012-95-1**		380 (193) (oc)				0.8–0.9		680 (360)	No	2	0	1	0
Mineral Seal Oil (Signal Oil) **64742-06-9**		275 (135) (oc)				0.8		480–680 (249–360)	No	2	1	1	0
Mineral Spirits Mineral Spirits, 360° **64742-88-7**	II	104 (40)	473 (245)	0.8 @212 (100)		0.8	3.9	300 (149)	No		1	2	0
Mineral Wax	See Wax, Ozocerite.												
Monochlorobenzene	See Chlorobenzene.												
Morpholine $OC_2H_4NHCH_2CH_2$ (ring) **110-91-8**		98 (37) (oc)	555 (290)	1.4	11.2	1.0	3.0	262 (128)	Yes	5 1	3	3	1
	Note: Decomposes at 489 (250). See NFPA 49 contained in this guide.												
Muriatic Ether	See Ethyl Chloride.												
Mustard Oil $C_3H_5N:C:S$ (Allyl Isothiocyanate) **57-06-7** **8007-40-7**	II	115 (46)				1.0+	3.4	304 (151)	No		3	2	1
Naphtha 49° Be-Coal Tar Type	II	107 (42)	531 (277)						No		2	2	0
Naphtha, Petroleum	See Petroleum Ether.												

Chemical Name Formula (Synonym) CAS No.	NFPA 30/ OSHA Class	Flash Point °F(°C)	Ignition Temp. °F(°C)	Flammable Limits Percent by Vol. Lower	Flammable Limits Percent by Vol. Upper	Sp.Gr. (Water =1)	Vapor Density (Air =1)	Boiling Point °F(°C)	Water Soluble	Extin-guishing Methods	Hazard Identification Health	Hazard Identification Flamma-bility	Hazard Identification Insta-bility
Naphtha, Safety Solvent	See Cleaning Solvent.												
Naphtha V.M. & P., 50° Flash **8032-32-4**	IB	50 (10)	450 (232)	0.9	6.7	<1	4.1	240–290 (116–143)	No	1	1	3	0
	Note: Flash point and ignition temperature will vary depending on the manufacturer.												
Naphtha V.M. & P., High Flash **8032-32-4**	IC	85 (29)	450 (232)	1.0	6.0	<1	4.3	280–350 (138–177)	No	1	1	3	0
	Note: Flash point and ignition temperature will vary depending on the manufacturer.												
Naphtha V.M. & P., Regular **8032-32-4**	IB	28 (−2)	450 (232)	0.9	6.0	<1		212–320 (100–160)	No	1	1	3	0
	Note: Flash point and ignition temperature will vary depending on the manufacturer.												
Naphthalene $C_{10}H_8$ (White Tar) **91-20-3**	IIIA	174 (79)	979 (526)	0.9	5.9	1.1	4.4	424 (218)	No		2	2	0
	Note: Melting point 176 (80). See NFPA 49 contained in this guide.												
β-Naphthol $C_{10}H_7OH$ (β-Hydroxy Naphthalene) (2-Naphthol) **135-19-3**	IIIB	307 (153)				1.22	4.98	545 (285)		2		1	0
	Note: Melting point 253 (123).												
1-Naphthylamine $C_{10}H_7NH_2$ **134-32-7**	IIIB	315 (157)				1.2		572 (300)	No	2	2	1	0
	Note: Melting point 122 (50).												
Natural Gas **8006-14-2**											1	4	0
	See Gas.												
Neatsfoot Oil **8002-64-0**	IIIB	470 (243)	828 (442)			0.9			No	2	1	1	0
	Note: Melting point 84–106 (29–41).												
Neohexane	See 2,2-Dimethylbutane.												
Neopentane	See 2,2-Dimethylpropane.												
Neopentyl Glycol $HOCH_2C(CH_3)_2CH_2OH$ (2,2-Dimethyl-1,3-Propanediol) **126-30-7**		265 (129) (oc)	750 (399)			1.1		410 (210)	Yes	2	1	1	0
	Note: Melting point 255–266 (124–130).												
Nickel Carbonyl $Ni(CO)_4$ **13463-39-3**	IB	<−4 (<−24)	140 (60)	2	34	1.32	5.89	110 (43)	No	4	4	3	3
	Note: Decomposes violently at 140 (60). See NFPA 49 contained in this guide.												
Nicotine $C_{10}H_{14}N_2$ **54-11-5**		214 (101)	471 (244)	0.7	4.0	1.0	5.6	475 (246)	Yes	2 5	3	1	0
Niobe Oil	See Methyl Benzoate.												
Nitric Ether	See Ethyl Nitrate.												
2,2′,2″-Nitrilotriethanol	See Triethanolamine.												
1,1′,1″-Nitrilotri-2-propanol	See Triisopropanolamine.												
p-Nitroaniline $NO_2C_6H_4NH_2$ **100-01-6**	IIIB	390 (199)				1.44	4.77	637 (336)	No	2	3	1	2
	Note: Melting point 298 (148). May decompose explosively in a fire. See NFPA 49 contained in this guide.												
Nitrobenzene $C_6H_5NO_2$ (Nitrobenzol) (Oil of Mirbane) **98-95-3**	IIIA	190 (88)	900 (482)	1.8 @ 200(93)		1.2	4.3	412 (211)	No	3	3	2	1
	See NFPA 49 contained in this guide.												
Nitrobenzol	See Nitrobenzene.												
1,3-Nitrobenzotrifluoride $C_6H_4NO_2CF_3$ (α,α,α-Trifluoronitrotoluene) **98-46-4**		217 (103) (oc)				1.44	6.59	397 (203)		2	3	1	1

Chemical Name Formula (Synonym) CAS No.	NFPA 30/ OSHA Class	Flash Point °F(°C)	Ignition Temp. °F(°C)	Flammable Limits Percent by Vol.		Sp.Gr. (Water = 1)	Vapor Density (Air = 1)	Boiling Point °F(°C)	Water Soluble	Extin-guishing Methods	Hazard Identification		
				Lower	Upper						Health	Flamma-bility	Insta-bility
Nitrobiphenyl $C_6H_5C_6H_4NO_2$	IIIB	290 (143)				1.2		626 (330)	No	2	2	1	0
Nitrocellulose (Cellulose Nitrate)		55 (13)							No	1 5	2	3	3
	See also Collodion and Pyroxylin Solution.												
M-Nitrochlorobenzene $C_6H_4ClNO_2$ **121-73-3**	IIIB	261 (127)				1.5		457 (236)	No	2	2	1	0
	Note: Melting point 111 (44). See NFPA 49 contained in this guide.												
p-Nitrochlorobenzene $C_6H_4ClNO_2$ (1-Chloro-4-Nitrobenzene) **100-00-5**	IIIB	261 (127)				1.37	5.44	468 (242)		2	2	1	3
	Note: Melting point 181 (83).												
Nitrocyclohexane $CH_2(CH_2)_4CHNO_2$ **1122-60-7**		190 (88) (oc)				1.07	4.46	403 (206) Decomposes			3	2	2
Nitroethane $C_2H_5NO_2$ **79-24-3**	IC	82 (28)	778 (414)	3.4		1.1	2.6	237 (114)	Slight	4 5	2	3	3
	Note: May explode on heating. See NFPA 49 contained in this guide.												
Nitroglycerine $C_3H_5(NO_3)_3$ (Glyceryl Trinitrate) **55-63-0**		Explodes	518 (270)			1.6		502 (261) Explodes	No		2	3	4
Nitromethane CH_3NO_2 **75-52-5**	IC	95 (35)	785 (418)	7.3		1.1	2.1	214 (101)	Slight	1 5	2	3	4
	Note: May detonate under high temperature and pressure conditions. See NFPA 49 contained in this guide.												
1-Nitronaphthalene $C_{10}H_7NO_2$ **86-57-7**	IIIB	327 (164)				1.3		579 (304)	No	2	1	1	0
	Note: Melting point 140 (60).												
1-Nitropropane $CH_3CH_2CH_2NO_2$ **108-03-2**	IC	96 (36)	789 (421)	2.2		1.0	3.1	268 (131)	Slight	5 1	2	3	2
	See NFPA 49 contained in this guide.												
2-Nitropropane $CH_3CH(NO_2)CH_3$ (sec-Nitropropane) **79-46-9**	IC	75 (24)	802 (428)	2.6	11.0	1.0 –	3.1	248 (120)	Slight	1 5	3	3	2
	See NFPA 49 contained in this guide.												
sec-Nitropropane	See 2-Nitropropane.												
m-Nitrotoluene $C_6H_4CH_3NO_2$ **99-08-1**	IIIB	223 (106)				1.16	4.73	450 (232)	No		3	1	1
	Note: Melting point 61 (16). See NFPA 49 contained in this guide.												
o-Nitrotoluene $C_6H_4CH_3NO_2$ **88-72-2**	IIIB	223 (106)				1.16	4.73	432 (222)	No	2	3	1	1
	Note: Melting point 25 (−4). See NFPA 49 contained in this guide.												
p-Nitrotoluene $NO_2C_6H_4CH_3$ **99-99-0**	IIIB	223 (106)				1.3	4.72	461 (238)	No	2	3	1	1
	Note: Melting point 125 (52).												
2-Nitro-p-toluidine $CH_3C_6H_3(NH_2)NO_2$ (4-Methyl-2-nitroaniline) **89-62-3**	IIIB	315 (157)				1.31	5.25			2	1	1	0
	Note: Melting point 259 (126).												
Nitrous Ether	See Ethyl Nitrite.												
Nonadecane $CH_3(CH_2)_{17}CH_3$ **629-92-5**	IIIB	>212 (>100)	446 (230)			0.79	9.27	628 (331)		2	1	1	0
	Note: Melting point 90 (32).												
Nonane C_9H_{20} **111-84-2**	IC	88 (31)	401 (205)	0.8	2.9	0.7	4.4	303 (151)	No	1	1	3	0
iso-Nonane $C_6H_{13}CH(CH_3)_2$ (2-Methyloctane)			428 (220)			0.71	4.43	290 (143)			0	3	0

Chemical Name Formula (Synonym) CAS No.	NFPA 30/ OSHA Class	Flash Point °F(°C)	Ignition Temp. °F(°C)	Flammable Limits Percent by Vol. Lower	Upper	Sp.Gr. (Water =1)	Vapor Density (Air =1)	Boiling Point °F(°C)	Water Soluble	Extin-guishing Methods	Hazard Identification Health	Flamma-bility	Insta-bility
iso-Nonane $C_5H_{11}CH(CH_3)C_2H_5$ (3-Methyloctane)			428 (220)			0.72	4.43	291 (144)			0	3	0
iso-Nonane $C_4H_9CH(CH_3)C_3H_7$ (4-Methyloctane)			437 (225)			0.72	4.43	288 (142)			0	3	0
Nonene C_9H_{18} (Nonylene) **27215-95-8**		78 (26) (oc)		0.7	3.7	0.7	4.35	270–290 (132–143)	No	1	1	3	1
Nonyl Acetate $CH_2COOC_9H_{19}$ **143-13-5**	IIIA	155 (68)				0.9	6.4	378 (192)	Very slight	5	1	2	0
Nonyl Alcohol	See Diisobutyl Carbinol.												
Nonylbenzene $C_9H_{19}C_6H_5$ **1081-77-2**	IIIB	210 (99)				0.9		468–486 (242–252)	No		0	1	0
tert-Nonyl Mercaptan $C_9H_{19}SH$ **25360-10-5**		154 (68) (oc)				0.9	5.53	370–385 (188–196)	No	5	1	2	0
Nonylnaphthalene $C_9H_{19}C_{10}H_7$ **27193-93-7**		<200 (<93)				0.9	8.8	626–653 (330–345)	No		0	2	0
Nonylphenol $C_6H_4(C_9H_{19})OH$ **25154-52-3**	IIIB	285 (141)		1.0		1.0–		559–567 (293–297)	Very slight	2 5	3	1	0
2,5-Norbornadiene C_7H_8 (NBD) **121-46-0**	IB	−6 (−21)				0.9	3.17	193 (89)	No	1	1	3	1
Octadecane $C_{18}H_{38}$ (n-Octadecane) **593-45-3**	IIIB	>212 (>100)	441 (227)			0.78	8.73	603 (317)		2	1	1	0
	Note: Melting point 82 (28).												
α-Octadecylene $CH_3(CH_2)_{15}CH:CH_2$ (1-Octadecene) **112-88-9**	IIIB	>212 (>100)	482 (250)			0.79	8.71	599 (315)		2	0	1	0
	Note: Melting point 64 (18).												
Octadecyltrichlorosi-lane $C_{18}H_{37}SiCl_3$ (Trichlorooctadecylsi-lane) **112-04-9**	IIIA	193 (89)				1.0		716 (380)	Yes		3	2	2 ~~W~~
Octadecyl Vinyl Ether	See Vinyl Octadecyl Ether.												
Octanal	See Caprylaldehyde.												
n-Octane $CH_3(CH_2)_6CH_3$ **111-65-9**	IB	56 (13)	403 (206)	1.0	6.5	0.7	3.9	258 (126)	No	1	1	3	0
1-Octanethiol $C_8H_{17}SH$ (n-Octyl Mercaptan) **111-88-6**		156 (69) (oc)				0.85	5.04	390 (199)	No	5	2	2	1
1-Octanol	See Octyl Alcohol.												
2-Octanol $CH_3CHOH(CH_2)_5CH_3$ **123-96-6**	IIIA	190 (88)				0.8	4.5	363 (184)	No		1	2	0
1-Octene $CH_2:C_7H_{14}$ **111-65-0**		70 (21) (oc)	446 (230)	0.7		0.7	3.9	250 (121)	No	1	1	3	0

Chemical Name Formula (Synonym) CAS No.	NFPA 30/ OSHA Class	Flash Point °F(°C)	Ignition Temp. °F(°C)	Flammable Limits Percent by Vol. Lower	Upper	Sp.Gr. (Water =1)	Vapor Density (Air =1)	Boiling Point °F(°C)	Water Soluble	Extin-guishing Methods	Hazard Identification Health	Flamma-bility	Insta-bility
2-Octene (Mixed cis and trans isomers) $CH_3CH{:}CHC_5H_{11}$ **111-67-1**		70 (21) (oc)				0.7	3.9	257 (125)	No	1	1	3	0
Octyl Acetate	See 2-Ethylhexyl Acetate.												
Octyl Alcohol $CH_3(CH_2)_6CH_2OH$ (1-Octanol) **111-87-5**	IIIA	178 (81)				0.8	4.5	381 (194)	No		1	2	0
Octylamine $CH_3(CH_2)_6CH_2NH_2$ (1-Aminooctane) **111-86-4**	IIIA	140 (60)				0.8	4.5	338 (170)	Slight	5	3	2	0
tert-Octylamine $(CH_3)_3CCH_2C(CH_3)_2NH_2$ (1,1,3,3-Tetramethyl-butylamine) **107-45-9**		91 (33) (oc)				1.41	4.46	284 (140)			3	3	0
Octyl Chloride $CH_3(CH_2)_7Cl$ **111-85-3** **628-61-5**	IIIA	158 (70)				0.9	5.1	359 (182)	No		1	2	0
Octylene Glycol **94-96-2**	See 2-Ethyl-1,3-Hexanediol.												
tert-Octyl Mercaptan $C_8H_{17}SH$ **141-59-3**		115 (46) (oc)				0.8	5.0	318–329 (159–165)	No		2	2	0
p-Octylphenyl Salicylate $C_{21}H_{26}O_3$		420 (216) (oc)	780 (416)							2	1	1	0
	Note: Melting point 162–165 (72–74).												
Oil of Mirbane	See Nitrobenzene.												
Oil of Wintergreen	See Methyl Salicylate.												
Oleic Acid $C_8H_{17}CH{:}CH\text{-}(CH_2)_7COOH$ (Red Oil) Distilled **112-80-1**	IIIB	372 (189) 364 (184)	685 (363)			0.9	9.7	547 (286)	No	2	1	1	0
Oleo Oil	IIIB	450 (232)				0.9		464 (240)	No	2	0	1	0
Olive Oil (Sweet Oil) **8001-25-0**	IIIB	437 (225)	650 (343)			0.9			No	2	0	1	0
Oxalic Ether	See Ethyl Oxalate.												
Oxammonium	See Hydroxylamine.												
Oxirane	See Ethylene Oxide.												
Palm Butter	See Palm Oil.												
Palm Kernel Oil (Palm Nut Oil) **8023-79-8**	IIIB	398 (203)				0.9			No	2	0	1	0
	Note: Melting point 78–86 (26–30).												
Palm Nut Oil	See Palm Kernel Oil.												
Palm Oil (Palm Butter) **8002-75-3**	IIIB	323 (162)	600 (316)			0.9			No	2			
	Note: Melting point 80–110 (27–43).												
Paraffin Oil, Mineral **8012-95-1**	IIIB	444 (229)								2			
	See also Lubricating Oil, Mineral.												
Paraffin Wax	See Wax, Paraffin.												

Chemical Name Formula (Synonym) CAS No.	NFPA 30/ OSHA Class	Flash Point °F(°C)	Ignition Temp. °F(°C)	Flammable Limits Percent by Vol. Lower	Upper	Sp.Gr. (Water =1)	Vapor Density (Air =1)	Boiling Point °F(°C)	Water Soluble	Extin-guishing Methods	Hazard Identification Health	Flamma-bility	Insta-bility
Paraformaldehyde $HO(CH_2O)_nH$ **30525-89-4**	IIIA	158 (70)	572 (300)	7.0	73	1.5	1.03	Decomposes	Slight	5	3	2	1
	Note: Melting point 248–356 (120–180). See NFPA 49 contained in this guide.												
Paraldehyde $(CH_3CHO)_3$ **123-63-7**		96 (36) (oc)	460 (238)	1.3		1.0 –	4.5	255 (124)	Slight	1 5	2	3	1
	See NFPA 49 contained in this guide.												
Peanut Oil (Cooking) (Katchung Oil) **8002-03-7**	IIIB	540 (282)	833 (445)			0.9			No	2	0	1	0
Pentaborane B_5H_9 **19624-22-7**		86 (30)	95 (35)	0.42	98	0.6	2.2	140 (60)	Reacts	1	4	4	2
	Note: Ignites spontaneously in air. Decomposes above 300 (149). See NFPA 49 contained in this guide.												
Pent-Acetate Mixture of Isomeric Amyl Acetates and Amyl Alcohols	IC	98 (37)				0.9		260 (127)	No	1	2	3	0
1,3-Pentadiene (mixture of cis and trans isomers) $CH_2:CHCH:CHCH_3$ (Piperylene) **504-60-9**	IB	−20 (−29)		2	8.3	0.7	2.35	109 (43)	No	1	2	3	2
1,2,3,4,5-Pentamethyl-benzene, 95% $C_6H(CH_3)_5$ (Pentamethylbenzene)	IIIB	200 (93)	800 (427) (est.)			0.9		449 (232)	No			2	0
Pentamethylene Dichloride	See 1,5-Dichloropentane.												
Pentamethylene Glycol	See 1,5-Pentanediol.												
Pentamethylene Oxide $O(CH_2)_4CH_2$ (Tetrahydropyran) **142-68-7**	IB	−4 (−20)				0.9	3.0	178 (81)	Yes	1 5	2	3	1
Pentanal	See Valeraldehyde.												
Pentane $CH_3(CH_2)_3CH_3$ **109-66-0**	IA	< −40 (< −40)	500 (260)	1.5	7.8	0.6	2.5	97 (36)	No	1	1	4	0
1,5-Pentanediol $HO(CH_2)_5OH$ (Pentamethylene Glycol) **111-29-5**		265 (129) (oc)	635 (335)			1.0 –		468 (242)	Yes	2 5	1	1	0
2,4-Pentanedione $CH_3COCH_2COCH_3$ (Acetyl Acetone) **123-54-6**	IC	93 (34)	644 (340)			1.0 –	3.5	284 (140)	Yes	5 1	2	3	0
Pentanoic Acid C_4H_9COOH (Valeric Acid) **109-52-4**		205 (96) (oc)	752 (400)	1.6	7.6	0.9	3.5	366 (186)	Very slight		3	1	0
1-Pentanol	See Amyl Alcohol.												
2-Pentanol	See Methyl Propyl Carbinol.												
3-Pentanol $CH_3CH_2CH(OH)CH_2CH_3$ (tert-n-Amyl Alcohol) **584-02-1**	II	105 (41)	815 (435)	1.2	9.0	0.8	3.0	241 (116)	Slight	5	1	2	0
1-Pentanol Acetate	See Amyl Acetate.												
2-Pentanol Acetate	See sec-Amyl Acetate.												
2-Pentanone	See Methyl Propyl Ketone.												

Chemical Name Formula (Synonym) CAS No.	NFPA 30/ OSHA Class	Flash Point °F(°C)	Ignition Temp. °F(°C)	Flammable Limits Percent by Vol.		Sp.Gr. (Water =1)	Vapor Density (Air =1)	Boiling Point °F(°C)	Water Soluble	Extin- guishing Methods	Hazard Identification		
				Lower	Upper						Health	Flamma- bility	Insta- bility
3-Pentanone	See Diethyl Ketone.												
Pentaphen $C_5H_{11}C_6H_4OH$ (p-tert-Amyl Phenol) **80-46-6**		232 (111) (oc)				0.9		482 (250)	No	2	3	1	0
	Note: Melting point 195 (91).												
Pentapropionyl Glucose	See Glucose Pentapropionate.												
1-Pentene $CH_3(CH_2)_2CH{:}CH_2$ (Amylene) **109-67-1**		0 (−18) (oc)	527 (275)	1.5	8.7	0.7	2.4	86 (30)	No	1	1	4	1
1-Pentene-cis	See β-Amylene-cis.												
2-Pentene-trans	See β-Amylene-trans.												
Pentylamine	See Amylamine.												
Pentyloxypentane	See Amyl Ether.												
Pentyl Propionate	See Amyl Propionate.												
1-Pentyne $HC{:}CC_3H_7$ (n-Propyl Acetylene) **627-19-0**	IB	<−4 (<−20)				0.69	2.35	104 (40)		1	1	3	3
Peracetic Acid (Less than 40%) CH_3COOOH **79-21-0**	II	105 (41)	392 (200)			1.23		221 (105)	Yes		3	2	4 OX
	Note: Decomposes violently at 230 (110). Explodes on heating. See NFPA 49 contained in this guide.												
Perchloroethylene $Cl_2C{:}CCl_2$ (Perc) (Perchloroethene) (Tetrachloroethylene) **127-18-4**		None	None		None	1.6	5.8	250 (121)	No		2	0	0
Perhydrophenanthrene $C_{14}H_{24}$ (Tetradecahydrophenanthrene) **5743-97-5**			475 (246)			0.9		187–192 (86–89)					0
Perilla Oil **68132-21-8**	IIIB	522 (272)				0.9			No	2	0	1	0
Petroleum, Crude, Sour		20–90 (−7–32)				<1			No	1	2	3	0
Petroleum, Crude, Sweet		20–90 (−7–32)				<1			No	1	1	3	0
Petroleum Ether (Benzine) (Naphtha, Petroleum) **64475-85-0**		<0 (<−18)	550 (288)	1.1	5.9	0.6	2.5	95–140 (35–60)	No	1	1	4	0
Petroleum Pitch	See Asphalt (Typical).												
Petroleum Sulfonate		400 (204) (oc)							No	2	0	1	0
β-Phellandrene $CH_2{:}CCH{:}CHCH[CH(CH_3)_2]CH_2CH_2$ [p-Mentha-1(7), 2-Diene] **555-10-2**	II	120 (49)				~0.9	4.68	340 (171)	No		0	2	0
Phenanthrene $(C_6H_4CH)_2$ (Phenanthrin) **85-01-8**		340 (171) (oc)				1.1		644 (340)	No	2	1	1	0
	Note: Melting point 212 (100).												

Chemical Name Formula (Synonym) CAS No.	NFPA 30/ OSHA Class	Flash Point °F(°C)	Ignition Temp. °F(°C)	Flammable Limits Percent by Vol.		Sp.Gr. (Water =1)	Vapor Density (Air =1)	Boiling Point °F(°C)	Water Soluble	Extin- guishing Methods	Hazard Identification		
				Lower	Upper						Health	Flamma- bility	Insta- bility
Phenethyl Alcohol $C_6H_5CH_2CH_2OH$ (Benzyl Carbinol) (Phenylethyl Alcohol) **60-12-8**	IIIB	205 (96)				1.0+		430 (221)	No	2	2	1	0
o-Phenetidine $H_2NC_6H_4OC_2H_5$ (2-Ethoxyaniline) (o-Amino-Phenetole) **94-70-2**	IIIA	178 (81)						442–446 (228–230)	No	5 2	1	2	0
p-Phenetidine $C_2H_5OC_6H_4NH_2$ (1-Amino-4-Ethoxybenzene) (p-Aminophenetole) **156-43-4**	IIIB	241 (116)				1.1		378–484 (192–251)	Very slight	2	2	1	0
Phenetole	See Ethoxybenzene.												
Phenol C_6H_5OH (Carbolic Acid) **108-95-2**	IIIA	175 (79)	1319 (715)	1.8	8.6	1.1	3.2	358 (181)	Yes	5	4	2	0
	Note: Melting point 108 (42). See NFPA 49 contained in this guide.												
2-Phenoxyethanol	See Ethylene Glycol Phenyl Ether.												
Phenoxy Ethyl Alcohol $C_6H_5O(CH_2)_2OH$ (2-Phenoxyethanol) (Phenyl Cellosolve) **122-99-6**		250 (121) (oc)				1.11	4.77	468 (242)		2	0	1	0
	Note: Melting point 58 (14).												
N-(2-Phenoxyethyl) Aniline $C_6H_5O(CH_2)_3NHC_6H_5$	IIIB	338 (170)				1.1		396 (202)	No	2	1	1	0
β-Phenoxyethyl Chloride	See β-Chlorophenetole.												
Phenylacetaldehyde $C_6H_5CH_2CHO$ (α-Toluic Aldehyde) **122-78-1**	IIIA	160 (71)				1.0+		383 (195)	No	5	3	2	1
Phenyl Acetate $CH_3COOC_6H_5$ (Acetylphenol) **122-79-2**	IIIA	176 (80)				1.1	4.7	384 (196)	Slight	5	1	2	0
Phenylacetic Acid $C_6H_5CH_2COOH$ (α-Toluic Acid) **103-82-2**	IIIB	>212 (>100)				1.1		504 (262)	Yes	5 2	2	1	0
	Note: Melting point 169–171 (76–77).												
Phenylamine	See Aniline.												
N-Phenylaniline	See Diphenylamine.												
Phenylbenzene	See Biphenyl.												
Phenyl Bromide	See Bromobenzene.												
1-Phenyl-2-Butene $C_6H_5CH_2CH{:}CHCH_3$		160 (71) (oc)				0.9	4.6	346 (174)				2	0
Phenyl Carbinol	See Benzyl Alcohol.												
Phenyl Chloride	See Chlorobenzene.												
Phenylcyclohexane	See Cyclohexylbenzene.												
Phenyl Didecyl Phosphite $(C_6H_5O)P(OC_{10}H_{21})_2$ **1254-78-0**		425 (218) (oc)				0.9				2	0	1	0

Chemical Name Formula (Synonym) CAS No.	NFPA 30/ OSHA Class	Flash Point °F(°C)	Ignition Temp. °F(°C)	Flammable Limits Percent by Vol. Lower	Upper	Sp.Gr. (Water =1)	Vapor Density (Air =1)	Boiling Point °F(°C)	Water Soluble	Extin-guishing Methods	Hazard Identification Health	Flamma-bility	Insta-bility
N-Phenyldiethanolamine $C_6H_5N(C_2H_4OH)_2$ **120-07-7**		385 (196) (oc)	730 (387)	0.7		1.1		376 (191)	No	2	2	1	0
	Note: Melting point 136 (58).												
Phenyldiethylamine	See N,N-Diethylaniline.												
Phenyl Diglycol Carbonate	See Diethylene Glycol Bis (Phenylcarbonate).												
Phenyl Di-o-Xenyl Phosphate $(C_{12}H_9O)_2POOC_6H_5$	IIIB	482 (250)				1.2		545–626 (285–330)	No	2	0	1	1
o-Phenylenediamine $NH_2C_6H_4NH_2$ (1,2-Diaminobenzene) **95-54-5**	IIIB	313 (156)		1.5			3.73	513 (267)		2	3	1	0
	Note: Melting point 284 (140).												
Phenylethane	See Ethylbenzene.												
N-Phenylethanolamine $C_6H_5NHC_2H_4OH$ (2-Anilinoethanol) (β-Anilinoethanol Ethoxyaniline) (β-Hydroxyethylaniline) **122-98-5**		305 (152) (oc)				1.1		545 (285)	Slight	2 5	3	1	0
β-Phenylethyl Acetate $C_6H_5CH_2CH_2OOCCH_3$ (β-Phenylethylacetate)		230 (110) (oc)				1.03	5.67	435 (224)		2	0	1	0
Phenylethyl Alcohol	See Phenethyl Alcohol.												
Phenylethylene	See Styrene.												
N-Phenyl-N-Ethylethanolamine $C_6H_5N(C_2H_5)C_2H_4OH$ **92-50-2**		270 (132) (oc)	685 (362)	0.8		1.0+		514 (268)@ 740 mm	Slight	2 5	3	1	0
Phenylhydrazine $C_6H_5NHNH_2$ **100-63-0**	IIIA	190 (88)	345 (174)			1.1	3.7	Decomposes	Slight	5	3	2	0
Phenylmethane	See Toluene.												
Phenylmethylethanolamine $C_6H_5N(CH_3)C_2H_4OH$ [2-(N-Methylaniline)-Ethanol]		280 (138) (oc)				1.07	5.22	378 (192) @ 100 mm		2	2	1	0
Phenyl Methyl Ketone	See Acetophenone.												
4-Phenylmorpholine $C_6H_5NC_2H_4OCH_2CH_2$ **92-53-5**		220 (104) (oc)				1.1		518 (270)	Slight	5 2	2	1	0
Phenylpentane	See Amylbenzene.												
o-Phenylphenol $C_6H_5C_6H_4OH$ **90-43-7**	IIIB	255 (124)	986 (530)			1.2		547 (286)	Slight	5 2	3	1	0
	Note: Melting point 134 (57).												
Phenylpropane	See Propylbenzene.												
2-Phenylpropane	See Cumene.												
Phenylpropyl Alcohol $C_6H_5(CH_2)_3OH$ (Hydrocinnamic Alcohol) (3-Phenyl-l-propanol) (Phenylethyl Carbinol) **122-97-4**	IIIB	212 (100)				1.0+		426 (219)	No	5	1	1	0

Chemical Name Formula (Synonym) CAS No.	NFPA 30/ OSHA Class	Flash Point °F(°C)	Ignition Temp. °F(°C)	Flammable Limits Percent by Vol. Lower	Upper	Sp.Gr. (Water =1)	Vapor Density (Air =1)	Boiling Point °F(°C)	Water Soluble	Extin-guishing Methods	Hazard Identification Health	Flamma-bility	Insta-bility
Phenylpropyl Aldehyde $C_6H_5CH_2CH_2CHO$ (3-Phenylpro-pionaldehyde) (Hydrocinnamic Aldehyde) **104-53-0**	IIIB	205 (96)				1.0+		430–439 (221–226)		5	1	1	0
o-Phenyltoluene $C_6H_5C_6H_4CH_3$ (2-Methylbiphenyl)	IIIB	>212 (>100)	923 (495)			1.01	5.82	500 (260)		2		1	0
Phenyl Trichloro Silane $C_6H_5SiCl_3$ [Trichloro(phenyl)silane] **98-13-5**		196 (91) (oc)				1.32	7.36	394 (201)			3	2	2 ~~W~~
Phorone $(CH_3)_2CCHCOCHC(CH_3)_2$ **504-20-1**	Note: Melting point 82 (28).	185 (85) (oc)				0.9	4.8	388 (198)	No		2	2	0
Phosphine PH_3 **7803-51-2**	See NFPA 49 contained in this guide.	Gas	212 (100)	1.6	98 (est.)	0.57@ 20 atm	1.17	−126 (−88)	No	6 Do not use halocar-bons	4	4	2
Phthalic Acid $C_6H_4(COOH)_2$ **88-99-3**	IIIB Note: Melting point 376 (191).	334 (168)				1.59	5.73	552 (289)			1	1	0
Phthalic Anhydride $C_6H_4(CO)_2O$ **85-44-9**	IIIB Note: Melting point 262 (128). See NFPA 49 contained in this guide.	305 (152)	1058 (570)	1.7	10.5	1.5		543 (284)	No	2	2	1	0
m-Phthalyl Dichloride	See Isophthaloyl Chloride.												
2-Picoline $CH_3C_5H_4N$ (2-Methylpyridine) **109-06-8**		102 (39) (oc)	1000 (538)			1.0−	3.2	262 (128)	No		3	3	0
4-Picoline $CH_3C_5H_4N$ **108-89-4**		134 (57) (oc)				1.0−	3.2	292 (144)	Yes	5	3	2	0
Pimelic Ketone	See Cyclohexanone.												
Pinane $C_{10}H_{18}$ **473-55-2**			523 (273)	0.7 @320 (160)	7.2 @320 (160)	0.8		336 (151)			0		0
α-Pinene $C_{10}H_{16}$ **80-56-8**	IC	91 (33)	491 (255)			0.9	4.7	312 (156)	No	1	1	3	0
Pine Oil **8002-09-3**	IIIA	172 (78) 138 (59)				0.9		367–439 (186–226)	No		2	2	0
Pine Pitch	IIIB Note: Melting point 148 (64).	285 (141)				1.1		490 (254)	No	2	0	1	0
Pine Tar **8011-48-1**	II	130 (54)	671 (355)					208 (98)	No		1	2	0
Pine Tar Oil (Wood Tar Oil)	IIIA	144 (62)				0.9			No		0	2	0
Piperazine $HNCH_2CH_2NHCH_2CH_2$ **110-85-0**	Note: Melting point 226–230 (108–110).	178 (81) (oc)	644 (340)	4	14	1.1	3.0	294 (146)	Slight	5	3	2	0
Piperidine $(CH_2)_5NH$ (Hexahydropyridine) **110-89-4**	IB See NFPA 49 contained in this guide.	61 (16)				0.9	3.0	223 (106)	Yes	1 5	3	3	0
Pogy Oil	See Menhaden Oil.												

Chemical Name Formula (Synonym) CAS No.	NFPA 30/ OSHA Class	Flash Point °F(°C)	Ignition Temp. °F(°C)	Flammable Limits Percent by Vol.		Sp.Gr. (Water =1)	Vapor Density (Air =1)	Boiling Point °F(°C)	Water Soluble	Extin- guishing Methods	Hazard Identification		
				Lower	Upper						Health	Flamma- bility	Insta- bility
Polyamyl Naphthalene		360 (182) (oc)				0.9		667–747 (353–397)	No	2	0	1	0
Polyethylene Glycols $OH(C_2H_5O)_nC_2H_4OH$ **25322-68-3**		360–550 (182–287) (oc)							Yes	5 2	1	1	0
Polyoxyethylene Lauryl Ether $C_{12}H_{25}O(OCH_2CH_2)_nOH$ **9002-92-0**	IIIB	>200 (>93)				0.95					0	1	0
Polypropylene Glycols $OH(C_3H_6O)_nC_3H_6OH$ **25322-69-4**		365 (185) (oc)				1.0+		Decomposes		5 2	0	1	0
Polyvinyl Alcohol **9002-89-5**		175 (79) (oc)							Yes	5	0	2	0
Poppy Seed Oil	IIIB	491 (255)				0.9			No	2	0	1	0
Potassium Xanthate $KS_2C\text{-}OC_2H_5$ **140-89-6**	IIIB	205 (96)			9.6	1.56	5.53	392 (200) Decomposes	Yes		1	1	0
Propanal	See Propionaldehyde.												
Propane $CH_3CH_2CH_3$ **74-98-6**		Gas	842 (450)	2.1	9.5		1.6	−44 (−42)	No	6	2	4	0
1,3-Propanediamine $NH_2CH_2CH_2CH_2NH_2$ (1,3-Diaminopropane) (Trimethylenediamine) **109-76-2**		75 (24) (oc)				0.9	2.6	276 (136)	Yes	1 5	3	3	0
1,2-Propanediol	See Propylene Glycol.												
1,3-Propanediol	See Trimethylene Glycol.												
1-Propanol	See Propyl Alcohol.												
2-Propanol	See Isopropyl Alcohol.												
2-Propanone	See Acetone.												
Propanoyl Chloride	See Propionyl Chloride.												
Propargyl Alcohol $HC{:}CCH_2OH$ (2-Propyn-1-ol) **107-19-7**	Note: May polymerize explosively. See NFPA 49 contained in this guide.	97 (36) (oc)				0.97	1.93	239 (115)	Yes	1	4	3	3
Propene	See Propylene.												
2-Propenylamine	See Allylamine.												
Propenyl Ethyl Ether $CH_3CH{:}CHOCH_2CH_3$ **928-55-2**		<20 (<−7) (oc)				0.8	1.3	158 (70)		1	2	3	0
β-Propiolactone $C_3H_4O_2$ **57-57-8**	IIIA	165 (74)		2.9		1.1	2.5	311 (155)	Yes	5	0	2	0
Propionaldehyde CH_3CH_2CHO (Propanal) **123-38-6**	IB See NFPA 49 contained in this guide.	−22 (−30)	405 (207)	2.6	17	0.8	2.0	120 (49)	Slight	1 5	2	3	2
Propionic Acid CH_3CH_2COOH **79-09-4**	II See NFPA 49 contained in this guide.	126 (52)	870 (465)	2.9	12.1	1.0−	2.5	297 (147)	Yes	5	3	2	0

Chemical Name Formula (Synonym) CAS No.	NFPA 30/ OSHA Class	Flash Point °F(°C)	Ignition Temp. °F(°C)	Flammable Limits Percent by Vol.		Sp.Gr. (Water =1)	Vapor Density (Air =1)	Boiling Point °F(°C)	Water Soluble	Extin-guishing Methods	Hazard Identification		
				Lower	Upper						Health	Flamma-bility	Insta-bility
Propionic Anhydride $(CH_3CH_2CO)_2O$ **123-62-6**	IIIA	145 (63)	545 (285)	1.3	9.5	1.0+	4.5	336 (169)	Decom-poses		3	2	1
Propionic Nitrile CH_3CH_2CN (Propionitrile) **107-12-0**	IB	36 (2)		3.1		0.78	1.90	207 (97)	Yes	1	4	3	1
Propionyl Chloride CH_3CH_2COCl (Propanoyl Chloride) **79-03-8**	IB	54 (12)				1.1	3.2	176 (80)	Decom-poses	1	3	3	2 ~~W~~
Propyl Acetate $C_3H_7OOCCH_3$ (Acetic Acid, n-Propyl Ester) **109-60-4**	IB	55 (13)	842 (450)	1.7 @ 100(38)	8	0.9	3.5	215 (102)	Slight	1 5	1	3	0
Propyl Alcohol $CH_3CH_2CH_2OH$ (1-Propanol) **71-23-8**	IC	74 (23)	775 (412)	2.2	13.7	0.8	2.1	207 (97)	Yes	1 5	1	3	0
Propylamine $CH_3(CH_2)_2NH_2$ **107-10-8**	IB See NFPA 49 contained in this guide.	−35 (−37)	604 (318)	2.0	10.4	0.7	2.0	120 (49)	Yes	1 5	3	3	0
Propylbenzene $C_3H_7C_6H_5$ (Phenylpropane) **103-65-1**	IC	86 (30)	842 (450)	0.8	6.0	0.9	4.1	319 (159)	No	1	1	3	0
2-Propybiphenyl $C_6H_5C_6H_4C_3H_7$	IIIB	>212 (>100)	833 (445)				6.77	~536 (~280)		2	0	1	0
n-Propyl Bromide C_3H_7Br (1-Bromopropane) **106-94-5**			914 (490)	4.6		1.35	4.34	160 (71)			2	2	0
n-Propyl Butyrate $C_3H_7COOC_3H_7$ **105-66-8**	IC	99 (37)				0.87	4.49	290 (143)		1	0	3	0
Propyl Carbinol	See Butyl Alcohol.												
Propyl Chloride C_3H_7Cl (1-Chloropropane) **540-54-5**	IB	<0 (<−18)	968 (520)	2.6	11.1	0.9	2.7	115 (46)	Very slight	1	2	3	0
Propyl Chlorothiolformate C_3H_7SCOCl	IIIA	145 (63)				1.1	4.8	311 (155)	No		2	2	0
Propylcyclohexane $C_6H_{11}CH_2CH_2CH_3$ **1678-92-8**		95 (35)	478 (248)			0.8		313–315 (156–157)			0		0
Propylcyclopentane $C_3H_7C_5H_9$ (1-Cyclopentylpropane)			516 (269)			0.8		269 (131)			0		0
Propylene $CH_2{:}CHCH_3$ (Propene) **115-07-1**		Gas	851 (455)	2.0	11.1		1.5	−53 (−47)	No	6	1	4	1
Propylene Aldehyde	See Crotonaldehyde.												
Propylene Carbonate $OCH_2CH_2CH_2OCO$ **108-32-7**		275 (135) (oc)				1.2		468 (242)	Yes	2 5	1	1	1
Propylene Chlorohydrin	See 2-Chloro-1-Propanol.												

Chemical Name Formula (Synonym) CAS No.	NFPA 30/ OSHA Class	Flash Point °F(°C)	Ignition Temp. °F(°C)	Flammable Limits Percent by Vol.		Sp.Gr. (Water =1)	Vapor Density (Air =1)	Boiling Point °F(°C)	Water Soluble	Extin-guishing Methods	Hazard Identification		
				Lower	Upper						Health	Flamma-bility	Insta-bility
sec-Propylene Chlorohydrin	See 1-Chloro-2-Propanol.												
Propylenediamine $CH_3CH(NH_2)CH_2NH_2$ **78-90-0**		92 (33) (oc)	780 (416)			0.9	2.6	246 (119)	Yes	1 5	3	3	0
Propylene Dichloride $CH_3CHClCH_2Cl$ (1,2-Dichloropropane) **78-87-5**	IB See NFPA 49 contained in this guide.	60 (16)	1035 (557)	3.4	14.5	1.2	3.9	205 (96)	No	4	2	3	0
Propylene Glycol $CH_3CHOHCH_2OH$ (Methyl Ethylene Glycol) (1,2-Propanediol) **57-55-6**	IIIB	210 (99)	700 (371)	2.6	12.5	1.0+	2.62	370 (188)	Yes	5	0	1	0
Propylene Glycol Acrylate $CH_2{:}CHCOO(C_3H_6)OH$ (Hydroxypropyl Acrylate) **25584-83-2** **999-61-1**	IIIB	207 (97)		1.4 @ 212 (100)		1.05	4.5	410 (210)	Yes	5	3	1	2
Propylene Glycol Isopropyl Ether	II	110 (43)				0.86		283 (140)	Yes				
Propylene Glycol Methyl Ether $CH_3OCH_2CHOHCH_3$ (1-Methoxy-2-propanol) **107-98-2**	IC	90 (32)		1.6	13.8	0.92	3.11	248 (120)	Yes	1	1	3	0
Propylene Glycol Methyl Ether Acetate (99% Pure) **108-65-6**	II	108 (42)	670 (354)	1.5 @ 392 (200)	7.0 @ 392 (200)	0.966	4.6	295 (146)	Slight	5	1	2	0
Propylene Oxide OCH_2CHCH_3 (ring) **75-56-9**	IA See NFPA 49 contained in this guide.	−35 (−37)	840 (449)	2.3	36	0.83	2.0	94 (35)	Yes	1 5	3	4	2
n-Propyl Ether $(C_3H_7)_2O$ (Dipropyl Ether) **111-43-3**	IB	70 (21)	370 (188)	1.3	7.0	0.75	3.53	194 (90)		1	1	3	1
Propyl Formate $HCOOC_3H_7$ **110-74-7**	IB	27 (−3)	851 (455)			0.9	3.0	178 (81)	Slight	1 5	2	3	0
Propyl Methanol	See Butyl Alcohol.												
Propyl Nitrate $CH_3CH_2CH_2NO_3$ **627-13-4**	IB Note: May explode on heating. Decomposes at 347 (175). See NFPA 49 contained in this guide.	68 (20)	347 (175)	2	100	1.1	3.6	231 (111)	Slight	1 5	2	3	3 OX
Propyl Propionate $CH_3CH_2COOCH_2$- CH_2CH_3 **106-36-5**		175 (79) (oc)				0.9	4.0	245 (118)	No		1	2	0
Propyltrichlorosilane $(C_3H_7)SiCl_3$ **141-57-1**	IC See NFPA 49 contained in this guide.	98 (37)				1.2	6.12	254 (123.5)	Reacts	1	3	3	1
Propyne $CH_3C{:}CH$ (Allylene) (Methylacetylene) **74-99-7**		Gas		1.7			1.4	−10 (−23)		6	1	4	3
Prussic Acid	See Hydrocyanic Acid.												
Pseudocumene	See 1,2,4-Trimethylbenzene.												
Pyridine C_5H_5N **110-86-1**	IB See NFPA 49 contained in this guide.	68 (20)	900 (482)	1.8	12.4	1.0−	2.7	239 (115)	Yes	1 5	3	3	0

Chemical Name Formula (Synonym) CAS No.	NFPA 30/ OSHA Class	Flash Point °F(°C)	Ignition Temp. °F(°C)	Flammable Limits Percent by Vol.		Sp.Gr. (Water =1)	Vapor Density (Air =1)	Boiling Point °F(°C)	Water Soluble	Extin-guishing Methods	Hazard Identification		
				Lower	Upper						Health	Flamma-bility	Insta-bility
Pyroxylin Solution	IC	80 (27) May be below.							No	1	1	4	0
	See Collodion and Nitrocellulose.												
Pyrrole $(CHCH)_2NH$ (Azole) **109-97-7**	II	102 (39)				1.0–	2.3	268 (131)	No		2	2	1
Pyrrolidine $NHCH_2CH_2CH_2CH_2$ (ring) (Tetrahydropyrrole) **123-75-1**	IB	37 (3)				0.9	2.5	186–189 (86–87)	Yes	5 1	2	3	1
2-Pyrrolidone $NHCOCH_2CH_2CH_2$ (ring) **616-45-5**		265 (129) (oc)				1.1	2.9	473 (245)	Yes	2 5	3	1	0
	Note: Melting point 77 (25).												
Quenching Oil	IIIB	365 (185)				0.9			No	2	1	1	0
Quinoline $C_6H_4N{:}CHCH{:}CH$ (ring) **91-22-5**	II	138 (59)	896 (480)	1.2		1.1	4.5	460 (238)	No		3	2	0
Range Oil	See Fuel Oil No. 1.												
Rapeseed Oil (Colza Oil) **8002-13-9**	IIIB	325 (163)	836 (447)			0.9			No	2	0	1	0
Red Oil	See Oleic Acid.												
Resorcinol $C_6H_4(OH)_2$ (Dihydroxybenzol) (1,3-Benzenediol) **108-46-3**	IIIB	261 (127)	1126 (608)	1.4 @ 392 (200)	1.28	3.80	531 (277)	352 (178) @ 16 mm	Yes	2	3	1	0
	Note: Melting point 232 (111).												
Rhodinol $CH_2{:}C(CH_3)(CH_2)_3CH$-$(CH_3)(CH_2)_2OH$ **6812-78-8**	IIIB	>212 (>100)				0.9		237–239 (114–115)@ 12 mm	No	2	0	1	0
Ricinus Oil	See Castor Oil.												
Rosin Oil **8002-16-2**	IIIB	266 (130)	648 (342)			1.0–		>680 (>360)	No	2	0	1	0
Rum	See Ethyl Alcohol and Water.												
Salicylaldehyde HOC_6H_4CHO (o-Hydroxy-benzaldehyde) **90-02-8**	IIIA	172 (78)				1.2		384 (196)	Slight	5	0	2	0
Safrole $C_3H_5C_6H_3O_2CH_2$ (4-Allyl-1,2-Methylene-Dioxybenzene) **94-59-7**	IIIB	212 (100)				1.1		451 (233)	No		1	1	0
Salicylic Acid HOC_6H_4COOH **69-72-7**	IIIB	315 (157)	1004 (540)	1.1 @ 392 (200)		1.5	4.8	Sublimes @ 169 (76)	No	2	1	1	0
	Note: Melting point 316–322 (158–161).												
Santalol $C_{15}H_{24}O$ (Arheol) **11031-45-1**	IIIB	>212 (>100)				1.0–		~572 (~300)	No	2		1	0
Sesame Oil **8008-74-0**	IIIB	491 (255)				0.9			No	2	0	1	0
Signal Oil	See Mineral Seal Oil, Typical.												

Chemical Name Formula (Synonym) CAS No.	NFPA 30/ OSHA Class	Flash Point °F(°C)	Ignition Temp. °F(°C)	Flammable Limits Percent by Vol.		Sp.Gr. (Water =1)	Vapor Density (Air =1)	Boiling Point °F(°C)	Water Soluble	Extin-guishing Methods	Hazard Identification		
				Lower	Upper						Health	Flamma-bility	Insta-bility
Silane SiH_4 (Silicon Hydride) **7803-62-5** See NFPA 49 contained in this guide.		Gas	Pyro-phoric	1.4	96 (est.)		1.3	−169 (−112)	Slight	Do not use halocar-bons.	1	4	3
Soy Bean Oil **8001-22-7**	IIIB	540 (282)	833 (445)			0.9			No	2	0	1	0
Sperm Oil No. 1 **8002-24-2** See also Sperm Oil No. 2	IIIB	428 (220) 460 (238)	586 (308)			0.9			No	2	0	1	0
Sperm Oil No. 2 See also Sperm Oil No. 1	IIIB	460 (238)											
Spindle Oil See Lubricating Oil, Spindle.													
Stearic Acid $CH_3(CH_2)_{16}COOH$ **57-11-4** Note: Melting point 157 (69).	IIIB	385 (196)	743 (395)			0.8		726 (386)	No	2	1	1	0
Stearyl Alcohol $CH_3(CH_2)_{17}OH$ (1-Octadecanol) **112-92-5** Note: Melting point 140–142 (60–61).		392 (200)	842 (450)			0.8	9.3	410 (210) @ 15 mm	No		0		0
Straw Oil **64742-34-3**	IIIB	315–361 (157–183)							No	2	1	1	0
Stoddard Solvent **8052-41-3**	II	100–140 (38–60)	444 (229)	0.9	6	0.8	4.8	300–399 (149–204)	No		1	2	0
Styrene $C_6H_5CH{:}CH_2$ (Cinnamene) (Phenylethylene) (Vinyl Benzene) **100-42-5** Note: Polymerizes. See NFPA 49 contained in this guide.	IC	88 (31)	914 (490)	0.9	6.8	0.9	3.6	295 (146)	No	1	2	3	2
Styrene Oxide $C_6H_5CHOCH_2$ **96-09-3**		165 (74) (oc)	929 (498)			1.1		381 (194)			1	2	0
Succinonitrile $NCCH_2CH_2CN$ (Ethylene Dicyanide) **110-61-2** Note: Melting point 130 (54).	IIIB	270 (132)				1.0−	2.1	509–513 (265–267)	Yes	2 5	2	1	0
Sulfolane $CH_2(CH_2)_3SO_2$ (Tetrahydrothiophene-1,1-Dioxide) (Tetramethylene Sulfone) **126-33-0** Note: Melting point 81 (27).		350 (177) (oc)				1.3		545 (285)	Yes	2	1	1	0
Sulfur S_8 **7704-34-9** Note: Melting point 239 (115). See NFPA 49 contained in this guide.	IIIB	405 (207)	450 (232)	3.3		1.8		832 (445)	No	2	2	1	0
Sulfur Chloride SCl_2 **10545-99-0** Note: Decomposes in water.						1.6 @ 15°C	3.55		Decom-poses		3	1	2 ₩
Sulfur Dichloride S_2Cl_2 **10025-67-9** **12771-08-3** See NFPA 49 contained in this guide.	IIIB	244 (118)	453 (234)			1.7	4.66	280 (138)	Decom-poses	2	4	1	2 ₩
Sweet Oil See Olive Oil.													
Sylvan See 2-Methylfuran.													
Tallow **61789-97-7** Note: Melting point 88–100 (31–38).	IIIB	509 (265)				0.9			No	2	0	1	0
Tallow Oil Note: Melting point 109 (43).	IIIB	492 (256)				0.9			No	2	0	1	0

Chemical Name Formula (Synonym) CAS No.	NFPA 30/ OSHA Class	Flash Point °F(°C)	Ignition Temp. °F(°C)	Flammable Limits Percent by Vol. Lower	Upper	Sp.Gr. (Water =1)	Vapor Density (Air =1)	Boiling Point °F(°C)	Water Soluble	Extin-guishing Methods	Hazard Identification Health	Flamma-bility	Insta-bility
Tannic Acid $(HO)_3C_6H_2CO_2C_6H_2(OH)_2$-COOH (Tannin) (Digallic Acid) **1401-55-4**		390 (199) (oc)	980 (527)					Decomposes @ 392 (200)	Yes	2	1	1	0
	Note: Material is a solid at ambient temperatures.												
Tartaric Acid (d, l) $(CHOHCO_2H)_2$ **d=87-69-4** **l=133-37-9**		410 (210) (oc)	797 (425)			1.76	5.18			2	2	1	0
	Note: Melting point 338 (170).												
Terephthalic Acid $C_6H_4(COOH)_2$ (para-Phthalic Acid) (TPA) (1,4-Benzenedi-carboxylic acid) **100-21-0**		500 (260) (oc)	925 (496)			1.5		Sublimes above 572 (300)	No	2	1	1	0
Terephthaloyl Chloride $C_6H_4(COCl)_2$ (Terephthalyl Dichloride) (p-Phthalyl Dichloride) (1,4-Benzenedicarbonyl Chloride) **100-20-9**	IIIB	356 (180)						498 (259)	Yes	2	3	1	1
	Note: Melting point 175 (79).												
o-Terphenyl $(C_6H_5)_2C_6H_4$ **84-15-1**		325 (163) (oc)				1.1		630 (332)	No	2	1	1	0
m-Terphenyl $(C_6H_5)_2C_6H_4$ **92-06-8**		375 (191) (oc)				1.2		685 (363)	No	2	1	1	0
	Note: Melting point 188 (87).												
Terpineol $C_{10}H_{17}OH$ (Terpilenol) **8000-41-7**	IIIA	195 (91)				0.9		417–435 (214–224)	No		1	2	0
Terpinyl Acetate $C_{10}H_{17}OOCCH_3$ **80-26-2**	IIIB	200 (93)				1.0–		428 (220)	Slight	5 2	1	1	0
Tetraamylbenzene $(C_5H_{11})_4C_6H_2$	IIIB	295 (146)				0.9		608–662 (320–350)	No	2	0	1	0
1,1,2,2-Tetrabromoethane $CHBr_2CHBr_2$ (Acetylene Tetrabromide) **79-27-6**			635 (335)			2.97	11.9	275 (135)			3	0	1
	See NFPA 49 contained in this guide.												
Tetrachlorobenzene	See 1,2,4,5-Tetrachlorobenzene.												
1,2,4,5-Tetrachloro-benzene $C_6H_2Cl_4$ **95-94-3**	IIIB	311 (155)				1.7	7.4	472 (245)	Very Slight	2	2	1	0
Tetrachloroethylene	See Perchloroethylene.												
Tetradecane $CH_3(CH_2)_{12}CH_3$ **629-59-4**	IIIB	212 (100)	392 (200)	0.5		0.8		487 (253)	No	2	1	1	0
Tetradecanol $C_{14}H_{29}OH$ **112-72-1**		285 (141) (oc)				0.8		507 (264)	No	2	0	1	0
	Note: Melting point 100 (38).												
1-Tetradecene $CH_2{:}CH(CH_2)_{11}CH_3$ **26952-13-6**	IIIB	230 (110)	455 (235)			0.8	6.8	493 (256)	No	2	1	1	0
tert-Tetradecyl Mercaptan $C_{14}H_{29}SH$ **28983-37-1**	IIIB	250 (121)				0.9		496–532 (258–278)		5 2	2	1	0

Chemical Name Formula (Synonym) CAS No.	NFPA 30/ OSHA Class	Flash Point °F(°C)	Ignition Temp. °F(°C)	Flammable Limits Percent by Vol.		Sp.Gr. (Water =1)	Vapor Density (Air =1)	Boiling Point °F(°C)	Water Soluble	Extin-guishing Methods	Hazard Identification		
				Lower	Upper						Health	Flamma-bility	Insta-bility
Tetraethoxypropane $(C_2H_5O)_4C_3H_4$		190 (88) (oc)				1.12	6.70	621 (327)			1	2	0
Tetra(2-Ethylbutyl) Silicate $[C_2H_5CH(C_2H_5)CH_2O]_4Si$ **133-37-9**		335 (168) (oc)				0.9		460 (238) @ 50 mm	No	2	1	1	0
Tetraethylene Glycol $HOCH_2(CH_2OCH_2)_3$- CH_2OH **112-60-7**		360 (182) (oc)				1.1	6.7	Decomposes	Yes	2 5	1	1	0
Tetraethylene Glycol Dibutyl Ether	See Dibutoxy Tetraglycol.												
Tetraethylene Glycol Dimethyl Ether	See Dimethoxy Tetraglycol.												
Tetraethylene Pentamine $H_2N(C_2H_4NH)_3C_2H_4NH_2$ **112-57-2**		325 (163) (oc)	610 (321)			1.0–		631 (333)	Yes	2 5	3	1	0
Tetra(2-Ethylhexyl) Silicate $[C_4H_9CH(C_2H_5)CH_2O]_4Si$ [Tetrakis(2-ethylhexyl) orthosilicate] **115-82-2**		390 (199) (oc)				0.9		460 (238) @ 50 mm	No	2	1	1	0
Tetraethyl Lead $Pb(C_2H_5)_4$ **78-00-2**	IIIB	200 (93)		1.8		1.6	8.6	Decomposes above 230 (110)	No		3	2	2 ₩
Tetraethyl Orthosilicate	See Ethyl Silicate.												
Tetrafluoroethylene $F_2C:CF_2$ (TFE) (Perfluoroethylene) **116-14-3**		Gas	392 (200)	10.0	50.0	1.5	3.87	–105 (–76)	No	6	2	4	3
	See NFPA 49 contained in this guide.												
Tetraglycol Dichloride	See Bis[2-(2-Chloroethoxy) Ethyl] Ether.												
1,2,3,6-Tetrahydro-benzaldehyde $CH_2CH:CHCH_2CH_2$- $CHCHO$ (ring) (3-Cyclohexene-1-Carboxaldehyde) **100-50-5**		135 (57) (oc)				1.0–	3.8	328 (164)	Slight	5	2	2	0
endo-Tetrahydrodi-cyclopentadiene $C_{10}H_{16}$ (Tricyclodecane) **2825-83-4**			523 (273)			0.9		379 (193)					0
	Note: Melting point 171 (77).												
Tetrahydrofuran $OCH_2CH_2CH_2CH_2$ (ring) (Diethylene Oxide) (Tetramethylene Oxide) **109-99-9**	IB	6 (–14)	610 (321)	2	11.8	0.9	2.5	151 (66)	Yes	1 5	2	3	1
	See NFPA 49 contained in this guide.												
Tetrahydrofurfuryl Alcohol $C_4H_7OCH_2OH$ **97-99-4**		167 (75) (oc)	540 (282)	1.5	9.7	1.1		352 (178) @ 743 mm	Yes	5	2	2	0
Tetrahydrofurfuryl Oleate $C_4H_7OCH_2OOCC_{17}H_{33}$	IIIB	390 (199)				0.9		392–545 (200–285) @ 16 mm	No	2	1	1	0
Tetrahydronaphthalene $C_6H_4(CH_2)_2C_2H_4$ (Tetralin) **119-64-2**	IIIA	160 (71)	725 (385)	0.8 @ 212 (100)	5.0 @ 302 (150)	1.0–	4.6	405 (207)	No		1	2	0

Chemical Name Formula (Synonym) CAS No.	NFPA 30/ OSHA Class	Flash Point °F(°C)	Ignition Temp. °F(°C)	Flammable Limits Percent by Vol. Lower	Flammable Limits Percent by Vol. Upper	Sp.Gr. (Water =1)	Vapor Density (Air =1)	Boiling Point °F(°C)	Water Soluble	Extin-guishing Methods	Hazard Identification Health	Hazard Identification Flamma-bility	Hazard Identification Insta-bility
Tetrahydropyran	See Pentamethylene Oxide.												
Tetrahydropyran-2-Methanol $OCH_2CH_2CH_2CH_2CH$- CH_2OH		200 (93) (oc)				1.0+	4.0	368 (187)	Yes	5	1	2	0
Tetrahydropyrrole	See Pyrrolidine.												
Tetralin	See Tetrahydronaphthalene.												
1,1,3,3-Tetramethoxy-propane $[(CH_3O)_2CH]_2CH_2$ **102-52-3**	IIIA	170 (77)				1.0−		361 (183)	Yes	5	1	2	0
1,2,3,4-Tetramethyl-benzene, 95% $C_6H_2(CH_3)_4$ (Prehnitene) **488-23-3**	IIIA	166 (74)	800 (427) (est.)			0.9		399–401 (204–205)	No		0	2	0
1,2,3,5-Tetramethyl-benzene, 85.5% $C_6H_2(CH_3)_4$ (Isodurene) **527-53-7**	IIIA	160 (71)	800 (427) (est.)			0.9		387–389 (197–198)	No		1	2	0
1,2,4,5-Tetramethyl-benzene, 95% $C_6H_2(CH_3)_4$ (Durene) **95-93-2**	II	130 (54)				0.8 @ 178 (81)	4.6	385 (196)	No		0	2	0
	Note: Melting point 174 (79).												
Tetramethylene	See Cyclobutane.												
Tetramethylene Glycol	See 1,4-Butanediol.												
Tetramethylene Oxide	See Tetrahydrofuran.												
Tetramethyl Lead $Pb(CH_3)_4$ **75-74-1**	II	100 (38)				1.6	6.5	Decomposes above 212 (100)	No		2	3	3 ~~W~~
2,2,3,3-Tetramethylpentane $(CH_3)_3CC(CH_3)_2CH_2CH_3$	IB	<70 (<21)	806 (430)	0.8	4.9	0.7	4.4	273 (134)		1	0	3	0
2,2,3,4-Tetramethylpentane $(CH_3)_3CCH(CH_3)$- $CH(CH_3)_2$	IB	<70 (<21)				0.74	4.43	270 (132)		1	0	3	0
Tetramethyl Tin $Sn(CH_3)_4$ **594-27-4**	IB	10 (12)		1.9		1.3	6.2	172 (78)	No	3	2	3	0
Tetraphenyl Tin $(C_6H_5)_4Sn$ **595-90-4**	IIIB	450 (232)				1.5	14.7	795 (424)	No	2	3	1	1
	Note: Melting point 439 (226).												
Tetrapropionyl Glucosyl Propionate	See Glucose Pentapropionate.												
Thialdine $SCH(CH_3)SCH(CH_3)$- $NHCHCH_3$ **638-17-5**		200 (93) (oc)				1.1		Decomposes	Slight	5		2	1
	Note: Melting point 112 (44).												
2,2-Thiodiethanol	See Thiodiglycol.												
Thiodiethylene Glycol	See Thiodiglycol.												

Chemical Name Formula (Synonym) CAS No.	NFPA 30/ OSHA Class	Flash Point °F(°C)	Ignition Temp. °F(°C)	Flammable Limits Percent by Vol.		Sp.Gr. (Water =1)	Vapor Density (Air =1)	Boiling Point °F(°C)	Water Soluble	Extin-guishing Methods	Hazard Identification		
				Lower	Upper						Health	Flamma-bility	Insta-bility
Thiodiglycol $(CH_2CH_2OH)_2S$ (Thiodiethylene Glycol) (Dihydroxyethyl Sulfide) [Bis(beta-Hydroxyethyl) Sulfide] (2,2-Thiodiethanol) **111-48-8**	IIIB	320 (160)	568 (298)			1.2		541 (283)	Yes	2 5	2	1	0
Thiophene SCH:CHCH:CH **110-02-1**	IB	30 (−1)				1.1	2.9	184 (84)	No	1	1	3	0
1,4-Thioxane $O(CH_2CH_2)_2S$ (1,4-Oxathiane) **15980-15-1**	II	108 (42)				1.12	3.59	300 (149)			1	2	0
Toluene $C_6H_5CH_3$ (Methylbenzene) (Phenylmethane) (Toluol) **108-88-3**	IB	40 (4)	896 (480)	1.1	7.1	0.9	3.1	231 (111)	No	1	2	3	0
	See NFPA 49 contained in this guide.												
Toluene-2,4-diisocyanate $CH_3C_6H_3(NCO)_2$ (TDI) (2,4-Tolylene Diisocyanate) (Toluene Diisocyanate) **108-88-3**	IIIB	260 (127)	1148 (620)	0.9	9.5	1.2	6.0	484 (251)	No Reacts	2	3	1	2
	See NFPA 49 contained in this guide.												
p-Toluenesulfonic Acid $C_6H_4(SO_3H)(CH_3)$ **104-15-4**	IIIB	363 (184)						295 (140)@ 20 mm	Yes	2	3	1	0
	Note: Melting point 220 (104.5).												
Toluhydroquinone $C_6H_3(OH)_2CH_3$ (Methylhydroquinone) **95-71-6**		342 (172) (oc)	875 (468)					545 (285)	Yes	2	1	1	0
	Note: Melting point 259 (126).												
o-Toluidine $CH_3C_6H_4NH_2$ (2-Methylaniline) **95-53-4**	IIIA	185 (85)	900 (482)	1.5		1.0−	3.7	392 (200)	No		3	2	0
	See NFPA 49 contained in this guide.												
p-Toluidine $CH_3C_6H_4NH_2$ (4-Methylaniline) **106-49-0**	IIIA	188 (87)	900 (482)	1.1	6.6	1.0+	3.9	392 (200)	No		3	2	0
	Note: Melting point 111 (44). See NFPA 49 contained in this guide.												
Toluol	See Toluene.												
m-Tolydiethanolamine $(HOC_2H_4)_2NC_6H_4CH_3$ (MTDEA)		400 (204) (oc)	740 (393)	0.6					No	2	2	1	0
	Note: Melting point 144 (62).												
2,4-Tolylene Diisocyanate	See Toluene-2,4-diisocyanate.												
o-Tolyl Phosphate	See Tri-o-Cresyl Phosphate.												
o-Tolyl p-Toluene Sulfonate $C_{14}H_{14}O_3S$	IIIB	363 (184)				1.2				2	1	1	0
Transformer Oil (Transil Oil)		295 (146) (oc)				0.9			No	2	1	1	0
Transil Oil	See Transformer Oil.												
Triacetin	See Glyceryl Triacetate.												
Tripentylamine $(C_5H_{11})_3N$ (Triamylamine) **621-77-2**		215 (102) (oc)				0.8		453 (234)	No	2	3	1	0
	See NFPA 49 contained in this guide.												

Chemical Name Formula (Synonym) CAS No.	NFPA 30/ OSHA Class	Flash Point °F(°C)	Ignition Temp. °F(°C)	Flammable Limits Percent by Vol. Lower	 Upper	Sp.Gr. (Water =1)	Vapor Density (Air =1)	Boiling Point °F(°C)	Water Soluble	Extin- guishing Methods	Hazard Identification Health	 Flamma- bility	 Insta- bility
Triamylbenzene $(C_5H_{11})_3C_6H_3$		270 (132) (oc)				0.9		575 (302)	No	2		1	0
Triamyl Borate $B(C_5H_{11}O)_3$ **621-78-3**		180 (82) (oc)				0.8	9.4	430 (221)				2	0
Tributylamine $(C_4H_9)_3N$ **102-82-9**	See NFPA 49 contained in this guide.	187 (86) (oc)				0.8	6.4	417 (214)	No		3	2	0
Tri-n-Butyl Borate $B(OC_4H_9)_3$ **688-74-4**		200 (93) (oc)				0.85	7.94	446 (230)			2	2	1
Tributyl Citrate $C_3H_4(OH)(COOC_4H_9)_3$ **77-94-1**	IIIB	315 (157)	695 (368)			1.0+		450 (232)	No	2	1	1	0
Tributyl Phosphate $PO_4(C_4H_9)_3$ (Butyl Phosphate) **126-73-8**		295 (146) (oc)	>900 (>482)			0.98	9.12	559 (293)	Slight	2	3	1	0
Tributylphosphine $(C_4H_9)_3P$ **998-40-3**		99–104 (37–40)	392 (200)			0.81		473 (245)	No		1	3	2
Tributyl Phosphite $(C_4H_9)_3PO_3$ **102-85-2**		248 (120) (oc)				0.9		244–250 (118–121)@ 7 mm	Decom- poses	2	2	1	1
1,2,4-Trichlorobenzene $C_6H_3Cl_3$ **120-82-1**	IIIB	222 (105)	1060 (571)	2.5 @ 302 (150)	6.6 @ 302 (150)	1.5	6.25	415 (213)	No	3	2	1	0
1,1,1-Trichloroethane CH_3CCl_3 (Methyl Chloroform) **71-55-6**	See NFPA 49 contained in this guide.	None	932 (500)	7.5	12.5	1.32	4.55	165 (74)	No		2	1	0
Trichloroethylene $ClHC{:}CCl_2$ **79-01-6**	See NFPA 49 contained in this guide.	None	788 (420)	8 @25°C 7.8 @ 100°C	10.5 @25°C 52 @ 100°C	1.5	4.5	188 (87)	No		2	1	0
1,2,3-Trichloropropane $CH_2ClCHClCH_2Cl$ (Allyl Trichloride) (Glyceryl Trichlorohydrin) **96-18-4**	IIIA	160 (71)	579 (304)	3.2 @ 120°C	12.6 @ 150°C	1.4	5.1	313 (156)	No	3	2	2	1
Trichlorosilane $HSiCl_3$ **10025-78-2**	See NFPA 49 contained in this guide.	7 (−14) (oc)		1.2	90.5	1.3	4.7	89 (32)	Decom- poses	Do not use halocar- bons	3	4	2 ~~W~~
Tri-o-Cresyl Phosphate $(CH_3C_6H_4)_3PO_4$ (o-Tolyl Phosphate) **78-30-8**	IIIB	437 (225)	725 (385)			1.2	12.7	770 (410) Decomposes	No	2	1	1	0
Tridecanol $CH_3(CH_2)_{12}OH$ **112-70-9**	Note: Melting point 86 (30).	250 (121) (oc)				0.8	6.9	525 (274)	No	2	0	1	0
2-Tridecanone	See Methyl Undecyl Ketone.												
Tridecyl Acrylate $CH_2{:}CHCOOC_{13}H_{27}$ **3076-04-8**		270 (132) (oc)				0.9		302 (150) @ 10 mm	No	2	1	1	0
Tridecyl Alcohol $C_{12}H_{25}CH_2OH$ (Tridecanol) **112-70-9**	Note: Melting point 88 (31).	180 (82) (oc)				0.8		485–503 (252–262)		5	1	2	0
Tridecyl Phosphite $(C_{10}H_{21}O)_3P$		455 (235) (oc)				0.9		356 (180)@ 0.1 mm	No	2	0	1	0

Chemical Name Formula (Synonym) CAS No.	NFPA 30/ OSHA Class	Flash Point °F(°C)	Ignition Temp. °F(°C)	Flammable Limits Percent by Vol. Lower	 Upper	Sp.Gr. (Water =1)	Vapor Density (Air =1)	Boiling Point °F(°C)	Water Soluble	Extin- guishing Methods	Hazard Identification Health	 Flamma- bility	 Insta- bility
Triethanolamine $(CH_2OHCH_2)_3N$ (2,2′,2″-Nitrilotriethanol) **102-71-6**	IIIB	354 (179)				1.1	5.1	650 (343)	Yes	2 5	2	1	0
	Note: Melting point 70 (21).												
1,1,3-Triethoxyhexane $CH(OC_2H_5)_2CH_2$- $CH(OC_2H_5)C_3H_7$		210 (99) (oc)				0.9	7.5	271 (133)@ 50 mm Decomposes @ 760 mm	No		1	1	0
Triethylaluminum $(C_2H_5)_3Al$ **97-93-8**		−63 (−53)				0.8		365 (185)			3	4	3 ₩
	Note: Ignites spontaneously in air. See NFPA 49 contained in this guide.												
Triethylamine $(C_2H_5)_3N$ **121-44-8**		16 (−7) (oc)	480 (249)	1.2	8.0	0.7	3.5	193 (89)	No	1 5	3	3	0
	See NFPA 49 contained in this guide.												
1,2,4-Triethylbenzene $(C_2H_5)_3C_6H_3$ **25340-18-5** **877-44-1**		181 (83) (oc)			56 @ 115°C	0.9	5.6	423 (217)	No			2	0
Triethylborane $(C_2H_5)_3B$ **97-94-9**	IB	−33 (−36)				0.7 @ 23°C	3.4	203 (95)			3	4	2 ₩
	Note: Ignites spontaneously in air.												
Triethyl Citrate $HOC(CH_2CO_2C_2H_5)$- $CO_2C_2H_5$ **77-93-0**	IIIB	303 (151)				1.1		561 (294)	Very slight	2	1	1	0
Triethylene Glycol $HOCH_2(CH_2OCH_2)_2$- CH_2OH (Dicaproate) (2,2-Ethylenedioxy- diethanol) **112-27-6**		350 (177) (oc)	700 (371)	0.9	9.2	1.1	5.2	546 (286)	Yes	2 5	1	1	0
Triethylene Glycol Diacetate $CH_3COO(CH_2CH_2O)_3$- $COCH_3$ (TDAC) **111-21-7**		345 (174) (oc)				1.1		572 (300)	Yes	5 2	0	1	0
Triethylene Glycol Dimethyl Ether $CH_3(OCH_2)_3OCH_3$ **112-49-2**		232 (111) (oc)				1.0−	4.7	421 (216)		2	1	1	0
Triethylene Glycol Ethyl Ether	See Ethoxytriglycol.												
Triethylene Glycol Methyl Ether	See Methoxytriglycol.												
Triethyleneglycol Monobutyl Ether $C_4H_9O(C_2H_4O)_3H$ **143-22-6**	IIIB	290 (143)				1.0+		270 (132)	Yes	5 2	2	1	0
Triethylenetetramine $H_2NCH_2(CH_2NHCH_2)_2$- CH_2NH_2 **112-24-3**	IIIB	275 (135)	640 (338)			1.0−		532 (278)	Yes	2 5	3	1	0
	See NFPA 49 contained in this guide.												
Triethyl Phosphate $(C_2H_5)_3PO_4$ (Ethyl Phosphate) **78-40-0**		240 (115) (oc)	850 (454)	1.2	10	1.1	6.28	408–424 (209–218)	Yes	5 2	1	1	1
Trifluorochloroethy- lene $CF_2:CFCl$ (R-1113) (Chlorotrifluoroethylene) **79-38-9**		Gas		8.4	38.7	1.31@ 5.7 atm	4.02	−18 (−28)		6	3	4	3

Chemical Name Formula (Synonym) CAS No.	NFPA 30/ OSHA Class	Flash Point °F(°C)	Ignition Temp. °F(°C)	Flammable Limits Percent by Vol.		Sp.Gr. (Water =1)	Vapor Density (Air =1)	Boiling Point °F(°C)	Water Soluble	Extin-guishing Methods	Hazard Identification		
				Lower	Upper						Health	Flamma-bility	Insta-bility
Triglycol Dichloride $ClCH_2(CH_3OCH_2)_2CH_2Cl$ **112-26-5**		250 (121) (oc)				1.2		466 (241)	No	2	2	1	0
Trihexyl Phosphite $(C_6H_{13})_3PO_3$ **6095-42-7**		320 (160) (oc)				0.9		275–286 (135–141) @ 2 mm	Decom- poses	2		1	0
	Note: Decomposes in water.												
Triisobutylaluminum $[(CH_3)_2CHCH_2]_3Al$ **100-99-2**						0.8		414 (212)	Reacts		3	4	3 ~~W~~
	Note: May ignite spontaneously in air. See NFPA 49 contained in this guide.												
Triisobutyl Borate $B(OC_4H_9)_3$		185 (85) (oc)				0.84	7.94	413 (212)			3	2	1
Triisopropanolamine $[(CH_3)_2COH]_3N$ (1,1′,1″-Nitrolotri-2-propanol) **122-20-3**		320 (160) (oc)	608 (320)	0.8	5.8	1.0–	6.60	584 (307)	Yes	2 5	3	1	0
	Note: Melting point 11 (44) (approx.).												
Triisopropylbenzene $C_6H_3(CH_3CHCH_3)_3$ **717-74-8**		207 (97) (oc)				0.9		495 (237)	No		1	2	0
Triisopropyl Borate $(C_3H_7O)_3B$ **5419-55-6**	IC	82 (28)				0.82	6.49	288 (142)		1		3	1
Trilauryl Trithiophosphite $[CH_3(CH_2)_{11}S]_3P$ (Tridodecyl trithiophosphite) **1656-63-9**		398 (203) (oc)				0.9				2	0	1	0
Trimethylaluminum $(CH_3)_3Al$ **75-24-1**		−1 (−18)				0.75		257–259 (125–126)			3	3	3 ~~W~~
	Note: Ignites spontaneously in air.												
Trimethylamine $(CH_3)_3N$ **75-50-3**		Gas	374 (190)	2.0	11.6	0.64	2.0	38 (3)	Yes	6	3	4	0
	See NFPA 49 contained in this guide.												
1,2,3-Trimethylbenzene $C_6H_3(CH_3)_3$ (Hemellitol) **526-73-8**	II	111 (44)	878 (470)	0.8	6.6	0.89	4.15	349 (176)			1	2	0
1,2,3-Trimethyl-benzene, 90.5% $C_6H_3(CH_3)_3$ (Hemimellitine)	II	128 (53)	895 (479)			0.9	4.1	347–351 (175–177)	No		1	2	0
1,2,4-Trimethylbenzene $C_6H_3(CH_3)_3$ (Pseudocumene) **95-63-6**	II	112 (44)	932 (500)	0.9	6.4	0.87	4.15	329 (165)	No		1	2	0
1,3,5-Trimethylbenzene $C_6H_3(CH_3)_3$ (Mesitylene) **108-67-8**	II	122 (50)	1039 (559)			0.9	4.1	328 (164)	No		2	2	0
Trimethyl Borate	See Methyl Borate.												
2,2,3-Trimethylbutane $(CH_3)_3C(CH_3)CHCH_3$ (Triptane—an isomer of Heptane) **464-06-2**	IB	<32 (<0)	774 (412)			0.69	3.46	178 (81)		1	1	3	0
2,3,3-Trimethyl-1-Butene $(CH_3)_3CC(CH_3):CH_2$ (Heptylene)	IB	<32 (<0)	707 (375)			0.71	3.39	172 (78)		1	0	3	0
Trimethyl Carbinol	See tert-Butyl Alcohol.												
Trimethylchlorosilane $(CH_3)_3SiCl$ **75-77-4**	IB	−18 (−28)	743 (395)	1.8	6.0	0.9	3.75	135 (57)	Yes	1	3	3	2 ~~W~~

Chemical Name Formula (Synonym) CAS No.	NFPA 30/ OSHA Class	Flash Point °F(°C)	Ignition Temp. °F(°C)	Flammable Limits Percent by Vol. Lower	Upper	Sp.Gr. (Water =1)	Vapor Density (Air =1)	Boiling Point °F(°C)	Water Soluble	Extin-guishing Methods	Hazard Identification Health	Flamma-bility	Insta-bility
1,3,5-Trimethylcyclo-hexane $(CH_3)_3C_6H_9$ (Hexahydromesitylene)			597 (314)			0.8		283 (139)			0		0
Trimethylcyclohexanol $CH(OH)CH_2C(CH_3)_2CH_2$- $CH(CH_3)CH_2$ **1321-60-4**		165 (74) (oc)				0.9	4.9	388 (198)	No			2	0
3,3,5-Trimethyl-1-Cyclohexanol $CH_2CH(CH_3)CH_2C$- $(CH_3)_2CH_2CHOH$ **116-02-9**		190 (88) (oc)				0.9	4.9	388 (198)	Slight	5	3	2	0
Trimethylene	See Cyclopropane.												
Trimethylenediamine	See 1,3-Propanediamine.												
Trimethylene Glycol $HO(CH_2)_3OH$ (1,3-Propanediol) **504-63-2**	IIIA	174 (345)	752 (400)			1.1	2.6	417 (214)	Yes	5	1	2	0
Trimethylethylene	See 2-Methyl-2-Butene.												
2,5,5-Trimethylheptane $C_2H_5C(CH_3)_2(CH_2)_2$- $CH(CH_3)_2$	II	<131 (<55)	527 (275)			0.73	4.91	304 (151)			0	2	0
2,2,5-Trimethylhexane $(CH_3)_3C(CH_2)_2CH(CH_3)_2$ **3522-94-9**		55 (13) (oc)				0.7	4.4	255 (124)	No	1		3	0
3,5,5-Trimethylhexanol $CH_3C(CH_3)_2CH_2CH$- $(CH_3)CH_2CH_2OH$ **3452-97-9**		200 (93) (oc)				0.8		381 (194)	No		2	2	0
2,6,8-Trimethyl-4-Nonanol $(CH_3)_2CHCH_2CH(OH)$- $CH_2CH(CH_3)CH_2CH$- $(CH_3)_2$ (2,4,8-Trimethyl-6-Nonanol) **123-17-1**		200 (93) (oc)				0.8		438 (226)	No		1	2	0
2,6,8-Trimethyl-4-Nonanone $(CH_3)_2CHCH_2CH$- $(CH_3)CH_2COCH_2CH$- $(CH_3)_2$ **123-18-2**		195 (91) (oc)				0.8	6.3	425 (218)	No		1	2	0
Trimethylolpropane Triacrylate $C_2H_5C(CH_2O$- $COCHCH_2)_3$ **15625-89-5**		300 (149) (oc)				1.5		392 (200)		2	2	1	2
2,2,3-Trimethylpentane $CH_3CH_2CH(CH_3)C(CH_3)_3$	IB	<70 (<21)	745 (346)			0.72	3.94	230 (110)		1	0	3	0
2,2,4-Trimethylpentane $(CH_3)_3CCH_2CH(CH_3)_2$ **540-84-1**	IB	10 (−12)	779 (415)	1.1	6.0	0.7	3.9	211 (99)	No	1	1	3	0
2,3,3-Trimethylpentane $CH_3CH_2C(CH_3)_2CH$- $(CH_3)_2$	IB	<70 (<21)	797 (425)			0.73	3.94	239 (115)		1	0	3	0
2,2,4-Trimethyl-1,3-Pentanediol $(CH_3)_2CHCH(OH)C$- $(CH_3)_2CH_2OH$ **144-19-4**	Note: Melting point 115–131 (46–55).	235 (113) (oc)	655 (346)			0.9		419–455 (215–235)	No	2	1	1	0

Chemical Name Formula (Synonym) CAS No.	NFPA 30/ OSHA Class	Flash Point °F(°C)	Ignition Temp. °F(°C)	Flammable Limits Percent by Vol. Lower	Upper	Sp.Gr. (Water =1)	Vapor Density (Air =1)	Boiling Point °F(°C)	Water Soluble	Extinguishing Methods	Hazard Identification Health	Flammability	Instability
2,2,4-Trimethyl-1,3-Pentanediol Diisobutyrate $C_{16}H_{30}O_4$ **144-19-4**		250 (121) (oc)	795 (424)	0.5 @ 342 (172)		0.9	9.9	536 (280)	No	2	1	1	0
2,2,4-Trimethyl-1,3-Pentanediol Isobutyrate $(CH_3)_2CHCH(OH)C(CH_3)_2CH_2OOCCH(CH_3)_2$ **25265-77-4**		248 (120) (oc)	740 (393)	0.6 @300 (149)	4.2 @393 (201)	1.0–	7.5	356–360 (180–182) @ 125 mm	No	2	1	1	0
2,2,4-Trimethylpentanediol Isobutyrate Benzoate $C_{19}H_{28}O_4$		325 (163) (oc)				1.0		167 (75) @ 10 mm		2	0	1	0
2,3,4-Trimethyl-1-pentene $H_2C:C(CH_3)CH(CH_3)CH(CH_3)_2$	IB	<70 (<21)	495 (257)			0.72	3.87	214 (101)		1	0	3	0
2,4,4-Trimethyl-1-pentene $CH_2:C(CH_3)CH_2C(CH_3)_3$ (Diisobutylene) **107-39-1**	IB	23 (–5)	736 (391)	0.8	4.8	0.7	3.8	214 (101)	No	1	1	3	0
2,4,4-Trimethyl-2-pentene $CH_3CH:C(CH_3)C(CH_3)_3$ **107-40-4**		35 (2) (oc)	581 (305)			0.7	3.8	221 (105)	No	1	2	3	0
3,4,4-Trimethyl-2-pentene $(CH_3)_3CC(CH_3):CHCH_3$ **598-96-9** **6095-42-7**	IB	<70 (<21)	617 (325)			0.74	3.87	234 (112)		1	0	3	0
Trimethyl Phosphite $(CH_3O)_3P$ **121-45-9**		130 (54) (oc)				1.0+	4.3	232–234 (111–112)	No		1	3	1
Trioctyl Phosphite $(C_8H_{17}O)_3P$ [Tris(2-Ethylhexyl) Phosphite]		340 (171) (oc)				0.9		212 (100) @ 0.01 mm	No	2	0	1	0
Trioxane $OCH_2OCH_2OCH_2$ **110-88-3** Note: Melting point 147 (64).		113 (45) (oc)	777 (414)	3.6	29			239 (115) Sublimes	Slight	5	2	2	3
Triphenylmethane $(C_6H_5)_3CH$ **519-73-3** Note: Melting point 200 (93).	IIIB	>212 (>100)				1.01	8.43	678 (359)		2	0	1	0
Triphenyl Phosphate $(C_6H_5)_3PO_4$ **115-86-6** Note: Melting point 122 (50).	IIIB	428 (220)				1.3		750 (399)	No	2	1	1	0
Triphenylphosphine See Triphenylphosphorus.													
Triphenyl Phosphite $(C_6H_5O)_3PO_3$ **101-02-0**		425 (218) (oc)				1.2		311–320 (155–160) @ 0.1 mm	No	2	2	1	1
Triphenylphosphorus $(C_6H_5)_3P$ (Triphenylphosphine) **603-35-0** Note: Melting point 176 (80).		356 (180) (oc)					9.0	711 (377)	No	2	2	1	0
Tripropyl Aluminum $(C_3H_7)_3Al$ **102-67-0** Note: Ignites spontaneously in air.											3	3	3 W
Tripropylamine $(CH_3CH_2CH_2)_3N$ **102-69-2**		105 (41) (oc)	356 (180)	0.7	5.6	0.8	4.9	313 (156)	Very slight		3	3	0

Chemical Name Formula (Synonym) CAS No.	NFPA 30/ OSHA Class	Flash Point °F(°C)	Ignition Temp. °F(°C)	Flammable Limits Percent by Vol.		Sp.Gr. (Water =1)	Vapor Density (Air =1)	Boiling Point °F(°C)	Water Soluble	Extin-guishing Methods	Hazard Identification		
				Lower	Upper						Health	Flamma-bility	Insta-bility
Tripropylene C_9H_{18} (Propylene Trimer)		75 (24) (oc)				0.7	4.35	271–288 (133–142)		1	0	3	0
Tripropylene Glycol $H(OC_3H_6)_3OH$ **24800-44-0** **1638-16-0**	IIIB	285 (141)		0.8	5.0	1.0+		514 (268)	Yes	2	0	1	0
Tripropylene Glycol Methyl Ether $HO(C_3H_6O)_2C_3H_6OCH_3$ **25498-49-1**	IIIB	250 (121)				0.97	7.12	470 (243)		2	1	1	0
Tris(2-Ethylhexyl) Phosphite	See Trioctyl Phosphite.												
Tung Oil (China Wood Oil) **8001-20-5**	IIIB Note: Melting point 88 (31).	552 (289)	855 (457)			0.9			No	2	0	1	0
Turbine Oil	See Lubricating Oil, Turbine.												
Turbo Fuels	See Jet Fuels.												
Turkey Red Oil (Castor Oil, Sulfated) **8002-33-3**	IIIB	476 (247)	833 (445)			1.0−			Yes	2 5	1	1	0
Turpentine **9005-90-7**	IC	95 (35)	488 (253)	0.8		<1		300 (149)	No	1	1	3	0
Ultrasene	See Kerosene, Deodorized.												
Undecane	See Hendecane.												
2-Undecanol $C_4H_9CH(C_2H_5)$- $C_2H_4CH(OH)CH_3$		235 (113) (oc)				0.8		437 (225)	No	2	1	1	0
Unsymmetrical Dimethylhydrazine	See 1,1-Dimethylhydrazine.												
Valeraldehyde $CH_3(CH_2)_3CHO$ (Pentanal) **110-62-3**		54 (12) (oc)	432 (222)	2.1	7.8	0.8	3.0	217 (103)	No	1	2	3	0
Valeric Acid	See Pentanoic Acid.												
Vinyl Acetate $CH_2{:}CHOOCCH_3$ (Ethenyl Ethanoate) **108-05-4**	IB Note: Polymerizes. See NFPA 49 contained in this guide.	18 (−8)	756 (402)	2.6	13.4	0.9	3.0	161 (72)	Slight	1 5	2	3	2
Vinylaceto-β-Lactone	See Diketene.												
Vinyl Acetylene $CH_2{:}CHC{⋮}CH$ (1-Buten-3-yne) **689-97-4**	See NFPA 49 contained in this guide.	Gas		21	100 Spont. decom-position	0.68 @ 1.7 atm	1.80	41 (5)	No	6	2	4	3
Vinyl Allyl Ether $CH_2{:}CHOCH_2CH_2O$- $(CH_2)_3CH_3$ (Allyl Vinyl Ether) **3917-15-5**		<68 (<20) (oc)				0.8		153 (67)	Very slight	1	1	3	0
Vinylbenzene	See Styrene.												
Vinylbenzylchloride $ClCH_2C_6H_4CH{:}CH_2$		220 (104) (oc)				1.1		444 (229)	No	2	2	1	
Vinyl Bromide **593-60-2**		<18 (<−8)	986 (530)	9	15	1.5	3.7	60 (15.8)	No		2	4	1
Vinyl Butyl Ether $CH_2{:}CHOC_4H_9$ (Butyl Vinyl Ether) **111-34-2**		15 (−9) (oc)	437 (255)			0.8	3.5	202 (94)	Slight	1 5	2	3	1

Chemical Name Formula (Synonym) CAS No.	NFPA 30/ OSHA Class	Flash Point °F(°C)	Ignition Temp. °F(°C)	Flammable Limits Percent by Vol. Lower	Upper	Sp.Gr. (Water =1)	Vapor Density (Air =1)	Boiling Point °F(°C)	Water Soluble	Extin-guishing Methods	Hazard Identification Health	Flamma-bility	Insta-bility
Vinyl Butyrate CH_2:$CHOCOC_3H_7$ **123-20-6**		68 (20) (oc)		1.4	8.8	0.9	4.0	242 (117)	Slight	1 5		3	2
Vinyl Chloride CH_2CHCl (Chloroethylene) **75-01-4**		Gas [−108.4 (−78) (oc)]	882 (472)	3.6	33.0	0.91	2.2	7 (−14)	No	6	2	4	2
	Note: Polymerizes. See NFPA 49 contained in this guide.												
Vinyl 2-Chloroethyl Ether CH_2:$CHOCH_2CH_2Cl$ (2-Chloroethyl Vinyl Ether) **110-75-8**		80 (27) (oc)				1.0+	3.7	228 (109)	Slight	1 5	2	3	1
Vinyl Crotonate CH_2:$CHOCOCH$:$CHCH_3$ **14861-06-4**		78 (26) (oc)				0.9	4.0	273 (134)	Slight	1 5	2	3	1
Vinyl Cyanide	See Acrylonitrile.												
4-Vinyl Cyclohexene C_8H_{12} **100-40-3**	IB	61 (16)	517 (269)	1	5.9	0.8	3.7	266 (130)		1	2	3	2
Vinyl Ether	See Divinyl Ether.												
Vinyl Ethyl Alcohol CH_2:$CH(CH_2)_2OH$ (3-Buten-1-ol) **627-27-0**	II	100 (38)		4.7	34	0.84	2.49	233 (112)	Yes		1	2	0
Vinylethylene Oxide	See Butadiene Monoxide.												
Vinyl Ethyl Ether CH_2:$CHOC_2H_5$ (Ethyl Vinyl Ether) **109-92-2**	IA	< −50 (< −46)	395 (202)	1.7	28	0.8	2.5	96 (36)	No	1 5	2	4	2
Vinyl 2-Ethylhexoate CH_2:$CHOCOCH(C_2H_5)$-C_4H_9		165 (74) (oc)				0.9	6.0	365 (185)	No		2	2	2
Vinyl 2-Ethylhexyl Ether $C_{10}H_{20}O$ (2-Ethylhexyl Vinyl Ether)		135 (57) (oc)	395 (202)			0.8	5.4	352 (178)	Slight	5	2	2	2
2-Vinyl-5-Ethylpyridine N:C(CH:CH_2)CH:CHC-(C_2H_5):CH		200 (93) (oc)				0.9		248 (120) @ 50 mm	No		2	2	2
Vinyl Fluoride CH_2:CHF **75-02-5**		Gas	860 (460)	2.6	21.7		1.6	−97.5 (−72)	Slight	6	2	4	2
Vinylidene Chloride CH_2:CCl_2 (1,1-Dichloroethylene) **75-35-4**	IA	−19 (−28)	1058 (570)	6.5	15.5	1.2	3.4	89 (32)	No	4	2	4	2
	Note: Polymerizes. See NFPA 49 contained in this guide.												
Vinylidene Fluoride CH_2:CF_2 **75-38-7**		Gas		5.5	21.3			−122.3 (−86)	Slight	6	1	4	2
Vinyl Isobutyl Ether CH_2:$CHOCH_2CH$-$(CH_3)CH_3$ (Isobutyl Vinyl Ether) **109-53-5**	IB	15 (−9)				0.8	3.5	182 (83)	Slight	1 5	2	3	2
Vinyl Isooctyl Ether CH_2:$CHO(CH_2)_5CH$-$(CH_3)_2$ (Isooctyl Vinyl Ether)	IIIA	140 (60)				0.8	5.4	347 (175)	No		1	2	0

Chemical Name Formula (Synonym) CAS No.	NFPA 30/ OSHA Class	Flash Point °F(°C)	Ignition Temp. °F(°C)	Flammable Limits Percent by Vol.		Sp.Gr. (Water =1)	Vapor Density (Air =1)	Boiling Point °F(°C)	Water Soluble	Extin-guishing Methods	Hazard Identification		
				Lower	Upper						Health	Flamma-bility	Insta-bility
Vinyl Isopropyl Ether $CH_2:CHOCH(CH_3)_2$ (Isopropyl Vinyl Ether) **926-65-8**	IB	−26 (−32)	522 (272)				3.0	133 (56)		1 5	2	3	2
Vinyl 2-Methoxyethyl Ether $CH_2:CHOC_2H_4OCH_3$ (1-Methoxy-2-Vinyloxyethane) **1663-35-0**		64 (18) (oc)				0.90	3.52	228 (109)		1	0	3	0
Vinyl Methyl Ether $CH_2:CHOCH_3$ (Methyl Vinyl Ether) **107-25-5**		Gas	549 (287)	2.6	39		2.0	43 (6)	Slight	6	2	4	2
Vinyl Octadecyl Ether $CH_2:CHO(CH_2)_{17}CH_3$ (Octadecyl Vinyl Ether) **930-02-9**	IIIB	350 (177)				0.8		297–369 (147–187) @ 5 mm	No	2	0	1	0
	Note: Melting point 82.4 (28).												
Vinyl Propionate $CH_2:CHOCOC_2H_5$ **105-38-4**		34 (1) (oc)				0.9	3.3	203 (95)	Slight	1 5	1	3	1
1-Vinylpyrrolidone $CH_2:CHNCOCH_2CH_2CH_2$ (Vinyl-2-Pyrrolidone) **88-12-0**		209 (98) (oc)				1.0+	3.8	205 (96) @ 14 mm	Yes	5	2	1	0
Vinyl-2-Pyrrolidone	See 1-Vinylpyrrolidone.												
Vinyl Toluene $CH_3C_6H_4CH:CH_2$ **25013-15-4**	II	127 (53)	1000 (538)	0.8	11.0	0.9	4.08	334 (168)	No		2	2	2
	See NFPA 49 contained in this guide.												
Vinyl Trichlorosilane $CH_2:CHSiCl_3$ **75-94-5**		70 (21) (oc)	505 (263)	3		1.3	5.61	195 (91)	Reacts	1	3	3	2 ₩
Water Gas	See Gas.												
Wax, Microcrystalline **63231-60-7**	IIIB	>400 (>204)				0.9				2	1	2	0
Wax, Ozocerite (Mineral Wax) **8021-55-4**	IIIB	236 (113)				0.9			No	2	0	1	0
Wax, Paraffin **8002-74-2**	IIIB	390 (199)	473 (245)			0.9		>700 (>371)	No	2	1	1	0
	Note: Melting point 120–167 (49–75).												
Whale Oil	IIIB	446 (230)	800 (427)			0.9			No	2	0	1	0
Whiskey	See Ethyl Alcohol and Water.												
White Tar	See Naphthalene.												
Wines Sherry and Port High	See Ethyl Alcohol and Water.												
Wood Alcohol	See Methyl Alcohol.												
Wood Tar Oil	See Pine Tar Oil.												
Wool Grease	See Lanolin.												
m-Xylene $C_6H_4(CH_3)_2$ (1,3-Dimethylbenzene) (m-Xylol) **108-38-3**	IC	77 (25)	982 (527)	1.1	7.0	0.9	3.7	282 (139)	No	1	2	3	0
	See NFPA 49 contained in this guide.												

Chemical Name Formula (Synonym) CAS No.	NFPA 30/ OSHA Class	Flash Point °F(°C)	Ignition Temp. °F(°C)	Flammable Limits Percent by Vol. Lower	Upper	Sp.Gr. (Water =1)	Vapor Density (Air =1)	Boiling Point °F(°C)	Water Soluble	Extin-guishing Methods	Hazard Identification Health	Flamma-bility	Insta-bility
o-Xylene $C_6H_4(CH_3)_2$ (1,2-Dimethylbenzene) (o-Xylol) **95-47-6**	IC	63 (17)	867 (463)	0.9	6.7	0.9	3.7	292 (144)	No	1	2	3	0
	See NFPA 49 contained in this guide.												
p-Xylene $C_6H_4(CH_3)_2$ (1,4-Dimethylbenzene) (p-Xylol) **106-42-3**	IC	77 (25)	984 (528)	1.1	7.0	0.9	3.7	281 (138)	No	1	2	3	0
	Note: Melting point 55 (13). See NFPA 49 contained in this guide.												
o-Xylidine $C_6H_3(CH_3)_2NH_2$ (o-Dimethylaniline) **87-59-2**	IIIB	206 (97)		1.0		1.0–		435 (224)	No		3	1	0
	See NFPA 49 contained in this guide.												
o-Xylol	See o-Xylene.												
Zinc Diethyl	See Diethylzinc.												
Zinc Stearate $Zn_{18}H_{35}O_2$ **557-05-1**		530 (277) (oc)	788 (420)			1.1					1	2	0
	Note: Melting point 262–266 (128–130).												

NFPA 432

1997 Edition

Storage of

Organic Peroxide Formulations

NFPA 432

Code for the

Storage of Organic Peroxide Formulations

1997 Edition

This edition of NFPA 432, *Code for the Storage of Organic Peroxide Formulations,* was prepared by the Technical Committee on Hazardous Chemicals and acted on by the National Fire Protection Association, Inc., at its Annual Meeting held May 19–22, 1997, in Los Angeles, CA. It was issued by the Standards Council on July 24, 1997, with an effective date of August 15, 1997, and supersedes all previous editions.

Changes other than editorial are indicated by a vertical rule in the margin of the pages on which they appear. These lines are included as an aid to the user in identifying changes from the previous edition.

This edition of NFPA 432 was approved as an American National Standard on August 15, 1997.

Origin and Development of NFPA 432

The development of NFPA 432 (formerly NFPA 43B in previous editions) began in 1969 with the tentative adoption by the Association of NFPA 499-T, *Code for the Storage and Transportation of Oxidizing Materials and Organic Peroxides.* As a result of suggestions by reviewers of this Tentative Code, the Technical Committee on Storage, Handling and Transportation of Hazardous Chemicals decided to replace NFPA 499-T with two codes, one for the storage of liquid and solid oxidizing materials and the other for organic peroxides.

The Technical Committee experienced great difficulty in developing NFPA 43B, primarily because initial attempts to classify burning behavior of the various organic peroxides considered only the peroxide itself. By 1975, it had become apparent to the Committee that any classification system would have to take into account the composition of each formulation (i.e., concentration of peroxide, active oxygen, and diluent) and the strength and size of the shipping container, if an accurate assessment of fire and explosion hazard were to be made. By analyzing the characteristics of most of the commercially available organic peroxide formulations and by conducting a limited number of full-scale fire tests, the Committee developed a valid classification scheme and storage requirements.

The first edition of NFPA 43B was adopted at the 1985 NFPA Fall Meeting.

The 1993 edition of NFPA 43B contained enhanced fire protection and storage requirements for all classes of organic peroxide formulations. The Committee on Hazardous Chemicals clarified the storage limitations for both sprinklered and nonsprinklered storage of all classes of organic peroxide formulations. The Committee also clarified the separation distance from the storage of incompatible materials. In addition, Appendix B contained expanded and updated tables of typical organic peroxide formulations that include more listed formulations and information on temperature control recommendations as well as hazard identification ratings.

For this 1997 edition, NFPA 43B was redesignated as NFPA 432. Provisions were added to address the classification of electrical equipment on the interior of any nonventilated, nonrefrigerated storage cabinet used for the storage of Class I, II, or III organic peroxide formulations. In addition, a table alphabetizing all the organic peroxide formulations was added to Appendix B.

Revisions to the tables of Typical Class Formulations include the following:

(a) Class I Formulations — The Health Hazard Identification Rating was revised for five organic peroxide formulations.

(b) Class II Formulations — The Health Hazard Identification Rating was revised for eight organic peroxide formulations.

(c) Class III Formulations — The Health Hazard Identification Rating was revised for 17 organic peroxide formulations, and the Flammability Hazard Identification Rating for cumyl hydroperoxide was also revised.

(d) Class IV Formulations — The Health Hazard Identification Rating was revised for nine organic peroxide formulations.

(e) Class V Formulations — The Health Hazard Identification Rating was revised for five organic peroxide formulations.

(f) The classification for 2,4-Pentanedione Peroxide was revised.

Other changes were editorial in nature to bring the document into conformance with the NFPA *Manual of Style.*

Technical Committee on Hazardous Chemicals

John A. Davenport, *Chair*
Industrial Risk Insurers, CT [I]

James E. Benge, Hercules Chemical Specialties Co., DE [U]
William J. Bradford, Brookfield, CT [SE]
James L. Daneker, Los Angeles City Fire Dept., CA [E]
Rep. NFPA Fire Service Section
August L. DeVico, II, Environmental Strategies & Applications, Inc., NJ [SE]
Henry L. Febo, Jr., Factory Mutual Research Corp., MA [I]
H. Dieter Heinz, Heinz Laboratories Int'l, CA [SE]
John M. Hoffmann, Safety Engr Laboratories, Inc., MI [SE]
Bart Howard, Davenport Fire Dept., IA [E]
Bruce A. Jacobsen, Olin Chemicals Corp., TN [M]
Janice King Jensen, U.S. Environmental Protection Agency, DC [I]
Brad Jones, Jacobson Warehouse Co. Inc., IA [U]
Roland J. Land, Alexander & Alexander of New York, Inc., NY [I]
George H. Matthews, N. Norwich, NY [SE]
Chester M. McCloskey, The Norac Co. Inc., CA [M]
Robert A. Michaels, RAM TRAC Corp., NY [SE]
David P. Nugent, Schirmer Engr Corp., IL [SE]
Anthony M. Ordile, Loss Control Assoc. Inc., PA [SE]
Gary A. Page, American Home Products, NJ [M]
George W. Rambo, GRCS Inc., VA [SE]
Sheila E. Toperosky, Akzo Nobel Chemicals, TX [M]
Rep. Society of the Plastics Industry Inc.
Gary F. Trojak, Chlorine Inst. Inc., DC [M]
Rep. The Chlorine Inst.
Michael A. Viggiani, George Eastman House, NY [U]
Matthew C. Woody, Des Moines Fire Dept., IA [E]

Alternates

Richard Cobb, The Norac Co. Inc., CA [M]
(Alt. to C. M. McCloskey)
Richard D. Gottwald, Society of the Plastics Industry Inc., DC [M]
(Alt. to S. E. Toperosky)
Donald J. Hoffmann, Safety Engr Laboratories, Inc., MI [SE]
(Alt. to J. M. Hoffmann)
Peter F. Langan, Industrial Risk Insurers, CT [I]
(Alt. to J. A. Davenport)
P. Kirk Mitchell, BioLab, Inc., GA [M]
(Voting Alt. to BLI Rep.)

Nonvoting

Charles H. Ke, U.S. Dept. of Transportation, DC
Samuel J. Porter, Lakeridge, VA
(Member Emeritus)
Robert W. VanDolah, CA
(Member Emeritus)

Martha H. Curtis, NFPA Staff Liaison

Committee Scope: This Committee shall have primary responsibility for documents on, and maintain current codes for, classes of hazardous chemicals and codes for specific chemicals where these are warranted by virtue of widespread distribution or special hazards.

This list represents the membership at the time the Committee was balloted on the text of this edition. Since that time, changes in membership may have occurred. A key to classifications is found at the back of this document.

NOTE: Membership on a committee shall not in and of itself constitute an endorsement of the Association or any document developed by the committee on which the member serves.

Contents

NFPA 432

Code for the

Storage of Organic Peroxide Formulations

1997 Edition

NOTICE: An asterisk (*) following the number or letter designating a paragraph indicates that explanatory material on the paragraph can be found in Appendix A.

Information on referenced publications can be found in Chapter 6 and Appendix C.

Chapter 1 General

1-1 Scope.

1-1.1 This code shall apply only to commercially available organic peroxide formulations in U.S. Department of Transportation- or Canadian Ministry of Transport-approved packages.

1-1.2 This code shall not apply to the storage of such formulations in process areas where they are manufactured or used.

1-1.3 This code does not apply to organic peroxide formulations that are capable of detonation in their normal shipping containers under conditions of fire exposure. Such formulations shall be handled and stored as Explosives 1.1 (formerly known as Class A) explosives in accordance with NFPA 495, *Explosive Materials Code.*

1-2 Purpose. The purpose of this code is to provide reasonable requirements for the safe storage of commercially available formulations containing organic peroxides.

1-3 Applicability of Other Documents. The requirements of NFPA 30, *Flammable and Combustible Liquids Code,* and NFPA 231, *Standard for General Storage,* shall apply where applicable and where they are more restrictive than this code.

1-4 Equivalency. Nothing in this standard is intended to prevent the use of systems, methods, or devices that provide equivalent protection from fire and explosion, provided that suitable data is available to demonstrate equivalency.

1-5 Definitions. For the purpose of this code, the following terms shall have the meanings given below.

Approved.* Acceptable to the authority having jurisdiction.

Authority Having Jurisdiction.* The organization, office, or individual responsible for approving equipment, an installation, or a procedure.

Deflagration. Propagation of a reaction zone at a velocity that is less than the speed of sound in the unreacted medium.

Detonation. Propagation of a reaction zone at a velocity that is at or above the speed of sound in the unreacted medium.

Explosive Decomposition. Rapid chemical reaction resulting in a large, almost instantaneous, release of energy. The term includes both deflagration and detonation.

Incompatible Materials. Materials that can initiate, catalyze, or accelerate the decomposition of organic peroxide formulations or that can cause hazardous reactions when in contact with such formulations. Information on incompatible materials for organic peroxide formulations can be found in material safety data sheets (MSDS) or manufacturers' product bulletins.

Labeled. Equipment or materials to which has been attached a label, symbol, or other identifying mark of an organization that is acceptable to the authority having jurisdiction and concerned with product evaluation, that maintains periodic inspection of production of labeled equipment or materials, and by whose labeling the manufacturer indicates compliance with appropriate standards or performance in a specified manner.

Listed.* Equipment, materials, or services included in a list published by an organization that is acceptable to the authority having jurisdiction and concerned with evaluation of products or services, that maintains periodic inspection of production of listed equipment or materials or periodic evaluation of services, and whose listing states that either the equipment, material, or service meets identified standards or has been tested and found suitable for a specified purpose.

Organic Peroxide. Any organic compound having a double oxygen or peroxy (-O-O-) group in its chemical structure.

Organic Peroxide Formulation.* A pure organic peroxide or a mixture of one or more organic peroxides with one or more other materials in various combinations and concentrations.

Organic Peroxide Storage Area. An area used for the storage of organic peroxide formulations.

Shall. Indicates a mandatory requirement.

Should. Indicates a recommendation or that which is advised but not required.

1-6* Classification of Organic Peroxide Formulations. For the purpose of this code, organic peroxide formulations shall be classified according to the system described in this section. The system is based on the behavior of certain specific formulations in their U.S. Department of Transportation- or Canadian Ministry of Transport-approved shipping containers and under conditions of fire exposure. *(See Appendix B for classification of typical organic peroxide formulations.)*

1-6.1 Class I shall describe those formulations that are capable of deflagration but not detonation.

1-6.2 Class II shall describe those formulations that burn very rapidly and that present a severe reactivity hazard.

1-6.3 Class III shall describe those formulations that burn rapidly and that present a moderate reactivity hazard.

1-6.4 Class IV shall describe those formulations that burn in the same manner as ordinary combustibles and that present a minimal reactivity hazard.

1-6.5 Class V shall describe those formulations that burn with less intensity than ordinary combustibles or do not sustain combustion and that present no reactivity hazard.

1-7 Classification of Storage Facilities.

1-7.1 *Segregated* storage refers to storage in the same room or inside area, but physically separated by distance from incompatible materials. Sills, curbs, intervening storage of nonhazardous compatible materials, and aisles shall be permitted to be used as aids in maintaining spacing. *(See Chapter 3.)*

1-7.2 *Cut-off* storage refers to storage in the same building or inside area, but physically separated from incompatible materials by partitions or walls. *(See Chapter 4.)*

1-7.3 *Detached* storage refers to storage in either an open outside area or a separate building containing no incompatible materials and located away from all other structures. *(See Chapter 5.)*

Chapter 2 Basic Requirements

2-1 Identification. All storage areas containing organic peroxide formulations shall be conspicuously identified by the words "Organic Peroxides" and by the class, as defined in Section 1-6.

2-1.1* When organic peroxide formulations having different classifications as defined by Section 1-6 are stored in the same area, the area shall be marked for the most severe class present.

2-1.2 Packages containing organic peroxide formulations shall be individually marked with the chemical name of the organic peroxide or with other pertinent information to allow proper area classification as required by this section.

2-1.3 Packages containing organic peroxide formulations that require temperature control shall be marked with the recommended storage temperature range.

2-2 Employee Instruction. Personnel involved in operations in organic peroxide storage areas shall be instructed in proper and safe handling of such materials, proper use of personal protective equipment, proper and safe disposal of spilled material, and proper emergency procedures. Manufacturers' instructions shall be consulted for each specific formulation.

2-3 Building Construction. Any construction materials that can be contacted by organic peroxide formulations shall be compatible with the materials stored.

2-4 Heating and Cooling.

2-4.1 Storage areas shall be maintained within the recommended storage temperature range for the materials stored. *(See Appendix B for compounds needing refrigeration systems.)*

2-4.2* Where the required storage temperature range extends beyond normal ambient temperatures, high or low temperature limit switches — as applicable — shall be provided in addition to the normal temperature controls. These limit switches shall actuate an alarm arranged to ensure prompt response.

2-4.3 Heating systems shall use hot water, low pressure (less than 15 psig [103 kPa gauge]) steam, or indirectly heated warm air. Cooling systems shall not utilize direct expansion of a flammable gas.

2-4.4 Heating coils, radiators, air diffusers, cooling coils, piping, and ducts shall be installed so as to prevent direct contact with containers and to prevent overheating or overcooling of the materials stored.

2-5 Electrical Installations.

2-5.1 Electrical installations shall meet all applicable requirements of NFPA 70, *National Electrical Code®*.

2-5.2 The interior of any refrigerator or freezer cabinet used for the storage of Class I, II, or III organic peroxide formulations shall be considered a Class I, Group D, Division 1 location as defined in Article 500 of NFPA 70, *National Electrical Code.* Any electrical equipment installed in the interior of such cabinets shall be approved for such use and shall be installed according to the requirements of Article 501 of NFPA 70, *National Electrical Code.*

2-5.3 The interior of any nonventilated, nonrefrigerated storage cabinet used for the storage of Class I, II, or III organic peroxide formulations shall be considered a Class I, Division 1 location as defined in Article 500 of NFPA 70, *National Electrical Code.*

2-5.4 Where the storage cabinet is ventilated, the electrical equipment shall be considered a Class I, Division 2 location as defined in Article 500 of NFPA 70, *National Electrical Code.* Mechanical ventilation systems shall provide at least 1 ft^3 per min per ft^2 of floor area (0.09 m^2 per min per 0.03 m^3).

2-6 Smoking. Smoking shall be prohibited in all organic peroxide storage areas. "No Smoking" signs shall be placed conspicuously at all entrances to and within storage areas.

2-7 Maintenance Operations.

2-7.1 Maintenance operations in organic peroxide storage areas shall be subject to prior review by and approval of supervisory personnel.

2-7.2 Cutting and welding operations in organic peroxide storage areas shall not be conducted until all organic peroxide formulations have been removed. Cutting and welding operations shall be conducted according to the requirements of NFPA 51B, *Standard for Fire Prevention in Use of Cutting and Welding Processes.*

2-8 Fire Protection.

2-8.1* Manual fire-fighting equipment shall be provided and maintained according to the requirements of NFPA 10, *Standard for Portable Fire Extinguishers,* and NFPA 14, *Standard for the Installation of Standpipe and Hose Systems.*

2-8.2* Where required by other provisions of this code, automatic sprinklers and water spray systems shall be designed and installed according to the requirements of NFPA 13, *Standard for the Installation of Sprinkler Systems,* and NFPA 15, *Standard for Water Spray Fixed Systems for Fire Protection,* and shall provide the following discharge densities:

Class I — 0.50 gpm/ft^2 (20.4 Lpm/m^2)
Class II — 0.40 gpm/ft^2 (16.3 Lpm/m^2)
Class III — 0.30 gpm/ft^2 (12.2 Lpm/m^2)
Class IV — 0.25 gpm/ft^2 (10.2 Lpm/m^2)

For Class I organic peroxide formulations, see 5-5.2.

2-8.2.1 The system shall be designed to provide the required density over a 3000 ft^2 (280 m^2) area for areas protected by a wet pipe sprinkler system or 3900 ft^2 (360 m^2) for areas protected by a dry pipe sprinkler system. The entire area of any building of less than 3000 ft^2 (280 m^2) shall be used as the area of application.

2-8.3 Where required, water supplies for automatic sprinklers, fire hydrants, and so forth, shall be provided in accordance with NFPA 24, *Standard for the Installation of Private Fire Service Mains and Their Appurtenances,* and shall be capable of supplying the anticipated demand for at least 90 minutes.

2-9 Housekeeping and Waste Disposal.

2-9.1 Any accumulation of combustible waste in organic peroxide storage areas shall be prohibited.

2-9.2* Spilled material and leaking or damaged containers and packages shall immediately be removed to a safe location for disposal.

2-9.3 Specific disposal procedures shall be established for all organic peroxide storage areas. Disposal procedures shall conform to all applicable federal, state, and local regulations and with the manufacturers' recommendations.

2-10 Storage Limitations.

2-10.1 Storage of organic peroxide formulations shall be limited to those areas within the scope of this code. The maximum allowable quantities of organic peroxide formulations that can be stored in a single area or building shall depend on the classification of the formulations and the classification of the storage facility, as set forth in Tables 2-10(a) and 2-10(b).

2-10.1.1 The quantity of Class III organic peroxide formulations as it appears in Table 2-10(a) in cut-off storage shall be permitted to be increased to 20,000 lb (9070 kg) if the walls or partitions providing the cut-off have a fire resistance rating of at least 4 hours.

2-10.1.2 Class I organic peroxide formulation cut-off storage as it appears in Table 2-10(b) shall have interior walls with a blast resistance of 432 psf (0.2 bar).

2-10.1.3* Class I organic peroxide formulation cut-off storage as it appears in Table 2-10(b) shall have deflagration venting provided for exterior walls.

2-10.2* Where two or more different classes of organic peroxide formulations are stored in the same area, the maximum quantity permitted shall be limited to the sum of the proportional amounts that each class bears to the maximum permitted for that class. The total of the proportional amounts shall not exceed 100 percent.

2-10.3 Where the storage area is protected by a specially engineered fire protection system acceptable to the authority having jurisdiction, the quantity of organic peroxide formulations shall be permitted to be increased.

2-10.4 Organic peroxide formulations shall not be stored where they can be exposed to explosive materials.

2-11 Storage Arrangements.

2-11.1 Storage shall be arranged to facilitate manual access and handling, to maintain pile stability, to minimize breakage and spillage, and to promote good housekeeping.

2-11.2 A clear space of at least 2 ft (0.6 m) shall be maintained between organic peroxide storage and uninsulated metal walls.

Table 2-10(a) Maximum Allowable Quantity of Organic Peroxide Formulations in Nonsprinklered Buildings

Class of Organic Peroxide Formulation	Segregated Storage		Cut-off Storage		Detached Storage Minimum Separation[1]					
					50 ft (15 m)		100 ft (30.5 m)		150 ft (46 m)	
	(lb)	(kg)	(lb)	(kg)	(lb)	(kg)	(lb)	(kg)	(lb)	(kg)
I	N/A	N/A	N/A	N/A	1000	454	4000	1810	10,000	4540
II	N/A	N/A	2000	907	20,000	9070	80,000	36,300	500,000	227,000
III	1500	680	3000	1360	70,000	31,800	200,000	90,700	750,000	340,000
IV	100,000	45,400	200,000	90,700	300,000	136,000	500,000	227,000	1,000,000	454,000
V	UNL	UNL	UNL	UNL	UNL	UNL	UNL	UNL	UNL	UNL

[1]Minimum separation means the distance from the line of property that is or can be built upon, including the opposite side of a public way, or the distance from the nearest important building on the same property.
N/A — Not Allowed
UNL — Unlimited

Table 2-10(b) Maximum Allowable Quantity of Organic Peroxide Formulations in Sprinklered Buildings

Class of Organic Peroxide Formulation	Segregated Storage		Cut-off Storage		Detached Storage Minimum Separation[1]					
					50 ft (15 m)		100 ft (30.5 m)		150 ft (46 m)	
	(lb)	(kg)	(lb)	(kg)	(lb)	(kg)	(lb)	(kg)	(lb)	(kg)
I	N/A	N/A	2000	907	2000	907	20,000	9070	175,000	79,400
II	4000	1810	50,000	22,700	100,000	45,400	200,000	90,700	UNL	UNL
III	50,000	22,700	100,000	45,400	200,000	90,700	UNL	UNL	UNL	UNL
IV	UNL	UNL	UNL	UNL	UNL	UNL	UNL	UNL	UNL	UNL
V	UNL	UNL	UNL	UNL	UNL	UNL	UNL	UNL	UNL	UNL

[1]Minimum separation means the distance from the line of property that is or can be built upon, including the opposite side of a public way, or the distance from the nearest important building on the same property.
N/A — Not Allowed
UNL — Unlimited

2-11.3 Separation Distance.

2-11.3.1 Incompatible materials and flammable liquids shall not be stored within 25 ft (7.6 m) of organic peroxide formulations. The effective separation distance shall be maintained by floor slope, drains, or dikes to prevent liquid leakage from encroaching on the organic peroxide formulation storage area.

Exception: Organic peroxide formulations that can also be classified as flammable liquids by their flash point shall be permitted to be stored with other organic peroxide formulations, and the more restrictive requirements of NFPA 30, Flammable and Combustible Liquids Code, or this code shall apply.

2-11.3.2 As an alternative to the 25-ft (7.6-m) separation distance, a 1-hr, liquid-tight fire barrier shall be permitted.

2-11.4 Only closed containers and packages shall be permitted in storage areas.

2-11.5 Storage of bags, drums, and other containers and packages of organic peroxide formulations shall be in accordance with Table 2-11.5.

Table 2-11.5 Provisions for Storage Arrangement by Class of Organic Peroxide Formulation

Class of Organic Peroxide Formulation	Max. Pile Height [ft (m)]	Max. Pile Width [ft (m)]	Min. Main Aisle Width [ft (m)]	Min. Additional Aisles Width [ft (m)]
I	6 (1.8)	4 (1.2)	8 (2.4)	4 (1.2)
II*	8 (2.4)	8 (2.4)	6 (1.8)	4 (1.2)
III*	8 (2.4)	8 (2.4)	6 (1.8)	4 (1.2)
IV	10 (3)	16 (4.9)	4 (1.2)	3 (0.9)
V	See 2-11.7.			

*See 2-11.6.

2-11.6* 55-gal (208-L) drum storage of Class II and Class III organic peroxide formulations shall be stored one high only.

2-11.7 Storage of Class V organic peroxide formulations shall meet the requirements of NFPA 231, *Standard for General Storage*, or NFPA 231C, *Standard for Rack Storage of Materials*, as applicable.

Chapter 3 Segregated Storage

3-1 Scope. This chapter shall apply to the storage of organic peroxide formulations when stored under segregated conditions as defined in Section 1-7 of this code and in quantities not exceeding those shown in Tables 2-10(a) and 2-10(b).

3-2 Basic Requirements. The basic requirements set forth in Chapter 2 shall apply to the segregated storage of organic peroxide formulations.

3-3 Building Construction. If there are any floors or open spaces located below the organic peroxide storage area, the floor of the storage area shall be made water-tight and shall be provided with drainage that leads to a safe location. Every means shall be taken to ensure that spilled material cannot run down into areas below the organic peroxide storage area.

3-4 Storage Arrangement.

3-4.1 A minimum of 8 ft (2.4 m) of clear space shall be maintained between organic peroxide storage and any other storage.

3-4.2 Segregated storage areas shall meet all applicable requirements of NFPA 231, *Standard for General Storage*, or NFPA 231C, *Standard for Rack Storage of Materials*, as applicable.

3-4.3* A clear space of at least 4 ft (1.2 m) shall be maintained between organic peroxide storage and any walls of combustible or limited-combustible construction.

3-5 Fire Protection. Automatic sprinkler protection shall be provided for segregated storage areas in accordance with 2-8.2 and 2-8.3, under the following conditions:

(a) Storage areas of combustible construction containing Classes II, III, or IV organic peroxide formulations

(b) Storage areas of noncombustible construction where quantities exceed the following:

1. 100,000 lb (45,400 kg) of Class IV organic peroxide formulations
2. 1500 lb (680 kg) of Class III organic peroxide formulations
3. Any quantity of Class II organic peroxide formulation

Chapter 4 Cut-off Storage

4-1 Scope. This chapter shall apply to the storage of organic peroxide formulations when stored under cut-off conditions as defined in Section 1-7 of this code and in quantities not exceeding those shown in Tables 2-10(a) and 2-10(b).

4-2 Basic Requirements. The basic requirements set forth in Chapter 2 shall apply to cut-off storage of organic peroxide formulations.

4-3 Building Construction.

4-3.1 Cut-off storage areas for Class I, Class II, or any refrigerated organic peroxide formulations shall be single story, without basements or crawl spaces.

4-3.2 Where any Class I organic peroxide formulations are stored in excess of 100 lb (45 kg), internal walls and any wall, roof, or ceiling that joins with another occupied building shall be capable of withstanding an internal overpressure of 432 psf (0.2 bar).

4-3.3 Where Class II or any refrigerated organic peroxide formulations are stored, any internal walls or any wall, roof, or ceiling that joins with another occupied building shall be capable of withstanding an internal overpressure of 125 psf (0.06 bar).

4-3.4* For Class I, Class II, or any refrigerated organic peroxide formulation that gives off flammable gases upon decomposition, the storage area shall be provided with deflagration venting.

4-3.5 Any walls common with another building shall have a fire resistance of at least 2 hours, as measured by the procedure described in NFPA 251, *Standard Methods of Fire Endurance of Building Construction and Materials.*

4-3.5.1 Any door or window openings in such walls shall be protected by approved fire doors and fire windows suitable for the opening and shall be installed according to NFPA 80, *Standard for Fire Doors and Fire Windows.*

4-4* Storage Arrangement. A clear space of at least 4 ft (1.2 m) shall be maintained between organic peroxide storage and any walls of combustible or limited-combustible construction.

4-5 Fire Protection.

4-5.1 Automatic sprinkler protection in accordance with 2-8.2 and 2-8.3 shall be provided for all storage areas of combustible construction, regardless of the class of formulation stored.

4-5.2 Automatic sprinkler protection shall be provided for all storage areas of noncombustible construction where any quantity of Class I organic peroxide formulations are stored.

4-5.3 Automatic sprinkler protection shall also be provided for all storage areas of noncombustible construction where quantities exceed the following:

(a) 2000 lb (907 kg) of Class II organic peroxide formulations

(b) 3000 lb (1360 kg) of Class III organic peroxide formulations

(c) 200,000 lb (90,700 kg) of Class IV organic peroxide formulations

Chapter 5 Detached Storage

5-1 Scope. This chapter shall apply to the storage of organic peroxide formulations when stored under detached conditions as defined in Section 1-7 and in quantities and at separation distances as specified in Tables 2-10(a) and 2-10(b).

5-2 Basic Requirements. The basic requirements set forth in Chapter 2 shall apply to detached storage of organic peroxide formulations.

5-3 Building Location.

5-3.1* Detached storage buildings shall be separated from the lines of property that are or can be built upon, including the opposite side of a public way, or from the nearest important building on the same property.

5-3.2 For Classes II, III, and IV organic peroxide formulations, detached storage buildings separated by less than 50 ft (15.3 m) shall be considered to be a single area when applying the limits for Tables 2-10(a) and 2-10(b).

5-3.3 For Class I organic peroxide formulations, detached storage buildings shall be separated from each other in accordance with Table 5-3.3.

Table 5-3.3 Separation of Individual Storage Buildings

Nonsprinklered				Automatic Sprinklered			
Quantity		Distance		Quantity		Distance	
(lb)	(kg)	(ft)	(m)	(lb)	(kg)	(ft)	(m)
1000	454	20	6	2000	907	20	6
4000	1810	75	23	20,000	9070	75	23
10,000	4540	100	30	175,000	79,400	100	30

5-4 Building Construction and Utilities.

5-4.1 Detached storage buildings shall be single story, without basement or crawl space.

5-4.2 Nonsprinklered buildings for storing more than 5000 lb (2270 kg) of Class I, Class II, or any refrigerated organic peroxide formulation that gives off flammable gases upon decomposition shall be built of noncombustible construction.

5-4.3* Buildings of combustible construction employing sun shields such as those illustrated in Figure A-5-4.3 shall be permitted to be used for detached storage buildings storing less than 5000 lb (2270 kg) of organic peroxide formulations in those areas where the temperature inside the storage building can approach or exceed the maximum recommended storage temperature.

5-5 Fire Protection.

5-5.1 Where required, automatic sprinkler systems and their water supplies shall meet the requirements of 2-8.2 and 2-8.3.

5-5.2 Where required for Class I organic peroxide formulations in quantities exceeding 2000 lb (907 kg), automatic sprinkler protection shall be open-head deluge-type, designed and installed in accordance with NFPA 13, *Standard for the Installation of Sprinkler Systems.*

Chapter 6 Referenced Publications

6-1 The following documents or portions thereof are referenced within this code as mandatory requirements and shall be considered part of the requirements of this code. The edition indicated for each referenced mandatory document is the current edition as of the date of the NFPA issuance of this code. Some of these mandatory documents might also be referenced in this code for specific informational purposes and, therefore, are also listed in Appendix C.

6-1.1 NFPA Publications. National Fire Protection Association, 1 Batterymarch Park, P.O. Box 9101, Quincy, MA 02269-9101.

NFPA 10, *Standard for Portable Fire Extinguishers,* 1994 edition.

NFPA 13, *Standard for the Installation of Sprinkler Systems,* 1996 edition.

NFPA 14, *Standard for the Installation of Standpipe and Hose Systems,* 1996 edition.

NFPA 15, *Standard for Water Spray Fixed Systems for Fire Protection,* 1996 edition.

NFPA 24, *Standard for the Installation of Private Fire Service Mains and Their Appurtenances,* 1995 edition.

NFPA 30, *Flammable and Combustible Liquids Code,* 1996 edition.

NFPA 51B, *Standard for Fire Prevention in Use of Cutting and Welding Processes,* 1994 edition.

NFPA 70, *National Electrical Code®,* 1996 edition.

NFPA 80, *Standard for Fire Doors and Fire Windows,* 1995 edition.

NFPA 231, *Standard for General Storage,* 1995 edition.

NFPA 231C, *Standard for Rack Storage of Materials,* 1995 edition.

NFPA 251, *Standard Methods of Fire Endurance of Building Construction and Materials,* 1995 edition.

NFPA 495, *Explosive Materials Code,* 1996 edition.

Appendix A Explanatory Material

This appendix is not part of the requirements of this NFPA document but is included for informational purposes only.

A-1-5 Approved. The National Fire Protection Association does not approve, inspect, or certify any installations, procedures, equipment, or materials; nor does it approve or evaluate testing laboratories. In determining the acceptability of installations, procedures, equipment, or materials, the authority having jurisdiction may base acceptance on compliance with NFPA or other appropriate standards. In the absence of such standards, said authority may require evidence of proper installation, procedure, or use. The authority having jurisdiction may also refer to the listings or labeling practices of an organization that is concerned with product evaluations and is thus in a position to determine compliance with appropriate standards for the current production of listed items.

A-1-5 Authority Having Jurisdiction. The phrase "authority having jurisdiction" is used in NFPA documents in a broad manner, since jurisdictions and approval agencies vary, as do their responsibilities. Where public safety is primary, the authority having jurisdiction may be a federal, state, local, or other regional department or individual such as a fire chief; fire marshal; chief of a fire prevention bureau, labor department, or health department; building official; electrical inspector; or others having statutory authority. For insurance purposes, an insurance inspection department, rating bureau, or other insurance company representative may be the authority having jurisdiction. In many circumstances, the property owner or his or her designated agent assumes the role of the authority having jurisdiction; at government installations, the commanding officer or departmental official may be the authority having jurisdiction.

A-1-5 Listed. The means for identifying listed equipment may vary for each organization concerned with product evaluation; some organizations do not recognize equipment as listed unless it is also labeled. The authority having jurisdiction should utilize the system employed by the listing organization to identify a listed product.

A-1-5 Organic Peroxide Formulation. Terms such as "accelerator," "catalyst," "initiator," and so forth, are sometimes used to describe organic peroxide formulations. These terms are misleading because they can also refer to materials that are not or do not contain organic peroxides, some of which might present increased hazard when mixed with organic peroxides.

A-1-6 Test procedures described in *United Nations Recommendation on Transportation of Dangerous Goods, Tests and Criteria* are useful in determining the classification of organic peroxide formulations.

A-2-1.1 The classification system described in Section 1-6 is used only to determine the storage requirements established by this code. It is not meant to be a substitute for the hazard identification system established by NFPA 704, *Standard System for the Identification of the Hazards of Materials for Emergency Response.* Since the hazard characteristics of organic peroxide formulations vary widely depending on the type of organic peroxide, the diluent, and their relative concentrations, each specific formulation will have to be rated individually according to the criteria established in NFPA 704.

A-2-4.2 Considerations should be given for maintaining proper refrigeration capability in the event of a loss of power. Some materials when frozen could cause separation of a carrier from the organic peroxide.

A-2-8.1 Manual fire-fighting equipment can consist of small hose equipped with adjustable spray nozzles or portable fire extinguishers suitable for Class A and for Class B:C fires, or both. Manual fire fighting in storage areas should be undertaken only by those having a clear understanding of the storage conditions and the characteristics of fires involving organic peroxides.

A-2-8.2 The use of high-expansion foam or liquid nitrogen flooding can be substituted for automatic sprinkler protection if installed subject to the approval of the authority having jurisdiction.

A-2-9.2 The method of disposal can vary depending on the specific formulation and materials with which they might have been contaminated. Refer to the manufacturer or the supplier of the specific formulation for advice.

A-2-10.1.3 See A-4-3.4.

A-2-10.2 For example, a sprinklered building, detached by 50 ft (15.3 m), can contain up to 500 lb (227 kg) of Class I, 50,000 lb (22,700 kg) of Class II, and 50,000 lb (22,700 kg) of Class III formulations, according to the following ratios:

Class I:

$$\frac{500\text{ lb}}{200\text{ lb (max)}} \times 100 = 25\% \qquad \frac{227\text{ kg}}{907\text{ kg (max)}} \times 100 = 25\%$$

Class II:

$$\frac{50{,}000\text{ lb}}{100{,}000\text{ lb (max)}} \times 100 = 50\% \qquad \frac{22{,}700\text{ kg}}{45{,}400\text{ kg (max)}} \times 100 = 50\%$$

Class III:

$$\frac{50{,}000\text{ lb}}{200{,}000\text{ lb (max)}} \times 100 = 25\% \qquad \frac{22{,}700\text{ lb}}{90{,}700\text{ lb (max)}} \times 100 = 25\%$$

In no case does the quantity in storage exceed the maximum for its class, nor does the sum of the percentages exceed 100 percent.

A-2-11.6 Since no commercially available Class I organic peroxide formulations are supplied in 55-gal (208-L) drums, there is no requirement for such storage.

A-3-4.3 For information on combustible or limited-combustible construction, see NFPA 220, *Standard on Types of Building Construction.*

A-4-3.4 In the venting equation, use the fuel characteristic constant for "gases with fundamental burning velocity less than 1.3 times that of propane." See NFPA 68, *Guide for Venting of Deflagrations,* for information on vent design. Refer to manufacturers' technical data for information on organic peroxide formulations that give off flammable gases upon decomposition.

A-4-4 For information on combustible or limited-combustible construction, see NFPA 220, *Standard on Types of Building Construction.*

A-5-3.1 For the purpose of this document, an important building is one that is occupied or that contains facilities vital to the operation of the plant.

A-5-4.3 Figure A-5-4.3 is an example of a building for storing less than 5000 lb (2270 kg) of organic peroxide formulations for detached storage as allowed by 5-4.3.

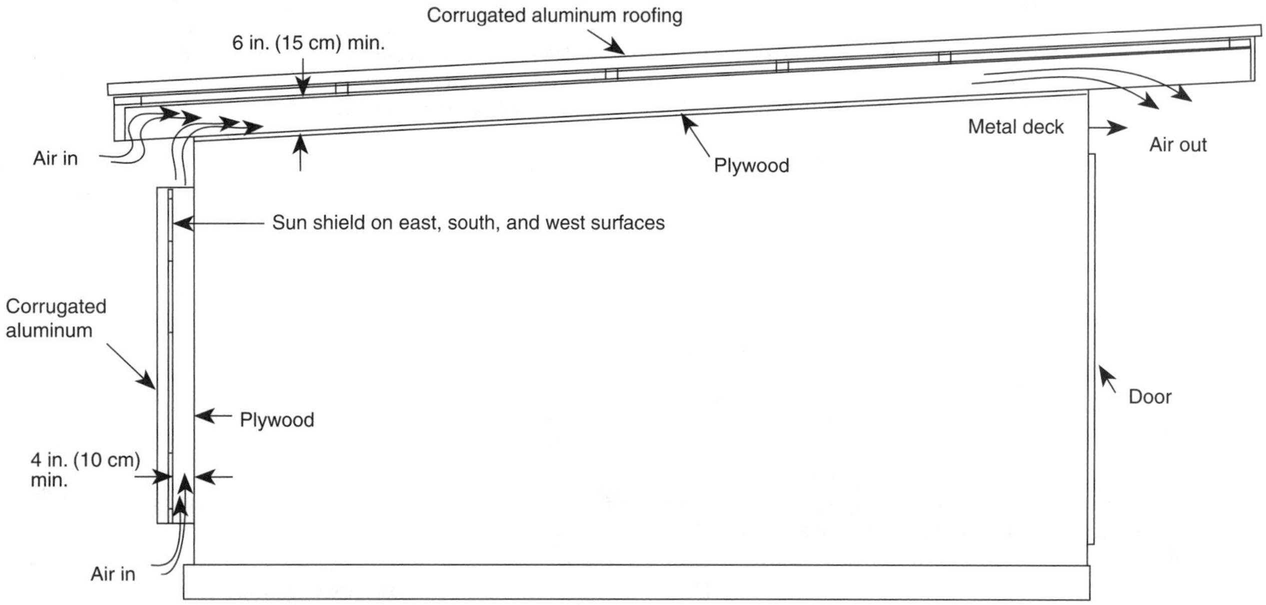

Figure A-5-4.3 Detached storage building for storing less than 5000 lb (2270 kg) of organic peroxide formulations.

Appendix B Typical Organic Peroxide Formulations

This appendix is not a part of the requirements of this NFPA document but is included for informational purposes only.

B-1 General. The assignment of the organic peroxide formulation classifications shown in the tables in this Appendix are based on the container sizes shown. A change in the container size could affect the classification.

For alphabetical listing of typical organic peroxide formulations, see Table B-1.

B-2 Class I Formulations.

B-2.1 Fire Hazard Characteristics. Class I formulations present a deflagration hazard through easily initiated, rapid explosive decomposition. Class I includes some formulations that are relatively safe only under closely controlled temperatures. Either excessively high or low temperatures can increase the potential for severe explosive decomposition.

B-2.2 Fire-Fighting Information. The immediate area should be evacuated and the fire should be fought from a remote location. Some damage to structures from overpressure can be expected should a deflagration occur.

B-2.3 Typical Class I Formulations. See Table B-2.3.

B-3 Class II Formulations.

B-3.1 Fire-Hazard Characteristics. Class II formulations present a severe fire hazard similar to Class I flammable liquids. The decomposition is not as rapid, violent, or complete as that produced by Class I formulations. As with Class I formulations, this class includes some formulations that are relatively safe when under controlled temperatures or when diluted.

B-3.2 Fire-Fighting Information. Fires should be fought from a safe distance, since a hazard exists from rupturing containers.

B-3.3 Typical Class II Formulations. See Table B-3.3.

B-4 Class III Formulations.

B-4.1 Fire Hazard Characteristics. Class III formulations present a fire hazard similar to Class II combustible liquids. They are characterized by rapid burning and high heat liberation due to decomposition.

B-4.2 Fire-Fighting Information. Caution should be observed due to possible unexpected increases in fire intensity.

B-4.3 Typical Class III Formulations. See Table B-4.3.

Table B-1 Class Index of Organic Peroxide Formulations

Organic Peroxide Formulation	Concentration	Diluent	Container	Class
t-Amyl Hydroperoxide	88	Water	55 gal (208 L)	III
t-Amyl Peroxyacetate	60	OMS	5 gal (19 L)	III
t-Amyl Peroxybenzoate	96	—	5 gal (19 L)	II
t-Amyl Peroxy-2-ethylhexanoate	96	—	55 gal (208 L)	III
t-Amyl Peroxyneodecanoate	75	OMS	5 gal (19 L)	III
t-Amyl Peroxypivalate	75	OMS	5 gal (19 L)	III
t-Butyl Cumyl Peroxide	95	—	55 gal (208 L)	IV
n-Butyl 4,4-Di(t-butylperoxy)valerate	98	—	5 gal(19 L)	II
t-Butyl Hydroperoxide	90	Water & t-BuOH	5 gal (19 L)	I
t-Butyl Hydroperoxide	70	DTBP & t-BuOH	55 gal (208 L)	II
t-Butyl Hydroperoxide	70	Water	55 gal (208 L)	IV
t-Butyl Peroxyacetate	75	OMS	5 gal (19 L)	I
t-Butyl Peroxyacetate	60	OMS	5 gal (19 L)	I
t-Butyl Peroxybenzoate	98	—	5 gal (19 L)	II
t-Butyl Peroxy-2-ethylhexanoate	97	—	5 gal (19 L)	III
t-Butyl Peroxy-2-ethylhexanoate	97	—	55 gal (208 L)	II
t-Butyl Peroxy-2-ethylhexanoate	50	DOP or OMS	5 gal (19 L)	IV
t-Butyl Peroxy-2-ethylhexanoate	50	DOP or OMS	55 gal (208 L)	III
t-Butylperoxy 2-Ethylhexyl Carbonate	95	—	5 gal (19 L)	III
t-Butyl Peroxyisobutyrate	75	OMS	5 gal (19 L)	II
t-Butylperoxy Isopropyl Carbonate	92	OMS	5 gal (19 L)	I
t-Butylperoxy Isopropyl Carbonate	75	OMS	5 gal (19 L)	II
t-Butyl Peroxymaleate	98	—	50 × 1 lb (50 × 0.5 kg)	I
t-Butyl Peroxyneodecanoate	75	OMS	5 gal (19 L)	III
t-Butyl Peroxypivalate	75	OMS	5 gal (19 L)	II
t-Butyl Peroxypivalate	45	OMS	5 gal (19 L)	IV
Cumyl Hydroperoxide	88	Cumene	55 gal (208 L)	III
Cumyl Peroxyneodecanoate	75	OMS	5 gal (19 L)	III
Cumyl Peroxyneoheptanoate	75	OMS	5 gal (19 L)	III
Diacetyl Peroxide	25	DMP	5 gal (19 L)	II
1,1-Di(t-amylperoxy)cyclohexane	80	OMS or BBP	5 gal (19 L)	III
Dibenzoyl Peroxide	98	—	1 lb (0.5 kg)	I
Dibenzoyl Peroxide	78	Water	25 lb (11 kg)	II
Dibenzoyl Peroxide	75	Water	25 lb (11 kg)	III
Dibenzoyl Peroxide	70	Water	25 lb (11 kg)	IV
Dibenzoyl Peroxide paste	55	Plasticizer	350 lb (160 kg)	III
Dibenzoyl Peroxide paste	55	Plasticizer & Water	350 lb (160 kg)	IV
Dibenzoyl Peroxide paste	50	Plasticizer	380 lb (170 kg)	III
Dibenzoyl Peroxide paste	50	Plasticizer & Water	380 lb (170 kg)	IV
Dibenzoyl Peroxide slurry	40	Water & Plasticizer	380 lb (170 kg)	IV
Dibenzoyl Peroxide slurry	40	Water	5 gal (19 L)	IV
Dibenzoyl Peroxide powder	35	Dicalcium Phosphate Dihydrate or Calcium Sulfate Dihydrate	100 lb (45 kg)	V

Table B-1 Class Index of Organic Peroxide Formulations (Continued)

Organic Peroxide Formulation	Concentration	Diluent	Container	Class
Dibenzoyl Peroxide powder	35	Starch	100 lb (45 kg)	IV
Di (4-t-butylcyclohexyl) Peroxydicarbonate	98	—	88 lb (40 kg)	III
Di-t-butyl Peroxide	99	—	55 gal (208 L)	III
2,2-Di(t-butylperoxy)butane	50	Toluene	1 gal (4 L)	I
1,1-Di(t-butylperoxy)cyclohexane	80	OMS or BBP	5 gal (19 L)	II
Di-sec-butyl Peroxydicarbonate	98	—	1 gal (4 L)	II
Di-sec-butyl Peroxydicarbonate	75	OMS	5 gal (19 L)	II
Di(2-t-butylperoxyisopropyl)benzene	96	—	100 lb (45 kg)	III
Di(2-t-butylperoxyisopropyl)benzene	40	Clay	100 lb (45 kg)	V
Di(butylperoxy) Phthalate	40	DBP	30 gal (110 L)	IV
1,1-Di-(t-butylperoxy)- 3,3,5-trimethylcyclohexane	75—95	—	5 gal (19 L)	II
1,1-Di-(t-butylperoxy)- 3,3,5-trimethylcyclohexane	40	Calcium Carbonate	100 lb (45 kg)	V
Dicetyl Peroxydicarbonate	85	—	20 kg (44 lb)	IV
2,4-Dichlorobenzoyl Peroxide	50	DBP & Silicone	5 gal (19 L)	III
Dicumyl Peroxide	98	—	55 gal (208 L)	IV
Dicumyl Peroxide	40	Clay or Calcium Carbonate	100 lb (45 kg)	V
Didecanoyl Peroxide	98	—	50 lb (23 kg)	III
Di(2-ethylhexyl) Peroxydicarbonate	97	—	1 gal (4 L)	II
Di(2-ethylhexyl) Peroxydicarbonate	40	OMS	5 gal (19 L)	IV
Diisopropyl Peroxydicarbonate	99	—	10 lb (4.5 kg)	I
Diisopropyl Peroxydicarbonate	30	Toluene	5 lb (2.3 kg)	III
Di-n-propyl Peroxydicarbonate	98	—	1 gal (4 L)	I
Di-n-propyl Peroxydicarbonate	85	OMS	1 gal (4 L)	I
Dilauroyol Peroxide	98	—	110 lb (50 kg)	IV
2,5-Dimethyl-2,5-di(benzoylperoxy)hexane	95	—	4 × 5 lb (4 × 2.3 kg)	II
2,5-Dimethyl-2,5-di(t-butylperoxy)hexane	92	—	30 gal (110 L)	III
2,5-Dimethyl-2,5-di(t-butylperoxy)hexane	47	Calcium Carbonate or Silica	100 lb (45 kg)	V
2,5-Dimethyl-2,5-di(2-ethylhexanoylperoxy) hexane	90	—	5 gal (19 L)	III
2,5-Dimethyl-2,5-dihydroperoxyhexane	70	Water	100 lb (45 kg)	II
Ethyl 3,3-Di(t-amylperoxy)butyrate	75	OMS	5 gal (19 L)	III
Ethyl 3,3-Di(t-amylperoxy)butyrate	40	Clay or Calcium Silicate	100 lb (45 kg)	V
p-Menthyl Hydroperoxide	54	Alcohols & Ketones	55 gal (208 L)	IV
Methyl Ethyl Ketone Peroxide	9% AO	DMP	5 gal (19 L)	III
Methyl Ethyl Ketone Peroxide	5.5% AO	DMP	5 gal (19 L)	IV
Methyl Ethyl Ketone Peroxide	9% AO	Water & Glycols	5 gal (19 L)	IV
Methyl Ethyl Ketone Peroxide and Cyclohexanone Peroxide mixture	9% AO	DMP	5 gal (19 L)	III
2,4-Pentanedione Peroxide	4% AO	Water & Solvent	5 gal (19 L)	IV
Peroxyacetic Acid	43	Water, HOAc, & H_20_2	30 gal (110 L)	II

NOTE: Diluents: OMS — odorless mineral spirits; t-Bu-OH — Tertiary Butanol; DTBP — Di-tertiary-butylperoxide; DOP — Dioctyl Phthalate; BBP — Butyl Benzyl Phthalate; DBP — Dibutyl Phthalate; DMP — Dimethyl Phthalate; HOAc — Acetic Acid; H_2O_2 — Hydrogen Peroxide.

Table B-2.3 Typical Class I Formulations

Organic Peroxide Formulation	Nominal Concentration, Weight Percent	Diluent	Individual Container Size	Temp. Control	Hazard Identification[1]		
					Health	Flamm.	Reactivity
t-Butyl Hydroperoxide	90	Water & t-BuOH	5 gal (19 L)		3	3	3
t-Butyl Peroxyacetate	75	OMS	5 gal (19 L)		1	3	3
t-Butyl Peroxyacetate	60	OMS	5 gal (19 L)		1	3	3
t-Butylperoxy Isopropyl Carbonate	92	OMS	5 gal (19 L)		1	3	3
t-Butyl Peroxymaleate	98	—	50 × 1 lb (50 × 0.5 kg)		2	3	3
Dibenzoyl Peroxide	98	—	1 lb (0.5 kg)		1	3	4
2,2-Di(t-butylperoxy)butane	50	Toluene	1 gal (4 L)		1	3	3
Diisopropyl Peroxydicarbonate	99	—	10 lb (4.5 kg)	R	2	3	4
Di-n-propyl Peroxydicarbonate	98	—	1 gal (4 L)	R	2	3	4
Di-n-propyl Peroxydicarbonate	85	OMS	1 gal (4 L)	R	2	3	3

R — Refrigeration recommended to reduce fire hazard.
OMS — Odorless Mineral Spirits
t-BuOH — tertiary-Butanol
[1]The column refers to NFPA 704, *Standard System for the Identification of the Hazards of Materials for Emergency Response,* hazard ratings for health, flammability, and reactivity. See NFPA 704 for details.

Table B-3.3 Typical Class II Formulations

Organic Peroxide Formulation	Nominal Concentration, Weight Percent	Diluent	Individual Container Size	Temp. Control	Hazard Identification[1]		
					Health	Flamm.	Reactivity
t-Amyl Peroxybenzoate	96	—	5 gal (19 L)		2	3	2
n-Butyl 4,4-Di(t-butylperoxy)valerate	98	—	5 gal (19 L)		2	3	2
t-Butyl Hydroperoxide	70	DTBP & t-BuOH	55 gal (208 L)		3	3	3
t-Butyl Peroxybenzoate	98	—	5 gal (19 L)		1	3	3
t-Butyl Peroxy-2-ethylhexanoate	97	—	55 gal (208 L)	R	1	3	3
t-Butyl Peroxyisobutyrate	75	OMS	5 gal (19 L)	R	2	3	3
t-Butylperoxy Isopropyl Carbonate	75	OMS	5 gal (19 L)		1	3	3
t-Butyl Peroxypivalate	75	OMS	5 gal (19 L)	R	2	3	3
Diacetyl Peroxide	25	DMP	5 gal (19 L)	T	2	3	3
Dibenzoyl Peroxide	78	Water	25 lb (11 kg)		1	2	3
1,1-Di(t-butylperoxy)cyclohexane	80	OMS or BBP	5 gal (19 L)		1	3	3
Di-sec-butyl Peroxydicarbonate	98	—	1 gal (4 L)	R	1	3	3
Di-sec-butyl Peroxydicarbonate	75	OMS	5 gal (19 L)	R	1	3	3
1,1-Di(t-butylperoxy)-3,3,5-trimethylcyclohexane	75–95	—	5 gal (19 L)		2	3	3
Di(2-ethylhexyl) Peroxydicarbonate	97	—	1 gal (4 L)	R	1	3	3
2,5-Dimethyl-2,5-di-(benzoylperoxy)hexane	95	—	4 × 5 lb (4 × 2.3 kg)		2	3	3
2,5-Dimethyl-2,5-dihydroperoxyhexane	70	Water	100 lb (45 kg)		2	3	3
Peroxyacetic Acid	43	Water HOAc & H_2O_2	30 gal (110 L)		3	2	3

R — Refrigeration recommended to reduce fire hazard.
T — Temperature control should be considered to reduce fire hazard depending on packaging size and recommendations in manufacturers' literature.
BBP — Butyl Benzyl Phthalate
DMP — Dimethyl Phthalate
DTBP — Di-tertiary-butyl Peroxide
HOAc — Acetic Acid
H_2O_2 — Hydrogen Peroxide
OMS — Odorless Mineral Spirits
t-BuOH — tertiary-Butanol
[1]The column refers to NFPA 704, *Standard System for the Identification of the Hazards of Materials for Emergency Response,* hazard ratings for health, flammability, and reactivity. See NFPA 704 for details.

Table B-4.3 Typical Class III Formulations

Organic Peroxide Formulation	Nominal Concentration, Weight Percent	Diluent	Individual Container Size	Temp. Control	Hazard Identification[1]		
					Health	Flamm.	Reactivity
t-Amyl Hydroperoxide	88	Water	55 gal (208 L)		3	3	2
t-Amyl Peroxyacetate	60	OMS	5 gal (19 L)		2	3	2
t-Amyl Peroxy-2-ethylhexanoate	96	—	55 gal (208 L)	R	0	3	2
t-Amyl Peroxyneodecanoate	75	OMS	5 gal (19 L)	R	1	3	2
t-Amyl Peroxypivalate	75	OMS	5 gal (19 L)	R	1	3	2
t-Butyl Peroxy-2-ethylhexanoate	97	—	5 gal (19 L)	R	1	3	2
t-Butyl Peroxy-2-ethylhexanoate	50	DOP or OMS	55 gal (208 L)	R	1	2	2
t-Butylperoxy 2-Ethylhexyl Carbonate	95	—	5 gal (19 L)		1	3	2
t-Butyl Peroxyneodecanoate	75	OMS	5 gal (19 L)	R	2	3	2
Cumyl Hydroperoxide	88	Cumene	55 gal (208 L)		3	2	2
Cumyl Peroxyneodecanoate	75	OMS	5 gal (19 L)	R	1	3	2
Cumyl Peroxyneoheptanoate	75	OMS	5 gal (19 L)	R	2	3	2
1,1-Di(t-amylperoxy)cyclohexane	80	OMS or BBP	5 gal (19 L)		2	3	2
Dibenzoyl Peroxide	75	Water	25 lb (11 kg)		1	2	2
Dibenzoyl Peroxide paste	55	Plasticizer	350 lb (160 kg)	T	1	2	2
Dibenzoyl Peroxide paste	50	Plasticizer	380 lb (170 kg)	T	1	2	2
Di(4-t-butylcyclohexyl) Peroxydicarbonate	98	—	88 lb (40 kg)		1	3	2
Di-t-butyl Peroxide	99	—	55 gal (208 L)		1	3	2
Di(2-t-butylperoxyisopropyl) benzene	96	—	100 lb (45 kg)		1	2	2
2,4-Dichlorobenzoyl Peroxide	50	DBP & Silicone	5 gal (19 L)	T	1	2	2
Didecanoyl Peroxide	98	—	50 lb (23 kg)	R	1	3	2
Diisopropyl Peroxydicarbonate	30	Toluene	5 gal (19 L)	R	2	3	2
2,5-Dimethyl-2,5-di-(2-ethylhexanoylperoxy)hexane	90	—	5 gal (19 L)	R	0	3	2
2,5-Dimethyl-2,5-di-(t-butylperoxy)hexane	92	—	30 gal (110 L)		2	3	2
Ethyl 3,3-Di(t-amylperoxy)butyrate	75	OMS	5 gal (19 L)		1	3	2
Ethyl 3,3-Di(t-butylperoxy)butyrate	75	OMS	5 gal (19 L)		2	2	2
Methyl Ethyl Ketone Peroxide	9% AO	DMP	5 gal (19 L)		3	2	2
Methyl Ethyl Ketone Peroxide and Cyclohexanone Peroxide mixture	9% AO	DMP	5 gal (19 L)		3	2	2

R — Refrigeration recommended to reduce fire hazard.
T — Temperature control should be considered to reduce fire hazard depending on packaging size and recommendations in manufacturers' literature.
AO — Active Oxygen
BBP — Butyl Benzyl Phthalate
DBP — Dibutyl Phthalate
DMP — Dimethyl Phthalate
DOP — Dioctyl Phthalate
OMS — Odorless Mineral Spirits
[1]The column refers to NFPA 704, *Standard System for the Identification of the Hazards of Materials for Emergency Response,* hazard ratings for health, flammability, and reactivity. See NFPA 704 for details.

B-5 Class IV Formulations.

B-5.1 Fire Hazard Characteristics. Class IV formulations present fire hazards that are easily controlled. Reactivity has little effect on fire intensity.

B-5.2 Fire-Fighting Information. Normal fire-fighting procedures can be used.

B-5.3 Typical Class IV Formulations. See Table B-5.3.

B-6 Class V Formulations.

B-6.1 Fire Hazard Characteristics. Class V formulations do not present severe fire hazards. Those that do burn, do so with less intensity than ordinary combustibles.

B-6.2 Fire-Fighting Information. Fire-fighting procedures need primarily consider the combustibility of containers.

B-6.3 Typical Class V Formulations. See Table B-6.3.

Table B-5.3 Typical Class IV Formulations

Organic Peroxide Formulation	Nominal Concentration, Weight Percent	Diluent	Individual Container Size	Temp. Control	Hazard Identification[1]		
					Health	Flamm.	Reactivity
t-Butyl Cumyl Peroxide	95	—	55 gal (208 L)		2	2	2
t-Butyl Hydroperoxide	70	Water	55 gal (208 L)		3	2	2
t-Butyl Peroxy-2-ethylhexanoate	50	DOP or OMS	5 gal (19 L)	R	1	2	2
t-Butyl Peroxypivalate	45	OMS	5 gal (19 L)	R	2	2	2
Dibenzoyl Peroxide	70	Water	25 lb (11 kg)		1	2	2
Dibenzoyl Peroxide paste	50	Plasticizer & Water	380 lb (170 kg)	T	1	2	2
Dibenzoyl Peroxide paste	55	Plasticizer & Water	350 lb (160 kg)	T	1	2	2
Dibenzoyl Peroxide slurry	40	Water & Plasticizer	80 lb (170 kg)	T	1	2	2
Dibenzoyl Peroxide slurry	40	Water	5 gal (19 L)		1	2	2
Dibenzoyl Peroxide powder	35	Starch	100 lb (45 kg)		1	2	2
Dicetyl Peroxydicarbonate	85	—	20 kg drums (44 lb)	T	1	2	2
Dicumyl Peroxide	98	—	55 gal (208 L)		2	2	2
Di(2-ethylhexyl) Peroxydicarbonate	40	OMS	5 gal (19 L)	R	1	2	2
Dilauroyl Peroxide	98	—	110 lb (50 kg)		1	2	2
Di(t-butylperoxy) Phthalate	40	DBP	30 gal (110 L)		2	2	2
p-Menthyl Hydroperoxide	54	Alcohols & Ketones	55 gal (208 L)	T	3	2	2
Methyl Ethyl Ketone Peroxide	5.5% AO	DMP	5 gal (19 L)		3	2	2
Methyl Ethyl Ketone Peroxide	9% AO	Water & Glycols	5 gal (19 L)		3	2	2
2,4-Pentanedione Peroxide	4% AO	Water & Solvent	5 gal (19 L)		2	1	1

R — Refrigeration recommended to reduce fire hazard.
T — Temperature control should be considered to reduce fire hazard depending on packaging size and recommendations in manufacturers' literature.
AO — Active Oxygen
DBP — Dibutyl Phthalate
DMP — Dimethyl Phthalate
DOP — Dioctyl Phthalate
OMS — Odorless Mineral Spirits
[1]The column refers to NFPA 704, *Standard System for the Identification of the Hazards of Materials for Emergency Response,* hazard ratings for health, flammability, and reactivity. See NFPA 704 for details.

Table B-6.3 Typical Class V Formulations

Organic Peroxide Formulation	Nominal Concentration, Weight Percent	Diluent	Individual Container Size	Temp. Control	Hazard Identification[1]		
					Health	Flamm.	Reactivity
Dibenzoyl Peroxide	35	Dicalcium Phosphate Dihydrate or Calcium Sulfate Dihydrate	100 lb (45 kg)		1	0	0
Di-(2-t-butylperoxyisopropyl)-benzene	40	Clay	100 lb (45 kg)		1	1	0
1,1-Di-(t-butylperoxy)-3,3,5-trimethylcyclohexane	40	Calcium Carbonate	100 lb (45 kg)		1	1	1
Dicumyl Peroxide	40	Clay or Calcium Carbonate	100 lb (45 kg)		1	1	1
2,5-Dimethyl-2,5-di-(t-butylperoxy)hexane	47	Calcium Carbonate or Silica	100 lb (45 kg)		1	1	1
Ethyl 3,3-Di-(t-butylperoxy)butyrate	40	Clay or Calcium Silicate	100 lb (45 kg)		1	1	1

AO — Active Oxygen

[1]The column refers to NFPA 704 , *Standard System for the Identification of the Hazards of Materials for Emergency Response,* ratings for health, flammability, and reactivity. See NFPA 704 for details.

Appendix C Referenced Publications

C-1 The following documents or portions thereof are referenced within this code for informational purposes only and are thus not considered part of the requirements of this code unless also listed in Chapter 6. The edition indicated here for each reference is the current edition as of the date of the NFPA issuance of this code.

C-1.1 NFPA Publications. National Fire Protection Association, 1 Batterymarch Park, P.O. Box 9101, Quincy, MA 02269-9101.

NFPA 68, *Guide for Venting of Deflagrations,* 1994 edition.

NFPA 220, *Standard on Types of Building Construction,* 1995 edition.

NFPA 704, *Standard System for the Identification of the Hazards of Materials for Emergency Response,* 1996 edition.

C-1.2 United Nations Publication. United Nations Publications, Sales Section, DC2-853, New York, NY 10017.

United Nations Recommendation on Transportation of Dangerous Goods, Tests and Criteria, Second Edition, 1990.

Index

NFPA 491

1997 Edition

Hazardous Chemical Reactions

NFPA 491

Guide to

Hazardous Chemical Reactions

1997 Edition

This edition of NFPA 491, *Guide to Hazardous Chemical Reactions,* was prepared by the Technical Committee on Classification and Properties of Hazardous Chemical Data and acted on by the National Fire Protection Association, Inc., at its Annual Meeting held May 19-22, 1997, in Los Angeles, CA. It was issued by the Standards Council on July 24, 1997, with an effective date of August 15, 1997, and supersedes all previous editions.

Changes other than editorial are indicated by a vertical rule in the margin of the pages on which they appear. These lines are included as an aid to the user in identifying changes from the previous edition.

This edition of NFPA 491 was approved as an American National Standard on August 15, 1997.

Origin and Development of NFPA 491

This guide was prepared by the Technical Committee on Classification and Properties of Hazardous Chemical Data. This 1997 edition is an extensive revision of the 1991 edition. The guide, originally published in 1975, revised in 1986, and reconfirmed in 1991, includes over 3500 entries of hazardous or potentially hazardous chemical reactions. As further information on hazardous reactions is accumulated, the Committee plans to publish revised editions. Those who know of references to reactions not included or who have personal knowledge of hazardous reactions are requested to send the information to the Committee Secretary, using the tear sheets at the end of the manual.

Technical Committee on Classification and Properties of Hazardous Chemical Data

F. Owen Kubias, *Chair*
Rocky River, OH [SE]

Robert A. Michaels, *Secretary*
RAM TRAC Corp., NY [SE]

Jacqueline E. Alpert, Underwriters Laboratories Inc., IL [RT]
Laurence G. Britton, Union Carbide Corp., WV [M]
Paul L. Errico, Ogden Services, CT [U]
Mark I. Grossman, Reliance Nat'l Risk Specialists, NY [I]
Ron A. Kirsch, MDL Information Systems, TN [SE]
Arthur A. Krawetz, Phoenix Chemical Laboratory Inc., IL [RT]
Jennifer L. Nelson, AT&T Co., NJ [U]
Rep. NFPA Industrial Fire Protection Section
Curtis G. Payne, U.S. Coast Guard (G-MSO-3), DC [U]
Gary Robinson, Liberty Mutual Insurance Co., IL [I]
Rep. The Alliance of American Insurers
William J. Satterfield, III, Industrial Risk Insurers, CT [I]
Norman E. Scheffler, The Dow Chemical Co., MI [M]
Norman V. Steere, Norman V. Steere Assoc. Inc., MN [SE]

Alternate

Robert A. Kingsbury, Underwriters Laboratories Inc., IL [RT]
(Alt. to J. E. Alpert)

Nonvoting

Howard H. Fawcett, Wheaton, MD (Member Emeritus)
Whitney Fay Long, SACLANTCEN, AE
Richard D. Tarr, U.S. Dept. of Transportation, DC
Jan Van der Linde, Samsom Chemical Publishers, The Netherlands
Ira Wainless, U.S. Dept. of Labor/OSHA, DC

Guy R. Colonna, NFPA Staff Liaison

Committee Scope: This Committee shall have primary responsibility for documents on the classification of the relative hazards of all chemical solids, liquids, and gases and to compile data on the hazard properties of these hazardous chemicals.

This list represents the membership at the time the Committee was balloted on the text of this edition. Since that time, changes in the membership may have occurred. A key to classifications is found at the back of this document.

NOTE: Membership on a committee shall not in and of itself constitute an endorsement of the Association or any document developed by the committee on which the member serves.

Contents

FOREWORD

This guide had its beginnings in an extensive literature survey conducted by the late George W. Jones of the U.S. Bureau of Mines during his work with NFPA and American Chemical Society Technical Committees. The current 1997 edition contains approximately 3550 documented reactions. Readers are encouraged to submit documentation of additional reactions to be considered for inclusion in this guide.

The purpose of the guide is to provide users of chemicals with a compilation of recorded experience with chemical reactions that have potential for danger. Thus, the abstracts presented here range from reactions that produce incandescence or flame at moderate or slightly elevated temperatures to those that produce explosions or detonations. However, when presenting such a large compilation of data as is presented in this guide, one must be aware of some possible limitations and considerations when using the data. Since some of the information was obtained from very old references, its validity may be questioned; many of the reported hazardous reactions may have been due to impurities or contaminants in the materials involved. At the same time, the user should be cautioned that the absence of a reaction from this listing in no way implies that combinations of materials may be mixed with impunity with or without heating. Similarly, the comments that may be appended to particular reactions regarding their violence should be tempered by consideration of quantities involved, temperatures, confinement, and many other factors.

For convenience, many potentially hazardous reaction mixtures have been brought together into groups. For example, the reactions of mixtures of inorganic perchlorates with many fuels can be quite violent. This association of different reactants in the same group should not be taken, however, as an indication that all such related compounds will react with equal rates or ease with a given fuel, that the violence will be equivalent in every case, or that potential contaminants such as moisture will have the same effect. The reader is warned that trace quantities of contaminants acting as catalysts may have a profound effect on the course and rate of the reaction. Unless there is unusual reactivity with air, oxygen, or water, the usual combustion reactions involving these oxidants have not been included for all possible fuel substances. Finally, any mixture of oxidizing and reducing agents should be suspected of being able to undergo a hazardous reaction.

Organization of this Guide

In this alphabetic tabulation, the reactions are presented in the following format:

PRIMARY ENTRY

Secondary Entries
Remarks and literature references.

For example,

ALUMINUM

Sodium Carbonate
When sodium carbonate was applied to redhot aluminum, an explosion occurred.
Price and Baker, *Chem. & Met. Eng.* **29:** 878 (1923).

means that aluminum and sodium carbonate react under the conditions stated and that the reference can be consulted for possible additional information. At the end of the guide, the full titles of the abbreviated names of references are listed.

This same reaction will also appear alphabetically under "sodium carbonate" as a cross-entry in bold-faced capital letters on the left margin as follows:

SODIUM CARBONATE
Aluminum
See ALUMINUM plus Sodium Carbonate.

The reactant under which the specific remarks are made (the Primary Entry) is chosen under an arbitrary system of priorities. Generally, the primary entry was selected from the higher on the following list:

CHEMICAL	EXAMPLE
Metallic Elements	Magnesium
Other Elements	Bromine
Classes of Compounds	Nitrates
Uncommon Compounds	Cesium Acetylene Carbide
Specific Compounds of a Class	Ammonium Nitrate
Common Acids	Nitric Acid
Common Bases	Sodium Hydroxide
Common Organic Compounds	Ethyl Alcohol
Nonchemical Names	Organic Matter

Additional guides for finding reactions in the manual are listed below:

1. There is a cross-reference of chemical names and synonyms. Synonyms are listed alphabetically with the corresponding primary entry and page number.

2. If the CAS number is available, the cross-reference of chemical names and CAS numbers can be used. The CAS numbers are listed in order with the name of the primary entry chemical.

3. When two chemical compounds are of equal importance, the first in alphabetic listing has usually received priority as the primary entry.

4. Most of the secondary entries appear also as primary cross-entries; exceptions are air, water, common chemical names like alcohol and ether, and trivial or common names like caustic soda or wood. For these common substances, refer to the other reactant or to the specific chemical name. Since so many reactions concern charcoal, this material is a primary entry.

5. For some common organic chemicals, popular names were used in preference to scientific nomenclature; for example, methyl bromide, rather than monobromomethane.

6. A chemical name is used in preference to its creator's name; thus, permonosulfuric acid, rather than Caro's acid.

7. A few proprietary names appear in preference to the relatively unknown chemical identification of the compound; e.g., Teflon® instead of polytetrafluoroethylene.

8. If no hazardous reaction is listed for a particular pair of chemicals, the reader should look up possible reactions between chemicals with similar properties. For example, if no reaction is given between cesium and hydrochloric acid, see sodium and hydrochloric acid. The violence of the reaction

between the similar chemicals might not be the same, but the combination should be regarded as suspect.

9. The guide does not list explosive fuel-air mixtures, but does list pyrophoric or hypergolic (self-igniting) mixtures.

10. The guide also lists a number of individual chemicals that explode or detonate spontaneously or in response to impact or heat. In such cases the chemical is listed as the primary entry, under which is printed the term, "self-reactive."

11. A number of entries by "families" of chemicals, e.g., nitrates, sulfates, aldehydes, and ethers, are included to facilitate the search for reactions. Frequently, these entries cross-refer to reactions of individual chemicals of the family.

12. Isomeric designations such as "iso" and "n" do not affect the alphabetic arrangement of chemical names in this guide.

References

An effort has been made to furnish references complete enough to lead the reader to the source of information. At the end of the guide, the full titles are listed for the abbreviated names of references that accompany the reactions. If a statement about a reaction might disclose proprietary information, the source is protected by the reference, "Confidential information furnished to NFPA."

Information on Errors and Omissions Welcomed

The Technical Committee on Classification and Properties of Hazardous Chemical Data will welcome comments on and criticisms of the present compilation. If a reader can cite more up- to-date references or experiences concerning any of the listed reactions, the information also will be welcomed. Similarly, the Committee would very much appreciate receiving brief details of incidents involving hazardous chemical reactions not yet included in the guide, so that these can be compiled and included in a later revision. Such material should be transmitted to Amy Spencer, Staff Liaison, Technical Committee on Classification and Properties of Hazardous Chemical Data, National Fire Protection Association, 1 Batterymarch Park, P.O. Box 9101, Quincy, MA 02269-9101. Tear-out pages for forwarding new material are at the back of the guide.

NFPA 491

Guide to

Hazardous Chemical Reactions

1997 Edition

ACETALDEHYDE CH_3CHO

Acetic Acid
Acetaldehyde was put in drums previously pickled with acetic acid. The acid caused the acetaldehyde to polymerize, and the drums became hot and vented.
MCA Case History **1764** (1971).

Acid Anhydrides
Condensation reaction of acetaldehyde with acid anhydrides, alcohols, ketones, and phenols can be violent.
Chem. Safety Data Sheet **SD-43** (1952).

Air
Acetaldehyde oxidizes readily in air to unstable peroxides that may explode spontaneously.
Chem. Safety Data Sheet **SD-43** (1952)

Alcohols
See ACETALDEHYDE plus Acid Anhydrides.
Chem. Safety Data Sheet **SD-43** (1952).

Ammonia (Anhydrous)
Reaction of anhydrous ammonia, hydrogen cyanide, or hydrogen sulfide can be violent.
Chem. Safety Data Sheet **SD-43** (1952).

Bromine
See BROMINE plus Acetaldehyde.

Chlorine
See CHLORINE plus Acetaldehyde.

Fluorine
See BROMINE plus Acetaldehyde.

Hydrogen Cyanide
See ACETALDEHYDE plus Ammonia (Anhydrous).

Hydrogen Sulfide
See ACETALDEHYDE plus Ammonia (Anhydrous).

Iodine
See BROMINE plus Acetaldehyde.

Ketones
See ACETALDEHYDE plus Acid Anhydrides.

Phenols
See ACETALDEHYDE plus Acid Anhydrides.

Phosphorus Isocyanate
See PHOSPHORUS ISOCYANATE plus Acetaldehyde.

Sodium Hydroxide
A violent polymerization of acetaldehyde results from reactions with alkaline materials such as sodium hydroxide.
Doyle (1966).

ACETIC ACID CH_3COOH

Acetaldehyde
See ACETALDEHYDE plus Acetic Acid.

2-Aminoethanol
Mixing acetic acid and 2-aminoethanol in a closed container caused the temperature and pressure to increase.
Flynn and Rossow (1970). See Note under complete reference.

Ammonium Nitrate
See AMMONIUM NITRATE plus Acetic Acid.

Ammonium Thiosulfate
See AMMONIUM THIOSULFATE plus Acetic Acid.

Bromine Pentafluoride
See BROMINE PENTAFLUORIDE plus Acetic Acid.

Chlorine Trifluoride
See TRIFLUORIDE plus Acetic Acid.

Chlorosulfonic Acid
Mixing glacial acetic acid and chlorosulfonic acid in a closed container caused the temperature and pressure to increase.
Flynn and Rossow (1970). See Note under complete reference.

Chromic Acid
See CHROMIC ANHYDRIDE plus Acetic Acid.

Chromic Anhydride and Acetic Anhydride
See CHROMIC ANHYDRIDE plus Acetic Acid and Acetic Anhy dride.

Diallyl Methyl Carbinol and Ozone
See DIALLYL METHYL CARBINOL plus Ozone and Acetic Acid.

Ethylene Diamine
Mixing acetic acid and ethylene diamine in a closed container caused the temperature and pressure to increase.
Flynn and Rossow (1970). See Note under complete reference.

Ethyleneimine
Mixing glacial acetic acid and ethyleneimine in a closed container caused the temperature and pressure to increase.
Flynn and Rossow (1970). See Note under complete reference.

Hydrogen Peroxide
See HYDROGEN PEROXIDE plus Acetic Acid.

Nitric Acid
See NITRIC ACID plus Acetic Acid.

Nitric Acid and Acetone
See NITRIC ACID plus Acetone and Acetic Acid.

Oleum
Mixing glacial acetic acid and oleum in a closed container caused the temperature and pressure to increase.
Flynn and Rossow (1970). See Note under complete reference.

Perchloric Acid
See PERCHLORIC ACID plus Acetic Acid.

Permanganates
See PERMANGANATES plus Acetic Acid.

Phosphorus Isocyanate
See PHOSPHORUS ISOCYANATE plus Acetaldehyde.

Phosphorus Trichloride
See PHOSPHORUS TRICHLORIDE plus Acetic Acid.

Potassium Hydroxide
Potassium hydroxide residue in a catalyst pot reacted violently when acetic acid was added.
MCA Case History **920** (1963).

Potassium Tert.-Butoxide
See ACETONE plus Potassium Tert.-Butoxide.

Sodium Hydroxide
See SODIUM HYDROXIDE plus Acetic Acid.

Sodium Peroxide
See SODIUM PEROXIDE plus Acetic Acid.

n-Xylene
During the production of terephthalic acid, n-xylene is oxidized in the presence of acetic acid. During these processes, detonating mix tures may be produced. Addition of a small amount of water may largely eliminate the risk of explosion.
B.I. Sraer, *Himiceskaja promyslennost* **46** (10): 27-30 (1970).

ACETIC ANHYDRIDE $CH_3COOCOCH_3$

2-Aminoethanol
Mixing acetic anhydride and 2-aminoethanol in a closed container caused the temperature and pressure to increase.
Flynn and Rossow (1970). See Note under complete reference.

Aniline
See ANILINE plus Acetic Anhydride.

Boric Acid
See BORIC ACID plus Acetic Anhydride.

Chlorosulfonic Acid
Mixing acetic anhydride and chlorosulfonic acid in a closed container caused the temperature and pressure to increase.
Flynn and Rossow (1970). See Note under complete reference.

Chromic Acid
See CHROMIC ANHYDRIDE plus Acetic Anhydride.

Chromic Anhydride
See CHROMIC ANHYDRIDE plus Acetic Anhydride.

Chromic Anhydride and Acetic Acid
See CHROMIC ANHYDRIDE plus Acetic Anhydride and Acetic Acid.

Ethylene Diamine
Mixing acetic anhydride and ethylene diamine in a closed container caused the temperature and pressure to increase.
Flynn and Rossow (1970). See Note under complete reference.

Ethyleneimine
Mixing acetic anhydride and ethyleneimine in a closed container caused the temperature and pressure to increase.
Flynn and Rossow (1970). See Note under complete reference.

Glycerol
A violent reaction occurs between these reactants in the presence of phosphorus oxychloride as a catalyst.
Hexagon Alpha Chi Sigma **40** (Oct. 1949).

Hydrochloric Acid
Mixing acetic anhydride and 36% hydrochloric acid in a closed con tainer caused the temperature and pressure to increase.
Flynn and Rossow (1970). See Note under complete reference.

Hydrofluoric Acid
Mixing acetic anhydride and 48.7% hydrofluoric acid in a closed container caused the temperature and pressure to increase.
Flynn and Rossow (1970). See Note under complete reference.

Hydrogen Peroxide
See HYDROGEN PEROXIDE plus Acetic Acid.

Nitric Acid
Mixing acetic anhydride and 70% nitric acid in a closed container caused the temperature and pressure to increase.
Flynn and Rossow (1970). See Note under complete reference.
See NITRIC ACID plus Acetic Anhydride.
See NITRIC ACID plus Acetic Acid.

Nitrogen Tetroxide
See NITROGEN TETROXIDE plus Acetic Anhydride.

Oleum
Mixing acetic anhydride and oleum in a closed container caused the temperature and pressure to increase.
Flynn and Rossow (1970). See Note under complete reference.

Perchloric Acid
See PERCHLORIC ACID plus Acetic Acid.
See PERCHLORIC ACID plus Acetic Anhydride.

Permanganates
See PERMANGANATES plus Acetic Acid.

Sodium Hydroxide
See SODIUM HYDROXIDE plus Acetic Anhydride.

Sodium Peroxide
See SODIUM PEROXIDE plus Acetic Acid.

Sulfuric Acid
Mixing acetic anhydride and 96% sulfuric acid in a closed container caused the temperature and pressure to increase.
Flynn and Rossow (1970). See Note under complete reference.

Water
The mixing of acetic anhydride with water can be dangerously explosive, especially when mineral acids are present.
Chem. and Eng. News **25:** 3458.

ACETONE CH_3COCH_3

Chloroform
A mixture of acetone and chloroform in a residue bottle exploded. Since addition of chloroform to acetone in the presence of a base will result in a highly exothermic

reaction, it is thought that a base may have been in the bottle.
MCA Case History **1661** (1970).

Chromic Anhydride
See CHROMIC ANHYDRIDE plus Acetone.

Chromyl Chloride
See CHROMYL CHLORIDE plus Acetone.

Hexachloromelamine
See HEXACHLOROMELAMINE plus Organic Contaminants.

Hydrogen Peroxide
See HYDROGEN PEROXIDE plus Organic Matter.

Nitric Acid and Acetic Acid
See NITRIC ACID plus Acetone and Acetic Acid.

Nitric Acid and Sulfuric Acid
See NITRIC ACID plus Acetone and Sulfuric Acid.

Nitrosyl Chloride
See NITROSYL CHLORIDE plus Acetone.

Nitrosyl Perchlorate
See NITROSYL PERCHLORATE plus Acetone.

Nitryl Perchlorate
See NITRYL PERCHLORATE plus Benzene.

Permonosulfuric Acid
See PERMONOSULFURIC ACID plus Acetone.

Potassium Tert.-Butoxide
Ignition occurs when potassium t-butoxide reacts with the follow ing: acetone, ethyl methyl ketone, methyl isobutyl ketone, methanol, ethanol, n-propanol, isopropanol, ethyl acetate, n-butyl acetate, n-propyl formate, acetic acid, sulfuric acid, methylene chloride, chloroform, carbon tetrachloride, epichlorohydrin, dimethyl carbon ate, and diethyl sulfate.
MCA Case History **1948** (1973).

Sodium Hypobromite
An explosion occurred during an attempt to prepare bromoform from acetone by the haloform reaction.
Chem. and Eng. News **9:**229 (1931).

Sulfuric Acid and Potassium Dichromate
Acetone ignited when it was accidentally splashed into a sulfuric acid-dichromate solution.
Wischmeyer (1969).

Thiodiglycol and Hydrogen Peroxide
See THIODIGLYCOL plus Hydrogen Peroxide and Acetone.

Trichloromelamine
See HEXACHLOROMELAMINE plus Organic Contaminants.

ACETONITRILE CH_3CN

Chlorosulfonic Acid
Mixing acetonitrile and chlorosulfonic acid in a closed container caused the temperature and pressure to increase.
Flynn and Rossow (1970). See Note under complete reference.

Erbium Perchlorate
In the preparation of anhydrous erbium perchlorate an acetonitrile extraction was made. During the final stages of the procedure a glossy material was formed that exploded when scratched with a spatula. It was concluded that acetonitrile was trapped in the glossy erbium perchlorate and that this material was shock-sensitive as are many organic-containing perchlorates.
J. Chem. Edu. **50** (6): A336-7 (1973).

Oleum
Mixing acetonitrile and oleum in a closed container caused the tem perature and pressure to increase.
Flynn and Rossow (1970). See Note under complete reference.

Sulfuric Acid
Mixing acetonitrile and 96% sulfuric acid in a closed container caused the temperature and pressure to increase.
Flynn and Rossow (1970). See Note under complete reference.

ACETYL BROMIDE CH_3COBr

Alcohols
Acetyl bromide reacts violently with alcohols or water.
Merck Index **7th Ed.** (1960).

Water
See ACETYL BROMIDE plus Alcohols.

ACETYL CHLORIDE CH_3COCl

Dimethyl Sulfoxide
See DIMETHYL SULFOXIDE plus Acyl Halides.

Ethyl Alcohol
Acetyl chloride reacts violently with ethyl alcohol or water.
Rose (1961).

Water
Acetyl chloride reacts violently with water.
Haz. Chem. Data (1966).

ACETYLENE $CH{\equiv}CH$

Brass
See COPPER plus Acetylene.

Bromine
See BROMINE plus Acetylene.

Cesium Hydride
See CESIUM HYDRIDE plus Acetylene.

Chlorine
See CHLORINE plus Acetylene.

Cobalt
See COBALT plus Acetylene.

Copper
See COPPER plus Acetylene.

Copper Salts
See COPPER SALTS plus Acetylene.

Cuprous Acetylide
See CUPROUS ACETYLIDE plus Acetylene.

Fluorine
See FLUORINE plus Acetylene.

Iodine
See IODINE plus Acetylene.

Mercuric Nitrate
See MERCURIC NITRATE plus Acetylene.

Mercury
See MERCURY plus Acetylene.

Mercury Salts
See MERCURY SALTS plus Acetylene.

Nitric Acid
See NITRIC ACID plus Acetylene.

Potassium
See POTASSIUM plus Acetylene.

Potassium Hydroxide
Ignition occurred when acetylene and potassium hydroxide came in contact. The incendivity of potassium hydroxide on acetylene and acetylene/nitrogen mixtures is reported in various temperature and pressure ranges.
H. P. Schildberg, M. Heider, B. Maurer, and W. Berthold, *Loss Pre vention and Safety Promotion in the Process Industries,* **1** (1995).

Rubidium Hydride
See RUBIDIUM HYDRIDE plus Acetylene.

Silver
See SILVER plus Acetylene.

Silver Salts
See MERCURY SALTS plus Acetylene.
See also SILVER NITRATE plus Acetylene and Ammonium Hydroxide.

Sodium Hydride
See SODIUM HYDRIDE plus Acetylene.

2-ACETYL-3-METHYLTHIOPHEN-4-ONE
$SC(COCH_3)=C(CH_3)COCH_2$ (ring: S bonded to CH_2)

(self-reactive)
A vacuum distillation of 2-acetyl-3-methylthiophen-4-one was being performed on a laboratory bench when suddenly there was an explosion.
MCA Guide for Safety, Appendix 3 (1972).

ACETYL NITRATE CH_3COONO_2

(self-reactive)
Acetyl nitrate has been reported to explode during vacuum distilla tion; also, when touched by a glass rod.
J. P. Wilaut, *Chem. Zentr.* **112** (I):384 (1943).
Pichet and Khotinsky, *Berichte* **40:**1164 (1907).

ACID ANHYDRIDES
(See also specific Anhydrides)

Acetaldehyde
See ACETALDEHYDE plus Acid Anhydrides.

ACIDS
(See also specific acid)

Acrolein
See ACROLEIN plus Sulfur Dioxide.

Benzyl Alcohol
Benzyl alcohol containing acidic constituents and dissolved iron was found to polymerize with a rapid temperature increase when heated in excess of 100°C. Amines, pyridene, and alkali hydroxides act as inhibitors and prevent polymerization.
Chem. Abst. **77**:7816w (1972).

Lithium Aluminum Hydride
See LITHIUM ALUMINUM HYDRIDE plus Water.

Nickel Nitride
See NICKEL NITRIDE plus Acids.

Sodium Ozonate
See SODIUM OZONATE plus Acids.

Thorium Phosphide
See THORIUM PHOSPHIDE plus Acids.

Tri-iso-Butyl Aluminum
See TRI-iso-BUTYL ALUMINUM plus Acids.

ACROLEIN $CH_2=CHCHO$

Acids
See ACROLEIN plus Sulfur Dioxide.

Alkalis
See ACROLEIN plus Sulfur Dioxide.

Amines
See ACROLEIN plus Sulfur Dioxide.
See SODIUM HYDROXIDE plus Acrolein.

2-Aminoethanol
Mixing acrolein and 2-aminoethanol in a closed container caused the temperature and pressure to increase.
Flynn and Rossow (1970). See Note under complete reference.

Ammonia
See SODIUM HYDROXIDE plus Acrolein.

Ammonium Hydroxide
Mixing acrolein and 28% ammonium hydroxide in a closed container caused the temperature and pressure to increase.
Flynn and Rossow (1970). See Note under complete reference.

Chlorosulfonic Acid
Mixing acrolein and chlorosulfonic acid in a closed container caused the temperature and pressure to increase.
Flynn and Rossow (1970). See Note under complete reference.

Ethylene Diamine
Mixing acrolein and ethylene diamine in a closed container caused the temperature and pressure to increase.
Flynn and Rossow (1970). See Note under complete reference.

Ethyleneimine
Mixing acrolein and ethyleneimine in a closed container caused the temperature and pressure to increase.
Flynn and Rossow (1970). See Note under complete reference.

Hydroxides
See SODIUM HYDROXIDE plus Acrolein.

Nitric Acid
Mixing acrolein and 70% nitric acid in a closed container caused the temperature and pressure to increase.
Flynn and Rossow (1970). See Note under complete reference.

Oleum
Mixing acrolein and oleum in a closed container caused the temper ature and pressure to increase.
Flynn and Rossow (1970). See Note under complete reference.

Potassium Hydroxide
See SODIUM HYDROXIDE plus Acrolein.

Sodium Hydroxide
See SODIUM HYDROXIDE plus Acrolein.

Sulfur Dioxide
Acrolein polymerizes with release of heat on contact with minor amounts of acids (including sulfur dioxide), alkalis, volatile amines, salts, thiourea, oxidants (air) and on exposure to light and heat.
BCISC **44:**174 (1973).

Sulfuric Acid
Mixing acrolein and 96% sulfuric acid in a closed container caused the temperature and pressure to increase.
Flynn and Rossow (1970). See Note under complete reference.

Thiourea
See ACROLEIN plus Sulfur Dioxide.

ACRYLAMIDE $H_2C=CHCONH_2$
It can polymerize violently on melting at 85°C.
Muir (1977).

ACRYLIC ACID $H_2C=CHCOOH$

2-Aminoethanol
Mixing acrylic acid and 2-aminoethanol in a closed container caused the temperature and pressure to increase.
Flynn and Rossow (1970). See Note under complete reference.

Ammonium Hydroxide
Mixing acrylic acid and 28% ammonium hydroxide in a closed con tainer caused the temperature and pressure to increase.
Flynn and Rossow (1970). See Note under complete reference.

Chlorosulfonic Acid
Mixing acrylic acid and chlorosulfonic acid in a closed container caused the temperature and pressure to increase.
Flynn and Rossow (1970). See Note under complete reference.

Ethylene Diamine
Mixing acrylic acid and ethylene diamine in a closed container caused the temperature and pressure to increase.
Flynn and Rossow (1970). See Note under complete reference.

Ethyleneimine
Mixing acrylic acid and ethyleneimine in a closed container caused the temperature and pressure to increase.
Flynn and Rossow (1970). See Note under complete reference.

Oleum
Mixing acrylic acid and oleum in a closed container caused the tem perature and pressure to increase.
Flynn and Rossow (1970). See Note under complete reference.

ACRYLONITRILE $CH_2=CHCN$

Acids (Strong)
See ACRYLONITRILE plus Sulfuric Acid and Water.

2-Aminoethanol
Mixing acrylonitrile and 2-aminoethanol in a closed container caused the temperature and pressure to increase.
Flynn and Rossow (1970). See Note under complete reference.

Bromine
See BROMINE plus Acrylonitrile.

Chlorosulfonic Acid
Mixing acrylonitrile and chlorosulfonic acid in a closed container caused the temperature and pressure to increase.
Flynn and Rossow (1970). See Note under complete reference.

Ethylene Diamine
Mixing acrylonitrile and ethylene diamine in a closed container caused the temperature and pressure to increase.
Flynn and Rossow (1970). See Note under complete reference.

Nitric Acid
Acrylonitrile and 70% Nitric Acid detonates at 90°C.
Flynn and Rossow (1970). See Note under complete reference.

Oleum
Mixing acrylonitrile and oleum in a closed container caused the temperature and pressure to increase.
Flynn and Rossow (1970). See Note under complete reference.

Potassium Hydroxide
See SODIUM HYDROXIDE plus Acrylonitrile.

Sodium Hydroxide
See SODIUM HYDROXIDE plus Acrylonitrile.

Sulfuric Acid
A mixture with concentrated sulfuric acid must be kept well chilled; otherwise, a vigorous exothermic reaction occurs.
Chem. Safety Data Sheet **SD-31:** 8 (1949).
A vigorous reaction between acrylonitrile and strong acids occurs with hydroquinone and powdered copper as catalysts. In the preparation of acrylic acid from these ingredients, using concentrated sulfuric acid, an eruption will occur in the flask, due to a strong exothermic reaction, unless the ingredients are kept well chilled.
F. J. Kaszuba, *Chem. and Eng. News* **30:** 824 (1952). Mixing acry lonitrile and 96% sulfuric acid in a closed container caused the temperature and pressure to increase.
Flynn and Rossow (1970). See Note under complete reference.

1,2,3,4-Tetrahydrocarbazole
See 1,2,3,4-TETRAHYDROCARBAZOLE plus Acrylonitrile.

ACRYLONITRILE-BUTADIENE COPOLYMER
$[-CH_2CH=CHCH_2CH_2CH(CN)-]n$

Fluorine
See FLUORINE plus Solid Nonmetals and Oxygen.

ACYL HALIDES

Dimethyl Sulfoxide
See DIMETHYL SULFOXIDE plus Acyl Halides.

AIR (LIQUID)

Charcoal
Explosions have occurred when liquid air contacts organic matter. A cracked tube of activated charcoal immersed in liquid air exploded violently.
J. Taylor, *J. Sci. Instr.* **5:** 24 (1928).

Diethyl Ether
See DIETHYL ETHER plus Air (Liquid).

Hydrocarbons
Almost any reducing agent and all hydrocarbons can form explosive mixtures with liquid air.
Chem. and Eng. News **27:** 2612 (1949).

ALCOHOLS

Acetaldehyde
See ACETALDEHYDE plus Acid Anhydrides.

Barium Perchlorate
See BARIUM PERCHLORATE plus Alcohols.

Chlorine
See ALCOHOLS plus Hypochlorous Acid.

Diethyl Aluminum Bromide
See DIETHYL ALUMINUM BROMIDE plus Air.

Ethylene Oxide
See ETHYLENE OXIDE plus Alcohols.

Hexamethylene Diiosocyanate
See ALCOHOLS plus Isocyanates.

Hydrogen Peroxide and Sulfuric Acid
Mixtures of alcohols with concentrated sulfuric acid and strong hydrogen peroxide can cause explosions. Examples: An explosion will occur if dimethylbenzylcarbinol is added to 90% hydrogen peroxide and then acidified with concentrated sulfuric acid. Mixtures of ethyl alcohol with concentrated hydrogen peroxide form powerful explosives. Mixtures of hydrogen peroxide and 1-phenyl-2-methyl propyl alcohol tend to explode if acidified with 70% sulfuric acid.
Chem. and Eng. News **45** (43): 73 (1967). *J. Org. Chem.* **28:** 1893 (1963).

Hypochlorous Acid
Alkyl hypochlorites are violently explosive. They are readily obtained by reacting hypochlorous acid and alcohols either in aque ous solution or in mixed water-carbon tetrachloride solutions. Obvi ously CHLORINE plus Alcohols would similarly produce alkyl hypochlorites. They decompose in the cold and explode on exposure to sunlight or heat. Tertiary hypochlorites are less unstable than secondary or primary hypochlorites.
Whitmore, 157 (1937). *Mellor,* **Supp. II, Part I:** 560 (1956).

Isocyanates
Base-catalyzed reactions of isocyanates such as hexamethylene diisocyanate with alcohols should generally be carried out in inert solvents. Such reactions in the absence of solvents often occur with explosive violence.
Wischmeyer (1969).

Lithium Aluminum Hydride
See LITHIUM ALUMINUM HYDRIDE plus Water.

Nitrogen Tetroxide
See NITROGEN TETROXIDE plus Alcohols.

Perchloric Acid
See PERCHLORIC ACID plus Alcohols.

Permonosulfuric Acid
See PERMONOSULFURIC ACID plus Alcohols.

Tri-iso-Butyl Aluminum
See TRI-iso-BUTYL ALUMINUM plus Acids.

ALKALI CARBONATES

Silicon
See SILICON plus Alkali Carbonates.

ALKALI HYDROXIDES

Zirconium
See ZIRCONIUM plus Alkali Hydroxides.

ALKALI METAL CHROMATES

Zirconium
See ZIRCONIUM plus Alkali Metal Salts.

ALKALI METAL DICHROMATES

Zirconium
See ZIRCONIUM plus Alkali Metal Salts.

ALKALI METAL MOLYBDATES

Zirconium
See ZIRCONIUM plus Alkali Metal Salts.

ALKALI METALS

Boron Trifluoride
Boron trifluoride reacts with incandescence when heated with alkali metals or alkaline earth metals, except magnesium.
Merck Index, p. 163 (1960).

Hydrazine and Ammonia
See HYDRAZINE plus Alkali Metals and Ammonia.

Maleic Anhydride
Maleic anhydride decomposes explosively in the presence of alkali metals.
Chem. Safety Data Sheet **SD-88** (1962).
Chem. Haz. Info. Series **C-71** (1960).

ALKALI METAL SULFATES

Zirconium
See ZIRCONIUM plus Alkali Metal Salts.

ALKALI METAL TUNGSTATES

Zirconium
See ZIRCONIUM plus Alkali Metal Salts.

ALKALINE EARTH METALS

Boron Trifluoride
See ALKALI METALS plus Boron Trifluoride.

ALKENES

Fluorine
See FLUORINE plus Alkenes.

ALKYD AZIDES

(heat sensitive)
See AZIDES, ORGANIC (heat sensitive).

ALKYLALUMINUM FLUOROALKOXIDES

Tests show that neat diethylaluminum 2,2,2-trifluoroethoxide (DEAL-FE) is shock sensitive. A slow exothermic decomposition occurs at about 75°C, and above 100°C, decomposition occurs violently.
Chem. and Eng. News, p.2 (April 2, 1990).

ALKYL AZIDES

(self-reactive)
Low molecular weight alkyl azides and diazido alkanes are considered to be particularly dangerous in the absence of suitable precautions. Introduction of more than one azide group into the molecule increases its instability.
Chem. and Eng. News **42** (31):6 (1964).

ALKYL BENZENES

Fluorine
See FLUORINE plus Alkyl Benzenes.

ALKYLISOTHIOUREA SALTS

Chlorine
See CHLORINE plus Alkylisothiourea Salts.

ALKYLPHOSPHINES

Chlorine
See CHLORINE plus Alkylphosphines.

ALLENE $H_2C=C=CH_2$

(self-reactive)
Pure allene can decompose explosively at two atmospheres.
Rutledge, p. 13 (1968).

ALLYL ALCOHOL $CH_2=CHCH_2OH$

Carbon Tetrachloride
A reaction between allyl alcohol and carbon tetrachloride produces trichlorobutylene epoxide (oxide) and dichlorobutylene epoxide (oxide), a mixture which during distillation proved to be unstable and detonated in the still.
Doyle (1969).

Chlorosulfonic Acid
Mixing allyl alcohol and chlorosulfonic acid in a closed container caused the temperature and pressure to increase.
Flynn and Rossow (1970). See Note under complete reference.

Diallyl Phosphite and Phosphorus Trichloride
See DIALLYL PHOSPHITE plus Allyl Alcohol and Phosphorus Trichloride.

Nitric Acid
Mixing allyl alcohol and 70% nitric acid in a closed container caused the temperature and pressure to increase.
Flynn and Rossow (1970). See Note under complete reference.

Oleum
Mixing allyl alcohol and oleum in a closed container caused the temperature and pressure to increase.
Flynn and Rossow (1970). See Note under complete reference.

Sodium Hydroxide
As a benzene extract of allyl benzenesulfonate was prepared from allyl alcohol and benzene sulfonyl chloride in the presence of aqueous sodium hydroxide, under vacuum distillation two fractions came off, then the temperature rose to 135°C, when the residue darkened and exploded.
W. T. Dye, and G.E. Ham, *Chem. and Eng. News* 28:3452 (1950).
This reaction was almost certainly a caustic-catalyzed polymerization of allyl alcohol.
Doyle (1966).

Sulfuric Acid
Mixing allyl alcohol and 96% sulfuric acid in a closed container caused the temperature and pressure to increase.
Flynn and Rossow (1970). See Note under complete reference.

Tri-n-Bromomelamine
These compounds exploded fifteen minutes after mixing at room temperature.
Chem. and Eng. News **30:**1916 (1952).

ALLYL BENZENESULFONATE $CH_2=CHCH_2OSO_2C_6H_5$

(self-reactive)
During distillation of crude allyl benzenesulfonate, from which the benzene solvent had been removed, two fractions came off—the first at 86–92°C and the second at 92–135°C—then the remaining residue darkened, thickened, and exploded probably owing to uncontrolled polymerization.
Chem. and Eng. News **28:**3452 (1950).

ALLYL CHLORIDE $CH_2=CHCH_2Cl$

Aluminum Chloride
See SULFURIC ACID plus Allyl Chloride.

Benzene and Diethyl Aluminum Chloride
See ALLYL CHLORIDE plus Benzene and Ethyl Aluminum Dichloride.

Benzene and Ethyl Aluminum Dichloride
It has been found that allyl chloride or other alkyl halides will react vigorously with benzene or toluene, even at minus 70°C, in the presence of ethyl aluminum dichloride or ethyl aluminum sesquichloride. Explosions have been reported.
Wischmeyer (1970).

Benzene and Ethyl Aluminum Sesquichloride
See ALLYL CHLORIDE plus Benzene and Ethyl Aluminum Dichloride.

Chlorosulfonic Acid
Mixing allyl chloride and chlorosulfonic acid in a closed container caused the temperature and pressure to increase.
Flynn and Rossow (1970). See Note under complete reference.

Ethylene Diamine
Mixing allyl chloride and ethylene diamine in a closed container caused the temperature and pressure to increase.
Flynn and Rossow (1970). See Note under complete reference.

Ethyleneimine
Mixing allyl chloride and ethyleneimine in a closed container caused the temperature and pressure to increase.
Flynn and Rossow (1970). See Note under complete reference.

Ferric Chloride
See SULFURIC ACID plus Allyl Chloride.

Lewis-Type Catalysts
See SULFURIC ACID plus Allyl Chloride.

Nitric Acid
Mixing allyl chloride and 70% nitric acid in a closed container caused the temperature and pressure to increase.
Flynn and Rossow (1970). See Note under complete reference.

Oleum
Mixing allyl chloride and oleum in a closed container caused the temperature and pressure to increase.
Flynn and Rossow (1970). See Note under complete reference.

Sodium Hydroxide
See SODIUM HYDROXIDE plus Allyl Chloride.

Sulfuric Acid
Mixing allyl chloride and 96% sulfuric acid in a closed container caused the temperature and pressure to increase.
Flynn and Rossow (1970). See Note under complete reference.
See SULFURIC ACID plus Allyl Chloride.

Toluene and Diethyl Aluminum Chloride
See ALLYL CHLORIDE plus Benzene and Ethyl Aluminum Dichloride.

Toluene and Ethyl Aluminum Dichloride
See ALLYL CHLORIDE plus Benzene and Ethyl Aluminum Dichloride.

Toluene and Ethyl Aluminum Sesquichloride
See ALLYL CHLORIDE plus Benzene and Ethyl Aluminum Dichloride.

Ziegler-Type Catalysts
See SULFURIC ACID plus Allyl Chloride.

ALLYLDIMETHYL ARSINE $CH_2CHCH_2AS(CH_3)_2$

Air
Dimethylallylarsine ignites in air and on filter paper.
Ellern, pp. 24, 25 (1968).

ALUMINUM Al

Ammonium Nitrate
A mixture of aluminum powder and ammonium nitrate can be used as an explosive. A number of explosions in which ammonium nitrate and aluminum are mixed with carbon, hydrocarbons, with or without oxidizing agents, have occurred.
Mellor **5:** 219 (1946-1947).

Ammonium Persulfate
A mixture of aluminum powder with ammonium persulfate powder and water may cause an explosion.
Pieters, p. 30 (1957).

Antimony Trichloride
See ALUMINUM plus Phosphorus Trichloride.

Arsenic Trichloride
See ALUMINUM plus Phosphorus Trichloride.

Barium Bromate
See ALUMINUM plus Bromates.

Barium Chlorate
See ALUMINUM plus Bromates.

Barium Iodate
See ALUMINUM plus Bromates.

Barium Sulfate
See ALUMINUM plus Sulfates.

Bismuth Trioxide
When bismuth trioxide is heated with powdered aluminum, the reduction occurs with explosive violence.
Mellor **9:** 649 (1946-1947). Ellern, pp. 244, 280 (1968).

Bromates
A combination of finely divided aluminum with finely divided bromates (also chlorates or iodates) of barium, calcium, magnesium, potassium, sodium, or zinc can be exploded by heat, percussion, and sometimes, light friction.
Mellor **2:** 310 (1946-1947).

Bromine
Bromine vapor reacts with warm aluminum foil with brilliant incandescence. The reaction is vigorous, even at 15°C.
Chem. News **121:** 178 (1920).
Mellor **1:** 135 (1946-1947).
Mellor **5:** 209 (1946-1947).

Calcium Bromate
See ALUMINUM plus Bromates.

Calcium Chlorate
See ALUMINUM plus Bromates.

Calcium Iodate
See ALUMINUM plus Bromates.

Calcium Sulfate
See ALUMINUM plus Sulfates.

Carbon Disulfide
Powdered aluminum burns in the vapor of carbon disulfide, sulfur dioxide, sulfur dichloride, nitrous oxide, nitric oxide, or nitrogen peroxide.
Mellor **5:** 209-212 (1946-1947).

Carbon Tetrachloride
A bomb containing powdered aluminum and carbon tetrachloride exploded violently when heated to 153°C.
C.C. Clogston, *UL Technical Report* **34** (1945).
A mixture of powdered aluminum and carbon tetrachloride in a ball mill exploded.
Chem. and Eng. News **32:** 258 (1954).
Impact sensitivity tests have shown that mixtures of carbon tetra chloride and aluminum will detonate.
ASESB Pot. Incid. **39** (1968).

Chlorates
See ALUMINUM plus Bromates.

Chlorinated Hydrocarbons
When hot vapors contact powdered aluminum, an explosion results.
Tech. Ind. Fire & Expl. Hazards **2:** 26 (1947).

Chlorine
Aluminum powder burns in chlorine, even at 20°C.
Mellor **2:** 92; **5:** 209 (1946-1947).

Chlorine Trifluoride
In the presence of carbon, the combination of chlorine trifluoride with aluminum, copper, lead, magnesium, silver, tin or zinc results in a violent reaction.
Mellor **2, Supp. 1:** (1956).
See also TRIFLUORIDE plus Elements.

Chlorofluorohydrocarbons
It has been experimentally determined that mixtures of powdered aluminum with monofluorotrichloroethane or with trifluorotrichlo roethane will flash or spark on heavy impact.
ASESB Pot. Incid. **39** (1968).
See also ALUMINUM plus Dichlorodifluoromethane.

Chloroform
Chloroform, methyl chloride, and carbon tetrachloride, and mixtures of these chemicals explode when in contact with aluminum powder or magnesium powder.
C.C. Clogston, *UL Technical Report* **34** (1945).

Chromic Anhydride
A violent reaction or flaming is likely in the reaction of chromic anhydride and aluminum powder.
Mellor **11:**237 (1946-1947).

Copper Oxide
A strong explosion occurred when aluminum was heated with copper oxide. With lead oxide, the crucible was broken to pieces and the doors of the furnace were blown off.
Mellor **5:**217-19 (1946-1947). Ellern, pp. 244, 280 (1968).

Diborane
Diborane reacts spontaneously with aluminum and lithium to form hydrides that ignite in air.
Haz. Chem. Data (1966).

Dichlorodifluoromethane
Destruction of the impellers in a centrifugal compressor occurred when abrasion exposed and heated fresh aluminum surfaces. These surfaces and dichlorodifluoromethane joined in a self-sustaining reaction with sufficient heat generation to melt and react much of the aluminum impeller material. Similar results were obtained in large test compressors using monochlorodifluoromethane. Follow-up laboratory test reactions between aluminum and (a) 1,1,2-trichloro-1,2,2-trifluoroethane; (b) monofluorotrichloromethane; (c) 1,2-dichloro-1,1,2,2-tetrafluoroethane; (d) dichlorodifluoromethane; (e) monobromotrifluoromethane; (f) monochlorodifluoromethane; (g) tetrafluoromethane established that vigorous reactions and heat outputs occurred in all cases. The vigor of the reactions and heat outputs increased in the given order, and were dependent on the combined effects of vapor pressure and degree of fluorination.
B. J. Eiseman, Jr., *ASHRAE Journal* **5:**63 (1963). C.C. Clogston, UL Technical Report **34** (1945). *Chem. and Eng. News* 39 (27):44 (1961);**39** (32): 4 (1961).

1,2-Dichloro-1,1,2,2- tetrafluoroethane
See ALUMINUM plus Dichlorodifluoromethane.

Ethylene Dichloride, Propylene Dichloride, and Orthodichlorobenzene
Orthodichlorobenzene had been mixed with ethylene dichloride and propylene dichloride.
This mixture dissolved the oxide coating from the aluminum containing vessel. Subsequent reaction between the aluminum vessel and the chlorinated olefins caused rupture of the vessel.
Doyle (1966).

Fluorine
See FLUORINE plus Metals.

Fluorochloro-lubricants
An explosive reaction occurs with fluorochloro oils or greases in contact with fresh aluminum surfaces under high loads. Examples cited: a spinning aluminum rod under pressure on an aluminum surface; a freshly bored aluminum cylinder under pressure from an aluminum piston; threading an aluminum rod into a dural tube with a fluorochloro oil as a lubricant.
Laccabue (1958).

Iodates
See ALUMINUM plus Bromates.

Iodine
Aluminum powder and iodine in close contact will ignite spontane ously.
Ellern, p. 46 (1968).

Iodine Monochloride
Aluminum foil, after continued contact with iodine monochloride, ignites spontaneously and burns with a bluish-white flame.
Mellor **2:** 119 (1946-1947).

Iron Oxide
The reaction of powdered aluminum and iron oxide, usually started by burning magnesium, proceeds vigorously, with evolution of intense heat. The mixture is known as "thermite."
Mellor **5:** 217-19 (1946-1947).
The reaction can be initiated by impact between an aluminum object and a rusty surface.
Morse (1966). *Abbey* (1964). *Health & Safety Inf.* **161** (1963).

Lead Oxides
The reduction of lead oxide by aluminum is violent. See also ALU MINUM plus Copper Oxide.
Mellor **7:** 658 (1946-1947). *Ellern,* pp. 244, 280 (1968).

Magnesium and Potassium Perchlorate
There have been three industrial explosions involving a photoflash composition containing potassium perchlorate with aluminum and magnesium powders.
ACS **146:** 210. *BM Info. Circ.* **7349** (1945).

Magnesium Bromate
See ALUMINUM plus Bromates.

Magnesium Chlorate
See ALUMINUM plus Bromates.

Magnesium Iodate
See ALUMINUM plus Bromates.

Manganese and Air
See MANGANESE plus Aluminum and Air.

Methyl Bromide
Methyl bromide in a steel tank reacted with an aluminum tube (part of a level gage) producing methyl aluminum bromide. When the latter was subsequently exposed to air, enough heat was produced to ignite the methyl bromide-compressed air mixture above the liquid level. The ensuing explosion shattered the tank.
Chem. Eng. Progr. **58** (8): 46-9 (1962).

Methyl Chloride
Methyl chloride in the presence of a small amount of aluminum chloride will attack powdered aluminum, forming spontaneously flammable (in air) aluminum trimethyl.
C. C. Clogston, *UL Technical Report* **34** (1945).
See also ALUMINUM plus Chlorinated Hydrocarbons.

Monobromotrifluoromethane
See ALUMINUM plus Dichlorodifluoromethane.

Monochlorotrifluoromethane
See ALUMINUM plus Dichlorodifluoromethane.

Monofluorotrichloromethane
See ALUMINUM plus Dichlorodifluoromethane.

Niobium Oxide and Sulfur
A mixture of aluminum, niobium oxide and sulfur caused a serious fire.
Poole (1971).

Nitrate-Nitrite and Organic Matter
Aluminum and aluminum alloys contaminated with organic matter are likely to explode in nitrate-nitrite salt baths.
Pieters, p. 30 (1957).

Nitrates
Two explosions occurred in mixtures containing aluminum dust, nitrates, water, sulfur, and vegetable glues.
Chem. and Eng. News **32:** 258 (1954).

Nitric Oxide
See ALUMINUM plus Carbon Disulfide.

Nitrogen Peroxide
See ALUMINUM plus Carbon Disulfide.

Nitrosyl Chloride
Aluminum is attacked by nitrosyl chloride when cold.
Mellor **5:** 212 (1946-1947).

Nitrous Oxide
See ALUMINUM plus Carbon Disulfide.

Oxygen
Flash bulbs containing aluminum foil plus oxygen, when ignited, cause similar bulbs up to 8 inches away to be ignited by radiated heat.
W. Zimmerman, *Naturwissenschaften* **18:** 857 (1930).
Liquid oxygen gives a detonable mixture when combined with powdered aluminum.
Kirschenbaum (1956).
A lecturer was demonstrating the ignition of powdered aluminum mixed with liquid oxygen when the mixture exploded. Seventeen persons were injured. This experiment, which is described in several places as a lecture demonstration, has been carried out success fully hundreds of times but there have been a few explosions when the conditions were just right.
Chem. and Eng. News **35** (25): 90 (June 17, 1957).

Palladium
If an aluminum sheath surrounding a palladium core of about .0025- inch diameter is heated to the melting point of aluminum, 600°C, an alloying reaction takes place with production of a brilliant flash and a temperature of 2,800°C.
Tricon (1965). *Woodcock* (1967). *U.S. Pat. Gaz.,* p. 224 (Nov. 3, 1959). *Ellern,* p. 279 (1968).

Performic Acid
Powdered aluminum decomposes performic acid violently.
Berichte **48:**1139 (1915).

Phosgene
See ALUMINUM plus Phosphorus Trichloride.

Phosphorus Trichloride
Powdered aluminum burns in the vapor of phosphorus trichloride, antimony trichloride, arsenic trichloride, and phosgene.
Mellor **5:**214 (1946-1947).

Potassium Bromate
See ALUMINUM plus Bromates.

Potassium Chlorate
See ALUMINUM plus Bromates.

Potassium Iodate
See ALUMINUM plus Bromates.

Potassium Sulfate
See ALUMINUM plus Sulfates.

Propylene Dichloride
An aluminum transfer line failed completely after only a few hours' service in refined propylene dichloride under hot weather conditions. Following this failure, a time sequence study illustrated the nature and rapidity with which this reaction may occur.
Chem. Abst. **52:**7986h (1958). *Corrosion* **14:** 186t-190t (1958).

Silicon and Lead Oxide
See SILICON plus Aluminum and Lead Oxide.

Silver Chloride
A reaction between silver chloride and aluminum, once started, proceeds with explosive violence.
Mellor **3:**402 (1946-1947).

Sodium Bromate
See ALUMINUM plus Bromates.

Sodium Carbide
See MERCURY plus Sodium Carbide.

Sodium Carbonate
When sodium carbonate was applied to red-hot aluminum, an explosion occurred.
Price and Baker, *Chem. & Met. Eng.* **29:**878 (1923).

Sodium Chlorate
See ALUMINUM plus Bromates.

Sodium Hydroxide
A 25 percent sodium hydroxide solution was filtered into a tank trailer thought to be made of mild steel. By the time it was discovered that the tank was made of aluminum, copious volumes of hydrogen were already boiling off.
MCA Case History **1115** (1965).
Aluminum reacts vigorously in sodium hydroxide.
Mellor **5:**207 (1946-1947).

Sodium Iodate
See ALUMINUM plus Bromates.

Sodium Peroxide
A mixture of sodium peroxide and aluminum powder reacts with incandescence. The mixture explodes when heated to redness. When the mixture is exposed to moist air, spontaneous ignition occurs.
Mellor **2:**490; **5:**217 (1946-1947).

Sodium Peroxide and Carbon Dioxide
When carbon dioxide gas is passed over a mixture of powdered aluminum and sodium peroxide, the mixture explodes.
Mellor **2:**490 (1946-1947).

Sodium Sulfate
See ALUMINUM plus Sulfates.

Sulfates
Violent explosions occur when potassium sulfate and sodium sulfate are melted with aluminum.
Chem. and Eng. News **32:** 258 (1954).
The reduction of barium sulfate and of calcium sulfate by aluminum is attended by violent explosions.
Mellor **5:**217-19 (1946-1947).

Sulfur Dichloride
See ALUMINUM plus Carbon Disulfide.

Sulfur Dioxide
See ALUMINUM plus Carbon Disulfide.

Tetrafluoromethane
See ALUMINUM plus Dichlorodifluoromethane.

Trichloroethylene
In the presence of dilute hydrochloric acid (0.1–0.2%) aluminum and trichloroethylene formed aluminum chloride, which catalyzed polymerization of the trichloroethylene with a very high release of heat. Under this condition subsequent oxidation of aluminum fines caused an explosion.
J. van Hints, *Veiligheid* **28:**121-23 (1952).
Fire and Accident Prev. (Dec. 22, 1953).

1,1,2-Trichloro-1,2,2- trifluoroethane
See ALUMINUM plus Dichlorodifluoromethane.

Zinc Bromate
See ALUMINUM plus Bromates.

Zinc Chlorate
See ALUMINUM plus Bromates.

Zinc Iodate
See ALUMINUM plus Bromates.

Zinc Peroxide
Zinc peroxide explodes when heated to about 212°C; and when mixed with aluminum powder or zinc powder, it burns with a dazzling light.
Mellor **4:**530 (1946-1947).

ALUMINUM AMINOBOROHYDRIDES

Air
Oily aluminum borohydrides are spontaneously flammable in air and are attacked by water.
A. B. Burg and C. L. Randolph, Jr., *J. Am. Chem. Soc.* **73:**953 (1951).

Water
See ALUMINUM AMINOBOROHYDRIDES plus Air.

ALUMINUM BROMIDE $AlBr_3$

Potassium
See POTASSIUM plus Aluminum Bromide.

Sodium
See SODIUM plus Aluminum Bromide.

ALUMINUM CARBIDE Al_4C_3

Lead Peroxide
Aluminum carbide reduces lead peroxide with incandescence.
Mellor **5:**872 (1946-1947).

Potassium Permanganate
Aluminum carbide reduces potassium permanganate with incandescence.
Mellor **5:**872 (1946-1947).

ALUMINUM CHLORIDE $AlCl_3$

(self-reactive)
After long storage of aluminum chloride in closed containers, an explosion often occurs when the container is opened.
Chem. Abst. **41:**6723d (1947).

Allyl Chloride
See SULFURIC ACID plus Allyl Chloride.

Ethylene
Ethylene in the presence of aluminum chloride may undergo a violent reaction.
Waterman, *J. Inst. Pet.* **33:**254 (1947).

Ethylene Oxide
See ETHYLENE OXIDE plus Aluminum Oxide.
See ETHYLENE OXIDE plus Acids and Bases.

Nitrobenzene and Phenol
Aluminum chloride added to nitrobenzene containing about 5% phenol caused a violent explosion.
Chem. and Eng. News **31:**4915 (1953).

Nitromethane and Organic Matter
Mixtures of nitromethane and aluminum chloride may explode when organic matter is present.
Chem. and Eng. News **26:**2257 (1948).

Oxygen Difluoride
See OXYGEN DIFLUORIDE plus Aluminum Chloride.

Perchloryl Fluoride and Benzene
See PERCHLORYL FLUORIDE plus Benzene and Aluminum Chloride.

Potassium
See POTASSIUM plus Aluminum Bromide.

Sodium
See SODIUM plus Aluminum Bromide.

Water
When water was added to sublimed anhydrous aluminum chloride, a very vigorous reaction with a release of much heat and toxic hydrogen chloride resulted.
Scott (1966).
This salt dissolves in water with hissing and much heat.
Mellor **5:**314 (1946-1947).

ALUMINUM FLUORIDE Alf_3

Potassium
See POTASSIUM plus Aluminum Bromide.

Sodium
See SODIUM plus Aluminum Bromide.

ALUMINUM HYDRIDE AlH_3

Air
Aluminum hydride will burn violently in air.
Lab. Govt. Chemist (1965).

Dimethyl Ether
Occasional explosions involving these materials have been traced to carbon dioxide impurity in the ether.
J. Am. Chem. Soc. **70:**877 (1948).

Oxygen
See OXYGEN plus Aluminum Hydride.

ALUMINUM HYDROXIDE $Al(OH)_3$

Bismuth
See BISMUTH plus Aluminum Hydroxide.

ALUMINUM HYPOPHOSPHITE $Al(PH_2O_2)_3$

Air
Aluminum hypophosphite releases spontaneously flammable phosphine at about 220°C.
Mellor **8, Supp. 3:**623 (1971).

ALUMINUM OXIDE Al_2O_3

Chlorine Trifluoride
See CHLORINE TRIFLUORIDE plus Aluminum Oxide.

Ethylene Oxide
See ETHYLENE OXIDE plus Aluminum Oxide.
See ETHYLENE OXIDE plus Acids and Bases.

ALUMINUM PHOSPHIDE AlP

Water
Aluminum phosphide yields phosphine on reaction with water. Phosphine is spontaneously flammable in air.
Merck Index, pp. 46, 823 (1968).

ALUMINUM TETRAAZIDOBORATE $Al[B(N_3)_4]_3$

(self-reactive)
This compound is very explosive on shock.
Mellor **8, Supp. 2:** 2 (1967).

ALUMINUM TETRAHYDROBORATE $Al(BH_4)_3$

Air
Oily liquid aluminum borohydrides are spontaneously flammable in air; the reaction is violent with air containing moisture.
Gaylord, p. 8 (1956). *Pease,* p. 1 (1950). H.I. Schlesinger et al., *J. Am. Chem. Soc.* **75:**210-211 (1953).

Oxygen
See OXYGEN plus Aluminum Borohydride.

Water
Aluminum borohydride will flame when in contact with water.
Ellern, p. 45 (1968).

AMINE PERCHOLORATES

(self-reactive)
There are a large number of amine perchlorates that ignite or explode at temperatures above 215°C.
J. Chem. Soc. **115:** 1006-10 (1909).
Analyst **80:** 415 (1955). *ACS* **146:** 211.

AMINES RNH_2

Acrolein
See ACROLEIN plus Sulfur Dioxide.
See SODIUM HYDROXIDE plus Acrolein.

Calcium Hypochlorite
See CALCIUM HYPOCHLORITE plus Amines.

Maleic Anhydride
See SODIUM HYDROXIDE plus Maleic Anhydride.

Nitrosyl Perchlorate
See NITROSYL PERCHLORATE plus Amines.

Sodium Hypochlorite
See CALCIUM HYPOCHLORITE plus Amines.

Tri-iso-Butyl Aluminum
See TRI-iso-BUTYL ALUMINUM plus Acids.

2-AMINOETHANOL $NH_2CH_2CH_2OH$

Acetic Acid
See ACETIC ACID plus 2-Aminoethanol.

Acetic Anhydride
See ACETIC ANHYDRIDE plus 2-Aminoethanol.

Acrolein
See ACROLEIN plus 2-Aminoethanol.

Acrylic Acid
See ACRYLIC ACID plus 2-Aminoethanol.

Acrylonitrile
See ACRYLONITRILE plus 2-Aminoethanol.

Chlorosulfonic Acid
Mixing 2-aminoethanol and chlorosulfonic acid in a closed container caused the temperature and pressure to increase.
Flynn and Rossow (1970). See Note under complete reference.

Epichlorohydrin
Mixing 2-aminoethanol and epichlorohydrin in a closed container caused the temperature and pressure to increase.
Flynn and Rossow (1970). See Note under complete reference.

Hydrochloric Acid
Mixing 2-aminoethanol and 36% hydrochloric acid in a closed container caused the temperature and pressure to increase.
Flynn and Rossow (1970). See Note under complete reference.

Hydrofluoric Acid
Mixing 2-aminoethanol and 48.7% hydrofluoric acid in a closed container caused the temperature and pressure to increase.
Flynn and Rossow (1970). See Note under complete reference.

Mesityl Oxide
See MESITYL OXIDE plus 2-Aminoethanol.

Nitric Acid
Mixing 2-aminoethanol and 70% nitric acid in a closed container caused the temperature and pressure to increase.
Flynn and Rossow (1970). See Note under complete reference.

Oleum
Mixing 2-aminoethanol and oleum in a closed container caused the temperature and pressure to increase.
Flynn and Rossow (1970). See Note under complete reference.

Propiolactone (BETA-)
Mixing 2-aminoethanol and propiolactone (BETA-) in a closed container caused the temperature and pressure to increase.
Flynn and Rossow (1970). See Note under complete reference.

Sulfuric Acid
Mixing 2-aminoethanol and 96% sulfuric acid in a closed container caused the temperature and pressure to increase.
Flynn and Rossow (1970). See Note under complete reference.

Vinyl Acetate
Mixing 2-aminoethanol and vinyl acetate in a closed container caused the temperature and pressure to increase.
Flynn and Rossow (1970). See Note under complete reference.

AMINOGUANIDINE NITRATE $CH_6N_4{\cdot}HNO_3$

(self-reactive)
Aminoguanidine nitrate in water solution exploded violently while being evaporated to dryness in vacuo on the steam bath.
H. Koopman, *Chem. Weekblad* **53:** 97, 98 (1957).

2-AMINOTHIAZOLE (SCHCHNC)NH_2

(self-reactive)
2-Aminothiazole ignited in a tray dryer and was entirely consumed. Stability tests show that 2-aminothiazole will ignite spontaneously in 3½ hours at 100°C.
MCA Case History **1587** (1969).

AMMONIA (ANHYDROUS) NH_3

Acetaldehyde
See ACETALDEHYDE plus Ammonia (Anhydrous).

Acrolein
See SODIUM HYDROXIDE plus Acrolein.

Boron
See BORON plus Ammonia.

Boron Triiodide
See BORON TRIIODIDE plus Ammonia.

Bromine
See BROMINE plus Ammonia.

Bromine Pentafluoride
See BROMINE PENTAFLUORIDE plus Acetic Acid.

Chloric Acid
See ANTIMONY plus Chloric Acid.

Chlorine
See CHLORINE plus Ammonia.

Chlorine Monoxide
See CHLORINE MONOXIDE plus Ammonia.

Chlorine Trifluoride
See CHLORINE TRIFLUORIDE plus Ammonia.

Chlorites
See CHLORITES plus Ammonia.

Chlorosilane
See CHLOROSILANE plus Ammonia.

Chromic Anhydride
See CHROMIC ANHYDRIDE plus Ammonia.

Chromium Trioxide
See CHROMIC ANHYDRIDE plus Ammonia.

Chromyl Chloride
See CHROMYL CHLORIDE plus Ammonia.

Ethylene Dichloride
Liquid ammonia and ethylene dichloride can cause an explosion when mixed.
Mukerjee (1970).

Ethylene Oxide
During manufacture of ethanolamine, an excess of ammonia during a period of high pressure resulted in an ammonia-ethylene oxide explosion.
MCA Case History **792** (1962).

Fluorine
See FLUORINE plus Ammonia.

Gold
See GOLD plus Ammonia.

Hexachloromelamine
See HEXACHLOROMELAMINE plus Organic Contaminants.

Hydrazine and Alkali Metals
See HYDRAZINE plus Alkali Metals and Ammonia.

Hydrogen Bromide
See HYDROGEN BROMIDE plus Ammonia.

Hypochlorous Acid
See HYPOCHLOROUS ACID plus Ammonia.

Iodine
See IODINE plus Ammonia.

Magnesium Perchlorate
See MAGNESIUM PERCHLORATE plus Ammonia.

Mercury
See MERCURY plus Ammonia. See also GOLD plus Ammonia.

Nitric Acid
See NITRIC ACID plus Ammonia.

Nitrogen Peroxide
See NITRIC OXIDE plus Ammonia.

Nitrogen Tetroxide
See NITROGEN TETROXIDE plus Ammonia.

Nitrogen Trichloride
See NITROGEN TRICHLORIDE plus Ammonia.

Nitrogen Trifluoride
See HYDROGEN plus Nitrogen Trifluoride.

Nitryl Chloride
See NITRYL CHLORIDE plus Ammonia.

Oxygen Difluoride
See OXYGEN DIFLUORIDE plus Ammonia.

Phosphorus Pentoxide
See PHOSPHORUS PENTOXIDE plus Ammonia.

Phosphorus Trioxide
See PHOSPHORUS TRIOXIDE plus Ammonia.

Picric Acid
See PICRIC ACID plus Ammonia.

Potassium and Arsine
See POTASSIUM plus Arsine and Ammonia.

Potassium and Phosphine
See POTASSIUM plus Phosphine and Ammonia.

Potassium and Sodium Nitrite
See POTASSIUM plus Sodium Nitrite and Ammonia.

Potassium Chlorate
See POTASSIUM CHLORATE plus Ammonia.

Potassium Ferricyanide
See POTASSIUM FERRICYANIDE plus Ammonia.

Potassium Mercuricyanide
See POTASSIUM MERCURICYANIDE plus Ammonia.

Silver
See GOLD plus Ammonia.

Silver Chloride
See SILVER CHLORIDE plus Ammonia.

Sodium and Carbon Monoxide
See SODIUM plus Carbon Monoxide and Ammonia.

Stibine
See STIBINE plus Ammonia.

Sulfur
See SULFUR plus Ammonia.

Sulfur Dichloride
See SULFUR DICHLORIDE plus Ammonia.

Tellurium Hydropentachloride
See TELLURIUM HYDROPENTACHLORIDE plus Ammonia.

Trichloromelamine
See HEXACHLOROMELAMINE plus Organic Contaminants.

AMMONIUM ACETATE CH_3COONH_4

Sodium Hypochlorite
See SODIUM HYPOCHLORITE plus Ammonium Acetate.

AMMONIUM AZIDE NH_4N_3

(self-reactive)
Ammonium azide decomposes at 160°C.
Mellor **8, Supp. 2:** 43 (1967).

AMMONIUM BROMIDE NH_4Br

Bromine Trifluoride
See BROMINE TRIFLUORIDE plus Ammonium Bromide.

Iodine Heptafluoride
See IODINE HEPTAFLUORIDE plus Ammonium Bromide.

Potassium
See POTASSIUM plus Ammonium Bromide.

AMMONIUM CARBONATE $(NH_4)_2CO_2$

Sodium Hypochlorite
See SODIUM HYPOCHLORITE plus Ammonium Acetate.

AMMONIUM CHLORATE NH_4ClO_3

(self-reactive)
The solid is an explosive compound. Solutions may decompose violently if much solid phase is present.
Mellor **2, Supp. 1:** 591 (1956).

AMMONIUM CHLORIDE NH_4Cl

Ammonium Nitrate
See AMMONIUM NITRATE plus Ammonium Chloride.

Bromine Trifluoride
See BROMINE TRIFLUORIDE plus Ammonium Bromide.

Iodine Heptafluoride
See IODINE HEPTAFLUORIDE plus Ammonium Bromide.

Potassium Chlorate
See POTASSIUM CHLORATE plus Ammonium Chloride.

AMMONIUM DICHROMATE $(NH_4)_2Cr_2O_7$

(self-reactive)
Ammonium dichromate decomposes vigorously with luminescence around 200°C. It is feebly explosive if confined.
Mellor **11:** 324 (1946-1947).

AMMONIUM HEXANITROCOBALTATE $(NH_4)_3CO(NO_2)_6$

(self-reactive)
Ammonium hexanitrocobaltate explodes at 230°C and is impact sensitive.
W. R. Tomlinson, Jr., and L. F. Audrieth, J. Chem. *Ed.* **27:** 606-9 (1950).

AMMONIUM HYDROXIDE NH_4OH

Acrolein
See ACROLEIN plus Ammonium Hydroxide.

Acrylic Acid
See ACRYLIC ACID plus Ammonium Hydroxide.

Chlorosulfonic Acid
See CHLOROSULFONIC ACID plus Ammonium Hydroxide.

Dimethyl Sulfate
Pure dimethyl sulfate and concentrated aqueous ammonia react extremely violently with one another.
Berichte **13:** 1700 (1880).

Fluorine
See FLUORINE plus Ammonium Hydroxide.

Gold and Aqua Regia
See GOLD plus Ammonium Hydroxide and Aqua Regia.

Hydrochloric Acid
See HYDROCHLORIC ACID plus Ammonium Hydroxide.

Hydrofluoric Acid
See HYDROFLUORIC ACID plus Ammonium Hydroxide.

Hydrogen Peroxide
See HYDROGEN PEROXIDE plus Ammonium Hydroxide.

Iodine
See IODINE plus Ammonium Hydroxide.

Nitric Acid
See NITRIC ACID plus Ammonium Hydroxide.

Oleum
See OLEUM plus Ammonium Hydroxide.

Propiolactone (BETA)
See PROPIOLACTONE (BETA) plus Ammonium Hydroxide.

Propylene Oxide
See PROPYLENE OXIDE plus Ammonium Hydroxide.

Silver Nitrate
See SILVER NITRATE plus Acetylene and Ammonium Hydroxide. See SILVER NITRATE plus Ammonium Hydroxide.

Silver Oxide
See SILVER OXIDE plus Ammonium Hydroxide.

Silver Oxide and Ethyl Alcohol
See SILVER OXIDE plus Aqueous Ammonia and Ethyl Alcohol.

Silver Permanganate
See SILVER PERMANGANATE plus Ammonium Hydroxide.

Sulfuric Acid
See SULFURIC ACID plus Ammonium Hydroxide.

AMMONIUM HYPOPHOSPHITE $NH_2PH_2O_2$

(self-reactive)
Ammonium hypophosphite liberates spontaneously flammable phosphine at about 240°C.
Mellor **8:** 880 (1946-1947).

AMMONIUM IODIDE NH_4I

Bromine Trifluoride
See BROMINE TRIFLUORIDE plus Ammonium Bromide.

Iodine Heptafluoride
See IODINE HEPTAFLUORIDE plus Ammonium Bromide.

Potassium
See POTASSIUM plus Ammonium Bromide.

AMMONIUM NITRATE NH_4NO_3

Acetic Acid
A mixture of ammonium nitrate and acetic acid ignites when warmed, especially if concentrated.
Von Schwartz, p. 322 (1918).

Aluminum
See ALUMINUM plus Ammonium Nitrate.

Ammonium Chloride
The decomposition of ammonium nitrate in the presence of ammonium chloride (0.1%) becomes violent around 175°C. The gases liberated contain chlorine.
Pascal **10:** 216 (1931-1934).

Antimony
See AMMONIUM NITRATE plus Metals (powdered).

Bismuth
See AMMONIUM NITRATE plus Metals (powdered).

Cadmium
See AMMONIUM NITRATE plus Metals (powdered).

Carbon
See CARBON plus Ammonium Nitrate.

Chlorides
See AMMONIUM NITRATE plus Ammonium Chloride.

Chromium
See AMMONIUM NITRATE plus Metals (powdered).

Cobalt
See AMMONIUM NITRATE plus Metals (powdered).

Contaminant
During the flame-cutting of a pipeline plugged with impure ammonium nitrate, the pipe contents exploded violently.
MCA Case History **873** (1963).

Copper
See AMMONIUM NITRATE plus Metals (powdered).
See COPPER plus Ammonium Nitrate.

Lead
See AMMONIUM NITRATE plus Metals (powdered).

Magnesium
See AMMONIUM NITRATE plus Metals (powdered).

Magnesium, Copper Sulfate (anhydrous), Potassium Chlorate and Water
See MAGNESIUM plus Copper Sulfate (anhydrous), Ammonium Nitrate, Potassium Chlorate and Water.

Metals (powdered)
Fused ammonium nitrate with powdered metals is often a violent and sometimes an explosive reaction. Zinc, cadmium, copper, magnesium, lead, cobalt, nickel, bismuth, chromium, and antimony are the metals that reacted in this way.
Mellor **Supp. I, Part I, 8:** 545 (1964).
See also SULFUR plus Ammonium Nitrate.
See also ALUMINUM plus Ammonium Nitrate.

Nickel
See AMMONIUM NITRATE plus Metals (powdered).

Organic Matter
Ammonium nitrate forms explosive mixtures with organic matter.
Hazardous Chemicals Data (1966); Lab. Govt. Chemist.

Phosphorus
See PHOSPHORUS plus Ammonium Nitrate.

Potassium and Ammonium Sulfate
See POTASSIUM plus Ammonium Sulfate and Ammonium Nitrate.

Sodium
See SODIUM plus Ammonium Nitrate.

Sodium Hypochlorite
See SODIUM HYPOCHLORITE plus Ammonium Acetate.

Sodium Perchlorate
See SODIUM PERCHLORATE plus Ammonium Alloy Nitrate.

Sodium-Potassium and Ammonium Sulfate
See POTASSIUM plus Ammonium Sulfate and Ammonium Nitrate.

Sulfur
See SULFUR plus Ammonium Nitrate.

Zinc
See ZINC plus Ammonium Nitrate.
See also AMMONIUM NITRATE plus Metals (powdered).

AMMONIUM NITRIDOOSMATE NH_4OsNO_3

(self-reactive)
Ammonium osmiamate decomposes explosively at 150°C.
Mellor **15:** 727 (1946-1947).

AMMONIUM OXALATE $(NH_4OOC\text{-})_2$

Sodium Hypochlorite
See SODIUM HYPOCHLORITE plus Ammonium Acetate.

AMMONIUM PERCHLORATE NH_4ClO_4

(self-reactive)
Ammonium perchlorate decomposes at 130°C and explodes at 380°C.
Mellor **2, Supp. 1:** 608 (1956).

Carbon
See CARBON plus Ammonium Perchlorate.

Dicyclopentadienyliron
Explosions have occurred in propellant formulations using dicyclopentadienyliron (ferrocene), as a burning rate catalyst. Although the definite cause has not been established, the most probable cause is the heat of friction between the mixer sidewall and the spatula while the latter was scraping through a mixture of ammonium perchlorate and sublimed recrystallized ferrocenes.
ASESB Expl. Report **211** (1966).

Ferrocene
See AMMONIUM PERCHLORATE plus Dicyclopentadienyliron.

Metals
See SULFUR plus Ammonium Perchlorate.

Organic Matter
See SULFUR plus Ammonium Perchlorate.

Sulfur
See SULFUR plus Ammonium Perchlorate.

AMMONIUM PERMANGANATE NH_4MnO_4

(self-reactive)
Dry ammonium permanganate is explosive at 60° C and is likely to explode when rubbed.
Lab. Govt. Chemist (1965).

AMMONIUM PERSULFATE $(NH_4)_2S_2O_8$

Aluminum
See ALUMINUM plus Ammonium Persulfate.

Sodium Peroxide
A mixture of ammonium persulfate and sodium peroxide will explode if subjected to crushing (in a mortar), heating, or if a stream of carbon dioxide is passed over it.
Mellor **10:** 464 (1946-1947).

AMMONIUM PHOSPHATE $NH_4H_2PO_4$

Sodium Hypochlorite
See SODIUM HYPOCHLORITE plus Ammonium Acetate.

AMMONIUM PICRATE $C_6H_2(NO_3)_3ONH_4$

(self-reactive)
Small traces of metallic picrates may lower appreciably the temperature at which such mixtures will explode.
Military Explosives, p. 96.

Metals
Explodes when heated to a temperature of about 300° C.
Military Explosives, p. 96.

AMMONIUM SALTS

(See also specific ammonium salt)

Potassium Chlorate
See POTASSIUM CHLORATE plus Ammonium Salts.

Sodium Nitrite
See SODIUM NITRITE plus Ammonium Salts.

AMMONIUM SULFATE $(NH_4)_2SO_4$

Potassium and Ammonium Nitrate
See POTASSIUM plus Ammonium Sulfate and Ammonium Nitrate.

Potassium Chlorate
See POTASSIUM CHLORATE plus Ammonium Sulfate.

Potassium Nitrite
See POTASSIUM NITRITE plus Ammonium Sulfate.

Sodium-Potassium Alloy and Ammonium Nitrate
See POTASSIUM plus Ammonium Sulfate and Ammonium Nitrate.

AMMONIUM TETRACHLOROCUPRATE $(NH_4)_2CuCl_4$

Potassium
See POTASSIUM plus Aluminum Bromide.

Sodium
See SODIUM plus Aluminum Bromide.

AMMONIUM TETRACHROMATE $(NH_4)_2Cr_4O_{13}$

(self-reactive)
Ammonium tetrachromate decomposes suddenly at 175°C.
Mellor **11:** 352 (1946-1947).

AMMONIUM TETRAPEROXYCHROMATE
$(NH_4)_3Cr\ (OO)_4$

(self-reactive)
Ammonium triperchromate explodes from percussion or if heated just to 50°C.
Mellor **11:** 356 (1946-1947).

Sulfuric Acid
Contact between these compounds results in an explosion.
Mellor **11:** 356 (1946-1947).

AMMONIUM THIOCYANATE NH_4SCN

Lead Nitrate
An explosion of guanidine nitrate demolished an autoclave built to withstand 50 atmospheres, in which it was being made from ammonium thiocyanate and lead nitrate. C. Schopf and H. Klapproth.
Angew. Chem. **49:** 23 (1936).

AMMONIUM THIOSULFATE $NH_4S_2O_3$

Acetic Acid
40–60% ammonium thiosulfate reacts under ambient conditions with 80% acetic acid to release sulfur dioxide. There is a mass yield of 25% SO_2 relative to the ammonium thiosulfate.
Acknowledge reported hazards as per correspondence from Gary H. Mosher.

Sodium Chlorate
See SODIUM CHLORATE plus Ammonium Thiosulfate.

AMMONIUM TRICHROMATE $(NH_4)_2Cr_3O_{10}$

(self-reactive)
Ammonium trichromate detonates at about 190°C.
Mellor **11:** 350 (1946-1947).

AMYL ALCOHOL $C_5H_{11}OH$

Hydrogen Trisulfide
See HYDROGEN TRISULFIDE plus Amyl Alcohol.

ANILINE $C_6H_5NH_2$

Acetic Anhydride
Mixing aniline and acetic anhydride in a closed container caused the temperature and pressure to increase.
Flynn and Rossow (1970). See Note under complete reference.

Chlorosulfonic Acid
Mixing aniline and chlorosulfonic acid in a closed container caused the temperature and pressure to increase.
Flynn and Rossow (1970). See Note under complete reference.

Hexachloromelamine
See HEXACHLOROMELAMINE plus Organic Contaminants.

Nitric Acid
See NITRIC ACID plus Aniline.

Nitric Acid, Nitrogen Tetroxide, and Sulfuric Acid
See UNSYMMETRICAL DIMETHYLHYDRAZINE plus Nitric Acid, Nitrogen Tetroxide, and Sulfuric Acid.

Nitrobenzene and Glycerine
In the reaction of these three ingredients to form quinoline, with ferrous sulfate as catalyst, there was too much sulfuric acid and too little water present. The resultant excessive temperature initiated a runaway reaction. The rupture disc and the manhole cover of the vessel blew out; the contents erupted from the vessel.
MCA Case History **1008** (1964).

Oleum
Mixing aniline and oleum in a closed container caused the temperature and pressure to increase.
Flynn and Rossow (1970). See Note under complete reference.

Ozone
See OZONE plus Aniline.

Perchloric Acid and Formaldehyde
See PERCHLORIC ACID plus Aniline and Formaldehyde.

Perchromates
See PERCHROMATES plus Aniline.

Performic Acid
See PERFORMIC ACID plus Aniline.

Potassium Peroxide
See SODIUM PEROXIDE plus Aniline.

Propiolactone (BETA-)
Mixing aniline and propiolactone (BETA-) in a closed container caused the temperature and pressure to increase.
Flynn and Rossow (1970). See Note under complete reference.

Silver Perchlorate
See SILVER PERCHLORATE plus Toluene.
See SILVER PERCHLORATE plus Acetic Acid.

Sodium Peroxide
See SODIUM PEROXIDE plus Aniline.

Sulfuric Acid
Mixing aniline and 96% sulfuric acid in a closed container caused the temperature and pressure to increase.
Flynn and Rossow (1970). See Note under complete reference.

Trichloromelamine
See HEXACHLOROMELAMINE plus Organic Contaminants.

ANISOYL CHLORIDE $CH_3OC_6H_4COCl$

(self-reactive)
A 5-pound bottle containing anisoyl chloride on the laboratory shelf exploded during the night. During cleanup, workers sustained painful eye burns. After several weeks storage in a dessicator at room temperature, a 200-gram bottle of commercial anisoyl chloride exploded with copious emission of hydrogen chloride.
Chem. and Eng. News **38** (34): 40 (1960); **38** (43): 5 (1960).

ANTHRACENE $C_6H_4(CH)_2C_6H_4$

Calcium Hypochlorite
See CALCIUM HYPOCHLORITE plus Anthracene.

Chromic Acid
See CHROMIC ANHYDRIDE plus Anthracene.

ANTIMONY Sb

Ammonium Nitrate
See AMMONIUM NITRATE plus Metals (powdered).

Bromine
Antimony is spontaneously flammable in fluorine, chlorine, or bromine. With iodine, the reaction produces heat, which can cause flame or even an explosion if the quantities are great enough.
Mellor **9:** 379 (1946-1947).

Bromine Trifluoride
Even at 10°C, bromine trifluoride reacts with antimony incandescently. Bromine trifluoride reacts similarly with arsenic, boron, bromine, iodine, phosphorus, and sulfur.
Mellor **2:** 113 (1946-1947).

Bromoazide
Bromoazide explodes on contact with antimony, arsenic, phosphorus, silver foil or sodium. It is very sensitive to shock and the result ing explosions appear to be spontaneous.
Mellor **8:** 336 (1946-1947).

Chloric Acid
Explosions of chloric acid have been due to the formation of explosive compounds with antimony, bismuth, ammonia, and organic matter.
Chem. Abst. **46:** 2805c (1952).

Chlorine
Antimony burns spontaneously in gaseous chlorine. With liquid chlorine, antimony ignites at 33°C.
Mellor **2:** 92-95; **9:** 379, 626 (1946-1947).

Chlorine Monoxide
See POTASSIUM plus Chlorine Monoxide.

Chlorine Trifluoride
Chlorine trifluoride reacts vigorously with antimony, arsenic, osmium, phosphorus, potassium, rhodium, selenium, silicon, sulfur, tellurium, or tungsten, producing flame.
Mellor **2, Supp. 1:** 156 (1956).

Fluorine
See ANTIMONY plus Bromine.

Iodine
See ANTIMONY plus Bromine.

Nitric Acid
The reaction of finely divided antimony and nitric acid can be violent.
Pascal **10:** 504 (1931-1934).

Potassium Nitrate
Powdered antimony mixed with an alkali nitrate explodes when heated.
Mellor **9:** 282 (1946-1947).

Potassium Permanganate
When antimony or arsenic and solid potassium permanganate are ground together, the metals ignite.
Mellor **12:** 322 (1946-1947).

Potassium Peroxide
See POTASSIUM plus Potassium Peroxide.

Sodium Nitrate
See ANTIMONY plus Potassium Nitrate.

Sodium Peroxide
Sodium peroxide oxidizes antimony, arsenic, copper, potassium, tin and zinc with incandescence.
Mellor **2:** 490-93 (1946-1947).

ANTIMONY COMPOUNDS (Trivalent)

Perchloric Acid
Trivalent antimony compounds tend to form explosive mixtures with perchloric acid when hot.
Analyst **84:** 215 (April 1959). *Chem. and Eng. News* **41** (31): 47 (1963).

ANTIMONYL CHLORIDE SbOCl

Bromine Trifluoride
See BROMINE TRIFLUORIDE plus Antimony Trioxide.

ANTIMONYL PERCHLORATE $SbOClO_4$

(self-reactive)
This chemical decrepitates when heated above 60°C.
Mellor **2, Supp. 1:** 613 (1956).

ANTIMONY PENTACHLORIDE $SbCl_5$

Oxygen Difluoride
Mixtures with chlorine, bromine, or iodine explode on warming. Antimony pentachloride with oxygen difluoride explodes mildly at 150°C.
A. G. Streng, *Chem. Reviews* (1963).

Phosphonium Iodide
Interaction at ambient temperature proceeds explosively.
Mellor (1947).

ANTIMONY PENTAFLUORIDE SbF_5
Phosphorus
See PHOSPHORUS plus Antimony Pentafluoride.

ANTIMONY SULFIDE Sb_2S_3;Sb_2S_5

(See also ANTIMONY TRISULFIDE)
Air
When the crystalline form of antimony trisulfide is heated in air, it burns with a blue flame.
Mellor **9:** 522 (1946-1947).

Cadmium Chlorate
See CHLORATES plus Antimony Sulfide.

Chlorates
See CHLORATES plus Antimony Sulfide.

Chloric Acid
Antimony sulfide and concentrated solutions of chloric acid react with incandescence.
Mellor **Supp. II, Part I:** 584 (1956).

Chlorine Monoxide
See CHLORINE MONOXIDE plus Calcium Phosphide.

Magnesium Chlorate
See CHLORATES plus Antimony Sulfide.

Thallic Oxide
See THALLIC OXIDE plus Antimony Sulfide.

Zinc Chlorate
See CHLORATES plus Antimony Sulfide.

ANTIMONY TRIBROMIDE $SbBr_3$

Potassium
See POTASSIUM plus Aluminum Bromide.

Sodium
See SODIUM plus Aluminum Bromide.

ANTIMONY TRICHLORIDE $SbCl_3$

Aluminum
See ALUMINUM plus Phosphorus Trichloride.

Potassium
See POTASSIUM plus Aluminum Bromide.

Sodium
See SODIUM plus Aluminum Bromide.

ANTIMONY TRIIODIDE SbI_3

Potassium
See POTASSIUM plus Aluminum Bromide.

Sodium
See SODIUM plus Aluminum Bromide.

ANTIMONY TRIOXIDE Sb_2O_3

Air
When powdered antimony trioxide is heated in air, it ignites and burns.
Mellor **9:** 425 (1946-1947).

Bromine Trifluoride
See BROMINE TRIFLUORIDE plus Antimony Trioxide.

ANTIMONY TRISULFIDE Sb_2S_3

Chlorine Monoxide
See CHLORINE MONOXIDE plus Calcium Phosphide.

Fluorine
See FLUORINE plus Antimony Trisulfide.

Hydrogen Peroxide
Hydrogen peroxide reacts vigorously with antimony trisulfide, arsenic trisulfide, cupric sulfide, lead sulfide, molybdenum disulfide, and ferrous sulfide.
Mellor **1:** 937 (1946-1947).

Potassium Chlorate
See POTASSIUM CHLORATE plus Antimony Trisulfide.

Potassium Nitrate
See POTASSIUM NITRATE plus Antimony Trisulfide.

Silver Oxide
See SILVER OXIDE plus Antimony Trisulfide.

ARSENIC As

Barium Bromate
See ARSENIC plus Bromates.

Barium Chlorate
See ARSENIC plus Bromates.

Barium Iodate
See ARSENIC plus Bromates.

Bromates
A combination of finely divided arsenic with finely divided bro mates (also chlorates and iodates) of barium, calcium, magnesium, potassium, sodium, or zinc can be exploded by heat, percussion, and sometimes, by light friction.
Mellor **2:** 310 (1946-1947).

Bromine Pentafluoride
Bromine pentafluoride reacts readily in the cold with arsenic, charcoal, selenium, sulfur, iodine, and alkaline chlorides, bromides, and iodides; ignition usually occurs. A few drops of the liquid falling in water produces an explosion.
Sidgwick, p. 1158 (1950).

Bromine Trifluoride
See ANTIMONY plus Bromine Trifluoride.

Bromoazide
See ANTIMONY plus Bromoazide.

Calcium Bromate
See ARSENIC plus Bromates.

Calcium Chlorate
See ARSENIC plus Bromates.

Calcium Iodate
See ARSENIC plus Bromates.

Cesium Acetylene Carbide
The carbide becomes incandescent when warmed in contact with arsenic.
Mellor **5:** 848-50 (1946-1947).

Chlorates
See ARSENIC plus Bromates.

Chlorine
Arsenic burns spontaneously in gaseous chlorine. With liquid chlorine, arsenic ignites at 33°C.
Mellor **2:** 92, 95; **9:** 626 (1946-1947).

Chlorine Monoxide
See POTASSIUM plus Chlorine Monoxide.

Chlorine Trifluoride
See ANTIMONY plus Chlorine Trifluoride.

Chromium Trioxide
Arsenic reacts with chromium trioxide with incandescence.
Mellor **11:** 232 (1946-1947).

Fluorine
See FLUORINE plus Arsenic.

Hypochlorous Acid
Arsenic ignites with hypochlorous acid.
Mellor **2:** 254 (1946-1947).

Iodates
See ARSENIC plus Bromates.

Iodine Pentafluoride
Iodine pentafluoride reacts spontaneously with sulfur, red phosphorus, silicon, bismuth, tungsten, and arsenic, usually with incandescence. Organic compounds react violently, usually carbonizing and often igniting.
Durrant, p. 515 (1953). *Sidgwick,* p. 1159 (1950).

Lithium
See LITHIUM plus Arsenic.

Magnesium Bromate
See ARSENIC plus Bromates.

Magnesium Chlorate
See ARSENIC plus Bromates.

Magnesium Iodate
See ARSENIC plus Bromates.

Nitrogen Tribromide
Nitrogen tribromide explodes violently in contact with arsenic or phosphorus.
Ann. Chim. et Phys. (2) **42:** 200.

Nitrogen Trichloride
Nitrogen trichloride explodes in contact with powdered arsenic. Also see NITROGEN TRICHLORIDE plus Ammonia.
Mellor **8:** 602 (1946-1947).

Potassium Bromate
See ARSENIC plus Bromates.

Potassium Chlorate
See ARSENIC plus Bromates.

Potassium Iodate
See ARSENIC plus Bromates.

Potassium Nitrate
A mixture of arsenic and potassium nitrate explodes when ignited.
Mellor **9:** 35 (1946-1947).

Potassium Permanganate
See ANTIMONY plus Potassium Permanganate.

Potassium Peroxide
See POTASSIUM plus Potassium Peroxide.

Rubidium Acetylene Carbide
Rubidium acetylene carbide becomes incandescent when warmed in contact with arsenic.
Mellor **5:** 849 (1946-1947).

Rubidium Carbide
A mixture of rubidium carbide and arsenic ignites when heated.
Mellor **5:** 848 (1946-1947).

Silver Nitrate
A mixture of sublimed arsenic ground with 10 times its weight of silver nitrate ignites immediately when shaken out on paper.
Mellor **3:** 470 (1946-1947).

Sodium Bromate
See ARSENIC plus Bromates.

Sodium Chlorate
See ARSENIC plus Bromates.

Sodium Iodate
See ARSENIC plus Bromates.

Sodium Peroxide
Sodium peroxide oxidizes arsenic with incandescence.
Mellor **2:** 490-93 (1946-1947).

Zinc Bromate
See ARSENIC plus Bromates.

Zinc Chlorate
See ARSENIC plus Bromates.

Zinc Iodate
See ARSENIC plus Bromates.

ARSENIC DISULFIDE As_2S_2

Air
Arsenic disulfide burns with a blue flame when heated in air.
Mellor **9:** 270 (1946-1947).

Chlorine
See CHLORINE plus Arsenic Disulfide.

Potassium Nitrate
See POTASSIUM NITRATE plus Arsenic Disulfide.

ARSENIC OXIDE As_2O_3; As_2O_5

Rubidium Carbide
See RUBIDIUM CARBIDE plus Arsenic Oxide.

ARSENIC SULFIDE As_2S_2; As_2S_3; As_2S_5

Cadmium Chlorate
See CHLORATES plus Arsenic Sulfide.

Chlorates
See CHLORATES plus Arsenic Sulfide.

Chloric Acid
Arsenic sulfide and concentrated solutions of chloric acid react with incandescence.
Mellor **Supp. II, Part I:** 584 (1956).

Magnesium Chlorate
See CHLORATES plus Arsenic Sulfide.

Zinc Chlorate
See CHLORATES plus Arsenic Sulfide.

ARSENIC TRICHLORIDE $AsCl_3$

Aluminum
See ALUMINUM plus Phosphorus Trichloride.

Aluminum Fluoride
See SODIUM plus Aluminum Bromide.

Ammonium Chlorocuprate
See SODIUM plus Aluminum Bromide.

Antimony Tribromide
See SODIUM plus Aluminum Bromide.

Antimony Trichloride
See SODIUM plus Aluminum Bromide.

Antimony Triiodide
See SODIUM plus Aluminum Bromide.

Arsenic Trichloride
See SODIUM plus Aluminum Bromide.

Arsenic Triiodide
See SODIUM plus Aluminum Bromide.

Potassium
See POTASSIUM plus Aluminum Bromide.

Sodium
See SODIUM plus Aluminum Bromide.

ARSENIC TRIFLUORIDE AsF_3

Phosphorus Trioxide
This reaction is very violent.
Mellor **8, Supp. 3:** 382 (1971).

ARSENIC TRIIODIDE AsI_3

Potassium
See POTASSIUM plus Aluminum Bromide.

Sodium
See SODIUM plus Aluminum Bromide.

ARSENIC TRIOXIDE As_2O_3

Chlorine Trifluoride
See CHLORINE TRIFLUORIDE plus Arsenic Trioxide.

Fluorine
See FLUORINE plus Arsenic Trioxide.

Hydrogen Fluoride
See HYDROGEN FLUORIDE plus Arsenic Trioxide.

Oxygen Difluoride
See OXYGEN DIFLUORIDE plus Aluminum Chloride.

Sodium Chlorate
See SODIUM CHLORATE plus Arsenic Trioxide.

ARSENIC TRISULFIDE As_2S_3

Hydrogen Peroxide
See ANTIMONY TRISULFIDE plus Hydrogen Peroxide.

Sulfur and Potassium Nitrate
See SULFUR plus Potassium Nitrate and Arsenic Trisulfide.

ARSINE AsH_3

Chlorine
See CHLORINE plus Arsine.

Nitric Acid
See NITRIC ACID plus Arsine.

Potassium and Ammonia
See POTASSIUM plus Arsine and Ammonia.

ASPHALT

Fluorine
See FLUORINE plus Common Materials and Oxygen.

AZIDES

(See also specific azide)

Carbon Disulfide
Carbon disulfide plus any of the azides produces violently explosive, extremely sensitive salts.
Mellor **8:** 338 (1946-1947).

Methylene Chloride
Explosive reaction can occur with methylene chloride and other halogenated solvents.
Chem. and Eng. News (Dec. 13, 1993).

AZIDES (ORGANIC)

(heat sensitive)
An explosion occurred during purification of 1,4-diazido-2-butene by high vacuum short path distillation.
Chem. and Eng. News, p. 2, (March 11, 1991).

Acids
Trace amounts of strong acid, certain metal salts, or conceivably other materials may catalyze explosive reactions with organic azides.
Chem. and Eng. News **42** (31): 6 (1964).

Metal Salts
See AZIDES (ORGANIC) plus Acids.

4-AZIDO-N,N-DIETHYLANILINE $NNNC_6H_4N(C_2H_5)_2$

(self-reactive)
An attempt to distill this compound resulted in violent decomposition.
NSC Newsletter, R & D Sec. (July 1973).

3-AZIDO-S-TRIAZOLE HC=N·N=C(N_3)NH

(self-reactive)
Samples of this compound detonated during melting point determinations, breaking combustion tubes.
DeNault, Marx and Takimoto, *J. Chem. Eng. Data* **13:** 514-516 (1968).

AZODICARBONAMIDE $H_2NCON{\cdot}NCONH_2$

A damaging explosion occurred during the manufacture of an azodicarbonamide formulation. It is reported that the event was a bottom-initiated spreading decomposition or deflagration that achieved very high mass rates due to a critical degree of confinement probably initiated by mechanical friction.
M. W. Whitmore, J. P. Gladwell, and P. V. Rutledge, *J. Loss Prev. Process Ind.,* **6** (3) (1993).

a,a′-AZODIISOBUTYRONITRILE [NCC(CH_3)2N=$]_2$

(self-reactive)
An explosion occurred when a solution of a,a′-azodiisobutyronitrile in acetone was concentrated in a glass-lined, steam-jacketed vessel.
P. J. Carlisle, *Chem. and Eng. News* **27:** 150 (1949).

BAKELITE

Fluorine
See FLUORINE plus Solid Nonmetals.

BARIUM Ba

Acids
Barium reacts violently with acids.
Lab. Govt. Chemist (1965).

Carbon Tetrachloride
A violent reaction occurred when small chunks of barium were cleaned by submerging in chemically pure carbon tetrachloride. See also BARIUM plus Trichlorotrifluoroethane.
Serious Acc. Series **23** (1952) and **Supp.** (Sept. 30, 1952).

Monofluorotrichloromethane
See BARIUM plus Trichlorotrifluoroethane.

Tetrachloroethylene
See BARIUM plus Trichlorotrifluoroethane.

Trichloroethylene
See BARIUM plus Trichlorotrifluoroethane.

Trichlorotrifluoroethane
It has been determined experimentally that mixtures of finely divided barium metal and a number of halogenated hydrocarbons possess an explosive capability. Specifically, impact sensitivity tests have shown that granular barium in contact with monofluorotrichloromethane, trichlorotrifluoroethane, carbon tetrachloride, trichloroethylene, or tetrachloroethylene can detonate.
ASESB Pot. Incid. **39** (1968). *Aero. and Astro.* **6** (3):82 (1968). *Chem. and Eng. News* **46** (9):38 (1968).

Water
Barium rapidly decomposes water. The heat of reaction is sufficient that the evolved hydrogen may ignite.
Lab. Govt. Chemist (1965).

BARIUM ALLOYS

Acids
Alloys containing a substantial proportion of barium react violently with acids.
Lab. Govt. Chemist (1965).

Water
Alloys containing a substantial proportion of barium rapidly decompose water. The heat of reaction is sufficient that the evolved hydrogen may ignite.
Lab. Govt. Chemist (1965).

BARIUM AZIDE $Ba(N_3)_2$

(self-reactive)
Barium azide decomposes at 275°C. It is explosively unstable.
Mellor **8, Supp. 2:** 43 (1967).

Air
Barium azide is spontaneously flammable in air.
Ripley (1966).

BARIUM BROMATE $Ba(BrO_3)_2$

Aluminum
See ALUMINUM plus Bromates.

Arsenic
See ARSENIC plus Bromates.

Carbon
See CARBON plus Bromates.

Copper
See COPPER plus Bromates.

Metal Sulfides
See METAL SULFIDES plus Bromates.

Organic Matter
See BROMATES plus Organic Matter.

Phosphorus
See PHOSPHORUS plus Bromates.

Sulfur
See SULFUR plus Bromates.

BARIUM CARBIDE BaC_2

Selenium
See SELENIUM plus Barium Carbide.

Sulfur
See SULFUR plus Barium Carbide.

Water
Barium carbide will flame in contact with water.
Ellern, p. 45 (1968).

BARIUM CHLORATE $Ba(ClO_3)_2$

Aluminum
See ALUMINUM plus Bromates.

Arsenic
See ARSENIC plus Bromates.

Carbon
See CARBON plus Bromates.

Charcoal
See CHLORATES plus Organic Matter.

Copper
See COPPER plus Bromates.

Manganese Dioxide
See CHLORATES plus Manganese Dioxide.

Metal Sulfides
See METAL SULFIDES plus Bromates.

Nitrogen Sulfide
See NITROGEN SULFIDE plus Barium Chlorate.

Organic Matter
See BROMATES plus Organic Matter.
See CHLORATES plus Organic Matter.

Phosphorus
See PHOSPHORUS plus Bromates.

Sulfur
See SULFUR plus Bromates. See SULFUR plus Chlorates.
See SULFUR plus Barium Chlorate.

BARIUM CHLORIDE $BaCl_2$

Bromine Trifluoride
See BROMINE TRIFLUORIDE plus Barium Chloride.

2-Furan Percarboxylic Acid
See 2-FURAN PERCARBOXYLIC ACID (self-reactive).

BARIUM HYDRIDE BaH_2

Air
See BARIUM HYDRIDE plus Water.

Water
Barium hydride reacts vigorously with water. If finely powdered, it ignites spontaneously in moist air or dry air.
Hurd, p. 48 (1952).

BARIUM HYPOPHOSPHITE $Ba(H_2PO_2)_2 \cdot H_2O$

Potassium Chlorate
See POTASSIUM CHLORATE plus Barium Hypophosphite.

BARIUM IODATE $Ba(IO_3)_2$

Aluminum
See ALUMINUM plus Bromates.

Arsenic
See ARSENIC plus Bromates.

Carbon
See CARBON plus Bromates.

Copper
See COPPER plus Bromates.

Metal Sulfides
See METAL SULFIDES plus Bromates.

Organic Matter
See BROMATES plus Organic Matter.

Phosphorus
See PHOSPHORUS plus Bromates.

Sulfur
See SULFUR plus Bromates.

BARIUM NITRATE $Ba(NO_3)_2$

Barium Dioxide, Magnesium,
See MAGNESIUM plus Barium Nitrate,

and Zinc
Barium Dioxide and Zinc.

BARIUM NITRIDOOSMATE $Ba(OsNO_3)_2$

(self-reactive)
Barium osmiamate detonates at 150°C.
Mellor **15:** 728 (1946-1947).

BARIUM OXIDE BaO

Hydrogen Sulfide
See HYDROGEN SULFIDE plus Soda Lime.

Hydroxylamine
Hydroxylamine is ignited on contact with barium oxide.
Mellor **8:** 291 (1946-1947).

Nitrogen Dioxide
See NITROGEN TETROXIDE plus Barium Oxide.

BARIUM PERCHLORATE $Ba(ClO_4)_2H_2O$

Alcohols
Reflux heating of an alcohol and barium perchlorate yields a perchloric ester, all of which are highly explosive.
Kirk and Othmer, Second Ed. **5:** 75 (1963).

BARIUM PEROXIDE BaO_2

Hydroxylamine
Reaction of an aqueous solution of hydroxylamine with barium dioxide causes flaming.
See also LEAD DIOXIDE plus Hydroxylamine.
Mellor **3:** 670 (1946-1947).

Magnesium, Zinc and Barium Nitrate
See MAGNESIUM plus Barium Nitrate, Barium Dioxide, and Zinc.

Organic Matter
Mixtures of barium peroxide and combustible, organic or readily oxidizable materials are explosive and are ignited easily by friction or on contact with a small amount of water.
Haz. Chem. Data (1969).

BARIUM RHODANIDE $Ba[\underline{N=C(O)CH_2SC(S)}]_2$

Sodium Nitrate
A mixture of the two may cause an explosion.
Pieters, p. 30 (1957).

BARIUM SULFATE $BaSO_4$

Aluminum
See ALUMINUM plus Sulfates.

BARIUM SULFIDE BaS

Chlorine Monoxide
See CHLORINE MONOXIDE plus Calcium Phosphide.

Lead Dioxide
Oxidizing agents like lead dioxide, potassium chlorate and potassium nitrate react vigorously when heated with sulfides of the alkaline earth group.
Mellor **3:** 745 (1946-1947).

Potassium Chlorate
See BARIUM SULFIDE plus Lead Dioxide.

Potassium Nitrate
See BARIUM SULFIDE plus Lead Dioxide.

BENZALDEHYDE C_6H_5CHO

Performic Acid
See PERFORMIC ACID plus Benzaldehyde.

BENZENE C_6H_6

Bromine Pentafluoride
See BROMINE PENTAFLUORIDE plus Acetic Acid.

Chlorine
See CHLORINE plus Benzene.

Chlorine Trifluoride
See CHLORINE TRIFLUORIDE plus Benzene.

Chromic Anhydride
See CHROMIC ANHYDRIDE plus Benzene.

Nitryl Perchlorate
See NITRYL PERCHLORATE plus Benzene.

Oxygen
See OXYGEN (LIQUID) plus Benzene.

Ozone
See OZONE plus Benzene.

Perchlorates
See PERCHLORATES plus Benzene.

Perchloryl Fluoride and Aluminum Chloride
See PERCHLORYL FLUORIDE plus Benzene and Aluminum Chloride.

Permanganates and Sulfuric Acid
See PERMANGANATES plus Sulfuric Acid and Benzene.

Potassium Peroxide
See SODIUM PEROXIDE plus Aniline.

Silver Perchlorate
See SILVER PERCHLORATE plus Benzene.
See SILVER PERCHLORATE plus Acetic Acid.
See SILVER PERCHLORATE plus Toluene.

Sodium Peroxide
See SODIUM PEROXIDE plus Aniline.

BENZENEDIAZONIUM 2-CARBOXYLATE HYDROCHLORIDE $N{\equiv}N\text{-}C_6H_4\text{-}2\text{-}CO_2{\cdot}HCl$

(self-reactive)
An explosion occurred during the transfer of dry crystals.
H.D. Embry, Chem. and Eng. News **49** (30): 3 (1971). R.M. Stiles et al., *J. Am. Chem. Soc.* **85,** p. 1795 (1963). C.A. Matuszak, *Chem. and Eng. News* **49** (24): 39 (1971).

BENZENEDIAZONIUM CHLORIDE C_6H_5NNCl

(self-reactive)
Phenylchlorodiazirine is extremely shock sensitive. It should not be handled in an undiluted state.
Chem. Eng. and News **48** (2): 10 (1970). W.H. Graham, *J. Am. Chem. Soc.* **87:** 4396 (1965). A. Padwa and D. Eastman, *J. Org. Chem.* **34:** 2728 (1969).

Hydrogen Sulfide
An explosive product is obtained when hydrogen sulfide and phenyl diazonium chloride are mixed.
Berichte **15:** 1683.

BENZENESULFONYL CHLORIDE $C_6H_5SO_2Cl$

Dimethyl Sulfoxide
See DIMETHYL SULFOXIDE plus Acyl Halides.

Methylformamide
See METHYL ISONITRILE (self-reactive).

BENZOTRIAZOLE $C_6H_4N_3H$

(self-reactive)
During the vacuum distillation of 2,000 lbs. of benzotriazole in a 500-gallon glass-lined kettle at 160°C and a pressure of 2 mm of mercury, the vessel suddenly pressurized, the temperature rose to a recorded 220°C, and the contents detonated. This same process had been in trouble-free operation for months.
Chem. and Eng. News **34:** 2450 (1956).

BENZOYL CHLORIDE C_6H_5COCl

Dimethyl Sulfoxide
See DIMETHYL SULFOXIDE plus Acyl Halides.

Sodium Azide and Potassium Hydroxide
See SODIUM AZIDE plus Benzoyl Chloride and Potassium Hydroxide.

BENZOYL PEROXIDE $(C_6H_5CO)_2O_2$

(See also DIBENZOYL PEROXIDE)

(self-reactive)
Benzoyl peroxide has been reported to explode for apparently no specific reason. Friction while opening bottles has caused other explosions. Purification of benzoyl peroxide in hot chloroform solutions has also resulted in several explosions. Purification in cold chloroform by addition of methanol is without danger.
Chem. and Eng. News **37:** 46 (Jan. 3, 1949).
Chem. Abst. **25:** 4127 (1931).

Carbon Tetrachloride and Ethylene
A reaction of ethylene, carbon tetrachloride and benzoyl peroxide caused an explosion.
R.O. Bolt, R.M. Joyce, *Chem. and Eng. News* **25:** 1866 (1947).

Methyl Methacrylate
Benzoyl peroxide was weighed into a stainless steel beaker that had been rinsed previously with methyl methacrylate. The peroxide catalyzed polymerization of the methacrylate and the build-up of heat was sufficient to ignite the remainder of the peroxide.
MCA Case History **996** (1964).

Organic Matter
While a bottle of benzoyl peroxide was being opened, it exploded. Organic matter may have been entrapped in the threads of the bottle. When cap was unscrewed, friction caused explosion.
G.R. Lappin, *Chem. and Eng. News* **26:** 3518 (1948).

BENZYL ALCOHOL $C_6H_5CH_2OH$

Acids
See ACIDS plus Benzyl Alcohol.

BENZYL FLUORIDE $C_6H_5CH_2F$
A bottle decomposed spontaneously after storage for approximately one year.
Chem. and Eng. News (August 20, 1990).

BENZYL SILANE $C_6H_5CH_2SiH_3$

Air
Benzyl silane is spontaneously flammable in air.
Lehman and Wilson, p. 53 (1949).

BENZYL SODIUM $C_6H_5CH_2Na$

Air
Benzyl sodium is spontaneously flammable in air.
Ellern (1961).

BERYLLIUM Be

Carbon Tetrachloride
It has been determined experimentally that a mixture of beryllium powder with carbon tetrachloride or with trichloroethylene will flash or spark on heavy impact.
ASESB Pot. Incid. **39** (1968).

Lithium
See LITHIUM plus Vanadium.

Phosphorus
The reaction between beryllium and the vapors of phosphorus proceeds with incandescence.
Mellor **8:** 842 (1946-1947).

Trichloroethylene
See BERYLLIUM plus Carbon Tetrachloride.

BERYLLIUM OXIDE BeO

Magnesium
See MAGNESIUM plus Beryllium Oxide.

BERYLLIUM TETRAHYDROBORATE $Be(BH_4)_2$

Air
Beryllium borohydride is spontaneously flammable in air.
Douda (1966).

Oxygen
See OXYGEN plus Beryllium Borohydride.

Water
See OXYGEN plus Beryllium Borohydride.

BIS (2-CHLOROETHYL) ETHER $ClCH_2CH_2OCH_2CH_2Cl$

Chlorosulfonic Acid
Mixing dichloroethyl ether and chlorosulfonic acid in a closed container caused the temperature and pressure to increase.
Flynn and Rossow (1970). See Note under complete reference.

Oleum
Mixing dichloroethyl ether and oleum in a closed container caused the temperature and pressure to increase.
Flynn and Rossow (1970). See Note under complete reference.

BIS(DIMETHYLSTIBINE) OXIDE $[(CH_3)_2Sb]_2O$

Air
Bisdimethylstibine oxide is spontaneously flammable in air.
Coates, p. 555 (1956).

BIS(ETHYLAMINO) CYCLOTRISILOXANE

$[(C_2H_5)_2N]_2SiOSiH_2OSiH_2O$

Air
Bisethylamino siloxane is spontaneously flammable in air.
Douda (1966).

BISMUTH Bi

Aluminum and Air
A mixture of bismuth hydroxide and aluminum hydroxide, coprecipitated, and reduced by hydrogen at 170°–210°C, is spontaneously flammable in air at ordinary temperatures.
Mellor **9:** 626 (1946-1947).

Ammonium Nitrate
See AMMONIUM NITRATE plus Metals (powdered).

Chloric Acid
See ANTIMONY plus Chloric Acid.

Chlorine
Powdered bismuth burns spontaneously in gaseous chlorine. With liquid chlorine, bismuth ignites at 80°C.
Mellor **2:** 92, 95; **9:** 626 (1946-1947).

Iodine Pentafluoride
See ARSENIC plus Iodine Pentafluoride.

Nitric Acid
If fuming nitric acid is poured over powdered bismuth, the metal becomes red hot.
Mellor **9:** 627 (1946-1947).

Perchloric Acid
When bismuth is heated with perchloric acid at 100° C or below, the metal dissolves slowly, but at 110° a brown coating forms, which on further heating explodes violently.
J. Am. Chem. Soc. **57:** 817-18 (May 1935).
ACS **146:** 188.
The preparation of a salt from these two chemicals is dangerous.
Mellor **2, Supp. 1:** 613 (1956).

BISMUTHIC ACID $HBiO_3$

Hydrofluoric Acid
When bismuthic acid is treated with 40 percent hydrofluoric acid at ordinary temperatures, a violent reaction occurs.
Mellor **9:** 657 (1946-1947).

BISMUTH PENTAFLUORIDE BiF_5

Water
Bismuth pentafluoride reacts violently with water, sometimes with ignition.
Brauer (1965).

BISMUTH PENTOXIDE Bi_2O_5

Bromine Trifluoride
See BROMINE TRIFLUORIDE plus Bismuth Pentoxide.

BISMUTH TRIBROMIDE $BiBr_3$

Potassium
See POTASSIUM plus Aluminum Bromide.

Sodium
See SODIUM plus Aluminum Bromide.

BISMUTH TRICHLORIDE $BiCl_3$

Potassium
See POTASSIUM plus Aluminum Bromide.

Sodium
See SODIUM plus Aluminum Bromide.

BISMUTH TRIIODIDE BiI_3

Potassium
See POTASSIUM plus Aluminum Bromide.

Sodium
See SODIUM plus Aluminum Bromide.

BISMUTH TRIOXIDE Bi_2O_3

Aluminum
See ALUMINUM plus Bismuth Trioxide.

Chlorine Trifluoride
See CHLORINE TRIFLUORIDE plus Arsenic Trioxide.

Potassium
See POTASSIUM plus Bismuth Trioxide.

Sodium
See SODIUM plus Bismuth Trioxide.

BIS(TRIFLUOROMETHYL) CHLOROPHOSPHINE $(CF_3)_2PCl$

Air
Bistrifluoromethyl chlorophosphine is spontaneously flammable in air.
Handbook Chem. Phys., p. C-428 (1970-1971).

BIS(TRIFLUOROMETHYL) CYANOPHOSPHINE $(CF_3)PCN$

Air
Bistrifluoromethyl cyanophosphine is spontaneously flammable in air.
Handbook Chem. Phys., p. C-428 (1970-1971).

BIS(TRIFLUOROMETHYL) PHOSPHINE $(CF_3)_2PH$

Air
Bistrifluoromethyl phosphine is spontaneously flammable in air.
Douda (1966). *Handbook Chem. Phys.*, p. C-428 (1970-1971).

BORAX $Na_2B_4O_7 \cdot 10H_2O$

Zirconium
See ZIRCONIUM plus .

BORIC ACID $B(OH)_3$

Acetic Anhydride
During an attempt to make triacetyl borate, a mixture of boric acid and acetic anhydride exploded when heated to 58-60°C.
M. L. Lerner. *Chem. and Eng. News.* **51:** (34) (Aug. 20, 1973).

Potassium
See POTASSIUM plus Boric Acid.

BORIC OXIDE B_2O_3

Calcium Oxide and Calcium Chloride
When a mixture of boric oxide and calcium oxide in any proportion is projected into fused calcium chloride, the mass becomes incandescent.
Mellor **5:** 141 (1946-1947).

BORON B

Ammonia
When amorphous boron is heated in dry ammonia, the reaction proceeds with incandescence and hydrogen is evolved.
Mellor **8:**109 (1946-1947).

Bromine
Boron ignites in bromine vapor at 700°C.
Mellor **5:** 15 (1946-1947).

Bromine Trifluoride
See ANTIMONY plus Bromine Trifluoride.

Cesium Carbide
See SILICON plus Cesium Carbide.

Chlorine
Boron burns spontaneously in gaseous chlorine.
Mellor **2:** 92, 95; **9:** 626 (1946-1947).
Boron ignites in chlorine at 410°C.
Mellor **5:** 15 (1946-1947).

Cupric Oxide
Boron reacts violently with cupric oxide after warming, melting glass tubing.
Mellor **5:** 17 (1946-1947).

Fluorine
Fluorine attacks boron at ordinary temperatures, the mass becoming incandescent.
Mellor **2:** 12; **5:** 15 (1946-1947).

Iodic Acid
Iodic acid attacks boron below 40°C and the mass becomes incandescent.
Mellor **5:** 15 (1946-1947).

Lead Dioxide
A mixture of boron and lead dioxide explodes violently when ground in a mortar.
Mellor **5:** 17 (1946-1947).

Nitric Acid
Concentrated nitric acid and boron react so violently that the mass is raised to incandescence.
Mellor **5:** 16 (1946-1947).

Nitric Oxide
See BORON plus Nitrous Oxide.

Nitrosyl Fluoride
The reaction between nitrosyl fluoride and boron (also phosphorus or silicon) is accompanied by incandescence.
Z. Anorg. Chemie **47:** 190.

Nitrous Oxide
Amorphous boron ignites when heated in dry nitrous oxide. With nitric oxide, the reaction proceeds with blinding flashes.
Mellor **8:** 109 (1946-1947).

Potassium Chlorate
The reaction of boron and fused potassium chlorate is vigorous.
Mellor **5:** 15 (1946-1947).

Potassium Nitrate
Portions of boron powder and potassium nitrate were blended, screened, and placed in aluminum containers. When one of the covered containers was accidentally dropped, there was a flash fire followed by explosions.
MCA Case History **1334** (1967).

Potassium Nitrite
Molten potassium nitrite is violently decomposed by boron.
Mellor **5:** 16 (1946-1947).

Rubidium Carbide
See SILICON plus Rubidium Carbide.

Silver Fluoride
Fused silver fluoride reacts explosively with boron at ordinary temperatures.
Mellor **3:** 389 (1946-1947).

Sulfur
A mixture of boron and sulfur becomes incandescent at 600°C.
Mellor **5:** 15 (1946-1947).

BORON ARSENOTRIBROMIDE BAs_2Br_3

Air
See OXYGEN plus Boron Arsenotribromide.

Oxygen
See OXYGEN plus Boron Arsenotribromide.

BORON BROMODIIODIDE $BBrI_2$

Water
Boron bromodiiodide hydrolyzes violently.
Mellor **5:** 136 (1946-1947).

BORON DIBROMOIODIDE BBr_2I

Water
Boron dibromoiodide hydrolyzes violently.
Mellor **5:** 136 (1946-1947).

BORON NITRIDE BN

Sodium Dioxide
When powdered boron nitride is added to molten sodium dioxide, the reaction proceeds with incandescence.
Mellor **8:** 111 (1946-1947).

BORON PHOSPHIDE BP

Nitrates
See BORON PHOSPHIDE plus Nitric Acid.

Nitric Acid
Boron phosphide ignites in concentrated nitric acid; with fused alkali nitrates, there is a deflagration.
Mellor **8:** 845-46 (1946-1947).

BORON PHOSPHODIIODIDE BPI_2

Chlorine
See CHLORINE plus Boron Phosphodiiodide.

Magnesium
See MAGNESIUM plus Boron Phosphodiiodide.

Mercury
See MERCURY plus Boron Phosphodiiodide.

BORON TRIAZIDE $B(N_3)_3$

(self-reactive)
Boron triazide, lithium boroazide, and silicon tetraazide and some of their intermediates are extremely sensitive and explosive.
Egon Wibergand Horst Michaud, *Z. Naturforsch.* **9b:** 497-500 (1954).

BORON TRIBROMIDE BBr_3

Potassium
See POTASSIUM plus Boron Tribromide.

Sodium
See SODIUM plus Aluminum Bromide.

Water
When boron tribromide and water are mixed, there is an explosion.
Mellor **5:** 134 (1946-1947). *BCISC* 41(1962):19 (1970).

BORON TRICHLORIDE BCl_3

Nitrogen Peroxide
Boron trichloride reacts energetically with nitrogen peroxide, phosphine, or fat and grease.
Mellor **5:** 132 (1946-1947).

Organic Matter
See BORON TRICHLORIDE plus Nitrogen Peroxide.

Oxygen
See OXYGEN plus Boron Trichloride.

Phosphine
See BORON TRICHLORIDE plus Nitrogen Peroxide.

BORON TRIFLUORIDE BF_3

Alkali Metals
See ALKALI METALS plus Boron Trifluoride.

Alkaline Earth Metals
See ALKALI METALS plus Boron Trifluoride.

Calcium Oxide
See CALCIUM OXIDE plus Boron Trifluoride.

BORON TRIFLUORIDE ETHERATE $BF_3{\cdot}(C_2H_5)_2O$

Lithium Aluminum Hydride
See LITHIUM ALUMINUM HYDRIDE plus Boron Trifluoride Etherate.

BORON TRIIODIDE BI_3

Ammonia
Ammonia reacts with boron triiodide with the development of much heat.
Mellor **5:** 136 (1946-1947).

Carbohydrates
See BORON TRIIODIDE plus Ethers.

Ethers
Boron triiodide and ethers or carbohydrates react vigorously.
Mellor **5:** 136 (1946-1947).

Phosphorus
See PHOSPHORUS plus Boron Triiodide.

Phosphoryl Chloride
See PHOSPHORYL CHLORIDE plus Boron Triiodide.

BORON TRISULFIDE B_2S_3

Chlorine
See CHLORINE plus Boron Trisulfide.

BRASS

Acetylene
See COPPER plus Acetylene.

Chlorine
See CHLORINE plus Brass.

Hydrogen Peroxide
See IRON plus Hydrogen Peroxide.

Lead Azide
See COPPER plus Lead Azide.

BROMATES

(See also specific bromates as primary entries or see under other reactants)

Acids and Metals (powdered)
See CHLORATES plus Metals (powdered).

Aluminum
See ALUMINUM plus Bromates.

Arsenic
See ARSENIC plus Bromates.

Calcium Hydride
A mixture of calcium hydride and bromates, chlorates or perchlorates explodes violently when rubbed in a mortar.
Mellor **3:** 651 (1946-1947).

Carbon
See CARBON plus Bromates.

Copper
See COPPER plus Bromates.

Metals (powdered)
See CHLORATES plus Metals (powdered).

Metal Sulfides
See METAL SULFIDES plus Bromates.

Organic Matter
A combination of finely divided organic matter with finely divided bromates (also chlorates or iodates) of barium, calcium, magnesium, potassium, sodium, or zinc can be exploded by heat, percussion, and sometimes, light friction.
Mellor **2:** 310 (1946-1947). *MCA Case History* **874** (1963).

Phosphonium Iodide
Bromates, chlorates or iodates when dry ignite in phosphonium iodide at ordinary temperatures.
Ann. Chim. et Phys. (2) **47:** 87.

Phosphorus
See PHOSPHORUS plus Bromates.

Strontium Hydride
A mixture of strontium hydride and bromates, chlorates, or perchlorates explodes violently when rubbed in a mortar.
Mellor **3:** 651 (1946-1947).

Sulfur
See SULFUR plus Bromates.

Sulfuric Acid and Metals
See CHLORATES plus Metals (powdered).

BROMIC ACID $HBrO_3$

Phosphonium Iodide
See PHOSPHONIUM IODIDE plus Bromic Acid.

BROMINE Br_2

Acetaldehyde
Combination of acetaldehyde with bromine, chlorine, fluorine, or iodine can be violent.
Chem. Safety Data Sheet **SD-43** (1952).

Acetylene
Acetylene can react explosively with bromine.
Von Schwartz, p. 142 (1918).

Acrylonitrile
During the drop-wise addition of bromine into a 500 ml. flask containing acrylonitrile, the periodic cooling with an ice bath was insufficient to prevent a runaway exothermic reaction. When the temperature of the reactants exceeded 40°C, the flask exploded.
MCA Case History **1214** (1966).

Aluminum
See ALUMINUM plus Bromine.

Ammonia
Ammonia plus bromine (with heat) explodes due to the formation of extremely sensitive nitrogen tribromide.
Mellor **2:** 95 (1946-1947).

Antimony
See ANTIMONY plus Bromine.

Boron
See BORON plus Bromine.

Calcium Nitride
Calcium nitride reacts in the cold with bromine, with incandescence.
Mellor **8:** 99 (1946-1947).

Cesium Acetylene Carbide
Cesium acetylene carbide burns in the vapors of bromine or iodine.
Mellor **5:** 844 (1946-1947).

Cesium Monoxide
At ordinary temperatures, cesium monoxide plus bromine, chlorine, fluorine or iodine reacts with incandescence. At temperatures above 150°C., a blue flame appears with fluorine. Chlorine and iodine act similarly.
Mellor **2:** 487 (1946-1947).

Chlorotrifluoroethylene and Oxygen
See CHLOROTRIFLUOROETHYLENE plus Bromine and Oxygen.

Copper Hydride
Copper hydride ignites in bromine, chlorine or fluorine.
Mellor **3:** 73 (1946-1947).

Cuprous Acetylide (Copper Carbide)
Cuprous acetylide is spontaneously flammable with bromine vapor, chlorine gas or fine iodine.
Mellor **5:** 852 (1946-1947).

Dimethyl Formamide
The use of dimethyl formamide as a solvent in one of the catalysis reactions of olefins and bromine resulted in the operation of a rupture disk on an autoclave. The investigation indicated that there was a highly exothermic reaction between dimethyl formamide and bro mine. In one instance mixing 40 cc of bromine and 150 cc of dime thyl formamide resulted in an increase of temperature to above 100°C and an increase in pressure to above 2000 psi.
H. A. Tayim and M. Absi, *Chem. & Ind.,* p. 347 (April 21, 1973).

Ethyl Phosphine
A mixture of ethyl phosphine and bromine, chlorine, or nitric acid (fuming) explodes.
Von Schwartz, pp. 324, 325 (1918).

Fluorine
See FLUORINE plus Bromine.

Germanium
See GERMANIUM plus Bromine.

Hydrogen
Hydrogen and bromine explode.
Mellor **Supp. I:** 707.

Iron Carbide
See CHLORINE plus Iron Carbide.

Isobutyrophenone
Bromine had been added dropwise at 21-31°C to a solution of isobutyrophenone in carbon tetrachloride. The flask was then packed in ice. After 15 minutes, the flask exploded.
MCA Guide for Safety, Appendix 3 (1972).

Lithium
See BROMINE plus Potassium.

Lithium Carbide
Lithium carbide burns vigorously and spontaneously in cold chlorine or fluorine. With bromine or iodine, the materials must be warm.
Mellor **5:** 848 (1946-1947).

Lithium Silicide
See FLUORINE plus Lithium Silicide.

Magnesium Phosphide
See CHLORINE plus Magnesium Phosphide.

Methyl Alcohol
A violent exothermic reaction of these materials occurred in a measuring cylinder.
MCA Case History **1863** (1972).

Nickel Carbonyl
The reaction between these liquids proceeds with explosive violence.
Mellor **2, Supp. 1:** 716 (1956). *J. Am. Chem. Soc.* **48:** 872-82 (1926).

Nitrogen Triiodide
Nitrogen triiodide explodes on contact with bromine, chlorine, or ozone, and is almost instantly decomposed by hydrogen sulfide.
Champion and Pellet, *Bull. Soc. Chim.* (2) **24:** 447 (1875). *Ann. Chim. et Phys.* (2) **42:** 200.
E. Schneider, *Report Anal. Chem.* **1:** 54 (1881).

Olefins
See BROMINE plus Dimethyl Formamide.

Oxygen Difluoride
A mixture of oxygen difluoride and bromine or iodine explodes on gentle warming.
Mellor **2, Supp. 1:** 192 (1956).

Ozone
See OZONE plus Bromine.

Phosphine
Phosphine ignites with bromine or chlorine at room temperature.
Berichte **3:** 660. *Merck Index,* p. 823 (1968).

Phosphorus
Ordinary phosphorus reacts with gaseous bromine with incandescence. Red phosphorus reacts with bromine (liquid) at ordinary temperatures with incandescence. Small pieces of yellow (white) phosphorus thrown into liquid bromine ignite and cause dangerous explosions.
Ann. Chim. et Phys. (2) **32:** 337. *Lowig* (1829).
See also PHOSPHORUS plus Chlorine.

Phosphorus Oxide
See CHLORINE plus Phosphorus Oxide.

Phosphorus Trioxide
Phosphorus trioxide, thrown into a jar of chlorine, ignites immedi ately and burns with a greenish flame. Phosphorus trioxide reacts violently with liquid bromine—generally ignites.
Thorpe and Tutton, *J. Chem. Soc.* **59:** 1019 (1891).

Potassium
The reaction between potassium and bromine (gas) is vigorous with incandescence. A violent explosion will occur if potassium is brought in contact with liquid bromine.
R. Cowper, *Chem. News* **47:** 70 (1883). *Sidgwick,* p. 65 (1950). *Mellor* **2:** 469 (1946-1947).
The system bromine-plus-sodium, however, requires a small impact to cause an explosion. The system bromine-plus-lithium requires a much larger impact to explode it.
H. Staudinger, *Z. Elektrochem.* **31:** 549-52 (1925).
Mellor **2, Supp. 3:** 1559.

Rubidium Acetylene Carbide
Rubidium acetylene carbide burns in cold bromine, chlorine, fluorine, or iodine (vapor).
Mellor **5:** 849 (1946-1947).

Rubidium Carbide
This carbide burns in bromine gas.
Mellor **5:** 848 (1946-1947).

Silver Azide
Bromine vapor diluted with some nitrogen plus silver or sodium azides formed bromoazide; explosions often occurred.
Mellor **8:** 330 (1946-1947).

Sodium
Finely divided sodium reacts with bromine with luminescence. Solid sodium plus liquid bromine can be caused to explode by mechanical shock. See also BROMINE plus Potassium.
Mellor **Supp. II, Part I:** 714 (1956).

Sodium Acetylene Carbide
Sodium acetylene carbide burns in cold chlorine or bromine.
Mellor **5:** 849 (1946-1947).

Sodium Carbide
Sodium carbide explodes on contact with bromine vapor or water.
Von Schwartz, p. 328 (1918).

Strontium Phosphide
Mixtures of these materials ignite at about 170°C.
Mellor **8:** 841 (1946-1947).

Tin
See TIN plus Bromine.

Uranium Dicarbide
Uranium dicarbide reacts with incandescence with warm fluorine; at 300°C. with chlorine; or at 390°C. with bromine.
Mellor **5:** 890-98 (1946-1947).

Zirconium Dicarbide
Zirconium dicarbide burns in fluorine, in the cold; in chlorine, at 250°C.; in bromine, at 300°C.; and in iodine, at 400°C.
Mellor **5:** 855-57 (1946-1947).

BROMINE AZIDE N_3Br

(self-reactive)
Spontaneous explosions have been observed with this compound.
Mellor **8, Supp. 2:** 50 (1967)
Mellor **8:** 336 (1946-1947).

Antimony
See ANTIMONY plus Bromoazide.

Arsenic
See ANTIMONY plus Bromoazide.

Diethyl Ether
A solution of bromoazide in ether is stable for a few hours, but after a time, or when being concentrated, it is likely to explode on shaking.
Mellor **8:** 327, 336, 338 (1946-1947).

Phosphorus
See ANTIMONY plus Bromoazide.

Silver
See ANTIMONY plus Bromoazide.

Sodium
See ANTIMONY plus Bromoazide.

BROMINE MONOFLUORIDE BrF

Organic Matter
See BROMINE MONOFLUORIDE plus water.

Water
Halogen fluorides react violently with water and organic compounds.
Mellor **2, Supp. 1:** 147 (1956).
See also CHLORINE TRIFLUORIDE plus Elements.

BROMINE PENTAFLUORIDE BrF_5

Acetic Acid
In reactions between bromine pentafluoride and acetic acid, ammonia, benzene, cellulose (in paper), ethyl alcohol, organic matter such as grease or wax, hydrogen sulfide, or methane, fire and explosions are likely.
Mellor **2, Supp. 1:** 172 (1956).

Ammonia
See BROMINE PENTAFLUORIDE plus Acetic Acid.

Arsenic
See ARSENIC plus Bromine Pentafluoride.

Benzene
See BROMINE PENTAFLUORIDE plus Acetic Acid.

Bromides (Alkaline)
See ARSENIC plus Bromine Pentafluoride.

Cellulose
See BROMINE PENTAFLUORIDE plus Acetic Acid.

Charcoal
See ARSENIC plus Bromine Pentafluoride.

Chlorides (Alkaline)
See ARSENIC plus Bromine Pentafluoride.

Chlorine
See CHLORINE plus Bromine Pentafluoride.

Ethyl Alcohol
See BROMINE PENTAFLUORIDE plus Acetic Acid.

Hydrogen Sulfide
See BROMINE PENTAFLUORIDE plus Acetic Acid.

Iodides (Alkaline)
See ARSENIC plus Bromine Pentafluoride.

Iodine
See ARSENIC plus Bromine Pentafluoride.
See IODINE plus Bromine Pentafluoride.

Metallic Halides
See BROMINE PENTAFLUORIDE plus Metal Oxides.

Metal Oxides
Bromine pentafluoride reacts violently with metal oxides and metallic halides.
Mellor **2, Supp. 1:** 172 (1956).

Metals
See METALS plus Bromine Pentafluoride.

Methane
See BROMINE PENTAFLUORIDE plus Acetic Acid.

Nitric Acid
Bromine pentafluoride reacts violently with strong nitric acid or strong sulfuric acid.
Mellor **2, Supp. 1:** 172 (1956).

Organic Matter
See BROMINE PENTAFLUORIDE plus Acetic Acid. See also BROMINE MONOFLUORIDE plus Water.

Selenium
See ARSENIC plus Bromine Pentafluoride.

Sulfur
See ARSENIC plus Bromine Pentafluoride.

Sulfuric Acid
See BROMINE PENTAFLUORIDE plus Nitric Acid.

Water
The reaction between bromine pentafluoride and water is very violent.
Mellor **2, Supp. 1:** 172 (1956).
See ARSENIC plus Bromine Pentafluoride.
See also BROMINE MONOFLUORIDE plus Water.

BROMINE TRIFLUORIDE BrF_3

(See also other reactants)

Ammonium Bromide
Bromine trifluoride reacts explosively with the following: ammonium bromide, ammonium chloride, ammonium iodide.
Mellor **2, Supp. 1:** 165 (1956).

Ammonium Chloride
See BROMINE TRIFLUORIDE plus Ammonium Bromide.

Ammonium Iodide
See BROMINE TRIFLUORIDE plus Ammonium Bromide.

Antimony
See ANTIMONY plus Bromine Trifluoride.

Antimonyl Chloride
See BROMINE TRIFLUORIDE plus Antimony Trioxide.

Antimony Trioxide
Bromine trifluoride produces a violent reaction with antimony trioxide, more violent with antimonyl chloride.
Mellor **2, Supp. 1:** 166 (1956).

Arsenic
See ANTIMONY plus Bromine Trifluoride.

Barium Chloride
Bromine trifluoride rapidly attacks the following salts: barium chloride, cadmium chloride, calcium chloride, cesium chloride, lithium chloride, rubidium chloride, silver chloride.
Mellor **2, Supp. 1:** 165 (1956).

Bismuth Pentoxide
Bromine trifluoride and bismuth pentoxide, manganous iodate, niobium pentoxide, or tantalum pentoxide react vigorously.
Mellor **2, Supp. 1:** 166, 173 (1956).

Boron
See ANTIMONY plus Bromine Trifluoride.

Bromine
See ANTIMONY plus Bromine Trifluoride.

Cadmium Chloride
See BROMINE TRIFLUORIDE plus Barium Chloride.

Calcium Chloride
See BROMINE TRIFLUORIDE plus Barium Chloride.

Carbon Monoxide
Bromine trifluoride and carbon monoxide react explosively at high temperatures or concentrations.
Mellor **2, Supp. 1:** 166 (1956).

Carbon Tetrachloride
Bromine trifluoride and carbon tetrachloride react vigorously.
Mellor **2, Supp. 1:** 167 (1956).

Carbon Tetraiodide
Flaming occurs when bromine trifluoride is dripped onto cooled carbon tetraiodide.
Mellor **2, Supp. 1:** 166 (1956).

Cesium Chloride
See BROMINE TRIFLUORIDE plus Barium Chloride.

Iodine
See ANTIMONY plus Bromine Trifluoride.

Lithium Chloride
See BROMINE TRIFLUORIDE plus Barium Chloride.

Manganous Iodate
See BROMINE TRIFLUORIDE plus Bismuth Pentoxide.

Metals
See METALS plus Bromine Trifluoride.

Molybdenum
See MOLYBDENUM plus Bromine Trifluoride.

Niobium
See NIOBIUM plus Bromine Trifluoride.

Niobium Pentoxide
See BROMINE TRIFLUORIDE plus Bismuth Pentoxide.

Organic Matter
See BROMINE MONOFLUORIDE plus Water.

Phosphorus
See ANTIMONY plus Bromine Trifluoride.

Platinic Bromide
Both platinic bromide and platinic chloride are vigorously attacked by bromine trifluoride.
Mellor **2, Supp. 1:** 165 (1956).

Platinic Chloride
See BROMINE TRIFLUORIDE plus Platinic Bromide.

Platinum and Potassium Fluoride
See PLATINUM plus Bromine Trifluoride and Potassium Fluoride.

Potassium Bromide
The following salts are rapidly attacked by bromine trifluoride: potassium bromide, potassium chloride, potassium iodide, rhodium tetrabromide, sodium bromide, sodium chloride, sodium iodide.
Mellor **2, Supp. 1:** 164 (1956).

Potassium Chloride
See BROMINE TRIFLUORIDE plus Potassium Bromide.

Potassium Iodide
See BROMINE TRIFLUORIDE plus Potassium Bromide.

Rhodium Tetrabromide
See BROMINE TRIFLUORIDE plus Potassium Bromide.

Rubidium Chloride
See BROMINE TRIFLUORIDE plus Barium Chloride.

Silver Chloride
See BROMINE TRIFLUORIDE plus Barium Chloride.

Sodium Bromide
See BROMINE TRIFLUORIDE plus Potassium Bromide.

Sodium Chloride
See BROMINE TRIFLUORIDE plus Potassium Bromide.

Sodium Iodide
See BROMINE TRIFLUORIDE plus Potassium Bromide.

Stannous Chloride
Bromine trifluoride and stannous chloride react with flame.
Mellor **2, Supp. 1:** 164 (1956).

Sulfur
See ANTIMONY plus Bromine Trifluoride.

Tantalum
See NIOBIUM plus Bromine Trifluoride.

Tantalum Pentoxide
See BROMINE TRIFLUORIDE plus Bismuth Pentoxide.

Tin
See TIN plus Bromine Trifluoride.

Titanium
See MOLYBDENUM plus Bromine Trifluoride.

Tungsten
See MOLYBDENUM plus Bromine Trifluoride.

Uranium Oxides
The reaction between bromine trifluoride and oxides of uranium (UO_2 UO_3, and U_3O_8) is rapid and quantitative below the boiling point of bromine trifluoride.
Mellor **2, Supp. 1:** 165 (1956).

Vanadium
See MOLYBDENUM plus Bromine Trifluoride.

Water
Bromine trifluoride reacts violently with water.
Handbook Chem. Phys., **47th Ed.:** B-160 (1966-1967).
Even at -50°C., water (present as 6-normal hydrochloric acid) reacted explosively with bromine trifluoride.
Swanson (1965).
See BROMINE MONOFLUORIDE plus Water.

BROMOACETYLENE $BrC{\equiv}CH$

Air
During the preparation of solid bromoacetylene an explosion occurred when air was drawn into the Volman trap containing the solid bromoacetylene. Although it was well known that gaseous bromoacetylene reacts violently with oxygen at room temperature, the explosion of the solid material at minus 190°C was surprising.
Chem. & Ind. (3) (1972).

1-BROMOACETYLENES $BrC{\equiv}CR$

(self-reactive)
The 1-bromoacetylenes should not be distilled. They sometimes explode, even when distilled at reduced pressure.
Rutledge, p. 136 (1968).

p-BROMOBENZOYL ACETANILIDE
p-$BrC_6H_4COC_6H_4NHCOCH_3$

Dimethyl Sulfoxide
After a solution of p-bromobenzoyl acetanilide in 600 ml of dimethyl sulfoxide had been heated on a steam bath (100°C) for 30 minutes, an explosion occurred.
Wischmeyer (1970).

BROMOBENZYL TRIFLUORIDE $BrC_6H_4CF_3$

Magnesium
See MAGNESIUM plus Bromobenzyl Trifluoride.

BROMODIBORANE $BrBH(H_2)BH_2$

Air
This compound burns with a pale green flame in air.
Mellor **5:** 37 (1946-1947).

BROMODIETHYLALUMINUM $(C_2H_5)_2AlBr$

Air
Diethyl aluminum bromide ignites spontaneously in air, water, and alcohol.
Chem. Eng. Progs. **62** (12): 116 (1966).

Alcohol
See DIETHYL ALUMINUM BROMIDE plus Air.

Water
See DIETHYL ALUMINUM BROMIDE plus Air.

2-BROMO-3,5-DIMETHOXYANILINE
$NH_2C_6H_2Br(OCH_3)_2$

(self-reactive)
During a laboratory distillation of a mixture of 3, 5-dimethoxyaniline, 2-bromo-3, 5-dimethoxyaniline and dibromo 3,5-dimethoxyaniline an explosion occurred. It was traced to the instability of the brominated compounds.
Wischmeyer (1970).

BROMOFORM $CHBr_3$

Lithium
See LITHIUM plus Bromoform.

Sodium-Potassium Alloy
See SODIUM-POTASSIUM ALLOY plus Bromoform.

3-BROMO-1-PROPYNE $CH{\equiv}CCH_2Br$

(self-reactive)
Pure propargyl bromide (aka 3-bromo-1-propyne) will decompose violently or detonate at temperatures as low as 220°C.
Wischmeyer (1966). R. D. Coffee and J. J. Wheeler, *Chem. Eng. Progr. Tech. Man.* **1:** 6-9 (1968).
Liquid propargyl bromide is easily ignited by impact from

such possible sources as "water hammer" or accidental pressurization of the aerated liquid.
D. R. Forshey, J. C. Cooper, G. H. Martindill and J. M. Kuchta, *Fire Tech.* **5** (2): 100-111 (1969).

Chloropicrin
Tests at the Bureau of Mines showed the mixture to be shock sensitive.
Forshey, Cooper, Martindill, and Kuchta, *Fire Tech.* **5** (2): 100-111 (1969).

BROMOSILANE SiH_3Br

Air
Bromosilane is spontaneously flammable in air.
Handbook Chem. Phys., p. B-132 (1970-1971).

BROMOTRICHLOROMETHANE $BrCCl_3$

Ethylene
During the uncatalyzed addition of bromotrichloromethane to ethylene a violent explosion occurred.
BCISC **33:** 131 (1962).
Chem. Abst. **57:** 9638 (1953).

BROMOTRIFLUOROMETHANE $CBrF_3$

Aluminum
See ALUMINUM plus Dichlorodifluoromethane.

BRONZE

Hydrogen Peroxide
See IRON plus Hydrogen Peroxide.

BUNA N

Fluorine
See FLUORINE plus Solid Nonmetals and Oxygen.

BUTADIENE $CH_2{=}CHCH{=}CH_2$; $CH{=}C{=}CHCH_3$

(self-reactive)
Butadiene, when heated under pressure, may undergo violent thermal decomposition.
Chem. and Eng. News **18:** 404 (1940).

Air
In contact with air, butadiene may form violently explosive peroxides, which can be exploded by mild heat or shock. Solid butadiene absorbs enough oxygen at subatmospheric pressures to make it explode violently when heated just above its melting point.
D. G. Hendry, F. R. Hendry and D. Scheutzle, *Ind. Eng. Chem. Prod. Res. Develop.* **7:** 145-151 (1968). D. G. Hendry et al, *Ind. Eng. Chem. Prod. Res. Develop.* **7:** 151-154 (1968). D. S. Alex ander, *Ind. Eng. Chem.* **51:** 733 (1959).

Chlorine Dioxide
See CHLORINE DIOXIDE plus Butadiene.

Crotonaldehyde
The Diels-Alder reaction between these chemicals under pressure is a logical approach to the preparation of a number of cyclic alde hydes, alcohols, and hydrocarbons. A destructive explosion, including a secondary gas explosion, occurred in carrying out this reaction.
K. W. Greenlee, *Chem. and Eng. News* **26:** 1985 (1948).

Phenol
See PHENOL plus Butadiene.

BUTADIYNE $HC{\equiv}CC{\equiv}CH$

Air
In the preparation of butadiyne (aka diacetylene) by adding 1,4- dichloro-2-butyne to 10% sodium hydroxide and a little dioxane at 100°C, no difficulty was experienced if the free diacetylene was collected at minus 25°C and held below that temperature. At temperatures above minus 25°C explosions would occur.
Rutledge, pp. 134-135 (1968).

n-BUTANE $CH_3CH_2CH_2CH_3$

Nickel Carbonyl and Oxygen
See NICKEL CARBONYL plus n-Butane and Oxygen.

1-BUTANETHIOL $CH_3(CH_2)_2CH_2SH$

Nitric Acid
See NITRIC ACID plus Organic Matter.

BUTYL ACETATE $C_4H_9OCOCH_3$

Potassium Tert.-Butoxide
See ACETONE plus Potassium Tert.-Butoxide.

t-BUTYL ALCOHOL $(CH_3)_3COH$

Hydrogen Peroxide
See HYDROGEN PEROXIDE plus t-Butyl Peroxide.

t-BUTYL AZIDOFORMATE $(CH_3)_3COCONNN$

Phosgene
In the formation of tert-butyl azidoformate by the addition of phosgene to alcohols followed by the addition of sodium nitride or hydrazoic acid in the presence of pyridine, reaction of phosgene with the azide can cause the formation of explosive carbazide. To prevent the reaction complete removal of excess phosgene is advocated by passing nitrogen into the solution prior to addition of the azide.
Chem. Abst. **73:** 14099h (1970). *Chem. Phar. Bull.* **18** (4): 850-851 (1970).

BUTYL DICHLOROBORANE C_4H_9BCl2

Air
Butyl boron dichloride is spontaneously flammable in air.
Buls, Bimonthly Rept. 5, p. 3 (1953).

BUTYL FLUORIDE C_4H_9F

Magnesium Perchlorate
See MAGNESIUM PERCHLORATE plus Butyl Fluoride.

t-BUTYL HYPOCHLORITE $CH_3C(CH_3)_2OCl$

(self-reactive)
Tertiary butyl hypochlorite requires very careful handling to avoid explosive decomposition under relatively mild conditions. At about 25°C., an ampoule containing 10 grams exploded violently after several minutes exposure to fluorescent and north window light.
Chem. and Eng. News **40** (42): 63 (1962).

t-BUTYL PEROXYACETATE $(CH_3)_3C\text{-}OO\text{-}COCH_3$

(self-reactive)
t-Butyl peracetate is sensitive to shock and heat.
Haz. Chem. Data, p. 77 (1973).

Organic Matter
Upon contact with t-butyl peracetate, combustible organic matter can ignite or give rise to an explosion.
Haz. Chem. Data, p. 77 (1973).

t-BUTYL PEROXYBENZOATE $(CH_3)_3C\text{-}OO\text{-}COC_6H_5$

Organic Matter
Organic substances can ignite or explode upon contact with t-butyl perbenzoate.
Haz. Chem. Data p. 79 (1973).

BUTYLLITHIUM LiC_4H_9

Air
Butyllithium above 20% in air can ignite spontaneously if the humidity exceeds 70%. Concentrations above 25% are pyrophoric at any humidity.
S. B. Mirviss *Ind. Eng. Chem.* **53** (1): Supp. 58A-60A (1961).
Handbook Chem. Phys., p. C-695 (1970-1971).

BUTYNEDIOL $HOCH_2C{\equiv}CCH_2OH$

Halides
See BUTYNEDIOL plus Hydroxides.

Hydroxides
Pure butynediol is nonexplosive. Small amounts of certain impurities—alkali hydroxides, alkaline earth hydroxides, halides—may cause explosive decomposition upon distillation. Butynediol should not be treated with basic catalysts in the absence of a solvent at room temperature and still less so at elevated temperature; other wise, uncontrollable decomposition may occur. In strong acids, contamination with mercury salts can also result in violent decomposition.
Kirk & Othmer, **Supp. II,** First Ed.: 45 (1960).

Mercury Salts and Acid
See BUTYNEDIOL plus Hydroxides.

n-BUTYRALDEHYDE $CH_3(CH_2)_2CHO$

Chlorosulfonic Acid
Mixing n-butyraldehyde and chlorosulfonic acid in a closed container caused the temperature and pressure to increase.
Flynn and Rossow (1970). See Note under complete reference.

Nitric Acid
Mixing n-butyraldehyde and 70% nitric acid in a closed container caused the temperature and pressure to increase.
Flynn and Rossow (1970). See Note under complete reference.

Oleum
Mixing n-butyraldehyde and oleum in a closed container caused the temperature and pressure to increase.
Flynn and Rossow (1970). See Note under complete reference.

Sulfuric Acid
Mixing n-butyraldehyde and 96% sulfuric acid in a closed container caused the temperature and pressure to increase.
Flynn and Rossow (1970). See Note under complete reference.

BUTYRIC ACID $C_4H_8O_2C_4H_8O_2$

Chromium Trioxide
A mixture of chromium trioxide and butyric acid became incandes cent on heating to 100°C.
R. D. Wilson, *Chem. & Ind.* (1957).

CADMIUM Cd

Ammonium Nitrate
See AMMONIUM NITRATE plus Metals (powdered).

Hydrazoic Acid
A violent explosion followed immersion of a cadmium rod in hydrazoic acid after about 30 minutes.
Mellor **8, Supp. 2:** 50 (1967).

Tellurium
See ZINC plus Selenium.

Zinc
See ZINC plus Selenium.

CADMIUM AMIDE $Cd(NH_2)_2$

Water
Cadmium amide, when wetted, heats spontaneously and can explode.
Mellor **8:** 261 (1946-1947).

CADMIUM AZIDE $Cd(N_3)_2$

(self-reactive)
This is an extremely hazardous substance, exploding when rubbed with a horn spatula.
Mellor **8, Supp. 2:** 25 (1967).

CADMIUM BROMIDE $CdBr_2$

Potassium
See POTASSIUM plus Aluminum Bromide.

CADMIUM CHLORATE $Cd(ClO_3)_2$

Antimony Sulfide
See CHLORATES plus Antimony Sulfide.

Arsenic Sulfide
See CHLORATES plus Arsenic Sulfide.

Copper Sulfide
See COPPER SULFIDE plus Cadmium Chlorate.

Stannic Sulfide
See STANNIC SULFIDE plus Cadmium Chlorate.

Stannous Sulfide
See STANNOUS SULFIDE plus Cadmium Chlorate.

CADMIUM CHLORIDE $CdCl_2$

Bromine Trifluoride
See BROMINE TRIFLUORIDE plus Barium Chloride.

Potassium
See POTASSIUM plus Aluminum Bromide.

CADMIUM CYANIDE $Cd(CN)_2$

Magnesium
See MAGNESIUM plus Cadmium Cyanide.

CADMIUM FLUORIDE CdF_2

Potassium
See POTASSIUM plus Ammonium Bromide.

CADMIUM-HEXAMMINE CHLORATE $Cd(NH_3)_6(ClO_3)_2$

(self-reactive)
This compound detonates when struck.
Mellor **2, Supp. 1:**592 (1956).

CADMIUM-HEXAMMINE PERCHLORATE
$Cd(NH_3)_6\ (ClO_4)_2$

(self-reactive)
This compound detonates when struck, but is less sensitive than hexamminocadmium chlorate.
Mellor **2, Supp. 1:** 592 (1956).

CADMIUM IODIDE CdI_2

Potassium
See POTASSIUM plus Aluminum Bromide.

CADMIUM NITRIDE Cd_3N_2

Acids
Cadmium nitride reacts explosively with dilute acids and bases.
Mellor **8, Supp. I, Part 1:** 161 (1964).

Bases
See CADMIUM NITRIDE plus Acids.

Water
Cadmium nitride explodes violently in contact with water.
Mellor **8:** 121, 122, 261 (1946-1947).

CADMIUM OXIDE CdO

Magnesium
See MAGNESIUM plus Beryllium Oxide.

CADMIUM SULFIDE CdS

Iodine Monochloride
See IODINE MONOCHLORIDE plus Cadmium Sulfide.

CADMIUM-TRIHYDRAZINE CHLORATE
$Cd(N_2H_4)_3(ClO_3)_2$

(self-reactive)
This compound detonates when struck.
Mellor **2, Supp. 1:** 592 (1956).

CADMIUM-TRIHYDRAZINE PERCHLORATE
$Cd(H_2NNH_2)_3(ClO_4)_2Cd$

(self-reactive)
This is an extremely explosive salt.
Mellor **8, Supp. 2:** 88 (1967).

CALCIUM Ca

Acids
Calcium reacts violently with acids.
Lab. Govt. Chemist (1965).

Air
Finely divided calcium burns spontaneously in air.
Mellor **3:** 637, 638, 651 (1946-1947).

Chlorine
Finely divided calcium burns spontaneously in chlorine. Solid calcium burns spontaneously in chlorine at elevated temperatures.
Mellor **3:** 637, 638, 651 (1946-1947).

Chlorine Trifluoride
Chlorine trifluoride combined with calcium or sodium forms a protective crust, but reaction is violent on heating.
Mellor **2, Supp. 1:** 156 (1956).

Fluorine
Finely divided or massive calcium burns spontaneously in fluorine at ordinary temperatures.
Mellor **3:** 637, 638, 651 (1946-1947).

Oxygen
Solid calcium ignites spontaneously in moist oxygen.
Chem. and Eng. News **26:** 1985 (1948).

Silicon
Calcium and silicon react violently if heated to 1,050°C.
Mellor **6:** 176, 177 (1946-1947).

Sulfur
A mixture of calcium and sulfur, when ignited, reacts explosively. Calcium burns in sulfur vapor with a brilliant flame. The reaction begins at about 400°C.
Perkin and Pratt, *Trans. Faraday Soc.* **3:** 176 (1908).
Mellor **3:** 639 (1946-1947).

Vanadium Oxide, Sulfur and Water
A mixture of calcium and vanadium oxide that was contaminated with sulfur and some moisture caused a severe fire.
Poole (1971).

Water
Calcium rapidly decomposes water. The heat of reaction is sufficient that the evolved hydrogen may ignite.
Lab. Govt. Chemist (1965).

CALCIUM ALLOYS

Acids
Calcium alloys react violently with acids.
Lab. Govt. Chemist (1965).

Water
Calcium alloys rapidly decompose water. The heat of reaction is sufficient that the evolved hydrogen may ignite.
Lab. Govt. Chemist (1965).

CALCIUM BROMATE $Ca(BrO_3)_2$

Aluminum
See ALUMINUM plus Bromates.

Arsenic
See ARSENIC plus Bromates.

Carbon
See CARBON plus Bromates.

Copper
See COPPER plus Bromates.

Metal Sulfides
See METAL SULFIDES plus Bromates.

Organic Matter
See BROMATES plus Organic Matter.

Phosphorus
See PHOSPHORUS plus Bromates.

Sulfur
See SULFUR plus Bromates.

CALCIUM CARBIDE CaC_2

Hydrogen Chloride
Calcium carbide reacts with hydrogen chloride gas with incandescence.
Mellor **5:** 862 (1946-1947).

Lead Fluoride
Calcium carbide mixed with lead fluoride, at ordinary temperatures, becomes incandescent.
Mellor **5:** 862-64 (1946-1947).

Magnesium
See MAGNESIUM plus Calcium Carbide.

Potassium Hydroxide and Chlorine
See DICHLOROACETYLENE plus Air.

Selenium
See SELENIUM plus Calcium Carbide.

Silver Nitrate
See SILVER NITRATE plus Calcium Carbide.

Sodium Peroxide
See SODIUM PEROXIDE plus Calcium Carbide.

Stannous Chloride
See STANNOUS CHLORIDE plus Calcium Carbide.

Sulfur
See SULFUR plus Calcium Carbide.

Water
The reaction between calcium carbide and water can produce enough heat to ignite the acetylene that is formed.
G.W. Jones, G.S. Scott, R.E. Kennedy & W.J. Huff, *BM Report Invest.* **3755** (1944).
Von Schwartz, p. 142 (1918).

CALCIUM CARBONATE $CaCO_3$

Fluorine
See FLUORINE plus Carbonates. See also FLUORINE plus Common Materials and Oxygen.

Magnesium and Hydrogen
See MAGNESIUM plus Hydrogen and Calcium Carbonate.

CALCIUM CHLORATE $Ca(ClO_3)_2$

Aluminum
See ALUMINUM plus Bromates.

Arsenic
See ARSENIC plus Bromates.

Carbon
See CARBON plus Bromates.

Charcoal
See CHLORATES plus Organic Matter.

Copper
See COPPER plus Bromates.

Manganese Dioxide
See CHLORATES plus Manganese Dioxide.

Metal Sulfides
See METAL SULFIDES plus Bromates.

Organic Acids (Dibasic)
See CHLORATES plus Organic Acids.

Organic Matter
See CHLORATES plus Organic Matter.

Phosphorus
See PHOSPHORUS plus Bromates.

Sulfur
See SULFUR plus Bromates.

CALCIUM CHLORIDE $CaCl_2$

Boric Oxide and Calcium Oxide
See BORIC OXIDE plus Calcium Oxide and Calcium Chloride.

Bromine Trifluoride
See BROMINE TRIFLUORIDE plus Barium Chloride.

2-Furan
See 2-FURAN PERCARBOXYLIC ACID

Percarboxylic Acid
(self-reactive).

CALCIUM CHLORITE $Ca(OCl)_2$

Chlorine
See CHLORINE plus Calcium Chlorite.

CALCIUM HEXAMMONIATE $Ca(NH_3)_6$

Air
Hexammino calcium is spontaneously flammable in air.
Ellern (1961).

CALCIUM HYDRIDE CaH_2

Air
Calcium hydride burns fiercely in air when heated.
Lab. Govt. Chemist (1965). NSC *Nat. Saf. News* **77** (2): 37-40 (1958).

Bromates
See BROMATES plus Calcium Hydride.

Chlorates
See BROMATES plus Calcium Hydride.

Perchlorates
See BROMATES plus Calcium Hydride.

Silver Fluoride
See SILVER FLUORIDE plus Calcium Hydride.

CALCIUM HYDROXIDE $Ca(OH)_2$

Maleic Anhydride
See SODIUM HYDROXIDE plus Maleic Anhydride.

Nitroethane
The nitroparaffins, in the presence of water, form salts with inorganic bases. The dry salts are explosive.
Chem. and Eng. News **30:** 2344 (1952).

Nitromethane
See CALCIUM HYDROXIDE plus Nitroethane.

Nitroparaffins
See CALCIUM HYDROXIDE plus Nitroethane.

Nitropropane
See CALCIUM HYDROXIDE plus Nitroethane.

Phosphorus
See PHOSPHORUS plus Alkaline Hydroxides.

CALCIUM HYPOCHLORITE $Ca(OCl)_2$

(See also HYPOCHLORITES)

Amines
Primary amines and calcium hypochlorite or sodium hypochlorite react to form normal chloroamines, which are explosive.
Kirk and Othmer **1:** 709 (1947).

Anthracene
Anthracene heats on contact with calcium hypochlorite.
Douglas and Thompson (1949).

Carbon
See CALCIUM HYPOCHLORITE plus Charcoal.

Carbon Tetrachloride
A severe explosion occurred when a carbon tetrachloride fire extin guisher was used to extinguish a fire in an open container of cal cium hypochlorite.
NSC *Newsletter, Chem. Sec.* (May 1972).

Charcoal
A mixture of equal parts of bleaching powder and finely divided charcoal exploded when heated in a closed vessel.
Halane—Prelim. Info. Sheet (1953). *Mellor* **2:** 254-62 (1946-1947).

Ethyl Alcohol
A little calcium hypochlorite added to ethyl alcohol or glycerol will result in a violent explosion after a short time.
Roblee (1966).

Glycerol
When mixed with calcium hypochlorite, glycerol may ignite spontaneously.
H. Fawcett, *Ind. Eng. Chem.* **51:** 89A-90A (1959).
See also CALCIUM HYPOCHLORITE plus Ethyl Alcohol.

Grease or Oil
A metal scoop kept in a drum of calcium hypochlorite was contaminated with grease or oil. Reaction with the contaminant initiated the violent decomposition of the hypochlorite.
MCA Case History **663** (1960).

Hydrochloric Acid
Reaction of these two chemicals releases copious quantities of chlorine gas.
Fawcett (1969).

Iron Oxide
This material has been the cause of many serious accidents caused by explosions in the containers. Oxygen is evolved by reaction between the hypochlorite and oxide catalysts.
A. H. Gill, *Ind. Eng. Chem.* **16:** 577 (1924).

Manganese Oxide
See CALCIUM HYPOCHLORITE plus Iron Oxide.

Mercaptans
Calcium hypochlorite and mercaptans will react violently.
Barrett (1973).

Methyl Carbitol
Fire occurred when a bag of calcium hypochlorite was inadvertently placed on a methyl carbitol spill on the floor.
Wischmeyer (1965).

Nitromethane
Nitromethane, either alone or in a mixture with methanol and castor oil (model airplane fuel) has a delayed but violent reaction with powdered calcium hypochlorite, especially when confined, as in a plastic bag.
H. Fawcett, *Hazards Home Chem.* (1963).

Organic Matter
Calcium hypochlorite contaminated with one percent of various common organic materials reacted when heated. The reaction varied from mild flame at 350°F. with wood, to violent explosion at 275°F. with oil.
Halane—Prelim. Info. Sheet.

Organic Sulfides
Dry calcium hypochlorite when mixed with organic sulfides causes a violent reaction with the possibility of a flash fire.
Stephenson (1973).

Phenol
This is an exothermic reaction producing toxic fumes, which may ignite.
H. Fawcett, *Ind. Eng. Chem.* **51:** 89A-90A (1959).

1-Propanethiol
An explosion occurred when 10 grams of calcium hypochlorite was dumped into a beaker containing 5 milliliters of 1-propanethiol. Identical results were obtained with ethanediol and isobutanethiol.
R. E. Barrett (1973).

Propyl Mercaptan
See CALCIUM HYPOCHLORITE plus Mercaptans.

Sulfur
See SULFUR plus Calcium Hypochlorite.

Turpentine
Calcium hypochlorite was placed in a turpentine can thought to be empty. A few minutes later reaction between the residual turpentine and the calcium hypochlorite resulted in an explosion.
Benson (1967).

CALCIUM HYPOPHOSPHITE $Ca(H_2PO_2)_2$

Air
Calcium hypophosphite decomposes when heated, forming phosphine, a spontaneously flammable gas in air.
Mellor **8:** 881 (1946-1947).

Nitric Acid
The salt ignites when nitric acid is poured onto it.
Mellor **8:** 883 (1946-1947).

Potassium Chlorate
A mixture of calcium hypophosphite and potassium chlorate exploded when being ground with quartz in a mortar. The mixture of calcium hypophosphite and potassium chlorate can be caused to explode by shock, heat, spark or friction.
Mellor **8:** 881 (1946-1947).

CALCIUM IODATE $Ca(IO_3)_2$

Aluminum
See ALUMINUM plus Bromates.

Arsenic
See ARSENIC plus Bromates.

Carbon
See CARBON plus Bromates.

Copper
See COPPER plus Bromates.

Metal Sulfides
See METAL SULFIDES plus Bromates.

Organic Matter
See BROMATES plus Organic Matter.

Phosphorus
See PHOSPHORUS plus Bromates.

Sulfur
See SULFUR plus Bromates.

CALCIUM-MANGANESE-SILICON

Acids
Calcium-manganese-silicon combinations evolve spontaneously flammable gas when in contact with acids.
Lab. Govt. Chemist (1965).

CALCIUM NITRIDE Ca_3N_2

Air
Calcium nitride is spontaneously flammable in air.
Von Schwartz, p. 322 (1918).

Bromine
See BROMINE plus Calcium Nitride.

Chlorine
See CHLORINE plus Calcium Nitride.

CALCIUM OXIDE (QUICKLIME) CaO

Boric Oxide and Calcium Chloride
See BORIC OXIDE plus Calcium Oxide and Calcium Chloride.

Boron Trifluoride
The reaction of calcium oxide and boron trifluoride forms a fused mass after warming.
Mellor **5:** 123 (1946-1947).

Chlorine Trifluoride
See CHLORINE TRIFLUORIDE plus Aluminum Oxide.

Fluorine
See FLUORINE plus Calcium Oxide.

Hydrofluoric Acid
Liquid hydrofluoric acid and calcium oxide react very violently.
Mellor **2, Supp. 1:** 129 (1956).

Phosphorus Pentoxide
Calcium oxide or sodium hydroxide reacts with phosphorus pentox ide extremely violently when initiated by local heating.
Mellor **8, Supp. 3:** 406 (1971).

Water
Addition of water to quicklime has generated temperatures as high as 800°C. (1,470°F.). Some reports describe the reaction as violent. Ignition of sulfur, gunpowder, wood, and straw by the heat of the quicklime-water reaction has been reported.
Mellor **3:** 673 (1946-1947). *Von Schwartz,* p. 325 (1918).

CALCIUM PERCHROMATE $Ca_3(CrOO_3)_2$

(self-reactive)
Calcium perchromate is a buff-colored powder that explodes at 100°C.
Mellor **11:** 359 (1946-1947).

CALCIUM PEROXIDE CaO_2

Polysulfide Polymers
Dry calcium peroxide floating on liquid polysulfide polymers containing mercaptan radicals caused flashing in small scale tests and ignition in plant scale processes.
R. Davis (1968).

CALCIUM PHOSPHIDE Ca_3P_2

Chlorine
See CHLORINE plus Calcium Phosphide.

Chlorine Monoxide
See CHLORINE MONOXIDE plus Calcium Phosphide.

Hydrochloric Acid
Calcium phosphide and hydrochloric acid undergo a very energetic reaction.
Mellor **8:** 841 (1946-1947).

Oxygen
See SULFUR plus Calcium Phosphide.

Sulfur
See SULFUR plus Calcium Phosphide.

Water
The reaction forms phosphine which is a spontaneously flammable gas (in moist air).
Von Schwartz, p. 327 (1918). *Lab. Govt. Chemist* (1965). *Douda* (1966).
Mellor **8:** 841 (1946-1947).

CALCIUM SILICIDE $CaSi_2$

Acids
Calcium silicide plus acids forms the gas, silicon hydride, which may ignite spontaneously in air.
Lab. Govt. Chemist (1965).

Fluorine
See FLUORINE plus Calcium Silicide.

CALCIUM-SILICON

Acids
Calcium-silicon combinations evolve spontaneously flammable gas when in contact with acids.
Lab. Govt. Chemist (1965).

CALCIUM SULFATE $CaSO_4$

Aluminum
See ALUMINUM plus Sulfates.

CALCIUM SULFIDE CaS

Lead Dioxide
See BARIUM SULFIDE plus Lead Dioxide.

Potassium Chlorate
See BARIUM SULFIDE plus Lead Dioxide.

Potassium Nitrate
See BARIUM SULFIDE plus Lead Dioxide.

CAMPHOR $C_{10}H_{16}O$

Chromic Anhydride
See CHROMIC ANHYDRIDE plus Naphthalene.

CARBIDES

(See also specific carbides as primary reactants or under other reactants)

Lithium
See LITHIUM plus Carbides.

Oxidizing Agents
Mixtures of carbides and oxidizing agents are explosive.
Mellor **5:** 848 (1946-1947).

Sulfuric Acid
See SULFURIC ACID plus Carbides.

CARBOHYDRATES

Boron Triiodide
See BORON TRIIODIDE plus Ethers.

CARBON C

Ammonium Nitrate
Explosions may occur when a mixture of these materials is heated.
Mellor **5:** 822 (1946-1947).

Ammonium Perchlorate
Ammonium perchlorate mixed with carbon (sugar charcoal) under goes exothermic decomposition below 240°C. Above 240°C, the reaction produces mild explosions.
Trans. Faraday Soc. **56:** 581-90 (1960).

Barium Bromate
See CARBON plus Bromates.

Barium Chlorate
See CARBON plus Bromates.

Barium Iodate
See CARBON plus Bromates.

Bromates
A combination of finely divided carbon with finely divided bromates (also chlorates or iodates) of barium, calcium, magnesium, potassium, sodium, or zinc will explode with heat, percussion, and sometimes light friction.
Mellor **2:** 310 (1946-1947).

Calcium Bromate
See CARBON plus Bromates.

Calcium Chlorate
See CARBON plus Bromates.

Calcium Hypochlorite
See CALCIUM HYPOCHLORITE plus Charcoal.

Calcium Iodate
See CARBON plus Bromates.

Chlorates
See CARBON plus Bromates.

Chlorine
See CHLORINE plus Carbon (Activated).

Chlorine and Chromyl Chloride
See CHLORINE plus Chromyl Chloride and Carbon.

Chlorine Monoxide
There is an immediate explosion when charcoal is added to chlorine monoxide.
Mellor **5:** 824 (1946-1947).

Fluorine
See FLUORINE plus Carbon.

2-Furan Percarboxylic Acid
See 2-FURAN PERCARBOXYLIC ACID (self-reactive).

Iodates
See CARBON plus Bromates.

Iodine Pentoxide
Iodine pentoxide reacts explosively when warmed with carbon, sulfur, sugar, resin, or powdered combustible elements.
Mellor **2:** 295 (1946-1947).

Lead Nitrate
Lead nitrate reacts with brilliant sparks when projected on red-hot carbon.
Mellor **7:** 863 (1946-1947).

Magnesium Bromate
See CARBON plus Bromates.

Magnesium Chlorate
See CARBON plus Bromates.

Magnesium Iodate
See CARBON plus Bromates.

Mercurous Nitrate
At high temperature, a mixture of mercurous nitrate and carbon decomposes explosively.
Mellor **4:** 987 (1946-1947).

Nitric Acid
Pulverized carbon reacts violently with nitric acid.
Pascal **10:** 504 (1931-1934).

Oils and Air
Fatty oils are spontaneously flammable when distributed in activated carbon. The carbon enormously increases the surface of oil exposed to the air.
C. W. Bahme, *NFPA Quarterly* **45:** 341 (1952).
Von Schwartz, p. 326 (1918).

Potassium and Air
See POTASSIUM plus Carbon and Air.

Potassium Bromate
See CARBON plus Bromates.

Potassium Chlorate
See CARBON plus Bromates.

Potassium Iodate
See CARBON plus Bromates.

Sodium Bromate
See CARBON plus Bromates.

Sodium Chlorate
See CARBON plus Bromates.

Sodium Iodate
See CARBON plus Bromates.

Sodium Sulfide
Mixtures of sodium sulfide and carbon are susceptible to spontaneous heating.
C. A. Browne, USDA Tech. Bull. **141** (1929).
J. Creevy, *Chem. Age* **44:** 257 (1941).

Zinc Bromate
See CARBON plus Bromates.

Zinc Chlorate
See CARBON plus Bromates.

Zinc Iodate
See CARBON plus Bromates.

Zinc Nitrate
Zinc nitrate explodes when sprinkled on hot carbon.
Mellor **4:** 655 (1946-1947).

CARBONATES

(See also specific carbonates under other reactants)

Aluminum
See ALUMINUM plus Sodium Carbonate.

Fluorine
See FLUORINE plus Carbonates.

Magnesium
See MAGNESIUM plus Carbonates.

Silicon
See SILICON plus Alkali Carbonates.

CARBON DIOXIDE CO_2

Aluminum and Sodium Peroxide
See ALUMINUM plus Sodium Peroxide and Carbon Dioxide.

Cesium Monoxide
See CESIUM MONOXIDE plus Carbon Dioxide.

Diethyl Magnesium
See DIETHYL MAGNESIUM plus Air.

Lithium
See LITHIUM plus Oxygen.
See LITHIUM plus Water.

Lithium Acetylene Carbide Diammino
See LITHIUM ACETYLENE CARBIDE DIAMMINO plus Carbon Dioxide.

Magnesium and Sodium Peroxide
See MAGNESIUM plus Sodium Peroxide and Carbon Dioxide.

Potassium
See POTASSIUM plus Carbon Dioxide.

Potassium Acetylene Carbide
See POTASSIUM ACETYLENE CARBIDE plus Carbon Dioxide.

Sodium
See SODIUM plus Carbon Dioxide.

Sodium Carbide
See SODIUM CARBIDE plus Carbon Dioxide.

Sodium-Potassium Alloy
See SODIUM-POTASSIUM ALLOY plus Carbon Dioxide.

Titanium
See TITANIUM plus Carbon Dioxide.

CARBON DISULFIDE CS_2

Aluminum
See ALUMINUM plus Carbon Disulfide.

Azides
Carbon disulfide plus any of the azides produces violently explosive, extremely sensitive salts.
Mellor **8:** 338 (1946-1947).

Cesium Azide
See CARBON DISULFIDE plus Azides.

Chlorine
See CHLORINE plus Carbon Disulfide.

Chlorine Monoxide
See CHLORINE MONOXIDE plus Carbon Disulfide.

Ethylene Diamine
Mixing carbon disulfide and ethylene diamine in a closed container caused the temperature and pressure to increase.
Flynn and Rossow (1970). See Note under complete reference.

Ethyleneimine
Mixing carbon disulfide and ethyleneimine in a closed container caused the temperature and pressure to increase.
Flynn and Rossow (1970). See Note under complete reference.

Fluorine
See FLUORINE plus Carbon Disulfide.

Lead Azide
See CARBON DISULFIDE plus Azides.

Lithium Azide
See CARBON DISULFIDE plus Azides.

Nitric Oxide
See NITRIC OXIDE plus Carbon Disulfide.

Nitrogen Dioxide
See NITROGEN TETROXIDE plus Carbon Disulfide.

Permanganates and Sulfuric Acid
See PERMANGANATES plus Sulfuric Acid and Benzene.

Potassium
See POTASSIUM plus Carbon Disulfide.

Potassium Azide
See CARBON DISULFIDE plus Azides.

Rubidium Azide
See CARBON DISULFIDE plus Azides.

Sodium Azide
See CARBON DISULFIDE plus Azides.

Zinc
See ZINC plus Carbon Disulfide.

CARBON MONOXIDE CO

Bromine Trifluoride
See BROMINE TRIFLUORIDE plus Carbon Monoxide.

Cesium Monoxide
See CESIUM MONOXIDE plus Carbon Dioxide.

Chlorine Trifluoride
See CHLORINE TRIFLUORIDE plus Ammonia.

Iodine Heptafluoride
See IODINE HEPTAFLUORIDE plus Carbon Monoxide.

Lithium and Water
See LITHIUM plus Carbon Monoxide and Water.

Nitrogen Trifluoride
See HYDROGEN plus Nitrogen Trifluoride.

Oxygen
See OXYGEN (LIQUID) plus Carbon Monoxide.

Oxygen Difluoride
See HYDROGEN plus Oxygen Difluoride.

Potassium and Oxygen
See POTASSIUM plus Carbon Monoxide and Oxygen.

Silver Oxide
See SILVER OXIDE plus Carbon Monoxide.

Sodium and Ammonia
See SODIUM plus Carbon Monoxide and Ammonia.

CARBON TETRABROMIDE CBr_4

Lithium
See LITHIUM plus Bromoform.

CARBON TETRACHLORIDE CCl_4

Allyl Alcohol
See ALLYL ALCOHOL, plus Carbon Tetrachloride.

Aluminum
See ALUMINUM plus Carbon Tetrachloride.

Aluminum Triethyl Sesquichlorides
See ALUMINUM TRIETHYL plus Carbon Tetrachloride.

Barium
See BARIUM plus Carbon Tetrachloride.

Benzoyl Peroxide and Ethylene
See BENZOYL PEROXIDE plus Carbon Tetrachloride and Ethylene.

Beryllium
See BERYLLIUM plus Carbon Tetrachloride.

Bromine Trifluoride
See BROMINE TRIFLUORIDE plus Carbon Tetrachloride.

Calcium Hypochlorite
See CALCIUM HYPOCHLORITE plus Carbon Tetrachloride.

Diborane
A violent explosion occurred when carbon tetrachloride was used on a borane fire.
Fawcett (1973).

Dimethyl Formamide
See DIMETHYL FORMAMIDE plus Carbon Tetrachloride.

Disilane
See DISILANE plus Carbon Tetrachloride.

Ethylene
Ethylene and carbon tetrachloride can react explosively under high pressures in the presence of organic peroxide catalysts.
R. O. Bolt, *Chem. and Eng. News* **25:** 1866 (1947).
R. M. Joyce, *Chem. and Eng. News* **25:** 1866-7 (1947).

Fluorine
See FLUORINE plus Carbon Tetrachloride.

Lithium
See LITHIUM plus Trichlorotrifluoroethane.
See LITHIUM plus Carbon Tetrachloride.

Magnesium
See ALUMINUM plus Chloroform.

Oxygen (Liquid)
See OXYGEN (LIQUID) plus Chlorinated Hydrocarbons.

Plutonium
See PLUTONIUM plus Carbon Tetrachloride.

Potassium
See POTASSIUM plus Carbon Tetrachloride.
See POTASSIUM plus Boron Tribromide.

Potassium Tert.-Butoxide
See ACETONE plus Potassium Tert.-Butoxide.

Silver Perchlorate and Hydrochloric Acid
See SILVER PERCHLORATE plus Carbon Tetrachloride and Hydrochloric Acid.

Sodium
See SODIUM plus Carbon Tetrachloride.
See SODIUM plus Cobaltous Bromide.

Sodium-Potassium Alloy
See SODIUM-POTASSIUM ALLOY plus Carbon Tetrachloride.

Tetrasilane
See TETRASILANE plus Carbon Tetrachloride.

Trisilane
See TRISILANE plus Carbon Tetrachloride.

Uranium
See URANIUM plus Carbon Tetrachloride.

Wax
An explosion occurred when a stream of carbon tetrachloride (fire extinguisher) was directed on burning wax.
Chem. and Eng. News **25:** 1866, 2852 (1947).
Chem. and Eng. News **26:** 957 (1948).

Zirconium
See ZIRCONIUM plus Carbon Tetrachloride.

CARBON TETRAIODIDE CI_4

Bromine Trifluoride
See BROMINE TRIFLUORIDE plus Carbon Tetraiodide.

CELLULOSE $(C_6H_{12}O_5)_x$

Bromine Pentafluoride
See BROMINE PENTAFLUORIDE plus Acetic Acid.

Fluorine
See FLUORINE plus Cellulose.

Hydrogen Peroxide
See HYDROGEN PEROXIDE plus Cellulose.

Sodium Hypochlorite
See SODIUM HYPOCHLORITE plus Oxalic Acid.

Sodium Nitrite
See SODIUM NITRITE plus Cellulose.

CERIUM Ce

Air
See RARE EARTH METALS plus Air.

Halogens
See RARE EARTH METALS plus Halogens.

Phosphorus
Cerium or lanthanum and phosphorus react violently at 400° – 500° C.
Mellor **8, Supp. 3:** 347, 252 (1971).

CERIUM HYDRIDE CeH_3

Air
Cerium hydride is spontaneously flammable in air.
Douda (1966).

CERIUM NITRIDE CeN

Acids
Cerium nitride sometimes reacts violently with dilute acids.
Mellor **8:** 121 (1946-1947).

Air
With moist air, cerium nitride undergoes spontaneous, incandescent oxidation. If a few drops of water are added to the cerium nitride, the heat developed is adequate to ignite the ammonia and hydrogen evolved.
Mellor **8:** 121 (1946-1947).

Water
The reaction of cerium nitride and water can produce enough heat to ignite the hydrogen and ammonia being evolved.
Mellor **8:** 121 (1946-1947).

CERIUM TETRAHYDROALUMINATE $Ce(AlH_4)_3$

Air
Cerium aluminohydride is spontaneously flammable in air.
Chem. Abst. **49:** 766e (1955). J. Aubrey and G. Monnier, *Comp. Rend.* **238:** 2534-2535 (1954).

CEROUS PHOSPHIDE CeP

Water
The reaction of cerous phosphide, lanthanum phosphide, or neodymium phosphide and water liberates spontaneously flammable phosphine.
Mellor **8, Supp. 3:** 347, 342, 348 (1971).

CESIUM Cs

Air
Cesium is spontaneously flammable in air at room temperature, if the surface of the cesium is clean.
Mellor **2:** 468 (1946-1947).

Chlorine
Chlorine vapors and cesium, lithium, or rubidium react with luminous flame.
Mellor **2, Supp. 1:** 380 (1956).

Oxygen
Cesium burns spontaneously in dry oxygen.
Mellor **2:** 468 (1946-1947).

Phosphorus
See PHOSPHORUS plus Cesium.

Water
At 20°C. the heat of reaction is adequate to ignite the hydrogen liberated in the reaction between water and cesium.
Mellor **2:** 469 (1946-1947).

CESIUM ACETYLIDE CsC_2H

Arsenic
See ARSENIC plus Cesium Acetylene Carbide.

Bromine
See BROMINE plus Cesium Acetylene Carbide.

Chlorine
See CHLORINE plus Cesium Acetylene Carbide.

Cupric Oxide
Cesium acetylene carbide explodes on contact with lead dioxide or cupric oxide at 350°C.
Mellor **5:** 849 (1946-1947).

Fluorine
See CHLORINE plus Cesium Acetylene Carbide.
See FLUORINE plus Cesium Acetylene Carbide.

Hydrogen Chloride
Cesium acetylene carbide burns in hydrogen chloride gas.
Mellor **5:** 849 (1946-1947).

Iodine
See IODINE plus Cesium Acetylene Carbide.

Lead Dioxide
See CESIUM ACETYLENE CARBIDE plus Cupric Oxide.

Nitrogen Dioxide
Cesium acetylene carbide ignites at about 100°C. in nitrogen dioxide.
Mellor **5:** 848-50 (1946-1947).

Phosphorus
See PHOSPHORUS plus Cesium Acetylene Carbide.

Sulfur Dioxide
Cesium acetylene carbide reacts with sulfur dioxide at ordinary temperatures, with incandescence.
Mellor **5:** 848-50 (1946-1947).

Sulfuric Acid
Cesium acetylene carbide burns with sulfuric acid.
Mellor **5:** 849 (1946-1947).

CESIUM AMIDE $CsNH_2$

Water
The reaction between cesium amide and water in the presence of air proceeds with incandescence.
Mellor **8:** 256 (1946-1947).

CESIUM AZIDE CsN_3

(self-reactive)
Cesium azide decomposes at 326°C.
Mellor **8, Supp. 2:** 43 (1967).

Carbon Disulfide
See CARBON DISULFIDE plus Azides.

CESIUM CARBIDE Cs_2C_2

Boron
See SILICON plus Cesium Carbide.

Ferric Oxide
Ferric oxide is reduced with incandescence when gently heated with cesium carbide.
Mellor **5:** 849 (1946-1947).

Hydrochloric Acid
Cesium carbide ignites in contact with hydrochloric acid unless the acid is dilute.
Mellor **5:** 848 (1946-1947).

Iodine
See IODINE plus Cesium Carbide.

Nitric Acid
A mixture of nitric acid and cesium carbide will explode.
Mellor **5:** 848 (1946-1947).

Silicon
See SILICON plus Cesium Carbide.

CESIUM CHLORIDE CsCl

Bromine Trifluoride
See BROMINE TRIFLUORIDE plus Barium Chloride.

CESIUM FLUORIDE NITROSYL FLUORIDE COMPLEX
$CsF\text{-}HNF_2$

(self-reactive)
This complex is an unstable compound at room temperature.
Lawless and Smith, pp. 39, 76 (1968).

CESIUM HYDRIDE CsH

Acetylene
In the presence of moisture, cesium hydride reacts vigorously, even at −60°C. When dry, no reaction occurs below 42°C.
Mellor **2:** 483 (1946-1947).

Oxygen
See OXYGEN plus Cesium Hydride.

CESIUM MONOXIDE Cs_2O

Bromine
See BROMINE plus Cesium Monoxide.

Carbon Dioxide
When heated, cesium monoxide burns in carbon monoxide or carbon dioxide.
Mellor **2:** 487 (1946-1947).

Carbon Monoxide
See CESIUM MONOXIDE plus Carbon Dioxide.

Chlorine
See BROMINE plus Cesium Monoxide.

Fluorine
See BROMINE plus Cesium Monoxide.

Iodine
See BROMINE plus Cesium Monoxide.

Sulfur Dioxide
Sulfur dioxide bleaches cesium monoxide at ordinary temperatures, and when heated the reaction is attended by incandescence.
Mellor **2:** 487 (1946-1947).

Water
Cesium monoxide is spontaneously flammable in air.
Brauer (1965).

CESIUM NITRIDE Cs_3N

Air
Cesium nitride burns in air and is readily attacked by chlorine, phosphorus, or sulfur.
Mellor **8:** 99, 101 (1946-1947).

Chlorine
See CESIUM NITRIDE plus Air.

Phosphorus
See CESIUM NITRIDE plus Air.

Sulfur
See CESIUM NITRIDE plus Air.

CESIUM PERFLUOROPROPOXIDE $CsOC_3F_7$

Fluorine
See FLUORINE plus Cesium Perfluoropropoxide.

CESIUM PHOSPHIDE Cs_3P

Water
Cesium phosphide reacts with water or moist air instantaneously to yield spontaneously flammable phosphine.
Van Wazer (1958).

CESIUM SILICIDE Cs_2Si_2

Water
The silicides of cesium, potassium, rubidium, and sodium ignite explosively in contact with water.
Ellern, p. 29 (1968). *Brauer* (1965).

CHARCOAL C

(See also CARBON)

Air
Charcoal is spontaneously flammable when freshly calcined.
Von Schwartz, p. 323 (1918).

Air (Liquid)
Explosions may occur when liquid air contacts organic matter. A cracked tube containing activated charcoal, when immersed in liquid air, caused a violent explosion.
J. Taylor, *J. Sci. Instr.* **5:** 24 (1928).

Barium Chlorate
See CHLORATES plus Organic Matter.

Bromine Pentafluoride
See ARSENIC plus Bromine Pentafluoride.

Calcium Chlorate
See CHLORATES plus Organic Matter.

Calcium Hypochlorite
See CALCIUM HYPOCHLORITE plus Charcoal.

Chlorine Monoxide
See CHLORINE MONOXIDE plus Charcoal.

Chlorine Trifluoride
See CHLORINE TRIFLUORIDE plus Charcoal.

Fluorine
See FLUORINE plus Common Materials and Oxygen.

Hydrogen Peroxide
See HYDROGEN PEROXIDE plus Charcoal.

Magnesium Chlorate
See CHLORATES plus Organic Matter.

Oxygen and Wood
See OXYGEN (LIQUID) plus Wood and Charcoal.

Perchlorates
See PERCHLORATES plus Charcoal.

Perchloric Acid
See PERCHLORIC ACID plus Charcoal.

Peroxides
See SODIUM PEROXIDE plus Aniline.

Phosphorus and Air
See PHOSPHORUS plus Charcoal and Air.

Potassium
See POTASSIUM plus Charcoal.

Potassium Chlorate
See CHLORATES plus Organic Matter.

Potassium Nitrate
See POTASSIUM NITRATE plus Ammonium Chloride.

Potassium Perchlorate
See PERCHLORATES plus Charcoal.

Ruthenium Tetroxide
See RUTHENIUM TETROXIDE plus Charcoal.

Silver Nitrate
See SILVER NITRATE plus Charcoal.

Sodium Chlorate
See CHLORATES plus Organic Matter.

Sodium Peroxide
See SODIUM PEROXIDE plus Aniline.

Sodium Peroxide and Silver Chloride
See SODIUM PEROXIDE plus Silver Chloride and Charcoal.

Sulfur
See SULFUR plus Charcoal.

Sulfur and Sodium Nitrate
See SULFUR plus Sodium Nitrate and Charcoal.

Water
An explosion was reported when water was directed on charred (still smoldering) sunflower screenings. The probable cause is the so-called "water gas reaction." The reaction is the partial oxidation- reduction reaction between carbon and water to form carbon monoxide and hydrogen and proceeds only when the carbon phase is at temperatures of at least 700-800°C.

Zinc Chlorate
See CHLORATES plus Organic Matter.
See ZINC CHLORATE plus Charcoal.

CHLORATES

(See also specific chlorates as primary entries and under other reactants)

Acids
All chlorates, when brought in contact with sulfuric acid or certain other strong acids, may give off chlorine dioxide, an explosive gas (See CHLORINE DIOXIDE, self-reactive). With concentrated sulfuric acid, a violent explosion is usual.
Latimer and Hildebrand (1940). *Von Schwartz,* p. 323 (1918).
Also see CHLORATES plus Organic Acids.

Acids and Metals (powdered)
See CHLORATES plus Metals (powdered).

Aluminum
See ALUMINUM plus Bromates.

Antimony Sulfide
Antimony sulfide reacts with incandescence with chlorates of cad mium, magnesium, or zinc.
Mellor **Supp. II, Part I:** 584 (1956).
A mixture of chlorates plus antimony sulfide, cyanides or thiocyanates explodes. The reaction may be caused by heat, shock, or friction.
Von Schwartz, p. 323 (1918). *Pieters,* p. 30 (1957).

Arsenic
See ARSENIC plus Bromates.

Arsenic Sulfide
Arsenic sulfide reacts with incandescence with chlorates of cadmium, magnesium, or zinc.
Mellor **Supp. II, Part I:** 584 (1956).

Calcium Hydride
See BROMATES plus Calcium Hydride.

Carbon
See CARBON plus Bromates.

Charcoal
See CHLORATES plus Organic Matter.

Copper
See COPPER plus Bromates.

Copper Sulfide
See COPPER SULFIDE plus Cadmium Chlorate.

Cyanides
See CHLORATES plus Antimony Sulfide.
See CYANIDES plus Chlorates. See POTASSIUM CYANIDE plus Sodium Chlorate.

Manganese Dioxide
A mixture of manganese dioxide plus chlorates of barium, calcium, magnesium, potassium, sodium, or zinc may liberate oxygen and heat explosively. The reaction may be originated by heat, shock, friction, age, or static electricity.
Chem. and Eng. News **30:** 3210. *Von Schwartz,* p. 323 (1918).

Mercury Tetratriphosphide
See MERCURY TETRATRIPHOSPHIDE plus Air.

Metals (powdered)
Some mixtures of chlorates and bromates with combustible sub stances, including powdered metals, are likely to ignite by friction or percussion. Strong acids have a very violent action on these sub stances and many mixtures of chlorates and combustible substances are set on fire if acted on by strong sulfuric acid.
Lab. Govt. Chemist (1965).

Metal Sulfides
See METAL SULFIDES plus Bromates. See COPPER SULFIDE plus Cadmium Chlorate.
See CHLORATES plus Antimony Sulfide.

Organic Acids (Dibasic)
When a mixture of chlorates and organic acids is heated above room temperature, explosive chlorine dioxide is evolved.
U.S. Pat. 2,338,268 (1944).

Organic Matter
A mixture of organic matter plus barium chlorate, calcium chlorate, magnesium chlorate, potassium chlorate, sodium chlorate, or zinc chlorate may liberate oxygen and heat explosively. A similar reaction occurs when manganese dioxide, sulfur, or charcoal is combined with these chlorates.
Chem. and Eng. News **30:** 3210. *Von Schwartz,* p. 323 (1918).

Phosphonium Iodide
See PHOSPHONIUM IODIDE plus Bromates.

Phosphorus
See PHOSPHORUS plus Bromates.
See PHOSPHORUS plus Chlorates.

Potassium Cyanide
A mixture of potassium cyanide and chlorates reacts explosively.
Bahme, p. 30 (1961).

Selenium
See SELENIUM plus Chlorates.

Sodium Hypophosphite
Mixtures of sodium hypophosphite and chlorates or nitrates will explode if moistened, then dried slowly over flame.
Chem. and Eng. News **25:** 3176-77 (1947).

Strontium Hydride
See BROMATES plus Strontium Hydride.

Sulfur
See SULFUR plus Chlorates. See CHLORATES plus Organic Matter.

Sulfur and Copper
See SULFUR plus Chlorates and Copper.

Sulfur Dioxide
Dry sulfur dioxide reacts on chlorates with evolution of chlorine peroxide which will flash at 60°C. and can explode.
Mellor **10:** 217 (1946-1947).

Sulfuric Acid
See CHLORATES plus Acids. See also SULFURIC ACID plus Carbides. See SODIUM CHLORATE plus Sulfuric Acid.
The reaction of chlorates and sulfuric acid (to form chlorine dioxide) may cause explosions.
Mellor **2, Supp. 1:** 521 (1956).

Sulfuric Acid and Metals
See CHLORATES plus Metals (powdered).

Thiocyanates
See THIOCYANATES plus CHLORATES.
See CHLORATES plus Antimony Sulfide.

Zinc
See ZINC plus Chlorates.

CHLORIC ACID $HClO_3$

(self-reactive)
Concentrations of chloric acid above 40% decompose.
Mellor **2, Supp. 1:** 576 (1956).

Ammonia
See ANTIMONY plus Chloric Acid.

Antimony
See ANTIMONY plus Chloric Acid.

Antimony Sulfide
See ANTIMONY SULFIDE plus Chloric acid.

Arsenic Sulfide
See ARSENIC SULFIDE plus Chloric Acid.

Bismuth
See ANTIMONY plus Chloric Acid.

Copper Sulfide
See COPPER SULFIDE plus Cadmium Chlorate.

Organic Matter
Chloric acid decomposes many organic substances with spontaneous ignition.
Mellor **2:** 310 (1946-1947).
See ANTIMONY plus Chloric Acid.

Phosphonium Iodide
See PHOSPHONIUM IODIDE plus Bromic Acid.

Stannic Sulfide
See STANNIC SULFIDE plus Chloric Acid.

Stannous Sulfide
See STANNOUS SULFIDE plus Chloric Acid.

CHLORINATED HYDROCARBONS

Aluminum
See ALUMINUM plus Chlorinated Hydrocarbons.

Oxygen (liquid)
See OXYGEN (LIQUID) plus Chlorinated Hydrocarbons.

Potassium
See POTASSIUM plus Chlorinated Hydrocarbons.

Sodium
See SODIUM plus Chlorinated Hydrocarbons.

CHLORINATED POLYETHYLENE

Fluorine
See FLUORINE plus Solid Nonmetals and Oxygen.

CHLORINE Cl_2

Acetaldehyde
See BROMINE plus Acetaldehyde.

Acetylene
Acetylene can react explosively with chlorine.
Von Schwartz, p. 142 (1918).

Alcohols
See ALCOHOLS plus Hypochlorous Acid.

Alkylisothiourea Salts
On long contact or with excess chlorine, explosions occur due to the formation of unstable nitrogen trichloride.
J. Am. Chem. Soc. **63:** 3520 (1941).

Alkylphosphines
Unless precautions are taken, the reaction of chlorine with alkylphosphines or dialkylphosphines is a vigorous decomposing reaction.
Mellor **8, Supp. 3:** 900 (1971).

Aluminum
See ALUMINUM plus Chlorine.

Ammonia
Ammonia plus chlorine (with heat) explodes due to the formation of extremely sensitive nitrogen trichloride. Excess chlorine (without heat) reacts similarly.
Mellor **2:** 95 (1946-1947). *Mathieson Chlorine* (1948).
Mellor **8, Supp. 2:** 330 (1964).

Antimony
See ANTIMONY plus Chlorine.

Arsenic
See ARSENIC plus Chlorine.

Arsenic Disulfide
Arsenic disulfide ignites in a rapid stream of chlorine.
Mellor **9:** 270 (1946-1947).

Arsine
When chlorine is bubbled into arsine, each bubble produces a flame.
Mellor **9:** 55 (1946-1947).
Mellor **2, Supp. 1:** 379 (1956).

Barium Phosphide
The phosphide ignites in chlorine at 90°C.
Mellor **8, Supp. 3:** 842 (1971).

Benzene
An explosion of benzene vapors and chlorine (inadvertently mixed) was initiated by light.
Report, Amer. Potash and Chemical Co.

Bismuth
See BISMUTH plus Chlorine.

Boron
See BORON plus Chlorine.

Boron Phosphodiiodide
Powdered magnesium and boron phosphodiiodide react with incandescence.
Mellor **8:** 845 (1946-1947).

Boron Trisulfide
Boron trisulfide ignites in chlorine, even if cold.
Mellor **5:** 144 (1946-1947).

Brass
Brass burns spontaneously in gaseous chlorine.
Mellor **2:** 95, 292; **9:** 626 (1946-1947).

Bromine Pentafluoride
Mixture of chlorine and bromine pentafluoride explodes on heating.
Mellor **2, Supp. 1:** 173 (1956).

Calcium
See CALCIUM plus Chlorine.

Calcium Carbide and Potassium Hydroxide
See DICHLOROACETYLENE plus Air.

Calcium Chlorite
The reaction of chlorine and a dilute solution of calcium chlorite evolves explosive chlorine dioxide.
Mellor **2, Supp. 1:** 382 (1956).
See also CHLORINE DIOXIDE (self-reactive).

Calcium Nitride
Calcium nitride reacts in the cold with chlorine, with incandescence.
Mellor **8:** 99 (1946-1947).

Calcium Phosphide
Mixtures of chlorine and calcium phosphide react readily at about 100°C.
Mellor **8:** 841 (1946-1947).

Carbon (Activated)
The mixture spontaneously ignites in the dry state.
Bahme, p. 28 (1961).

Carbon Disulfide
When liquid chlorine was added to carbon disulfide in an iron cylin der, the iron catalyzed an explosive reaction.
MCA Case History **971** (1964).

Cesium
See CESIUM plus Chlorine.

Cesium Acetylene Carbide
Cesium acetylene carbide burns in cold chlorine or fluorine.
Mellor **5:** 849 (1946-1947).

Cesium Monoxide
See BROMINE plus Cesium Monoxide.

Cesium Nitride
See CESIUM NITRIDE plus Air.

Chromyl Chloride and Carbon
The reaction of a mixture of chlorine and chromyl chloride with red-hot carbon sometimes causes a violent reaction or explosion.
Mellor **11:** 395 (1946-1947).

Copper
See COPPER plus Chlorine.

Copper Hydride
See BROMINE plus Copper Hydride.

Cuprous Acetylide
See BROMINE plus Cuprous Acetylide.

Dialkylphosphines
See CHLORINE plus Alkylphosphines.

Diborane
Diborane explodes in contact with chlorine at ordinary temperatures.
Mellor **5:** 37 (1946-1947).

Dibutyl Phthalate
See CHLORINE plus Polypropylene.

Diethyl Ether
When ether is poured into chlorine gas an explosion results.
Bernthsen (1912).

Diethyl Zinc
Diethyl zinc is spontaneously flammable in air or chlorine.
Handbook Chem. Phys., p. C-715 (1970-1971).

Drawing Wax
See CHLORINE plus Polypropylene

Ethane
Chlorine and ethane have produced explosions.
Chem. Abst. **31:** 85025 (1937). W. W. Lawrence and S. E. Cook, *Ind. Eng. Chem. Proc. Dev.* **9** (1): 47-49 (1970).

Ethylene
Ethylene reacts explosively with chlorine in sunlight or ultraviolet light.
Haz. Chem. Data (1966).
The reaction of chlorine and ethylene is explosive at room temperature over yellow mercuric oxide, mercurous oxide, or silver oxide.
Mellor **2, Supp. 1:** 380 (1956).

Ethyleneimine
Ethyleneimine plus chlorine forms an explosive compound, 1-chlo roethyleneimine.
Ethyleneimine.

S-Ethyl Isothiourea Sulfate
An explosion occurred during the chlorination of S-ethyl isothiourea sulfate and formamidine thiolacetic acid-HCl. Formation of spontaneously explosive nitrogen trichloride was the suggested cause.
J. Am. Chem. Soc. **63:** 3530-32 (1941).

Ethyl Phosphine
A mixture of ethyl phosphine and chlorine explodes.
Von Schwartz, pp. 324, 325 (1918).

Fluorine
Reaction of chlorine and fluorine is accompanied by flames. In the presence of a spark, a violent explosion occurs.
Mellor **2, Supp. 1:** 58 (1956).

Formamidine Thiolacetic Acid-HCl
See CHLORINE plus S-Ethyl Isothiourea Sulfate.

Germanium
See GERMANIUM plus Chlorine.

Glycerol
See CHLORINE plus Polypropylene.

Hydrazine
Hydrazine ignites in contact with chlorine.
Mellor **8:** 313 (1946-1947).

Hydrocarbons
In a chemical process, chlorine inadvertently contacted hydrocarbon vapors at about 60 psig. An explosion ruptured the pipeline.
MCA Case History **1035** (1964).
Chlorine reacts vigorously with most hydrocarbons, causing ignition with some, e.g., turpentine.
Mathieson Chlorine. Mellor **2, Supp. I:** 404.
During treatment of naphtha with an aqueous caustic-hypochlorite solution to remove objectionable odors, an explosion occurred in the mixer. Just before the detonation, liquid chlorine had been added to strengthen the hypochlorite solution. The explosion is attributed to the highly exothermic liquid phase reaction of chlorine and saturated hydrocarbons.
Chem. Eng. Progs. **58(6):** 71-74 (1962).
Mellor **2, Supp. 1:** 380 (1956).

Hydrogen
A mixture of hydrogen and chlorine is exploded by almost any form of energy (heat, sunlight, sparks, etc.). Explosive range: 5% to 95%.
Mathieson Chlorine.

Hydrogen Peroxide and Potassium Hydroxide
Red luminescence occurs during reaction of chlorine and hydrogen peroxide in strong potassium hydroxide solution.
Mellor **2, Supp. 1:** 378 (1956).

Hydroxylamine
Hydroxylamine is spontaneously flammable in chlorine.
Mellor **8:** 288 (1946-1947).

Iodine
The reaction of liquid chlorine and iodine is violent.
Mellor **2, Supp. 1:** 378 (1956).

Iron
See IRON plus Chlorine.

Iron Carbide
Iron carbide burns in chlorine below 100°C with incandescence and behaves similarly with bromine at about 100°C.
Mellor **5:** 858 (1946-1947).

Linseed Oil
See CHLORINE plus Polypropylene.

Lithium
See CESIUM plus Chlorine.

Lithium Acetylene Carbide Diammino
See LITHIUM ACETYLENE CARBIDE DIAMMINO plus Carbon Dioxide.

Lithium Carbide
See BROMINE plus Lithium Carbide.

Lithium Silicide
See FLUORINE plus Lithium Silicide.

Magnesium
See MAGNESIUM plus Chlorine.

Magnesium Phosphide
Magnesium phosphide burns brilliantly when heated in chlorine or bromine vapors.
Mellor **8:** 842 (1946-1947).

Manganese
See MANGANESE plus Chlorine.

Manganese Ditritaphosphide
This phosphide ignites when gently heated in chlorine.
Mellor **8:** 853 (1946-1947).

Mercuric Oxide
Chlorine reacts rapidly at room temperature with both mercuric oxide and silver oxide.
Mellor **2, Supp. 1:** 381 (1956).

Mercuric Sulfide
Mercuric sulfide burns in chlorine with incandescence.
Mellor **4:** 952 (1946-1947).

Mercury
See MERCURY plus Chlorine.

Mercury Tetratriphosphide
See MERCURY TETRATRIPHOSPHIDE plus Air.

Methane
The reaction of chlorine and methane is explosive at room temperature over yellow mercuric oxide.
Mellor **2, Supp. 1:** 380 (1956).

Niobium (Columbium)
See NIOBIUM plus Chlorine.
See NIOBIUM plus Fluorine.

Nitrogen Triiodide
See BROMINE plus Nitrogen Triiodide.

Oxomonosilane
The polymer of oxomonosilane ignites in air or chlorine.
Mellor **6:** 234 (1946-1947).

Oxygen Difluoride
The reaction between chlorine and oxygen difluoride produces a reddish-brown solid that explodes at about minus 10°C.
Mellor **2, Supp. 1:** 182 (1956).
A mixture of chlorine and oxygen fluoride explodes on gentle warming. Puffs or more violent explosions occur if mixture is in copper tubing at 300°C.
Mellor **2, Supp. 1:** 192 (1956).

Oxygen Difluoride and Copper
See CHLORINE plus Oxygen Difluoride.

Phosphine
See BROMINE plus Phosphine.

Phosphorus
See PHOSPHORUS plus Chlorine.

Phosphorus and Heptane
See PHOSPHORUS plus Chlorine and Heptane.

Phosphorus Isocyanate
The reaction of phosphorus isocyanate and chlorine is vigorous, forming a yellow oil.
Mellor **8, Supp. 3:** 585 (1971).

Phosphorus Oxide
When phosphorus oxide is thrown into a jar of chlorine vapor, it ignites instantly. It reacts violently with liquid bromine and generally ignites.
Mellor **8:** 897 (1946-1947).

Phosphorus Trioxide
See BROMINE plus Phosphorus Trioxide.

Polychlorinated Biphenyl
Liquid chlorine reacts exothermically with polychlorinated biphenyl heat transfer liquid.
W. A. Statesir, *Chem. Eng. Progs.* **69** (4): 52-54 (1973).

Polydimethylsiloxane
See CHLORINE plus Polypropylene.

Polypropylene
Liquid chlorine reacts explosively with polypropylene, drawing wax, polydimethyl-siloxane, dibutyl phthalate, glycerol, and linseed oil.
W. A. Statesir, *Chem. Eng. Progs.* **69** (4): 52-54 (1973).

Potassium
See POTASSIUM plus Chlorine.

Potassium Acetylene Carbide
Potassium acetylene carbide ignites spontaneously in cold chlorine, forming hydrogen chloride plus carbon.
Mellor **5:** 849 (1946-1947) *Comp. Rend.* **127:** 916. *Comp. Rend.* **136:** 1220.

Potassium Hydride
Potassium hydride burns in fluorine or chlorine spontaneously.
Mellor **2:** 483 (1946-1947).

Rubber
Rubber will burn in liquid chlorine. During chlorination of rubber, an explosion occurred causing pressure of over 1,100 psi.
Chem. and Eng. News **26:** 3369.

Rubidium
See CESIUM plus Chlorine.

Rubidium Acetylene Carbide
See BROMINE plus Rubidium Acetylene Carbide.

Silicon
See SILICON plus Chlorine.

Silicon Hydride
Silicon hydride ignites in a chlorine atmosphere.
Mellor **6:** 219 (1946-1947).

Silver Oxide
See CHLORINE plus Mercuric Oxide.

Sodium
See SODIUM plus Chlorine.

Sodium Acetylene Carbide
See BROMINE plus Sodium Acetylene Carbide.

Sodium Carbide
See SODIUM CARBIDE plus Carbon Dioxide.
This carbide burns in chlorine gas.
Mellor **5:** 848 (1946-1947).

Sodium Hydride
Sodium hydride is spontaneously flammable in fluorine. With chlorine, moisture must also be present.
Mellor **2:** 483 (1946-1947).

Stannous Fluoride
The reaction of chlorine and stannous fluoride occurs with flaming.
Mellor **2, Supp. 1:** 382 (1956).

Stibine
See STIBINE plus Ammonia.

Strontium Phosphide
Mixtures of these materials ignite at about 30°C.
Mellor **8:** 841 (1946-1947).

Sulfamic Acid
An explosion occurred when chlorine was being passed at room temperature into a reaction mixture which included sulfamic acid and water. It is suspected that nitrogen trichloride, a very sensitive explosive, was formed.
Short (1966).

Tellurium
Warm chlorine attacks tellurium with incandescence.
Mellor **11:** 26, 40 (1946-1947).

Tetramethyl Diarsine
Tetramethyl diarsine is spontaneously flammable in chlorine.
ACS **15** (1923).

Thorium
See THORIUM plus Chlorine.

Tin
See TIN plus Chlorine.

Tungsten Dioxide
When tungsten dioxide is heated in chlorine the reaction occurs with incandescence.
Mellor **11:** 851 (1946-1947).

Turpentine
See CHLORINE plus Hydrocarbons.

Uranium
Uranium ignites spontaneously if chlorine is heated to 150°C.
Mellor **12:** 31, 32 (1946-1947).

Uranium Dicarbide
See BROMINE plus Uranium Dicarbide.

Vanadium
Powdered vanadium explodes with chlorine, even at 0°C.
Mellor **Supp. II, Part I:** 715 (1956).

Zinc
See ZINC plus Chlorine.

Zirconium Dicarbide
See BROMINE plus Zirconium Dicarbide.

CHLORINE AZIDE N_3Cl

(self-reactive)
Chlorine azide is spontaneously explosive.
Mellor **8:** 336 (1946-1947).
Mellor **8, Supp. 2:** 50 (1967).

Butadiene-1, 3
Chlorine dioxide mixed with butadiene, ethane, ethylene, methane or propane always explodes spontaneously.
J.K.K. Ip and P. Gray, *Comb. & Flame* **19:** 117-129 (1972).

Ethane
See CHLORINE DIOXIDE plus Butadiene.

Ethylene
See CHLORINE DIOXIDE plus Butadiene.

Methane
See CHLORINE DIOXIDE plus Butadiene.

Propane
See CHLORINE DIOXIDE plus Butadiene.

CHLORINE FLUOROXIDE ClOF

(self-reactive)
Chlorine fluoroxide is explosively unstable.
Mellor **2, Supp. 1:** 182 (1956).

CHLORINE MONOFLUORIDE ClF

Organic Matter
See BROMINE MONOFLUORIDE plus Water.

Water
See BROMINE MONOFLUORIDE plus Water.

CHLORINE DIOXIDE ClO_2

(self-reactive)
With over 10% chlorine dioxide in air at pressures from 0.1 to 1.0 atmosphere, chlorine dioxide is violently explosive. Explosion may be initiated by almost any form of energy such as sunlight, heat, or sparks.
Chem. and Eng. News **29:** 5030 (1951).

Difluoroamine
The gas phase reaction of chlorine dioxide and difluoroamine is explosive.
Lawless and Smith, p. 171 (1968).

Fluorine
See FLUORINE plus Chlorine Dioxide.

Mercury
See MERCURY plus Chlorine Dioxide.

Organic Matter
Organic material in contact with chlorine dioxide can be exploded by shock or sparks.
R.F. Stedman, *Chem. and Eng. News* **29:** 5030 (1951).

Phosphorus
See PHOSPHORUS plus Chlorine Dioxide.

Potassium Hydroxide
See POTASSIUM HYDROXIDE plus Chlorine Dioxide.

Sugar
See SULFUR plus Chlorine Dioxide.

Sulfur
See SULFUR plus Chlorine Dioxide.

CHLORINE FLUORIDE ClF

Tellurium
See TELLURIUM plus Chlorine Fluoride.

CHLORINE MONOXIDE Cl_2O

(self-reactive)
Chlorine monoxide is highly explosive if heated rapidly or over heated locally.
Mellor **2, Supp. 1:** 517 (1956).

Ammonia
A mixture of chlorine monoxide and ammonia explodes.
Mellor **2:** 241, 242 (1946-1947).

Antimony
See POTASSIUM plus Chlorine Monoxide.

Antimony Sulfide
See CHLORINE MONOXIDE plus Calcium Phosphide.

Arsenic
See POTASSIUM plus Chlorine Monoxide.

Barium Sulfide
See CHLORINE MONOXIDE plus Calcium Phosphide.

Calcium Phosphide
Calcium phosphide causes chlorine monoxide to explode; chlorine monoxide also causes explosions with sulfides of barium, tin, antimony and mercury.
Mellor **2:** 242 (1946-1947).

Carbon
See CHLORINE MONOXIDE plus Charcoal.

Carbon Disulfide
Chlorine monoxide explodes in contact with carbon disulfide vapor.
Mellor **6:** 110 (1946-1947).

Charcoal
An immediate explosion occurs when charcoal is added to chlorine monoxide.
Mellor **5:** 822-30 (1946-1947).

Hydrogen Sulfide
A mixture of chlorine monoxide and hydrogen sulfide explodes.
Mellor **2:** 241-42 (1946-1947).

Mercury Sulfide
See CHLORINE MONOXIDE plus Calcium Phosphide.

Metal Sulfides
See CHLORINE MONOXIDE plus Calcium Phosphide.

Nitric Oxide
A mixture of nitric oxide and chlorine monoxide can be explosive.
Ann. Chim. et Phys. (2) **57:** 225.

Organic Matter
Chlorine monoxide often explodes violently in contact with organic compounds.
Mellor **2, Supp. 1:** 520 (1956).
See POTASSIUM plus Chlorine Monoxide.

Phosphine
Chlorine monoxide explodes on contact with phosphine.
Taylor (1831).

Phosphorus
See CHLORINE MONOXIDE plus Calcium Phosphide.

Sulfur
See POTASSIUM plus Chlorine Monoxide.

Tin Sulfides
See CHLORINE MONOXIDE plus Calcium Phosphide.

Turpentine
See POTASSIUM plus Chlorine Monoxide.

CHLORINE TRIFLUORIDE ClF_3

Acetic Acid
The reaction between chlorine trifluoride and acetic acid is very violent, sometimes explosive.
Mellor **2, Supp. 1:** 155 (1956).

Aluminum
See ALUMINUM plus Chlorine Trifluoride.

Aluminum Oxide
Chlorine trifluoride reacts violently, producing flame, with aluminum oxide, calcium oxide, chromium oxide, lead dioxide, magnesium oxide, manganese dioxide, molybdenum trioxide, tantalum pentoxide, tungsten trioxide, or vanadium pentoxide.
Mellor **2, Supp. 1:** 157 (1956).
See also CHLORINE TRIFLUORIDE plus Elements.

Ammonia
Chlorine trifluoride causes an explosive reaction with ammonia, carbon monoxide, hydrogen sulfide, sulfur dioxide, or hydrogen.
Mellor **2, Supp. 1:** 157 (1956).

Antimony
See ANTIMONY plus Chlorine Trifluoride.

Arsenic
See ANTIMONY plus Chlorine Trifluoride.

Arsenic Trioxide
Chlorine trifluoride produces a violent reaction without flame in presence of arsenic trioxide, bismuth trioxide, lanthanum oxide, phosphorus pentoxide, or stannic oxide.
Mellor **2, Supp. 1:** 157 (1956).
See also CHLORINE TRIFLUORIDE plus Elements.

Benzene
The reaction between chlorine trifluoride and benzene is very violent, sometimes explosive.
Mellor **2, Supp. 1:** 155 (1956).

Bismuth Trioxide
See CHLORINE TRIFLUORIDE plus Arsenic Trioxide.

Calcium
See CALCIUM plus Chlorine Trifluoride.

Calcium Oxide
See CHLORINE TRIFLUORIDE plus Aluminum Oxide.

Carbon Monoxide
See CHLORINE TRIFLUORIDE plus Ammonia.

Charcoal
Chlorine trifluoride causes charcoal, glass wool (rapidly etched with traces of moisture), or graphite to burst into flame.
Mellor **2, Supp. 1:** 157 (1956).

Chlorotrifluoroethylene Polymer (Kel-F Oil) and water
While chlorine trifluoride was being passed through Kel-F Oil for disposal the inadvertent introduction of mois ture set up the exothermic water-plus-chlorine trifluoride reaction. The heat evolved initiated a violent reaction with the Kel-F Oil.
Chem. and Eng. News **43** (20): 41 (1965).

Chromic Anhydride
Chlorine trifluoride and chromic anhydride react violently with evolution of brown fumes.
Mellor **2, Supp. 1:** 157 (1956).
Mellor **11:** 230 (1946-1947).

Chromic Oxide
Reaction between chlorine trifluoride and chromic oxide is accompanied by incandescence.
Mellor **11:** 181 (1946-1947).

Chromium Oxide
See also CHLORINE TRIFLUORIDE plus Aluminum Oxide.

Copper
See ALUMINUM plus Chlorine Trifluoride.

Diethyl Ether
The reaction between chlorine and diethyl ether is very violent, sometimes explosive.
Mellor **2, Supp. 1:** 155 (1956).

Elements
Most chemical elements are attacked explosively by chlorine trifluoride. Most oxides behave the same way. Glass wool catches fire in the vapor. One drop of the liquid sets fire to paper, cloth, or wood. The reaction is violent with water or ice.
Sidgwick, p. 1156 (1950). *Matheson Gas Data,* p. 108 (1961).

Glass
Glass wool catches fire readily in the vapor. Chlorine trifluoride flowing in glass tubing at excessive rates or pressures can cause the glass to burn.
Sidgwick, p. 1156 (1950). *Yunker* (1966).
See also CHLORINE TRIFLUORIDE plus Charcoal.

Graphite
See CHLORINE TRIFLUORIDE plus Charcoal.

Hydrogen
See CHLORINE TRIFLUORIDE plus Ammonia.

Hydrogen Sulfide
See CHLORINE TRIFLUORIDE plus Ammonia.

Iodine
See CHLORINE TRIFLUORIDE plus Mercuric Iodide.

Iridium
See IRIDIUM plus Chlorine Trifluoride.

Iron
See IRON plus Chlorine Trifluoride.

Lanthanum Oxide
See CHLORINE TRIFLUORIDE plus Arsenic Trioxide.

Lead
See ALUMINUM plus Chlorine Trifluoride.

Lead Dioxide
See CHLORINE TRIFLUORIDE plus Aluminum Oxide.

Magnesium
See ALUMINUM plus Chlorine Trifluoride.

Magnesium Oxide
See CHLORINE TRIFLUORIDE plus Aluminum Oxide.

Manganese Dioxide
See MANGANESE DIOXIDE plus Chlorine Trifluoride.
See also CHLORINE TRIFLUORIDE plus Aluminum Oxide.

Mercuric Iodide
Combination of chlorine trifluoride and mercuric iodide, tungsten carbide, or iodine results in a reaction with flame.
Mellor **2, Supp. 1:** 157 (1956).

Molybdenum
See MOLYBDENUM plus Chlorine Trifluoride.

Molybdenum Trioxide
See MOLYBDENUM TRIOXIDE plus Chlorine Trifluoride.
See also CHLORINE TRIFLUORIDE plus Aluminum Oxide.

Nitric Acid (Fuming)
Combination of chlorine trifluoride and fuming nitric acid, potassium carbonate, potassium iodide, silver nitrate, 10% sodium hydroxide or sulfuric acid results in a violent reaction.
Mellor **2, Supp. 1:** 157 (1956).

Nitroaromatic Compounds
See NITROAROMATIC COMPOUNDS plus Chlorine Trifluoride.

Organic Matter
Chlorine trifluoride is compatible with other oxidizers such as OF_2 and ClO_3F, but reacts violently with organics.
See also CHLORINE TRIFLUORIDE plus Elements.
Lawless and Smith, p. 114 (1968).
Mellor **2, Supp. 1:** 155 (1956).
See also BROMINE MONOFLUORIDE plus Water.

Osmium
See ANTIMONY plus Chlorine Trifluoride.

Oxides
See CHLORINE TRIFLUORIDE plus Elements.

Phosphorus
See ANTIMONY plus Chlorine Trifluoride.

Phosphorus Pentoxide
See CHLORINE TRIFLUORIDE plus Arsenic Trioxide.

Potassium
See ANTIMONY plus Chlorine Trifluoride.

Potassium Carbonate
See CHLORINE TRIFLUORIDE plus Nitric Acid.

Potassium Iodide
See CHLORINE TRIFLUORIDE plus Nitric Acid.

Rhodium
See ANTIMONY plus Chlorine Trifluoride.

Rubber
When chlorine trifluoride is in contact with rubber a violent reaction occurs.
Mellor **2, Supp. 1:** 156 (1956).

Selenium
See ANTIMONY plus Chlorine Trifluoride.

Silicon
See ANTIMONY plus Chlorine Trifluoride.

Silver
See ALUMINUM plus Chlorine Trifluoride.

Silver Nitrate
See CHLORINE TRIFLUORIDE plus Nitric Acid.

Sodium
See CALCIUM plus Chlorine Trifluoride.

Sodium Hydroxide
See CHLORINE TRIFLUORIDE plus Nitric Acid.

Stannic Oxide
See CHLORINE TRIFLUORIDE plus Arsenic Trioxide.

Sulfur
See ANTIMONY plus Chlorine Trifluoride.

Sulfur Dioxide
See CHLORINE TRIFLUORIDE plus Ammonia.

Sulfuric Acid
See CHLORINE TRIFLUORIDE plus Nitric Acid.

Tantalum Pentoxide
See CHLORINE TRIFLUORIDE plus Aluminum Oxide.

Tellurium
See ANTIMONY plus Chlorine Trifluoride.

Tin
See ALUMINUM plus Chlorine Trifluoride.

Tungsten
See ANTIMONY plus Chlorine Trifluoride.

Tungsten Carbide
See CHLORINE TRIFLUORIDE plus Mercuric Iodide.

Tungsten Trioxide
See TUNGSTEN TRIOXIDE plus Chlorine Trifluoride. See also CHLORINE TRIFLUORIDE plus Aluminum Oxide.

Vanadium Pentoxide
See CHLORINE TRIFLUORIDE plus Aluminum Oxide.

Water
See CHLORINE TRIFLUORIDE plus Elements.
See also BROMINE MONOFLUORIDE plus Water.

Zinc
See ALUMINUM plus Chlorine Trifluoride.

CHLORINE TRIOXIDE ClO_3

(self-reactive)
Explosions occurred during preparation of chlorine trioxide.
Mellor **2, Supp. 1:** 540 (1956).

Ethyl Alcohol
No really safe conditions exist under which ethyl alcohol and chlorine oxides can be handled.
Mellor **2, Supp. 1:** 540 (1956).

Organic Matter
Chlorine trioxide reacts violently, even explosively, with stopcock grease, wood, most forms of organic matter.
Mellor **2, Supp. 1:** 540 (1956).

Phosphorus
See PHOSPHORUS plus Chlorine Trioxide.

Phosphorus Pentachloride
When chlorine trioxide is passed over phosphorus pentachloride, there is often a vigorous explosion, explosive chlorine monoxide being formed.
Bull. Acad. Belg. (2) **38:** 503 (1814).

Water
Chlorine trioxide reacts vigorously and may explode with water.
Mellor **2, Supp. 1:** 540 (1956).

CHLORITES

(See also specific chlorites)

Ammonia
This reaction produces ammonium chlorite, which is a shock-sensitive compound.
Federoff **3:** C-254 (1966).

Organic Matter
See CHLORITES plus Metals.

Metals
Finely divided metallic or organic substances, if mixed with chlorites, are highly flammable and may be ignited by friction.
Lab. Govt. Chemist (1965).

CHLOROACETALDEHYDE OXIME $ClCH_2CH{=}NOH$

(self-reactive)
Separation of chloroacetaldehyde oxime from ether by distillation must not be carried out too far or a violent explosion will occur.
MCA Guide for Safety, Appendix 3 (1972).

CHLOROACETONE $ClCH_2COCH_3$

(self-reactive)
Chloroacetone had turned black during storage for two years on a shelf in dull diffused light. A few days after the bottle of chloroacetone was moved, it exploded. The chloroacetone had polymerized to a black rubber-like substance.
Ind. & Eng. Chem. News **9:** 184 (1931).

CHLOROACETYLENE $HC{\equiv}CCl$

(self-reactive)
See POTASSIUM HYDROXIDE plus 1,2-Dichloroethylene.

Air
See POTASSIUM HYDROXIDE plus 1,2-Dichloroethylene.

m-CHLOROANILINE DIAZONIUM CHLORIDE
$NH_2{\cdot}C_6H_4N({\equiv}N)Cl$

Sodium Bisulfide
See SODIUM SULFIDE plus Diazonium Salts and Diazonium Chloride Salts.

Sodium Polysulfide
See SODIUM SULFIDE plus Diazonium Salts and Diazonium Chloride Salts.

Sodium Sulfide
See SODIUM SULFIDE plus Diazonium Salts and Diazonium Chloride Salts.

CHLOROAZODIN $ClN{=}C(NH_2)N{=}NC(NH_2)NCl$

(self-reactive)
Chloroazodin decomposes explosively at about 155°C. The decomposition is accelerated by contact with metals.
Merck Index, p. 240 (1968).

CHLOROBENZENE C_6H_5Cl

Dimethyl Sulfoxide
See DIMETHYL SULFOXIDE plus Acyl Halides.

Silver Perchlorate
See SILVER PERCHLORATE plus Acetic Acid.

5-CHLOROBENZOTRIAZOLE $NHN{=}NC_6H_3Cl$

(self-reactive)
5-Chlorobenzotriazole spontaneously burst into flame while being packaged.
H. S. Hopps, *Chem. and Eng. News* **49** (30): 3 (1971).
J. Chem. Eng. Data **17:** 108 and 109 (1972).

3-CHLOROCYCLOPENTENE $(\text{-}CH{=}CHCHClCH_2CH_2\text{-})$

(self-reactive)
Thirty-five grams of 3-chlorocyclopentene exploded one day after it was made.
Merck Safety Report (April 1962).

CHLORODIBORANE $ClBH(H_2)BH_2$

Air
This compound is spontaneously flammable in air.
Mellor **5:** 37 (1946-1947). *Douda* (1966).

CHLORODIETHYLALUMINUM $(C_2H_5)_2AlCl$

Benzene and Allyl Chloride
See ALLYL CHLORIDE plus Benzene and Ethyl Aluminum Dichloride.

Toluene and Allyl Chloride
See ALLYL CHLORIDE plus Benzene and Ethyl Aluminum Dichloride.

Water
Diethyl aluminum chloride reacts violently with water.
Rose (1961).

CHLORODIETHYLBISMUTHINE $(C_2H_5)_2BiCl$

Air
Diethyl bismuth chloride is spontaneously flammable in air.
Coates, p. 161 (1956).

CHLORODIETHYLBORANE $(C_2H_5)_2BCl$

Air
Diethyl boron chloride is spontaneously flammable in air.
Buls, Bimonthly Rept. 5, p. 3 (1953).

2-CHLORO-1, 1-DIETHOXYETHANE $(C_2H_5O)_2CHCH_2Cl$

Sodium Amide
See SODIUM AMIDE plus 1,1-Diethoxy-2-Chloroethane.

CHLORODIISOBUTYLALUMINUM $AlCl(C_4H_9)_2$

Air
Diisobutyl aluminum chloride ignites spontaneously in air.
J. E. Knap, R. E. Leach et al., *Ind. Eng. Chem.* **49** (5): 874-879 (1957).

CHLORO (DIMETHYLAMINO) DIBORANE $(CH_3)_2NB_2H_4Cl$

Air
Dimethylamino chlorodiborane is spontaneously flammable in air.
A. B. Burg and C. L. Randolph, Jr., *J. Am. Chem. Soc.* **71:** 3451- 3455 (1949).

1-CHLORO-2, 4-DINITROBENZENE $(O_2N)_2C_6H_3Cl$

(self-reactive)
An explosion may occur when the solvent symmetrical tetrachlorethane is almost removed in the chlorinolysis of 2, 4-dinitrophenyl disulfide.
MCA Guide for Safety, Appendix 3 (1972).
2, 4-Dinitrochlorobenzene has been known to detonate at about 300°F. It can be detonated by shock or heat under confinement that will permit high pressure build-up.
Haz. Chem. Data, p. 85 (1966).

Hydrazine Hydrate
See HYDRAZINE HYDRATE plus 2, 4-Dinitrochlorobenzene.
See also 2, 4-Dinitrochlorobenzene.

x-CHLORO-2, 4-DINITROTOLUENE $C_6H_3(NO_2)_2CH_2Cl$

(self-reactive)
2,4-Dinitrochlorotoluene has been known to detonate at about 300°F. It can be exploded by shock or heat under confinement that will permit high pressure build-up.
Van Dolah (1966).

CHLORODIPROPYLBORANE $(C_3H_7)_2BCl$

Air
Dipropylchloroborine is spontaneously flammable in air.
Douda (1966).

2-CHLOROETHANOL $ClCH_2CH_2OH$

Chlorosulfonic Acid
Mixing ethylene chlorohydrin and chlorosulfonic acid in a closed container caused the temperature and pressure to increase.
Flynn and Rossow (1970). See Note under complete reference.

Ethylene Diamine
Mixing ethylene chlorohydrin and ethylene diamine in a closed container caused the temperature and pressure to increase.
Flynn and Rossow (1970). See Note under complete reference.

Sodium Hydroxide
See SODIUM HYDROXIDE plus Chlorohydrin.

2-CHLOROETHYLENIMINE $CHCl=C=NH$

(self-reactive)
A distilled 50-gram quantity, after sitting in an amber bottle for three months, exploded suddenly. A black residue indicated it may have polymerized.
Chem. and Eng. News **42** (8): 41 (1964); *Chem. and Eng. News* **36** (43): 52 (1958).

N-CHLOROETHYLENIMINE $ClNCH_2CH_2$

(self-reactive)
MCA Guide for Safety, Appendix 3 (1972).

CHLOROFLUOROHYDROCARBONS

Aluminum
See ALUMINUM plus Chlorofluorohydrocarbons.

CHLOROFORM Cl_3CH

Acetone
See ACETONE plus Chloroform.

Aluminum
See ALUMINUM plus Chlorinated Hydrocarbons and ALUMINUM plus Chloroform.

Disilane
See DISILANE plus Carbon Tetrachloride.

Lithium
See LITHIUM plus Chloroform.

Magnesium
See MAGNESIUM plus Chloroform.

Nitrogen Tetroxide
See NITROGEN TETROXIDE plus 1,2-Dichloroethane.

Perchloric Acid and Phosphorus Pentoxide
See PHOSPHORUS PENTOXIDE plus Perchloric Acid and Chloroform.

Potassium
See POTASSIUM plus Chloroform.

Potassium Hydroxide and Methyl Alcohol
See SODIUM HYDROXIDE plus Chloroform and Methyl Alcohol.

Potassium Tert.-Butoxide
See ACETONE plus Potassium Tert.-Butoxide.

Sodium
See SODIUM plus Chloroform.

Sodium Hydroxide and Methyl Alcohol
See SODIUM HYDROXIDE plus Chloroform and Methyl Alcohol.

Sodium Methylate
See SODIUM METHYLATE plus Chloroform.

Sodium-Potassium Alloy
See SODIUM-POTASSIUM ALLOY plus Carbon Tetrachloride.
See LITHIUM plus Chloroform.

3-CHLORO-2-METHYLFURAN $OCCH_3=CClCH=CH$

(self-reactive)
A small sample (20 milliliters) had been made, distilled and allowed to stand over the weekend. During the weekend it exploded.
MCA Guide for Safety, Appendix 3 (1972).

Lithium Aluminum Hydride and Ethyl Acetate
A mixture of chlorinated organic compounds consisting principally of 3-CHLORO-2-METHYLFURAN was subjected to reductive dechlorination with lithium aluminum hydride, after which ethyl acetate was added in small increments to decompose excess lithium aluminum hydride. After a few drops had been added, a violent explosion occurred.
Chem. & Ind. **14:** 432 (1957).

4-CHLORO-2-NITROANILINE $NO_2(Cl)C_6H_3NH_2$

Nitric Acid
In a large scale-up of the method for preparing 4-chloro-2,6-dini troaniline by reacting nitric acid with 4-chloro-2-nitroaniline, an unexpected strong evolution of heat was experienced. The exotherm was found due to the simultaneous formation of two explosive products the isomer 2-chloro-4,6-dinitroaniline and also 4-chloro- 3,6-dinitrophenyldiazonium-2-oxide. The latter is very shock sensitive.
MCA Case History **1489** (1968).

CHLORONITROTOLUENES

Sodium Hydroxide
The feed stream into a tank of mixed chloronitrotoluenes became inadvertently contaminated with caustic. The runaway reaction within the tank ripped the tank open in spite of a 10-inch relief vent.
MCA Case History **907** (1963).

p-CHLOROPHENYL ISOCYANATE ClC_6H_4NCO

(self-reactive)
A violent explosion occurred in a laboratory during vacuum distillation of p-chlorophenyl isocyanate that had been prepared by the Curtius reaction of p-chlorobenzoylazide.
Chem. & Ind. **38:** 1625 (1965).

CHLOROPICRIN Cl_3CNO_2

(self-reactive)
Tank car volumes of this material may detonate under certain condi tions. There is a critical volume above which sufficient shock may cause detonation.
Chem. and Eng. News **50** (38): 13 (1972).

Propargyl Bromide
See PROPARGYL BROMIDE plus Chloropicrin.

3-CHLORO-1-PROPYNE $CH\equiv CCH_2Cl$

(self-reactive)
See PROPARGYL BROMIDE. Liquid propargyl chloride is much less susceptible to this type ignition.
D. R. Forshey et al., *Fire Tech.* **5** (2):100-111 (1969).

CHLOROSILANE $ClSiH_3$
Silane and chlorosilanes can explode when mixed with various halocarbons and ignited.
Plant Operations Progress, Britton (1990).

Ammonia
With insufficient ammonia, chlorosilane forms trisilylammonia which is spontaneously flammable in air.
Mellor **8:** 262 (1946-1947).

CHLOROSILANES ClxSiHy
Chloropentamethyl disilane and related heavy chlorosilanes may be thermally unstable and some are shock sensitive.
Chem. and Eng. News (June 4, 1990), *Plant Operations Progress,* Britton (1990) -Silanes

Air
The chlorosilicon hydrides are spontaneously flammable in air.
Ellern, p. 22 (1968).

CHLOROSULFURIC ACID $ClSO_2OH$

Acetic Acid
See ACETIC ACID plus Chlorosulfonic Acid.

Acetic Anhydride
See ACETIC ANHYDRIDE plus Chlorosulfonic Acid.

Acetonitrile
See ACETONITRILE plus Chlorosulfonic Acid.

Acrolein
See ACROLEIN plus Chlorosulfonic Acid.

Acrylic Acid
See ACRYLIC ACID plus Chlorosulfonic Acid.

Acrylonitrile
See ACRYLONITRILE plus Chlorosulfonic Acid.

Allyl Alcohol
See ALLYL ALCOHOL plus Chlorosulfonic Acid.

Allyl Chloride
See ALLYL CHLORIDE plus Chlorosulfonic Acid.

2-Aminoethanol
See 2-AMINOETHANOL plus Chlorosulfonic Acid.

Ammonium Hydroxide
Mixing chlorosulfonic acid and 28% ammonia in a closed container caused the temperature and pressure to increase.
Flynn and Rossow (1970). See Note under complete reference.

Aniline
See ANILINE plus Chlorosulfonic Acid.

n-Butyraldehyde
See n-Butyraldehyde plus Chlorosulfonic Acid.

Creosote Oil
Mixing chlorosulfonic acid and creosote oil in a closed container caused the temperature and pressure to increase.
Flynn and Rossow (1970). See Note under complete reference.

Cresol
See CRESOL plus Chlorosulfonic Acid.

Cumene
See CUMENE plus Chlorosulfonic Acid.

Dichloroethyl Ether
See DICHLOROETHYL ETHER plus Chlorosulfonic Acid.

Diethylene Glycol Monomethyl Ether
See DIETHYLENE GLYCOL MONOMETHYL ETHER plus Chlorosulfonic Acid.

Diisobutylene
See DIISOBUTYLENE plus Chlorosulfonic Acid.

Diisopropyl Ether
See DIISOPROPYL ETHER plus Chlorosulfonic Acid.

Epichlorohydrin
See EPICHLOROHYDRIN plus Chlorosulfonic Acid.

Ethyl Acetate
See ETHYL ACETATE plus Chlorosulfonic Acid.

Ethyl Acrylate
See ETHYL ACRYLATE plus Chlorosulfonic Acid.

Ethylene Chlorohydrin
See ETHYLENE CHLOROHYDRIN plus Chlorosulfonic Acid.

Ethylene Cyanohydrin
See ETHYLENE CYANOHYDRIN plus Chlorosulfonic Acid.

Ethylene Diamine
See ETHYLENE DIAMINE plus Chlorosulfonic Acid.

Ethylene Glycol
See ETHYLENE GLYCOL plus Chlorosulfonic Acid.

Ethylene Glycol Monoethyl Ether Acetate
See ETHYLENE GLYCOL MONOETHYL ETHER ACETATE plus Chlorosulfonic Acid.

Ethyleneimine
See ETHYLENEIMINE plus Chlorosulfonic Acid.

Glyoxal
See GLYOXAL plus Chlorosulfonic acid.

Heptane
Stirred mixtures of chlorosulfonic acid (aka chlorosulfuric acid) and heptane or similar alkanes can cause a reaction liberating large volumes of hydrogen chloride, sulfur dioxide, and other gases.
Chem. and Eng. News (Dec. 11, 1989).

Hydrochloric Acid
Mixing chlorosulfonic acid and 36% hydrochloric acid in a closed container caused the temperature and pressure to increase.
Flynn and Rossow (1970). See Note under complete reference.

Hydrofluoric Acid
Mixing chlorosulfonic acid and 48.7% hydrofluoric acid in a closed container caused the temperature and pressure to increase.
Flynn and Rossow (1970). See Note under complete reference.

Hydrogen Peroxide
Permonosulfonic acid was being prepared by reacting chlorosulfonic acid and 90% hydrogen peroxide. A sam-

ple was stored over night at 0°C, then removed to a test tube rack. In ten minutes it exploded.
Chem. and Eng. News **33:** 3336 (1955).
See also PERMONOSULFURIC ACID plus Acetone.

Isoprene
See ISOPRENE plus Chlorosulfonic Acid.

Mesityl Oxide
See MESITYL OXIDE plus Chlorosulfonic acid.

Metallic Powders
See CHLOROSULFONIC ACID plus Organic Matter.

Methyl Ethyl Ketone
See METHYL ETHYL KETONE plus Chlorosulfonic Acid.

Nitric Acid
Mixing chlorosulfonic acid and 70% nitric acid in a closed container caused the temperature and pressure to increase.
Flynn and Rossow (1970). See Note under complete reference.

2-Nitropropane
Mixing chlorosulfonic acid and 2-nitropropane in a closed container caused the temperature pressure to increase.
Flynn and Rossow (1970). See Note under complete reference.

Organic Matter
This material is dangerous in contact with combustible materials, nitrates, chlorates, metallic powders, carbides, picrates and fulmi nates. It develops great heat in contact with water.

Chem. Safety Data Sheet **SD-33** (1949).

Phosphorus
See PHOSPHORUS plus Chlorosulfonic Acid.

Propiolactone (BETA-)
See PROPIOLACTONE (BETA-) plus Chlorosulfonic Acid.

Propylene Oxide
See PROPYLENE OXIDE plus Chlorosulfonic Acid.

Pyridine
See PYRIDINE plus Chlorosulfonic Acid.

Sodium Hydroxide
See SODIUM HYDROXIDE plus Chlorosulfonic Acid.

Styrene Monomer
See STYRENE MONOMER plus Chlorosulfonic Acid.

Sulfolane
See SULFOLANE plus Chlorosulfonic Acid.

Sulfuric Acid
Mixing chlorosulfonic acid and 96% sulfuric acid in a closed container caused the temperature and pressure to increase.
Flynn and Rossow (1970). See Note under complete reference.

Vinyl Acetate
See VINYL ACETATE plus Chlorosulfonic Acid.

Vinylidene Chloride
See VINYLIDENE CHLORIDE plus Chlorosulfonic Acid.

Water
See CHLOROSULFONIC ACID plus Organic Matter.

CHLOROTHION $(CH_3O)_2P(S)OC_6H_3ClNO_2$

(self-reactive)
When a sample was heated in a small test tube it decomposed and in a few minutes the residue exploded.
J.B. McPherson and G.A. Johnson, *Agri. Food Chem.* **4** (1): 42 (1956).

4-CHLORO-o-TOLUIDINE DIAZONIUM CHLORIDE SALT
$NH_2C_6H_3(Cl)CH_2N(\equiv N)Cl$

Sodium Bisulfide
See SODIUM SULFIDE plus Diazonium Salts and Diazonium Chloride Salts.

Sodium Polysulfide
See SODIUM SULFIDE plus Diazonium Salts and Diazonium Chloride Salts.

Sodium Sulfide
See SODIUM SULFIDE plus Diazonium Salts and Diazonium Chloride Salts.

CHLOROTRIFLUOROETHYLENE $ClFC=CF_2$

Bromine and Oxygen
Addition of bromine to a mixture of chlorotrifluoroethylene and oxygen causes an explosion. One of the products of the reaction is chlorotrifluoroethylene peroxide, which explodes when heated.
R.N. Haszeldine and F. Nyman, *J. Chem. Soc.* **1959:** 1084-1090 (1959).

Chlorine Trifluoride and Water
See CHLORINE TRIFLUORIDE plus Chlorotrifluoroethylene Polymer and Water.

CHLOROTRIFLUOROETHYLENE PEROXIDE
CF_2ClCOF

(self-reactive)
Chlorotrifluoroethylene peroxide explodes when heated.
R.N. Haszeldine and F. Nyman, *J. Chem. Soc.* **1959:** 1084-90 (1959).

CHLOROTRIFLUOROMETHANE $CClF_3$

Aluminum
See ALUMINUM plus Dichlorodifluoromethane.

CHLOROTRIMETHYLSILANE $(CH_3)_3SiCl$

Water
Trimethyl chlorosilane reacts violently with water yielding heat and white acid fumes.
Title 46 (1970).

CHROMATES

Hydrazine
Hydrazine is decomposed explosively by chromates and chromic anhydride.
Mellor **11:** 234 (1946-1947).

CHROMIC ANHYDRIDE CrO_3
(CHROMIC ACID, CHROMIUM VI OXIDE, CHROMIUM TRIOXIDE)

Acetic Acid
Acetic acid or acetic anhydride can explode with chromic acid if not kept cold.
Von Schwartz, p. 321 (1918).

Acetic Anhydride
During the preparation of chromyl acetate by the direct reaction of chromic anhydride on acetic anhydride without the use of diluting solvents, a violent explosion occurred.
J.G. Dawber, *Chem. & Ind.* **23:** 973 (Part I, 1964).
See also CHROMIC ANHYDRIDE plus Acetic Acid.

Acetic Anhydride and Acetic Acid
Acetic anhydride was gradually being titrated into a mixture of chromic anhydride and acetic acid in a 20-gallon, glass-lined tank. After 1½ hours of this procedure, the contents of the reactor exploded.
Doyle (1966).

Acetone
An attempt to purify acetone by refluxing with chromic anhydride led to an explosion and fire when the acetone was first brought into contact with the chromic anhydride.
Robert Delhez, *Chem. & Ind.*: 931 (Sept. 8, 1956).

Aluminum
See ALUMINUM plus Chromic Anhydride.

Ammonia
Ammonia gas decomposes the dry trioxide with incandescence at ordinary temperatures.
Mellor **11:** 161 (1946-1947).
Mellor **11:** 233 (1946-1947).

Anthracene
Anthracene will burst into flame on contact with chromic acid.
Douglas and Thompson (1949).

Arsenic
See ARSENIC plus Chromium Trioxide.

Benzene
Benzene ignites in contact with powdered chromic anhydride.
Mellor **11:** 235 (1946-1947).

Camphor
See CHROMIC ANHYDRIDE plus Naphthalene.

Chlorine Trifluoride
See CHLORINE TRIFLUORIDE plus Chromic Anhydride.

Chromous Sulfide
Ignition occurs when chromium trioxide comes in contact with a small proportion of chromium sulfide.
Mellor **11:** 430 (1946-1947).

Diethyl Ether
These compounds react violently at room temperature.
Mellor **11:** 235 (1946-1947).

Dimethyl Formamide
A violent reaction occurred when chromic anhydride was added rapidly or in large lumps to dimethyl formamide.
Chem. and Eng. News **48** (28): 4 (July 6, 1970).

Ethyl Alcohol
Chromic anhydride ignites ethyl alcohol.
Durrant, p. 990 (1962).

Glycerol
See CHROMIC ANHYDRIDE plus Naphthalene.

Hydrocarbons
Chromic anhydride ignites many hydrocarbons.
Campbell and Young, *Science* **104:** 353 (1946).

Hydrogen Sulfide
When hydrogen sulfide is passed over heated chromium trioxide, decomposition occurs with incandescence.
Mellor **11:** 232 (1946-1947).
See also CHROMIC ANHYDRIDE plus Naphthalene.

Methyl Alcohol
A laboratory preparation of hexa-aquochromic sulfate required the reduction of chromic anhydride by methyl alcohol. When the alcohol was contacted by the anhydride, an explosion and fire resulted.
Delhez (1967).

Naphthalene
Naphthalene, camphor, glycerol, or turpentine will react violently with chromic anhydride.
Haz. Chem. Data, p. 68 (1967).

Organic Matter
A container of 50 kilograms of chromic anhydride exploded when laid on the ground. The container may have been contaminated with an oxidizable substance.
Chem. Abst. **31:** 4010 (1937).

Phosphorus
See PHOSPHORUS plus Chromium Trioxide.

Potassium
See POTASSIUM plus Chromium Trioxide.

Potassium Ferricyanide
While these two compounds were being mixed, an explosion occurred when the dust was ignited by a spark.
Mich. Occ. Health **7:** No. 2, p. 2 (Winter 1962).

Pyridine
During the preparation of a chromium trioxide-pyridine complex, the proportion of the trioxide was increased. Since the trioxide dis solves in the pyridine by swelling, then rapidly dissolving with evo lution of heat, the excessive amount of chromium trioxide produced overheating, which resulted in an explosion and fire.
MCA Case History **1284** (1967).

Selenium
See SELENIUM plus Chromium Trioxide.

Sodium
See SODIUM plus Chromium Trioxide.

Sodium Amide
See SODIUM AMIDE plus Chromic Anhydride.

Sulfur
See SULFUR plus Chromic Anhydride.

Turpentine
See CHROMIC ANHYDRIDE plus Naphthalene.

CHROMIC-HEXAMMINE NITRATE $[Cr(NH_3)_6](NO_3)_3$

(self-reactive)
Hexammine chromium nitrate explodes at 265°C and is impact sensitive.
W.R. Tomlinson, Jr., and L.F. Audrieth, *J. Chem. Edu.* **27:** 606-609 (1950).

CHROMIUM Cr

Ammonium Nitrate
See AMMONIUM NITRATE plus Metals (powdered).

Hydrogen Peroxide
See IRON plus Hydrogen Peroxide.

Lithium
See LITHIUM plus Vanadium.

Nitric Oxide
Pyrophoric chromium unites with nitric oxide with incandescence.
Mellor **11:** 162 (1946-1947).

Potassium Chlorate
Chromium is attacked vigorously by fused potassium chlorate, producing vivid incandescence.
Mellor **11:** 163 (1946-1947).

Sulfur Dioxide
Pyrophoric chromium unites with sulfur dioxide with incandescence.
Mellor **11:** 161 (1946-1947).

CHROMIUM-AMMINE NITRATES

(self-reactive)
Chromium-ammine nitrates may be impact-sensitive: $Cr(NH_3)_5NO_2(NO_3)_2$ detonates when heated.
Mellor **11:** 477 (1946-1947).

CHROMIUM-AMMINE PERCHLORATES

(self-reactive)
Chromium-ammine perchlorates may be impact-sensitive.
Mellor **11:** 477 (1946-1947).

CHROMIUM OXIDE Cr_2O_3
(CHROMIC OXIDE, CHROMIUM III OXIDE, CHROMIUM SESQUIOXIDE)

Chlorine Trifluoride
See CHLORINE TRIFLUORIDE plus Chromic Oxide.

Glycerol
Contact between the two may produce an explosion.
Merck Index, 7th Ed., p. 489 (1960). *Pieters,* p. 30 (1957).

Lithium
See LITHIUM plus Chromic Oxide.

Oxygen Difluoride
See OXYGEN DIFLUORIDE plus Aluminum Chloride.

CHROMIUM TETRACHLORIDE $CrCl_4$

Potassium
See POTASSIUM plus Aluminum Bromide.

Sodium
See SODIUM plus Chromium Tetrachloride.

CHROMIUM TRIAMMINOTETROXIDE $Cr(NH_3)_3O_4$

(self-reactive)
Chromium triamminotetroxide detonates and becomes incandescent when heated.
Mellor **11:** (1946-1947).

CHROMIUM TRICHLORIDE $CrCl_3$

Lithium
See LITHIUM plus Chromium Trichloride.

CHROMIUM TRIFLUORIDE CrF_3

Potassium
See POTASSIUM plus Ammonium Bromide.

CHROMOUS OXIDE CrO

Air
Chromous monoxide is spontaneously flammable in air.
Ellern (1968).

CHROMOUS SULFIDE CrS

Chromic Anhydride
See CHROMIC ANHYDRIDE plus Chromous Sulfide.

Fluorine
See FLUORINE plus Chromous Sulfide.

CHROMYL CHLORIDE CrO_2Cl_2

Acetone
Alcohol, ether and acetone react with chromyl chloride with incandescence. Turpentine is ignited by chromyl chloride.
Mellor **11:** 396 (1946-1947).

Ammonia
Chromyl chloride causes ammonia and ethyl alcohol to ignite.
Durrant, p. 991 (1962).

Chlorine and Carbon
See CHLORINE plus Chromyl Chloride and Carbon.

Diethyl Ether
See CHROMYL CHLORIDE plus Acetone.

Ethyl Alcohol
See CHROMYL CHLORIDE plus Ammonia.

Fluorine
See FLUORINE plus Chromyl Chloride.

Phosphorus
See PHOSPHORUS plus Chromyl Chloride.

Phosphorus Trichloride
Each drop of chromyl chloride added to well-cooled phosphorus trichloride produces a hissing noise, incandescence, and sometimes an explosion.
Mellor **11:** 395 (1946-1947).

Sodium Azide
See SODIUM AZIDE plus Chromyl Chloride.

Sulfur
See SULFUR plus Chromyl Chloride.

Sulfur Monochloride
If chromyl chloride vapor is passed through a narrow jet into the vapor of sulfur monochloride, vivid combustion occurs.
Mellor **11:** 394 (1946-1947).

Turpentine
See CHROMYL CHLORIDE plus Acetone.

COBALT Co

Acetylene
Pyrophoric cobalt decomposes acetylene in the cold and the metal becomes incandescent.
Mellor **14:** 513 (1946-1947).

Air
Pyrophoric cobalt, a black powder, burns brilliantly when exposed to air.
Mellor **14:** 453 (1946-1947).

Ammonium Nitrate
See AMMONIUM NITRATE plus Metals (powdered).

COBALT-HEXAMMINE CHLORATE $Co(NH_3)_6(ClO_3)_2$

(self-reactive)
This compound detonates when struck.
Mellor **2, Supp. 1:** 592 (1956).

COBALT-HEXAMMINE CHLORITE $Co(NH_3)_6ClO_23H_2O$

(self-reactive)
Hexamminocobaltic chlorite contains an explosive combination of ions.
Mellor **2, Supp. 1:** 575 (1956).
Cobalt ammine azides explode violently on impact.
Mellor **8, Supp. 2:** 48 (1967).

COBALT-HEXAMMINE PERCHLORATE
$Co(NH_3)_6(ClO_4)_2$

(self-reactive)
This compound detonates when struck but is less sensitive than hexamminocobalt chlorate.
Mellor **2, Supp. 1:** 592 (1956).

COBALT NITRIDE CoN

Air
Cobalt nitride is spontaneously flammable in air.
Brauer (1965).
Mellor **8, Supp. 1:** 238 (1964).

COBALT-PENTAMMINE AZIDE PERCHLORATE
$[Co(NH_3)_5N_3](ClO_4)_2$

Phenyl Isocyanate and Nitrosyl Perchlorate
See PHENYL ISOCYANATE plus Cobalt Pentammine Triazo Perchlorate and Nitrosyl Perchlorate.

COBALT-PENTAMMINE HYPOPHOSPHITE PERCHLORATE $[Co(NH_3)_5]H_2PO_2(ClO_4)_2$

(self-reactive)
When a chemist touched a platinum wire (temperature uncertain) into the freshly prepared chemical to make a flame test, the preparation exploded.
Serious Acc. Series **253** (1965).

COBALTIC DIHYDROPHOSPHIDE $Co(PH_2)_3$

Air
Cobalt triphosphine is spontaneously flammable in air.
J. Zehr, *Staub* **22** (11): 494-508 (1962).

COBALTIC FLUORIDE CoF_3

Silicon
See SILICON plus Colbatic Fluoride.

COBALTIC-HEXAMMINE IODATE $[Co(NH_3)_6](IO_3)_3$

(self-reactive)
Hexammine cobalt iodate explodes at 355°C and is impact sensi tive.
W. R. Tomlinson, Jr. and L. F. Audrieth,
J. Chem. Edu. **27:** 606-609 (1950).

COBALTIC-HEXAMMINE PERCHLORATE
$[Co(NH_3)_6](ClO_4)_3$

(self-reactive)
Hexammine cobalt perchlorate explodes at 360°C and is impact sensitive.
W. R. Tomlinson, Jr. and L. F. Audrieth,
J. Chem. Edu. **27:** 606-609 (1950).

COBALTIC-PENTAMMINE AZIDE $CoN_3(NH_3)_5(N_3)_2$

(self-reactive)
Cobalt ammine azide exploded violently on impact.
Mellor **8, Supp. 4:** 48 (1967).

COBALTIC-PENTAMMINE CHLORITE
$Co(NH_3)_5Cl(ClO_2)_2$

(self-reactive)
Pentamminochlorocobaltic chlorite contains an explosive combination of ions.
Mellor **2, Supp. 1:** 575 (1956).

COBALTOUS BROMIDE $CoBr_2$

Potassium
See POTASSIUM plus Boron Tribromide.

Sodium
See SODIUM plus Cobaltous Bromide.

COBALTOUS CHLORIDE $CoCl_2$

Potassium
See POTASSIUM plus Boron Tribromide.

Sodium
See SODIUM plus Cobaltous Bromide.

COBALTOUS CYANIDE $Co(CN)_2$

Magnesium
See MAGNESIUM plus Cadmium Cyanide.

COBALTOUS HYPOPHOSPHITE $CO(PH_2O_2)_2$

(self-reactive)
Cobaltous hypophosphite liberates spontaneously flammable phosphine above 150°C.
Mellor **8:** 889 (1946-1947).

COBALTOUS-PENTAMMINE CHLORO-PERCHLORATE
$[Co(NH_3)_5Cl]ClO_4$

(self-reactive)
Cobaltous-pentammine chloro-perchlorate explodes at 320°C and is impact sensitive.
J. Chem. Educ. **27:** 606-609 (1950).

COBALTOUS-PENTAMMINE NITRITO-N NITRATE
$[Co(NH_3)_5NO_2]NO_3$

(self-reactive)
Nitropentammine cobalt nitrate explodes at 310°C and is impact sensitive.
W. R. Tomlinson, Jr. and L. F. Audrieth, *J. Chem. Edu.* **27:** 606-609 (1950).

COBALTOUS-TRIHYDRAZINE CHLORATE
$CO(N_2H_4)_3(ClO_3)_2$

(self-reactive)
This compound detonates when struck.
Mellor **2, Supp. 1:** 592 (1956).

COKE

Fluorine
See FLUORINE plus Common Materials and Oxygen.

COPPER Cu

Acetylene
Unstable acetylides form when acetylene is passed over copper that has been heated enough to form a tarnish of oxide coating. In the presence of wet acetylene and ammonia, copper and brasses down to 60 percent copper react readily to form explosive acetylides.
Brameld, Clark and Seyfond, *J. Soc. Chem. Ind.* **66:** 346-53 (1947). G. Benson, *Comp. Gas Bull.* 1950-83. *Miller,* pp. 484-6 (1965). *Rutledge,* p. 84 (1968).

Ammonium Nitrate
See AMMONIUM NITRATE plus Metals (powdered).
Mellor **8, Supp. 1:** 546 (1964).

Barium Bromate
See COPPER plus Bromates.

Barium Chlorate
See COPPER plus Bromates.

Barium Iodate
See COPPER plus Bromates.

Bromates
A combination of finely divided copper with finely divided bromates (also chlorates or iodates) of barium, calcium, magnesium, potassium, sodium, or zinc will explode with heat, percussion, and sometimes light friction.
Mellor **2:** 310 (1946-1947).

Calcium Bromate
See COPPER plus Bromates.

Calcium Chlorate
See COPPER plus Bromates.

Calcium Iodate
See COPPER plus Bromates.

Chlorates
See COPPER plus Bromates.

Chlorine
Copper foil burns spontaneously in gaseous chlorine.
Mellor **2:** 92, 95 (1946-1947). *Mellor* **9:** 626 (1946-1947).
Copper reacts vigorously with chlorine at around 320° C.
Mellor **2, Supp. 1:** 380 (1956).

Chlorine and Oxygen Difluoride
See CHLORINE plus Oxygen Difluoride.

Chlorine Trifluoride
See ALUMINUM plus Chlorine Trifluoride.

Ethylene Oxide
Copper and other acetylide-forming metals should not be used in process equipment handling ethylene oxide because of the danger of the possible presence of acetylene. See COPPER plus Acetylene.
L. G. Hess and V. V. Tilton, *Ind. Eng. Chem.* **42:** 1251-8 (1950).

Fluorine
See FLUORINE plus Copper. See also FLUORINE plus Metals.

Hydrazine Mononitrate
See ZINC plus Hydrazine Mononitrate.

Hydrazoic Acid
Explosions resulted from corrosion of brass parts of a vacuum gage and water jet vacuum pump on prolonged contact with hydrozoic acid vapors.
Chem. & Ind. **10,** p. 444 (1973).

Hydrochloric Acid
A reaction occurred at a slow rate that released hydrogen which built up pressure in a closed system resulting in an explosion of a glass container.
Chem. and Eng. News, p. 4, (July 29, 1991); and p. 2, (Sept. 16, 1991).

Hydrogen Peroxide
See IRON plus Hydrogen Peroxide.

Hydrogen Sulfide
If a mixture of air and hydrogen sulfide is passed over powdered copper, the mixture may heat to redness.
Mellor **10:** 140 (1946-1947).

Iodates
See COPPER plus Bromates.

Lead Azide
Lead azide, when in contact with copper, zinc, or alloys containing copper or zinc, forms, over a period of time, the extremely sensitive copper and zinc azides which on slight disturbance can set off the main body of lead azide.
Federoff **1:** A532, A551 (1960).
Mustaparta (1966).

Magnesium Bromate
See COPPER plus Bromates.

Magnesium Chlorate
See COPPER plus Bromates.

Magnesium Iodate
See COPPER plus Bromates.

Phosphorus
The reacting mass formed by the mixture of phosphorus and copper, iron, nickel, or platinum can become incandescent when heated.
Mellor **8, Supp. 3:** 228 (1971).

Potassium Bromate
See COPPER plus Bromates.

Potassium Chlorate
See COPPER plus Bromates.

Potassium Iodate
See COPPER plus Bromates.

Potassium Peroxide
See POTASSIUM plus Potassium Peroxide and POTASSIUM plus Potassium Tetroxide.

Sodium Azide
See SODIUM AZIDE plus Copper.

Sodium Bromate
See COPPER plus Bromates.

Sodium Chlorate
See COPPER plus Bromates.

Sodium Iodate
See COPPER plus Bromates.

Sodium Peroxide
Sodium peroxide oxidizes copper with incandescence.
Mellor **2:** 490-93 (1946-1947).

Sulfur and Chlorates
See SULFUR plus Chlorates and Copper.

Zinc Bromate
See COPPER plus Bromates.

Zinc Chlorate
See COPPER plus Bromates.

Zinc Iodate
See COPPER plus Bromates.

COPPER OXYCHLORIDE Cu_2OCl_2

Potassium
See POTASSIUM plus Boric Acid.

COPPER SALTS

Acetylene
Many copper salts form dangerous acetylides. The copper acetylides formed in ammoniacal or caustic solutions with cupric salts and acetylene are more explosive than those derived from cuprous salts.
Brameld, Clark and Seyfond, *J. Soc. Chem. Ind.* **66:** 346-53 (1947). G. Benson, *Comp. Gas Bull.* 1950-83. *Miller,* pp. 484-6 (1965).

Hydrazine
Copper salts promote the decomposition of hydrazine.
Chem. and Eng. News **48** (48): 97 (Nov. 16, 1970). See also CUPRIC OXIDE plus Hydrazine.

Nitromethane
Nitromethane and salts of copper, silver, gold or mercury spontaneously form explosive materials.
Chem. and Eng. News **49** (23): 6 (1971).

CREOSOTE OIL

Chlorosulfonic Acid
See CHLOROSULFURIC ACID plus Creosote Oil.

CRESOL $CH_3C_6H_4OH$

Chlorosulfonic Acid
Mixing cresol and chlorosulfonic acid in a closed container caused the temperature and pressure to increase.
Flynn and Rossow (1970). See Note under complete reference.

Nitric Acid
Mixing cresol and 70% nitric acid in a closed container caused the temperature and pressure to increase.
Flynn and Rossow (1970). See Note under complete reference.

Oleum
Mixing cresol and oleum in a closed container caused the temperature and pressure to increase.
Flynn and Rossow (1970). See Note under complete reference.

CROTONALDEHYDE $CH_3CH=CHCHO$

Butadiene-1,3
See BUTADIENE-1,3 plus Crotonaldehyde.

CUMENE $C_6H_5CH(CH_3)_2$

Chlorosulfonic Acid
Mixing Cumene and chlorosulfonic acid in a closed container caused the temperature and pressure to increase.
Flynn and Rossow (1970). See Note under complete reference.

Nitric Acid
Mixing cumene and 70% nitric acid in a closed container caused the temperature and pressure to increase.
Flynn and Rossow (1970). See Note under complete reference.

Oleum
Mixing cumene and oleum in a closed container caused the temper ature and pressure to increase.
Flynn and Rossow (1970). See Note under complete reference.

CUMENE HYDROPEROXIDE $C_6H_5C(CH_3)_2OOH$

Contaminants may catalyze decomposition at lower temperatures.
Chem. and Eng. News (May 31, 1993).

(self-reactive)
At concentrations of 91 and 95%, cumene hydroperoxide decomposed violently at about 150°C.
A. Le Roux, *Mem. Poudres* **37:** 49-58 (1955).

Sodium Iodide
See SODIUM IODIDE plus Cumene Hydroperoxide.

CUPRIC AZIDE $CU(N_3)_2$

(self-reactive)
Spontaneous explosions have been observed with this compound.
Mellor **8, Supp. 2:** 50 (1967).
See SODIUM AZIDE plus Copper.

CUPRIC BROMIDE $CuBr_2$

Potassium
See POTASSIUM plus Aluminum Bromide.

CUPRIC CHLORIDE $CuCl_2$

Potassium
See POTASSIUM plus Aluminum Bromide.

Sodium
See SODIUM plus Aluminum Bromide.

CUPRIC CHLORITE $Cu(ClO_2)_2$

(self-reactive)
Cupric chlorite explodes violently on percussion. In the dry state it decomposes within 12 days.
Mellor **2, Supp. 1:** 574 (1956).

CUPRIC-DIHYDRAZINE CHLORATE $Cu(H_2NNH_2)_2ClO_3$

(self-reactive)
This is an extremely explosive salt and will detonate on drying.
Mellor **8, Supp. 2:** 88 (1967).
Mellor **2, Supp. 1:** 592 (1956).

CUPRIC HYPOPHOSPHITE $Cu(PH_2O_2)_2$

(self-reactive)
Cupric hypophosphite forms impact-sensitive ammunition-priming mixtures.
Mellor **8, Supp. 3:** 623 (1971).
Cupric hypophosphite explodes suddenly at about 90°C.
Mellor **8:** 883 (1946-1947).

CUPRIC NITRATE $Cu(NO_3)_2$

Paper
On prolonged contact with cupric nitrate in the presence of moisture paper will ignite spontaneously.
Ellern, p. 46 (1968).

Potassium Ferrocyanide
A finely ground mixture of potassium ferrocyanide and cupric nitrate when dried at 220°C exploded within a few minutes.
Chem. Abst. **77:** 13431f (1972).

Tin
See TIN plus Cupric Nitrate.

CUPRIC NITRIDE Cu_3N_2

Nitric Acid
Concentrated nitric acid plus cupric nitride explodes with great violence.
Mellor **8:** 100 (1946-1947).

CUPRIC OXIDE CuO

Aluminum
See ALUMINUM plus Copper Oxide.

Boron
See BORON plus Cupric Oxide.

Cesium Acetylene Carbide
See CESIUM ACETYLENE CARBIDE plus Cupric Oxide.

Hydrazine
Hydrazine reacts vigorously with cupric oxide.
Mellor **3:** 137 (1946-1947).

Magnesium
See MAGNESIUM plus Cupric Oxide.

Phospham
See PHOSPHAM plus Cupric Oxide.

Potassium
See POTASSIUM plus Cupric Oxide.

Rubidium Acetylene Carbide
See RUBIDIUM ACETYLENE CARBIDE plus Cupric Oxide.

Sodium
See SODIUM plus Cupric Oxide.

Titanium
See TITANIUM plus Cupric Oxide.

Zirconium
See ZIRCONIUM plus Cupric Oxide.

CUPRIC PHOSPHIDE Cu_3P_2

Potassium Chlorate
When copper phosphide is mixed with oxidizing agents, such as potassium chlorate, it explodes on impact.
Mellor **8:** 839 (1946-1947).

Potassium Nitrate
When copper phosphide is mixed with potassium nitrate and heated, an explosion occurs.
Mellor **8:** 839 (1946-1947).

Water
On contact with water, copper phosphide yields phosphine, which is spontaneously flammable.
Schwab (1970).

CUPRIC SALTS

Sodium Hypobromite
See SODIUM HYPOBROMITE plus Cupric Salts.

CUPRIC SULFATE $CuSO_4$

Hydroxylamine
Anhydrous copper sulfate causes hydroxylamine to ignite and the hydrated salt is vigorously reduced.
Mellor **8:** 292 (1946-1947).

Magnesium
See MAGNESIUM plus Cupric Sulfate.

CUPRIC SULFIDE CuS

Cadmium Chlorate
Copper sulfide explodes on contact with a concentrated solution of chloric acid or chlorates of cadmium, magnesium, or zinc.
Mellor **Supp. II, Part I:** 584 (1956).

Chlorates
See COPPER SULFIDE plus Cadmium Chlorate.

Chloric Acid
See COPPER SULFIDE plus Cadmium Chlorate.

Hydrogen Peroxide
See ANTIMONY TRISULFIDE plus Hydrogen Peroxide.

Magnesium, Ammonium Nitrate, Potassium Chlorate and Water
See MAGNESIUM plus Copper Sulfate (anhydrous), Ammonium Nitrate, Potassium Chlorate and Water.

Magnesium Chlorate
See COPPER SULFIDE plus Cadmium Chlorate.

Zinc Chlorate
See COPPER SULFIDE plus Cadmium Chlorate.

CUPRIC-TETRAMMINE CHLORATE $Cu(NH_3)_4(ClO_3)_2$

(self-reactive)
This compound will detonate when struck.
Mellor **2, Supp. 1:** 592 (1956).

CUPRIC-TETRAMMINE PERCHLORATE $Cu(NH_3)_4(ClO_4)_2$

(self-reactive)
This compound will detonate when struck but is less sensitive than tetramminocupric chlorate.
Mellor **2, Supp. 1:** 592 (1956).

CUPROUS AZIDE CuN_3

(self-reactive)
Cuprous azide decomposes at 205°C. It is explosively unstable.
Mellor **8, Supp. 2:** 43 (1967).

CUPROUS BROMIDE CuBr

Potassium
See POTASSIUM plus Aluminum Bromide.

CUPROUS CARBIDE Cu_2C_2

(self-reactive)
Cuprous acetylide is explosive and can be detonated by percussion or when heated above 100°C.
Mellor **5:** 851, 852 (1946-1947). *Rutledge,* p. 84 (1968).

Acetylene
If warmed in air or oxygen for several hours, it explodes when brought in contact with acetylene.
Mellor **5:** 851, 852 (1946-1947).

Bromine
See BROMINE plus Cuprous Acetylide.

Chlorine
See BROMINE plus Cuprous Acetylide.

Iodine
See BROMINE plus Cuprous Acetylide.

Silver Nitrate
Cuprous acetylide and silver nitrate give off an explosive mixture.
Mellor **5:** 853 (1946-1947). J. K. Luchs, *Photo. Sci. Eng.* **10** (6): 334-7 (1966).

CUPROUS CHLORIDE CuCl
Potassium
See POTASSIUM plus Aluminum Bromide.

CUPROUS CYANIDE CuCN
Magnesium
See MAGNESIUM plus Cadmium Cyanide.

CUPROUS HYDRIDE Cu_2H_2

Air
Dry copper hydride is spontaneously flammable in air.
Von Schwartz, p. 156 (1964).

Bromine
See BROMINE plus Copper Hydride.

Chlorine
See BROMINE plus Copper Hydride.

Fluorine
See BROMINE plus Copper Hydride.

CUPROUS IODIDE CuI
Potassium
See POTASSIUM plus Aluminum Bromide.

CUPROUS NITRIDE Cu_3N

Nitric Acid
See CUPRIC NITRIDE plus Nitric Acid.
See CUPROUS NITRIDE plus Sulfuric Acid.

Sulfuric Acid
The reaction of cuprous nitride and sulfuric or nitric acid is violent.
Mellor **8, Supp. 1:** 154 (1964).

CUPROUS TETRAHYDROALUMINATE $CuAlH_4$

Air
Copper aluminohydride is spontaneously flammable in air.
J. Aubrey and G. Monnier, *Comp. Rend.* **238:** 2534-2535 (1954).

CYANIDES
(See also specific cyanides as primary entries or under other reactants)

Chlorates
Violent explosion occurs if cyanide salt is melted with nitrite salt. The melt explodes if cyanide plus chlorate or nitrite is heated to 450°C.
Von Schwartz, pp. 299, 327 (1918).
Also see ANTIMONY SULFIDE plus Chlorates.

Fluorine
See FLUORINE plus Chlorides.

Magnesium
See MAGNESIUM plus Cadmium Cyanide.

Nitrates
See NITRATES plus Cyanides.

Nitric Acid
See NITRIC ACID plus Cyanides.

Nitrites
See CYANIDES plus Chlorates.
See NITRITES plus Potassium Cyanide.

CYANOACETIC ACID $NCCH_2COOH$

Furfuryl Alcohol
See FURFURYL ALCOHOL plus Cyanoacetic Acid.

CYANOACETYL CHLORIDE $NCCH_2COCl$

(self-reactive)
Cyanoacetyl chloride was prepared from cyanoacetic acid and phos phorus pentachloride. Following distillation of the volatile material, the crude cyanoacetyl chloride was

placed in a hood in a stoppered, 1-liter flask. About 24 hours later the flask exploded.
Wischmeyer (1967).

CYANODIMETHYLARSINE $(CH_3)AsCN$

Air
Dimethylcyanoarsine is spontaneously flammable in air.
Ripley (1966).

2-CYANOETHANOL $HOCH_2CH_2CN$

Sulfuric Acid
Concentrated sulfuric acid reacts violently with both ethylene cyanohydrin and epichlorohydrin.
Confidential information furnished to NFPA.

CYANOGEN NCCN

Fluorine
See FLUORINE plus Cyanogen.

Oxygen
See OXYGEN (LIQUID) plus Cyanogen.

CYANOGEN AZIDE NCNNN

(self-reactive)
Cyanogen azide explodes when shocked mechanically or thermally.
Chem. and Eng. News **43** (52): 29, 30 (Dec. 27, 1965).

CYANOGEN IODIDE NCI

Phosphorus
See PHOSPHORUS plus Cyanogen Iodide.

CYANURIC CHLORIDE N=CClN=CClN=CCl (ring)

Dimethyl Sulfoxide
See DIMETHYL SULFOXIDE plus Acyl Halides.

Water
Cyanuric chloride acts autocatalytically with water at a temperature of about 30°C to produce cyanuric acid, hydrochloric acid and heat. An explosion occurred during an industrial process in which cyanuric chloride and water were mixed. The refrigeration had been turned off. Pressure built up in the reactor and blew gaskets, allowing flammable vapors to fill the building. The explosion occurred when the vapors were ignited.
MCA Case History **1869** (1972).

CYCLOHEXANE C_6H_{12}

Nitrogen Dioxide
Through an error, liquid nitrogen dioxide instead of gaseous was fed into a nitration column containing hot cyclohexane. An explosion resulted.
MCA Case History **128** (1962).

CYCLOHEXANOL $C_6H_{11}OH$

Nitric Acid
See NITRIC ACID plus Cyclohexanol.

CYCLOHEXANONE $CO(CH_2)_4CH_2$ (ring)

Nitric Acid
See NITRIC ACID plus Cyclohexanone.

CYCLOPENTADIENYLCHROMIUM DINITROSYL DIMER $[C_5H_5(NO)_2Cr]_2$

(self-reactive)
A glass vial of the dimer in the sample compartment of a laser Raman spectrophotometer exploded on excitation by the helium-neon beam.
Chem. & Ind. No. **7:** 201 (1969). R. B. King and M. B. Bisnette, *Inorg. Chem.* **3:** 79 (1964).

DECABORANE (14) $B_{10}H_{14}$

Oxygen
See OXYGEN plus Decaborane.

DEXTROSE $C_6H_{12}O_6$

Sodium Peroxide and Potassium Nitrate
See SODIUM PEROXIDE plus Dextrose and Potassium Nitrate.

DIACETYL PEROXIDE $(CH_3CO)_2O_2$

(self-reactive)
Acetyl peroxide is unpredictable. Five grains of it being removed from an ice chest detonated violently.
Chem. and Eng. News **26:** 3197 (1948).
Pure diacetyl peroxide is a severe explosion hazard.
Cond. Chem. Dict. **10:** (1971).
See also HYDROGEN PEROXIDE plus Acetic Anhydride.

Diethyl Ether
Solid acetyl peroxide in contact with ether or any volatile solvent may explode violently. A 5-gram portion in ether detonated while being carried.
L. P. Kuhn, *Chem. and Eng. News* **26:** 3197 (1948); E.S. Shanley, Chem. and Eng. News **27:** 175 (1949).

Organic Materials
See ACETYL PEROXIDE plus Solvents.

Solvents
Acetyl peroxide is extremely shock-sensitive. When a solution of acetyl peroxide in any volatile solvent is evaporated, the concentration may become high enough for spontaneous explosions. Acetyl peroxide is a powerful oxidizing agent; it may cause ignition of organic materials on contact.
Chem. and Eng. News **26:** 3197 (1948). *Chem. and Eng. News* **27:** 175 (1949).

DIALKYLPHOSPHINES

Chlorine
See CHLORINE plus Alkylphosphines.

DIALLYL METHYL CARBINOL $(CH_2=CHCH_2)_2C(OH)CH_3$

Ozone and Acetic Acid
During the preparation of β-hydroxy-β-methyl glutaric acid using 75 grams of diallyl methyl carbinol, the material had been ozonized and allowed to stand overnight. Glacial acetic acid had been added and the mixture was being concentrated under vacuum in a desiccator. After 1½ hours the mixture exploded. Previous preparations using 12.6 grams were successful.
Chem. and Eng. News. **51** (6): 29 (Feb. 5, 1973).

DIALLYL PHOSPHITE $(C_3H_5O)_2POH$

(self-reactive)
Diallyl phosphite is made from allyl alcohol and phosphorus trichloride. When the product is distilled in vacuo in a carbon dioxide stream, explosions usually occur after about two-thirds is distilled.
Zh. Obshch. Khim. **21:** 658-62 (1951).

DIAMIDOPHOSPHOROUS ACID $POH(NH_2)_2$

Water
This material dissolves in water with such violence that the mass becomes incandescent.
Mellor **8:** 704 (1946-1947).

DI-o-AZIDOBENZOYL PEROXIDE $[C_6H_4(N_3)CO]_2O_2$

(self-reactive)
A 2-gram sample of the crystalline material on a sintered glass funnel detonated "with extreme violence" when touched with a metal spatula. A build-up of static charge on the sintered glass may have initiated the decomposition.
Chem. and Eng. News **41** (48): 45; **41** (52): 5 (1963).

1,3-DIAZIDOPROPENE $N_3CH=CHCH_2N_3$

(self-reactive)
In the determination of the weight of a sample of 1,3-diazidopropene, a violent explosion occurred.
J. H. Bover and F. C. Canter, *Chem. Reviews* **54:** 32, 33 (1954).

DIAZOCYCLOPENTADIENE $NN=CCH=CHCH=CH$

(self-reactive)
Diazocyclopentadiene should be handled cautiously since during one preparation a violent explosion took place after distillation.
F. Ranairez and S. Levy, *J. Org. Chem.* **23:** 2036-7 (1958).

DIAZOMALONIC ACID $(HOCO)_2C=NN$

(self-reactive)
Six grams of impure diazomalonic acid was being distilled under 3 millimeters pressure in a 50 milliliter flask. After three minutes of heating, during which no product was obtained, the flask exploded.
NSC Newsletter, Campus Safety **3** (1973).

DIAZOMETHANE $NN=CH_2$

(self-reactive)
Diazomethane will undergo violent thermal decomposition. Above 200°C, the vapor may explode violently. Explosions at low temperatures can occur if traces of organic matter are present.
J. Phys. Chem. **35:** 1493 (1931).

Organic Matter
See DIAZOMETHANE (self-reactive).

DIAZONIUM CHLORIDE SALTS

Sodium Sulfide
See SODIUM SULFIDE plus Diazonium Salts and Diazonium Chloride Salts.

DIAZONIUM PERCHLORATES

(self-reactive)
Diazonium perchlorates are particularly hazardous, being exploded by the slightest shock when dry.
Berichte **39:** 3146-8 (1906). *German Pat.* 258,679 (Apr. 27, 1911). *ACS* **146:** 213.

DIAZONIUM SALTS

Sodium Bisulfide
See DIAZONIUM SALTS plus Thiophenates.

Sodium Sulfide
See SODIUM SULFIDE plus Diazonium Salts and Diazonium Chloride Salts.
See DIAZONIUM SALTS plus Thiophenates.

Thiophenates
This reaction is often quoted as a route to diaryl sulfides without mention of explosive hazards. Unstable p-chlorodiazobenzene thiophenyl ether has been prepared by this route. Two reactions of this type were attempted and in both cases explosive compounds were produced. Also, reported explosions from reactions of diazonium salts with xanthates, sodium bisulfide, and sodium sulfide are attributed to formation of diazo ethers or related compounds.
BCISC **40** (158): 17-18 (1969).

Xanthates
See DIAZONIUM SALTS plus Thiophenates.

DIBENZOYL PEROXIDE $(C_6H_5CO)_2O_2$

N,N-Dimethylaniline
Explosive decomposition occurred when finely ground benzoyl per oxide was allowed to react with N,N-dimethylaniline by breaking an ampoule containing 0.5 grams of dimethylaniline in an auto clave.
L. Horner and C. Betzel, *Chem. Ber.* **86:** 1071-72 (1953).

Lithium Aluminum Hydride
An attempted reduction of benzoyl peroxide with lithium aluminum hydride resulted in an explosion.
D.A. Sutton, *Chem. & Ind.* **1951:** 272 (1951).

DIBENZYL CHLOROPHOSPHONATE $(C_6H_5CH_2O)_2POCl$

(self-reactive)
Dibenzylchlorophosphonate can decompose violently during vacuum distillation.
Chem. and Eng. News **28:** 3452 (Oct. 2, 1950).
J. Chem. Soc. 1106-10 (1948).

DIBENZYL PHOSPHITE $(C_6H_5CH_2O)_2PHO$

(self-reactive)
Dibenzyl phosphite can decompose violently during vacuum distillation.
Chem. and Eng. News **28:** 3452 (Oct. 2, 1950).
J. Chem. Soc. **385** (1945).

DIBORANE $BH_2(H_2)BH_2$

Aluminum
See ALUMINUM plus Diborane.

Carbon Tetrachloride
See CARBON TETRACHLORIDE plus Diborane.

Chlorine
See CHLORINE plus Diborane.

Halogenated Hydrocarbons
Diborane reacts violently with halogenated hydrocarbons (as in vaporizing liquid fire extinguishing agents).
Haz. Chem. Data (1966).

Nitric Acid
See NITRIC ACID plus Diborane.

Nitrogen Trifluoride
See NITROGEN TRIFLUORIDE plus Diborane.

Oxygen
See OXYGEN plus Diborane.

Phosphorus Trifluoride
See PHOSPHORUS TRIFLUORIDE plus Diborane.

Water
Diborane ignites spontaneously in moist air.
Haz. Chem. Data (1966). E. L. Poling and H. P. Simons, *Ind. Eng. Chem.* **50:** 1695-1698 (1958). P. L. Sampl and H. P. Simons, *Ind. Eng. Chem.* **50:** 1699-1702 (1958).

2,6-DIBROMO-p-BENZOQUINONE-4-CHLORIMINE
$O=C_6H_2Br_2=NCL$

(self-reactive)
While thin layer chromatograms were being dried with a hot-air dryer, a 25-gram bottle of 2,6-dibromo-p-benzoquinone-4-chlorimine, one to two feet away, exploded.
Chem. & Ind. **37:** 1551 (1967).

DIBROMOBORYL-PHOSPHINE Br_2BPH_2

Air
Dibromoborine phosphine is spontaneously flammable in air.
Douda (1966).

2,6-DIBROMO-N-CHLOROBENZOQUINONIMINE
$OC_6H_2(Br)_2NCl$

(self-reactive)
This chromatographic reagent can decompose violently under readily obtainable laboratory conditions. After a small quantity exploded on a laboratory reagent shelf, tests were made on one- half-gram quantities in a thermal stability bomb. When the temperature was raised gradually to 120°C, a violent exothermic reaction raised the pressure to 1,800 psi and burst the rupture diaphragm. A second sample held at 60°C decomposed similarly after 3 hours. Tests on the chlorocompound 2,6-DICHLOROQUINONECHLORIMIDE showed similar, but less severe instability.
Chem. and Eng. News **45** (50):54 (Dec. 11, 1967).
Chem. & Ind. **37:** 1551 (Sept. 1967).

DIBROMOMALONONITRILE $CBr_2(CN)_2$

Sodium Azide
See SODIUM AZIDE plus Dibromomalononitrile.

DIBROMOTRIMETHYLALUMINUM $(CH_3)_3AlBr_2$

Air
Trimethyl aluminum bromide is spontaneously flammable in air.
Chem. Eng. Progs. **63** (7): 126 (1967).

DIBUTYL CHLOROBORANE $(C_4H_9)_2BCl$

Air
Dibutyl boron chloride is spontaneously flammable in air.
Buls, Bimonthly Rept. **8,** p. 4 (1953).

DIBUTYL ETHER $C_4H_9OC_4H_9$

Nitrogen Trichloride
See NITROGEN TRICHLORIDE plus Di-n-Butyl Ether.

DIBUTYLMAGNESIUM $(C_4H_9)_2Mg$

Air
Dibutylmagnesium is spontaneously flammable in air.
Douda (1966).

2,6-DI-t-BUTYL-4 NITROPHENOL
$HOC_6H_3[C(CH_3)\ _2CH_3]_2$

(self-reactive)
This material exploded violently after being warmed for two to three minutes on a steam bath.
ASESB Expl. Report **24** (1961).

2,6-DI-t-BUTYLPHENOL $HOC_6H_3[C(CH_3)_2CH_3]_2$

Nitric Acid
See NITRIC ACID plus Di-t-Butylphenol.

DIBUTYL PHTHALATE $(C_4H_9OCO)_2C_6H_4$

Chlorine
See CHLORINE plus Polypropylene.

DIBUTYL SULFOXIDE $(C_4H_9)_2SO$

Perchloric Acid
See PERCHLORIC ACID plus Dibutyl Sulfoxide.

DICHLORINE HEPTOXIDE Cl_2O_7

(self-reactive)
Dichlorine heptoxide explodes violently under a blow or when heated rapidly.
Mellor **2, Supp. 1:** 542 (1956).

DICHLOROACETYLENE $ClC=CCl$

(self-reactive)
During synthesis of dichloroacetylene, the dichloroacetylene acci dentally condensed and collected in a water trap. When the chemist attempted to sample the material in the trap, a violent explosion occurred. Since dichloroacetylene is reported to be shock-sensitive, the touching of the sample could have initiated the detonation.
MCA Case History **1989** (1974).

Air
Dichloroacetylene ignites or explodes on contact with air.
MCA Case History **495** (1956); **1065,** (1965).
When moist chlorine was passed over calcium carbide and potassium hydroxide, a solution of 58% dichloroacetylene was collected in ether. The solution burned spontaneously and filled the laboratory with phosgene. When the head was removed from a steel bomb used for one of the experiments, contact with air caused an explosion that drove the base of the bomb through the floor.
R. Reemschneider and K. Brendel, *Ann. Chem.* **640:** 5(1961). *Rutledge,* p. 138 (1968).

DICHLOROBENZENE ClC_6H_4Cl

Aluminum
See ALUMINUM plus Ethylene Dichloride, Propylene Dichloride, and Orthodichlorobenzene.

DICHLORODIETHYLDIAMMINE COBALT PERCHLORATE $[Co(Cl)_2(C_2H_5)_2(NH_2)_2]ClO_4$

(self-reactive)
Dichlorodiethyldiammine cobalt perchlorate explodes at 300°C and is impact sensitive.
W. R. Tomlinson, Jr., and L. F. Audrieth, *J. Chem. Edu.* **27:** 606- 609 (1950).

DICHLORODIFLUOROMETHANE CCl_2F_2

Aluminum
See ALUMINUM plus Dichlorodifluoromethane.

DICHLORODIMETHYLSILANE $(CH_3)_2SiCl_2$

Water
Dimethyldichlorosilane reacts violently with water.
Title 46 (1970).

DICHLORO(DISILYLAMINO)BORANE $(SiH_3)2NBCl_2$

Air
Disilylamino dichloroborane is spontaneously flammable in air.
Douda (1966).

DICHLOROETHYLALUMINUM $C_2H_5AlCl_2$

Air
Ethyl aluminum dichloride is spontaneously flammable in air.
Douda (1966).

Benzene and Allyl Chloride
See ALLYL CHLORIDE plus Benzene and Ethyl Aluminum Dichloride.

Toluene and Allyl Chloride
See ALLYL CHLORIDE plus Benzene and Ethyl Aluminum Dichloride.

Water
Ethyl aluminum dichloride reacts violently with water.
Rose (1961).

DICHLOROETHYLBORANE $C_2H_5BCl_2$

Air
Ethyl boron dichloride is spontaneously flammable in air.
Buls, Bimonthly Rept. 5, p. 3 (1953).

1,2-DICHLOROETHYLENE $ClCH=CHCl$

Nitrogen Tetroxide
See NITROGEN TETROXIDE plus 1,2-Dichloroethane.

Potassium Hydroxide
See POTASSIUM HYDROXIDE plus 1,2-Dichloroethylene.

Sodium
See SODIUM plus 1,2-Dichloroethylene.

Sodium Hydroxide
See SODIUM plus 1,2-Dichloroethylene.

DICHLOROFLUORAMINE Cl_2NF

(self-reactive)
Dichlorofluoramine is explosive in the liquid state.
Lawless and Smith, p. 88 (1968).

1,6-DICHLORO-2,4-HEXADIYNE $(Cl{\cdot}CH_2{\equiv}C\text{-})_2$

(self-reactive)
1, 6-dichloro-2, 4-hexadiyne is shock-sensitive. P.E. Drieder and H.V. Isaacson,
Chem. and Eng. News **50** (12): 51 (1972).

DICHLOROMETHANE $ClCH_2Cl$

Nitrogen Tetroxide
See NITROGEN TETROXIDE plus 1,2-Dichloroethane.

Oxygen (Liquid)
See OXYGEN (LIQUID) plus Chlorinated Hydrocarbons.

Potassium
See POTASSIUM plus Chloroform.

Sodium
See POTASSIUM plus Chloroform.

Sodium-Potassium Alloy
See SODIUM-POTASSIUM ALLOY plus Carbon Tetrachloride.

N,N-DICHLOROMETHYLAMINE CH_3NCl_2

Sodium Sulfide
N,N-dichloromethylamine exploded violently on addition of sodium sulfide.
Biul. Wojskowej Akad. Tech. **8** (48): 75-9 (1959).

1,2-DICHLOROPROPANE $ClCH_2CHClCH_3$

Aluminum
See ALUMINUM plus Ethylene Dichloride, Propylene Dichloride and Orthodichlorobenzene. See ALUMINUM plus Propylene Dichloride.

DICHLOROSILANE H_2SiCl_2
Dichlorosilane explodes immediately on contact with strong solid oxidants such as nitrate/nitrite mixtures.
Plant Operations Progress, Britton (1990).

1,2-DICHLORO-1,1,2,2-TETRAFLUOROETHANE $CClF_2CF_2Cl$

Aluminum
See ALUMINUM plus Dichlorodifluoromethane.

DICYANDIAZIDE $NCN=C(NNN)_2$

(self-reactive)
Dicyandiazide is a shock-sensitive compound.
Chem. and Eng. News **43** (52): 29, 30 (Dec. 27, 1965).

2,2-DIETHOXYCYCLODISILOXANE $(C_2H_5O)_2\underline{SiOSiH_2O}$

Air
Diethoxycyclodisiloxane is spontaneously flammable in air.
Kaufman (1961).

DIETHYLALUMINUM HYDRIDE $(C_2H_5)_2AlH$

Air
Diethyl aluminum hydride ignites spontaneously in air.
Fire Haz. Prop. (1969).

DIETHYLAMINE $C_4H_{11}N$

Cellulose Nitrate
Cellulose nitrate of high surface area (dry or alcohol-wet guncotton or scrap) spontaneously ignited in contact with diethylamine used as curing agent for epoxide resins.
ABCM Quarterly Safety Summary (1956); *Bretherick* (1979).

Dicyanofurazan
Contact of dicyanofurazan, or its N-oxide, with diethylamine or mixtures of nitrogenous bases is instantaneously explosive.
Denson, D. B., *Chem. Abst.* (1973).

DIETHYLARSINE $(C_2H_5)_2AsH$

Air
Diethylarsine is spontaneously flammable in air.
Douda (1966).

DIETHYL AZODICARBOXYLATE
$C_2H_5OCON{=}NCOOC_2H_5$

(self-reactive)
A sample decomposed upon attempted distillation with sufficient violence to shatter the distillation apparatus.
Org. Syntheses **28,** p. 59 (1948).

DIETHYLCADMIUM $(C_2H_5)_2Cd$

Air
Diethylcadmium fumes explode in air.
Brauer (1965).

DIETHYL (3-DIETHYLAMINOPROPYL) ALUMINUM
$(C_2H_5)_2Al(CH_2)_3N(C_2H_5)_2$

Air
Diethyl 3-diethylaminopropyl aluminum is spontaneously flammable in air.
Douda (1966).

DIETHYL ETHER $C_2H_5OC_2H_5$
Forms unstable peroxides upon prolonged contact with air which can concentrate and explode during distillation/evaporation.

Acetyl Peroxide
See ACETYL PEROXIDE plus Diethyl Ether.

Air
See also OXYGEN plus Diethyl Ether.

Air (Liquid)
A mixture of liquid air and diethyl ether exploded spontaneously.
Z. Angew. Chem. **40:** 1317. *MCA Case History* **616** (1960).

Bromoazide
See BROMOAZIDE plus Diethyl Ether.

Chlorine
See CHLORINE plus Diethyl Ether.

Chlorine Trifluoride
See CHLORINE TRIFLUORIDE plus Diethy Ether.

Chromic Anhydride
See CHROMIC ANHYDRIDE plus Diethyl Ether.

Chromyl Chloride
See CHROMYL CHLORIDE plus Acetone.

Lithium Aluminum Hydride
See LITHIUM ALUMINUM HYDRIDE plus Diethyl Ether.

Nitrosyl Perchlorate
See NITROSYL PERCHLORATE plus Diethyl Ether.

Nitryl Perchlorate
See NITRYL PERCHLORATE plus Benzene.

Ozone
See OZONE plus Diethyl Ether.

Perchloric Acid
See PERCHLORIC ACID plus Diethyl Ether.

Permanganates and Sulfuric Acid
See PERMANGANATES plus Sulfuric Acid and Benzene.

Potassium Peroxide
See SODIUM PEROXIDE plus Aniline.

Sodium Peroxide
See SODIUM PEROXIDE plus Aniline.

Triethyl Aluminum and Air
See TRIETHYL ALUMINUM plus Diethyl Ether and Air.

Trimethyl Aluminum and Air
See TRIMETHYL ALUMINUM plus Diethyl Ether and Air.

DIETHYLMAGNESIUM $(C_2H_5)_2Mg$

Air
Diethylmagnesium is spontaneously flammable in air; it explodes violently on contact with water and will glow and catch fire even in carbon dioxide. It must be handled in high vacuum, or under dry nitrogen or hydrogen.
Merck Index, p. 359 (1968).

Carbon Dioxide
See DIETHYL MAGNESIUM plus Air.

Water
See DIETHYL MAGNESIUM plus Air.

DIETHYLPHOSPHINE $(C_2H_5)_2PH$

Air
Diethylphosphine is spontaneously flammable in air.
Von Schwartz, p. 323 (1918).

DIETHYL PEROXIDE $C_2H_5OOC_2H_5$

(self-reactive)
See OXYGEN plus Ethers.

DIETHYL PEROXYDICARBONATE $[C_2H_5OCOO\text{-}]_2$

(self-reactive)
Diethyl peroxydicarbonate decomposes rapidly at room temperature, sometimes with an explosion. It becomes

hazardous above 10°C. One must avoid allowing it to crystallize.
Kirk and Othmer, Second Ed. **14:** 801, 803 (1963).

DIETHYL SULFATE $(C_2H_5O)_2SO_2$

Metals and Water
The presence of moisture in a metal container of diethyl sulfate caused formation of sulfuric acid which reacted with the metal to release hydrogen which pressurized and exploded the container.
Chem. Abst. **28:** 2908 (1934).
Angew. Chem. Intern. Ed. Engl. **47:** 105 (1934).

Potassium Tert.-Butoxide
See ACETONE plus Potassium Tert.-Butoxide.

DIETHYL TELLURIDE $(C_2H_5)_2Te$

Air
Diethyl telluride is spontaneously flammable in air.
Ellern, pp. 24-25 (1968).

1,2-DIETHYLTETRAIODODIALUMINUM
$C_2H_5I_2Al_2I_2C_2H_5$

Air
1,2-Diethyl tetraiodo dialuminum is spontaneously flammable in air.
Douda (1966).

DIETHYLZINC $(C_2H_5)_2Zn$

Air
Diethyl zinc is spontaneously flammable in air.
Douda (1966). *Handbook Chem. Phys.*, p. C-715 (1970-1971).
Mellor **1:** 376 (1946-1947).
See also CHLORINE plus Diethyl Zinc.

Chlorine
See CHLORINE plus Diethyl Zinc.

Hydrazine
See ZINC DIAMIDE plus Hydrazine.

Water
Diethyl zinc reacts violently with water.
Brauer (1965).

2,4-DIETHYNYL-5-METHOXYTOLUENE
$(CH{\equiv}C\text{-})_2C_6H_2(CH_3)OCH_3$

(self-reactive)
The polymer of this material explodes thermally.
Chem. Abst. **75:** 19831 (1971).

2,4-DIETHYNYL-5-METHYLPHENOL
$(CH=C\text{-})_2C_6H_2(OH)CH_3$

(self-reactive)
This compound is unstable in light and air.
Chem. Abst. **75:** 19831 (1971).

DIFLUORAMINE NHF_2

(self-reactive)
A small flask of gaseous difluoramine in a train of glass apparatus broke loose and exploded when it fell to the concrete floor. A nearby glass U-tube containing liquid difluoramine at minus 80°C exploded either from the shock of the first explosion or from the inrush of air after the apparatus broke.
MCA Case History **768** (1961).
Difluoramine has a tendency to explode when in the solid state or during the process of freezing or melting.
Lawless and Smith, pp. 70-71 (1968).

Chlorine Dioxide
See CHLORINE DIOXIDE plus Difluoramine.

DIFLUORINE PEROXIDE O_2F_2

Organic Matter
Even at minus 160°C or below a violent reaction or an explosion results when dioxygen difluoride reacts with any organic material and most inorganic materials containing hydrogen.
Solomon, Kacmarck, and McDonough, *J. Chem. Eng. Data* **13** (4): 529-531 (1968).

Sulfur Trioxide
The reaction of sulfur trioxide and oxygen difluoride is very vigor ous and explosions occur if the reaction is carried out in the absence of a solvent.
Solomon, Kacmarck and McDonough, *J. Chem. Eng. Data* **13** (4): 529-531 (1968).

DIFLUORODIAZENE N_2F_2

(self-reactive)
Studies of the isomerization of difluorodiazine in a copper tube indicated that the cis form is much less stable than the trans.
Lawless and Smith, pp. 42, 43 (1968).

DIGERMANE Ge_2H_6

Air
Digermane ignites spontaneously in air.
Ellern, p. 22 (1968).

DIHYDRAZINOZINC CHLORATE $Zn(N_2H_4)_2(ClO_3)_2$

(self-reactive)
This compound detonates when struck.
Mellor **2, Supp. 1:** 592 (1956).
See ZINC-HYDRAZINE CHLORATE.

1, 6-DIIODO-2,4-HEXADIYNE $(I\text{-}CH_2C{\equiv}C\text{-})_2$

(self-reactive)
1, 6-diiodo-2,4-hexadiyne is shock-sensitive.
P.E. Drieder and H.V. Isaacson, *Chem. and Eng. News* **50** (12): 51 (1972).

DIIODOMETHANE ICH_2I

Sodium-Potassium Alloy
See SODIUM-POTASSIUM ALLOY plus Diiodomethane.

DIISOAMYL ZINC $((CH_3)_2CHC_2H_4)_2Zn$

Air
Isoamyl zinc is spontaneously flammable in air.
Dangerous Chem. Code, p. 343 (1951).

DIISOBUTYLALUMINUM HYDRIDE $(C_4H_9)_2AlH$

Air

Diisobutyl aluminum hydride is spontaneously flammable in air.
Rose (1961).

DIISOBUTYLENE $CH_2{=}C(CH_3)CH_2C(CH_3)_3$

Chorosulfonic Acid

Mixing diisobutylene and chlorosulfonic acid in a closed container caused the temperature and pressure to increase.
Flynn and Rossow (1970). See Note under complete reference.

Oleum

Mixing diisobutylene and oleum in a closed container caused the temperature and pressure to increase.
Flynn and Rossow (1970). See Note under complete reference.

Sulfuric Acid

Mixing diisobutylene and 96% sulfuric acid in a closed container caused the temperature and pressure to increase.
Flynn and Rossow (1970). See Note under complete reference.

DIISOBUTYL ZINC $[(CH_3)_2CHCH_2]_2Zn$

Air

Isobutyl zinc is spontaneously flammable in air.
Dangerous Chem. Code, p. 343 (1951).

DIISOPROPYLBERYLLIUM $(C_3H_7)_2Be$

Water

Diisopropyl beryllium reacts explosively with water.
G.E. Coates and F. Glockling, *J. Chem. Soc.* **106:** 22 (1954).

DIISOPROPYL ETHER $(CH_3)_2CHOCH(CH_3)_2$

Air

A flask of diisopropyl ether was being heated on a steam bath with gentle shaking when an explosion occurred. In a second instance, an explosion occurred after practically all the ether had been distilled.
MCA Guide for Safety, Appendix 3 (1972).
Diisopropyl ether and air form highly explosive peroxides.
Wischmeyer (1969).

Air or Oxygen

See OXYGEN plus Ethers.
See OXYGEN plus Isopropyl Ether.

Chlorosulfonic Acid

Mixing diisopropyl ether and chlorosulfonic acid in a closed container caused the temperature and pressure to increase.
Flynn and Rossow (1970). See Note under complete reference.

Nitric Acid

Mixing diisopropyl ether and 70% nitric acid in a closed container caused the temperature and pressure to increase.
Flynn and Rossow (1970). See Note under complete reference.

DIISOPROPYL PEROXYDICARBONATE $[(CH_3)_2CHOC(O)O\text{-}]_2$

(self-reactive)

Diisopropyl perdicarbonate decomposes rapidly at room temperature and sometimes explodes. It becomes hazardous above 10°C. It should not be allowed to crystallize.
Kirk and Othmer, Second Ed. **14:** 801, 803 (1963).

Organic Matter

Upon contact with diisopropyl peroxydicarbonate, combustible organic materials can ignite or explode.
Haz. Chem. Data p. 121 (1973).

DIKETENE $H_2C_3H_2CO_2$

Diketene residues awaiting incineration in a tank trailer decomposed violently on standing, and blew off the dome cover and ignited. *Vervalin* (1973).

Acids or Bases

Presence of mineral, or Lewis acids, or bases including amines, will catalyze violent polymerization.
Hazardous Chemicals Data, NFPA 49 (1971).

1,2-DIMETHOXYETHANE $CH_2(OCH_3)CH_2(OCH_3)$

Lithium Aluminum Hydride

See LITHIUM ALUMINUM HYDRIDE plus 1,2-Dimethoxy ethane.

2,2-DIMETHOXYPROPANE $CH_3C(OCH_3)_2CH_3$

Manganese Perchlorate and Ethyl Alcohol

See ETHYL ALCOHOL plus Manganese Perchlorate and 2,2-Dimethoxypropane.

Nickel Perchlorate

See NICKEL PERCHLORATE plus 2,2-Dimethoxypropane.

DIMETHYLAMINE C_2H_7N

Maleic Anhydride

Maleic anhydride decomposes exothermically, evolving carbon dioxide in the presence of dimethylamine.
Vogler, et al., *J. Chem. Eng. Data* (1963).

N, N-DIMETHYLANILINE $C_6H_5N(CH_3)_2$

Benzoyl Peroxide

See BENZOYL PEROXIDE plus N, N-Dimethylaniline.

DIMETHYLARSINE $(CH_3)_2AsH$

Air

Dimethylarsine is spontaneously flammable in air.
Douda (1966). *Handbook Chem. Phys.,* p. C-681 (1970-1971).

DIMETHYL CARBONATE $CH_3OCOOCH_3$

Potassium Tert.-Butoxide

See ACETONE plus Potassium Tert.-Butoxide.

DIMETHYL ETHER CH_3OCH_3

Aluminum Hydride

See ALUMINUM HYDRIDE plus Dimethyl Ether.

Lithium Aluminum Hydride
See LITHIUM ALUMINUM HYDRIDE plus Dimethyl Ether.

DIMETHYL FORMAMIDE $HCON(CH_3)_2$

Bromine
See BROMINE plus Dimethyl Formamide.

Carbon Tetrachloride
Dimethyl formamide and carbon tetrachloride react violently at temperatures above 65°C.
Kittila, p. 165 (1967).

Chlorinated Hydrocarbons
Some halogenated hydrocarbons reacted with dimethyl formamide in the presence of iron at moderate temperatures.
Kittila, p. 165 (1967).

Chromic Anhydride
See CHROMIC ANHYDRIDE plus Dimethyl Formamide.

2,5-Dimethylpyrrole and Phosphorus
See 2,5-DIMETHYLPYRROLE plus Phosphorus Oxychloride and Dimethyl Formamide.

Hexachlorobenzene
Dimethyl formamide and hexachlorobenzene react violently above 65°C.
Kittila, p. 165 (1967).

Magnesium Nitrate
This mixture undergoes spontaneous decomposition. Nitrates of sodium, lithium, lead, copper and silver do not react under similar conditions.
Kittila, p. 165 (1967).

Methylene Diisocyanate
Methylene diisocyanate polymerized violently on contact with dimethyl formamide.
Kittila, p. 122 (1967).

Organic Nitrates
Dimethyl formamide undergoes spontaneous decomposition in the presence of organic nitrates.
du Pont Prod. Inf. Bull., Dimethylformamide.

Phosphorus Trioxide
Dimethyl formamide, dimethyl sulfoxide, dimethyl sulfite, or methanol and phosphorus trioxide react very violently, often charring.
Mellor **8, Supp. 3:** 382 (1971).

Triethyl Aluminum
Dimethyl formamide and triethyl aluminum form an explosive mixture when heated together.
du Pont Prod. Inf. Bull., Dimethylformamide.

uns-DIMETHYLHYDRAZINE (UDMH) $(CH_3)_2NNH_2$

Air
Unsymmetrical dimethyl hydrazine, when spread on a large surface, may ignite spontaneously.
Def. Res. and Eng., pp. 299-300 (1963).
Three manufacturers of dimethylhydrazine reported that they did not believe this substance to be spontaneously flammable in air.
(As reported from personal telephone conversations in 1998 between NFPA Technical Committee member Ron Kirsch and Aldrich, Fluka and Janssen Chemica.)
However, one manufacturer did report it is spontaneously flammable in air.
(As reported from personal telephone conversations in 1999 between NFPA Technical Committee member Curtis Payne and Raphael Traggianese of Arch Chemicals.)

Hydrogen Peroxide
Spontaneous ignition of UDMH can occur on contact with oxidants like hydrogen peroxide and fuming nitric acid.
Haz. Chem. Data (1966).

Nitric Acid
See NITRIC ACID plus Dimethylhydrazine.

Nitric Acid (Fuming)
See UNSYMMETRICAL DIMETHYL HYDRAZINE plus Hydrogen Peroxide.

Nitric Acid, Nitrogen Tetroxide, and Sulfuric Acid
Combinations of unsymmetrical dimethylhydrazine, aniline, or furfuryl alcohol as fuels with hydrogen peroxide or a mixture of nitric acid-nitrogen tetroxide-sulfuric acid as oxidizers ignite with little delay and are used as propellants.
Chem. Abst. **51:** 3961d (1957); **63:** 4067h (1965).
Brennstoff-Chem. **46** (4): 117-24 (1965).

Nitric Oxide
See NITRIC OXIDE plus Unsymmetrical Dimethylhydrazine.

DIMETHYLMAGNESIUM $(CH_3)_2Mg$

Air
Dimethylmagnesium is spontaneously flammable in air.
Coates, p. 29 (1956).

DIMETHYL MALONATE $CH_2(COOCH_3)_2$

Methyl Azide
See METHYL AZIDE plus Dimethyl Malonate.

DIMETHYLMANGANESE $(CH_3)_2Mn$

Air
Dimethylmanganese is spontaneously flammable in air.
Zeiss, p. 432 (1960).

2,5-DIMETHYLPYRROLE $(CH_3)_2C_4H_3N$

Phosphorus Oxychloride and Dimethyl Formamide
A complex of phosphorus oxychloride and dimethyl formamide was formed, then 2,5-dimethylpyrrole was added slowly. Internal temperature was 15°C. When only a part of the 2,5-dimethylpyrrole had been added the chemist noted that a vortex was no longer being formed by the stirrer. When he agitated the flask, the mixture erupted.
MCA Case History **1460** (1968).

DIMETHYL SULFATE $(CH_3)_2SO_4$

Ammonium Hydroxide
See AMMONIUM HYDROXIDE plus Dimethyl Sulfate.

Sodium Azide
See SODIUM AZIDE plus Dimethyl Sulfate.

DIMETHYL SULFITE $SO_3(CH_3)_2$

Phosphorus Trioxide
See DIMETHYL FORMAMIDE plus Phosphorus Trioxide.

DIMETHYL SULFOXIDE $(CH_3)_2SO$

Acetyl Chloride
See DIMETHYL SULFOXIDE plus Acyl Halides.

Acyl Halides
Dimethyl sulfoxide decomposes violently on contact with a wide range of acyl halides, aryl halides and related compounds. Exam ples are phenyl and tolyl chloride, acetyl chloride, benzenesulfonyl chloride, benzoyl chloride, cyanuric chloride, phosphorus chloride, phosphorus oxychloride, and thionyl chloride. Dimethyl sulfoxide should be used with caution in exploratory reactions.
Chem. and Eng. News **35** (9): 87 (1957). *BCISC* **39** (154): 15 (1968). *Chem. Ind.* **40:** 1706-1707 (1967).

Benzenesulfonyl Chloride
See DIMETHYL SULFOXIDE plus Acyl Halides.

Benzoyl Chloride
See DIMETHYL SULFOXIDE plus Acyl Halides.

p-Bromobenzoyl Acetanilide
See p-BROMOBENZOYL ACETANILIDE plus Dimethyl Sulfoxide.

Cyanuric Chloride
See DIMETHYL SULFOXIDE plus Acyl Halides.

Iodine Pentafluoride
The reaction of dimethyl sulfoxide and iodine pentafluoride can be controlled to give a number of products, but the unmoderated reaction is quite violent because of the predominant formation of gaseous fluoromethanes and sulfuroxyfluorides as the temperature increases.
E.M. Lawless, *Chem. and Eng. News* **47** (12): 8, 109 (1969).

Magnesium Perchlorate
In the preparation of anhydrous dimethyl sulfoxide by vacuum distillation from anhydrous magnesium perchlorate, an explosion occurred.
MCA Case History **1187** (1966). *Karasch* (1961). *Chem. and Eng. News* **43** (37): 62 (1965).

Methyl Bromide
See METHYL BROMIDE plus Dimethyl Sulfoxide.

Perchloric Acid
An explosion occurs when 70% perchloric acid contacts sulfoxides.
MCA Case History **1187** (1966). *Karasch* (1961).
See also SULFOXIDES plus Perchloric Acid.

Periodic Acid
In periodic-dimethyl sulfoxide oxidizing systems, violent explosions can occur if the concentration of periodic acid is too strong. For example, in oxidizing glycopyranosides an explosion took place at a 1.5N concentration of the periodic acid.
R. J. Yu and C. T. Bishop, *Can. J. Chem.* **45:** 2195 (1967). *Chem. and Eng. News* **44** (15): 48 (1966). *J. Am. Chem. Soc.* **90** (7): 1924 (1968).

Phenyl Chloride
See DIMETHYL SULFOXIDE plus Acyl Halides.

Phosphorus Oxychloride
See DIMETHYL SULFOXIDE plus Acyl Halides.

Phosphorus Trichloride
See DIMETHYL SULFOXIDE plus Acyl Halides.

Phosphorus Trioxide
See DIMETHYL FORMAMIDE plus Phosphorus Trioxide.

Potassium Permanganate
A mixture of the two will flash instantaneously.
Ellern, p. 50 (1968).

Silver Fluoride
Dimethyl sulfoxide is violently reactive with fluorinating agents such as silver fluoride.
Chem. and Eng. News **47** (12): 8, 109 (1969).

Sodium Hydride
The reaction of these two reagents to prepare methyl sulfinyl carbanion can cause explosions.
Chem. and Eng. News **44** (14): 48 (1966); **44** (24): **7** (1966).

Thionyl Chloride
See DIMETHYL SULFOXIDE plus Acyl Halides.

Tolyl Chloride
See DIMETHYL SULFOXIDE plus Acyl Halides.

DINITROANILINE HYDROCHLORIDE
$(O_2N)_2C_6H_3NH_2 \cdot HCl$

Nitrosylsulfuric Acid
See NITROSYLSULFURIC ACID plus Dinitroaniline Hydrochloride.

2,4-DINITROBENZENE SULFENYL CHLORIDE
$(NO_2)_2C_6H_3SCl$

(self-reactive)
An explosion may occur when the solvent symmetrical tetrachlore thane is almost removed in the chlorinolysis of 2,4-dinitrophenyl disulfide.
MCA Guide for Safety, Appendix 3 (1972).

2,4-DINITROCHLOROBENZENE $(O_2N)_2C_6H_3Cl$

(self-reactive)
B. D. Halpern, *Chem. and Eng. News*, **29:** 2666 (1951).

DINITROGEN PENTOXIDE O_2NONO_2

Ozone
See OZONE plus Dinitrogen Pentoxide.

2,4-DINITROPHENYL DISULFIDE $[(O_2N)_2C_6H_3S\text{-}]_2$

Tetrachlorethane
See 2, 4-DINITROBENZENE SULFENYL-CHLORIDE (self- reactive).

DINITROSOPENTAMETHYLENETETRAMINE
$(ON)_2(CH_2)_5N_4$

(self-reactive)
This chemical is a blowing agent with an exothermic decomposition slightly above its melting point of 203°C.
Ellern, p. 161 (1968).

DIOXANE $\underline{OCH_2CH_2OCH_2CH_2}$

Hydrogen and Nickel (Raney)
See HYDROGEN plus Dioxane and Nickel (Raney).

Silver Perchlorate
See SILVER PERCHLORATE plus Toluene.

DIPEROXYTEREPHTHALIC ACID $(HOOOC)_2C_6H_4$

(self-reactive)
This acid explodes under the influence of a shock or an increase in temperature.
Chem. Reviews **45:** 14, 15 (1949).

DIPHENYLAMINE $(C_6H_5)_2NH$

Hexachloromelamine
See HEXACHLOROMELAMINE plus Organic Contaminants.

Trichloromelamine
See HEXACHLOROMELAMINE plus Organic Contaminants.

DIPHENYL DIAZOSULFIDE $(C_6H_5N_2)_2S$

Air
Phenyldiazosulfide explodes when air-dried.
Chem. and Eng. News **29:** 5473 (1951).

1,2-DIPHENYLETHYLENE $C_6H_5CH=CHC_6H_5$

Oxygen
See OXYGEN plus Diphenylethylene.

DIPHENYLTETRACETYLENE $(C_6H_5C=CC=C)_2$

(self-reactive)
Diphenyltetracetylene was stable for at least 13 months at room temperature in the dark. When placed on a metallic plate, it decomposed explosively with much soot.
Chem. Abst. **45:** 7082 (1962).

DIPHOSPHINE H_2PPH_2

Air
The liquid is spontaneously flammable in air and the presence of a trace of the vapor makes phosphine and other combustible gases spontaneously flammable in air.
Mellor **8:** 829 (1946-1947).
Mellor **1:** 376 (1946-1947).
Mellor **8, Supp. 3:** 273 (1971).

DIPHOSPHORYL CHLORIDE $P_2O_3Cl_2$

Water
The vigorous hydrolysis of pyrophosphoryl chloride is like that of phosphorus pentoxide.
Mellor **8, Supp. 3:** 505.

DIPROPARGYL ETHER $(CH=CCH_2)_2O$

Air
An explosion occurred in a 50-gallon stainless steel still during the distillation of dipropargyl ether.
MCA Guide for Safety, Appendix 3 (1972).

DIPROPYLALUMINUM HYDRIDE $(C_3H_7)_2AlH$

Air
Di-n-propylaluminum hydride ignites spontaneously in air.
Aluminum Alkyls, p. 21. *Fire Haz. Prop.* (1969).

Water
Di-n-propylaluminum hydride reacts violently with water.
Aluminum Alkyls, p. 21.

DIPROPYLZINC $(C_3H_7)_2Zn$

Air
Di-n-propyl zinc is spontaneously flammable in air.
Douda (1966).

DISILANE (SILICOETHANE) Si_2H_6

Air
See OXYGEN plus Disilane.

Carbon Tetrachloride
Disilane explodes violently when mixed with carbon tetrachloride; reacts vigorously with incandescence in contact with chloroform.
Mellor **6:** 223 (1946-1947).

Chloroform
See DISILANE plus Carbon Tetrachloride.

Oxygen
See OXYGEN plus Disilane.

Sulfur Hexafluoride
Disilane explodes violently in contact with sulfur hexafluoride.
Mellor **6:** 223 (1946-1947).

DISILOXANE $(SiH_3)_2O$

Air
See SILANES plus Air.

(DISILYLAMINO) DIBORANE $B_2H_5N(SiH_3)_2$

Air
Disilylamino diborane is spontaneously flammable in air.
Douda (1966).

DISULFURYL AZIDE $(N_3SO_2)_2O$

(self-reactive)
Pyrosulfuryl azide decomposes explosively below 80°C.
Mellor **8, Supp. 2:** 36 (1967).

DIVANADIUM DODECACARBONYL $V_2(CO)_{12}$

Air
Divanadium dodecacarbonyl is spontaneously flammable in air.
R. L. Pruett and J. E. Wyman, *Chem. and Ind.* **9** (1): 119-120 (1960).

DIVINYL ETHER $(CH_2=CH)_2O$

Air
See OXYGEN plus Ethers.

Oxygen
See OXYGEN plus Ethers.

DIVINYLZINC $(CH_2=CH)_2Zn$

Air
Divinyl zinc is spontaneously flammable in air.
Zeiss (1960).

DOWICIL 100 [1-(3-CHLOROALLYL)-3,5,7-TRIAZO-1-AZONIAADAMANTANE CHLORIDE]
$C_6H_{12}N_4$-$(CH_2CHCHCl)Cl$

Hydrogen Chloride
This compound is stable below 120°C if kept dry and away from hydrogen chloride. Both water and hydrogen chloride will cause chemical decomposition. Decomposition is immediate with hydro genchloride; it is somewhat slower in water.
Dowicil

Water
See DOWICIL 100 plus Hydrogen Chloride.

DYSPROSIUM Dy

Air
See RARE EARTH METALS plus Air.

Halogens
See RARE EARTH METALS plus Halogens.

ENDRIN $C_{12}H_8OCl_6$

Parathion
See PARATHION plus Endrin.

EPICHLOROHYDRIN OCH_2CHCH_2Cl

2-Aminoethanol
See 2-AMINOETHANOL plus Epichlorohydrin.

Chlorosulfonic Acid
Mixing epichlorohydrin and 2-aminoethanol in a closed container caused the temperature and pressure to increase.
Flynn and Rossow (1970). See Note under complete reference.

Ethylene Diamine
See ETHYLENE DIAMINE plus Epichlorohydrin.

Ethyleneimine
Mixing epichlorohydrin and ethyleneimine in a closed container caused the temperature and pressure to increase.
Flynn and Rossow (1970). See Note under complete reference.

Nitric Acid
Mixing epichlorohydrin and 70% nitric acid in a closed container caused the temperature and pressure to increase.
Flynn and Rossow (1970). See Note under complete reference.

Oleum
Mixing epichlorohydrin and oleum in a closed container caused the temperature and pressure to increase.
Flynn and Rossow (1970). See Note under complete reference.

Potassium Tert.-Butoxide
See ACETONE plus Potassium Tert.-Butoxide.

Sulfuric Acid
See ETHYLENE CYANOHYDRIN plus Sulfuric Acid.
Mixing epichlorohydrin and 96% sulfuric acid in a closed container caused the temperature and pressure to increase.
Flynn and Rossow (1970). See Note under complete reference.

ERBIUM Er

Air
See RARE EARTH METALS plus Air.

Halogens
See RARE EARTH METALS plus Halogens.

ERBIUM PERCHLORATE $Er(ClO_4)_3$

Acetonitrile
See ACETONITRILE plus Erbium Perchlorate.

ESTERS

Nitrates
See NITRATES plus Esters.

ETHANE C_2H_6

Chlorine
See CHLORINE plus Ethane.

Chlorine Dioxide
See CHLORINE DIOXIDE plus Butadiene.

1,2-ETHANETHIOL $HSCH_2CH_2SH$

Calcium Hypochlorite
See CALCIUM HYPOCHLORITE plus 1-Propanethiol.

ETHERS
(See also specific ethers)

Air or Oxygen
Peroxides form on standing and are very dangerous.
Bahme, p. 46 (1961).

Boron Triiodide
See BORON TRIIODIDE plus Ethers.

ETHOXYACETYLENE $C_2H_5OC{\equiv}CH$

Ethylmagnesium Iodide
See ETHYLMAGNESIUM IODIDE plus Ethoxyacetylene.

(4-ETHOXYBUTYL) DIETHYLALUMINUM
$(C_2H_5)_2Al(CH_2)_4OC_2H_5$

Air
Diethyl-4-ethoxybutylamine is spontaneously flammable in air.
Douda (1966).

2-(2-ETHOXYETHOXY)ETHYL ACETATE
$CH_3COOCH_2CH_2OCH_2CH_2OC_2H_5$

Chlorosulfonic Acid
Mixing ethyl glycol monoethyl ether acetate and chlorosulfonic acid in a closed container caused the temperature and pressure to increase.
Flynn and Rossow (1970). See Note under complete reference.

Oleum
Mixing ethylene glycol monoethyl ether acetate and oleum in a closed container caused the temperature and pressure to increase.
Flynn and Rossow (1970). See Note under complete reference.

ETHOXYETHYNYLCARBINOL $C_2H_5OCHOHC{\equiv}CH$

(self-reactive)
Violent explosions have been recorded in the use of this material.
Rutledge, p. 35 (1968).

ETHOXYTRIETHYLDIPHOSPHINYL OXIDE
$(C_2H_5)_2POP(C_2H_5)(OC_2H_5)$

Air
Triethyl ethoxy diphosphinyl oxide is spontaneously flammable in air.
Kaufman (1961).

ETHYL ACETATE $C_2H_5COOCH_3$

Chlorosulfonic Acid
Mixing ethyl acetate and chlorosulfonic acid in a closed container caused the temperature and pressure to increase.
Flynn and Rossow (1970). See Note under complete reference.

Lithium Aluminum Hydride and 2-Chloromethylfuran
See 2-CHLOROMETHYLFURAN plus Lithium Aluminum Hydride and Ethyl Acetate.

Oleum
Mixing ethylacetate and oleum in a closed container caused the temperature and pressure to increase.
Flynn and Rossow (1970). See Note under complete reference.

Potassium Tert.-Butoxide
See ACETONE plus Potassium Tert.-Butoxide.

ETHYL ACETOACETATE $C_2H_5OCOCH_2COCH_3$

Tribromoneopentyl Alcohol and Zinc
Tribromoneopentyl alcohol, ethyl acetoacetate and zinc were being reacted to prepare the zinc chelate of tribromoneopentyl acetoace tate. When the reaction had proceeded to where 80% of the by-product ethanol had been removed, a violent decomposition occurred.
Wischmeyer (1972). U.S. Pat. 3,578,619 (1971).

ETHYL ACRYLATE $C_2H_5OCOCH=CH_2$

Chlorosulfonic Acid
Mixing ethyl acrylate and chlorosulfonic acid in a closed container caused the temperature and pressure to increase.
Flynn and Rossow (1970). See Note under complete reference.

ETHYL ALCOHOL CH_3CH_2OH

Acetyl Chloride
See ACETYL CHLORIDE plus Ethyl Alcohol.

Ammonium Hydroxide and Silver Oxide
See SILVER OXIDE plus Aqueous Ammonia and Ethyl Alcohol.

Bromine Pentafluoride
See BROMINE PENTAFLUORIDE plus Acetic Acid.

Calcium Hypochlorite
See CALCIUM HYPOCHLORITE plus Ethyl Alcohol.

Chlorine Trioxide
See CHLORINE TRIOXIDE plus Alcohol.

Chromic Anhydride
See CHROMIC ANHYDRIDE plus Ethyl Alcohol.

Chromyl Chloride
See CHROMYL CHLORIDE plus Ammonia.

Cyanuric Acid
See CYANURIC ACID plus Water.

Hydrogen Peroxide
The addition of alcohols to highly concentrated hydrogen peroxide forms powerful explosives which can be detonated by shock.
Bahme, p. 9 (1961).

Hydrogen Peroxide and Sulfuric Acid
See ALCOHOLS plus Hydrogen Peroxide and Sulfuric Acid.

Iodine, Methyl Alcohol, and Mercuric Oxide
See IODINE plus Ethyl Alcohol, Methyl Alcohol, and Mercuric Oxide.

Manganese Perchlorate and 2,2-Dimethoxypropane
A violent explosion occurred when manganese perchlorate, absolute alcohol and 2,2-dimethoxypropane were gently refluxed for about two hours under a stream of nitrogen.
Chem. and Eng. News **48** (28): 6 (July 6, 1970).

Mercuric Nitrate
See MERCURIC NITRATE plus Ethyl Alcohol.

Nitric Acid
See NITRIC ACID plus Ethyl Alcohol.

Perchlorates
See PERCHLORATES plus Benzene.

Perchloric Acid
See PERCHLORIC ACID plus Ethyl Alcohol.

Permanganates and Sulfuric Acid
See PERMANGANATES plus SULFURIC Acid and Benzene.

Permanganic Acid
See PERMANGANIC ACID plus Ethyl Alcohol.

Potassium Superoxide
See POTASSIUM SUPEROXIDE plus Ethyl Alcohol.

Potassium Tert.-Butoxide
See ACETONE plus Potassium Tert.-Butoxide.

Silver and Nitric Acid
See SILVER plus Ethyl Alcohol and Nitric Acid.

Silver Nitrate
See SILVER NITRATE plus Ethyl Alcohol.

Silver Perchlorate
See SILVER PERCHLORATE plus Benzene.

Sodium Hydrazide
See SODIUM HYDRAZIDE plus Air.

Uranyl Perchlorate
See URANYL PERCHLORATE plus Ethyl Alcohol.

m-ETHYLANILINE $C_2H_5C_6H_4NH_2$

Nitric Acid
See NITRIC ACID plus m-Ethylaniline.

ETHYLENE $CH_2=CH_2$

Aluminum Chloride
See ALUMINUM CHLORIDE plus Ethylene.

Benzoyl Peroxide and Carbon Tetrachloride
See BENZOYL PEROXIDE plus Carbon Tetrachloride and Ethylene.

Bromotrichloromethane
See BROMOTRICHLOROMETHANE plus Ethylene.

Carbon Tetrachloride
See CARBON TETRACHLORIDE plus Ethylene.

Chlorine
See CHLORINE plus Ethylene.

Chlorine Dioxide
See CHLORINE DIOXIDE plus Butadiene.

Hydrogen
Ethylene undergoes flame reaction with hydrogen at elevated pressure. Products are similar to ethylene decomposition products. Various catalysts including reduced iron oxides and purification bed packings may cause initiation.
L. G. Britton, "Decomposition Flame Propagation Limits of Ethylene and Mixtures with Other Gases;" Paper 8e, 30th Annual Loss Prevention Symposium, AIChE, New Orleans, Feb. 1996.

Nitrogen Dioxide
See NITROGEN TETROXIDE plus Olefins.

Nitromethane and Aluminum Chloride
A mixture of ethylene with nitromethane-aluminum chloride catalyst in an autoclave exploded at a temperature below 40°C.
F. M. Cowen and O. Rorso, *Chem. and Eng. News* **26:** 2257 (1948).
See also ALUMINUM CHLORIDE plus Nitromethane and Organic Matter.

Ozone
See OZONE plus Ethylene.

ETHYLENEDIAMINE $H_2NCH_2CH_2NH_2$

Acetic Acid
See ACETIC ACID plus Ethylene Diamine.

Acetic Anhydride
See ACETIC ANHYDRIDE plus Ethylene Diamine.

Acrolein
See ACROLEIN plus Ethylene Diamine.

Acrylic Acid
See ACRYLIC ACID plus Ethylene Diamine.

Acrylonitrile
See ACRYLONITRILE plus Ethylene Diamine.

Allyl Chloride
See ALLYL CHLORIDE plus Ethylene Diamine.

Carbon Disulfide
See CARBON DISULFIDE plus Ethylene Diamine.

Chlorosulfonic Acid
Mixing ethylene diamine and chlorosulfonic acid in a closed container caused the temperature and pressure to increase.
Flynn and Rossow (1970). See Note under complete reference.

Epichlorohydrin
Mixing ethylene diamine and epichlorohydrin in a closed container caused the temperature and pressure to increase.
Flynn and Rossow (1970). See Note under complete reference.

Ethylene Chlorohydrin
See ETHYLENE CHLOROHYDRIN plus Ethylene Diamine.

Hydrochloric Acid
Mixing ethylene diamine and 36% hydrochloric acid in a closed container caused the temperature and pressure to increase.
Flynn and Rossow (1970). See Note under complete reference.

Mesityl Oxide
See MESITYL OXIDE plus Ethylene Diamine.

Nitric Acid
Mixing ethylene diamine and 70% nitric acid in a closed container caused the temperature and pressure to increase.
Flynn and Rossow (1970). See Note under complete reference.

Oleum
Mixing ethylene diamine and oleum in a closed container caused the temperature and pressure to increase.
Flynn and Rossow (1970). See Note under complete reference.

Propiolactone (BETA-)
Mixing ethylene diamine and propiolactone (beta-) in a closed container caused the temperature and pressure to increase.
Flynn and Rossow (1970). See Note under complete reference.

Silver Perchlorate
See SILVER PERCHLORATE plus Ethylenediamine.

Sulfuric Acid
Mixing ethylene diamine and 96% sulfuric acid in a closed container caused the temperature and pressure to increase.
Flynn and Rossow (1970). See Note under complete reference.

Vinyl Acetate

Mixing ethylene diamine and vinyl acetate in a closed container caused the temperature and pressure to increase.
Flynn and Rossow (1970). See Note under complete reference.

ETHYLENEDIAMINE DIPERCHLORATE

$NH_2CH_2CH_2NH_2(ClO_4)_2$

(self-reactive)

This compound is an explosive that exceeds the power and brisance of TNT.
ACS **146:**206. *Chem. Reviews* **44:**419-45 (1949).

ETHYLENE DICHLORIDE $ClCH_2CH_2Cl$

Aluminum

See ALUMINUM plus Ethylene Dichloride, Propylene Dichloride, and Orthodichlorobenzene.

Ammonia

See AMMONIA plus Ethylene Dichloride.

Dimethyl Amino Propyl Amine

A tank of dimethyl amino propyl amine exploded violently when it reacted with wet ethylene dichloride which was the tank's previous contents. Investigation revealed that this combination can be extremely hazardous.
Doyle (1973).

ETHYLENE DIOXYAMINE PERCHLORATE

$CH_2CH_2ONHOHClO_4$

(self-reactive)

An explosion occurred in a laboratory during synthesis of ethylene dioxyamine perchlorate. It is believed that during some stage of purification of the material a low order explosion occurred.
BCISC **41** (162): 18 (April-June 1970).

ETHYLENE GLYCOL HOC_2H_4OH

Chlorosulfonic Acid

Mixing ethylene glycol and chlorosulfonic acid in a closed container caused the temperature and pressure to increase.
Flynn and Rossow (1970). See Note under complete reference.

Oleum

Mixing ethylene glycol and oleum in a closed container caused the temperature and pressure to increase.
Flynn and Rossow (1970). See Note under complete reference.

Sulfuric Acid

Mixing ethylene glycol and 96% sulfuric acid in a closed container caused the temperature and pressure to increase.
Flynn and Rossow (1970). See Note under complete reference.

ETHYLENE OXIDE $(CH_2)_2O$

Acids and Bases

Alkali metal hydroxides; acids; anhydrous chlorides of iron, tin, and aluminum; pure oxides of iron and aluminum; and metallic potassium are some of the catalysts that may cause liquid ethylene oxide to rearrange and/or polymerize, liberating heat.
L. G. Hess and V. V. Tilton, *Ind. Eng. Chem.* **42:** 1251-8 (1950). A. K. Gupta, *J. Soc. Chem. Ind.* **68:** 179-83 (1949). B. Beam, L. L. Simpson, G. Viera, *Chem. Eng. Progs.* (April 1992).

Alcohols

Explosions occur, although infrequently, from the combination of ethylene oxide and alcohols or mercaptans.
Chem. and Eng. News **20:** 1318 (1942).

Aluminum Chloride

See ETHYLENE OXIDE plus Acids and Bases. See ETHYLENE OXIDES plus Aluminum Oxide.

Aluminum Oxide

Ethylene oxide may polymerize violently when in contact with highly catalytic surfaces such as anhydrous chlorides of iron, tin and aluminum, or the pure oxides of aluminum and iron.
Hazardous Chemicals Data (1966).
See also ETHYLENE OXIDE plus Acids and Bases.

Ammonia

See AMMONIA plus Ethylene Oxide.

Copper

See COPPER plus Ethylene Oxide.

Insulation

Ethylene oxide reacts with water in porous insulation, forming low molecular weight polyethylene glycols. Under certain conditions these glycols can spontaneously ignite.
L. Britton, *Plant Operations Progress* (1990).

Iron Chlorides

See ETHYLENE OXIDE plus Acids and Bases. See ETHYLENE OXIDE plus Aluminum Oxide.

Iron Oxides

See ETHYLENE OXIDE plus Acids and Bases. See ETHYLENE OXIDE plus Aluminum Oxide.

Magnesium Perchlorate

See MAGNESIUM PERCHLORATE plus Ethylene Oxide.

Mercaptans

See ETHYLENE OXIDE plus Alcohols.

Potassium

See POTASSIUM plus Ethylene Oxide. See ETHYLENE OXIDE plus Acids and Bases.

Tin Chlorides

See ETHYLENE OXIDE plus Acids and Bases. See ETHYLENE OXIDE plus Aluminum Oxide.

ETHYLENEIMINE $NHCH_2CH_2$

(self-reactive)

Undiluted ethyleneimine can polymerize violently in the presence of acids or acid-forming materials.
Ethyleneimine.

Acetic Acid

See ACETIC ACID plus Ethyleneimine.

Acetic Anhydride

See ACETIC ANHYDRIDE plus Ethyleneimine.

Acrolein
See ACROLEIN plus Ethyleneimine.

Acrylic Acid
See ACRYLIC ACID plus Ethyleneimine.

Allyl Chloride
See ALLYL CHLORIDE plus Ethyleneimine.

Carbon Disulfide
See CARBON DISULFIDE plus Ethyleneimine.

Chlorine
See CHLORINE plus Ethyleneimine.

Chlorosulfonic Acid
Mixing ethyleneimine and chlorosulfonic acid in a closed container caused the temperature and pressure to increase.
Flynn and Rossow (1970). See Note under complete reference.

Epichlorohydrin
See EPICHLOROHYDRIN plus Ethyleneimine.

Glyoxal
See GLYOXAL plus Ethyleneimine.

Hydrochloric Acid
Mixing ethyleneimine and 36% hydrochloric acid in a closed container caused the temperature and pressure to increase.
Flynn and Rossow (1970). See Note under complete reference.

Hydrofluoric Acid
Mixing ethyleneimine and 48.7% hydrofluoric acid in a closed container caused the temperature and pressure to increase.
Flynn and Rossow (1970). See Note under complete reference.

Nitric Acid
Mixing ethyleneimine and 70% nitric acid in a closed container caused the temperature and pressure to increase.
Flynn and Rossow (1970). See Note under complete reference.

Oleum
See OLEUM plus Ethyleneimine.

Propiolactone (BETA-)
Mixing ethyleneimine and propiolactone (BETA-) in a closed container caused the temperature and pressure to increase.
Flynn and Rossow (1970). See Note under complete reference.

Silver
See SILVER plus Ethyleneimine.

Sodium Hypochlorite
Chlorination of ethyleneimine with sodium hypochlorite gives the explosive compound, 1-chloroethyleneimine.
A.F. Graefe and R.E. Meyer, J. *Am. Chem. Soc.* **80:** 3939 (1958).

Sulfuric Acid
Mixing ethyleneimine and 96% sulfuric acid in a closed container caused the temperature and pressure to increase.
Flynn and Rossow (1970). See Note under complete reference.

Vinyl Acetate
See VINYL ACETATE plus Ethyleneimine.

ETHYL HYPOCHLORITE CH_3CH_2OCl

(self-reactive)
Ethyl hypochlorite decomposes explosively when exposed to light and rapidly even in its absence.
Mellor **2, Supp. 1:** 560 (1956).
See also ALCOHOLS plus Hypochlorous Acid.

ETHYLIODOMETHYLARSINE $(CH_3)(C_2H_5)AsI$

Air
Methyl ethyliodoarsine occasionally ignites spontaneously in air.
ACS **15** (1923).

S-ETHYLISOTHIOUREA SULFATE
$NH_2C(NH)SC_2H_5{\cdot}H_2SO_4$

Chlorine
See CHLORINE plus S-Ethyl Isothiourea Sulfate.

ETHYLLITHIUM C_2H_5Li

Air
Ethyl lithium is spontaneously flammable in air.
Ellern (1961).

ETHYLMAGNESIUM IODIDE C_2H_5MgI

Ethoxyacetylene
A laboratory scale-up of this reaction had failed to yield the desired Grignard end-product. After one hour, the reaction vessel exploded.
Chem. and Eng. News **44** (8): 40 (1966).

ETHYLMETHYLARSINE $HAs(CH_3)(C_2H_5)$

Air
Ethylmethylarsine is spontaneously flammable in air.
Ellern, pp. 24-25 (1968).

ETHYL METHYL ETHER $CH_3OC_2H_5$

Air
See OXYGEN plus Ethers.

Lithium Aluminum Hydride
See LITHIUM ALUMINUM HYDRIDE plus Dimethyl Ether.

Oxygen
See OXYGEN plus Ethers.

ETHYL METHYL KETONE $CH_3COC_2H_5$

Chlorosulfonic Acid
Mixing methyl ethyl ketone and chlorosulfonic acid in a closed container caused the temperature and pressure to increase.
Flynn and Rossow (1970). See Note under complete reference.

Oleum
Mixing methyl ethyl ketone and oleum in a closed container caused the temperature and pressure to increase. *Flynn and Rossow* (1970). See Note under complete reference.

Potassium Tert.-Butoxide
See ACETONE plus Potassium Tert.-Butoxide.

5-ETHYL-2-METHYLPYRIDINE
$N=C(CH_3)CH=CHC(C_2H_5)=CH$ (ring closure between N and CH)

Nitric Acid
See NITRIC ACID plus 2-Methyl-5-Ethylpyridine.
See NITRIC ACID plus 5-Ethyl-2-Methyl Pyridine.

ETHYL NITRITE C_2H_5ONO

(self-reactive)
The decomposition of ethyl nitrite above 194°F can be violently explosive.
Chem. Haz. Data (1969).

ETHYL PERCHLORATE $C_2H_5ClO_4$

(self-reactive)
This compound is an explosive that exceeds the power and brisance of TNT.
ACS **146: 296. Chem. Reviews 44:** 419-45 (1949).

ETHYLPHOSPHINE $C_2H_5PH_2$

Bromine
See BROMINE plus Ethyl Phosphine.

Chlorine
See BROMINE plus Ethyl Phosphine.

Nitric Acid
See BROMINE plus Ethyl Phosphine.

5-ETHYL-2-PICOLINE $C_8H_{11}N$

Nitric Acid
This reaction results in the formation of 5-(1,1 dinitroethyl)-2- picoline, an explosive compound. In addition, the reaction itself is potentially violent, especially in closed systems.
H. Rubenstein, G. Hazen, and R. Zerfing, Chem. Eng. Data **12:** 149- 50 (1967).

ETHYL SODIO-ACETOACETATE
$C_2H_5OCOCH=CO(Na)CH_3$

2-Iodo-3, 5-Dinitrobiphenyl
See 2-IODO-3, 5-DINITROBIPHENYL plus Ethyl Sodio-Acetoacetate.

ETHYLSODIUM C_2H_5Na

Air
Ethyl sodium is spontaneously flammable in air.
Douda (1966).

EUROPIUM

Air
See RARE EARTH METALS plus Air.

Halogens
See RARE EARTH METALS plus Halogens.

FERRIC BROMIDE $FeBr_3$

Potassium
See POTASSIUM plus Boron Tribromide.

Sodium
See SODIUM plus Cobaltous Bromide.

FERRIC CHLORIDE $FeCl_3$

Allyl Chloride
See SULFURIC ACID plus Allyl Chloride.

Potassium
See POTASSIUM plus Boron Tribromide.

Sodium
See SODIUM plus Cobaltous Bromide.

FERRIC FERROCYANIDE $Fe_4[Fe(CN)_6]_3$

Lead Chromate
See LEAD CHROMATE plus Ferric Ferrocyanide.

FERRIC HYPOPHOSPHITE $Fe(PH_2O_2)_3$

(self-reactive)
Ferric hypophosphite forms impact-sensitive ammunition-priming mixtures.
Mellor **8, Supp. 3:** 623 (1971).

FERRIC OXIDE Fe_2O_3

Aluminum
See ALUMINUM plus Iron Oxide.

Calcium Hypochlorite
See CALCIUM HYPOCHLORITE plus Lead Oxide.

Cesium Carbide
See CESIUM CARBIDE plus Ferric Oxide.

Ethylene Oxide
See ETHYLENE OXIDE plus Acids and Bases. See ETHYLENE OXIDE plus Aluminum Oxide.

FERRIC OXIDE (HYDRATED) $Fe_2O_3XH_2O$

Hydrogen Sulfide
See HYDROGEN SULFIDE plus Hydrated Iron Oxide.

FERROCENE $(C_5H_5)_2Fe$

Ammonium Perchlorate
See AMMONIUM PERCHLORATE plus Dicyclopentadienyliron.

FERROUS BROMIDE $FeBr_2$

Potassium
See POTASSIUM plus Boron Tribromide.

Sodium
See SODIUM plus Cobaltous Bromide.

FERROUS CHLORIDE $FeCl_2$

Ethylene Oxide
See ETHYLENE OXIDE plus Acids and Bases.
See ETHYLENE OXIDE plus Aluminum Oxide.

Potassium
See POTASSIUM Plus Boron Tribromide.

Sodium
See SODIUM plus Ferrous Chloride.

FERROUS IODIDE FeI_2

Potassium
See POTASSIUM plus Boron Tribromide.

Sodium
See SODIUM plus Cobaltous Bromide.

FERROUS OXIDE FeO

Air
Ferrous oxide is spontaneously flammable in air.
Chem. Abst. **45:** 3276i (1951).

Ethylene Oxide
See ETHYLENE OXIDE plus Acids and Bases. See ETHYLENE OXIDE plus Aluminum Oxide.

Fluorine
See FLUORINE plus Ferrous Oxide.

Nitric Acid
When pyrophoric iron oxide is gently warmed with nitric acid, the oxide becomes incandescent.
Mellor **13:** 716 (1946-1947).

Sulfur Dioxide
When ferrous oxide, prepared at 300°C., is heated in sulfur dioxide, the mass becomes incandescent.
Mellor **13:** 715 (1946-1947).

FERROUS SULFIDE FeS

Air
Moist ferrous sulfide readily oxidizes in air and the heat evolved may cause incandescence. When ground in a mortar, the mass becomes incandescent.
Mellor **14:** 157 (1946-1947).

Hydrogen Peroxide
See ANTIMONY TRISULFIDE plus Hydrogen Peroxide.

Lithium
See LITHIUM plus Ferrous Sulfide.

FLUOBORIC ACID

Acetic Anhydride
Dehydration of the aqueous 48 percent acid by addition to the anhydride is rather exothermic, and caution is advised.
Bretherick (1979).

FLUORINE F_2

Acetaldehyde
See BROMINE plus Acetaldehyde.

Acetylene
Acetylene and fluorine will react violently.
Chem. Safety Data Sheet **SD-7** (1957).

Acrylonitrile-Butadiene Copolymer
See FLUORINE plus Solid Nonmetals and Oxygen.

Alkali Oxides
The oxides of the alkalies and alkaline earths are vigorously attacked by fluorine gas with incandescence.
Mellor **2:** 13 (1946-1947).

Alkaline Earth Oxides
See FLUORINE plus Alkali Oxides.

Alkenes
Fluorine causes unsaturated hydrocarbons to ignite spontaneously.
Mellor **2, Supp. 1:** 55 (1956).

Alkylbenzenes
Fluorine causes aromatic hydrocarbons to ignite spontaneously.
Mellor **2, Supp. 1:** 55 (1956).

Aluminum
See FLUORINE plus Metals.

Ammonia
Fluorine and ammonia burst into flame.
Mellor **1:** 12; **8:** 216 (1946-1947).
Mellor **8, Supp. 2:** 329 (1964).

Ammonium Hydroxide
Combination of fluorine and ammonium hydroxide results in flames and explosion.
Mellor **2, Supp. 1:** 56 (1956).

Antimony
See ANTIMONY plus Bromine.

Antimony Trisulfide
The reaction at ordinary temperatures between fluorine and antimony trisulfide is accompanied by a blue flame.
Mellor **9:** 522 (1946-1947).

Arsenic
Fluorine vigorously reacts with arsenic at ordinary temperatures.
Mellor **9:** 34 (1946-1947).

Arsenic Trioxide
Fluorine reacts violently with arsenic trioxide.
Mellor **9:** 101 (1946-1947).

Asphalt
See FLUORINE plus Common Materials and Oxygen.

Bakelite®
See FLUORINE plus Solid Nonmetals.

Boron
See BORON plus Fluorine.

Bromides
See FLUORINE plus Chlorides.

Bromine
Bromine unites with fluorine at ordinary temperatures with a luminous flame, forming bromine trifluoride.
Mellor **2:** (1946-1947).

Buna N
See FLUORINE plus Solid Nonmetals and Oxygen.

Calcium
See CALCIUM plus Fluorine.

Calcium Carbonate
See FLUORINE plus Carbonates.

Calcium Oxide
Even when cold, fluorine will attack calcium oxide, evolving much heat and some light.
Mellor **3:** 663 (1946-1947).

Calcium Silicide
Calcium silicide burns readily in fluorine.
Mellor **6:** 169 (1946-1947).

Carbon
Graphitic or crystallized carbon tends to react explosively with fluorine after an intermediate induction period in a manner similar to that of ice.
NASA SP- **3037:** 53, 84.
Mellor **5:** 822-30: **2:** 310 (1946-1947).
Mellor **2, Supp. 1:** 60 (1956).

Carbonates
The carbonates of sodium, lithium, calcium and lead in contact with fluorine are decomposed at ordinary temperatures with incandescence.
Mellor **2:** 13 (1946-1947).

Carbon Disulfide
A mixture of fluorine and carbon disulfide ignites at ordinary temperatures.
Mellor **2:** 13; **6:** 111 (1946-1947).

Carbon Tetrachloride
The reaction is violent and sometimes explosive.
NASA SP-**3037:** 82. *Mellor* **2, Supp. I.** 198 (1956).

Cellulose
Fluorine in contact with cotton produces a violent explosion.
Mellor **2, Supp. 1:** 54 (1956).

Cesium Acetylene Carbide
Cesium acetylene carbide burns in cold fluorine.
Mellor **5:** 849 (1946-1947).

Cesium Monoxide
See BROMINE plus Cesium Monoxide.

Cesium Perfluoro-propoxide
During preparation of perfluoropropyl hypofluorite, the intermediate cesium compound was being fluorinated with a 50/50 fluorine-nitrogen mix at minus 50°C. After 10 hours addition of fluorine, the set-up exploded.
Chem. and Eng. News **43** (9): 36 (1965). *MCA Case History* **1045** (1964).

Charcoal
See FLUORINE plus Common Materials and Oxygen.

Chlorides
Chlorides, bromides, iodides and cyanides are generally vigorously attacked by fluorine in the cold.
Mellor **2:** 13 (1946-1947).

Chlorinated Polyethylene
See FLUORINE plus Solid Nonmetals.

Chlorine
See CHLORINE plus Fluorine.

Chlorine Dioxide
The uncontrolled reaction between chlorine dioxide and fluorine is explosive.
Lawless and Smith, p. 133 (1968).
Mellor **2, Supp. 1:** 532 (1956).

Chromous Sulfide
Chromous sulfide combines with fluorine with incandescence.
Mellor **11:** 430 (1946-1947).

Chromyl Chloride
Fluorine reacts with chromyl chloride, producing flame at certain concentrations.
Mellor **2, Supp. 1:** 64 (1956).

Coke
See FLUORINE plus Common Materials and Oxygen.

Common Materials and Oxygen
Spill tests of 100% liquid fluorine, 30% liquid fluorine-in-oxygen, and 100% liquid oxygen on various common materials demonstrated the following effects of the fluorine content: asphalt and also crushed limestone (calcium carbonate) burned with sputtering and small flames; JP-4 fuel produced loud, rapid explosions and a large fireball; coke burned with a small flame; charcoal burned smoothly with a large, brilliant fireball; and rich soil burned with a bright flame.
NASA SP- **3037:** 110-119 (1967).

Copper
When fluorine flows too rapidly or under too much pressure in copper tubing, the copper burns in the fluorine atmosphere. See also FLUORINE plus Metals.
Yunker (1966). *Cady* (1966).

Copper Hydride
See BROMINE plus Copper Hydride.

Cyanides
See FLUORINE plus Chlorides.

Cyanogen
Cyanogen is decomposed by fluorine gas at ordinary temperatures with the production of a white flame.
Mellor **2:** 13 (1946-1947).

Ferrous Oxide
Fluorine does not act in the cold on ferrous oxide, but with gentle heat a reaction sets in with incandescence.
Mellor **13:** 715 (1946-1947).

Graphite
Graphite burns in a stream of fluorine. See also FLUORINE plus Carbon.
Mellor **2, Supp. I:** 198 (1956).

Halogenated Compounds
See FLUORINE plus Hydrogen.

Hexafluoropropylene- Vinylidene Fluoride Copolymer
See FLUORINE plus Solid Nonmetals and Oxygen.

Hydrazine
Spontaneous ignition occurs when these chemicals are mixed.
Mellor **8, Supp. 2:** 95 (1967).

Hydriodic Acid
The reaction of fluorine with gaseous hydriodic acid is accompanied by flame.
Mellor **2:** 12 (1946-1947).

Hydrobromic Acid
The reaction of fluorine with gaseous or aqueous hydrobromic acid is accompanied by flame.
Mellor **2:** 12 (1946-1947).

Hydrocarbons
Violent explosions are encountered when attempts are made to fluorinate hydrocarbons in the liquid phase with elementary fluorine. Many lubricants burn in fluorine.
Mellor **2: Supp. I:** 198 (1956).
NASA SP- **3037:** 82-84 (1967).
Mellor **2, Supp. 1:** 55 (1956).

Hydrochloric Acid
The reaction of fluorine with gaseous or aqueous hydrochloric acid is accompanied by flame.
Mellor **2:** 12, 204-6 (1946-1947).

Hydrofluoric Acid (Aqueous)
If fluorine is passed into a 50 percent solution of hydrofluoric acid, there is an energetic reaction with the water and it is accompanied by flame.
Mellor **2:** 12 (1946-1947).

Hydrogen
Hydrogen and fluorine combine with extreme violence. The reactions of most organic compounds with fluorine occur explosively. Even halogenated organic materials burn or explode in a fluorine atmosphere. The reaction with water is violent even at minus 210°C.
Matheson Gas Data, p. 215 (1961). *Stecher,* pp. 301-2 (1953).
Fluorine and hydrogen react as low as minus 210°C when impurities are present.
Mellor **1:** 327 (1946-1947).

Hydrogen Azide
See AZINE FLUORIDE (self-reactive).

Hydrogen Sulfide
Fluorine ignites in contact with hydrogen sulfide.
Mellor **10:** 133 (1946-1947).

Iodides
See FLUORINE plus Chlorides.

Iodine
Iodine unites with fluorine at ordinary temperatures with a luminous flame.
Mellor **2:** 12 (1946-1947).

Iridium
See IRIDIUM plus Fluorine.

Iron
See FLUORINE plus Metals. See also IRON plus FLUORINE.

JP-4 Fuel
See FLUORINE plus Common Materials and Oxygen.

Lead Carbonate (Basic)
White lead burns in fluorine. See also FLUORINE plus Carbonates.
NASA SP- **3037:** 83 (1967).

Lead Oxide and Glycerol
A mixture of litharge and glycerol burns in fluorine.
NASA SP- **3037:** 84 (1967).

Limestone (crushed)
See FLUORINE plus Common Materials and Oxygen.

Lithium Carbide
See BROMINE plus Lithium Carbide.

Lithium Carbonate
See FLUORINE plus Carbonates.

Lithium Silicide
When lithium silicide is warmed with gaseous fluorine, a reaction takes place with incandescence. With chlorine, bromine, and iodine a higher temperature is required.
Mellor **6:** 169 (1946-1947).

Lucite®
See FLUORINE plus Solid Nonmetals and Oxygen.

Magnesium
See MAGNESIUM plus Fluorine.

Manganese
See MANGANESE plus Fluorine.

Manganous Oxide
See FLUORINE plus Trimanganese Tetroxide.

Manufactured Gas
Unlighted manufactured gas issuing from a gas jet is immediately ignited by fluorine gas.
Mellor **2:** 13 (1946-1947).

Mercuric Cyanide
Fluorine and mercuric cyanide react vigorously when gently heated, producing flames.
Mellor **2, Supp. 1:** 63 (1956).

Metals
Metals (powdered) are in general attacked by fluorine at ordinary temperatures. If the temperature is raised nearly all the metals are vigorously attacked with incandescence.
Mellor **2:** 13 (1946-1947).
Some average ignition temperatures (°F) of various metals in fluorine are: aluminum, greater than 1220; copper, 692; iron, 672; molybdenum, 205; monel, 396; nickel, 1162; stainless steel (No. 302), 681; and tungsten, 283.
NASA SP- **3037:** 79-80 (1967).

Molybdenum
See FLUORINE plus Metals. See also MOLYBDENUM plus FLUORINE.

Monel®
See FLUORINE plus Metals.

Neoprene
When pieces of neoprene are dropped into liquid fluorine slight explosions occur and the neoprene burns. Neoprene covered fiber glass exploded in liquid fluorine. See also FLUORINE plus Solid Nonmetals.
NASA SP- **3037:** 84
Mellor **2, Supp. 1:** 54 (1956).
Chem. and Eng. News **26:** 3336-7 (1948).

Nickel
See FLUORINE plus Metals.

Nickel Monoxide
Nickel monoxide becomes incandescent in fluorine gas.
Ann. Chim. et Phys. (5) **21:** 199, 386.
NASA SP- **3037:** 84.

Niobium (Columbium)
See NIOBIUM plus Fluorine.

Nitric Acid
If fluorine is passed into nitric acid, each bubble of gas is attended by the decomposition of the acid and accompanied by flame.
Ann. Chim. et Phys. (6) **24:** 224.

Fluorine in contact with nitric acid creates a danger of explosion if acid is not 100% strength.
Mellor **8, Supp. 2:** 319 (1967).

Nitric Oxide
Fluorine reacts immediately with nitric oxide with a pale yellow flame.
Ann. Chim. et Phys. (8) **9:** 221.
Mellor **2, Supp. 1:** 54 (1956).

Nitrogen Dioxide
Fluorine and nitrogen dioxide react vigorously when heated.
Mellor **2, Supp. 1:** 54 (1956).

Nylon
See FLUORINE plus Solid Nonmetals and Oxygen.

Organic Matter (Leather)
Fluorine in contact with leather causes it to smolder and char.
Mellor **2, Supp. 1:** 54 (1956).

Perchloric Acid
Reaction of fluorine and perchloric acid produces fluorine perchlorate, a highly reactive material.
Mellor **2, Supp. 1:** 59 (1956).
See also FLUORINE PERCHLORATE (self-reactive).
The action of fluorine gas in 60-72% perchloric acid leads to the formation of fluorine perchlorate, a very unstable gas that explodes under the most diverse physical and chemical influences.
Pascal **16:** 316 (1931-1934). *Kirk and Othmer, Second Ed.* **5:** 74 (1963).

Perfluoropropionyl Fluoride
Fluorination of perfluoropropionyl fluoride to synthesize perfluoropropionyl hypofluorite in the presence of activated cesium fluoride catalyst involves potential explosion hazards. No temperature change was noted during the 10-hour addition of fluorine at minus 40°C, but the setup exploded at the finish of the addition.
MCA Case History **1045** (1965).
Chem. and Eng. News **43:** 36 (March 1, 1965).

Phenol-Formaldehyde Resin
See FLUORINE plus Solid Nonmetals and Oxygen.

Phosphorus
Fluorine reacts with red or yellow phosphorus at ordinary temperatures and the reaction is accompanied by incandescence.
Mellor **8:** 785 (1946-1947).
Mellor **2, Supp. 1:** 60 (1956).
See also PHOSPHORUS plus Chlorine.

Phosphorus Pentachloride
When phosphorus pentachloride is treated with fluorine, the entire mass becomes incandescent.
Moissan, p. 134 (1900).

Phosphorus Trichloride
Phosphorus trichloride reacts with fluorine with incandescence.
Moissan, p. 134 (1900).

Phosphorus Trifluoride
A yellow flame appears when fluorine contacts phosphorus trifluoride.
Comp. Rend. **138:** 789.

Polyamide
See FLUORINE plus Solid Nonmetals and Oxygen.

Polychloroprene
See FLUORINE plus Solid Nonmetals and Oxygen.

Polyethylene
See FLUORINE plus Solid Nonmetals and Oxygen.

Polymethylmethacrylate
See FLUORINE plus Solid Nonmetals and Oxygen.

Polytetrafluoroethylene
See FLUORINE plus Solid Nonmetals and Oxygen.

Polyurethane
See FLUORINE plus Solid Nonmetals and Oxygen.

Polyvinylchloride Acetate
See FLUORINE plus Solid Nonmetals and Oxygen.

Potassium
See POTASSIUM plus Fluorine.

Potassium Hydride
See CHLORINE plus Potassium Hydride.

Potassium Nitrate
Fluorine attacks potassium nitrate to give fluorine nitrate.
Mellor **2, Supp. 1:** 62 (1956).
See also FLUORINE NITRATE (self-reactive).

Potassium Perchlorate
The action at low pressure of fluorine on potassium perchlorate produces fluorine perchlorate, which is very unstable and explodes easily.
Pascal **16:** 316 (1931-1934).

Rhenium
See RHENIUM plus Fluorine.

Rubber (LS-53 and LS-63)
See FLUORINE plus Solid Nonmetals and Oxygen.

Rubidium Acetylene Carbide
See BROMINE plus Rubidium Acetylene Carbide.

Selenium
Selenium, silicon, or sulfur ignites in fluorine gas at ordinary temperatures.
Mellor **2:** 11-13; **6:** 161-4 (1946-1947).

Silicon
See FLUORINE plus Selenium.

Silver Cyanide
Fluorine and silver cyanide react with explosive violence at ordinary temperatures.
Mellor **2, Supp. 1:** 63 (1956).

Sodium
See SODIUM plus Fluorine.

Sodium Acetate
Fluorine and sodium acetate produce an explosive reaction involving formation of diacetyl peroxide.
Mellor **2, Supp. 1:** 56 (1956).
See also DIACETYL PEROXIDE (self-reactive).

Sodium Carbonate
See FLUORINE plus Carbonates.

Sodium Hydride
See CHLORINE plus Sodium Hydride.

Sodium Silicate
Sodium silicate (water glass) burns in fluorine.
NASA SP- **3037:** 82 (1967).

Soil (rich)
See FLUORINE plus Common Materials and Oxygen.

Solid Nonmetals and Oxygen
Numerous nonmetal materials were tested statically on gaseous and liquid fluorine-oxygen mixtures with 50 to 100% fluorine. Substances that burned or reacted violently were: Tygon® (polyvinyl chloride-acetate), nylon (polyamide), Bakelite® (phenol-formaldehyde resin), polyethylene, neoprene (polychloroprene), Buna N (acrylonitrile-butadiene copolymer), LS-53 and LS-63 Rubber (trifluoropropyl methyl polysiloxane), Viton A® (vinylidene fluoride-hexafluoropropylene copolymer) and polyurethane foam. Under dynamic conditions, i.e., flow and pressure, other materials such as Lucite® (polymethyl methacrylate), Teflon® (polytetrafluoroethylene), and CPE products (chlorinated polyethylenes) also ignited in fluorine-oxygen mixtures.
NASA SP- **3037:** 87-110 (1967).

Stainless Steel (302)
See FLUORINE plus Metals.

Strontium Phosphide
Mixtures of these materials ignite at room temperatures.
Mellor **8:** 841 (1946-1947).

Sulfur
See FLUORINE plus Selenium.

Sulfur Dioxide
Each bubble of sulfur dioxide gas led into a container of fluorine produces an explosion.
Mellor **2:** 1 (1946-1947)

Tantalum
Fluorine attacks powdered tantalum with incandescence.
Mellor **9:** 891 (1946-1947).
Fluorine reacts vigorously with tantalum. The metal should not be used to handle it.
Mellor **2, Supp. 1:** 62 (1956).

Teflon®
See FLUORINE plus Solid Nonmetals and Oxygen.

Tellurium
Fluorine attacks tellurium with incandescence.
Mellor **11:** 26, 40 (1946-1947).

Thallium
Fluorine acts so vigorously on thallium that the metal becomes incandescent.
Mellor **5:** 421, 434 (1946-1947).

Thallous Chloride
Fluorine and thallous chloride react violently, melting the product.
Mellor **2, Supp. 1:** 63 (1956).

Titanium
When titanium is fractured in a liquid fluorine atmosphere, it ignites. With catalysis, titanium has ignited in gaseous fluorine at minus 113°F.
NASA SP- **3037:** 70 (1967).

Trifluoropropyl Methyl Polysiloxane
See FLUORINE plus Solid Nonmetals and Oxygen.

Trimanganese Tetroxide
Fluorine and trimanganese tetroxide or manganous oxide react vigorously below 100°C, even when diluted with nitrogen.
Mellor **2, Supp. 1:** 64 (1956).

Tungsten
The reaction between fluorine and tungsten is accompanied by incandescence. See also FLUORINE plus Metals.
Mellor **11:** 730 (1946-1947).

Tungsten Carbide
Tungsten carbide becomes incandescent in cold fluorine.
Mellor **5:** 890 (1946-1947).

Tygon®
See FLUORINE plus Solid Nonmetals and Oxygen.

Uranium
Electrolytic uranium, as fine powder, is vigorously attacked by fluorine, and burns. Uranium ignites spontaneously in cold fluorine.
Mellor **2:** 13; **12:** 31, 32 (1946-1947).

Uranium Carbide
See BROMINE plus Uranium Dicarbide.

Viton A®
See FLUORINE plus Solid Nonmetals and Oxygen.

Water
Water *vapor* will react combustively with fluorine; an explosive reaction occurs between liquid fluorine and ice, after an intermediate induction period.
NASA SP- **3037:** 52 (1967).
If liquid air which has stood for some time is treated with fluorine, a precipitate is formed which is very likely to explode. Explosive material is thought to be fluorine hydrate.
Mellor **2:** 11 (1946-1947).
See also FLUORINE plus Hydrogen.

Zinc
Zinc burns in moist fluorine.
Mellor **4:** 476 (1946-1947).

Zirconium Dicarbide
See BROMINE plus Zirconium Dicarbide.

FLUORINE AZIDE N_3F

(self-reactive)
Azine fluoride was detected in the products obtained from the reaction of fluorine with nitrogen-diluted hydrogen azide. The liquid is extremely shock- and light-sensitive and often explodes on vaporization.
Lawless and Smith, p. 104 (1968).
Fluorine azide is extremely unstable and easily decomposes explosively.
Mellor **2, Supp. 1:** 59 (1956).
Mellor **8, Supp. 2:** 24 (1967).

FLUORINE FLUOROSULFATE FSO_2OF

(self-reactive)
Fluorine fluorosulfate, which has a vapor pressure of 10 atmospheres at room temperature, was distilled cold into a steel cylinder rated at 135 atmospheres. When the cylin-

der reached room temperature, it exploded. The violence indicated a chemical explosion.
Chem. and Eng. News **44:** 40 (Feb. 21, 1966).
MCA Case History **1189** (1966).

FLUORINE NITRATE $FONO_2$

(self-reactive)
Fluorine nitrate explodes on slight concussion.
Merck Index, p. 464 (1968).

FLUORINE PERCHLORATE $FOClO_3$

(self-reactive)
Pure fluorine perchlorate exploded in three attempts to determine its freezing point. The gas readily explodes on contact with a small flame or spark.
ACS **146:** 209. *J. Am. Chem. Soc.* **69:** 667-8 (1947).
Mellor **2, Supp. 1:** 59, 184 (1956).
See also POTASSIUM PERCHLORATE plus Fluorine.

Organic Matter
Fluorine perchlorate undergoes explosive decomposition on contact with grease, dirt, or rubber tubing.
Mellor **2, Supp. 1:** 184 (1956).

Potassium Iodide
A sample of fluorine perchlorate exploded on contact with a potassium iodide solution.
ACS **146:** 209-10. *J. Am. Chem. Soc.* **69:** 667-8 (1947).
Fluorine perchlorate in contact with potassium iodide can cause an explosion.
Mellor **2, Supp. 1:** 184 (1956).

FLUORINE PEROXIDE F_2O_2

(self-reactive)
Fluorine peroxide is a very unstable vapor above minus 100°C, decomposing to fluorine and oxygen gases.
Mellor **2, Supp. 1:** 194 (1956).

FLUOROACETYLENE HC≡CF

(self-reactive)
Fluoroacetylene is a colorless gas that freezes at minus 196°C to a white solid, which melts to a liquid whose boiling point is a little below minus 80°C. The liquid sometimes explodes with great force. The silver salt detonates when warmed, and the mercury salt decomposes violently without detonation when warmed.
Rutledge, p. 135 (1968).

FLUOROCHLORO-LUBRICANTS

Aluminum
See ALUMINUM plus Fluorochloro-lubricants.

FLUORODIMETHYLARSINE $(CH_3)_2AsF$

Air
Dimethylfluoroarsine is spontaneously flammable in air.
Ripley (1966).

1-FLUORO-2,2-DINITROETHANE $CH_2FCH(NO_3)_2$

Air
Abnormal operating conditions during the nitration process in preparation of dinitrofluoroethane caused the operator to relieve the vacuum by introducing air. The resulting reaction with air caused an explosion.
MCA Case History **784** (1962).

FORMALDEHYDE HCHO

Nitrogen Dioxide
The slow reaction between nitrogen dioxide and formaldehyde becomes explosive in the region of 180°C.
F. H. Pollard and P. Woodward, *Trans. Faraday Soc.* **45:** 767-770 (1949).

Perchloric Acid and Aniline
See PERCHLORIC ACID plus Aniline and Formaldehyde.

Performic Acid
See PERFORMIC ACID plus Formaldehyde.

FORMAMIDINE THIOLACETIC ACID HYDROCHLORIDE $NH_2C(NH)SCH_2COOH{\cdot}HCl$

Chlorine
See CHLORINE plus S-Ethyl Isothiourea Sulfate.

FORMIC ACID HCOOH

Furfuryl Alcohol
See FURFURYL ALCOHOL plus Formic Acid.

Hydrogen Peroxide
See HYDROGEN PEROXIDE plus Formic Acid and Organic Matter.

Thallium Trinitrate Trihydrate
See THALLIUM TRINITRATE TRIHYDRATE plus Formic Acid.

FURAN-2-PEROXYCARBOXYLIC ACID
OCH = CHCH = CCOOOH

(self-reactive)
This acid explodes when heated to 30 to 40°C, or at room temperature upon addition of organic or inorganic materials such as carbon black, calcium chloride, barium chloride, strontium chloride or magnesium chloride.
Chem. Reviews **45:** 15, 16 (1949).

FURFURYL ALCOHOL $OCH=CHCH=CCH_2OH$

Cyanoacetic Acid
An explosion occurred in a laboratory when cyanoacetic acid was reacted with furfuryl alcohol in an attempt to form the ester, furfuryl cyanoacetate. The explosion occurred a few minutes after the agitator was turned on and the heat applied.
MCA Case History **858** (1963).

Formic Acid
During an attempt to prepare furfuryl formate from furfuryl alcohol and concentrated formic acid, an explosion occurred.
Chem. and Eng. News **18:** 72 (1940).

Mineral Acids
Furfuryl alcohol will polymerize rapidly, and sometimes with explosive violence, in the presence of strong mineral acids.
Hexagon Alpha Chi Sigma (October 1949).

Nitric Acid
See NITRIC ACID plus Organic Matter.
See NITRIC ACID plus Furfuryl Alcohol.
See also NITRIC ACID plus Diborane.

Nitric Acid, Nitrogen Tetroxide, and Sulfuric Acid
See UNSYMMETRICAL DIMETHYLHYDRAZINE plus Nitric Acid, Nitrogen Tetroxide, and Sulfuric Acid.

GADOLINIUM Gd

Air
See RARE EARTH METALS plus Air.

Halogens
See RARE EARTH METALS plus Halogens.

GALLIC ACID $(OH)_3C_6H_2COOH$

Potassium Chlorate
See POTASSIUM CHLORATE plus Gallic Acid.

GALLIUM HYDRIDE Ga_2H_6

Air
Gallium hydride is spontaneously flammable in air.
Hurd, p. 99 (1952).

GALLIUM PERCHLORATE $Ga(ClO_3)_3$

Urea
The double salt formed decomposes violently on heating.
Mellor **2, Supp. 1:** 611 (1956).

GERMANE (GERMANIUM HYDRIDE) GeH_4

Air
The germanium hydrides are spontaneously flammable in air.
Fawcett (1965). *Brauer* (1965).

GERMANIUM Ge

Bromine
When heated in bromine, germanium burns with a yellowish flame.
Mellor **7:** 260 (1946-1947).

Chlorine
When germanium is heated in chlorine, it burns with a bluish-white flame. Powdered germanium ignites spontaneously in chlorine at ordinary temperatures.
Mellor **7:** 260 (1946-1947).

Nitric Acid
The action of concentrated nitric acid on powdered germanium is very violent.
Mellor **7:** 260 (1946-1947).

Oxygen
Germanium burns with incandescence when heated in oxygen.
Mellor **7:** 260 (1946-1947).

Potassium Chlorate
See GERMANIUM plus Potassium Nitrate.

Potassium Nitrate
Mixture of germanium with potassium nitrate or potassium chlorate explodes when heated.
Mellor **7:** 261 (1946-1947).

GERMANIUM HYDRIDE GeH_4

Air
See GERMANE plus Air.

GERMANIUM HYDRIDES GeH_4; Ge_2H_6; Ge_3H_8

Air
The germanium hydrides decompose in air, often bursting into flames.
Brauer (1965).

GERMANIUM SULFIDE GeS_2

Potassium Nitrate
When germanium sulfide is mixed with potassium nitrate and heated, it explodes.
Mellor **7:** 274 (1946-1947).

GERMANIUM TETRACHLORIDE $GeCl_4$

Water
Germanium tetrachloride is decomposed by water and much heat is developed.
Mellor **7:** 270 (1946-1947).

GERMANIUM TETRAIODIDE GeI_4

Air
The vapor of germanium tetraiodide is flammable in air.
Mellor **7:** 272, 273 (1946-1947).

GLASS

Chlorine Trifluoride
See CHLORINE TRIFLUORIDE plus Charcoal.

GLYCERIDES $(RCOOCH_2)CHOCOR$

Nitric Acid and Sulfuric Acid
See NITRIC ACID plus Sulfuric Acid and Glycerides.

GLYCEROL $HOCH_2CHOHCH_2OH$

Acetic Anhydride
See ACETIC ANHYDRIDE plus Glycerol.

Aniline and Nitrobenzene
See ANILINE plus Nitrobenzene and Glycerine.

Calcium Hypochlorite
See CALCIUM HYPOCHLORITE plus Glycerol and CALCIUM HYPOCHLORITE plus Ethyl Alcohol.

Chlorine
See CHLORINE plus Polypropylene.

Chromic Anhydride
See CHROMIC ANHYDRIDE plus Naphthalene.

Chromium Oxide
See CHROMIUM OXIDE plus Glycerol.

Fluorine and Lead Oxide
See FLUORINE plus Lead Oxide and Glycerol.

Perchloric Acid and Lead Oxide
See LEAD OXIDE plus Perchloric Acid and Glycerine.

Potassium Permanganate
See POTASSIUM PERMANGANATE plus Glycerol.

Potassium Peroxide
See SODIUM PEROXIDE plus Aniline.

Silver Perchlorate
See SILVER PERCHLORATE plus Acetic Acid.

Sodium Peroxide
See SODIUM PEROXIDE plus Aniline.

GLYCOL ETHERS

Perchloric Acid
See PERCHLORIC ACID plus Glycol Ethers.

GLYCOLONITRILE $HOCH_2CN$

(self-reactive)
A bottle containing freshly purified glycolonitrile sat for a week before a portion of it was removed. Six days later, the remainder polymerized and exploded the bottle.
Chem. and Eng. News **42** (48): 50 (Nov. 28, 1966).

GLYCOL PERCHLORATES

(self-reactive)
Glycol perchlorate and epichlorohydrin perchlorate are more explosive than nitroglycerine. Ethylene glycol perchlorate is so sensitive that a few drops of water cause a violent explosion.
ACS **146:** 214. *Berichte* **42:** 2031-4 (1909).

GLYCOLS

Perchloric Acid
See PERCHLORIC ACID plus Glycol Ethers.

GLYOXAL OCHCHO

(self-reactive)
See GLYOXAL plus Water.

Air
Mixtures with air may explode.
Merck Index, p. 502 (1968).
See also GLYOXAL plus Water.

Chlorosulfonic Acid
Mixing glyoxal and chlorosulfonic acid in a closed container caused the temperature and pressure to increase.
Flynn and Rossow (1970). See Note under complete reference.

Ethyleneimine
Mixing glyoxal and ethyleneimine in a closed container caused the temperature and pressure to increase.
Flynn and Rossow (1970). See Note under complete reference.

Nitric Acid
See NITRIC ACID plus Glyoxal.

Oleum
Mixing glyoxal and oleum in a closed container caused the temperature and pressure to increase.
Flynn and Rossow (1970). See Note under complete reference.

Sodium Hydroxide
See SODIUM HYDROXIDE plus Glyoxal.

Water
Glyoxal polymerizes quickly on standing, on contact with water (violent reaction), or when dissolved in solvents containing water.
Merck Index, p. 502 (1968).

GOLD Au

Ammonia
The reaction between ammonia and gold, silver, or mercury produces fulminate-like compounds of variable and uncertain composition that explode when dried. Severe accidents have occurred.
Chem. Abst. **60:** 12, 14327 (1964).
Mellor **3:** 579-84 (1946-1947).
Allison (1966). J. K. Luchs, *Phot. Sci. Eng.* **10:** 334-7 (1966).

Ammonium Hydroxide and Aqua Regia
In an effort to precipitate finely divided gold from aqua regia, ammonium hydroxide was substituted for ammonium oxalate. When the gold precipitate was heated in a muffle furance with other metals to produce an alloy, an explosion occurred.
U. Wash. Occ. Health Newsletter **16** (1967).

Hydrogen Peroxide
Finely divided gold and a strong hydrogen peroxide solution may explode.
Mellor **1:** 936 (1946-1947).

GOLD CYANIDE AuCN; $Au(CN)_3 3H_2O$

Magnesium
See MAGNESIUM plus Gold Cyanide.

GOLD SALTS

Nitromethane
See COPPER SALTS plus Nitromethane.

GRAPHITE C

Chlorine Trifluoride
See CHLORINE TRIFLUORIDE plus Charcoal.

Fluorine
See FLUORINE plus Charcoal.

Potassium
See POTASSIUM plus Charcoal.

Potassium Superoxide
See POTASSIUM plus Graphite and Air.
Also see POTASSIUM plus Graphite and Potassium Superoxide.

GUANIDINE PERCHLORATE $(NH_2)_3CClO_4$

(self-reactive)
Guanidine perchlorate is unusually sensitive to initiation and has extraordinary explosive power.
ACS **146:** 213 *Davis* (1943).

HAFNIUM TETRAHYDROBORATE $Hf(BH_4)_4$

Air
Hafnium borohydride burns violently when exposed to air.
Gaylord, p. 58 (1966).

HALOGEN FLUORIDES

Organic Matter
See BROMINE MONOFLUORIDE plus Water.
See individual fluoride plus Organic Matter.

HALOGENS

Cerium
See RARE EARTH METALS plus Halogens.

Dysprosium
See RARE EARTH METALS plus Halogens.

Erbium
See RARE EARTH METALS plus Halogens.

Europium
See RARE EARTH METALS plus Halogens.

Gadolinium
See RARE EARTH METALS plus Halogens.

Hafnium
See RARE EARTH METALS plus Halogens.

Holmium
See RARE EARTH METALS plus Halogens.

Lutetium
See RARE EARTH METALS plus Halogens.

Neodymium
See RARE EARTH METALS plus Halogens.

Praseodymium
See RARE EARTH METALS plus Halogens.

Rare Earth Metals
See RARE EARTH METALS plus Halogens.

Samarium
See RARE EARTH METALS plus Halogens.

Terbium
See RARE EARTH METALS plus Halogens.

Thulium
See RARE EARTH METALS plus Halogens.

Tri-iso-Butyl Aluminum
See TRI-iso-BUTYL ALUMINUM plus Acids.

Ytterbium
See RARE EARTH METALS plus Halogens.

Yttrium
See RARE EARTH METALS plus Halogens.

N-HALOIMIDES (INCLUDING TRICHLOROISOCYANURIC ACID)

Alcohols, Amines, Diallyl Sulfide,Hydrazine, or Xylene
Many of the reactions of several N-chloro- and N-bromo-imides are extremely violent or explosive.
Bretherick (1978).

HEPTANE C_7H_{16}

Phosphorus and Chlorine
See PHOSPHORUS plus Chlorine and Heptane.

HEXABORANE (10) B_6H_{10}

Air
Boron hexahydride is spontaneously flammable in air.
Douda (1966).

HEXABORANE (12) B_6H_{12}

Air
This hydride is spontaneously flammable in air.
Mellor **5:** 36 (1946-1947).
Douda (1966).

HEXACHLOROBENZENE C_6Cl_6

Dimethyl Formamide
See DIMETHYL FORMAMIDE plus Hexachlorobenzene.

HEXACHLOROMELAMINE
$N=C(NCl_2)N=C(NCl_2)N=C(NCl_2)$

Acetone
See HEXACHLOROMELAMINE plus Organic Contaminants.

Ammonia
See HEXACHLOROMELAMINE plus Organic Contaminants.

Aniline
See HEXACHLOROMELAMINE plus Organic Contaminants.

Diphenylamine
See HEXACHLOROMELAMINE plus Organic Contaminants.

Organic Contaminants
Organic contaminants added to hexachloromelamine cause a very rapid reaction to take place with or without visible flame. Contaminants tested were acetone, aniline, diphenylamine, ammonia and others. The hexachloromelamine would explode if the amount were large and confined. Trichloromelamine behaves similarly; however, it consumes itself less rapidly, but with more flame and fume production. After the contaminant is added, there is a delay of several seconds before anything happens.
Ventrone (1968).

Turpentine
See HEXACHLOROMELAMINE plus Organic Contaminants.

1,5-HEXADIEN-3-YNE $H_2C=CHC \equiv CCH=CH_2$

Air
Divinylacetylene reacts with oxygen to form an explosive peroxide polymer. Divinylacetylene must be handled in an oxygen-free atmosphere. After experiments are completed the equipment should be rinsed immediately with solvents containing a polymerization inhibitor to prevent formation of unstable films. Handy and Bensen, *J. Org. Chem.* **27:** 39 (1962).

2, 4-HEXADIYN-1, 6-BISCHLOROSULFITE
$(ClSOOCH_2C \equiv C-)_2$

(self-reactive)
See THIONYL CHLORIDE plus 2, 4-Hexadiyn-1, 6-Diol.

2, 4-hexadiyn-1, 6-bischlorosulfite is shock-sensitive and decomposes violently upon distillation.
P. E. Drieder and H. V. Isaacson, *Chem. and Eng. News* **50** (12): 51 (1972).

2, 4-HEXADIYN-1, 6-DIOL $(HOCH_2C{\equiv}C\text{-})_2$

Phosgene
See PHOSGENE plus 2, 4-Hexadiyn-1, 6-Diol.

Thionyl Chloride
See THIONYL CHLORIDE plus 2, 4-Hexadiyn-1, 6-Diol.

HEXAFLUOROPROPYLENE-VINYLIDINE COPOLYMER

Fluorine
See FLUORINE plus Solid Nonmetals and Oxygen.

HEXAMETHYLBENZENE $C_6(CH_3)_6$

Nitromethane
The electro-oxidation of various methyl benzenes was being stud ied. During the reactions, violent explosions occurred at the auxiliary electrode.
Chem. and Eng. News **49** (23): 6 (1971).

HEXAMETHYLENE DIISOCYANATE $OCN(CH_2)_6NCO$

Alcohols
See ALCOHOLS plus Isocyanates.

HEXAMETHYLENETETRAMINE $(CH_2)_6N_4$

Sodium Peroxide
See SODIUM PEROXIDE plus Hexamethylenetetramine.

HOLMIUM Ho

Air
See RARE EARTH METALS plus Air.

Halogens
See RARE EARTH METALS plus Halogens.

HYDRAZINE H_2NNH_2

Air
Hydrazine may ignite spontaneously while absorbed on porous materials such as earth, asbestos, cloth, or wood unless the heat of the gradual hydrazine-air reaction has a chance to dissipate. Spontaneous ignition can occur with hydrogen peroxide and nitric acid. Contact with many metallic oxide surfaces may lead to flaming decomposition.
Haz. Chem. Data (1966).
Mellor **8, Supp. 2:** 95 (1967).

Alkali Metals and Ammonia
Explosive metal hydrazides form when hydrazine and alkali metals are mixed in liquid ammonia.
Mellor **8, Supp. 2:** 73 (1967).

Chlorine
See CHLORINE plus Hydrazine.

Chromates
See CHROMATES plus Hydrazine.

Cupric Oxide
See CUPRIC OXIDE plus Hydrazine.

Cupric Salts
See CUPRIC SALTS plus Hydrazine.

Fluorine
See FLUORINE plus Hydrazine.

Hydrogen Peroxide
See HYDRAZINE plus Air.
Mellor **8, Supp. 2:** 95 (1967).

Iron Oxide
While boiling a sample of a polyester fiber in hydrazine in a glass beaker, the technician used a somewhat rusty pair of metal tweezers to handle the sample. When the tweezers were put in the solution, the solution ignited. The ignition temperature of hydrazine varies from 75°F in the presence of iron oxide to 518°F in a glass container.
MCA Case History 1893 (1973).

Metallic Oxides
See HYDRAZINE plus Air.

Nickel
See NICKEL plus Hydrazine.

Nickel Perchlorate
See NICKEL PERCHLORATE plus Hydrazine.

Nitric Acid
See HYDRAZINE plus Air.
Spontaneous ignition occurs when these chemicals are mixed.
Mellor **8, Supp. 2:** 95 (1967).

Nitrous Oxide
See NITROUS OXIDE plus Lithium Hydride.

Oxygen
See OXYGEN plus Hydrazine.

Oxygen (liquid)
See OXYGEN (LIQUID) plus Hydrazine.

Potassium Dichromate
See POTASSIUM DICHROMATE plus Hydrazine.

Sodium Dichromate
See POTASSIUM DICHROMATE plus Hydrazine.

Tetryl
During the measurement of shock sensitivity of a mixture containing hydrazine, a drop of the hydrazine mixture fell inadvertently on the tetryl donor explosive. The tetryl immediately burst into flame.
ASESB Operational Incident Report **105.**

Zinc Diamide
See ZINC DIAMIDE plus Hydrazine.

Zinc Diethyl
See ZINC DIAMIDE plus Hydrazine.

HYDRAZINE AZIDE $H_2NNH_3N_3$

(self-reactive)
This is an explosive salt.
Mellor **8, Supp. 2:** 86 (1967).

Air
When hydrazine azide is rapidly heated in air, as by a white-hot wire, the salt decomposes violently. Similar ex-

plosions occur when a detonator is used. The moist salt is also explosive.
Mellor **8:** 344 (1946-1947).

HYDRAZINE CHLORITE $H_2NNH_3ClO_2$

(self-reactive)
This is an explosive salt, highly flammable when dry.
Mellor **8, Supp. 2:** 85 (1967).
Mellor **2, Supp. 1:** 573 (1956).

HYDRAZINE HYDRATE $H_2NNH_2{\cdot}H_2O$

2,4-Dinitrochlorobenzene
This reaction is exothermic; it shattered the reaction flask.
Wischmeyer (1967).

Mercuric Oxide
See MERCURIC OXIDE plus Hydrazine Hydrate.

Sodium
See SODIUM plus Hydrazine Hydrate.

Stannous Chloride
See STANNOUS CHLORIDE plus Hydrazine Hydrate.

HYDRAZINE MONONITRATE $H_2NNH_2HNO_3$

Copper
See ZINC plus Hydrazine Mononitrate.

Metal Carbides
See ZINC plus Hydrazine Mononitrate.

Metal Nitrides
See ZINC plus Hydrazine Mononitrate.

Metal Oxides
See ZINC plus Hydrazine Mononitrate.

Metal Sulfides
See ZINC plus Hydrazine Mononitrate.

Zinc
See ZINC plus Hydrazine Mononitrate.

HYDRAZINE NITRATE $H_2NNH_3NO_3$

(self-reactive)
This explosive salt is less stable than ammonium nitrate.
Mellor **8, Supp. 2:** 86 (1967).

HYDRAZINE PERCHLORATE $H_2NNH_3ClO_4$

(self-reactive)
Dry hydrazine perchlorate can be detonated by shock or friction.
ACS-**146:** 209.
Comp. Rend. **228:** 1497-8 (1949).
Mellor **8, Supp. 2:** 85 (1967).

HYDRAZINE SELENATE $H_2NNH_2SeO_3OH$

(self-reactive)
This salt is explosive.
Mellor **8, Supp. 2:** 85 (1967).

HYDRAZOIC ACID N_3H

Cadmium
See CADMIUM plus Hydrazoic Acid.

Copper
See COPPER plus Hydrazoic Acid.

Nickel
See NICKEL plus Hydrazoic Acid.

Nitric Acid
The reaction of hydrazoic acid and nitric acid is energetic.
Mellor **8, Supp. 2:** 4 (1967).

HYDRIODIC ACID HI

(See also HYDROGEN IODIDE)

Fluorine
See FLUORINE plus Hydriodic Acid.

Perchloric Acid
See PERCHLORIC ACID plus Hydriodic Acid.

HYDROBROMIC ACID HBr

Fluorine
See FLUORINE plus Hydrobromic Acid.

HYDROCARBONS

Chlorine
See CHLORINE plus Hydrocarbons.

Fluorine
See FLUORINE plus Hydrocarbons.

Magnesium Perchlorate
See MAGNESIUM PERCHLORATE plus Hydrocarbons.

HYDROCHLORIC ACID HCl

(See also HYDROGEN CHLORIDE)

Acetic Anhydride
See ACETIC ANHYDRIDE plus Hydrochloric Acid.

2-Aminoethanol
See 2-AMINOETHANOL plus Hydrochloric Acid.

Ammonium Hydroxide
Mixing hydrochloric acid and 28% ammonia in a closed container caused the temperature and pressure to increase.
Flynn and Rossow (1970). See Note under complete reference.

Calcium Phosphide
See CALCIUM PHOSPHIDE plus Hydrochloric Acid.

Chlorosulfonic Acid
See CHLOROSULFONIC ACID plus Hydrochloric Acid.

Ethylene Diamine
See ETHYLENE DIAMINE plus Hydrochloric Acid.

Ethyleneimine
See ETHYLENEIMINE plus Hydrochloric Acid.

Oleum
See OLEUM plus Hydrochloric Acid.

Perchloric Acid
The hydronium compound decomposes spontaneously with violence.
Mellor **2, Supp. 1:** 613 (1956).

Propiolactone (BETA-)
See PROPIOLACTONE (BETA-) plus Hydrochloric Acid.

Propylene Oxide
See PROPYLENE OXIDE plus Hydrochloric Acid.

Silver Perchlorate and Carbon Tetrachloride
See SILVER PERCHLORATE plus Carbon Tetrachloride and Hydrochloric Acid.

Sodium Hydroxide
See SODIUM HYDROXIDE plus Hydrochloric Acid.

Sulfuric Acid
Mixing 36% hydrochloric acid and 96% sulfuric acid in a closed container caused the temperature and pressure to increase.
Flynn and Rossow (1970). See Note under complete reference.

Uranium Phosphide
See URANIUM PHOSPHIDE plus Hydrochloric Acid.

Vinyl Acetate
See VINYL ACETATE plus Hydrochloric Acid.

HYDROFLUORIC ACID HF

(See also HYDROGEN FLUORIDE)

Acetic Anhydride
See ACETIC ANHYDRIDE plus Hydrofluoric Acid.

2-Aminoethanol
See 2-AMINOETHANOL plus Hydrofluoric Acid.

Ammonium Hydroxide
Mixing 48.7% hydrofluoric acid and 28% ammonia in a closed container caused the temperature and pressure to increase.
Flynn and Rossow (1970). See Note under complete reference.

Bismuthic Acid
See BISMUTHIC ACID plus Hydrofluoric Acid.

Calcium Oxide
See CALCIUM OXIDE plus Hydrofluoric Acid.

Chlorosulfonic Acid
See CHLOROSULFONIC ACID plus Hydrofluoric Acid.

Ethylene Diamine
See ETHYLENE DIAMINE plus Hydrofluoric Acid.

Ethyleneimine
See ETHYLENEIMINE plus Hydrofluoric Acid.

Fluorine
See FLUORINE plus Hydrofluoric Acid.

Nitric Acid and Lactic Acid
See NITRIC ACID plus Lactic Acid and Hydrofluoric Acid.

Oleum
See OLEUM plus Hydrofluoric Acid.

Propiolactone (BETA-)
See PROPIOLACTONE (BETA-) plus Hydrofluoric Acid.

Propylene Oxide
See PROPYLENE OXIDE plus Hydrofluoric Acid.

Sodium
See SODIUM plus Hydrofluoric Acid.

Sodium Hydroxide
See SODIUM HYDROXIDE plus Hydrofluoric Acid.

Sulfuric Acid
Mixing 48.7% hydrofluoric acid and 96% sulfuric acid in a closed container caused the temperature and pressure to increase.
Flynn and Rossow (1970). See Note under complete reference.

Vinyl Acetate
See VINYL ACETATE plus Hydrofluoric Acid.

HYDROGEN H_2

Air and Platinum
Finely divided platinum and some other metals will cause a mixture of hydrogen and oxygen to explode at ordinary temperatures. If a jet of hydrogen in air impinges on platinum black, the metal becomes hot enough to ignite the gas.
Mellor **1:** 325; **16:** 146 (1946-1947).

Bromine
See BROMINE plus Hydrogen.

Chlorine
See CHLORINE plus Hydrogen.

Chlorine Trifluoride
See CHLORINE TRIFLUORIDE plus Ammonia.

Dioxane and Nickel (Raney)
Dioxane reacts explosively with hydrogen and Raney nickel above 210°C.
Organic Synthesis, **Coll. Vol. III:** 182 (1955).

Fluorine
See FLUORINE plus Hydrogen.

Lithium
See LITHIUM plus Hydrogen.

Magnesium and Calcium Carbonate
See MAGNESIUM plus Hydrogen and Calcium Carbonate.

Nitroanisole
Catalytic hydrogenation of nitroanisole in the presence of nickel catalyst has resulted in an explosion.
J. Am. Chem. Soc. **53:** 2417 (1931).

Nitrogen Trifluoride
Explosive reactions occur upon ignition of mixtures of nitrogen trifluoride with good reducing agents such as ammonia, carbon mon oxide, hydrogen, hydrogen sulfide or methane.
Lawless and Smith, p. 34 (1968).

Oxygen Difluoride
Mixtures of hydrogen, carbon monoxide, or methane and oxygen difluoride are exploded when a spark is discharged.
Mellor **2, Supp. 1:** 192 (1956).

Oxygen and Platinum
See HYDROGEN plus Air and Platinum.

Palladium and Isopropyl Alcohol
When a stream of hydrogen entrained isopropyl alcohol

vapors and palladium particles, the mixture caught fire on exposure to air.
Confidential information furnished to NFPA.

1-Pentol
An explosion and subsequent investigation revealed that heating 1′- pentol and 1′′-pentol under hydrogen pressure is extremely dangerous. It appears to cause this acetylenic compound to break down suddenly to elemental carbon, hydrogen, and carbon monoxide with the release of sufficient energy to develop pressures in excess of 1,000 atmospheres. The presence of small quantities of sulfuric acid or potassium hydroxide reduces the temperature of instability of 1-pentol. Also heating 1-pentol isomers above 100°C during vacuum distillation should be avoided to prevent polymerization.
F. Lorenz, *AIChE Loss Prevention,* 1967, p. 1.

HYDROGEN AZIDE HN_3

Fluorine
See AZINE FLUORIDE (self-reactive).

HYDROGEN BROMIDE HBr

Ammonia
The reaction is vigorous even at minus 80°C with intensely dried reactants.
Mellor **2, Supp. 1:** 737 (1956).

Ozone
See OZONE plus Hydrogen Bromide.

HYDROGEN CHLORIDE HCl

(See also HYDROCHLORIC ACID)

Calcium Carbide
See CALCIUM CARBIDE plus Hydrogen Chloride.

Cesium Acetylene Carbide
See CESIUM ACETYLENE CARBIDE plus Hydrogen Chloride.

Cesium Carbide
See CESIUM CARBIDE plus Hydrochloric Acid.

Dowicil 100
See DOWICIL 100 plus Hydrogen Chloride.

Lithium Silicide
See LITHIUM SILICIDE plus Hydrogen Chloride.

Magnesium Boride
See MAGNESIUM BORIDE plus Hydrochloric Acid.

Mercuric Sulfate
See MERCURIC SULFATE plus Hydrogen Chloride.

Rubidium Acetylene Carbide
See RUBIDIUM ACETYLENE CARBIDE plus Hydrochloric Acid.

Rubidium Carbide
See RUBIDIUM CARBIDE plus Hydrochloric Acid.

Sodium
See SODIUM plus Hydrochloric Acid.
See SODIUM plus Hydrogen Chloride.

HYDROGEN CYANIDE HCN

(self-reactive)
Hydrogen cyanide containing water up to 10% was polymerized in glass ampoules at 50-60°C or catalyzed at room temperature under the effect of a minute amount of alkali. In view of the possibility of running into dangerous conditions with a water content of 2-5%, it is important to keep it below this range.
J. Chem. Soc. Japan Ind. Chem. Sec. **71** (8): 1119-1123 (1968).

Acetaldehyde
See ACETALDEHYDE plus Ammonia (Anhydrous).

HYDROGEN DIPHOSPHIDE P_2H

Air
Hydrogen diphosphide in air ignites when suddenly heated to 100°C., or when struck with a hammer.
Mellor **8:** 831 (1946-1947).

HYDROGEN FLUORIDE HF

(See also HYDROFLUORIC ACID)

Arsenic Trioxide
Hydrogen fluoride and arsenic trioxide react with incandescence.
Mellor **9:** 101 (1946-1947).

Phosphorus Pentoxide
See PHOSPHORUS PENTOXIDE plus Hydrogen Fluoride.

HYDROGEN IODIDE HI

(See also HYDRIODIC ACID)

Magnesium
See MAGNESIUM plus Hydrogen Iodide.

Nitric Acid
When hydrogen iodide is passed through fuming nitric acid, each bubble produces a red flame with the separation of iodine.
Berichte **3:** 3660.

Ozone
See OZONE plus Hydrogen Iodide.

Potassium
See POTASSIUM plus Hydrogen Iodide.

Potassium Chlorate
See POTASSIUM CHLORATE plus Hydrogen Iodide.

HYDROGEN PEROXIDE H_2O_2

Acetic Acid
Even dilute hydrogen peroxide added to dilute acetic acid and heated will initiate an exothermic reaction with production of per acetic acid which will explode at 110°C.
Weed (1966).

Acetic Anhydride
Addition of hydrogen peroxide to acetic anhydride yields peroxyacetic acid; but an excess of acetic anhydride reacts with peroxyacetic acid yielding diacetyl peroxide, which is very unstable and explodes readily.
Chem. Reviews **45:** 5 (1949).
See also HYDROGEN PEROXIDE plus Acetic Acid.
See also PERACETIC ACID plus Acetic Anhydride.

Acetone
See HYDROGEN PEROXIDE plus Organic Matter.

Alcohols and Sulfuric Acid
See ALCOHOLS plus Hydrogen Peroxide and Sulfuric Acid.

Ammonium Hydroxide
A mixture of ammonium hydroxide and hydrogen peroxide exploded.
Chem. and Eng. News, p. 2 (July 23, 1990).

Antimony Trisulfide
See ANTIMONY TRISULFIDE plus Hydrogen Peroxide.

Arsenic Trisulfide
See ANTIMONY TRISULFIDE plus Hydrogen Peroxide.

Brass
See IRON plus Hydrogen Peroxide.

Bronze
See IRON plus Hydrogen Peroxide.

t-Butyl Alcohol
The preparation of di tertiary butyl peroxide by the addition of tertiary butyl alcohol to a mixture of hydrogen peroxide and sulfuric acid (2 to 1 weight ratio of 78% sulfuric acid to 50% hydrogen per oxide) has resulted in severe explosions particularly during the early stages of large batches.
T.A. Schenach, *Chem. and Eng. News.* **51** (6): 39 (Feb. 5, 1973).

Cellulose
Hydrogen peroxide plus cellulose (in cotton) ignites spontaneously.
Mellor **1:** 938 (1946-1947).

Charcoal
Charcoal mixed with a trace of manganese dioxide ignites immediately in contact with hydrogen peroxide.
Mellor **1:** 938 (1946-1947).

Chlorine and Potassium Hydroxide
See CHLORINE plus Hydrogen Peroxide and Potassium Hydroxide.

Chlorosulfonic Acid
See CHLOROSULFURIC ACID plus Hydrogen Peroxide.

Chromium
See IRON plus Hydrogen Peroxide.

Copper
See IRON plus Hydrogen Peroxide.

Cupric Sulfide
See ANTIMONY TRISULFIDE plus Hydrogen Peroxide.

Dimethylbenzylcarbinol and Sulfuric Acid
See ALCOHOLS plus Hydrogen Peroxide and Sulfuric Acid.

Ethyl Alcohol
See ETHYL ALCOHOL plus Hydrogen Peroxide.

Ethyl Alcohol and Sulfuric Acid
See ALCOHOLS plus Hydrogen Peroxide and Sulfuric Acid.

Ferrous Sulfide
See ANTIMONY TRISULFIDE plus Hydrogen Peroxide.

Formic Acid and Organic Matter
A chemist working with a 50-50 mixture of formic acid and 90 percent hydrogen peroxide, introduced a small amount of organic material into the solution. When the reaction had subsided, the container was removed to a workbench. Later, when the flask was picked up, the material exploded violently.
Chem. and Eng. News **28:** 418 (1950).

Gold
See GOLD plus Hydrogen Peroxide.

Hydrazine
See HYDRAZINE plus Air.
See HYDRAZINE plus Hydrogen Peroxide.

Hydrogen Selenide
See HYDROGEN SELENIDE plus Hydrogen Peroxide.

Iron
See IRON plus Hydrogen Peroxide.

Ketones and Nitric Acid
See KETONES plus Nitric Acid and Hydrogen Peroxide.

Lead
See IRON plus Hydrogen Peroxide.

Lead Dioxide
See LEAD DIOXIDE plus Hydrogen Peroxide.

Lead Monoxide
See LEAD DIOXIDE plus Hydrogen Peroxide.

Lead Sulfide
See ANTIMONY TRISULFIDE plus Hydrogen Peroxide.

Magnesium
See MAGNESIUM plus Hydrogen Peroxide.

Manganese
See IRON plus Hydrogen Peroxide.

Manganese Dioxide
See MANGANESE DIOXIDE plus Hydrogen Peroxide.

Mercuric Oxide
See LEAD DIOXIDE plus Hydrogen Peroxide.

Mercurous Oxide
See MERCUROUS OXIDE plus Hydrogen Peroxide.

Molybdenum Disulfide
See ANTIMONY TRISULFIDE plus Hydrogen Peroxide.

Nitric Acid
This mixture is unstable when more than 50% of acid is present.
Mellor **8, Supp. 2:** 315 (1967).

Organic Matter
Under certain circumstances, hydrogen peroxide is capable of developing an explosive power in excess of its weight equivalent of TNT when mixed with organic compounds; the acetone-hydrogen peroxide system is a good example.
Chem. Safety Data Sheet **SD-53** (1955). **SD-53 Supp. A** (1961). **SD-53 Supp. B** (1961).
BCISC **36:** 29 (July-Sept. 1969). *BCISC* **40** (158): 17 (1969).
Chem. in Brit. **5** (1): 36 (1969).
Chem. in Brit. **5** (6): 287 (1969).

1-Phenyl-2-methyl-propyl Alcohol and Sulfuric Acid

See ALCOHOLS plus Hydrogen Peroxide and Sulfuric Acid.

Platinum
See PLATINUM plus Hydrogen Peroxide.

Potassium
See LEAD DIOXIDE plus Hydrogen Peroxide.

Potassium Permanganate
See POTASSIUM PERMANGANATE plus Hydrogen Peroxide.

Silver
See IRON plus Hydrogen Peroxide.
See SILVER plus Hydrogen Peroxide.

Sodium
See LEAD DIOXIDE plus Hydrogen Peroxide.

Sodium Iodate
See SODIUM IODATE plus Hydrogen Peroxide.

Sulfuric Acid
A 50-50 mixture of concentrated sulfuric acid and 30% hydrogen peroxide (piranha solution) is susceptible to spontaneous and unpredictable explosive decomposition.
Chem. and Eng. News, p. 2 (April 23, 1990).

Thiodiglycol
See THIODIGLYCOL plus Hydrogen Peroxide.

Unsymmetrical Dimethyl Hydrazine
See UNSYMMETRICAL DIMETHYL HYDRAZINE plus Hydrogen Peroxide.

HYDROGEN SELENIDE SeH_2

Hydrogen Peroxide
Hydrogen selenide and hydrogen peroxide undergo a very swift decomposition.
Mellor **1:** 941 (1946-1947).

Nitric Acid
Fuming nitric acid reacts with incandescence with hydrogen selenide.
Berichte **3:** 658.

HYDROGEN SULFIDE H_2S

Acetaldehyde
See ACETALDEHYDE plus Ammonia (Anhydrous).

Barium Oxide, Mercurous Oxide and Air
See HYDROGEN SULFIDE plus Soda Lime.

Barium Oxide, Nickel Oxide and Air
See HYDROGEN SULFIDE plus Soda Lime.

Bromine Pentafluoride
See BROMINE PENTAFLUORIDE plus Acetic Acid.

Chlorine Monoxide
Hydrogen sulfide ignites in contact with chlorine monoxide.
Mellor **10:** 134 (1946-1947).

Chlorine Trifluoride
See CHLORINE TRIFLUORIDE plus Ammonia.

Chromic Anhydride
See CHROMIC ANHYDRIDE plus Hydrogen Sulfide.
Also see CHROMIC ANHYDRIDE plus Naphthalene.

Copper
See COPPER plus Hydrogen Sulfide.

Fluorine
See FLUORINE plus Hydrogen Sulfide.

Hydrated Iron Oxide
A pyrophoric iron sulfide was made from hydrated iron oxide and hydrogen sulfide under gasoline.
Ellern, p. 33 (1968).

Lead Dioxide
See LEAD DIOXIDE plus Hydrogen Sulfide.

Nitric Acid
Fuming nitric acid reacts with incandescence with hydrogen sulfide.
Berichte **3:** 658.
Chem. Safety Data Sheet **SD-5,** p. 6.

Nitrogen Iodide
See BROMINE plus Nitrogen Triiodide.

Nitrogen Trichloride
See NITROGEN TRICHLORIDE plus Ammonia.

Nitrogen Trifluoride
See HYDROGEN plus Nitrogen Trifluoride.

Oxygen Difluoride
See OXYGEN DIFLUORIDE plus Hydrogen Sulfide.

Phenyl Diazonium Chloride
See PHENYL DIAZONIUM CHLORIDE plus Hydrogen Sulfide.

Soda Lime (Sodium Hydroxide and Calcium Oxide) and Air
The reaction between hydrogen sulfide and soda lime is attended with incandescence in the presence of air; in oxygen, there is a violent explosion. Mixtures of barium oxide with mercurous or nickel oxide also react vigorously with hydrogen sulfide in air and vivid incandescence or explosions may result.
Mellor **10:** 140 (1946-1947).

Sodium
See SODIUM plus Hydrogen Sulfide.

Sodium Peroxide
When hydrogen sulfide is passed over sodium peroxide, a very vigorous reaction occurs, even in the absence of air, and the reaction may be accompanied by flame.
Mellor **10:** 132 (1946-1947).

HYDROGEN TELLURIDE H_2Te

Nitric Acid
See NITRIC ACID plus Hydrogen Telluride.

HYDROGEN TRISULFIDE HSSSH

Amyl Alcohol
The decomposition of amyl alcohol by hydrogen trisulfide is explosively violent.
Mellor **10:** 158 (1946-1947).

Iron Oxide (Magnetite)
See HYDROGEN TRISULFIDE plus Lead Oxide.

Lead Oxide
Lead oxide, stannic oxide, and magnetite (Fe_3O_4) brought about a violent decomposition of hydrogen trisulfide.
Mellor **10:** 159 (1946-1947).

Potassium Permanganate
Potassium permanganate decomposes hydrogen trisulfide so rapidly that sufficient heat is liberated to ignite the trisulfide.
Mellor **10:** 159 (1946-1947).

Stannic Oxide
See HYDROGEN TRISULFIDE plus Lead Oxide.

HYDROQUINONE $C_6H_4(OH)_2$

Sodium Hydroxide
See SODIUM HYDROXIDE plus Hydroquinone.

HYDROXIDES

(See also specific hydroxides as primary entries or see under other reactants)

Acrolein
See SODIUM HYDROXIDE plus Acrolein.

4-HYDROXY-3, 5-DINITROBENZENEAR SONIC ACID $4,3,5,1\text{-}OHC_6H_2(NO_2)_2AsO_3H_2$

(self-reactive)
This compound and its metallic salts may be as explosive as its close relative picric acid. When a wet cake of the acid was heated an explosion occurred that was accompanied by liberation of arsenic or arsine.
M. A. Phillips, *Chem. & Ind.* **1947:** 61.

a-HYDROXYISOBUTYRONITRILE $(CH_3)_2COHCN$

Sulfuric Acid
During addition of sulfuric acid to a vat of acetone cyanhydrin, pressure produced by rapid reaction ruptured the vessel explosively.
Occupancy Fire Record **FR57-5:** 5 (1957).

HYDROXYLAMINE NH_2OH

Barium Dioxide
See BARIUM DIOXIDE plus Hydroxylamine.

Barium Oxide
See BARIUM OXIDE plus Hydroxylamine.

Chlorine
See CHLORINE plus Hydroxylamine.

Copper Sulfate
See COPPER SULFATE plus Hydroxylamine

Lead Dioxide
See LEAD DIOXIDE plus Hydroxylamine.

Oxidants
Hydroxylamine is a powerful reducing agent, particularly when anhydrous. It explodes on contact with air above 70°C. Barium dioxide will ignite aqueous hydroxylamine.
Mellor (1941); *Brauer* (1963).

Phosphorus Pentachloride
See PHOSPHORUS TRICHLORIDE plus Hydroxylamine.

Phosphorus Trichloride
See PHOSPHORUS TRICHLORIDE plus Hydroxylamine.

Potassium Dichromate
See POTASSIUM DICHROMATE plus Hydroxylamine.

Potassium Permanganate
See POTASSIUM PERMANGANATE plus Hydroxylamine.

Sodium
See SODIUM plus Hydroxylamine.

Zinc
See ZINC plus Hydroxylamine.

HYDROXYLAMINE HYPOPHOSPHITE $NH_2OHPH_2O_2$

(self-reactive)
Hydroxylamine hypophosphite detonates above 100° C.
Mellor **8:** 880 (1946-1947).

HYDROXYLAMINES

(See also under other reactants)

(self-reactive)
Several scale-ups of previously successful hydroxylamine reactions have resulted in explosions, e.g.: 1) During preparation of an oxime from an aldehyde, an ether solution of the reaction mixture, containing hydroxylamine hydrochloride decomposed violently under vacuum distillation at 80°C. 2) The hydrochloride can be made to decompose exothermically at 140°C. and solid hydroxylamine sulfate will explode when heated to 170°C. 3) A mixture containing the hydrochloride, pyridine, and sodium acetate in a stainless steel autoclave at 90°C. suddenly heated and pressurized to 5000 psi to rupture the relief disk.
Chem. Process (Chicago) **26:** 30 (1963).

4-HYDROXY-3-METHOXYBENZALDEHYDE $CH_3O(HO)C_6H_3CHO$

(See also VANILLIN)

Bromine
See BROMINE plus Methyl Alcohol.

Perchloric Acid
See PERCHLORIC ACID plus Ethyl Alcohol.

Potassium Tert.-Butoxide
See ACETONE plus Potassium Tert.-Butoxide.

Tetrachlorobenzene and Sodium Hydroxide
See SODIUM HYDROXIDE plus Tetrachlorobenzene and Methyl Alcohol.

n-HYDROXYMETHYLACRYLAMIDE $HOCH_2NHCOCH=CH_2$

Contaminant
Among four fiber drums of this chemical, two of which had never been opened, excessive heat, smoke, crackling, and small flames were noted. Very small amounts of contaminant are believed to have catalyzed this polymerization reaction, but storage in exces sively heated areas can also start the reaction.
Coventry (1965). *Spence* (1966).

3-HYDROXYPROPIONITRILE $HOCH_2CH_2CN$

Chlorosulfonic Acid
Mixing ethylene cyanohydrin and chlorosulfonic acid in a closed container caused the temperature and pressure to increase.
Flynn and Rossow (1970). See Note under complete reference.

Oleum
See OLEUM plus Ethylene Cyanohydrin.

Sodium Hydroxide
See SODIUM HYDROXIDE plus Ethylene Cyanohydrin.

Sulfuric Acid
Mixing ethylene cyanohydrin and 96% sulfuric acid in a closed container caused the temperature and pressure to increase.
Flynn and Rossow (1970). See Note under complete reference.

HYPOCHLORITES

(See also specific hypochlorites as primary entries or under other reactants)

Urea
Hypochlorites react with urea to form nitrogen trichloride which explodes spontaneously in air.
J. Am. Chem. Soc. **63:** 3530-32.

HYPOCHLOROUS ACID HOCl

Alcohols
See ALCOHOLS plus Hypochlorous Acid.

Ammonia
Gaseous ammonia explodes in contact with hypochlorous acid; toxic chlorine is liberated.
Mellor **8:** 217 (1946-1947).

Arsenic
See ARSENIC plus Hypochlorous Acid.

HYPOPHOSPHITES

(See also specific hypophosphites as primary entries or see under other reactants)

Perchloric Acid
Some inorganic materials, such as hypophosphites, tend to form explosive mixtures with perchloric acid when hot. When a precipitate of scandium hypophosphite was heated in a perchloric acid solution, the perchloric acid concentrated from evaporation and the mixture of perchloric acid with the inorganic reducing compound exploded violently.
Analyst **84:** 215 (April 1959). *NSC Newsletter, Chem. Sec.* (Novem ber 1966).

HYPOPHOSPHORIC ACID $H_4P_2O_6$

Mercuric Nitrate
See MERCURIC NITRATE plus Hypophosphoric Acid.

HYPOPHOSPHOROUS ACID H_3PO_2

Mercuric Oxide
See MERCURIC OXIDE plus Hypophosphorous Acid.

INDANE $CH_2CH{=}CHC_6H_4$

Nitric Acid and Sulfuric Acid
In the preparation of 4 and 5 nitroindanes according to the procedure of Lindner and Brukin (*Chem. Ber.* **60,** 435 (1925)) the crude nitro mix was distilled in vacuo. After allowing the pot to cool, air was admitted to the residue. After a short period the pot erupted. A second preparation exploded at the beginning of the distillation.
G.W. Grebble, *Chem. and Eng. News* **51** (6): 39 (Feb. 5, 1973).

INDIUM In

Sulfur
When indium is heated with sulfur, the elements unite with incandescence.
Mellor **5:** 393 (1946-1947).

INDIUM MONOXIDE InO

Air
Indium monoxide is spontaneously flammable in air.
Ellern (1961).

IODATES

(See also specific iodates as primary entries or under other reactants)

Aluminum
See ALUMINUM plus Bromates.

Arsenic
See ARSENIC plus Bromates.

Carbon
See CARBON plus Bromates.

Copper
See COPPER plus Bromates.

Metal Sulfides
See METAL SULFIDES plus Bromates.

Organic Matter
See BROMATES plus Organic Matter.

Phosphonium Iodide
See BROMATES plus Phosphonium Iodide.

Phosphorus
See PHOSPHORUS plus Bromates.

Sulfur
See SULFUR plus Bromates.

IODIC ACID HIO_3

Boron
See BORON plus Iodic Acid.

Phosphonium Iodide
See PHOSPHONIUM IODIDE plus Bromic Acid.

IODINE I_2

Acetaldehyde
See BROMINE plus Acetaldehyde.

Acetylene
Acetylene can react explosively with iodine.
Von Schwartz, p. 142 (1918).

Aluminum
See ALUMINUM plus Iodine.

Ammonia
Mixture explodes spontaneously.
Von Schwartz, p. 324 (1918).

Ammonium Hydroxide
The reaction of excess iodine with strong aqueous ammonium hydroxide forms explosive iodide.
Mellor **8, Supp. 1:** 330 (1964).
Nitrogen iodides, which detonate on drying, are formed from concentrated solutions.
Mellor **2, Supp. 1:** 851 (1956).

Antimony
See ANTIMONY plus Bromine.

Bromine Pentafluoride
See ARSENIC plus Bromine Pentafluoride.
An immediate reaction with evolution of heat occurs between iodine and bromine pentafluoride.
Mellor **2, Supp. 1:** 173 (1956).

Cesium Acetylene Carbide
Cesium Acetylene Carbide burns in the vapors of iodine.
Mellor **5:** 844 (1946-1947).

Cesium Carbide
Cesium carbide, rubidium carbide or lithium carbide (after warming) burn in iodine vapor.
Mellor **5:** 848 (1946-1947).

Cesium Monoxide
See BROMINE plus Cesium Monoxide.

Chlorine
See CHLORINE plus Iodine.

Chlorine Trifluoride
See CHLORINE TRIFLUORIDE plus Mercuric Iodide.

Cuprous Acetylide
See BROMINE plus Cuprous Acetylide.

Ethyl Alcohol, Methyl Alcohol, and Mercuric Oxide
The Petrov method of preparing 1-iodo-2-ethoxy-3-butene calls for addition of 15 grams of mercuric oxide to 0.11 molar ethyl alcohol in 25 ml of methyl alcohol, followed by 25 grams of powdered iodine at -10 to -15°C, filtration, and dilution. A change in the procedure used 1 molar ethyl alcohol. While the alcohol was being distilled off under vacuum, a violent explosion occurred.
Chem. and Eng. News **44** (42): 7 (October 17, 1966).
Chem. Abst. **44:** 1003-d (1950).

Fluorine
See FLUORINE plus Iodine.

Lithium
A highly luminous reaction occurs at room temperature, between iodine and lithium, potassium, and sodium.
Mellor **2, Supp. 1:** 848 (1956).

Lithium Carbide
See BROMINE plus Lithium Carbide.
See IODINE plus Cesium Carbide.

Lithium Silicide
See FLUORINE plus Lithium Silicide.

Magnesium
See MAGNESIUM plus Iodine.

Oxygen Difluoride
See BROMINE plus Oxygen Difluoride.

Phosphorus
Ordinary (white or yellow) phosphorus unites with iodine at ordinary temperatures. Even at minus 24°C., heat is developed. The product is spontaneously flammable in air. With red phosphorus, the reaction does not occur at ordinary temperatures; but when warmed, it reacts without incandescence.
C.L. Gazzaniga, *Bibl. Univ. Geneve* **54:** 186 (1833).
See also PHOSPHORUS plus Oxygen.

Potassium
Potassium burns on contact with liquid iodine.
Mellor **2:** 469 (1946-1947).
Iodine and potassium vapors at 0.001 mm pressure react with luminescence.
Mellor **2, Supp. 3:** 1563 (1963).

Rubidium Acetylene Carbide
See BROMINE plus Rubidium Acetylene Carbide.

Rubidium Carbide
See IODINE plus Cesium Carbide.

Silver Azide
Silver azide in a cold ethereal solution of iodine gives a yellow explosive, iodoazide.
Mellor **8:** 336-7 (1946-1947).

Sodium Hydride
Sodium hydride reacts with iodine with incandescence at 100°C.
Mellor **2:** 483 (1946-1947).

Zirconium Dicarbide
See BROMINE plus Zirconium Dicarbide.

IODINE AZIDE N_3I

(self-reactive)
Iodine azide is spontaneously explosive.
Mellor **8:** 336 (1946-1947).
Mellor **8, Supp. 2:** 50 (1967).

IODINE HEPTAFLUORIDE IF_7

Ammonium Bromide
Iodine heptafluoride reacts violently with ammonium bromide, ammonium chloride or ammonium iodide.
Mellor **2, Supp. 1:** 179 (1956).

Ammonium Chloride
See IODINE HEPTAFLUORIDE plus Ammonium Bromide.

Ammonium Iodide
See IODINE HEPTAFLUORIDE plus Ammonium Bromide.

Carbon Monoxide
Carbon monoxide burns in gaseous iodine heptafluoride.
Mellor **2, Supp. 1:** 179 (1956).

Organic Matter
See BROMINE MONOFLUORIDE plus Water.

Sulfuric Acid
In reaction between iodine heptafluoride and sulfuric acid, the acid becomes effervescent.
Mellor **2, Supp. 1:** 185 (1956).

Water
See BROMINE MONOFLUORIDE plus Water.

IODINE MONOBROMIDE IBr

Phosphorus
See PHOSPHORUS plus Iodine Monobromide.

Potassium
See POTASSIUM plus Iodine Monobromide.

Sodium
See SODIUM plus Ferrous Chloride.
See SODIUM plus Iodine Monobromide.

IODINE MONOCHLORIDE ICl

Aluminum Foil
See ALUMINUM plus Iodine Monochloride.

Cadmium Sulfide
The reaction between iodine monochloride and cadmium sulfide, lead sulfide, silver sulfide, or zinc sulfide is vigorous.
Mellor **2, Supp. 1:** 502 (1956).

Lead Sulfide
See IODINE MONOCHLORIDE plus Cadmium Sulfide.

Organic Matter
Iodine monochloride produces a vigorous reaction with cork, rubber and other organic substances.
Mellor **2, Supp. 1:** 500 (1956).

Phosphorus
See PHOSPHORUS plus Iodine Monobromide.

Phosphorus Trichloride
The reaction of iodine monochloride and phosphorus trichloride is intensely exothermal.
Mellor **2, Supp. 1:** 502 (1956).

Potassium
See POTASSIUM plus Iodine Monochloride.

Rubber
See IODINE MONOCHLORIDE plus Organic Matter.

Silver Sulfide
See IODINE MONOCHLORIDE plus Cadmium Sulfide.

Sodium
See POTASSIUM plus Iodine Monochloride.
See SODIUM plus Iodine Monochloride.

Zinc Sulfide
See IODINE MONOCHLORIDE plus Cadmium Sulfide.

IODINE PENTAFLUORIDE IF_5

Arsenic
See ARSENIC plus Iodine Pentafluoride.

Bismuth
See ARSENIC plus Iodine Pentafluoride.

Dimethyl Sulfoxide
See DIMETHYL SULFOXIDE plus Iodine Pentafluoride.

Organic Matter
See ARSENIC plus Iodine Pentafluoride.
See also BROMINE MONOFLUORIDE plus Water.
See also IODINE PENTAFLUORIDE plus Water.

Phosphorus
See ARSENIC plus Iodine Pentafluoride.

Potassium
See POTASSIUM plus Iodine Pentafluoride.

Silicon
See ARSENIC plus Iodine Pentafluoride.

Sodium
See POTASSIUM plus Iodine Pentafluoride.

Sulfur
See ARSENIC plus Iodine Pentafluoride.

Tetrafluoroethylene and Limonene
Compressed gas cylinders made of tetrafluoroethylene were being purged with nitrogen. Failure of a ball check valve in a related system caused the purge gas to be contaminated with iodine pentafluo ride. The iodine pentafluoride reacted with the polymerization inhibitor, limonene, in the TFE, generating enough heat to cause deflagration of the cylinder material.
MCA Case History **1520** (1968).

Tetraiodoethylene
Explosions occur with too rapid admixture of iodine pentafluoride and tetraiodoethylene.
Mellor **2, Supp. 1:** 176 (1956).

Tungsten
See ARSENIC plus Iodine Pentafluoride.

Water
Iodine pentafluoride reacts violently with water.
Matheson Gas Data, p. 254 (1961).
The reaction between iodine pentafluoride and water is violent. Water-containing materials and many organics also react violently.
Mellor **2, Supp. 1:** 176 (1956).
See also BROMINE MONOFLUORIDE plus water.

IODINE PENTOXIDE I_2O_5

Carbon
See CARBON plus Iodine Pentoxide.

Organic Matter
See CARBON plus Iodine Pentoxide.

Sulfur
See CARBON plus Iodine Pentoxide.

IODODIACETYLENE HC≡CC≡CI

(self-reactive)
Iododiacetylene detonates if scratched in light.
Rutledge, p. 137 (1968).

IODODIMETHYLARSINE $(CH_3)AsI$

Air
Dimethyliodarsine is spontaneously flammable in air.
Ripley (1966).

2-IODO-3, 5-DINITROBIPHENYL $IC_6H_2(NO_2)_2C_6H_5$

Ethyl Sodio-Acetoacetate
The condensation of 2-iodo-3, 5-dinitrobiphenyl with ethyl sodio-aceto-acetate should be carried out with only

5-6 grams of the 2- iodo-3, 5-dinitrobiphenyl since larger amounts lead to explosions.
S.H. Zahur and I.K. Kocker.
J. Indian Chem. Soc. **32:** 491 (1955).

IODOFORM CHI_3

Lithium
See LITHIUM plus Bromoform.

3-IODO-1-PHENYL-1-PROPYNE $C_6H_5C{\equiv}C{\cdot}CH_2I$

(self-reactive)
While being distilled at about 180°C 3-iodo-1-phenyl-1-propyne detonated.
Chem. and Eng. News **50** (23): 86, 87 (June 5, 1972).

2-IODOXYBENZOIC ACID (PERIODINANE)

Dry material is shock sensitive. Also explodes when heated under confinement.
Chem. and Eng. News (July 16, 1990).

IRIDIUM Ir

Chlorine Trifluoride
Chlorine trifluoride reacts with iridium with incandescence.
Mellor **15:** 745 (1946-1947).
Mellor **2, Supp. 1:** 156 (1956).

Fluorine
Powdered iridium and fluorine react vigorously at 260° C, forming the hexafluoride.
Mellor **2, Supp. 1:** 65 (1956).

Oxygen Difluoride
An incandescent reaction occurs when any of the following metals are warmed gently in gaseous oxygen difluoride: iridium, osmium, palladium, platinum, rhodium, ruthenium.
Mellor **2, Supp. 1:** 192 (1956).

IRIDIUM-AMMINE NITRATES

(self-reactive)
Iridium-ammine nitrates may be impact-sensitive. $Ir(NH_3)_5OH(NO_3)_3$ and $Ir\ (NH_3)_5Cl(NO_3)_3$ detonate at red heat.
Mellor **15:** 787 (1946-1947).

IRIDIUM-AMMINE PERCHLORATES

(self-reactive)
Iridium-ammine perchlorates may be impact-sensitive.
Mellor **15:** 787 (1946-1947).

IRON Fe

(For iron compounds see also FERRIC and FERROUS compounds)

Chlorine
Hot iron (wire) burns in chlorine gas.
Mellor **2:** 95, 469 (1946-1947).
Mellor **2, Supp. 1:** 380 (1956).

Chlorine Trifluoride
Chlorine trifluoride reacts with iron with incandescence.
Mellor **13:** 315 (1946-1947).
Mellor **2, Supp. 1:** 156 (1956).

Fluorine
Powdered iron reacts with fluorine below redness with incandescence.
Mellor **13:** 314 (1946-1947).

Hydrogen Peroxide
Violent decomposition of hydrogen peroxide (52% by weight or greater) may be caused by contact with many substances, such as iron, copper, chromium, brass, bronze, lead, silver, manganese, etc., and their salts.
Chem. Safety Data Sheet **SD-53** (1955); **SD-53 Supp. A** (1961); **SD-53 Supp. B** (1961).
Iron and hydrogen peroxide ignite immediately if a trace of manganese dioxide is present.
Mellor **1:** 938 (1946-1947).

Nitrogen Dioxide
Reduced iron decomposes nitrogen dioxide at ordinary temperatures with incandescence.
Mellor **13:** 342 (1946-1947).

Phosphorus
See COPPER plus Phosphorus.

Sodium Carbide
See MERCURY plus Sodium Carbide.

Sulfuric Acid
While steel piping, which had held sulfuric acid in cold climates during the winter, was being refitted, two explosions occurred; these were possibly due to trapped hydrogen from the acid-metal reaction.
Chem. and Eng. News **29:** 1770 (1951). *Chem. and Eng. News* **30:** 707 (1952).

IRON CARBIDE FeC_2

Bromine
See CHLORINE plus Iron Carbide.

Chlorine
See CHLORINE plus Iron Carbide.

IRON OXIDE Fe_2O_3

Hydrazine
See HYDRAZINE plus Iron Oxide.

IRON OXIDE (MAGNETITE) Fe_3O_4

Hydrogen Trisulfide
See HYDROGEN TRISULFIDE plus Iron Oxide.

IRON PENTACARBONYL $Fe(CO)_5$

Air
Iron pentacarbonyl is spontaneously flammable in air.
R. Kamo, *IIT Progs. Rept. 1,* p. 23 (1962).

ISOAMYL NITRITE $(CH_3)_2CHCH_2CH_2ONO$

(self-reactive)
Vapors will explode when heated.
Von Schwartz and Salter, p. 322 (1940).

ISOBUTANETHIOL $(CH_3)_2CHCH_2SH$

Calcium Hypochlorite
See CALCIUM HYPOCHLORITE plus 1-Propanethiol.

ISOBUTYL METHYL KETONE $CH_3COCH_2CH(CH_3)_2$

Potassium Tert.-Butoxide
See ACETONE plus Potassium Tert.-Butoxide.

ISOBUTYROPHENONE $(CH_3)_2CHCOC_6H_5$

Bromine
See BROMINE plus Isobutyrophenone.

ISOCYANATES
See ALCOHOLS plus Isocyanates.

ISOCYANOETHANE C_2H_5NC

(self-reactive)
Ethyl isonitrile is reported to have exploded when heated on a hot plate.
Chem. and Eng. News **46** (42): 7 (1968).

ISOCYANOMETHANE CH_3NC

(self-reactive)
The dehydration of n-methyl formamide by benzenesulfonyl chloride in tributylamine solution produces methyl isonitrile. In a subsequent distillation, the isonitrile was allowed to go to dryness and the flask exploded.
Chem. and Eng. News **46** (42): 7 (1968).

ISOPRENE $CH_2=C(CH_3)CH=CH_2$

Chlorosulfonic Acid
Mixing isoprene and chlorosulfonic acid in a closed container caused the temperature and pressure to increase.
Flynn and Rossow (1970). See Note under complete reference.

Nitric Acid
Mixing isoprene and 70% nitric acid in a closed container caused the temperature and pressure to increase.
Flynn and Rossow (1970). See Note under complete reference.

Oleum
Mixing isoprene and oleum in a closed container caused the temperature and pressure to increase.
Flynn and Rossow (1970). See Note under complete reference.

Sulfuric Acid
Mixing isoprene and 96% sulfuric acid in a closed container caused the temperature and pressure to increase.
Flynn and Rossow (1970). See Note under complete reference.

ISOPROPYL ALCOHOL $(CH_3)_2CHOH$

Air
Forms unstable peroxides upon prolonged contact with air which can concentrate and explode during distillation/evaporation.
Chem. and Eng. News, p. 4 (Jan. 2, 1989).

Hydrogen and Palladium
See HYDROGEN plus Palladium and Isopropyl Alcohol.

Nitroform
See NITROFORM plus Isopropyl Alcohol.

Oleum
See OLEUM plus Isopropyl Alcohol.

Phosgene
The reaction between isopropyl alcohol and phosgene forms isopropyl chloroformate and hydrogen chloride. In the presence of iron salts thermal decomposition can occur, which in some cases can become explosive.
Konstantinov, I.I, Pereslegina, L.S., Zhuravlev, E.Z., and Gusev, Yu. M.
Tr. po Khim. i Khim. Teknol. **10** (2): 171-4 (1967).

Potassium Tert.-Butoxide
See ACETONE plus Potassium Tert.-Butoxide.

ISOPROPYL CHLOROFORMATE $(CH_3)_2CHOCOCl$

(self-reactive)
Isopropylchloroformate stored in a refrigerator exploded.
Wischmeyer (1973).
See also ISOPROPYL ALCOHOL plus Phosgene.

ISOPROPYL HYPOCHLORITE $(CH_3)_2CHOCl$

(self-reactive)
Isopropyl hypochlorite decomposes explosively when exposed to light and rapidly even in its absence.
Mellor **2, Supp. 1:** 550 (1956).
See also ALCOHOLS plus Hypochlorous Acid.

JP-4 FUEL

Fluorine
See FLUORINE plus Common Materials and Oxygen.

KETONES

(See also specific ketones)

Acetaldehyde
See ACETALDEHYDE plus Acid Anhydrides.

Nitric Acid
See NITRIC ACID plus Ketones (Cyclic).

Nitric Acid and Hydrogen Peroxide
These reactants produce solids or oils that are highly explosive. The reaction itself proceeds explosively with excess of nitric acid or inadequate cooling.
Trans. Roy. Soc. Can. **Sect. III 44:** 1934-5 (1954).

Perchloric Acid
See PERCHLORIC ACID plus Glycol Ethers.

LACTIC ACID $CH_3CHOHCOOH$

Nitric Acid and Hydrofluoric Acid
See NITRIC ACID plus Lactic Acid and Hydrofluoric Acid.

LANTHANUM La

Air
See RARE EARTH METALS plus Air.

Halogens
See RARE EARTH METALS plus Halogens.

Phosphorus
See CERIUM plus Phosphorus.

LANTHANUM OXIDE La_2O_3

Chlorine Trifluoride
See CHLORINE TRIFLUORIDE Plus Arsenic Trioxide.

LANTHANUM PHOSPHIDE LaP

Water
See CEROUS PHOSPHIDE plus Water.

LEAD Pb

Ammonium Nitrate
See AMMONIUM NITRATE plus Metals (powdered)

Chlorine Trifluoride
See ALUMINUM plus Chlorine Trifluoride.

Hydrogen Peroxide
See IRON plus Hydrogen Peroxide.

Sodium Azide
See SODIUM AZIDE plus Copper.

Sodium Carbide
See MERCURY plus Sodium Carbide.

Zirconium
An alloy of 10% to 70% zirconium plus lead will ignite when struck with a hammer.
U.S. Pat. 2,611,316 (1952).

LEAD ACETATE $(CH_3COO)_2Pb$

Potassium Bromate
See POTASSIUM BROMATE plus Lead Acetate.

LEAD AZIDE $Pb(N_3)_2$

(self-reactive)
Lead azide decomposes at 250°C. It is explosively unstable.
Mellor **8, Supp. 2:** 43 (1967).
See also SODIUM AZIDE plus Copper.

Brass
See COPPER plus Lead Azide.

Calcium Stearate
In the production of lead azide, addition of calcium stearate was tried for the first time. An explosion ensued. Cause not understood.
MCA Case History **949** (1963).

Carbon Disulfide
See CARBON DISULFIDE plus Azides.

Copper
See COPPER plus Lead Azide.

Zinc
See COPPER plus Lead Azide.

LEAD CARBONATE $PbCO_3$

Fluorine
See FLUORINE plus Carbonates and FLUORINE plus Lead Carbonate (Basic).

LEAD CARBONATE (BASIC) $2PbCO_3{\cdot}Pb(OH)_2$

Fluorine
See FLUORINE plus Lead Carbonate (Basic) and FLUORINE plus Carbonates.

LEAD CHLORATE $Pb(ClO_3)_3$

Sulfur
See SULFUR plus Lead Chlorate.

LEAD CHLORITE $Pb(ClO_2)_2$

(self-reactive)
Lead chlorite has detonator properties but its behavior is somewhat unpredictable.
Mellor **2, Supp. 1:** 574 (1956).

Sulfur
See SULFUR plus Lead Chlorite.

LEAD CHROMATE $PbCrO_4$

Ferric Ferrocyanide
While these two chemicals were being ground together in a ball mill to form chrome green, a spark initiated a reaction that produced a fierce fire in the pigment.
Chem. Process (Chicago) **30:** 118 (August 1967)

LEAD CYANIDE $Pb(CN)_2$

Magnesium
See MAGNESIUM plus Cadmium Cyanide.

LEAD DIOXIDE PbO_2

(See also LEAD OXIDE)

Aluminum Carbide
See ALUMINUM CARBIDE plus Lead Peroxide.

Barium Sulfide
See BARIUM SULFIDE plus Lead Dioxide.

Boron
See BORON plus Lead Dioxide.

Calcium Sulfide
See BARIUM SULFIDE plus Lead Dioxide.

Cesium Acetylene Carbide
See CESIUM ACETYLENE CARBIDE plus Cupric Oxide.

Chlorine Trifluoride
See CHLORINE TRIFLUORIDE plus Aluminum Oxide.

Hydrogen Peroxide
Hydrogen peroxide reacts violently with lead dioxide, lead monoxide, mercuric oxide, potassium, and sodium.
Mellor **1:** 937 (1946-1947).

Hydrogen Sulfide
When hydrogen sulfide is passed over moist or dry lead dioxide, the mass becomes red-hot, producing a blue flame.
Mellor **7:** 689 (1946-1947).

Hydroxylamine
A mixture of hydroxylamine with barium dioxide or lead dioxide ignites.
Mellor **8:** 291 (1946-1947).

Molybdenum
See MOLYBDENUM plus Lead Dioxide.

Performic Acid
See PERFORMIC ACID plus Lead Dioxide.

Phenyl Hydrazine
Lead dioxide reacts instantly and vigorously with phenyl hydrazine.
Mellor **7:** 637 (1946-1947).

Phosphorus
See PHOSPHORUS plus Lead Dioxide.

Phosphorus Trichloride
When lead dioxide is added to warm phosphorus trichloride, the mixture becomes incandescent.
Mellor **7:** 690 (1946-1947).

Sulfur
See SULFUR plus Lead Dioxide.

Sulfuryl Chloride
See SULFURYL CHLORIDE plus Lead Dioxide.

Tungsten
See MOLYBDENUM plus Lead Dioxide.

Zirconium
See ZIRCONIUM plus Cupric Oxide.

LEAD FLUORIDE PbF_2

Calcium Carbide
See CALCIUM CARBIDE plus Lead Fluoride.

Fluorine
See FLUORINE plus Lead Fluoride.

LEAD HYPOPHOSPHITE $Pb(PH_2O_2)_2$

(self-reactive)
Lead hypophosphite forms impact-sensitive ammunition-priming mixtures.
Mellor **8, Supp. 3:** 623 (1971).

Lead Nitrate
This mixture forms a highly explosive double salt with rate of detonation greater than that of mercury fulminate.
Mellor **8:** 887 (1946-1947).

LEAD IMIDE PbNH

Acids
See LEAD IMIDE plus Water.

Water
Lead imide explodes when heated or when treated with water or dilute acids.
Mellor **8:** 265 (1946-1947).

LEAD MONOXIDE PbO

Hydrogen Peroxide
See LEAD DIOXIDE plus Hydrogen Peroxide.

Lithium Carbide
See LITHIUM CARBIDE plus Lead Monoxide.

LEAD NITRATE $Pb(NO_3)_2$

Ammonium Thiocyanate
See AMMONIUM THIOCYANATE plus Lead Nitrate.

Carbon
See CARBON plus Lead Nitrate.

Lead Hypophosphite
See LEAD HYPOPHOSPHITE plus Lead Nitrate.

LEAD OXIDE PbO; PbO_2; Pb_2O_3; Pb_3O_4

(See also LEAD DIOXIDE)

Aluminum
See ALUMINUM plus Lead Oxide.

Cesium Acetylene Carbide
See CESIUM ACETYLENE CARBIDE plus Cupric Oxide.

Fluorine and Glycerol
See FLUORINE plus Lead Oxide and Glycerol.

Hydrogen Trisulfide
See HYDROGEN TRISULFIDE plus Lead Oxide.

Perchloric Acid and Glycerine
Over a period of time, perchloric acid fumes from a laboratory hood condensed on the cover plate of the exhaust fan, which was sealed with a cement of glycerine and litharge (lead monoxide). When a workman tapped the plate with a chisel, a violent explosion caused two injuries and one fatality.
Serious Acc. Series **184** (1962).

Rubidium Acetylene Carbide
See RUBIDIUM ACETYLENE CARBIDE plus Lead Oxide.

Rubidium Carbide
See RUBIDIUM CARBIDE plus Lead Oxide.

Silicon and Aluminum
See SILICON plus Aluminum and Lead Oxide.

Sodium
See SODIUM plus Lead Oxide.

Sulfur Trioxide
The reaction between sulfur trioxide and lead oxide is attended by white luminescence.
Mellor **7:** 654 (1946-1947).

Titanium
See TITANIUM plus Cupric Oxide.

Zirconium
See ZIRCONIUM plus Cupric Oxide.

LEAD OXYCHLORIDE Pb_2OCl_2

Potassium
See POTASSIUM plus Boric Acid.

LEAD PERCHLORATE $Pb(ClO_4)_2$

Methyl Alcohol
A flask containing a saturated solution of anhydrous lead perchlorate dissolved in methyl alcohol exploded when it was disturbed.
ACS **146:** 209. *J Am. Chem. Soc.* **52:** 2391-6 (1930).

LEAD PEROXIDE PbO_2

(See also LEAD DIOXIDE)

Potassium
See POTASSIUM plus Boric Acid.

LEAD PHOSPHITE $Pb(H_2PO_3)_2$

(self-reactive)
A fiber drum of lead diphosphite caught fire apparently without any external cause. Since phosphite salts decom-

pose rapidly at elevated temperatures (200°C), it is believed a gradual decomposition took place, yielding lead phosphate, water, and phosphine. Phosphine, in turn, is spontaneously flammable in air and was the probable secondary cause of the fire.
Schwab (1967). *Kirk and Othmer* **10:** 489 (1947).

LEAD STYPHNATE $PbO_2C_6H(NO_2)_3$

(self-reactive)
This compound is a weak but highly sensitive explosive.
Urbanski, Vol. III, p. 213 (1967).
An employee was removing a beaker of lead styphnate from a laboratory oven when he apparently bumped the beaker on the side of the oven. A detonation occurred.
MCA Case History **957** (1966).
Three kilograms of lead styphnate detonated from an unknown cause in the anteroom of a dry-house. Wet material in two adjacent drying rooms did not detonate.
Chem. Abst. **26:** 5210 (1932).

LEAD SULFATE $PbSO_4$

Potassium
See POTASSIUM plus Boric Acid.

LEAD SULFIDE PbS

Iodine Monochloride
See IODINE MONOCHLORIDE plus Cadmium Sulfide.

Hydrogen Peroxide
See ANTIMONY TRISULFIDE plus Hydrogen Peroxide.

LEAD TETRAAZIDE $Pb(N_3)_4$

(self-reactive)
Lead tetraazide is too unstable to be isolated. The ammonium double salt is an unstable explosive compound.
Mellor **8, Supp. 2:** 22 (1967).

LEWIS-TYPE CATALYSTS

Allyl Chloride
See SULFURIC ACID plus Allyl Chloride.

LIMESTONE (CRUSHED)

Fluorine
See FLUORINE plus Common Materials and Oxygen.

LIMONENE $C_{10}H_{16}$

Iodine Pentafluoride and Tetrafluoroethylene
See IODINE PENTAFLUORIDE plus Tetrafluoroethylene and Limonene.

LINSEED OIL

Chlorine
See CHLORINE plus Polypropylene.

LITHIUM Li

Air
Lithium is spontaneously flammable in air if heated to 180°C., if the surface of the metal is clean. See also LITHIUM plus Oxygen.
Mellor **2:** 468 (1946-1947).

Arsenic
The reaction of lithium is violent with both strongly heated arsenic and phosphorus.
Mellor **2, Supp. 1:** 77 (1956).

Beryllium
See LITHIUM plus Vanadium.

Bromine
See BROMINE plus Potassium.

Bromoform
Lithium mixed with the following compounds can explode on impact: bromoform, carbon tetrabromide, chloroform, iodoform, methyl dichloride, and methyl diiodide.
Mellor **2, Supp. 2:** 83 (1961).

Carbides
Molten lithium attacks carbides and silicates.
Mellor **2, Supp. 2:** 84 (1961).

Carbon Dioxide
See LITHIUM plus Oxygen.
See also LITHIUM Plus Water.

Carbon Monoxide and Water
The product of the reaction between lithium and carbon monoxide, lithium carbonyl, detonates violently with water, igniting gaseous products.
Mellor **2, Supp. 2:** 88 (1961).

Carbon Tetrabromide
See LITHIUM plus Bromoform.

Carbon Tetrachloride
There was no reaction when a drop or two of carbon tetrachloride was added to burning lithium. When the quantity was eventually increased to about 25 cc of carbon tetrachloride, a violent explosion occurred.
Allison (1968).
See also LITHIUM plus Trichlorotrifluoroethane.
A billet-cutting knife initiated a violently explosive reaction between lithium and carbon tetrachloride.
Mellor **2, Supp. 2:** (1961).
See also LITHIUM plus Water.

Chlorine
See CESIUM plus Chlorine.

Chloroform
Chloroform with various alkali metals is impact-sensitive as follows: weak explosion with lithium; fairly strong with sodium; strong with potassium; and violent with sodium-potassium.
H. Staudinger, *Z. Electrochem.* **31:** 549-52 (1925).
See LITHIUM plus Bromoform.

Chromic Oxide
The reaction of lithium and chromic oxide occurs around 180°C with consequent temperature rise to 965°C.
Mellor **2, Supp. 2:** 81 (1961).

Chromium
See LITHIUM plus Vanadium.

Chromium Trichloride
On dusting a lithium strip with either chromium trichloride or zirconium tetrachloride then warming in a nitrogen atmosphere, the lithium burns vigorously, presumably forming lithium nitride.
BCISC **40** (158): 17 (1968).

Cobalt Alloys
Molten lithium attacks the following alloys: cobalt alloys, iron alloys, manganese alloys, nickel alloys.
Mellor **2, Supp. 2:** 80 (1961).

Diborane
See ALUMINUM plus Diborane.

Ferrous Sulfide
The reaction of lithium and ferrous sulfide occurs around 260°C with consequent temperature rise to 945°C.
Mellor **2, Supp. 2:** 82 (1961).

Halogenated Hydrocarbons
See LITHIUM plus Oxygen.

Hydrogen
Lithium burns in gaseous hydrogen.
Mellor **1:** 327 (1946-1947).

Iodine
See IODINE plus Lithium.

Iodoform
See LITHIUM plus Bromoform.

Iron Alloys
See LITHIUM plus Cobalt Alloys.

Maleic Anhydride
See ALKALI METALS plus Maleic Anhydride.

Manganese Alloys
See LITHIUM plus Cobalt Alloys.

Methyl Dichloride
See LITHIUM plus Bromoform.

Methyl Diiodide
See LITHIUM plus Bromoform.

Molybdenum Trioxide
The reaction of lithium and molybdenum trioxide occurs at about 180°C with consequent temperature rise to 1400°C.
Mellor **2, Supp. 2:** 82 (1961).

Monofluorotrichloromethane
See LITHIUM plus Trichlorotrifluoroethane.

Nickel Alloys
See LITHIUM plus Cobalt Alloys.

Niobium Pentoxide
The reaction of lithium and niobium pentoxide occurs around 320°C, with consequent temperature rise to 490°C.
Mellor **2, Supp. 2:** 81 (1961).

Nitric Acid
When 15 ml. of nitric acid were poured onto 15 grams of lithium in an attempt to dissolve the metal, a small fire started in the flask. In less than a minute, the reaction was so vigorous that burning lithium was thrown upward in the laboratory hood.
Acc. and Fire Prev. Inf. (March 31, 1954).

Nitrogen
See LITHIUM plus Oxygen; also LITHIUM plus Trichlorotrifluoroethane.
The reaction of lithium and nitrogen increases greatly as the metal melts.
Mellor **2, Supp. 2:** 77 (1961).

Organic Matter
Molten lithium attacks plastics and rubber.
Mellor **2, Supp. 2:** 84 (1961).

Oxygen
Lithium will burn in air, oxygen, nitrogen, and carbon dioxide. The susceptibility of molten lithium surfaces to spontaneous ignition is increased by the presence of lithium oxides or nitrides. These reactions and the reaction with water are extremely violent at higher temperatures. Contact with halogenated hydrocarbons can produce extremely violent reactions, especially on impact.
ASESB Pot. Incid. **39** (1968).
Haz. Chem. Data (1966).

Phosphorus
See LITHIUM plus Arsenic.
See PHOSPHORUS plus Cesium.

Platinum
Platinum and molten lithium react violently at 540°C plus or minus 20°. An intermetallic compound is formed.
Chem. and Eng. News **39** (5): 42 (January 30, 1961).

Rubber
See LITHIUM plus Organic Matter.

Silicates
See LITHIUM plus Carbides.

Sodium Chloride
Sodium chloride extinguishant should not be used on lithium fires since the reaction releases sodium and results in a more violent fire.
Fatt and Tashima, p. 32.

Sodium Nitrite
Lithium reacts with sodium nitrite to form lithium sodium hydronitrite, a compound which decomposes violently around 100°–130°C.
Mellor **2, Supp. 2:** 78 (1961).

Sulfur
The reaction of lithium and sulfur is very violent when either is molten, starting with explosive violence.
Mellor **2, Supp. 2:** 74 (1961).

Tantalum Pentoxide
The reaction of lithium and tantalum pentoxide occurs around 410°C with consequent temperature rise to 595°C.
Mellor **2, Supp. 2:** 81 (1961).

Tetrachloroethylene
See LITHIUM plus Trichlorotrifluoroethane.

Titanium Dioxide
The reaction of lithium and titanium dioxide occurs around 200°C with a flash of light; the temperature can reach 900°C.
Mellor **2, Supp. 2:** 81 (1961).

Trichloroethylene
See LITHIUM plus Trichlorotrifluoroethane.

Trichlorotrifluoroethane
It has been determined experimentally that mixtures of lithium shavings and a number of halogenated hydrocarbons possess an explosive capability. Specifically, impact sensitivity tests have shown that lithium shavings in contact with monofluorotrichlo romethane, trichlorotrifluor-

oethane, carbon tetrachloride, trichloroethylene, or tetrachloroethylene can detonate.
ASESB Pot. Incid. **39** (1968).

Tungsten Trioxide
The reaction of lithium and tungsten trioxide occurs at about 200°C with consequent temperature rise to 1030°C.
Mellor **2, Supp. 2:** 82 (1961).

Vanadium
Molten lithium at 180°C attacks vanadium, beryllium, or chromium severely.
Mellor **2, Supp. 2:** 80 (1961).

Vanadium Pentoxide
The reaction of lithium and vanadium pentoxide occurs around 400°C; the temperature then rises rapidly to 768°C.
Mellor **2, Supp. 2:** 81 (1961).

Water
See LITHIUM plus Oxygen.
Liquid lithium is readily ignited and reacts with most extinguishing agents, including water, carbon tetrachloride and carbon dioxide.
Mellor **2, Supp. 2:** 71 (1961).

Zirconium Tetrachloride
See LITHIUM plus Chromium Trichloride.

LITHIUM ACETYLENE CARBIDE DIAMMINO
$LiC{\equiv}CHNH_3$

Carbon Dioxide
Lithium acetylene carbide diammino burns on contact with carbon dioxide, chlorine, sulfur dioxide, and water.
Mellor **5:** 849 (1946-1947).

Chlorine
See LITHIUM ACETYLENE CARBIDE DIAMMINO plus Carbon Dioxide.

Sulfur Dioxide
See LITHIUM ACETYLENE CARBIDE DIAMMINO plus Carbon Dioxide.

Water
See LITHIUM ACETYLENE CARBIDE DIAMMINO plus Carbon Dioxide.

LITHIUM ALUMINUM HYDRIDE $LiAlH_4$

Air
Lithium aluminum hydride can burn in heated or moist air.
Haz. Chem. Data, p. 101 (1966).
Lab. Govt. Chemist (1965).

Alcohols
See LITHIUM ALUMINUM HYDRIDE plus Water.

Acids
See LITHIUM ALUMINUM HYDRIDE plus Water.

Benzoyl Peroxide
See BENZOYL PEROXIDE plus Lithium Aluminum Hydride.

Boron Trifluoride Etherate
In a laboratory effort to prepare diborane gas from these reactants, the boron trifluoride etherate in ether was frozen at liquid nitrogen temperature, lumps of lithium aluminum hydride were added, and the system was evacuated. Because of insufficient vacuum, the connection between the apparatus and the vacuum source was reopened. When this action jarred the reaction flask, an explosion and orange flame resulted. The presence of oxides in the etherate probably initiated the reaction.
Chem. and Eng. News **45** (20): 51 (1967); **45** (27): **7** (1967).

2-Chloromethylfuran and Ethyl Acetate
See 2-CHLOROMETHYLFURAN plus Lithium Aluminum Hydride and Ethyl Acetate.

Diethylene Glycol Dimethyl Ether
A violent explosion occurred when lithium aluminum hydride was being used to dry diethylene glycol dimethyl ether. About 75 percent of the ether had been distilled when the explosion occurred.
R. M. Adams, *Chem. and Eng. News* **31:**2334 (1953).
MCA Case History **1494** (1968).

Diethyl Ether
With aluminum chloride as a catalyst, occasional explosions involving these materials have been traced to carbon dioxide as an impurity in the ether.
J. Am. Chem. Soc. **70:** 877 (1948).

1,2-Dimethoxyethane
When the solvent, dimethoxyethane was poured into a funnel previously used to introduce the hydride into a reaction flask, a fire ignited in the funnel.
MCA Case History **1182** (1966).

Dimethyl Ether
Use of lithium aluminum hydride to dry methyl ethers may cause explosions, which are attributed to solubility of carbon dioxide. High concentrations of peroxides were found to be present.
MCA Guide for Safety, Appendix 3 (1972).

Methyl Ethyl Ether
See LITHIUM ALUMINUM HYDRIDE plus Dimethyl Ether.

Nitriles and Water
The nitrile reaction with an ether solution of the hydride was conducted in a flask equipped with a reflux condenser having a drying tube. After the apparatus had stood over the weekend, moisture worked back into the flask through the ground glass joint. The lubricant had evidently been dissolved by the ether. When the moisture reached the reactants in the flask an explosion resulted.
NSC Newsletter, Chem. Sec. (April 1967).

Perfluorosuccinamide
Perfluorosuccinamide was added to an ether solution of lithium aluminum hydride in a nitrogen atmosphere. Hydrolysis was then attempted but as the second drop of water was added, a violent explosion occurred.
MCA Guide for Safety, Appendix 3 (1972).

Perfluorosuccinamide and Water
Perfluorosuccinamide was added to an ether solution of lithium aluminum hydride in an atmosphere of nitrogen. When hydrolysis of the mixture was attempted, a violent explosion and fire occurred after the second drop of water was added.
T.S. Reid and G.H. Smith, *Chem. and Eng. News* **29:** 3042 (1951).

Tetrahydrofuran
See TETRAHYDROFURAN plus Lithium Aluminum Hydride.

Water
Lithium aluminum hydride reacts vigorously with hydroxy compounds: water, alcohols, carboxylic acids.
Mellor **2, Supp. 2:** 142 (1961).

LITHIUM AMIDE $LiNH_2$

Water
Lithium amide reacts readily with water and develops a dangerous amount of heat.
Chaney (1948). *Chapman* (1948). F. W. Bergstrom and W. C. Fernelius, *Chem. Reviews* **12:** 61 (1933).

LITHIUM AZIDE LiN_3

Carbon Disulfide
See AZIDES plus Carbon Disulfide.

LITHIUM CARBIDE Li_2C_2

Bromine
See BROMINE plus Lithium Carbide.

Chlorine
See BROMINE plus Lithium Carbide.

Fluorine
See BROMINE plus Lithium Carbide.

Iodine
See BROMINE plus Lithium Carbide.
See IODINE plus Cesium Carbide.

Lead Monoxide
Lithium carbide in the presence of lead monoxide is reduced with great vigor and with incandescence. *Mellor* **5:** 849 (1946-1947).

Phosphorus
See PHOSPHORUS plus Lithium Carbide.

Selenium
See SULFUR plus Lithium Carbide.

Sulfur
See SULFUR plus Lithium Carbide.

LITHIUM CARBONATE Li_2CO_3

Fluorine
See FLUORINE plus Carbonates.

LITHIUM CHLORIDE LiCl

Bromine Trifluoride
See BROMINE TRIFLUORIDE plus Barium Chloride.

LITHIUM HEXAPHENYLTUNGSTATE ETHERATE
$Li_3W(C_6H_5)_63(C_2H_5)_2O$

Air
Triphenyl tungsten-tris(phenyl lithium)-tri (diethyl ether) is spontaneously flammable in air.
Douda (1966).

LITHIUM HYDRIDE LiH

Nitrous Oxide
See NITROUS OXIDE plus Lithium Hydride.

Oxygen (Liquid)
See OXYGEN (LIQUID) plus Lithium Hydride.

LITHIUM METHYLIDE CH_2Li_2

Air
Methylene dilithium is spontaneously flammable in air.
Douda (1966).

LITHIUM PHOSPHIDE Li_3P

Water
Lithium phosphide reacts with water to form spontaneously flammable phosphine.
Van Wazer (1958).

LITHIUM SILICIDE Li_6Si_2

Bromine
See FLUORINE plus Lithium Silicide.

Fluorine
See FLUORINE plus Lithium Silicide.

Hydrogen Chloride
Lithium silicide in contact with hydrogen chloride becomes incandescent. When dilute hydrochloric acid is used, a gas spontaneously flammable in air is evolved.
Mellor **6:** 170 (1946-1947).

Nitric Acid
Lithium silicide reacts explosively with nitric acid, producing nitrogen dioxide and silica.
Mellor **6:** 170 (1946-1947).

Phosphorus
See PHOSPHORUS plus Lithium Silicide.

Selenium
See PHOSPHORUS plus Lithium Silicide.

Sulfuric Acid
When lithium silicide is placed on sulfuric acid, it becomes incandescent.
Mellor **6:** 170 (1946-1947).

Tellurium
See PHOSPHORUS plus Lithium Silicide.

Water
The reaction between lithium silicide and water is very violent; a spontaneously flammable gas is evolved.
Mellor **6:** 170 (1946-1947).

LITHIUM TETRAHYDROBORATE $LiBH_4$

Cellulosic Material
Lithium borohydride is likely to ignite in contact with cellulosic materials.
Lab. Govt. Chemist (1965).

Water
Lithium borohydride is likely to ignite when moistened with water.
Lab. Govt. Chemist (1965). *Gaylord,* p. 22 (1956).

LITHIUM TETRAMETHYLBORATE $LiB(CH_3)_4$

Water
Lithium tetramethyl borate may ignite spontaneously in moist air.
Dreisback, pp. 93-94 (1961).

LITHIUM TRI-tert-BUTOXYALUMINATE
$LiAl[OC(CH_3)_3]_3H$

Water
Lithium aluminum tri-tert-butoxyhydride reacts with water to form hydrogen. Ignition sometimes occurs.
Rose (1961).

LUCITE®

Fluorine
See FLUORINE plus Solid Nonmetals and Oxygen.

LUTETIUM Lu

Air
See RARE EARTH METALS plus Air.

Halogens
See RARE EARTH METALS plus Halogens.

MAGNESIUM Mg

Air
Magnesium ribbon and fine magnesium shavings can be ignited at air temperatures of about 950°F and very finely divided magnesium powder has been ignited at air temperatures below 900°F.
Magnesium Standard, p. 4 (1967).

Aluminum and Potassium Perchlorate
See ALUMINUM plus Magnesium and Potassium Perchlorate.

Ammonium Nitrate
See AMMONIUM NITRATE plus Metals (powdered).

Barium Nitrate, Barium Dioxide and Zinc
A mixture consisting of barium dioxide, barium nitrate, magnesium and zinc exploded from an unknown cause, demolishing a small plant.
Sprengstoffe, Waffen u. Munitions (1905).

Beryllium Oxide
Oxides of beryllium, cadmium, mercury, molybdenum and zinc can react explosively with magnesium when heated.
Mellor **4:** 272 (1946-1947).

Boron Phosphodiiodide
Powdered magnesium and boron phosphodiiodide react with incandescence.
Mellor **8:** 845 (1946-1947).

Bromobenzyl Trifluoride
Bromobenzyl trifluoride was added to magnesium turnings in sodium-dried ether at a rate so as to maintain reflux. After a period of time an explosion occurred.
MCA Case History **1834** (1972).

Cadmium Cyanide
Magnesium reacts with incandescence when heated with cyanides of cadmium, cobalt, copper, lead, nickel, or zinc.
Mellor **4:** 271 (1946-1947).

Cadmium Oxide
See MAGNESIUM plus Beryllium Oxide.

Calcium Carbide
Magnesium reacts with incandescence when heated in air with calcium carbide.
Mellor **4:** 271 (1946-1947).

Carbonates
A mixture of the two may cause an explosion.
Pieters, p. 30 (1957).

Carbon Tetrachloride
See MAGNESIUM plus Trichloroethylene; also ALUMINUM plus Chloroform.

Chlorine
Magnesium exposed to moist chlorine is spontaneously flammable.
Mellor **4:** 267 (1946-1947).

Chlorine Trifluoride
See ALUMINUM plus Chlorine Trifluoride.

Chloroform
When chloroform or methyl chloride (or mixtures of both) contacts magnesium, an explosion occurs.
C.C. Clogston, *UL Technical Report* **34:** 15 (1945).

Cobalt Cyanide
See MAGNESIUM plus Cadmium Cyanide.

Copper Cyanide
See MAGNESIUM plus Cadmium Cyanide.

Copper Sulfate (anhydrous), Ammonium Nitrate, Potassium Chlorate and Water
The water permits both the exothermic reaction of $Mg + Cu^{++}$ to give $Cu + Mg^{++}$ and the metathetical reaction of the salts, which produces the unstable ammonium chlorate. The mixture is unstable and hazardous.
Ellern, p. 46 (1968).

Cupric Oxide
The reduction of heated cupric oxide by admixed magnesium is accompanied by incandescence and an explosion.
Mellor **3:** 138 (1946-1947).

Cupric Sulfate
The action of magnesium on a solution of cupric sulfate is attended by the evolution of hydrogen.
Mellor **3:** 247 (1946-1947).

Fluorine
Magnesium exposed to moist fluorine is spontaneously flammable.
Mellor **4:** 267 (1946-1947).

Gold Cyanide
Cyanides of gold or mercury decompose to the metals and cyanogen. The latter reacts explosively with magnesium.
Mellor **4:** 271 (1946-1947).

Hydrogen and Calcium Carbonate
When a mixture of magnesium and calcium carbonate is heated in a current of hydrogen, a violent explosion occurs.
Mellor **4:** 272 (1946-1947).

Hydrogen Iodide
Magnesium burns momentarily in hydrogen iodide.
Mellor **2:** 206 (1946-1947).

Hydrogen Peroxide
Magnesium mixed with a trace of manganese dioxide ignites immediately in contact with hydrogen peroxide.
Mellor **1:** 938 (1946-1947).

Iodine
Magnesium burns vigorously when heated in iodine vapor.
Mellor **4:** 267 (1946-1947).

Lead Cyanide
See MAGNESIUM plus Cadmium Cyanide.

Mercuric Oxide
See MAGNESIUM plus Beryllium Oxide.

Mercury Cyanide
See MAGNESIUM plus Gold Cyanide.

Methyl Chloride
See MAGNESIUM plus Chloroform.

Molybdenum Trioxide
When molybdenum trioxide is heated with molten magnesium, a violent detonation occurs.
H.N. Warren, *Chem. News* **64:** 75 (1891).
See MAGNESIUM plus Beryllium Oxide.

Nickel Cyanide
See MAGNESIUM plus Cadmium Cyanide.

Nitric Acid
A mixture of finely divided magnesium and nitric acid is explosive.
Pieters, p. 28 (1957).

Nitrogen Dioxide
Magnesium, phosphorus or sulfur burns vigorously in nitrogen dioxide.
Comp. Rend. **116:** 756

Oxygen (Liquid)
Liquid oxygen (LOX) gives a detonable mixture when combined with *powdered* magnesium.
Kirschenbaum (1956).

Performic Acid
Powdered magnesium can decompose performic acid violently.
Berichte **48:** 1139 (1915).

Phosphates
A mixture of the two may cause an explosion.
Pieters, p. 30 (1957).

Potassium Chlorate
An explosion occurred during heating of a mixture of potassium chlorate and magnesium.
Chem. and Eng. News **14:** 451 (1936).

Potassium Perchlorate
Powdered magnesium plus potassium (or sodium) perchlorate is a friction-sensitive explosive mixture.
V.E. Ready, *Safety Eng. Reports* (1947).

Silver Nitrate
A mixture of the two ingredients will burst into flame on moistening. The water causes electrochemical exchange between the magnesium and the silver ion. The heat of reaction of this exchange provokes the pyrochemical effect.
Ellern, p. 46 (1968).

Silver Oxide
See SILVER OXIDE plus Magnesium.

Sodium Perchlorate
See MAGNESIUM plus Potassium Perchlorate.

Sodium Peroxide
Sodium peroxide oxidizes magnesium powder with incandescence. The mixture explodes when heated to redness. When the mixture is exposed to moist air, spontaneous combustion occurs.
Mellor **2:** 490; **5:** 217 (1946-1947).

Sodium Peroxide and Carbon Dioxide
When carbon dioxide gas is passed over a mixture of powdered magnesium and sodium peroxide, the mixture explodes.
Mellor **2:** 490 (1946-1947).

Stannic Oxide
Stannic oxide, heated with magnesium, explodes.
Mellor **7:** 401 (1946-1947).

Sulfates
A mixture of the two may cause an explosion.
Pieters, p. 30 (1957).

Trichloroethylene
It has been determined experimentally that a mixture of magnesium powder with trichloroethylene or with carbon tetrachloride will flash or spark under heavy impact.
ASESB Pot. Incid. **39** (1968).

Zinc Cyanide
See MAGNESIUM plus Cadmium Cyanide.

Zinc Oxide
See MAGNESIUM plus Beryllium Oxide.

MAGNESIUM ALLOYS

Air
Magnesium alloy powders containing more than 50% magnesium readily ignite in air.
Lab. Govt. Chemist (1965).
Magnesium Standard, p. 5 (1967).

MAGNESIUM ALUMINUM PHOSPHIDE Mg_3AlP_3

Water
In contact with water or damp air, magnesium aluminum phosphide evolves phosphine, which is spontaneously flammable in air.
Lab. Govt. Chemist (1965).

MAGNESIUM BORIDE Mg_3B_2

Hydrochloric Acid
Magnesium boride, when treated with concentrated hydrochloric acid, produces a spontaneously flammable gas.
Mellor **5:** 25 (1946-1947).

MAGNESIUM BROMATE $Mg(BrO_3)_2$

Aluminum
See ALUMINUM plus Bromates.

Arsenic
See ARSENIC plus Bromates.

Carbon
See CARBON plus Bromates.

Copper
See COPPER plus Bromates.

Metal Sulfides
See METAL SULFIDES plus Bromates.

Organic Matter
See BROMATES plus Organic Matter.

Phosphorus
See PHOSPHORUS plus Bromates.

Sulfur
See SULFUR plus Bromates.

MAGNESIUM CHLORATE $Mg(ClO_3)_2$

Aluminum
See ALUMINUM plus Bromates.

Antimony Sulfide
See CHLORATES plus Antimony Sulfide.
See METAL SULFIDES plus Bromates.

Arsenic
See ARSENIC plus Bromates.

Arsenic Sulfide
See CHLORATES plus Arsenic Sulfide. See METAL SULFIDES plus Bromates.

Carbon
See CARBON plus Bromates.

Charcoal
See CHLORATES plus Organic Matter.

Copper
See COPPER plus Bromates.

Copper Sulfide
See COPPER SULFIDE plus Cadmium Chlorate.

Manganese Dioxide
See CHLORATES plus Manganese Dioxide.

Metal Sulfides
See METAL SULFIDES plus Bromates.

Organic Acids (Dibasic)
See CHLORATES plus Organic Acids.

Organic Matter
See BROMATES plus Organic Matter. See CHLORATES plus Organic Matter.

Phosphorus
See PHOSPHORUS plus Bromates.

Stannic Sulfide
See STANNIC SULFIDE plus Cadmium Chlorate. See METAL SULFIDES plus Bromates.

Stannous Sulfide
See STANNIC SULFIDE plus Cadmium Chlorate.
See METAL SULFIDES plus Bromates.

Sulfur
See SULFUR plus Bromates. See CHLORATES plus Organic Matter.

MAGNESIUM CHLORIDE $MgCl$

2-Furan Percarboxylic Acid
See 2-FURAN PERCARBOXYLIC ACID (self-reactive).

MAGNESIUM HYDRIDE MgH_2

Air
Magnesium hydride ignites spontaneously in air.
Merck Index, p. 637 (1968).

Water
Magnesium hydride ignites violently with water.
Merck Index, p. 637 (1968).

MAGNESIUM HYDROXIDE $Mg(OH)_2$

Maleic Anhydride
See SODIUM HYDROXIDE plus Maleic Anhydride.

Phosphorus
See PHOSPHORUS plus Alkaline Hydroxide.

MAGNESIUM HYPOPHOSPHITE $Mg(PH_2O_2)_2$

(self-reactive)
Magnesium hypophosphite liberates spontaneously flammable phosphine when heated.
Mellor **8:** 885 (1946-1947).

MAGNESIUM IODATE $Mg(IO_3)_2$

Aluminum
See ALUMINUM plus Bromates.

Arsenic
See ARSENIC plus Bromates.

Carbon
See CARBON plus Bromates.

Copper
See COPPER plus Bromates.

Metal Sulfides
See METAL SULFIDES plus Bromates.

Organic Matter
See BROMATES plus Organic Matter.

Phosphorus
See PHOSPHORUS plus Bromates.

Sulfur
See SULFUR plus Bromates.

MAGNESIUM METHYLIDE CH_2Mg

Air
Methylene magnesium is spontaneously flammable in air.
Coates, p. 29 (1956).

MAGNESIUM NITRATE $Mg(NO_3)_2$

Dimethyl Formamide
See DIMETHYL FORMAMIDE plus Magnesium Nitrate.

MAGNESIUM OXIDE MgO

Chlorine Trifluoride
See CHLORINE TRIFLUORIDE plus Aluminum Oxide.

Phosphorus Pentachloride
See PHOSPHORUS PENTACHLORIDE plus Magnesium Oxide.

MAGNESIUM PERCHLORATE $Mg(ClO_4)_2$

Acids (Mineral)
Magnesium perchlorate should not be contacted by mineral acids because of the danger of explosion.
ACS **146:** 208. *Chem. Weekblad.* **38:** 85 (1941); **54:** 277 (1958). *Ind. & Eng. Chem. News* **17:** 70 (1939).

Ammonia
Magnesium perchlorate was contained in a small steel refrigeration-type drying tube and the ammonia was passed through it (after the system was evacuated) in small increments in an attempt to further desiccate it. It was noted that the outside of the drying tube was warm to the touch. Shortly thereafter the tube exploded violently.
F.F. Chapman (1973).

Butyl Fluoride
The butyl fluoride content of hydrocarbon gases being dried by magnesium perchlorate hydrolyzed. Reaction of the acid formed with the perchlorate caused an explosion.
ACS **146:** 208-9. *Chem. Weekblad.* **38:** 85 (1941); **54:** 277 (1958). *Ind. & Eng. Chem. News* **17:** 70 (1939).

Dimethyl Sulfoxide
See DIMETHYL SULFOXIDE plus Magnesium Perchlorate.

Ethylene Oxide
Drying gaseous ethylene oxide with magnesium perchlorate resulted in an explosion.
NSC Newsletter, Chem. Sec. (Oct. 1959).

Hydrocarbons
Magnesium perchlorate, used in drying hydrocarbon gases, exploded when it was heated to 220°C.
ACS **146:**208-9, *Chem. Weekblad.* **38:**85 (1941); **54:**277 (1958). *Ind. & Eng. Chem. News* **17:** 70 (1939).
Magnesium perchlorate, used in drying unsaturated hydrocarbons, exploded on being heated to 220°C.
P. M. Heertjes and J. P. W. Houtman, *Chem. Weekblad* **38:**85 (1941).

Organic Matter
Several instances of explosions from using magnesium perchlorate as a drying agent for organic matter have been documented.
Chem. and Eng. News **43** (37):62 (1965); **43** (47):5 (1965).

Phosphorus
See PHOSPHORUS plus Magnesium Perchlorate.

Trimethyl Phosphite
As soon as trimethyl phosphite contacted a small quantity of mag nesium perchlorate in a small flask there was a brilliant flash and a loud explosion that shattered the flask.
Allison (1968).

MAGNESIUM PHOSPHIDE Mg_3P_2

Bromine
See CHLORINE plus Magnesium Phosphide.

Chlorine
See CHLORINE plus Magnesium Phosphide.

Nitric Acid
Nitric acid oxidizes magnesium phosphide with incandescence.
Mellor **8:**842 (1946-1947).

Water
Magnesium phosphide produces spontaneously flammable phos phine and diphosphine on contact with water.
Douda (1966).

MAGNESIUM-TITANIUM ALLOY

Nitric Acid
See TITANIUM-MAGNESIUM ALLOY plus Nitric Acid.

MALEIC ANHYDRIDE OCOCH=CHCO

Raw maleic anhydride was being distilled at reduced pressure (0.2 bar) in a plate column 3 m in diameter × 10 m high. The base temperature was 165°C, but several hours into the distillation, the temperature began to rise at an increasing rate, reaching 260°C in 3 hours. At this point the column pressure exceeded atmospheric pressure and the safety valves opened, emitting "violent" jets of white vapor. The column then exploded with one fragment weighing over a ton landing 200 m away. The primary explosion was followed by a secondary combustion of the vapors and a fireball.
Louis A. Medard, *Accidental Explosions* **2:** 769 (1989).

Alkali Metals
See ALKALI METALS plus Maleic Anhydride.

Amines
See SODIUM HYDROXIDE and Maleic Anhydride; also SODIUM HYDROXIDE plus Pyridine or other Tertiary Amines.

Calcium Hydroxide
See SODIUM HYDROXIDE plus Maleic Anhydride.

Caustic Soda
In 1960 a factory was cleaning an apparatus with caustic soda. One valve was not water tight in the off position and a small amount of caustic soda was introduced into a 3-cu m stainless steel vessel containing maleic anhydride. Heat of hydration and neutralization triggered an exothermic reaction with gas emission. The vessel exploded and two people were killed by the fragments.
Louis A. Medard, *Accidental Explosions* **2:** 769 (1989).

Lithium
See ALKALI METALS plus Maleic Anhydride.

Potassium
See ALKALI METALS plus Maleic Anhydride.

Potassium Hydroxide
See SODIUM HYDROXIDE plus Maleic Anhydride.

Pyridine or Other Tertiary Amines
A 0.1 percent solution of pyridine in maleic anhydride at 185°C. gives an exothermic decomposition with rapid evolution of gas.
Chem. and Eng. News **42** (8):41 (1964). *Chem. Haz. Info. Series* **C- 71,** p. 5 (1960).

Sodium
See ALKALI METALS plus Maleic Anhydride.

Sodium Hydroxide
See SODIUM HYDROXIDE plus Maleic Anhydride.

MANGANESE Mn

Aluminum and Air
During a fire in an industrial bag filter, a mixture of aluminum and manganese dusts was inadvertently released from the hopper below the bag and a drastic explosion resulted.
Occ. Haz. **28:**44-6 (November 1966).

Chlorine
Heated manganese ignites in chlorine and burns brilliantly. Powdered manganese ignites in chlorine and burns brilliantly.
Mellor **12:**185-7 (1946-1947).

Fluorine
When powdered manganese is exposed to fluorine, the reaction takes place with incandescence.
Mellor **12:**344 (1946-1947).

Hydrogen Peroxide
See IRON plus Hydrogen Peroxide.

Nitric Acid
Concentrated nitric acid reacts with powdered manganese with incandescence and a feeble explosion.
Mellor **12:**188 (1946-1947).

Nitrogen Dioxide
Manganese or potassium ignites in nitrogen dioxide.
Ann. Chim. et Phys. (2) **2:**317.

Phosphorus
When manganese is heated in the vapor of phosphorus at a very dull red heat, union occurs with incandescence.
Mellor **8:**853 (1946-1947).

Sulfur Dioxide
Pyrophoric manganese burns with a brilliant flame when heated in sulfur dioxide vapor.
Mellor **12:**187 (1946-1947).

MANGANESE ALLOYS

Lithium
See LITHIUM plus Cobalt Alloys.

MANGANESE DIOXIDE MnO_2

Chlorates
See CHLORATES plus Manganese Dioxide.

Chlorine Trifluoride
Chlorine trifluoride reacts with manganese dioxide with incandescence.
Mellor **12:**254 (1946-1947).
See also CHLORINE TRIFLUORIDE plus Aluminum Oxide.

Hydrogen Peroxide
Powdered manganese dioxide dropped into a concentrated solution of hydrogen peroxide may cause an explosion.
Mellor **1:**936, 938 (1946-1947).

Permonosulfuric Acid
See PERMONOSULFURIC ACID plus Manganese Dioxide. See PLATINUM plus Permonosulfuric Acid.

Potassium Azide
When manganese dioxide is gently heated with potassium azide the reaction is very violent.
Mellor **8:**347 (1946-1947).

Rubidium Acetylene Carbide
See RUBIDIUM ACETYLENE CARBIDE plus Manganese Dioxide.

Sodium Peroxide
See SODIUM PEROXIDE plus Manganese Dioxide.

MANGANESE HEPTOXIDE Mn_2O_7

(self-reactive)
About three cubic centimeters of manganese heptoxide, stored in a brown glass bottle, exploded 5 or 6 hours after its preparation from sulfuric acid and potassium permanganate.
Delhez (1967).

Organic Matter
When these materials are mixed, explosions may result.
A. M. Patterson, *Chem. and Eng. News* **26:**711 (1948). J. R. Archer, *Chem. and Eng. News* **26:**205 (1948).
See also POTASSIUM PERMANGANATE plus Sulfuric Acid.

MANGANESE TRIFLUORIDE MnF_3

Glass
When manganese trifluoride is heated in a glass vessel, there is a violent reaction involving the silicon in the glass, since silicon tet rafluoride is released.
Mellor **12:**344 (1946-1947).

MANGANOCENE $Mn(C_5H_5)_2$

Air
Biscyclopentadienyl manganese is spontaneously flammable in air.
Douda (1966).

MANGANOUS BROMIDE $MnBr_2$

Potassium
See POTASSIUM plus Ammonium Bromide.

MANGANOUS CHLORIDE $MnCl_2$

Potassium
See POTASSIUM plus Aluminum Bromide.

Sodium
See SODIUM plus Ferrous Chloride.

Zinc
See ZINC plus Manganese Chloride.

MANGANOUS HYPOPHOSPHITE $Mn(PH_2O_2)_2$

(self-reactive)
Manganous hypophosphite detonates above 200°C.
Mellor **8:**889 (1946-1947).

MANGANOUS IODATE $Mn(IO_3)_3$

Bromine Trifluoride
See BROMINE TRIFLUORIDE plus Bismuth Pentoxide.

MANGANOUS IODIDE MnI_2

Potassium
See POTASSIUM plus Ammonium Bromide.

MANGANOUS OXIDE MnO

Calcium Hypochlorite
See CALCIUM HYPOCHLORITE plus Iron Oxide.

Fluorine
See FLUORINE plus Trimanganese Tetroxide.

MANGANOUS PERCHLORATE $Mn(ClO_4)_2 6H_2O$

Ethyl Alcohol and 2,2-Dimethoxypropane
See ETHYL ALCOHOL plus Manganese Perchlorate and 2,2- Dimethoxypropane.

MANGANOUS PHOSPHIDE Mn_3P_2

Chlorine
See CHLORINE plus Manganese Ditritaphosphide.

MANGANOUS SULFIDE MnS

Air
Red manganese sulfide, when dried in vacuo, becomes red-hot when exposed to air.
Mellor **12:** 344 (1946-1947).

MANGANOUS TETRAHYDROALUMINATE $Mn(AlH_4)_2$

Air
Manganese aluminohydride is spontaneously flammable in air.
Chem. Abst. **49:** 766e (1955). J. Aubrey and G. Monnier, *Comp. Rend.* **238:** 2534-2535 (1954).

MERCAPTANS RSH

Calcium Hypochlorite
See CALCIUM HYPOCHLORITE plus Mercaptans.

MERCURIC AZIDE $Hg(N_3)_2$

(self-reactive)
Mercuric azide decomposes at 190°C. It is explosively unstable.
Mellor **8, Supp. 2:** 43 (1967).

MERCURIC BROMIDE $HgBr_2$

Sodium
See SODIUM plus Ferrous Chloride.

Potassium
See POTASSIUM plus Aluminum Bromide.

MERCURIC CHLORIDE $HgCl_2$

Potassium
See POTASSIUM plus Aluminum Bromide.

Sodium
See SODIUM plus Ferrous Chloride.

MERCURIC CHLORITE $Hg(ClO_2)_2$

(self-reactive)
Mercuric chlorite is an explosive salt.
Mellor **2, Supp. 1:** 575 (1956).

MERCURIC CYANIDE $Hg(CN)_2$

Fluorine
See FLUORINE plus Mercuric Cyanide.

Magnesium
See MAGNESIUM plus Gold Cyanide.

MERCURIC CYANIDE OXIDE $Hg_2(CN)_2O$

(self-reactive)
Several instances are cited where explosions have occurred in handling or manipulating this substance. Rubbing the material is a frequent cause of the explosions.
Chem. Abst. **16:** 2010 (1972).
Chem. Abst. **11:** 300 (1917).

MERCURIC FLUORIDE HgF_2

Potassium
See POTASSIUM plus Aluminum Bromide.

Sodium
See SODIUM plus Ferrous Chloride.

MERCURIC IODIDE HgI_2

Chlorine Trifluoride
See CHLORINE TRIFLUORIDE plus Mercuric Iodide.

Potassium
See POTASSIUM plus Aluminum Bromide.

Sodium
See SODIUM plus Ferrous Chloride.

MERCURIC NITRATE $Hg(NO_3)_2$

Acetylene
Acetylene forms a sensitive acetylide when passed into an aqueous solution of mercuric nitrate.
Mellor **4:** 933 (1946-1947).

Ethyl Alcohol
Alcohols should not be mixed with mercuric nitrate, as explosive mercury fulminate may be formed.
Bahme, p. 9 (1961).

Hypophosphoric Acid
Mercuric nitrate is violently reduced to mercury by hypophosphoric acid.
Mellor **4:** 993 (1946-1947).

Phosphine
The reaction of these materials gives a yellow precipitate which explodes when heated or subjected to shock.
Mellor **4:** 993 (1946-1947).

Sulfur
See SULFUR plus Mercuric Nitrate.

Unsaturates; Aromatics
Mercuric nitrate reacts with unsaturates and aromatics with violence if given time to generate enough heat.
J. Ball, *Chem. and Eng. News* **26:** 3300 (1948).

MERCURIC NITRIDE Hg_3N_2

(self-reactive)
Mercuric nitride is said to be very explosive.
Mellor **8:** 107 (1946-1947).

Sulfuric Acid
Mercuric nitride explodes when brought in contact with sulfuric acid.
Mellor **8:** 108 (1946-1947).

MERCURIC OXIDE HgO

Chlorine
See CHLORINE plus Mercuric Oxide.

Hydrazine Hydrate
When hydrazine hydrate is dropped on mercuric oxide, an explosion may occur.
Mellor **8:** 318 (1946-1947).

Hydrogen Peroxide
See LEAD DIOXIDE plus Hydrogen Peroxide.

Hypophosphorous Acid
Hypophosphorous acid reduces mercuric oxide explosively to the metal.
Mellor **4:** 778 (1946-1947).

Iodine, Methyl Alcohol, and Ethyl Alcohol
See IODINE plus Ethyl Alcohol, Methyl Alcohol, and Mercuric Oxide.

Magnesium
See MAGNESIUM plus Beryllium Oxide.

Phospham
See PHOSPHAM plus Cupric Oxide.

Phosphorus
See PHOSPHORUS plus Mercuric Oxide.

Sodium-Potassium Alloy
See SODIUM-POTASSIUM plus Mercuric Oxide.

Sulfur
See SULFUR plus Mercuric Oxide.

MERCURIC SULFATE $HgSO_4$

Hydrogen Chloride
Absorption of gaseous hydrogen chloride on mercuric sulfate becomes violent at 125°C.
Mellor **2, Supp. 1:** 462 (1956).

MERCURIC SULFIDE HgS

Chlorine
See CHLORINE plus Mercuric Sulfide.

Chlorine Monoxide
See CHLORINE MONOXIDE plus Calcium Phosphide.

Silver Oxide
See SILVER OXIDE plus Antimony Trisulfide.

MERCUROUS AZIDE HgN_3

(self-reactive)
Mercurous azide decomposes at 210°C. It is explosively unstable.
Mellor **8, Supp. 2:** 43 (1967).

MERCUROUS CHLORIDE HgCl

Potassium
See POTASSIUM plus Aluminum Bromide.

Sodium
See SODIUM plus Ferrous Chloride.

MERCUROUS HYPOPHOSPHATE $Hg_4P_2O_6$

(self-reactive)
Mercurous hypophosphate decomposes explosively.
Mellor **8, Supp. 3:** 651 (1971).

MERCUROUS NITRATE $HgNO_3$

Carbon
See CARBON plus Mercurous Nitrate.

Phosphorus
See PHOSPHORUS plus Mercurous Nitrate.

MERCUROUS OXIDE Hg_2O

Hydrogen Peroxide
Mixture reacts with explosive violence.
V. Autropoff, *J. Prakt. Chem.* **77:** 316 (1908).

Hydrogen Sulfide, Barium Oxide and Air
See HYDROGEN SULFIDE plus Soda Lime.

Potassium
See POTASSIUM plus Mercurous Oxide.

Sodium
See POTASSIUM plus Mercurous Oxide.

Sulfur
See SULFUR plus Mercurous Oxide.

MERCURY Hg

Acetylene
Insoluble, explosive acetylide is formed with mercury.
Von Schwartz, p. 142 (1918).

Ammonia
Mercury and ammonia can produce explosive compounds. A residue resulting from such a reaction exploded when an attempt was made to clean out the residue with a steel rod.
C. Van Brunt, *Science* **65:** 63-4 (1927). L.M. Henderson, *Ind. & Eng. Chem. News* **10:** 73 (1932). *Chem. and Eng. News* **25:** 2138 (1947).
See also GOLD plus Ammonia.

Boron Phosphodiiodide
When thrown into mercury vapor, boron phosphodiiodide ignites at once.
Mellor **8:** 845 (1946-1947).

Chlorine
Flame forms with chlorine jet over mercury surface at 200°–300°C.
Mellor **2, Supp. 1:** 381 (1956).

Chlorine Dioxide
Chlorine dioxide and liquid mercury explode violently.
Mellor **2:** 288 (1946-1947). *Von Schwartz,* p. 142 (1918).

Methyl Azide
Methyl azide in the presence of mercury was shown to be potentially explosive.
C.L. Currie and B. Darwent, *Can. J. Chem.* **41:** 1048 (1963).

Sodium Carbide
Ground mixtures of sodium carbide and mercury, aluminum, lead, or iron can react vigorously.
Mellor **5:** 848 (1946-1947).

MERCURY SALTS

Acetylene
Mercury salts and silver salts give acetylides from ammoniacal solutions in the same way copper salts do. The dried acetylides are extremely sensitive and violent.

G. Benson, *Comp. Gas Bull.* (Oct. 18, 1950); J.K. Luchs, *Phot. Sci. Eng.* 10:334-7 (1966).

Butynediol and Acid
See BUTYNEDIOL plus Hydroxides.

Nitromethane
See COPPER SALTS plus Nitromethane.

MERCURY TETRAPHOSPHIDE Hg_3P_4

Air
Mercury tetratriphosphide ignites when warmed in air, or in chlo rine at ordinary temperatures. Mixed with potassium chlorate, it explodes by percussion.
Comp. Rend. **115:** 230.

Chlorates
See MERCURY TETRATRIPHOSPHIDE plus Air.

Chlorine
See MERCURY TETRATRIPHOSPHIDE plus Air.

Potassium Chlorate
See MERCURY TETRATRIPHOSPHIDE plus Air.

MESITYLENE $C_6H_3(CH_3)_3$

Nitric Acid
See NITRIC ACID plus Mesitylene.

MESITYL OXIDE $(CH_3)_2C{=}CHCOCH_3$

2-Aminoethanol
Mixing mesityloxide and 2-aminoethanol in a closed container caused the temperature and pressure to increase.
Flynn and Rossow (1970). See Note under complete reference.

Chlorosulfonic Acid
Mixing mesityl oxide and chlorosulfonic acid in a closed container caused the temperature and pressure to increase.
Flynn and Rossow (1970). See Note under complete reference.

Ethylene Diamine
Mixing mesityl oxide and ethylene diamine in a closed container caused the temperature and pressure to increase.
Flynn and Rossow (1970). See Note under complete reference.

Nitric Acid
Mixing mesityl oxide and nitric acid in a closed container caused the temperature and pressure to increase.
Flynn and Rossow (1970). See Note under complete reference.

Oleum
Mixing mesityl oxide and oleum in a closed container caused the temperature and pressure to increase.
Flynn and Rossow (1970). See Note under complete reference.

Sulfuric Acid
Mixing mesityl oxide and 96% sulfuric acid in a closed container caused the temperature and pressure to increase.
Flynn and Rossow (1970). See Note under complete reference.

METALLIC HALIDES

Bromine Pentafluoride
See BROMINE PENTAFLUORIDE plus Metal Oxides.

METAL OXIDES

Bromine Pentafluoride
See BROMINE PENTAFLUORIDE plus Metal Oxides.

Performic Acid
Metal oxides catalyze the decomposition of performic acid, resulting in an explosion.
Grignard **11:** 179 (1935-1954).

METALS

Ammonium Nitrate
See AMMONIUM NITRATE plus Metals (powdered).

Bromine Pentafluoride
Very violent reactions may occur between bromine pentafluoride and powdered or warmed metals.
Mellor **2, Supp. 1:** 172 (1956).

Bromine Trifluoride
Halogen fluorides appear to react with all metals. The reaction is vigorous when no film forms.
Mellor **2, Supp. 1:** 163 (1956).

Chlorates
See CHLORATES plus Metals (powdered).

Performic Acid
Metals catalyze the decomposition of performic acid and can make it explosive.
Grignard **11:** 179 (1935-1954).

METAL SULFIDES

Bromates
A combination of finely divided metal sulfides with finely divided bromates (also chlorates and iodates) of barium, calcium, magnesium, potassium, sodium, and zinc can be exploded by heat, percussion and, sometimes, light friction.
Mellor **2:** 310 (1946-1947).

Chlorates
See METAL SULFIDES plus Bromates. See COPPER SULFIDE plus Cadmium Chlorate.

Chloric Acid
See COPPER SULFIDE plus Cadmium Chlorate. See ANTIMONY SULFIDE plus Chloric Acid.

Hydrazine Mononitrate
See ZINC plus Hydrazine Mononitrate.

Iodates
See METAL SULFIDES plus Bromates.

Silver Oxide
See SILVER OXIDE plus Antimony Trisulfide.

METHANE CH_4

Bromine Pentafluoride
See BROMINE PENTAFLUORIDE plus Acetic Acid.

Chlorine
See CHLORINE plus Methane.

Chlorine Dioxide
See CHLORINE DIOXIDE plus Butadiene.

Nitrogen Trifluoride
See HYDROGEN plus Nitrogen Trifluoride.

Oxygen (Liquid)
See OXYGEN (LIQUID) plus Methane.

Oxygen Difluoride
See HYDROGEN plus Oxygen Difluoride.

METHANOL CH_3OH

Chromic Anhydride
See CHROMIC ANHYDRIDE plus Methyl Alcohol.

Iodine, Ethyl Alcohol and Mercuric Oxide
See IODINE plus Ethyl Alcohol, Methyl Alcohol, and Mercuric Oxide.

Lead Perchlorate
See LEAD PERCHLORATE plus Methyl Alcohol.

Perchloric Acid
See PERCHLORIC ACID plus Ethyl Alcohol.

Phosphorus Trioxide
See DIMETHYL FORMAMIDE plus Phosphorus.

Potassium Hydroxide and Chloroform
See SODIUM HYDROXIDE plus Chloroform and Methyl Alcohol.

Sodium Hydroxide and Chloroform
See SODIUM HYDROXIDE plus Chloroform and Methyl Alcohol.

p-METHOXYBENZYL FORMATE $CH_3OC_6H_4CH_2OCHO$

Phosgene
In the formation of p-methoxybenzyl formate by the addition of phosgene to alcohols followed by the addition of sodium nitride or hydrazoic acid in the presence of pyridine, reaction of phosgene with the azide can cause the formation of explosive carbazide. To prevent the reaction, complete removal of excess phosgene is advocated by passing nitrogen into the solution prior to addition of the azide.
Chem. Abst. **73:** 14099h (1970). *Chem. Phar. Bull.* **18** (4): 850-851 (1970).

2-METHOXYETHANOL $HOCH_2CH_2OCH_3$

Air
Ethylene glycol monomethyl ether forms peroxides that are highly explosive.
Wischmeyer (1969).

2(2-METHOXYETHOXY) ETHANOL
$CH_3OCH_2CH_2OCH_2CH_2OH$

Calcium Hypochlorite
See CALCIUM HYPOCHLORITE plus Methyl Carbitol.

Chlorosulfonic Acid
Mixing diethylene glycol monomethyl ether and chlorosulfonic acid in a closed container caused the temperature and pressure to increase.
Flynn and Rossow (1970). See Note under complete reference.

Oleum
Mixing diethylene glycol monomethyl ether and oleum in a closed container caused the temperature and pressure to increase.
Flynn and Rossow (1970). See Note under complete reference.

BIS(2-METHOXYETHYL)ETHER $(CH_3OCH_2CH_2)_2O$

Lithium Aluminum Puthene Hydride
See LITHIUM ALUMINUM HYDRIDE plus Diethylene Glycol Dimethyl Ether.

METHYL AZIDE CH_3N_3

(self-reactive)
Methyl and ethyl azides are stable at room temperatures but are likely to detonate upon rapid heating.
J. H. Bover and F. C. Canter, *Chem. Reviews* **54:** 32-3 (1954).

Dimethyl Malonate and Sodium Methylate
A serious explosion occurred in the condensation of methyl azide with dimethyl malonate in the presence of sodium methylate.
Ch. Grundmann and H. Haldenwanger, *Angew Chem.* **62A:** 410 (1950).

Mercury
See MERCURY plus Methyl Azide.

METHYL 2-AZIDOBENZOATE $CH_3OCOC_6H_4$-2-NNN

(self-reactive)
During distillation of this material the apparatus exploded.
Wischmeyer (1972).

METHYL BROMIDE CH_3Br

Aluminum
See ALUMINUM plus Methyl Bromide.

Dimethyl Sulfoxide
A reaction between methyl bromide and dimethyl sulfoxide resulted in an explosion that shattered the apparatus.
Scaros and Serauskas (1973).

METHYL CARBITOL $CH_3OCH_2CH_2OCH_2CH_2OH$

Calcium Hypochlorite
See CALCIUM HYPOCHLORITE plus Methyl Carbitol.

METHYL CHLORIDE CH_3Cl

Aluminum
See ALUMINUM plus Methyl Chloride.

Magnesium
See MAGNESIUM plus Chloroform.

Potassium
See POTASSIUM plus Chloroform.

Sodium
See POTASSIUM plus Chloroform.
See SODIUM plus Methyl Chloride.

Sodium-Potassium Alloy
See SODIUM-POTASSIUM ALLOY plus Carbon Tetrachloride.

METHYLCOPPER CH_3Cu

Air
Methyl copper explodes violently when allowed to dry in air.
Coates, p. 172 (1956).

4-METHYLCYCLOHEXANONE
$\underline{CH_2COCH_2CH_2CH(CH_3)CH_2}$

Nitric Acid Puthene
See NITRIC ACID plus 4-Methylcyclohexanone.

METHYL-bis (DIETHYLBORYL) AMINE
$[(C_2H_5)_2B]_2NCH_3$

Air
n-Methyl n,n-bis diethylborinicimide is spontaneously flammable in air.
Buls, Bimonthly Rept. 6, p. 3 (1953).

METHYLENE CHLORIDE $ClCH_2Cl$
(See also DICHLOROMETHANE)

Lithium
See LITHIUM plus Bromoform.

N-Methyl-N-Nitroso Urea and Potassium Hydroxide
See N-METHYL-N-NITROSO UREA plus Potassium Hydroxide and Methylene Chloride.

Potassium Tert.-Butoxide
See ACETONE plus Potassium Tert.-Butoxide.

Sodium-Potassium Alloy
See SODIUM-POTASSIUM ALLOY plus Methyl Dichloride.

METHYLENE DIISOCYANATE $OCN\text{-}CH_2\text{-}NCO$

Dimethyl Formamide
See DIMETHYL FORMAMIDE plus Methylene Diisocyanate.

METHYLENE IODIDE ICH_2I

Lithium
See LITHIUM plus Bromoform.

METHYL FORMAMIDE CH_3NHCHO

Benzenesulfonyl Chloride
See METHYL ISONITRILE (self-reactive).

METHYLHYDRAZINE CH_3NHNH_2

Air
Exposure of monomethylhydrazine in air on a large surface may result in spontaneous ignition.
Def. Res. and Eng., p. 27 (1963).

METHYL HYPOCHLORITE CH_3OCl

(self-reactive)
Methyl hypochlorite decomposes explosively when exposed to light and rapidly even in its absence.
Mellor **2, Supp. 1:** 550 (1956).
See also ALCOHOLS plus Hypochlorus Acid.

METHYLLITHIUM CH_3Li

Air
Methyllithium is spontaneously flammable in air.
Douda (1966).
Mellor **2, Supp. 2:** 91 (1961).

METHYL METHACRYLATE $CH_2=C(CH_3)COOCH_3$

Benzoyl Peroxide
See BENZOYL PEROXIDE plus Methyl Methacrylate.

METHYL METHACRYLATE POLYMER

Fluorine
See FLUORINE plus Solid Nonmetals and Oxygen.

N-METHYL-N-NITROSO UREA $ON\text{-}N(CH_3)CONH_2$

Potassium Hydroxide and Methylene Chloride
Diazomethane was being prepared by portion-wise additions of N-methyl-N-nitroso urea to a flask containing 40% potassium hydroxide and methylene chloride. At the fourth addition a loud detonation occurred.
MCA Guide for Safety, p. 301 (1972).

METHYL PARATHION $(CH_3O)_2P(S)OC_6H_4NO_2$

(self-reactive)
When a sample was heated in a small test tube it decomposed and in a few minutes the residue exploded.
J. B. McPherson and G. A. Johnson, *Agri. Food Chem.* **4** (1): 42 (1956).

2-METHYL-3-PHENYL-1-PROPANOL

$C_6H_5CH_2CH(CH_3)CH_2OH$

Hydrogen Peroxide and Sulfuric Acid
See ALCOHOLS plus Hydrogen Peroxide and Sulfuric Acid.

METHYL PERCHLORATE CH_3ClO_4

(self-reactive)
Methyl, ethyl, and propyl perchlorates are oily liquids of extraordinary explosive power, extremely sensitive to heat, shock, and friction.
ACS **146:** 214. *Berichte* **42:** 4390-4 (1909).
Z. Anorg. Chemie **228:** 341-51 (1936).

METHYLPHOSPHINE CH_3PH_2

Air
Methyl phosphine is spontaneously flammable in air.
Hurd, p. 128 (1952).

METHYLSILYLAMINO DIBORANE $(B_2H_5)N(CH_3)(SiH_3)$

Air
Methyl silyamino diborane is spontaneously flammable in air.
Douda (1966).

METHYLSODIUM CH_3Na

Air
Methyl sodium is spontaneously flammable in air.
Douda (1966).

METHYL(TRIFLUOROPROPYL)POLYSILOXANE

Fluorine
See FLUORINE plus Solid Nonmetals and Oxygen.

MOLYBDENUM Mo

Bromine Trifluoride
Powdered molybdenum, powdered titanium, and powdered vanadium all react with bromine trifluoride, producing incandescence.
Mellor **2, Supp. 1:** 164 (1956).
Reaction between molybdenum or tungsten and bromine trifluoride is vigorous. No protective film forms with the volatile hexafluoride of the metal.
Mellor **2, Supp. 1:** 163 (1956).

Chlorine Trifluoride
Chlorine trifluoride acts on powdered molybdenum with incandescence.
Z. Anorg. Chemie **190:** 270.
Mellor **2, Supp. 1:** 156 (1956).

Fluorine
Fluorine acts on powdered molybdenum with incandescence. Other interhalogen compounds containing fluorine may act similarly.
Z. Anorg. Chemie **190:** 270.

Lead Dioxide
Powdered molybdenum or tungsten mixed with lead dioxide becomes incandescent when heated.
Mellor **7:** 691 (1946-1947).

MOLYBDENUM DISULFIDE MoS_2

Hydrogen Peroxide
See ANTIMONY TRISULFIDE plus Hydrogen Peroxide.

MOLYBDENUM TRIOXIDE MoO_3

Chlorine Trifluoride
Chlorine trifluoride attacks molybdenum trioxide with incandescence.
Z. Anorg. Chemie **190:** 270.
See also CHLORINE TRIFLUORIDE plus Aluminum Oxide.

Lithium
See LITHIUM plus Molybdenum Trioxide.

Magnesium
See MAGNESIUM plus Molybdenum Trioxide.

Potassium
See POTASSIUM plus Molybdenum Trioxide.

Sodium
See POTASSIUM plus Molybdenum Trioxide.

MONEL®

Fluorine
See FLUORINE plus Metals.

MONOAMMONIUM PHOSPHATE $NH_4H_2PO_4$

Sodium
See SODIUM plus Monoammonium Phosphate.

Sodium Bicarbonate
See SODIUM BICARBONATE plus Monoammonium Phosphate.

MORPHOLINE $OCH_2CH_2NHCH_2CH_2$

Cellulose Nitrate
Cellulose nitrate of high surface area (dry or alcohol-wet guncotton or scrap) spontaneously ignited in contact with morpholine used as a curing agent for epoxide resins.
ABCM Quarterly Safety Summary (1956); *Bretherick* (1979).

NAPHTHALENE $C_{10}H_8$

Chromic Anhydride
See CHROMIC ANHYDRIDE plus Naphthalene.

NEODYMIUM Nd

Air
See RARE EARTH METALS plus Air.

Halogens
See RARE EARTH METALS plus Halogens.

Nitrogen
Neodymium and nitrogen react vigorously.
Mellor **8, Supp. 1:** 164 (1964).

Phosphorus
Neodymium and phosphorus react vigorously at 400°–500°C.
Mellor **8, Supp. 3:** 347 (1971).

NEODYMIUM PHOSPHIDE NdP

Nitric Acid
Neodymium phosphide and nitric acid react violently.
Mellor **8, Supp. 3:** 348 (1971).

Water
See CEROUS PHOSPHIDE plus Water.

NEOPRENE $(CH_2{=}CClCH{=}CH_2)_X$

Fluorine
See FLUORINE plus Solid Nonmetals and Oxygen.

Fluorine (liquid)
See FLUORINE plus Neoprene.

NICKEL Ni

Ammonium Nitrate
See AMMONIUM NITRATE plus Metals (powdered).

Fluorine
See FLUORINE plus Metals.

Hydrazine
The catalytic decomposition of hydrazine in the presence of Raney nickel may be vigorous at room temperature.
Mellor **8, Supp. 2:** 83 (1967).

Hydrazoic Acid
Raney nickel and hydrazoic acid undergo a vigorous decomposition.
Mellor **8, Supp. 2:** 4 (1967).

Hydrogen and Dioxane
See HYDROGEN plus Dioxane and Nickel (Raney).

Performic Acid
Powdered nickel can decompose performic acid violently.
Berichte **48:** 1139 (1915).

Phosphorus
See COPPER plus Phosphorus.

Selenium
When powdered nickel is heated with selenium or sulfur, the elements unite with incandescence.
Berichte **14:** 2823. *Comp. Rend.* **131:** 557. G. Little, *Ann. Chem.* **112:** 211 (1859).

Sulfur
See SULFUR plus Nickel.

Titanium and Potassium Perchlorate
Mixtures containing potassium perchlorate with nickel and titanium powders and infusorial earth gave severe explosions during a friction test. Very small sparks—less than those available from static electricity on the human body—can ignite the mixture.
ACS **146:** 210. *BM Info. Circ.* **7349** (1945).

NICKEL ALLOYS

Lithium
See LITHIUM plus Cobalt Alloys.

NICKEL BROMIDE $NiBr_2$

Potassium
See POTASSIUM plus Aluminum Bromide.

NICKEL CARBONYL $Ni(CO)_4$

Air
In the presence of air, nickel carbonyl forms a deposit which becomes peroxidized. This tends to decompose and ignite. See also NICKEL CARBONYL plus n-Butane and Oxygen.
Edgerton & Radra-Kanchana, *Proc. Roy. Soc.* **A225:** 427 (1954).

Bromine
See BROMINE plus Nickel Carbonyl.

n-Butane and Oxygen
Nickel carbonyl vapor explodes in air or oxygen at 20°C and a partial pressure of 15 mm. Addition of nickel carbonyl to an n-butane-oxygen mixture causes explosion at 20–40°C
C. E. J. Badin, P. C. Hunter, R. N. Pease, *J. Am. Chem. Soc.* 70: 2055–6 (1948).

Oxygen
See NICKEL CARBONYL plus n-Butane and Oxygen.

NICKEL CHLORIDE $NiCl_2$

Potassium
See POTASSIUM plus Aluminum Bromide.

NICKEL CHLORITE $Ni(ClO_2)_2$

(self-reactive)
The dihydrate of nickel chlorite explodes when heated to 100°C.
Mellor **2, Supp. 1:** 574 (1956).

NICKEL CYANIDE $Ni(CN)_2$

Magnesium
See MAGNESIUM plus Cadmium Cyanide.

NICKEL FLUORIDE NiF_2

Potassium
See POTASSIUM plus Ammonium Bromide.

NICKEL-HEXAMMINE CHLORATE $Ni(NH_3)_6(ClO_3)_2$

(self-reactive)
This compound detonates when struck.
Mellor **2, Supp. 1:** 592 (1956)

NICKEL-HEXAMMINE PERCHLORATE $Ni(NH_3)_6(ClO_4)_2$

(self-reactive)
This compound detonates when struck but is less sensitive than hexamminonickel chlorate.
Mellor **2, Supp. 1:** 592 (1956).

NICKEL HYPOPHOSPHITE $Ni(PH_2O_2)_2$

(self-reactive)
Nickel hypophosphite liberates spontaneously flammable phosphine above 100°C.
Mellor **8:** 890 (1946-1947).

NICKEL IODIDE NiI_2

Potassium
See POTASSIUM plus Aluminum Bromide.

NICKEL MONOXIDE NiO

Fluorine
See FLUORINE plus Nickel Monoxide.

Hydrogen Sulfide, Barium Oxide and Air
See HYDROGEN SULFIDE plus Soda Lime.

NICKEL NITRIDE Ni_3N

Acids
The reaction of nickel nitride and acids may be explosive with high acid concentrations and heat.
Mellor **8, Supp. 1:** 238 (1964).

NICKEL PERCHLORATE $Ni(ClO_4)_2$

2,2-Dimethoxypropane
When nickel perchlorate and 2,2-dimethoxypropane were heated, a violent reaction occurred.
Chem. and Eng. News **48** (28): 7-8 (Oct. 26, 1970).
See also 2,2-DIMETHOXYPROPANE plus Manganese Perchlorate and Ethyl Alcohol.

Hydrazine
The blue precipitate formed from nickel perchlorate and hydrazine in water exploded violently when a glass stirring rod was introduced into the suspension.
ACS **146:** 209. *Helv. Chim. Acta.* **34:** 2084-5 (1951).

NICKEL-TRIHYDRAZINE CHLORATE $Ni(N_2H_4)_3(ClO_3)_2$

(self-reactive)
This compound detonates when struck.
Mellor **2, Supp. 1:** 592 (1956).

NICKEL-TRIHYDRAZINE NITRATE $Ni(NO_3)3H_2NNH_2$

(self-reactive)
A small amount of thoroughly washed, dry trihydrazine nickel nitrate exploded about ten minutes after exposure to the atmosphere.
H. Ellern and D. E. Olander, *J. Chem. Edu.* **32:**24 (1955).

NIOBIUM (COLUMBIUM) Nb

Bromine Trifluoride
Niobium and tantalum each reacts with bromine trifluoride with incandescence.
Mellor **2, Supp. 1:** 164 (1956).

Chlorine
Powdered niobium reacts energetically with chlorine.
Mellor **2, Supp. 1:** 381 (1956).
See NIOBIUM plus Fluorine.

Fluorine
At ordinary temperatures, niobium (columbium) becomes incandescent in the presence of fluorine. It ignites when gently heated in chlorine.
Mellor **9:** 849 (1946-1947).

NIOBIUM PENTOXIDE Nb_2O_5

Aluminum and Sulfur
See ALUMINUM plus Niobium Oxide and Sulfur.

Bromine Trifluoride
See BROMINE TRIFLUORIDE plus Bismuth Pentoxide.

Lithium
See LITHIUM plus Niobium Pentoxide.

NITRATE-NITRITE

Aluminum
See ALUMINUM plus Nitrate-Nitrite and Organic Matter.

Organic Matter
See ALUMINUM plus Nitrate-Nitrite and Organic Matter.

NITRATES

(See also specific nitrates as primary entries or under other reactants)

Aluminum
See ALUMINUM plus Nitrates.

Boron Phosphide
See BORON PHOSPHIDE plus Nitric Acid.

Cyanides
Addition of cyanides to a molten nitrate bath (or vice versa) will result in an explosion.
NBFU Research Report **2** (1950).

Esters
A mixture of the two may cause an explosion.
Pieters, p. 30 (1957).

Phospham
A mixture of phospham and a nitrate explodes when heated.
H. Rose, *Ann. Phys.* **24:** 308 (1832).

Phosphorus
See PHOSPHORUS plus Nitrates.

Sodium Cyanide
See NITRATES plus Cyanides.

Sodium Hypophosphite
See CHLORATES plus Sodium Hypophosphite.

Stannous Chloride
A mixture of the two may cause an explosion.
Pieters, p. 30 (1957).

Thiocyanates
See THIOCYANATES plus Chlorates.

NITRIC ACID HNO_3

Acetic Acid
Acetic acid or acetic anhydride can explode with nitric acid if not kept cold.
Von Schwartz, p. 321 (1918). *Comp Rend.* **269** (15): 1114-1116 (1968).

Acetic Anhydride
See NITRIC ACID plus Acetic Acid.
See ACETIC ANHYDRIDE plus Nitric Acid.
Experiments demonstrate that mixtures containing more than 50% by weight of nitric acid in acetic anhydride may act as detonating explosives under certain conditions. An indication is given of the percentage mixtures of acetic anhydride-nitric acid which could be detonated using a priming charge and detonator.
BCISC **42** (166): 2 (1971).

Acetone and Acetic Acid
An etching reagent of equal parts of acetone, concentrated nitric acid, and 75 percent acetic acid exploded four hours after it was prepared and placed in a closed bottle. A correspondent pointed out that this formulation is similar to the method of preparing tetranitromethane, a sensitive explosive.
Chem. and Eng. News **38** (43): 56 (1960); **38** (46): 5 (1960).

Acetone and Sulfuric Acid
Acetone will decompose violently when brought in contact with mixed sulfuric-nitric acids. This will occur especially if the reaction is in a confined or a narrow-mouthed container.
Ind. Eng. Chem. **51:** 59A (April 1959).

Acetylene
Concentrated nitric acid on acetylene gives trinitromethane, which melts at 15°C and is explosive in the liquid state.
Kirk and Othmer **9:** 430-2 (1947).

Acrolein
See ACROLEIN plus Nitric Acid.

Acrylonitrile
See ACRYLONITRILE plus Nitric Acid.

Allyl Alcohol
See ALLYL ALCOHOL plus Nitric Acid.

Allyl Chloride
See ALLYL CHLORIDE plus Nitric Acid.

2-Aminoethanol
See 2-AMINOETHANOL plus Nitric Acid.

Ammonia
Ammonia gas burns in an atmosphere of nitric acid vapor.
Mellor **8:** 219 (1946-1947).
See NITRIC ACID plus Diborane.

Ammonium Hydroxide
Mixing 70% nitric acid and 28% ammonium hydroxide in a closed container caused the temperature and pressure to increase.
Flynn and Rossow (1970). See Note under complete reference.
Mellor **8, Supp. 1:** 349 (1964).

Aniline
Aniline ignites spontaneously in the presence of red fuming nitric acid.
Kit and Evered, pp. 238-42 (1960).
A self-flammable fuel is prepared by adding a hydrocarbon to a mixture of concentrated nitric acid and an oxidation catalyst. The hydrocarbon contains a combustion initiator made up of aniline, dimethyl aniline, xylidene, and iron pentacarbonyl.
Aniline, p. 85 (1964).
Aromatic amines (e.g., aniline or toluidine) in triethylamine solution are ignited rapidly by red fuming nitric acid at temperatures of minus 76° or lower.
Aero. Tech. Note **3884** (1956).
Brennstoff-Chem. **46** (4): 117-24 (1965). *Chem. Abst.* **51:** 3961d (1957); **63:** 4067h (1965).
See also NITRIC ACID plus Diborane.

Anion Exchange Resins
If hydroxyl-form anion exchange resins are contacted by nitric acid solutions of excessive strength (e.g. 6 molar), rapid heating and resulting gaseous degradation products can pressurize and damage the ion-exchange vessel.
Van Slyke (1967). *Reactor Fuel Process.* **7** (4): 297-303 (Fall 1964). *AEC Research and Devel. Report, B N WL*-476 (January 1967).

Anion Exchange Resins and Dichromate
Dichromate loadings as low as 0.05 grams per cubic centimeter of resin in contact with 7 molar nitric acid can cause a runaway reaction.
Ignition temperature is 92°C and decreases with increasing dichromate loading.
AEC Research and Devel. Report BNWL-**144** (August 1965).

Antimony
See ANTIMONY plus Nitric Acid.

Arsine
Fuming nitric acid reacts explosively with arsine.
Mellor **9:** 56 (1946-1947).

Bismuth
See BISMUTH plus Nitric Acid.

Boron
See BORON plus Nitric Acid.

Boron Decahydride
See BORON DECAHYDRIDE plus Nitric Acid.

Boron Phosphide
See BORON PHOSPHIDE plus Nitric Acid.

Bromine Pentafluoride
See BROMINE PENTAFLUORIDE plus Nitric Acid.

n-Butyraldehyde
See n-BUTYRALDEHYDE plus Nitric Acid.

Calcium Hypophosphite
See CALCIUM HYPOPHOSPHITE plus Nitric Acid.

Carbon
See CARBON plus Nitric Acid.

Cesium Carbide
See CESIUM CARBIDE plus Nitric Acid.

4-Chloro-2-Nitroaniline
See 4-CHLORO-2-NITROANILINE plus Nitric Acid.

Chlorine Trifluoride
See CHLORINE TRIFLUORIDE plus Nitric Acid.

Chlorosulfonic Acid
See CHLOROSULFONIC ACID plus Nitric Acid.

Cresol
See CRESOL plus Nitric Acid.

Cumene
See CUMENE plus Nitric Acid.

Cupric Nitride
See CUPRIC NITRIDE plus Nitric Acid.

Cuprous Nitride
See CUPROUS NITRIDE plus Sulfuric Acid.

Cyanides
This mixture produces an explosive reaction.
Scott (1967).

Cyclic Ketones
The cyclic ketones are far more susceptible to violent reaction than are the corresponding cyclic alcohols.
Chem. and Eng. News **37** (35): 48 (Aug. 31, 1959).

Cyclohexanol
Cyclohexanol and nitric acid can react at room temperature to form a violently explosive material.
Chem. & Ind. **1971:** (19) (1971).

Cyclohexanone
Acid burns resulted from the violent reaction of nitric acid with cyclohexanone.
Dept. of Commerce PB Report **73591.**

Diborane
Mixtures of fuming nitric acid and any of the following are self-igniting: diborane, aniline, terpenes, furfuryl alcohol, and ammonia.
Mellor **8, Supp. 2:** 341 (1967).

2,6-Di-t-Butylphenol
These ingredients, reacted in a medium of acetic acid, form 2,6-di-t-butyl-4-nitrophenol. Two grams of this nitro compound exploded violently after warming on a steam bath for 2-3 minutes. (Possibly a polynitro derivative was the explosive.)
ASESB Expl. Report **24** (1961).

Diisopropyl Ether
See DIISOPROPYL ETHER plus Nitric Acid.

Epichlorohydrin
See EPICHLOROHYDRIN plus Nitric Acid.

Ethyl Alcohol
Stirring a mixture of concentrated nitric acid and ethyl alcohol results in a reaction that starts slowly and accelerates to an explosion.
Becker (1965).
A solution of 190-proof ethyl alcohol plus nitric acid (15 percent), being used to etch bismuth, decomposed vigorously and sprayed the surrounding area.
Chem. and Eng. News **27:** 1396 (1949).
See SILVER plus Ethyl Alcohol and Nitric Acid.

m-Ethylaniline
m-Ethylaniline ignites spontaneously in the presence of red fuming nitric acid.
Kit and Evered, pp. 238-42 (1960).

Ethylene Diamine
See ETHYLENE DIAMINE plus Nitric Acid.

Ethyleneimine
See ETHYLENEIMINE plus Nitric Acid.

5-Ethyl-2-Methyl Pyridine
These materials were placed in a small auto-clave and heated and stirred for 40 minutes. The emergency vent was opened due to a sudden pressure rise. A violent explosion occurred 90 seconds later.
R.L. Frank, *Chem. and Eng. News* **30:** 3348 (1952).

5-Ethyl-2-Picoline
See 5-ETHYL-2-PICOLINE plus Nitric Acid.

Ethyl Phosphine
See BROMINE plus Ethyl Phosphine.

Ferrous Oxide
See FERROUS OXIDE plus Nitric Acid.

Fluorine
See FLUORINE plus Nitric Acid.

Furfuryl Alcohol
Furfuryl alcohol is ignited immediately by concentrated nitric acid.
MCA Case History **193** (1952).
See also NITRIC ACID plus Diborane.

Germanium
See GERMANIUM plus Nitric Acid.

Glyoxal
Mixing 70% nitric acid and glyoxal in a closed container caused the temperature and pressure to increase.
Flynn and Rossow (1970). See Note under complete reference.

Hydrazine
See HYDRAZINE plus Air.
See HYDRAZINE plus Nitric Acid.

Hydrazoic Acid
See HYDRAZOIC ACID plus Nitric Acid.

Hydrogen Iodide
See HYDROGEN IODIDE plus Nitric Acid.

Hydrogen Peroxide
See HYDROGEN PEROXIDE plus Nitric Acid.

Hydrogen Selenide
See HYDROGEN SELENIDE plus Nitric Acid.

Hydrogen Sulfide
See HYDROGEN SULFIDE plus Nitric Acid.

Hydrogen Telluride
Cold fuming nitric acid ignites hydrogen telluride, sometimes explosively.
Pascal **10:** 505 (1931-1934).

Indane and Sulfuric Acid
See INDANE plus Nitric Acid and Sulfuric Acid.

Isoprene
See ISOPRENE plus Nitric Acid.

Ketones and Hydrogen Peroxide
See KETONES plus Nitric Acid and Hydrogen Peroxide.

Lactic Acid and Hydrofluoric Acid
A mixture of 5 parts lactic acid, 5 parts nitric acid, 2 parts water, and 1 part hydrofluoric acid being stored in a plastic bottle ruptured with explosive force.
Scott (1967). *NSC Newsletter Aero. Sec.* (May 1967).

Lithium
See LITHIUM plus Nitric Acid.

Lithium Silicide
See LITHIUM SILICIDE plus Nitric Acid.

Magnesium
See MAGNESIUM plus Nitric Acid.

Magnesium Phosphide
See MAGNESIUM PHOSPHIDE plus Nitric Acid.

Magnesium-Titanium Alloy
See TITANIUM-MAGNESIUM ALLOY plus Nitric Acid.

Manganese
See MANGANESE plus Nitric Acid.

Mesitylene
During oxidation of mesitylene with nitric acid in an autoclave at 115°C to give 3,5-dimethyl benzoic acid a violent explosion occurred. The reaction was attributed to local overheating, formation of a trinitro compound 1,3,5-tri(nitromethyl) benzene, and to violent decomposition of the latter. Smaller scale preparations with better temperature control were uneventful.
Wilma et al, *Angew. Chem. Intern, Ed. Engl.* **74:** 465 (1962).

Mesityl Oxide
See MESITYL OXIDE plus Nitric Acid.

2-Methyl-5-Ethylpyridine
Chem. and Eng. News **51** (34) 142 (1973).

4-Methylcyclohexanone
The oxidation by nitric acid of 4-methylcyclohexanone to form a dicarboxylic acid resulted in a violent explosion. The methylcyclohexanone was added gradually to the mixture held at 69 to 77°C. After an hour of this procedure, the mixture exploded.
Chem. and Eng. News **37** (35): 48 (1959).

Neodymium Phosphide
See NEODYMIUM PHOSPHIDE plus Nitric Acid.

Nitrobenzene
Mixtures of nitric acid and nitrobenzene are detonable, depending on the amount of water present.
Chem. and Eng. News **41** (37):89 (1963).
A series of mixtures of nitric acid with one or more of

mono- and di-nitrobenzenes have been shown to possess high explosive properties.
Urbanski (1967).

Oleum
See OLEUM plus Nitric Acid.

Organic Matter
Nitric acid ignites spontaneously with some organic compounds, such as furfuryl alcohol and butyl mercaptan.
S.V. Gunn, *J. Am. Rocket Soc.* **22:** 33 (1952).
Barrere & Moutet, *Symposium Comb.* **(Fifth):** 170-81 (1954).

Phosphine
See PHOSPHINE plus Nitric Acid.

Phosphonium Iodide
See PHOSPHONIUM IODIDE plus Nitric Acid.

Phosphorus
See PHOSPHORUS plus Nitric Acid.

Phosphorus Tetratriiodide
See PHOSPHORUS TETRATRIIODIDE plus Nitric Acid.

Phosphorus Trichloride
See PHOSPHORUS TRICHLORIDE plus Nitric Acid.

Phthalic Acid
See PHTHALIC ANHYDRIDE plus Nitric Acid.

Phthalic Anhydride
See PHTHALIC ANHYDRIDE plus Nitric Acid.

Potassium Hypophosphite
See POTASSIUM HYPOPHOSPHITE plus Nitric Acid.

Propiolactone (BETA-)
See PROPIOLACTONE (BETA-) plus Nitric Acid.

Propylene Oxide
See PROPYLENE OXIDE plus Nitric Acid.

Pyridine
See PYRIDINE plus Nitric Acid.

Rubidium Carbide
See RUBIDIUM CARBIDE plus Nitric Acid.

Selenium
See SELENIUM plus Nitric Acid.

Selenium Iodophosphide
See SELENIUM IODOPHOSPHIDE plus Nitric Acid.

Silver and Ethyl Alcohol
See SILVER plus Ethyl Alcohol and Nitric Acid.

Sodium
See SODIUM plus Nitric Acid.

Sodium Azide
See SODIUM AZIDE plus Nitric Acid.

Sodium Hydroxide
See SODIUM HYDROXIDE plus Nitric Acid.

Stibine
See STIBINE plus Nitric Acid.

Sulfamic Acid
See SULFAMIC ACID plus Nitric Acid.

Sulfuric Acid and Glycerides
Sulfuric acid, nitric acid and fat were placed in a tightly closed container. Within 10 minutes, the container exploded.
Chem. and Eng. News **51** (31): 32 (1973).

Terpenes
See NITRIC ACID plus Diborane.

Tetraboron Decahydride
See TETRABORON DECAHYDRIDE plus Nitric Acid.

Thiocyanates
See THIOCYANATES plus Nitric Acid.

Thiophene
See THIOPHENE plus Nitric Acid.

Titanium
See TITANIUM plus Nitric Acid.

Titanium Alloy
See TITANIUM ALLOY plus Nitric Acid.

Titanium-Magnesium Alloy
See TITANIUM-MAGNESIUM ALLOY plus Nitric Acid.

Toluene and Sulfuric Acid
If conditions are not properly controlled, the reaction of toluene with nitric acid is extremely violent especially in the presence of sulfuric acid, which takes up the water formed. Part of the hazard is from the formation of nitrocresols, which react and decompose violently on further nitration.
Urbanski **1:** 139, 931 (1964).

Toluidine
See NITRIC ACID plus Aniline.

Triazine
Nitrolysis of triazine with 99% nitric acid in a trifluoroacetic anhydride solvent caused a violent explosion at 36°C.
Rolston (1972).

Unsymmetrical Dimethyl Hydrazine
See UNSYMMETRICAL DIMETHYL HYDRAZINE plus Hydrogen Peroxide.
Also see UNSYMMETRICAL DIMETHYL-HYDRAZINE plus Nitric Acid, Nitrogen Tetroxide, and Sulfuric Acid.

Uranium
See URANIUM plus Nitric Acid.

Uranium-Neodymium Alloy
See URANIUM-NEODYMIUM ALLOY plus Nitric Acid.

Uranium-Neodymium-Zirconium Alloy
See URANIUM-NEODYMIUM-ZIRCONIUM ALLOY plus Nitric Acid.

Vinyl Acetate
See VINYL ACETATE plus Nitric Acid.

Vinylidene Chloride
See VINYLIDENE CHLORIDE plus Nitric Acid.

Zinc
See ZINC plus Nitric Acid.

Zirconium-Uranium Alloys
See ZIRCONIUM-URANIUM ALLOYS plus Nitric Acid.

NITRIC OXIDE NO

Aluminum
See ALUMINUM plus Carbon Disulfide.

Boron
See BORON plus Nitrous Oxide.

Carbon Disulfide
A mixture of nitric oxide with the vapor of carbon disulfide gives a green luminous flame.
Mellor **8:** 436 (1946-1947).
These compounds react explosively with emission of light.
Mellor **8, Supp. 2:** 232 (1967).

Chlorine Monoxide
See CHLORINE MONOXIDE plus Nitric Oxide.

Chromium
See CHROMIUM plus Nitric Oxide.

Fluorine
See FLUORINE plus Nitric Oxide.

Fuels
Nitric oxide will burn with nearly all fuels which will burn with air.
Symposium Comb. **(Fourth):** 420 (1952).

Hydrocarbons
See NITRIC OXIDE plus Fuels.

Nitrogen Trichloride
See NITROGEN TRICHLORIDE plus Ammonia.

Ozone
See OZONE plus Nitric Oxide.

Phosphine
See PHOSPHINE plus Nitric Oxide.

Phosphorus
See PHOSPHORUS plus Nitric Oxide.

Rubidium Carbide
See RUBIDIUM CARBIDE plus Sulfur Dioxide.

Sodium Monoxide
See SODIUM MONOXIDE plus Nitric Oxide.

Unsymmetrical Dimethylhydrazine
This mixture ignites on sparking.
Mellor **8, Supp. 2:** 234 (1967).

Uranium
See URANIUM plus Nitric Oxide.

NITRILES

Lithium Aluminum Hydride and Water
See LITHIUM ALUMINUM HYDRIDE plus Nitriles and Water.

NITRITES
(See also specific nitrites as primary entries or see under other reactants)

Ammonium Salts
A violent explosion occurs if an ammonium salt is melted with a nitrite salt.
Von Schwartz, p. 299 (1918).

Cyanides
See CYANIDES plus Chlorates.

Potassium Cyanide
A mixture of the two may cause an explosion.
Pieters, p. 30 (1957).
A molten salt bath containing nitrite salts was carefully cleaned before reuse with cyanide-containing salts. However, when the furnace was reheated, a violent reaction and eruption took place. Presumably a residue of nitrite had remained.
Scott (1966).

o-NITROANILINE DIAZONIUM SALT
$O_2NC_6H_3(NO_2)NNX$

Sodium Bisulfide
See SODIUM SULFIDE plus Diazonium Salts and Diazonium Chloride Salts.

Sodium Polysulfide
See SODIUM SULFIDE plus Diazonium Salts and Diazonium Chloride Salts.

Sodium Sulfide
See SODIUM SULFIDE plus Diazonium Salts and Diazonium Chloride Salts.

NITROANILINES

Sulfuric Acid
A series of o- and p-nitroaniline derivatives and analogues when heated with sulfuric acid to above 200°C undergo a vigorous reaction. o-Nitroaniline reacts almost explosively.
J. F. Hodgson, *Chem. & Ind.* (1968); *Bretherick* (1978).

NITROANISOLE $O_2NC_6H_4OCH_3$

(self-reactive)
The explosion of 400 grams of o-nitroanisole during reduction using nickel as a catalyst has been reported.
J. Am. Chem. Soc. **53:** 2808 (1931).

Hydrogen
See HYDROGEN plus Nitroanisole.

NITROAROMATIC COMPOUNDS

Chlorine Trifluoride
Solutions of nitroaromatic compounds in chlorine trifluoride are extremely sensitive to shock.
Mellor **2, Supp. 1:** 156 (1956).

NITROBENZENE $C_6H_5NO_2$

Aluminum Chloride and Phenol
See ALUMINUM CHLORIDE plus Nitrobenzene and Phenol.

Aniline and Glycerine
See ANILINE plus Nitrobenzene and Glycerine.

Nitric Acid
See NITRIC ACID plus Nitrobenzene.

Nitrogen Tetroxide
See NITROGEN TETROXIDE plus Nitrobenzene.

Silver Perchlorate
See SILVER PERCHLORATE plus Acetic Acid.

NITROBENZENESULFONIC ACID $O_2NC_6H_4SO_3H$

(self-reactive)
Nitrobenzene sulfonic acid is known to decompose violently at about 200°C.
MCA Case History **1482** (1968).

o-NITROBENZOYLACETIC ACID
$O_2NC_6H_4COCH_2COOH$

Thionyl Chloride
See THIONYL CHLORIDE plus o-Nitrobenzoylacetic Acid.

N-NITRO-N′2,4-DINITROPHENYLUREA
$(NO_2)_2C_6H_3NHCONHNO_2$

(self-reactive)
This compound is an explosive of less power than picric acid, but of greater sensitivity to friction and impact.
Chem. and Eng. News **18:** 72 (1940).

NITROETHANE $C_2H_5NO_2$

Calcium Hydroxide
See CALCIUM HYDROXIDE plus Nitroethane.

Hydrocarbons
Nitroethane and other nitro compounds are mild oxidizers and should not be heated with easily oxidized hydrocarbons under confinement.
Chem. and Eng. News **30:** 2344 (1952).

Hydroxides
See CALCIUM HYDROXIDE plus Nitroethane.

Inorganic Bases
See CALCIUM HYDROXIDE plus Nitroethane.

Potassium Hydroxide
See CALCIUM HYDROXIDE plus Nitroethane.

Sodium Hydroxide
See CALCIUM HYDROXIDE plus Nitroethane.

NITROFORM $CH(NO_2)_3$

Isopropyl Alcohol
Solutions of 90% nitroform in 10% isopropyl alcohol in polyethylene bottles exploded. Nitroform, especially when the concentration is 50% or greater, dissolves with evolution of heat. This heat is sufficient to initiate the reaction.
ASESB Expl. Report **175.** *MCA Case History* **1010** (1964).

NITROGEN N_2

Lithium
See LITHIUM plus Oxygen.
See LITHIUM plus Nitrogen.

Neodymium
See NEODYMIUM plus Nitrogen.

Titanium
See TITANIUM plus Nitrogen.

NITROGEN DIOXIDE NO_2; N_2O_4
(See also NITROGEN PEROXIDE)

Cyclohexane
See CYCLOHEXANE plus Nitrogen Dioxide.

Fluorine
See FLUORINE plus Nitrogen Dioxide.

Formaldehyde
See FORMALDEHYDE plus Nitrogen Dioxide.

NITROGEN IODIDE NI_3

Ozone
See OZONE plus Nitrogen Iodide.

NITROGEN IODIDES

(self-reactive)
See IODINE plus Ammonium Hydroxide.

NITROGEN PENTOXIDE N_2O_5

Sodium Carbide
See SODIUM CARBIDE plus Nitrogen Pentoxide.

NITROGEN PEROXIDE NO_2; N_2O_4
(See also NITROGEN TETROXIDE)

Acetic Anhydride
This reaction in the attempt to synthesize tetranitromethane resulted in a violent explosion.
Van Dolah (1967).

Aluminum
See ALUMINUM plus Carbon Disulfide.

Ammonia
Solid nitrogen tetroxide reacts explosively with liquid ammonia. With gaseous ammonia, slow reactions start even when cold.
Comp. Rend. **116:** 756. Parker & Wolfhard, *Symposium Comb.* **(Fourth):** 420 (1952).
See NITRIC OXIDE plus Ammonia.

Barium Oxide
When nitrogen dioxide is passed over barium oxide (at 200°C.) the oxide becomes red-hot and fumes.
Ann. Chim. et Phys. (2) **2:** 317.

Boron Trichloride
See BORON TRICHLORIDE plus Nitrogen Peroxide.

Carbon Disulfide
Explosives can be prepared from nitrogen dioxide plus carbon disulfide. They can be heated to 200°C without explosion, but can be detonated with mercury fulminate.
E. Turpin, *German Pat.* 19,676 (1881).

Cesium Acetylene Carbide
See CESIUM ACETYLENE CARBIDE plus Nitrogen Dioxide.

Chloroform
See NITROGEN TETROXIDE plus 1,2-Dichloroethane.

1,2-Dichloroethane
Nitrogen tetroxide forms explosive mixtures with incompletely halogenated hydrocarbons.
Turley (1964). *Chem. and Eng. News* **42** (47): 53 (1964).

Dichloroethylene
See NITROGEN TETROXIDE plus 1,2-Dichloroethane.

Ethylene
See NITROGEN TETROXIDE plus Olefins.

Fuels
Nitrogen dioxide burns readily with all fuels which burn in air.
Parker & Wolfhard, *Symposium Comb.* (**Fourth**): 420 (1952).
See NITROGEN TETROXIDE plus Organic Matter.

Hydrocarbons
See NITROGEN TETROXIDE plus Fuels.

Iron
See IRON plus Nitrogen Dioxide.

Magnesium
See MAGNESIUM plus Nitrogen Dioxide.

Manganese
See MANGANESE plus Nitrogen Dioxide.

Methylene Chloride
See NITROGEN TETROXIDE plus 1,2-Dichloroethane.

Olefins
Nitrogen dioxide and olefins form extremely unstable nitrosates or nitrosites. Sabatier & Senderens, *Comp. Rend.* **116:** 756 (1893).

Organic Matter
Mixtures of nitrogen tetroxide and hydrocarbons are high explosives and some combinations are very hazardous.
Damon (1965).
See NITROGEN TETROXIDE plus Fuels.
See NITROGEN TETROXIDE plus Organic Matter.

Ozone
See OZONE plus Nitrogen Dioxide.

Phospham
See PHOSPHAM plus Nitrogen Dioxide.

Phosphorus
See MAGNESIUM plus Nitrogen Dioxide.

Potassium
See MANGANESE plus Nitrogen Dioxide.

Propylene
During an experiment to produce lactic acid by oxidizing propylene with nitrogen tetroxide, a violent explosion occurred. See also NITROGEN TETROXIDE plus Olefins.
Fawcett (1966). B.B. Brandt, et al., *Khim. Prom. SSSR* **3:** 204-10 (1961).

Sodium
See SODIUM plus Nitrogen Peroxide.

Sulfur
See MAGNESIUM plus Nitrogen Dioxide.

Tetrachloroethane (Asymmetrical)
See NITROGEN TETROXIDE plus 1,2-Dichloroethane.

1,1,1-Trichloroethane
See NITROGEN TETROXIDE plus 1,2-Dichloroethane.

Trichloroethylene
See NITROGEN TETROXIDE plus 1,2-Dichloroethane.

Tungsten Carbide
See TUNGSTEN CARBIDE plus Nitrogen Dioxide.

NITROGEN TETROXIDE N_2O_4

Alcohols
An explosion of these materials killed a research worker in a 1955 accident.
Mellor **8, Supp. 2:** 264 (1967).

Nitrobenzene
Mixtures of nitrogen tetroxide and nitrobenzene qualify as military explosives.
Mellor **8, Supp. 2:** 264 (1967).

Petroleum
An explosion of these materials killed 17 workers and devastated a plant in Bodio, Switzerland.
Mellor **8, Supp. 2:** 264 (1967).

Toluene
A mixture of these chemicals caused an explosion at an industrial plant in Zschornewitz.
Mellor **8, Supp. 2:** 264 (1967).

NITROGEN TRIBROMIDE NBr_3

Arsenic
See ARSENIC plus Nitrogen Tribromide.

Phosphorus
See ARSENIC plus Nitrogen Tribromide.
See PHOSPHORUS plus Nitrogen Bromide.

NITROGEN TRICHLORIDE NCl_3

Ammonia
Nitrogen trichloride explodes on contact with concentrated ammonia, arsenic, hydrogen sulfide, nitric oxide, organic matter, ozone, phosphine, phosphorus, potassium cyanide, potassium hydroxide, or selenium.
H. Davy, *Phil. Trans. Roy. Soc. London* **103:** 242 (1813). *Comp. Rend.* **70:** 539. E. Schneider, *Report Anal. Chem.* **1:** 54 (1881).

Arsenic
See ARSENIC plus Nitrogen Trichloride. See HYPOCHLORITES plus Urea.

Dibutyl Ether
During preparation of nitrogen trichloride by bubbling chlorine into an aqueous solution of ammonium sulfate and 100 ml. of the ether, 50 ml. of the ether-NCl_3 mixture over ammonium sulfate solution was stored in a refrigerator. Five minutes later, the mixture exploded violently.
Chem. and Eng. News **44** (31): 46 (1966).

Grease
Nitrogen trichloride is an explosive substance. Even grease from fingers can cause explosion.
Ann. Chim. et Phys. (1) **86:** 37.

Hydrogen Sulfide
See NITROGEN TRICHLORIDE plus Ammonia.

Nitric Oxide
See NITROGEN TRICHLORIDE plus Ammonia.

Organic Matter
See NITROGEN TRICHLORIDE plus Ammonia.

Ozone
See NITROGEN TRICHLORIDE plus Ammonia.
See OZONE plus Nitrogen Trichloride.

Phosphine
See NITROGEN TRICHLORIDE plus Ammonia.

Phosphorus
See NITROGEN TRICHLORIDE plus Ammonia.

Potassium Cyanide
See NITROGEN TRICHLORIDE plus Ammonia.

Potassium Hydroxide
See NITROGEN TRICHLORIDE plus Ammonia.

Selenium
See NITROGEN TRICHLORIDE plus Ammonia.

NITROGEN TRIFLUORIDE NF_3

Ammonia
See HYDROGEN plus Nitrogen Trifluoride.

Carbon Monoxide
See HYDROGEN plus Nitrogen Trifluoride.

Diborane
Studies of nitrogen trifluoride and diborane revealed no interaction at room temperature and 1-8 atmospheres pressure. When the mixtures were handled as liquids at low temperatures, violent explosions occurred, even when precautions were made to eliminate OF_2 impurities.
Lawless and Smith, pp. 34-35 (1968).

Hydrogen
See HYDROGEN plus Nitrogen Trifluoride.

Hydrogen Sulfide
See HYDROGEN plus Nitrogen Trifluoride.

Methane
See HYDROGEN plus Nitrogen Trifluoride.

Tetrafluorohydrazine
Several hundred grams of a crude reaction mixture involving nitrogen trifluoride and tetrafluorohydrazine had been collected in a small stainless steel cylinder. During opening of valves to measure cylinder pressure, the cylinder exploded, killing one man and injuring another.
MCA Case History **683** (1966).

NITROGEN TRIIODIDE NH_3NI_3

(self-reactive)
Nitrogen triiodide explodes under very slight shock.
Van Dolah (1966). *Chem. and Eng. News* **46** (9): 38 (1968).
Latimer and Hildebrand, p. 202 (1951).

Acids
Addition of concentrated acids causes nitrogen triiodide to explode.
Ann. Chim. et Phys. (2) **69:** 88. *J. Am. Chem. Soc.* **10:** 332. *Comp. Rend.* **97:** 526.

Bromine
See BROMINE plus Nitrogen Triiodide.

Chlorine
See BROMINE plus Nitrogen Triiodide.

Hydrogen Sulfide
See BROMINE plus Nitrogen Triiodide.

Ozone
See BROMINE plus Nitrogen Triiodide.

NITROGEN TRIOXIDE N_2O_3

Phosphine
Phosphine gas ignites spontaneously if a trace of nitrogen trioxide is added.
T. Graham, *Edin. Roy. Soc.* **13:** 88 (1835).

NITROGLYCERIN $C_3H_5(ONO_2)_3$

Ozone
See OZONE plus Nitroglycerin.

NITROMETHANE O_2NCH_3

Aluminum Chloride and Organic Matter
See ALUMINUM CHLORIDE plus Nitromethane and Organic Matter.

Calcium Hydroxide
See CALCIUM HYDROXIDE plus Nitroethane.

Calcium Hypochlorite
See CALCIUM HYPOCHLORITE plus Nitromethane.

Hexamethylbenzene
See HEXAMETHYLBENZENE plus Nitromethane.

Hydrocarbons
See NITROETHANE plus Hydrocarbons.

Hydroxides
See CALCIUM HYDROXIDE plus Nitroethane.

Inorganic Bases
See CALCIUM HYDROXIDE plus Nitroethane.

Organic Amines
Nitromethane plus organic amines forms sensitive explosive mixtures.
Van Dolah (1966).

Potassium Hydroxide
See CALCIUM HYDROXIDE plus Nitroethane.

Sodium Hydroxide
See CALCIUM HYDROXIDE plus Nitroethane.

NITROPARAFFINS

Aluminum Chloride and Organic Matter
See ALUMINUM CHLORIDE plus Nitromethane and Organic Matter.

Calcium Hydroxide
See CALCIUM HYDROXIDE plus Nitroethane.

Hydrocarbons
See NITROETHANE plus Hydrocarbons.

Hydroxides
See CALCIUM HYDROXIDE plus Nitroethane.

Inorganic Bases
See CALCIUM HYDROXIDE plus Nitroethane.

Potassium Hydroxide
See CALCIUM HYDROXIDE plus Nitroethane.

Sodium Hydroxide
See CALCIUM HYDROXIDE plus Nitroethane.

o-NITROPHENOL $HO\text{-}C_6H_4\text{-}2NO_2$

Potassium Hydroxide
See POTASSIUM HYDROXIDE plus o-Nitrophenol.

o-NITROPHENYLACETIC ACID $O_2NC_6H_4CH_2COOH$

Thionyl Chloride
See THIONYL CHLORIDE plus o-Nitrobenzoylacetic Acid.

o-NITROPHENYLACETYL CHLORIDE
$O_2NC_6H_4CH_2COCl$

(self-reactive)
Two explosions are reported: In one case, the solvent-free residue decomposed violently, generating black smoke and a red flame. In the other case, the residue exploded as soon as the chloroform solvent was evaporated. A similar finding with o-nitrobenzoyl chloride is referenced.
Chem. and Eng. News **42** (13):39 (1964).
Chem. and Eng. News **23:** 2394 (1945).
J. Am. Chem. Soc. **68:** 344 (1946).
May and Baker Ltd., *Chem. and Ind.* **39** (1946).

m-NITROPHENYLDIAZONIUM PERCHLORATE
$NO_2C_6H_4N(\equiv N)ClO_4$

(self-reactive)
This compound is very sensitive to heat and shock.
ACS **146:** 205. *Davis* (1943).

NITROPROPANE $CH_3CH_2CH_2NO_2$

Calcium Hydroxide
See CALCIUM HYDROXIDE plus Nitroethane.

Hydrocarbons
See NITROETHANE plus Hydrocarbons.

Hydroxides
See CALCIUM HYDROXIDE plus Nitroethane.

Inorganic Bases
See CALCIUM HYDROXIDE plus Nitroethane.

Potassium Hydroxide
See CALCIUM HYDROXIDE plus Nitroethane.

Sodium Hydroxide
See CALCIUM HYDROXIDE plus Nitroethane.

2-NITROPROPANE $CH_3CHNO_2CH_3$

Chlorosulfonic Acid
See CHLOROSULFURIC ACID plus 2-Nitropropane.

Oleum
See OLEUM plus 2-Nitropropane.

NITROSOPHENOL ONC_6H_4OH

Acids
Nitrosophenol explodes on heating or on addition of concentrated acids.
Beilstein, p. 600 (1909).

NITROSYL AZIDE ONNNN

(self-reactive)
This unstable yellow compound decomposes even at minus 50°C.
Mellor **8, Supp. 2:** 22 (1967).

NITROSYL CHLORIDE ONCl

Acetone
Nitrosyl chloride sealed in a tube with a residue of acetone in the presence of platinum catalyst gave an explosive reaction.
Chem. and Eng. News **35** (43): 60 (1957).

Aluminum
See ALUMINUM plus Nitrosyl Chloride.

NITROSYL FLUORIDE ONF

Boron
See BORON plus Nitrosyl Fluoride.

Halogenated Olefin
Excessive quantities of the two reactants in a reaction vessel caused the vessel to explode.
MCA Case History **928** (1963).

Phosphorus
See BORON plus Nitrosyl Fluoride.

Silicon
See BORON plus Nitrosyl Fluoride.

Sodium
See SODIUM plus Nitrosyl Fluoride.

NITROSYL PERCHLORATE $ONOClO_3$

(self-reactive)
Decomposition of nitrosyl perchlorate begins just below 100°C. Above 100°C (115–120°C) a low order explosion occurs.
H. Gerding and W.F. Haak, *Chem. Weekblad* **52:** 282-3 (1956).

Acetone
Nitrosyl perchlorate ignites and explodes with acetone.
Hoffman & Zedtwitz, *Ann. Chem.* **42:** 2031 (1909).

Amines
Explosions occur with mixtures of nitrosyl perchlorate and primary amines. Hoffman & Zedtwitz, *Ann. Chem.* **42:** 2031 (1909).

Cobalt Pentammine Triazo Perchlorate and Phenyl Isocyanate
See PHENYL ISOCYANATE plus Cobalt Pentammine Triazo Perchlorate and Nitrosyl Perchlorate.

Diethyl Ether
Nitrosyl perchlorate ignites and explodes with diethyl ether.
Hoffman & Zedtwitz, *Ann. Chem.* **42:** 2031 (1909).

Metal Salts
The hot reaction of nitrosyl perchlorate with metal salts, which is a way to prepare perchorates, forms salts that are very explosive.
Kirk and Othmer, Second Ed. **5:** 69 (1963).

NITROSYLSULFURIC ACID $O=NOSO_2OH$

Dinitroaniline Hydrochloride
An explosion occurred during the diazotization using nitrosylsulfuric acid which resulted in several fatalities. Subsequent tests have shown that this was due to the high concentration of reactants in the mixture.
MCA Case History **1763** (1971).

NITROTOLUENES

Nitric Acid
A series of mixtures of nitric acid with one or more of di- and tri-nitrotoluenes have been shown to possess high explosive properties.
Urbanski (1967).

p-NITROTOLUENE $O_2NC_6H_4CH_3$

Sulfuric Acid
para-Nitrotoluene and sulfuric acid exploded at 80°C.
Chem. and Eng. News **27:** 2504.

NITROUS ACID HNO_2

Phosphine
See PHOSPHINE plus Nitrous Acid.

Phosphorus Trichloride
See PHOSPHORUS TRICHLORIDE plus Nitric Acid.

NITROUS OXIDE N_2O

(self-reactive)
This compound decomposes explosively at high temperatures.
Mellor **8, Supp. 2:** 207 (1967).

Aluminum
See ALUMINUM plus Carbon Disulfide.

Boron
See BORON plus Nitrous Oxide.

Hydrazine
See NITROUS OXIDE plus Lithium Hydride.

Lithium Hydride
Spontaneous ignition occurs when nitrous oxide and lithium hydride or hydrazine are mixed.
Mellor **8, Supp. 2:** 214 (1967).

Phenyl-Lithium
See PHENYL-LITHIUM plus Nitrous Oxide.

Phosphine
See PHOSPHINE plus Nitrous Oxide.

Sodium
See SODIUM plus Nitrogen Peroxide.

Tungsten Carbide
See TUNGSTEN CARBIDE plus Nitrogen Dioxide.

NITRYL CHLORIDE O_2NCl

Ammonia
Liquid ammonia reacts violently with nitryl chloride, even at minus 75°C.
J. Am. Chem. Soc. **74:** 3408-10 (1952).
Mellor **8, Supp. 1:** 331 (1964).

Stannic Bromide
The reaction between nitryl chloride and stannic bromide or stannic iodide occurs with violence.
J. Am. Chem. Soc. **74:** 3408 (1952).

Stannic Iodide
See NITRYL CHLORIDE plus Stannic Bromide.

Sulfur Trioxide
Liquid sulfur trioxide reacts violently with nitryl chloride, even at 75°C.
J. Am. Chem. Soc. **74:** 3409 (1952).

NITRYL FLUORIDE O_2NF

Phosphorus
See PHOSPHORUS plus Nitryl Fluoride.

Potassium
See POTASSIUM plus Nitryl Fluoride.

NITRYL PERCHLORATE O_2NOClO_3

Acetone
See NITRYL PERCHLORATE plus Benzene.

Benzene
Nitronium perchlorate reacts with benzene, giving a slight explosion and flash. With acetone and diethyl ether, the reaction produces a sharper explosion.
Chem. and Eng. News **38** (15):5 (1960).

Diethyl Ether
See NITRYL PERCHLORATE plus Benzene.

Organic Matter
Nitryl perchlorate reacts with organic matter with a violence ranging from slight explosions to sharp detonations accompanied by fire.
ACS **146:**210. *Can. J. Research* **18** (B):358-62 (1940).

NYLON

Fluorine
See FLUORINE plus Solid Nonmetals and Oxygen.

OLEUM $H_2SO_4SO_3$

Acetic Acid
See ACETIC ACID plus Oleum.

Acetic Anhydride
See ACETIC ANHYDRIDE plus Oleum.

Acetonitrile
See ACETONITRILE plus Oleum.

Acrolein
See ACROLEIN plus Oleum.

Acrylic Acid
See ACRYLIC ACID plus Oleum.

Acrylonitrile
See ACRYLONITRILE plus Oleum.

Allyl Alcohol
See ALLYL ALCOHOL plus Oleum.

Allyl Chloride
See ALLYL CHLORIDE plus Oleum.

2-Aminoethanol
See 2-AMINOETHANOL plus Oleum.

Ammonium Hydroxide
Mixing oleum and 28% ammonium hydroxide in a closed container caused the temperature and pressure to increase.
Flynn and Rossow (1970). See Note under complete reference.

Aniline
See ANILINE plus Oleum.

n-Butyraldehyde
See n-BUTYRALDEHYDE plus Oleum.

Cresol
See CRESOL plus Oleum.

Cumene
See CUMENE plus Oleum.

Dichloroethyl Ether
See DICHLOROETHYL ETHER plus Oleum.

Diethylene Glycol Monomethyl Ether
See DIETHYLENE GLYCOL MONOMETHYL ETHER plus Oleum.

Diisobutylene
See DIISOBUTYLENE plus Oleum.

Epichlorohydrin
See EPICHLOROHYDRIN plus Oleum.

Ethyl Acetate
See ETHYL ACETATE plus Oleum.

Ethylene Cyanohydrin
Mixing oleum and ethylene cyanohydrin in a closed container caused the temperature and pressure to increase.
Flynn and Rossow (1970). See Note under complete reference.

Ethylene Diamine
See ETHYLENE DIAMINE plus Oleum.

Ethylene Glycol
See ETHYLENE GLYCOL plus OLEUM.

Ethylene Glycol Monoethyl Ether Acetate
See ETHYLENE GLYCOL MONOETHYL ETHER ACETATE plus Oleum.

Ethyleneimine
Mixing oleum and ethyleneimine in a closed container caused the temperature and pressure to increase.
Flynn and Rossow (1970). See Note under complete reference.

Glyoxal
See GLYOXAL plus Oleum.

Hydrochloric Acid
Mixing oleum and 36% hydrochloric acid in a closed container caused the temperature and pressure to increase.
Flynn and Rossow (1970). See Note under complete reference.

Hydrofluoric Acid
Mixing oleum and 48.7% hydrofluoric acid in a closed container caused the temperature and pressure to increase.
Flynn and Rossow (1970). See Note under complete reference.

Isoprene
See ISOPRENE plus Oleum.

Isopropyl Alcohol
Mixing oleum and isopropyl alcohol in a closed container caused the temperature and pressure to increase.
Flynn and Rossow (1970). See Note under complete reference.

Mesityl Oxide
See MESITYL OXIDE plus Oleum.

Methyl Ethyl Ketone
See METHYL ETHYL KETONE plus Oleum.

Nitric Acid
Mixing oleum and 70% nitric acid in a closed container caused the temperature and pressure to increase.
Flynn and Rossow (1970). See Note under complete reference.

2-Nitropropane
Mixing oleum and 2-nitropropane in a closed container caused the temperature and pressure to increase.
Flynn and Rossow (1970). See Note under complete reference.

Propiolactone (BETA-)
Mixing oleum and propiolactone (BETA-) in a closed container caused the temperature and pressure to increase.
Flynn and Rossow (1970). See Note under complete reference.

Propylene Oxide
Mixing oleum and propylene oxide in a closed container caused the temperature and pressure to increase.
Flynn and Rossow (1970). See Note under complete reference.

Pyridine
Mixing oleum and pyridine in a closed container caused the temperature and pressure to increase.
Flynn and Rossow (1970). See Note under complete reference.

Sodium Hydroxide
See SODIUM HYDROXIDE plus Oleum.

Styrene Monomer
Mixing oleum and styrene monomer in a closed container caused the temperature and pressure to increase.
Flynn and Rossow (1970). See Note under complete reference.

Sulfolane
Mixing oleum and sulfolane in a closed container caused the tem perature and pressure to increase.
Flynn and Rossow (1970). See Note under complete reference.

Vinyl Acetate
Mixing oleum and vinyl acetate in a closed container caused the temperature and pressure to increase.
Flynn and Rossow (1970). See Note under complete reference.

Vinylidene Chloride
Mixing oleum and vinylidene chloride in a closed container caused the temperature and pressure to increase.
Flynn and Rossow (1970). See Note under complete reference.

ORGANIC MATTER

Acetyl Peroxide
See ACETYL PEROXIDE plus Solvents.

Aluminum Chloride and Nitromethane
See ALUMINUM CHLORIDE plus Nitromethanes and Organic Matter.

Ammonium Nitrate
See AMMONIUM NITRATE plus Organic Matter.

Ammonium Perchlorate
See SULFUR plus Ammonium Perchlorate.

Barium Peroxide
See BARIUM PEROXIDE plus Organic Matter.

Benzoyl Peroxide
See BENZOYL PEROXIDE plus Organic Matter.

Boron Trichloride
See BORON TRICHLORIDE plus Nitrogen Peroxide.

Bromates
See BROMATES plus Organic Matter.

Bromine Monofluoride
See BROMINE MONOFLUORIDE plus Water.

Bromine Pentafluoride
See BROMINE PENTAFLUORIDE plus Acetic Acid.

Bromine Trifluoride
See BROMINE MONOFLUORIDE plus Water.

t-Butyl Peracetate
See t-BUTYL PERACETATE plus Organic Matter.

t-Butyl Perbenzoate
See t-BUTYL PERBENZOATE plus Organic Matter.

Calcium Hypochlorite
See CALCIUM HYPOCHLORITE plus Organic Matter.

Chlorates
See BROMATES plus Organic Matter.

Chloric Acid
See CHLORIC ACID plus Organic Matter.
See ANTIMONY plus Chloric Acid.

Chlorine
See BROMINE MONOFLUORIDE plus Water.

Chlorine Dioxide
See CHLORINE DIOXIDE plus Organic Matter.

Chlorine Monoxide
See POTASSIUM plus Chlorine Monoxide.
See CHLORINE MONOXIDE plus Organic Matter.

Chlorine Trifluoride
See CHLORINE TRIFLUORIDE plus Organic Matter.
See also BROMINE MONOFLUORIDE plus Water.

Chlorine Trioxide
See CHLORINE TRIOXIDE plus Organic Matter.

Chlorosulfonic Acid
See CHLOROSULFURIC ACID plus Organic Matter.

Chromic Anhydride
See CHROMIC ANHYDRIDE plus Organic Matter.

Diazomethane
See DIAZOMETHANE (self-reactive).

Diisopropyl Peroxydicarbonate
See DIISOPROPYL PEROXYDICARBONATE plus Organic Matter.

Dioxygen Difluoride
See DIOXYGEN DIFLUORIDE plus Organic Matter.

Fluorine
See FLUORINE plus Neoprene.
See FLUORINE plus Organic Matter.

Fluorine Perchlorate
See FLUORINE PERCHLORATE plus Organic Matter.

Halogen Fluorides
See BROMINE MONOFLUORIDE plus Water; see individual fluoride plus organic matter.

Hydrogen Peroxide
See HYDROGEN PEROXIDE plus Organic Matter.

Hydrogen Peroxide and Sulfuric Acid
See ALCOHOLS plus Hydrogen Peroxide and Sulfuric Acid.

Iodates
See BROMATES plus Organic Matter.

Iodine Heptafluoride
See BROMINE MONOFLUORIDE plus Water.

Iodine Monochloride
See IODINE MONOCHLORIDE plus Organic Matter.

Iodine Pentafluoride
See ARSENIC plus Iodine Pentafluoride.
See also BROMINE MONOFLUORIDE plus Water.
See also IODINE PENTAFLUORIDE plus Water.

Iodine Pentoxide
See CARBON plus Iodine Pentoxide.

Liquid Air
See CHARCOAL plus Liquid Air.

Lithium
See LITHIUM plus Organic Matter.

Magnesium Perchlorate
See MAGNESIUM PERCHLORATE plus Organic Matter.

Manganese Heptoxide
See MANGANESE HEPTOXIDE plus Organic Matter.

Mercuric Nitrate
See MERCURIC NITRATE plus Unsaturates; Aromatics.

Nitrate-Nitrite
See ALUMINUM plus Nitrate-Nitrite and Organic Matter.

Nitric Acid
See NITRIC ACID plus Organic Matter.

Nitric Oxide
See NITRIC OXIDE plus Fuels.

Nitroethane
See NITROETHANE plus Hydrocarbons.

Nitrogen Trichloride
See NITROGEN TRICHLORIDE plus Ammonia; Grease.

Nitromethane
See NITROMETHANE plus Hydrocarbons.

Nitryl Perchlorate
See NITRYL PERCHLORATE plus Organic Matter.

Oxygen
See OXYGEN plus Clothing.

Ozone
See OZONE plus Organic Matter.

Peracetic Acid
See PERACETIC ACID plus Organic Matter.

Perchlorates
See PERCHLORATES plus Organic Matter.

Perchloric Acid
See PERCHLORIC ACID plus Organic Fibers.

Permanganates and Sulfuric Acid
See PERMANGANATES plus Sulfuric Acid and Benzene.

Permanganic Acid
See PERMANGANIC ACID (self-reactive).

Permonosulfuric Acid
See PERMONOSULFURIC ACID plus Cotton; Organic Matter.

Peroxides
See PEROXIDES plus Organic Matter.

Phosphoric Anhydride and Water
See PHOSPHORIC ANHYDRIDE plus Organic Matter and Water.

Phosphorus Oxychloride
See PHOSPHORUS OXYCHLORIDE plus Organic Matter.

Phosphorus Trichloride
See PHOSPHORUS OXYCHLORIDE plus Organic Matter.

Potassium Oxides
See POTASSIUM plus Air.

Potassium Permanganate
See POTASSIUM PERMANGANATE plus Organic Matter.

Sodium Chlorate
See SODIUM CHLORATE plus Organic Matter.

Sodium Chlorite
See SODIUM CHLORITE plus Organic Matter.

Sodium Peroxide
See SODIUM PEROXIDE plus Organic Matter.

Stannous Nitrate
See STANNOUS NITRATE plus Organic Matter.

Sulfur Monochloride
See SULFUR MONOCHLORIDE plus Organic Matter.

ORGANIC PERCHLORATES

(self-reactive)
Almost any organic perchlorate decomposes when heated. The ammoniacal and aminiacal compounds seem more sensitive than the others. The amine perchlorates have explosion temperatures in the range of 250°C to 300°C. None explodes below 200°C.
ACS **146:** 204-20 (1960).

ORGANIC SULFIDES RSR

Calcium Hypochlorite
See CALCIUM HYPOCHLORITE plus Organic Sulfides.

OSMIUM Os

Chlorine Trifluoride
See ANTIMONY plus Chlorine Trifluoride.

Oxygen Difluoride
See IRIDIUM plus Oxygen Difluoride.

OSMIUM-AMMINE NITRATES

(self-reactive)
Osmium-ammine nitrates may be impact-sensitive. $Os(NH_3)_4O_2(NO_3)_2$ crystals are very unstable.
Mellor **15:** 727 (1946-1947).

OSMIUM-AMMINE PERCHLORATES

(self-reactive)
Osmium-ammine perchlorates may be impact-sensitive.
Mellor **15:** 727 (1946-1947).

OXALIC ACID HOCOCOOH

Furfuryl Alcohol
See FURFURYL ALCOHOL plus Oxalic Acid.

Silver
See SILVER plus Oxalic Acid.

Sodium Chlorite
See SODIUM CHLORITE plus Oxalic Acid.

Sodium Hypochlorite
See SODIUM HYPOCHLORITE plus Oxalic Acid.

OXALYL BROMIDE BrCOCOBr

Sodium-Potassium Alloy
See SODIUM-POTASSIUM ALLOY plus Oxalyl Bromide.

OXALYL CHLORIDE ClCOCOCl

Sodium-Potassium Alloy
See SODIUM-POTASSIUM ALLOY plus Oxalyl Bromide.

OXIDIZING AGENTS

Carbides
See CARBIDES plus Oxidizing Agents.

OXODISILANE $H_3SiSiHO$

Air
Oxodisilane is spontaneously flammable in air.
Z. Anorg. Chemie **117:** 209. *Hurd,* pp. 36, 73 (1952).

OXOSILANE H_2SiO

Air
Oxosilane is spontaneously flammable in air.
Z. Anorg. Chemie **117:** 209.
See also CHLORINE plus Oxomonosilane.

Chlorine
See CHLORINE plus Oxomonosilane.

OXYGEN O_2

Aluminum
See ALUMINUM plus Oxygen.

Aluminum Borohydride
Explosive reaction occurs at temperatures as low as 20°C. Explosive range: 5% to 90%.
J. Am. Chem. Soc. **71:** 2950.

Aluminum Hydride
Aluminum hydride is spontaneously flammable in oxygen or air.
Lockheed, p. 8 (1960).

Beryllium Borohydride
Beryllium borohydride reacts explosively with oxygen or water.
A. J. Stosick, *Acta Crystallogr.* **5** (1): 15 (1952).

Boron Arsenotribromide
In contact with air or oxygen, this material is readily oxidized, and in most cases ignites spontaneously.
Mellor **9:** 57 (1946-1947).

Boron Decahydride
Boron decahydride ignites spontaneously when exposed to air or oxygen.
Mellor **5:** 36 (1946-1947).

Boron Trichloride
Oxygen and boron trichloride react vigorously on sparking.
Mellor **5:** 131 (1946-1947).

Butane and Nickel Carbonyl
See NICKEL CARBONYL plus n-Butane and Oxygen.

Calcium
See CALCIUM plus Oxygen.

Calcium Phosphide
See SULFUR plus Calcium Phosphide.

Cesium
See CESIUM plus Oxygen.

Cesium Hydride
Cesium hydride ignites in oxygen at room temperature.
Brauer (1965).

Chlorotrifluoroethylene and Bromine
See CHLOROTRIFLUOROETHYLENE plus Oxygen and Bromine.

Clothing
The normal 2-3 percent oxygen enrichment of air supplied to an air-supplied suit was upset by failure of the air-oxygen mix valve so that the enrichment was 68-76 percent. A worker who had disconnected supply and exhaust lines removed his helmet and lighted a cigarette. Apparently a spark from the cigarette lighted his oxygen-saturated underwear and also the pressure suit.
MCA Case History **884** (1963).

Decaborane
Decaborane is spontaneously flammable in oxygen.
Chem. Safety Data Sheet **SD 84** (1961).

Diborane
Oxygen and diborane form spontaneously explosive mixtures.
A. T. Whately and R. N. Pease, *J. Am. Chem. Soc.* **76:** 1997-1999 (1954).

Diethyl Ether
See OXYGEN plus Ethers.

Diphenylethylene
An explosion was observed at the auto-oxidation of diphenylethylene with oxygen under high pressure at low temperature.
H. Staudinger, *Z. Electrochem.* **31:** 549-52 (1925).

Disilane
Disilane, trisilane, or tetrasilane, when mixed with oxygen or air at ordinary temperatures, ignites or explodes.
Mellor **6:** 232-4 (1946-1947).

Ethers
In the presence of oxygen or air, ethers form peroxides which may explode spontaneously or when heated.
Haz. Chem. Data (1966). *MCA Case History* **616** (1960).
Ethyl ether forms peroxides which may explode when heated to about 100°C.
Chem. Safety Data Sheet **SD-29** (1965).
Isopropyl ether, which had stood on the shelf a long time, exploded when the stuck cap on the bottle was freed.
MCA Case History **603** (1960).

Germanium
See GERMANIUM plus Oxygen.

Hydrazine
Oxygen and hydrazine form explosive mixtures.
Mellor **8, Supp. 2:** 72 (1967).

Hydrogen
See HYDROGEN plus Air; Oxygen.

Isopropyl Ether
Isopropyl ether tends to react with oxygen from the air to form unstable peroxides which may detonate with extreme violence. Several incidents are cited.
NSC Newsletter, Chem. Sec. (May 1966).
See also OXYGEN plus Ethers.

Lithium
See LITHIUM plus Oxygen.

Nickel Carbonyl and Butane
See NICKEL CARBONYL plus n-Butane and Oxygen.

Organic Materials
See OXYGEN plus Clothing.

Oxygen Difluoride and Water
Violent explosions resulted when a spark was discharged in a mixture containing 25-70% oxygen difluoride in oxygen over water.
Mellor **2, Supp. 1:** 191 (1956).

Phosphine
This reaction is explosive at ordinary temperatures.
Mellor **8, Supp. 3:** 281 (1971).

Phosphorus
See PHOSPHORUS plus Oxygen.

Phosphorus Trifluoride
Phosphorus trifluoride does not burn in air, but if it is mixed with oxygen, the gases explode.
Comp. Rend. **138:** 789. *Mellor* **8:** 995 (1946-1947).

Phosphorus Trioxide
See PHOSPHORUS TRIOXIDE plus Air.

Polyurethane
In the form of foam, polyurethane, and also polyvinyl

chloride, have exploded when saturated with liquid oxygen.
Ind. Saf. Equip., p. 54 (June 1964).

Polyvinyl Chloride
See OXYGEN plus Polyurethane.

Potassium and Carbon Monoxide
See POTASSIUM plus Carbon Monoxide and Oxygen.

Potassium Peroxide
The reaction of oxygen and potassium peroxide is violent at pressures of oxygen as low as 10 mm.
Mellor **2, Supp. 3:** 1626 (1963).

Rubidium
See RUBIDIUM plus Oxygen.

Selenium
See SELENIUM plus Oxygen.

Sodium Hydride
Sodium hydride in oxygen ignites at 230°C.
Mellor **2:** 483 (1946-1947).

Teflon® (Polytetrafluoroethylene)
Teflon® ignited at 1,300°F in a 5 psia pure oxygen atmosphere, when used as a 20 AWG wire insulation. Polyolefin insulation ignites at about 1,100°F under the same conditions.
N.A. Aviation (1964).
The combustion of Teflon® in oxygen to give carbonyl fluoride is highly exothermic but a large ignition source is required. The minimum ignition temperature is 465°C even under 7500 psi of oxygen gas.
The ignition of Teflon® tubing at −61°C in supercritical oxygen at 900 psi required a hot nickel-chromium wire as an initiator.
Chem. and Eng. News, p. 2 (October 7, 1991).

Tetrafluorohydrazine
An explosive reaction of these two chemicals is likely in the presence of organic matter.
Mellor **8, Supp. 2:** 113 (1967).

Tetrasilane
See OXYGEN plus Disilane.

Titanium Alloy
See TITANIUM ALLOY plus Oxygen.

1,1,1-Trichloroethane
The sides of a 5,000 psi autoclave were bulged by an explosive reaction between oxygen and 1,1,1-trichloroethane when the pressurized mixture was brought up to 100°C and 790 psi and allowed to stand for three hours.
Chem. and Eng. News **35** (43): 60 (1957).

Trichloroethylene
The explosion of an oxygen pipe under pressure (400 psi) in a metallurgical factory was apparently due to the remains of trichloroethylene which was used for the previous cleaning of the pipes. Tests showed it was possible to make a stoichiometric mixture of trichloroethylene and oxygen vapors explode.
U. Weber, *Chim. Ind. (Paris)* **90** (3): 178-83 (1963).

Trisilane
See OXYGEN plus Disilane.

OXYGEN (LIQUID) O_2

Aluminum
See ALUMINUM plus Oxygen.

Asphalt
During transfer of liquid oxygen from a factory reservoir to a tanker truck, some of the liquid leaked from a coupling to the asphalt surface below. When the trucker dropped a hammer on this surface, a violent explosion formed a crater 20 inches square by 4 inches deep in the asphalt and broke windows nearby.
U. Weber, *Chim. Ind. (Paris)* **90** (3); 178-83 (1963).

Benzene
Liquid oxygen (LOX) gives an explosive mixture when combined with benzene.
Kirschenbaum (1956).

Carbon Monoxide
Liquid oxygen gives an explosive mixture when combined with *liquid* carbon monoxide.
Kirschenbaum (1956).

Carbon Tetrachloride
See OXYGEN (LIQUID) plus Chlorinated Hydrocarbons.

Chlorinated Dye Penetrants
See OXYGEN (LIQUID) plus Chlorinated Hydrocarbons.

Chlorinated Hydrocarbons
Several halogenated solvents reacted explosively with liquid oxygen when ignited with a high energy source: 1,1,1-trichloroethane, methylene chloride, trichloroethylene, chlorinated dye penetrants, and carbon tetrachloride. The carbon tetrachloride exploded only mildly. Behavior of these chemicals is similar with nitrogen tetroxide.
Chem. and Eng. News **43** (24): 41 (1965).
BM Report Invest. **6766** (1966)

Cyanogen
Liquid oxygen gives an explosive mixture when combined with *liquid* cyanogen.
Kirschenbaum (1956).

Fuels
Liquid oxygen plus ordinary fuels, hydrocarbons, and many other organic compounds are powerful explosives.
BM Bull. **472** (1949). *Kirschenbaum* (1956).
MCA Case Histories **824** (1962) and **865** (1963).
Houghton (1966).

Hydrazine
Spontaneous ignition occurs when these chemicals are mixed.
Mellor **8, Supp. 2:** 95 (1967).

Hydrocarbons
See OXYGEN (LIQUID) plus Fuels.

Lithium Hydride
Liquid oxygen gives an explosive mixture when combined with lithium hydride.
Kirschenbaum (1956).

Magnesium
See MAGNESIUM plus Oxygen.

Methane
Liquid oxygen gives an explosive mixture when combined with liquid methane.
Kirschenbaum (1956).

Methylene Chloride
See OXYGEN (LIQUID) plus Chlorinated Hydrocarbons.

Oil
Traces of oil on the ball bearing of a centrifugal pump reacted with liquid oxygen being transferred by the pump. The heat of reaction vaporized the oxygen and the pump burst from pressurization.
U. Weber, *Chim. Ind. (Paris)* **90** (3): 178-83 (1963).

Paraformaldehyde
Liquid oxygen gives an explosive mixture when combined with paraformaldehyde.
Kirschenbaum (1956).

Titanium
See TITANIUM plus Oxygen.

1,1,1-Trichloroethane
See OXYGEN (LIQUID) plus Chlorinated Hydrocarbons.

Trichloroethylene
See OXYGEN (LIQUID) plus Chlorinated Hydrocarbons.

Wood and Charcoal
In a plant manufacturing liquid and gaseous oxygen, spruce wood flooring encased in iron sheeting was charred by an undetected, smoldering fire started by a welding spark. Subsequent leakage of liquid oxygen saturated the charred wood and a violent explosion resulted.
U. Weber, *Chim. Ind. (Paris)* **90** (3): 178-83 (1963).

OXYGEN DIFLUORIDE OF_2

Aluminum Chloride
A vigorous reaction occurs between oxygen difluoride and aluminum chloride, arsenic trioxide, chronic oxide, or phosphorus pentoxide.
Mellor **2, Supp. 1:** 192 (1956).

Ammonia
Oxygen difluoride and ammonia react immediately with white fumes.
Mellor **2, Supp. 1:** 192 (1956).

Arsenic Trioxide
See OXYGEN DIFLUORIDE plus Aluminum Chloride.

Bromine
See BROMINE plus Oxygen Difluoride.

Carbon Monoxide
See HYDROGEN plus Oxygen Difluoride.

Chlorine
See CHLORINE plus Oxygen Difluoride.

Chlorine and Copper
See CHLORINE plus Oxygen Difluoride.

Chromic Oxide
See OXYGEN DIFLUORIDE plus Aluminum Chloride.

Hydrogen
See HYDROGEN plus Oxygen Difluoride.

Hydrogen Sulfide
Oxygen difluoride and hydrogen sulfide explode on mixing.
Mellor **2, Supp. 1:** 192 (1956).

Iodine
See BROMINE plus Oxygen Difluoride.

Iridium
See IRIDIUM plus Oxygen Difluoride.

Methane
See HYDROGEN plus Oxygen Difluoride.

Osmium
See IRIDIUM plus Oxygen Difluoride.

Oxygen and Water
See OXYGEN plus Oxygen Difluoride and Water.

Palladium
See IRIDIUM plus Oxygen Difluoride.

Phosphorus Pentoxide
See OXYGEN DIFLUORIDE plus Aluminum Chloride.

Platinum
See IRIDIUM plus Oxygen Difluoride.

Rhodium
See IRIDIUM plus Oxygen Difluoride.

Ruthenium
See IRIDIUM plus Oxygen Difluoride.

Silica
Liquid oxygen difluoride and 60/80 mesh silica gel at about 254 mm. pressure and 196°C exploded. The presence of moisture was suspected.
A.G. Streng, *Chem. Rev.* **63** (6):607-624 (1963).
Chem. and Eng. News **43** (7):41 (1965); **43** (15):41 (1965).

OZONE O_8

Aniline
Aniline in an atmosphere of ozone forms as one of the products a white, gelatinous explosive compound, ozobenzene.
Mellor **1:** 911 (1946-1947).

Benzene
Benzene in an atmosphere of ozone forms formic, acetic, oxalic, and other acids as well as a white gelatinous explosive compound called ozobenzene.
Mellor **1:** 911 (1946-1947). R.W. Murray, *Acc. Chem. Res.* **1**(10): 313 (1968).

Bromine
Severe explosions occur in attempts to form tribromine octoxide from these reactants.
Mellor **2, Supp. 1:** 748 (1956).

Diallyl Methyl Carbinol and Acetic Acid
See DIALLYL METHYL CARBINOL plus Ozone and Acetic Acid.

Diethyl Ether
A mixture of ether and ozone forms aldehyde and acetic acid and a heavy liquid, ethyl peroxide, which is explosive.
Mellor **1:** 911 (1946-1947).

Dinitrogen Pentoxide
Mixtures of ozone and dinitrogen pentoxide are flammable or explosive.
Mellor **8, Supp. 2:** 276 (1967).

Ethylene
Ozone and ethylene react explosively.
Berichte **38:** 3837.
Mellor **1:** 911 (1946-1947).

Hydrogen Bromide
These chemicals react instantaneously, exploding except at low pressure of 2–3 mm mercury.
Mellor **2, Supp. 1:** 736 (1956).

Hydrogen Iodide
The reaction between these chemicals is even more energetic than between ozone and hydrogen bromide.
Mellor **2, Supp. 1:** 736 (1956).

Nitric Oxide
Mixtures of nitric oxide and ozone explode even when the quantity of ozone is small.
Mellor **8:** 432 (1946-1947).
Mixtures of ozone and nitric oxide explode violently at liquid-air temperatures.
Mellor **8, Supp. 2:** 164 (1967).

Nitrogen Dioxide
Nitrogen dioxide and ozone react with the evolution of light, and often explode.
Pinkus & Schulthess, *J. Chem. Phys.* **18:** 366 (1920).

Nitrogen Trichloride
See NITROGEN TRICHLORIDE plus Ammonia.
A mixture of ozone and nitrogen trichloride will explode.
Mellor **1:** 911 (1946-1947).

Nitrogen Triiodide
See BROMINE plus Nitrogen Triiodide.
Ozone and nitrogen triiodide form an explosive mixture.
Mellor **1:** 911 (1946-1947).

Nitroglycerin
Ozone and nitroglycerin explode on mixing.
Mellor **1:** 911 (1946-1947).

Organic Liquids
When some organic liquids are dropped into liquid ozone, explosions sometimes result. This phenomenon was observed in ozone that was formed by neutron or gamma-ray excitation of liquid oxygen. Also ozone itself was observed to decompose with small explosions in such an environment.
F.E. Adley, *Nucl. Sci. Abstr.* **17:** 18 (1962).

Organic Matter
Liquid ozone is particularly likely to explode when it reaches the boiling point of the ozone or when brought in contact with oxidizable substances.
Mellor **1:** 894 (1946-1947).

Stibine
Stibine and ozone explode at 90°C.
Berichte **38:** 3837.
Mellor **1:** 907 (1946-1947).

PALLADIUM Pd

Aluminum
See ALUMINUM plus Palladium.

Hydrogen and Isopropyl Alcohol
See HYDROGEN plus Palladium and Isopropyl Alcohol.

Oxygen Difluoride
See IRIDIUM plus Oxygen Difluoride.

Sulfur
Sulfur and palladium react with incandescence.
J. J. Berzelius, *Acad. Handl.* **33:** 175 (1813).

PALLADIUM-AMMINE NITRATES

(self-reactive)
Palladium-ammine nitrates may be impact-sensitive. $Pd(NH_3)_2(NO_3)_2$ and Pd $(NH_3)_4(NO_3)_2$ detonate violently when heated.
Mellor **15:** 685 (1946-1947).

PALLADIUM-AMMINE PERCHLORATES

(self-reactive)
Palladium-ammine perchlorates may be impact-sensitive.
Mellor **15:** 684 (1946-1947).

PARAFORMALDEHYDE $(HCHO)_n$

Oxygen
See OXYGEN (LIQUID) plus Paraformaldehyde.

PARALDEHYDE

Nitric Acid
Oxidation of paraldehyde to glyoxal by action of nitric acid is subject to an induction period, and the reaction can become violent if the paraldehyde is added too fast. Presence of nitrous acid eliminates the induction period.
Bretherick (1978).

PARATHION $(C_2H_5O)_2P(S)OC_6H_4NO_2$

(self-reactive)
When a sample was heated in a small test tube it decomposed and in a few minutes the residue exploded.
J.B. McPherson and G.A. Johnson, *Agri. Food Chem.* **4** (1): 42 (1956).

Endrin
While a mixture of parathion and endrin were being blended into a petroleum solvent an exothermic reaction occurred which caused some of the solvent to vaporize. The solvent vapor-air mixture exploded. Overheating, possibly caused by mechanical agitation, started the exothermic reaction.
Doyle (1973).

PENTABORANE (9) B_5H_9

Air
Pentaborane is spontaneously flammable in air.
Handbook Chem. Phys. (1958). *Sevegin* (1963).

PENTACHLOROETHANE C_2HCl_5

Sodium-Potassium Alloy
See SODIUM-POTASSIUM ALLOY plus Bromoform.

PENTAMETHYLDIALUMINUM HYDRIDE
$(CH_3)_3Al_2H(CH_3)_2$

Air
Pentamethyl aluminum hydride is spontaneously flammable in air.
Hurd, p. 98 (1952).

PENTOL (3-METHYL-2-PENTEN-4YN-1-OL)
$CH{\equiv}CC(CH_3)=CHCH_2OH$

Hydrogen
See HYDROGEN plus 1-Pentol.

Sodium Hydroxide
See SODIUM HYDROXIDE plus Pentol.

"PER" ACIDS (PERFORMIC, PERACETIC, etc.)

Olefins
Reactions between "per" acids and olefins are vigorously exothermic. Means should be provided for dissipation of heat.
Chem. and Eng. News **28:** 418, 3067 (1950).
See also "PEROXY" ACIDS

PERCHLORATES

(See also specific perchlorates as primary entries or under other reactants)

Benzene
Certain metal perchlorates recrystallized from benzene or ethyl alcohol can explode spontaneously.
J. Am. Chem. Soc. **62** (10): 3524 (October 1940).

Calcium Hydride
See BROMATES plus Calcium Hydride.

Charcoal
Perchlorates explode when melted with reducing agents or when projected into red-hot charcoal.
Berichte **39:** 3146.

Ethyl Alcohol
See PERCHLORATES plus Benzene.

Metals
When perchlorates are mixed with finely divided metals, the mixture may be explosive.
ACS **146:** 188. *Lab. Govt. Chemist* (1965).

Organic Matter
Perchlorates will render organic matter easily flammable. When perchlorates are mixed with finely divided organic matter, they may be explosive.
ACS **146:** 188. *Lab. Govt. Chemist* (1965).

Reducing Agents
See PERCHLORATES plus Charcoal.

Strontium Hydride
See BROMATES plus Strontium Hydride.

Sulfur
See SULFUR plus Perchlorates.

Sulfuric Acid
A mixture of the two may cause an explosion.
Pieters, p. 30 (1957).

PERCHLORIC ACID $HClO_4$

(self-reactive)
Anhydrous perchloric acid can decompose explosively at atmospheric pressure. On storage even in the dark, the anhydrous acid becomes discolored owing to decomposition products, e.g. chlorine dioxide, and may explode spontaneously.
ACS **146:** 190.
After an animal carcass was dissolved in nitric acid, fat was skimmed off and 125 milliliters of perchloric acid was added. The sample was heated on a hot plate to dryness in a 1-liter beaker after which two samples were placed on a stainless steel steam tray (steam off). When the samples were touched, they exploded.
Chem. and Eng. News. **51** (6): 29 (Feb. 5, 1973).

Acetic Acid
Explosions involving these materials have occurred in electrolytic polishing baths. The violence in some cases approached that of a true high explosive.
ACS **146:** 193. *Rev. Met.* **46:** 549-60 (1949).
Mem. Poudres **32:** 179-96 (1950). *Report L.A. Fire Department.*
NFPA Quarterly **40** (4): 275-78 (April 1947).

Acetic Acid and Acetic Anhydride
Mixtures of these three ingredients have varying degrees of sensitivity to shock. Vapors above the heated mixtures are flammable.
ACS **146:** 193-4. *Rev Met.* **46:** 549-60 (1949).
Mem. Poudres **32:** 179-96 (1950).

Acetic Anhydride
An electropolishing mixture of 170 gallons of 68–72% perchloric acid and 70 gallons of acetic anhydride exploded with devastating effect some time after the refrigerative temperature control of the tank had been turned off. A plastic holder had been inserted into the solution just before the explosion.
ACS **146:** 187. *BM Explos. Div. Rep.* **3034-C-443** (1947).
The addition of acetic anhydride to an aqueous solution of perchloric acid causes the formation of acetic acid which can react violently with the perchloric acid.
Rev. Met. **46** (8): 549-560 (1949).
Mem. Poudres **32:** 179-196 (1950).

Alcohols
The contact of hot, concentrated perchloric acid with alcohols or cellulose is particularly dangerous.
ACS **146:** 189, 195. E. M. Harris, *Chem. Eng.* **56** (1):116-7 (1949).

Aniline and Formaldehyde
Aniline treated with perchloric acid, then formaldehyde, gives a resinous condensation product which burns with explosive violence.
Aniline, p. 85 (1964). *U. S. Pat.* 2,871,224.

Antimony Compounds (trivalent)
See ANTIMONY COMPOUNDS (trivalent) plus Perchloric Acid.

Bismuth
See BISMUTH plus Perchloric Acid.

Cellulose
See PERCHLORIC ACID plus Alcohols.

Charcoal
A drop of anhydrous perchloric acid on charcoal causes a violent explosion.
ACS **146:** 188.

Dibutyl Sulfoxide
A 70% perchloric acid solution reacts instantly and explosively on contact with dibutyl sulfoxide.
Wischmeyer (1973).

Diethyl Ether
A drop of anhydrous perchloric acid in ether causes a violent explosion.
ACS **146:** 188. *Am. Chem. J.* **23:** 444 (1900).

Dimethyl Sulfoxide
See DIMETHYL SULFOXIDE plus Perchloric Acid.

Ethyl Alcohol
In mineral analysis the potassium cation is sometimes identified by adding perchloric acid in the presence of ethyl alcohol concentration. Explosions frequently occur that are due to the spontaneous decomposition of ethyl perchlorate formed during concentration and of residual perchloric acid. With methyl alcohol, the reaction is identical except that the methyl perchlorate that is formed is very explosive.
Analyst **80:** 10 (1955).

Fluorine
See FLUORINE plus Perchloric Acid.

Glycerine and Lead Oxide
See LEAD OXIDE plus Glycerine and Perchloric Acid.

Glycol Ethers
Glycol ethers, glycols, ketones, and alcohols undergo violent decomposition in contact with 68–72% perchloric acid.
ACS **146:** 195. *U.S. Patent* 2,504,119.

Glycols
See PERCHLORIC ACID plus Glycol Ethers.

Hydriodic Acid
Perchloric acid ignites with hydriodic acid.
Am. Chem. J. **23:** 444 (1900).

Hydrochloric Acid
See HYDROCHLORIC ACID plus Perchloric Acid.

Hydrogen
The explosion temperature of hydrogen-perchloric acid vapor mixtures is lowered from 400 to 215°C by the presence of steel particles.
ACS **146:** 189. *Angew. Chem.* **52:** 616-18 (1939).

Hypophosphites
See HYPOPHOSPHITES plus Perchloric Acid.

Ketones
See PERCHLORIC ACID plus Glycol Ethers.

Methyl Alcohol
See PERCHLORIC ACID plus Ethyl Alcohol.

Nitrogen Iodide
See NITROGEN TRIIODIDE plus Acids.

Nitrosophenol
See NITROSOPHENOL plus Acids.

Organic Matter
Perchloric acid can cause fire or explosion in most organic materials. Example: When bis(2-hydroxyethyl)-terephthalate, being refluxed with 5% perchloric acid in ethyl alcohol, was allowed to go to dryness, there was a violent explosion. A similar mixture, containing also ethylene glycol, flashed brightly after 18 hours refluxing. See also the other organic entries under perchloric acid.
Wheeler (1969).

Paper
A drop of anhydrous perchloric acid on paper can cause a violent explosion.
ACS **146:** 188.

Phosphorus Pentoxide
See PERCHLORIC ACID plus Sulfuric Acid.

Phosphorus Pentoxide and Chloroform
See PHOSPHORUS PENTOXIDE plus Perchloric Acid and Chloroform.

Sodium Iodide
See SODIUM IODIDE plus Perchloric Acid.

Steel
Explosions may occur when 72 percent perchloric acid is used for determination of chromium in steel. These explosions are apparently due to the formation of mixtures of perchloric acid vapor and hydrogen, catalyzed by the presence of steel particles. The presence of steel burnings lowered the explosion temperatures of such mix tures to 215°C. Addition of a little water to keep their boiling temperature at 150 to 160°C prevented the formation of explosive gas mixtures.
ACS **146,** p. 189 (1960).

Sulfoxides
See SULFOXIDES plus Perchloric Acid.

Sulfuric Acid
It is fairly easy to produce the dangerous anhydrous perchloric acid from either its salts or its aqueous solutions by heating with high-boiling acids and dehydrating agents such as sulfuric acid and phosphorus pentoxide.
NSC Data Sheet **D-311.** *ACS* **146:** 71.
Pascal **16:** 298 (1931-1934).

Sulfur Trioxide
The reaction of anhydrous perchloric acid with sulfur trioxide is violent and accompanied by the evolution of considerable heat, even when diluted with an inert solvent such as chloroform.
Pascal **16:** 300-303 (1931-1934).

Wood
A drop of anhydrous perchloric acid on wood fibers or dust causes a violent explosion. See also PERCHLORIC ACID plus Cellulose or plus Paper.
ACS **146:** 188.
Gordon, Young & Campbell, *Science* **104:** 353 (1946).

PERCHLORYL FLUORIDE $FClO_3$

Benzene and Aluminum Chloride
During the synthesis of perchloryl benzene by the action of perchloryl fluoride on benzene in the presence of aluminum chloride, there also forms a hazardous nitration product which may explode. The product is apparently nitrochlorobenzene, which is shock-sensitive.
Chem. and Eng. News **38** (4): 62 (1960).

Sodium Methylate
Sodium methylate, as it was being added to a mixture of perchloryl fluoride and methyl alcohol, underwent an explosive reaction with perchloryl fluoride in the vapor phase above the liquid. When the sodium methylate and methyl alcohol were mixed before the addition of perchloryl fluoride, no explosion occurred.
Chem. and Eng. News **37** (28): 60 (1959).

PERCHROMATES

Aniline
A mixture of aniline and a perchromate gives rise to an explosive reaction as the temperature is increased.
Rüst and Ebert, p. 297 (1948).

Pyridine
Heating a mixture of pyridine and a perchromate can lead to an explosion.
Rüst and Ebert, p. 297 (1948).

Quinoline
Heating a mixture of quinoline and perchromate can produce an explosion.
Rüst and Ebert, p. 297 (1948).

PERFLUOROPROPIONYL FLUORIDE F_3CCF_2COF

Fluorine
An explosion occurred during the investigation of a new method of forming perfluoropropionyl hypofluorite. The method involved cooling the reactor to minus 50°C after which a 50–50 fluorine-nitrogen mixture was added to perfluoropropionyl fluoride. It is possible that a small amount of water, which may have been introduced due to the low temperature, converted some of the perfluoropropionyl fluoride to the perfluoropropionic acid, a precursor for the formation of one of the acyl hypofluorites. The latter are known to be explosive.
MCA Case History **1045** (1966).
See FLUORINE plus Perfluropropionyl Fluoride.

PERFLUOROSUCCINAMIDE $F_2NCOCF_2CF_2CONF_2$

Lithium Aluminum Hydride and Water
See LITHIUM ALUMINUM HYDRIDE plus Perfluorosuccinamide and Water.

PERFLUOROTOLUENE $C_6H_5CH_3F_4$

Perfluorotoluene has been reported to explode when heated with oxygen at a pressure of 2000 psig and 200°C.
Chem. and Eng. News, p. 2 (Sept. 23, 1991); p. 2 (October 7, 1991); p. 2 (Dec. 16, 1991); and p. 2 (March 30, 1992).

PERIODATES $MeIO_4$

(self-reactive)
The metaperiodates ($MeIO_4$) in some cases decompose with explosive violence when strongly heated. Ammonium periodate may explode even on gentle friction, e.g., when touched with a spatula.
Ellern, p. 288 (1968). *Remy* **1:** 814 (1956).

PERIODIC ACID HIO_4

Dimethyl Sulfoxide
See DIMETHYL SULFOXIDE plus Periodic Acid.

PERMANGANATES

(See also specific permanganates as primary entries or see under other reactants)

Acetic Acid
Acetic acid or acetic anhydride can explode with permanganates if not kept cold.
Von Schwartz, p. 34 (1918).

Acetic Anhydride Sulfuric Acid and Benzene
See PERMANGANATES plus Acetic Acid. Explosions can occur when permanganates that have been treated with sulfuric acid come in contact with benzene, carbon disulfide, diethyl ether, ethyl alcohol, petroleum, or organic matter.
Von Schwartz, p. 327 (1918).

PERMANGANIC ACID $HMnO_4$

(self-reactive)
Above 3°C permanganic acid is unstable and decomposes explosively. It is a violent oxidant and the following classes of organic chemicals explode into flame on contact with it: alcohols, alkanes, aryl hydrocarbons, greases, cycloalkanes, alkylamines, amides, and ethers. Carbon tetrachloride, chloroform and dichloromethane do not burn.
J. Am. Chem. Soc. **91** (22): 6200-6201 (1969).
Chem. Abst. **72:** 17982f (1970).

Ethyl Alcohol
Alcohols should not be mixed with permanganic acid, as they may spontaneously explode.
Bahme, p. 9 (1961).

Organic Matter
See PERMANGANIC ACID (self-reactive).

PERMONOSULFURIC ACID (CARO'S ACID) H_2SO_5

Acetone
Inadvertent addition of acetone to a solution containing permono sulfuric acid resulted in a violent explosion. The permonosulfuric acid had been formed by reaction between hydrogen peroxide and sulfuric acid during an analytical procedure.
Wood (1966). *NSC Newsletter, Chem. Sec.* (1961). *J. Am. Chem. Soc.* **59:** 552-7 (1937).

Alcohols
Permonosulfuric acid in contact with primary or secondary alcohols often produces explosions.
J. Am. Chem. Soc. **59:** 552 (1937).

Cotton
If 92% permonosulfuric acid is brought in contact with cotton, in a few seconds there is a violent reaction accompanied by a yellow flame.
Z. Angew. Chem. **22:** 1713.

Hydrogen Peroxide
See HYDROGEN PEROXIDE plus Sulfuric Acid.

Manganese Dioxide
The decomposition of 92% permonosulfuric acid is explosive in the presence of smooth or finely divided manganese dioxide or silver.
Z. Angew. Chem. **22:** 1713.

Organic Matter
Too concentrated permonosulfuric acid in any organic medium may prove dangerous.
J. Am. Chem. Soc. **59:** 552 (1937).

Platinum
See PLATINUM plus Permonosulfuric Acid.

Silver
See PERMONOSULFURIC ACID plus Manganese Dioxide.

PEROXIDES ROOR

(See also specific peroxides or see under other reactants)

Organic Matter
Peroxides may cause ignition of organic materials.
Lab. Govt. Chemist (1965).

Thiocyanates
See THIOCYANATES plus Oxidizing Agents.

PEROXYACETIC ACID CH_3COOOH

Acetic Anhydride
Acetic anhydride and peracetic acid react readily to form acetyl peroxide which is an extremely sensitive explosive.
MCA Case History **1795** (1971).
See also HYDROGEN PEROXIDE plus Acetic Anhydride.

Olefins
See "PER" ACIDS plus Olefins.

Organic Matter
Upon contact with peracetic acid, organic materials can ignite or result in explosions.
Haz. Chem. Data, p. 214 (1973); *Chem. and Eng. News* (March 11, 1991).

"PEROXY" ACIDS (PERFORMIC, PERACETIC, etc.)

(self-reactive)
Peracids should be handled only in small quantities and with extreme care when pure or very concentrated. Organic peracids, such as peracetic acid, are so unstable that they may explode during distillation, even under reduced pressure.
Kirk and Othmer, Second Ed. **14:** 809 (1963).
Grignard **11:** 90 (1935-1954).

PEROXYCAMPHORIC ACID $C_3H_{14}(COOOH)_2$

(self-reactive)
Percamphoric acid explodes when heated rapidly from 80 to 100°C.
Chem. Reviews **45:** 15 (1949).

PEROXYTRICHLOROACETIC ACID $Cl_3CCOOOH$

(self-reactive)
Pertrichloroacetic acid is very unstable. Decomposition products include phosgene, chlorine, hydrochloric acid and carbon monoxide.
Chem. Reviews **45** (1): 10 (1949).

PEROXYFORMIC ACID OCHOOH

(self-reactive)
Performic acid is an unstable compound capable of undergoing rapid, spontaneous exothermal decomposition at room temperature, even in the absence of foreign substances. It is shock sensitive.
Chem. and Eng. News **28:** 3067 (Sept. 4, 1950).
Chem. Reviews **45:** 4, 7 (1949).
Chem. and Eng. News **30:** 3041 (1952).

Aluminum
See ALUMINUM plus Performic Acid.

Aniline
Aniline is oxidized violently by performic acid when the acid strength is more than 60% by weight.
Berichte **48:** 1139 (1915).

Benzaldehyde
Benzaldehyde is oxidized violently by performic acid.
Berichte **48:** 1139 (1915).

Formaldehyde
Formaldehyde is oxidized violently by concentrated performic acid.
Berichte **48:** 1139 (1915).

Lead Dioxide
A concentrated solution of performic acid can explode upon contact with powdered lead dioxide.
Berichte **48:** 1139 (1915).

Magnesium
See MAGNESIUM plus Performic Acid.

Metal Oxides
See METAL OXIDES plus Performic Acid.

Metals
See METAL plus Performic Acid.

Nickel
See NICKEL plus Performic Acid.

Olefins
See "PER" ACIDS plus Olefins.

Phosphorus
See PHOSPHORUS plus Performic Acid.

Sodium Nitride
Sodium nitride can decompose performic acid explosively.
Berichte **48:** 1139 (1915).

Zinc
See ZINC plus Performic Acid.

PETROLEUM

Nitrogen Tetroxide
See NITROGEN TETROXIDE plus Petroleum.

PHENOL C_6H_5OH

Aluminum Chloride and Nitrobenzene
See ALUMINUM CHLORIDE plus Nitrobenzene and Phenol.

Butadiene
Reaction of the two ingredients, catalyzed by boron trifluoride diethyletherate, and in a petroleum ether solution, pressurized the capped bottle, causing the bottle to explode.
MCA Case History **790** (1962).

Calcium Hypochlorite
See CALCIUM HYPOCHLORITE plus Phenol.

PHENOL-FORMALDEHYDE RESIN

Fluorine
See FLUORINE plus Solid Nonmetals and Oxygen.

PHENOLS

Acetaldehyde
See ACETALDEHYDE plus Acid Anhydrides.

b-PHENYLBORACYCLOPENTANE $C_6H_5B(CH_2)_4$

Air
Phenyl cyclotetramethylene borine is spontaneously flammable in air.
Douda (1966).

p-PHENYLENEDIAMINE PERCHLORATE $C_6H_4(NH_2)_2$•CLO_4

(self-reactive)
This compound was believed in 1910 to be the most powerful explosive substance known.
ACS **146:** 213. *Berichte* **43:** 2624-30 (1910).

PHENYLHYDRAZINE $C_6H_5NHNH_2$

Lead Dioxide
See LEAD DIOXIDE plus Phenylhydrazine.

n-PHENYLHYDROXYLAMINE HYDROCHLORIDE C_6H_5NHOH•HCl

(self-reactive)
In an attempt to stabilize some phenylhydroxylamine for safekeeping, 700 grams were made into the hydrochloride, but after it had been in the laboratory about two weeks, it exploded with considerable force.
Wallace (1966).

PHENYL ISOCYANATE C_6H_5NCO

Cobalt Pentammine Triazo Perchlorate and Nitrosyl Perchlorate.
The reaction mixture was stirred and proceeded normally for 2–3 minutes. When stirring was interrupted, the mixture exploded.
Chem. and Eng. News **46** (8): 39 (1968).

PHENYLLITHIUM C_6H_5Li

Air
Phenyl lithium is spontaneously flammable in air.
Ellern (1961).

Nitrous Oxide
The reaction of phenyl-lithium produces unstable lithium phenylazoxide as a product.
Mellor **2, Supp. 2:** 93 (1961).

PHENYLSILVER C_6H_5Ag

(self-reactive)
Phenyl silver is explosive at room temperature.
Coates, p. 173 (1956).

PHENYL SULFIDE SALTS

Diazonium Salts
See DIAZONIUM SALTS plus Thiophenates.

PHENYLVANADOCENE $(C_5H_5)_2VC_6H_5$

Air
Phenyl dicyclopentadienyl vanadium is spontaneously flammable in air.
Zeiss, p. 234 (1960).

PHOSGENE $OCCl_2$

Aluminum
See ALUMINUM plus Phosphorus Trichloride.

tert-Butyl Azidoformate
See tert-BUTYL AZIDOFORMATE plus Phosgene.

2, 4-Hexadiyn-1, 6-Diol
Phosgene and 2, 4-hexadiyn-1, 6-diol react to form 2, 4-hexadiyn-1, 6-bischloroformate, which is a shock-sensitive compound.
P. E. Driedger and H. V. Isaacson, *Chem. and Eng. News* **50** (12): 51 (1972).

Isopropyl Alcohol
See ISOPROPYL ALCOHOL plus Phosgene.

Potassium
See POTASSIUM plus Phosgene.

Sodium
See SODIUM plus Phosgene.

PHOSPHAM PN_2H

Air
Phospham ignites in air at slightly elevated temperatures and burns with a white flame.
H. Rose, *Ann. Phys.* **52:** 62 (1841).

Cupric Oxide
A mixture of phospham and cupric oxide or mercuric oxide decomposes with incandescence.
Wohler & Liebig, *Ann. Chem.* **11:** 139 (1834).

Mercuric Oxide
See PHOSPHAM plus Cupric Oxide.

Nitrates
See NITRATES plus Phospham.

Nitrogen Dioxide
Phospham ignites in nitrogen dioxide (nitrogen peroxide) vapors.
H. Rose, *Ann. Phys.* **24:** 308 (1832).

PHOSPHATES

Magnesium
See MAGNESIUM plus Phosphates.

PHOSPHINE PH_3

Air
Dry phosphine is spontaneously flammable in cold air.
H. Rose, *Ann. Phys.* **14:** 183 (1828). *Z. Anorg. Chemie* **180:** 32. *Handbook Chem. Phys.* **40:** 582 (1958). *MCA Case History* **1066** (1965).
See also PHOSPHINES plus Air.

Boron Trichloride
See BORON TRICHLORIDE plus Nitrogen Peroxide.

Bromine
See BROMINE plus Phosphine.

Chlorine
See BROMINE plus Phosphine.

Chlorine Monoxide
See CHLORINE MONOXIDE plus Phosphine.

Mercuric Nitrate
See MERCURIC NITRATE plus Phosphine.

Nitric Acid
Phosphine is violently decomposed by concentrated nitric acid, and flame is produced.
Warm fuming nitric acid, dropped in a container of phosphine gas, produces an explosion.
T. Graham, *Edin. Roy. Soc.* **13:** 88 (1835).

Nitric Oxide
Phosphine plus nitric oxide can be ignited by the addition of oxygen.
Berzelius **1, i:** 485 (1825).

Nitrogen Trichloride
See NITROGEN TRICHLORIDE plus Ammonia.

Nitrogen Trioxide
See NITROGEN TRIOXIDE plus Phosphine.

Nitrous Acid
Phosphine gas ignites spontaneously if a trace of nitrous acid is added.
T. Graham, *Edin. Roy. Soc.* **13:** 88 (1835).

Nitrous Oxide
A mixture of nitrous oxide and phosphine can be exploded by a spark.
Comp. Rend. **18:** 652.

Oxygen
See OXYGEN plus Phosphine.

Potassium and Ammonia
See POTASSIUM plus Phosphine and Ammonia.

Silver Nitrate
See SILVER NITRATE plus Phosphine.

PHOSPHINES PH_3; P_2H_4; $(P_2H_4)_3$; PxHy

(self-reactive)
The higher phosphines (beyond Diphosphine) decompose rapidly in light at room temperature.
Mellor **8, Supp. 3:** 274 (1971).

Air
If the P_2H_4 is removed by passing the PH_3 and P_2H_4 through concentrated sulfuric acid, the P_2H_4 does not catch fire in air below 150°C. The PH_3 is spontaneously flammable in cold air. Solid $(P_2H_4)_3$ ignites at 160°C.
Z. Anorg. Chemie **180:** 32. *Handbook Chem. Phys.* **40th Ed.:** 582 (1958).

PHOSPHONITRILE AZIDE-TRIMER

(self-reactive)
This is a highly explosive compound, readily detonated by friction.
Mellor **8, Supp. 2:** 23 (1967).

PHOSPHONIUM IODIDE PH_4I

Bromates
See BROMATES plus Phosphonium Iodide.

Bromic Acid
Phosphonium iodide ignites at ordinary temperatures in contact with bromic, chloric or iodic acid.
Ann. Chim. et Phys. (2) **47:** 87.

Chlorates
See PHOSPHONIUM IODIDE plus Bromates.

Chloric Acid
See PHOSPHONIUM IODIDE plus Bromic Acid.

Iodates
See PHOSPHONIUM IODIDE plus Bromates.

Iodic Acid
See PHOSPHONIUM IODIDE plus Bromic Acid.

Nitric Acid
Phosphonium iodide ignites spontaneously when mixed with nitric acid at ordinary temperatures.
Ann. Chim. et Phys. (2) **47:** 87.

Silver Nitrate
Phosphonium iodide reacts vigorously with dry silver nitrate with development of much heat.
Ann. Chim. et Phys. (2) **47:** 87.

PHOSPHONIUM PERCHLORATE $2PH_3 \cdot 3HClO_4$

(self-reactive)
Violent explosions have occurred in spite of every precaution.
Helv. Chim. Acta **17:** 222-4 (1934).
This is a very explosive salt and cannot be dried.
Mellor **8, Supp. 3:** 274 (1971).

PHOSPHORUS P

Air
White (yellow) phosphorus ignites spontaneously in air—even in a rarefied atmosphere.
A. D. Backe, *Schweigger's Jour.* **63:** 478 (1831).
Latimer and Hildebrand, p. 210 (1940).

Alkaline Hydroxides
Phosphorus boiled with alkaline hydroxides yields mixed phosphines which may ignite spontaneously in air.
Z. Anorg. Chemie **121:** 73. *Sidgwick* **1:** 729 (1950).
See PHOSPHORUS plus Potassium Hydroxide.

Ammonium Nitrate
A mixture of white (or yellow) phosphorus and ammonium nitrate can be exploded by percussion.
J. W. Slater, *Chem. Gaz.* **11:** 329 (1853).

Antimony Pentafluoride
Phosphorus ignites in contact with antimony pentafluoride.
Mellor **9:** 467 (1946-1947).

Barium Bromate
See PHOSPHORUS plus Bromates.

Barium Chlorate
See PHOSPHORUS plus Bromates.

Barium Iodate
See PHOSPHORUS plus Bromates.

Beryllium
See BERYLLIUM plus Phosphorus.

Boron Triiodide
See BORON TRIIODIDE plus Phosphorus. White or red phosphorus and boron triiodide react with incandescence.
Mellor **5:** 136 (1946-1947).

Bromates
A combination of finely divided phosphorus with finely divided bromates (also chlorates or iodates) of barium, calcium, magnesium, potassium, sodium, or zinc will explode with heat, percussion, and, sometimes, light friction.
Mellor **2:** 310 (1946-1947).

Bromine
See BROMINE plus Phosphorus.

Bromine Trifluoride
See ANTIMONY plus Bromine Trifluoride.

Bromoazide
See ANTIMONY plus Bromoazide.

Calcium Bromate
See PHOSPHORUS plus Bromates.

Calcium Chlorate
See PHOSPHORUS plus Bromates.

Calcium Iodate
See PHOSPHORUS plus Bromates.

Cerium
See CERIUM plus Phosphorus.

Cesium
Phosphorus reacts vigorously below 250°C with any of the following materials: cesium, lithium, potassium, rubidium, sodium, sulfur.
Mellor **8, Supp. 3:** 228 (1971).

Cesium Acetylene Carbide
Cesium acetylene carbide becomes incandescent when warmed in contact with phosphorus.
Mellor **5:** 848-50 (1946-1947).

Cesium Nitride
See CESIUM NITRIDE plus Air.

Charcoal and Air
Phosphorus sprinkled with animal charcoal ignites at 15.5°C in the open air.
Mellor **8:** 771 (1946-1947).

Chlorates
A mixture of red phosphorus and chlorates bursts into flames after a few moments. Moist chlorates explode on contact with white phosphorus.
Mellor **2, Supp. 1:** 584 (1956).
See PHOSPHORUS plus Bromates. See PHOSPHORUS plus Potassium Chlorate.

Chlorine
Phosphorus burns spontaneously in gaseous chlorine.
Mellor **2:** 92, 95; **9:** 626 (1946-1947).
Phosphorus (white or yellow) burns in chlorine gas with a pale green light. Red phosphorus reacts with chlorine at ordinary temperatures. Finely divided red phosphorus ignites spontaneously in chlorine at ordinary temperatures.
Moissan, p. 125 (1900).
The reaction of phosphorus and chlorine, fluorine, or bromine is highly exothermic.
All can explode in contact with white phosphorus.
Mellor **8, Supp. 3:** 228 (1971).
The reaction of white phosphorus and liquid chlorine is explosive.
Mellor **2, Supp. 1:** 379 (1956).

Chlorine Dioxide
Phosphorus ignites spontaneously in chlorine dioxide and may explode.
Mellor **2:** 289 (1946-1947).

Chlorine and Heptane
Flaming occurs when liquid chlorine in heptane is added to red phosphorus at 0°C.
Mellor **2, Supp. 1:** 379 (1956).

Chlorine Monoxide
See POTASSIUM plus Chlorine Monoxide.

Chlorine Trifluoride
See ANTIMONY plus Chlorine Trifluoride.

Chlorine Trioxide
Ordinary phosphorus (white or yellow) reacts explosively with chlorine trioxide.
Ann. Chim. et Phys. (3) **7:** 298.

Chlorosulfonic Acid
Yellow phosphorus reacts feebly with chlorosulfonic acid if cold. At temperatures from 25 to 30°C, the reaction begins vigorously (with evolution of hydrogen chloride and sulfur dioxide) and ends with an explosion. With red phosphorus a higher temperature is necessary to start the reaction.
Berichte **15:** 417.

Chromic Acid
See PHOSPHORUS plus Chromium Trioxide.

Chromic Anhydride
See PHOSPHORUS plus Chromium Trioxide.

Chromium Trioxide
Phosphorus reacts explosively with molten chromium trioxide.
Ann. Chim. et Phys. (6) **5:** 468.
Mellor **11:** 234 (1946-1947).

Chromyl Chloride
Chromyl chloride explodes with moistened phosphorus. (Light is emitted at the same time.)
Ann. Chim. et Phys. (2) **31:** 435. *Comp. Rend.* **5:** 753. T. Thomson, *Phil. Trans. Roy. Soc. London* **117:** 195 (1827).

Copper
See COPPER plus Phosphorus.

Cyanogen Iodide
Phosphorus (molten) plus cyanogen iodide reacts with incandescence to produce phosphorus iodide.
F. Wohler, *Gilbert's Ann.* **69:** 281 (1821).

Fluorine
See FLUORINE plus Phosphorus.

Iodates
See PHOSPHORUS plus Bromates. See PHOSPHORUS plus Potassium Iodate.

Iodine
See IODINE plus Phosphorus.

Iodine Monobromide
Phosphorus reacts violently with molten iodine monobromide or iodine monochloride.
Mellor **8, Supp. 3:** 264.

Iodine Monochloride
See PHOSPHORUS plus Iodine Monobromide.

Iodine Pentafluoride
See ARSENIC plus Iodine Pentafluoride.

Iron
See COPPER plus Phosphorus.

Lanthanum
See CERIUM plus Phosphorus.

Lead Dioxide
When lead dioxide and red phosphorus are ground the mass ignites; with yellow phosphorus, there is an explosion.
Mellor **7:** 690 (1946-1947).

Lithium
See LITHIUM plus Arsenic. See also PHOSPHORUS plus Cesium.

Lithium Carbide
A mixture of lithium carbide and phosphorus burns if the mixture is warm.
Mellor **5:** 848 (1946-1947).

Lithium Silicide
Lithium silicide attacks phosphorus, selenium or tellurium with incandescence.
Mellor **6:** 169 (1946-1947).

Magnesium Bromate
See PHOSPHORUS plus Bromates.

Magnesium Chlorate
See PHOSPHORUS plus Bromates.

Magnesium Iodate
See PHOSPHORUS plus Bromates.

Magnesium Perchlorate
A student was injured by an explosion when he attempted to mix these two chemicals in the laboratory.
1965 Sum. Serious Acc. (1966).

Manganese
See MANGANESE plus Phosphorus.

Mercuric Oxide
A mixture of mercuric oxide and phosphorus explodes when struck with a hammer and when boiled with water and phosphorus.
Mellor **4:** 778 (1946-1947).

Mercurous Nitrate
A mixture of mercurous nitrate and phosphorus explodes violently when struck with a hammer.
Mellor **4:** 987 (1946-1947).

Neodymium
See NEODYMIUM plus Phosphorus.

Nickel
See COPPER plus Phosphorus.

Nitrates
A mixture of the two may cause an explosion.
Pieters, p. 30 (1957).

Nitric Acid
Phosphorus ignites in the vapor of nitric acid and burns with an intense white light.
Berrere & Moutet, *Symposium Comb.* (**Fifth**): 170-81 (1954).

Nitrogen Bromide
Nitrogen bromide explodes violently in contact with phosphorus.
Mellor **8, Supp. I, Part 2:** 707 (1964).

Nitrogen Dioxide
See MAGNESIUM plus Nitrogen Dioxide.

Nitrogen Tribromide
See ARSENIC plus Nitrogen Tribromide.

Nitrogen Trichloride
See NITROGEN TRICHLORIDE plus Ammonia.

Nitrosyl Fluoride
See BORON plus Nitrosyl Fluoride.

Nitryl Fluoride
Red phosphorus and nitryl fluoride react at room temperature.
Mellor **8, Supp. 3:** 264 (1971).

Oxygen
Phosphorus and oxygen or iodine undergo a vigorous reaction at room temperature.
Mellor **8, Supp. 3:** 228 (1971).

Performic Acid
Red phosphorus is violently oxidized by performic acid.
Grignard **11:** 179 (1935-1954).
Berichte **48:** 1139 (1915).

Platinum
See COPPER plus Phosphorus.

Potassium
See PHOSPHORUS plus Cesium.

Potassium Bromate
See PHOSPHORUS plus Bromates.

Potassium Chlorate
If a drop of solution of phosphorus in carbon disulfide is placed on powdered potassium chlorate, an explosion occurs as the solvent evaporates.
R. Bottger, *Repert. Pharm.* **24:** 725 (1875).
Ellern, p. 50 (1968).
See also PHOSPHORUS plus Bromates.

Potassium Hydroxide
When phosphorus is boiled with a solution of sodium or potassium hydroxide, phosphine gas is evolved which is spontaneously flammable.
Mellor **8:** 804-5 (1946-1947).
See PHOSPHORUS plus Alkaline Hydroxides.

Potassium Iodate
If red or white phosphorus is mixed with potassium iodate and moistened with a few drops of water, the mixture reacts violently, sometimes explosively.
J. Am. Chem. Soc. **49:** 9 (1927).
See also PHOSPHORUS plus Bromates.

Potassium Nitride
Potassium nitride unites with sulfur or phosphorus when heated, forming a highly flammable mixture.
Mellor **8:** 99 (1946-1947).

Potassium Permanganate
Crystals of potassium permanganate explode vigorously when ground with phosphorus.
Mellor **12:** 322 (1946-1947).

Potassium Peroxide
A mixture of phosphorus and potassium peroxide causes fire or explosion.
Mellor **2:** 490-93 (1946-1947). *Von Schwartz,* p. 328 (1918).

Rubidium
See PHOSPHORUS plus Cesium.

Rubidium Acetylene Carbide
Rubidium acetylene carbide ignites in contact with molten sulfur. It becomes incandescent when warmed in contact with phosphorus.
Mellor **5:** 849 (1946-1947).

Selenium Monochloride
White phosphorus mixed with selenium monochloride explodes.
Mellor **8, Supp. 3:** 264 (1971).

Selenium Oxychloride
Red phosphorus reacts in the cold with selenium oxychloride evolving light and heat; white phosphorus reacts explosively.
Mellor **10:** 906 (1946-1947).

Selenium Oxyfluoride
This mixture ignites spontaneously.
Mellor **8, Supp. 3:** 264 (1971).

Selenium Tetrafluoride
This mixture produces a violent reaction.
Mellor **8, Supp. 3:** 264 (1971).

Silver Nitrate
A mixture of silver nitrate and phosphorus explodes violently when struck with a hammer.
Mellor **3:** 470 (1946-1947).

Silver Oxide
When amorphous phosphorus is ground with silver oxide, the mixture ignites.
Mellor **3:** 377 (1946-1947).

Sodium
See PHOSPHORUS plus Cesium.

Sodium Bromate
See PHOSPHORUS plus Bromates.

Sodium Carbide
Sodium carbide burns vigorously in phosphorus vapor.
Mellor **5:** 848-50 (1946-1947).

Sodium Chlorate
See PHOSPHORUS plus Bromates.

Sodium Chlorite
Red phosphorus and sodium chlorite react in aqueous suspension in a strongly exothermic manner. The reaction can have a sudden, almost explosive stage.
Mellor **8, Supp. 3:** 645 (1971).

Sodium Hydroxide
See PHOSPHORUS plus Potassium Hydroxide and PHOSPHORUS plus Alkaline Hydroxides.

Sodium Iodate
See PHOSPHORUS plus Bromates.

Sodium Peroxide
Phosphorus and sodium peroxide react with flame or explosion.
Mellor **2:** 490-93 (1946-1947). *Von Schwartz,* p. 328 (1918).

Sulfur
When a mixture of sulfur and yellow phosphorus is warmed, the two elements unite in all proportions with vivid combustion and powerful explosions.
Ann. Chim. et Phys. (1) **4:** 1. *Ann. Chim. et Phys.* (2) **67:** 332. *Comp. Rend.* **96:** 1499, 1771. R. Bottger, *J. Prakt. Chem.* (1) **12:** 357 (1837).
See PHOSPHORUS plus Cesium.

Sulfur Trioxide
Yellow phosphorus ignites after exposure to the vapor of sulfur trioxide. A piece of phosphorus dropped into liquid sulfur trioxide reduces the latter with violence. When the pieces of phosphorus are large, the heat raises the temperature of the phosphorus sufficiently to cause ignition.
F. C. Vogel, *Schweigger's Jour.* **4:** 121 (1812).

Sulfuric Acid
Yellow phosphorus ignites when placed in boiling concentrated sulfuric acid.
A. Oppenheim, *Bull. Soc. Chim.* (2) **1:** 163 (1864).

Thorium
When thorium is heated with phosphorus, they unite with incandescence.
J. J. Berzelius, *Svenska Akad.,* p. 1 (1829).

Vanadium Oxytrichloride
This mixture produces an explosive reaction below 100°C with more than small amounts.
Mellor **8, Supp. 3:** 264 (1971).

Zinc Bromate
See PHOSPHORUS plus Bromates.

Zinc Chlorate
See PHOSPHORUS plus Bromates.

Zinc Iodate
See PHOSPHORUS plus Bromates.

Zirconium
Phosphorus and zirconium react with incandescence when heated in a vacuum.
Mellor **7:** 114-16 (1946-1947).

PHOSPHORUS CYANIDE P_3CN

Air
This very reactive cyanide ignites in air when touched with a warm rod.
Mellor **8, Supp. 3:** 583 (1971).

Water
Phosphorus cyanide reacts violently with water.
Mellor **8, Supp. 3:** 583 (1971).

PHOSPHORUS HEXAOXYTETRASULFIDE $P_4O_6S_4$

Water
This sulfide decomposes rapidly in moist air.
Mellor **8, Supp. 3:** 437 (1971).

PHOSPHORUS ISOCYANATE P_3OCN

Acetaldehyde
Phosphorus isocyanate and acetaldehyde, acetic acid, silver nitrate, or sulfuric acid react violently.
Mellor **8, Supp. 3:** 585 (1971).

Acetic Acid
See PHOSPHORUS ISOCYANATE plus Acetaldehyde.

Chlorine
See CHLORINE plus Phosphorus Isocyanate.

Silver Nitrate
See PHOSPHORUS ISOCYANATE plus Acetaldehyde.

Sulfuric Acid
See PHOSPHORUS ISOCYANATE plus Acetaldehyde.

Water
The hydrolysis of phosphorus isocyanate is rapid.
Mellor **8, Supp. 3:** 585 (1971).

PHOSPHORUS PENTACHLORIDE PCl_5

Chlorine Trioxide
See CHLORINE TRIOXIDE plus Phosphorus Pentachloride.

Fluorine
See FLUORINE plus Phosphorus Pentachloride.

Hydroxylamine
See PHOSPHORUS TRICHLORIDE plus Hydroxylamine.

Magnesium Oxide
These materials react with brilliant incandescence.
Mellor **8:** 1016 (1946-1947).

Phosphorus Trioxide
See PHOSPHORUS TRIOXIDE plus Phosphorus Pentachloride.

Potassium
See POTASSIUM plus Boron Tribromide.

Sodium
See SODIUM plus Phosphorus Pentachloride.
See SODIUM plus Cobaltous Bromide.

Water
Phosphorus pentachloride reacts violently with water.
Oldbury Chemicals, p. 9.

PHOSPHORUS PENTASULFIDE P_2S_5

Water
Phosphorus pentasulfide heats spontaneously, and may ignite, in the presence of moisture.
Haz. Chem. Data (1969).

PHOSPHORUS PENTOXIDE P_2O_5

Ammonia
Reaction of phosphorus pentoxide and ammonia is rapid, contrary to older reports.
Mellor **8, Supp. 1:** 331 (1964).
This is a vigorous reaction.
Mellor **8, Supp. 3:** 403 (1971).

Calcium Oxide
See CALCIUM OXIDE plus Phosphorus Pentoxide.

Chlorine Trifluoride
See CHLORINE TRIFLUORIDE plus Arsenic Trioxide.

Hydrogen Fluoride
Phosphorus pentoxide unites with hydrogen fluoride vigorously, even at 19.5°C.
G. Gore, *Proc. Roy. Soc.* **17:** 256 (1869).

Oxygen Difluoride
See OXYGEN DIFLUORIDE plus Aluminum Chloride.

Perchloric Acid
See PERCHLORIC ACID plus Sulfuric Acid.

Perchloric Acid and Chloroform
A violent explosion occurs if a solution of perchloric acid in chloroform is poured on phosphorus pentoxide.
J. Am. Chem. Soc. **23:** 444 (1901).

Potassium
See POTASSIUM plus Phosphorus Pentoxide.

Propargyl Alcohol
Addition of phosphorus pentoxide to propargyl alcohol caused the alcohol to burst into flame.
Monroe (1966).

Sodium
See POTASSIUM plus Phosphorus Pentoxide.

Sodium Carbonate
See SODIUM CARBONATE plus Phosphorus Pentoxide.

Sodium Hydroxide
See CALCIUM OXIDE plus Phosphorus Pentoxide.

Water
Phosphorus pentoxide reacts violently with water.
Oldbury Chemicals, p. 9.

Water and Organic Matter
Mixed with water and combustible material, phosphoric anhydride produces great heat and often ignites the combustible material.
Chem. Safety Data Sheet **SD-23:** 3 (1948).

PHOSPHORUS TETRAOXYTRISULFIDE $P_4O_4S_3$

Water
The sulfide ignites if moistened with a little water.
Mellor **8, Supp. 3:** 437 (1971).

PHOSPHORUS TRIBROMIDE PBr_3

Potassium
See POTASSIUM plus Boron Tribromide.

Ruthenium Tetroxide
See RUTHENIUM TETROXIDE plus Phosphorus Tribromide.

Sodium
See SODIUM plus Phosphorus Tribromide.
See SODIUM plus Cobaltous Bromide.

PHOSPHORUS TRICHLORIDE PCl_3

Acetic Acid
Several laboratory explosions have occurred using this reaction to form acetyl chloride. Poor heat control probably caused formation of phosphine.
J. Am. Chem. Soc. **60:** 488 (1938).

Aluminum
See ALUMINUM plus Phosphorus Trichloride.

Chromyl Chloride
See CHROMYL CHLORIDE plus Phosphorus Trichloride.

Diallyl Phosphite and Allyl Alcohol
See DIALLYL PHOSPHITE plus Allyl Alcohol and Phosphorus Trichloride.

Dimethyl Sulfoxide
See DIMETHYL SULFOXIDE plus Acyl Halides.

Fluorine
See FLUORINE plus Phosphorus Trichloride.

Hydroxylamine
Ignition occurs when hydroxylamine is mixed with phosphorus trichloride or phosphorus pentachloride.
Mellor **8:** 290 (1946-1947).

Iodine Monochloride
See IODINE MONOCHLORIDE plus Phosphorus Trichloride.

Lead Dioxide
See LEAD DIOXIDE plus Phosphorus Trichloride.

Nitric Acid
An explosion occurs when phosphorus trichloride is brought in contact with nitric or nitrous acid.
Comp. Rend. **28:** 86.

Nitrous Acid
See PHOSPHORUS TRICHLORIDE plus Nitric Acid.

Organic Matter
See PHOSPHORUS OXYCHLORIDE plus Organic Matter.

Potassium
See POTASSIUM plus Phosphorus Trichloride.

Sodium
See SODIUM plus Phosphorus Trichloride.

Water
The reaction between water and phosphorus trichloride is extremely violent. The reaction may be due to the formation of phosphine or elemental phosphorus. The possible presence of hydrogen may intensify these flashes of fire.
Chem. Safety Data Sheet **SD-27** (1948).

PHOSPHORUS TRIFLUORIDE PF_3

Diborane
The reaction product of this combination, borane-phosphorus trifluoride compound, is spontaneously flammable in air.
Mellor **8, Supp. 3:** 442 (1971).

Fluorine
See FLUORINE plus Phosphorus Trifluo ride.

Oxygen
See OXYGEN plus Phosphorus Trifluoride.

PHOSPHORUS TRIOXIDE P_4O_6

Air
Melted phosphorus trioxide readily ignites in air. When thrown into oxygen (heated to 50–60°C.), it instantly ignites with a flame of almost blinding brilliance.
W.E. Downey, *J. Chem. Soc.* **125:** 347 (1924).

Ammonia
If ammonia is passed over phosphorus trioxide, which has been melted by the warmth of the hand, a somewhat violent reaction occurs and the mass ignites. The reaction is slow if the materials are kept cold.
Thorpe and Tutton, *J. Chem. Soc.* **59:** 1019 (1891). *Mellor* **8:** 898 (1946-1947).

Arsenic Trifluoride
See ARSENIC TRIFLUORIDE plus Phosphorus Trioxide.

Bromine
See BROMINE plus Phosphorus Trioxide. See also CHLORINE plus Phosphorus Oxide.

Chlorine
See BROMINE plus Phosphorus Trioxide. See also CHLORINE plus Phosphorus Oxide.

Dimethyl Formamide
See DIMETHYL FORMAMIDE plus Phosphorus Trioxide.

Dimethyl Sulfoxide
See DIMETHYL FORMAMIDE plus Phosphorus Trioxide.

Dimethyl Sulfite
See DIMETHYL FORMAMIDE plus Phosphorus Trioxide.

Methanol
See DIMETHYL FORMAMIDE plus Phosphorus Trioxide.

Oxygen
See PHOSPHORUS TRIOXIDE plus Air.

Phosphorus Pentachloride
The reaction between phosphorus trioxide and phosphorus pentachloride is violent at ordinary temperatures.
Thorpe and Tutton, *J. Chem. Soc.* **57:** 545 (1890).

Sulfur
See SULFUR plus Phosphorus Trioxide.

Sulfur Monochloride
Sulfur monochloride acts with great violence on phosphorus trioxide.
Thorpe and Tutton, *J. Chem. Soc.* **59:** 1019 (1891). *Mellor* **8:** 898 (1946-1947).

Water
With quantities of phosphorus trioxide exceeding a couple of grams, hot water produces a violent explosion.
Thorpe and Tutton, *J. Chem. Soc.* **59:** 1019 (1891). *Mellor* **8:** 897 (1946-1947).

PHOSPHORYL BROMODIFLUORIDE $POBrF_2$

Water
See PHOSPHORYL FLUORIDE plus Water.

PHOSPHORYL CHLORIDE $POCl_3$

Boron Triiodide
Phosphoryl chloride and boron triiodide react vigorously.
Mellor **5:** 136 (1946-1947).

2,5-Dimethylpyrrole and Dimethyl Formamide
See 2,5-DIMETHYLPYRROLE plus Phosphorus Oxychloride and Dimethyl Formamide.

Dimethyl Sulfoxide
See DIMETHYL SULFOXIDE plus Acyl Halides.

Organic Matter
Fibrous organic matter (wood, etc.), when dry, readily absorbs phosphorus oxychloride. When thus absorbed, it may constitute a fire hazard. Both phosphorus oxychlo-

ride and phosphorus trichloride are strongly corrosive and may set fire to combustible material.
Chem. Safety Data Sheet **SD-26** (1948). B. L. Heustis, *Safety Eng.* **54:** 95 (1927).

Sodium
See SODIUM plus Phosphoryl Chloride.

Water
When water reacts with phosphorus oxychloride, there is little warning; first a little bubbling and then a rapid acceleration and pressure increase. Small quantities of phosphorus oxychloride were emptied into a scrap nickel drum containing about 28 pounds of water. After a delay of 15 to 30 minutes, the drum exploded.
MCA Task Group, POCl (Jan. 19, 1967).
MCA Case History **1274** (1967). *MCA Case History* **793** (1962). *Chem. Safety Data Sheet* **SD-26** (1948).

PHOSPHORYL CHLORODIFLUORIDE $POClF_2$

Water
See PHOSPHORYL FLUORIDE plus Water.

PHOSPHORYL DIBROMOFLUORIDE $POBr_2F$

Water
See PHOSPHORYL FLUORIDE plus Water.

PHOSPHORYL DICHLOROFLUORIDE $POCl_2F$

Water
See PHOSPHORYL FLUORIDE plus Water.

PHOSPHORYL FLUORIDE POF_3

Water
The hydrolysis of phosphoryl fluoride and the halofluorides (phosphoryl chlorodifluoride, phosphoryl dichlorofluoride, phosphoryl bromodifluoride, and phosphoryl dibromofluoride) is a vigorous reaction.
Mellor **8, Supp. 3:** 458 (1971).

PHTHALIC ACID $HOCOC_6H_4COOH$

Nitric Acid
See PHTHALIC ANHYDRIDE plus Nitric Acid.

PHTHALIC ANHYDRIDE $\underline{C_6H_4COOCO}$

Nitric Acid
The exothermic nitration of phthalic acid or phthalic anhydride by a fuming nitric acid—sulfuric acid mixture may give mixtures of the potentially explosive phthaloyl nitrates or nitrites or their nitro derivatives. Formation of these compounds may be avoided if the nitrating mixture is extensively diluted with sulfuric acid and if a small (1.5 mole equivalent) of nitric acid is present.
Chem. & Ind. **20:** 790 (1972). *Chem. & Ind.* **17:** 664 (1972).

PICRATES

(See also specific picrates as primary entries and under other reactants.)

Sulfuric Acid
See SULFURIC ACID plus Carbides.

PICRIC ACID $(NO_2)_3C_6H_2OH$

Ammonia
Ammonia and metals with picric acid give results similar to bases.
Military Explosives.
See also PICRIC ACID plus Bases.

Bases
Picric acid and bases form explosive salts. The salts with heavy metals (e.g., lead) are very sensitive to primary explosives.
Davis, pp. 164-68 (1943).

Concrete
Contact between picric acid and concrete floors leads to the formation of more explosion-sensitive salts, such as calcium picrate.
Urbanski **1:** 518 (1964).

Metals
See PICRIC ACID plus Bases.

PIPERIDINE $CH_2CH_2CH_2CH_2CH_2NH$

Dicyanofurazan
Contact of dicyanofurazan, or its N-oxide, with piperidine or mixtures of nitrogenous bases is instantaneously explosive.
D. B. Denson, *Chem. Abst.* (1973).

1-Perchlorylpiperidine
It has exploded violently on contact with piperidine.
D. L. Gardner, et al., *J. Org. Chem.* (1964).

N-Nitrosoacetanilide
The dry anilide exploded on contact with a drop of piperidine.
R. Huisgen, *Ann.* (1951).

PLATINUM Pt

Bromine Trifluoride and Potassium Fluoride
Platinum is attacked by bromine trifluoride at 280°C in presence of potassium fluoride.
Mellor **2, Supp. 1:** 164 (1956).

Hydrogen and Oxygen
See HYDROGEN plus Oxygen and Platinum.

Hydrogen Peroxide
A little platinum black dropped into a hydrogen peroxide solution may cause an explosion.
Mellor **1:** 936 (1946-1947).

Lithium
See LITHIUM plus Platinum.

Oxygen Difluoride
See IRIDIUM plus Oxygen Difluoride.

Permonosulfuric Acid
The decomposition of 92 percent permonosulfuric acid is explosive in the presence of smooth or finely divided platinum, manganese dioxide or silver.
Mellor **10:** 483 (1946-1947).

Phosphorus
See COPPER plus Phosphorus.

PLATINIC BROMIDE $PtBr_4$

Bromine Trifluoride
See BROMINE TRIFLUORIDE plus Platinic Bromide.

PLATINIC CHLORIDE $PtCl_4$

Bromine Trifluoride
See BROMINE TRIFLUORIDE plus Platinic Bromide.

PLATINOUS HYPOPHOSPHITE $Pt(PH_2O_2)_2$

(self-reactive)
Platinous hypophosphite liberates spontaneously flammable phosphine above 130°C.
Mellor **8:** 890 (1946-1947).

PLATINUM-AMMINE NITRATES

(self-reactive)
Platinum-amine nitrates may be impact-sensitive. $Pt(NH_3)_2NO_3$ and $Pt(NH_3)_4(OH)_2$ $(NO_3)_2$ detonate when heated.
Mellor **16:** 412 (1946-1947).

PLATINUM-AMMINE PERCHLORATES

(self-reactive)
Platinum-ammine perchlorates may be impact-sensitive.
Mellor **16:** 412 (1946-1947).

PLUTONIUM Pu

Air
See PLUTONIUM plus Water.

Carbon Tetrachloride
Plutonium metal chips degreased in carbon tetrachloride and allowed to drain for five minutes ignited spontaneously. When the burning chips were inadvertently dropped into the carbon tetrachloride container, an explosion resulted.
Ser. Acc. Series No. **246** (1965).

Water
Pyrophoric products form on plutonium and particularly on certain alloys if they are stored for long periods in closed containers. When a container is opened, spontaneous ignition may occur. Plutonium corrosion is accelerated by atmospheric moisture and a hydride is formed. This corrosion also occurs in moist inert gases. The corrosion products are frequently pyrophoric.
Wick, pp. 148-152, 331-332, 338 (1967).

PLUTONIUM HYDRIDE PuH_2

Air
Plutonium hydride in some forms is spontaneously flammable in air. See also PLUTONIUM plus Carbon Tetrachloride and PLUTONIUM plus Water.
Chem. and Eng. News **36** (8): 64 (1958).

POLYAMIDE

Fluorine
See FLUORINE plus Solid Nonmetals and Oxygen.

POLYCHLORINATED BIPHENYL

Chlorine
See CHLORINE plus Polychlorinated Biphenyl.

POLYDIMETHYLSILOXANE $[-Si(CH_3)_2O-]_X$

Chlorine
See CHLORINE plus Polypropylene.

POLYETHYLENE

Fluorine
See FLUORINE plus Solid Nonmetals and Oxygen.

POLYISOBUTYLENE $[CH_2=C(CH_3)_2]_X$

Silver Peroxide
See SILVER PEROXIDE plus Polyisobutylene.

POLYPHOSPHORYL CHLORIDES

Water
These polymers hydrolyze violently.
Mellor **8, Supp. 3:** 507 (1971).

POLYPROPYLENE $(CH_2=CHCH_3)_X$

Chlorine
See CHLORINE plus Polypropylene.

Potassium Permanganate
See POTASSIUM PERMANGANATE plus Polypropylene.

POLYSULFIDE POLYMERS

Calcium Peroxide
See CALCIUM PEROXIDE plus Polysulfide Polymers.

POLYURETHANE

Fluorine and Oxygen
See FLUORINE plus Solid Nonmetals and Oxygen.

POTASSIUM K
(See also IODINE plus Lithium)

Acetylene
Molten potassium ignites in acetylene.
M. Berthelot, *Bull. Soc. Chim.* (2) **5:** 188 (1866).

Air
The oxidation of potassium may proceed so rapidly that the heat generated melts and ignites the metal. This is particularly the case where pressure is applied at ordinary temperatures; the metal then liquefies where the pressure is applied, and takes fire.
Sidgwick **1** (1950).
Potassium burns in moist air at room temperature.
Mellor **2:** 468 (1946-1947).
Potassium is spontaneously flammable in air at room temperature if the surface of the metal is clean.
Mellor **2:** 468 (1946-1947).
The higher oxides of potassium, formed in air, react explosively with pure potassium, sodium, sodium-potassium alloys, and organic matter.
Mellor **2, Supp. 3:** 1559 (1963).

Aluminum Bromide
A mixture of potassium and any of the following metallic halides produces a strong explosion on impact: aluminum bromide, aluminum chloride, aluminum fluoride, ammonium chlorocuprate, antimony tribromide, antimony trichloride, antimony triiodide, arsenic trichloride, arsenic triiodide, bismuth tribromide, bismuth trichloride, bismuth triiodide, cadmium bromide, cadmium chloride, cad mium iodide, chromium tetrachloride, cupric bromide, cupric chloride, cuprous bromide, cuprous chloride, cuprous iodide, manganous chloride, mercuric bromide, mercuric chloride, mercuric fluoride, mercuric

iodide, mercurous chloride, nickel bromide, nickel chloride, nickel iodide, silicon tetrachloride, silver fluoride, stannic chloride, stannic iodide (with sulfur), stannous chloride, sulfur dibromide, thallous bromide, vanadium pentachloride, zinc bromide, zinc chloride, and zinc iodide.
Mellor **2, Supp. 3:** 1571 (1963).

Aluminum Chloride
See POTASSIUM plus Aluminum Bromide.

Aluminum Fluoride
See POTASSIUM plus Aluminum Bromide.

Ammonium Chlorocuprate
See POTASSIUM plus Aluminum Bromide.

Ammonium Bromide
A mixture of potassium and any of the following compounds produces a weak explosion on impact: ammonium bromide, ammonium iodide, cadmium fluoride, chromium trifluoride, manganous bromide, manganous iodide, nickel fluoride, potassium chlorocuprate, silver chloride, silver iodide, strontium iodide, thallous chloride, and zinc fluoride.
Mellor **2, Supp. 3:** 1571 (1963).

Ammonium Iodide
See POTASSIUM plus Ammonium Bromide.

Ammonium Sulfate and Ammonium Nitrate
A mixture of ammonium sulfate and ammonium nitrate can easily be exploded by potassium or sodium-potassium alloy.
H. Staudinger, *Z. Elektrokem.* **31:** 549-52 (1925).

Antimony Tribromide
See POTASSIUM plus Aluminum Bromide.

Antimony Trichloride
See POTASSIUM plus Aluminum Bromide.

Antimony Triiodide
See POTASSIUM plus Aluminum Bromide.

Arsenic Trichloride
See POTASSIUM plus Aluminum Bromide.

Arsenic Triiodide
See POTASSIUM plus Aluminum Bromide.

Arsine and Ammonia
Potassium and arsine react vigorously in liquid ammonia at minus 78°C. The product reacts vigorously with air.
Mellor **2, Supp. 3:** 1579 (1963).

Bismuth Tribromide
See POTASSIUM plus Aluminum Bromide.

Bismuth Trichloride
See POTASSIUM plus Aluminum Bromide.

Bismuth Triiodide
See POTASSIUM plus Aluminum Bromide.

Bismuth Trioxide
Potassium reduces heated bismuth trioxide to the metal and the reaction is accompanied by incandescence. Similar results are obtained with sodium.
Mellor **9:** 649 (1946-1947).

Boric Acid
A mixture of potassium and any of the following compounds may explode on impact: boric acid, copper oxychloride, lead oxychloride, lead peroxide, lead sulfate, silver iodate, sodium iodate, and vanadium oxychloride.
Mellor **2, Supp. 3:** 1571 (1963).

Boron Tribromide
A mixture of potassium and any of the following halide compounds produces a very violent explosion on impact: boron tribromide, carbon tetrachloride, cobaltous bromide, cobaltous chloride, ferric bromide, ferric chloride, ferrous bromide, ferrous chloride, ferrous iodide, phosphorus pentachloride, phosphorus tribromide and sulfur dichloride.
Mellor **2, Supp. 3:** 1571 (1963).

Bromine
See BROMINE plus Potassium.

Cadmium Bromide
See POTASSIUM plus Aluminum Bromide.

Cadmium Chloride
See POTASSIUM plus Aluminum Bromide.

Cadmium Fluoride
See POTASSIUM plus Ammonium Bromide.

Cadmium Iodide
See POTASSIUM plus Aluminum Bromide.

Carbon
See POTASSIUM plus Graphite and Potassium Superoxide.

Carbon Dioxide
Mixture of solid forms of potassium and carbon dioxide (as dry ice) explodes when subjected to shock.
Mellor **2, Supp. 3:** 1568 (1963).

Carbon Disulfide
Heated potassium ignites in the vapor of carbon disulfide. Potassium and carbon disulfide can be exploded by pressure or friction.
Von Schwartz, p. 327. *Ann. Phys.* **6:** 444 (1826).

Carbon Monoxide and Oxygen
The reaction of potassium and carbon monoxide forms an explosive carbonyl compound, potassium carbonyl, which reacts violently with oxygen.
Mellor **2, Supp. 3:** 1567 (1963).
See also SODIUM CARBONYL plus Air.

Carbon Tetrachloride
Potassium and its alloys form explosive mixtures with carbon tetrachloride.
H.N. Gilbert, *Chem. and Eng. News* **26:** 2604 (1948).
See POTASSIUM plus Boron Tribromide.

Charcoal
Both charcoal and graphite react vigorously with liquid potassium.
Mellor **2, Supp. 3:** 1566 (1963).

Chlorinated Hydrocarbons
Potassium and its alloys form explosive mixtures with chlorinated hydrocarbons.
H. N. Gilbert, *Chem. and Eng. News* **26:** 2604 (1948).

Chlorine
Potassium burns spontaneously in dry chlorine.
Mellor **2:** 469 (1946-1947).

Chlorine Monoxide
Mere contact of chlorine monoxide gas with paper, caoutchouc (India rubber), turpentine, sulfur, potassium, phosphorus, charcoal, arsenic, or antimony is attended by a violent explosion.
Mellor **2:** 241 (1946-1947).

Chlorine Trifluoride
See ANTIMONY plus Chlorine Trifluoride.

Chloroform
The alkali metals react explosively with chloroform, dichloromethane, and methyl chloride.
See LITHIUM plus Chloroform.
Z. Electrochem. **31:** 549 (1925).

Chromium Tetrachloride
See POTASSIUM plus Aluminum Bromide.

Chromium Trifluoride
See POTASSIUM plus Ammonium Bromide.

Chromium Trioxide
Sodium or potassium reacts with chromium trioxide with incandescence.
Mellor **11:** 237 (1946-1947).

Cobaltous Bromide
See POTASSIUM plus Boron Tribromide.

Cobaltous Chloride
See POTASSIUM plus Boron Tribromide.

Copper Oxychloride
See POTASSIUM plus Boric Acid.

Cupric Bromide
See POTASSIUM plus Aluminum Bromide.

Cupric Chloride
See POTASSIUM plus Aluminum Bromide.

Cupric Oxide
Cupric oxide is reduced to metallic copper when heated with potassium at a temperature below its melting point. The reaction proceeds with vivid incandescence.
Berichte **24.**

Cuprous Bromide
See POTASSIUM plus Aluminum Bromide.

Cuprous Chloride
See POTASSIUM plus Aluminum Bromide.

Cuprous Iodide
See POTASSIUM plus Aluminum Bromide.

Dichloromethane
See POTASSIUM plus Chloroform.

Ethylene Oxide
Ethylene oxide is dangerously reactive with metallic potassium.
Chem. Safety Data Sheet **SD-38:** 11 (1951).
See ETHYLENE OXIDE plus Acids and Bases.

Ferric Bromide
See POTASSIUM plus Boron Tribromide.

Ferric Chloride
See POTASSIUM plus Boron Tribromide.

Ferrous Bromide
See POTASSIUM plus Boron Tribromide.

Ferrous Chloride
See POTASSIUM plus Boron Tribromide.

Ferrous Iodide
See POTASSIUM plus Boron Tribromide.

Fluorine
Potassium burns spontaneously in dry fluorine.
Mellor **2:** 469 (1946-1947).

Graphite
See POTASSIUM plus Charcoal.

Graphite and Air
See POTASSIUM plus Graphite and Potassium Superoxide.

Graphite and Potassium Superoxide
Potassium superoxide forms on the surface of either solid or molten potassium metal. Attempts to extinguish burning potassium with powdered graphite have resulted in violent explosions.
Chem. Abst. **63** (1): 424 (July 5, 1965).
Mellor **2, Supp. 3:** 1566 (1963).

Hydrogen Iodide
Potassium burns momentarily in hydrogen iodide; the flame then goes out.
M. Ribalkin, *Bull. Acad. St. Petersbourg* (2) **1:** 279 (1889).
A very violent explosion results when a mixture of potassium and hydrogen iodide is struck by a hammer.
Mellor **2, Supp. 3:** 1563 (1963).

Hydrogen Peroxide
See LEAD DIOXIDE plus Hydrogen Peroxide.

Iodine
See IODINE plus Potassium.
See IODINE plus Lithium.

Iodine Monobromide
Potassium in contact with molten iodine monobromide creates a strong explosion.
Mellor **2, Supp. 3:** 1563 (1963).

Iodine Monochloride
Potassium explodes in contact with iodine monochloride, but the reaction of sodium is very slow.
A. Vogel, *Kastner's Arch.* **10:** 119 (1827).
Berichte **31:** 892.
Mellor, **2, Supp. 1:** 501 (1956).
Mellor, **2, Supp. 3:** 1563 (1963).

Iodine Pentafluoride
A mixture of iodine pentafluoride and potassium or sodium (molten) will explode.
Mellor **2:** 114 (1946-1947).

Lead Oxychloride
See POTASSIUM plus Boric Acid.

Lead Peroxide
See POTASSIUM plus Boric Acid.

Lead Sulfate
See POTASSIUM plus Boric Acid.

Maleic Anhydride
See ALKALI METALS plus Maleic Anhydride.

Manganous Bromide
See POTASSIUM plus Ammonium Bromide.

Manganous Chloride
See POTASSIUM plus Aluminum Bromide.

Manganous Iodide
See POTASSIUM plus Ammonium Bromide.

Mercuric Bromide
See POTASSIUM plus Aluminum Bromide.

Mercuric Chloride
See POTASSIUM plus Aluminum Bromide.

Mercuric Fluoride
See POTASSIUM plus Aluminum Bromide.

Mercuric Iodide
See POTASSIUM plus Aluminum Bromide.

Mercurous Chloride
See POTASSIUM plus Aluminum Bromide.

Mercurous Oxide
Molten sodium or potassium decomposes mercurous oxide with slight explosion.
J. B. Senderens, *Bull. Soc. Chim.* (3)**6:** 802 (1891).

Methyl Chloride
See POTASSIUM plus Chloroform.

Molybdenum Trioxide
Molybdenum trioxide is reduced by either potassium or sodium with incandescence.
Z. Anorg. Chemie **190:** 270.

Nickel Bromide
See POTASSIUM plus Aluminum Bromide.

Nickel Chloride
See POTASSIUM plus Aluminum Bromide.

Nickel Fluoride
See POTASSIUM plus Ammonium Bromide.

Nickel Iodide
See POTASSIUM plus Aluminum Bromide.

Nitrogen Dioxide
Potassium ignites in nitrogen dioxide at ordinary temperatures.
Mellor **8:** 544 (1946-1947).
See also MANGANESE plus Nitrogen Dioxide.

Nitryl Fluoride
Heated potassium metal burns with a lilac flame in vapor of nitryl fluoride.
Mellor **2, Supp. 3:** 1566 (1963).

Peroxides
See ANTIMONY plus Sodium Peroxide.

Phosgene
Mixture of potassium and phosgene explodes when subjected to shock.
Mellor **2, Supp. 3:** 1568 (1963).

Phosphine and Ammonia
Potassium and phosphine react in liquid ammonia to form potassium dihydrophosphide, a spontaneously flammable solid.
Mellor **8, Supp. 3:** 283 (1971).

Phosphorus
See PHOSPHORUS plus Cesium.

Phosphorus Pentachloride
See POTASSIUM plus Boron Tribromide.

Phosphorus Pentoxide
When phosphorus pentoxide is warmed with potassium or sodium, the mixture becomes incandescent.

H. Davy, *Phil. Trans. Roy. Soc. London* **102:** 405 (1812).

Phosphorus Tribromide
See POTASSIUM plus Boron Tribromide.

Phosphorus Trichloride
Potassium burns vigorously in the vapor of phosphorus trichloride.
H. Davy, *Phil. Trans. Roy. Soc. London* **100:** 231 (1810); **101:** 1 (1811).

Potassium Chlorocuprate
See POTASSIUM plus Ammonium Bromide.

Potassium Oxides
See POTASSIUM plus Air.

Potassium Ozonide
Potassium in contact with the following oxides causes an explosive reaction: potassium ozonide, potassium peroxide, potassium super oxide.
Mellor **2, Supp. 3:** 1577 (1963).

Potassium Peroxide
Potassium peroxide oxidizes many metals with incandescence; e.g., potassium, arsenic, antimony, tin, zinc, and copper.
Mellor **2:** 490-3 (1946-1947).
See POTASSIUM plus Potassium Ozonide.

Potassium Superoxide
Potassium metal sometimes forms an orange-yellow coating of tetroxide, even under mineral oil. A 2 cc. lump of such potassium, while being sliced with a stainless steel knife, suddenly exploded and burned.
Short (1966). *Health & Safety Info.* **257** (March 31, 1967).
Potassium superoxide scale being chipped off metallic potassium was driven into the underlying metal, and caused a violent explosion.
H. N. Gilbert, *Chem. and Eng. News* **26:** 2604 (1948).
See POTASSIUM plus Potassium Ozonide.

Selenium
See SELENIUM plus Potassium.

Selenium Monochloride
When potassium is added to selenium monochloride at ordinary temperatures, the mixture explodes violently.
Mellor **10:** 896 (1946-1947).
Mellor **2, Supp. 3:** 1564 (1963).

Selenium Oxychloride
When potassium is brought in contact with selenium oxychloride in the cold, a violent explosion occurs.
Mellor **10:** 908 (1946-1947).

Silicon Tetrachloride
See POTASSIUM plus Aluminum Bromide.

Silver Bromide
See SODIUM plus Silver Bromide.

Silver Chloride
See SODIUM plus Silver Bromide.
See POTASSIUM plus Ammonium Bromide.

Silver Fluoride
See SODIUM plus Silver Bromide.
See POTASSIUM plus Aluminum Bromide.

Silver Iodate
See POTASSIUM plus Boric Acid.

Silver Iodide
See SODIUM plus Silver Bromide.
See POTASSIUM plus Ammonium Bromide.

Sodium Iodate
See POTASSIUM plus Boric Acid.

Sodium Nitrite and Ammonia
Solutions of potassium and sodium nitrite in liquid ammonia form disodium nitrite, which is very reactive and easily explosive.
Mellor **2, Supp. 3:** 1566 (1963).

Sodium Peroxide
Sodium peroxide oxidizes potassium with incandescence.
Mellor **2:** 490-93 (1946-1947).

Stannic Chloride
See POTASSIUM plus Aluminum Bromide.

Stannic Iodide and Sulfur
See POTASSIUM plus Aluminum Bromide.

Stannic Oxide
Stannic oxide is reduced by potassium or sodium at gentle heat and the reaction is accompanied by incandescence.
Mellor **7:** 401 (1946-1947).

Stannous Chloride
See POTASSIUM plus Aluminum Bromide.

Strontium Iodide
See POTASSIUM plus Ammonium Bromide.

Sulfur
Vapors of potassium and sulfur react with chemiluminescence at 300°C and low pressures.
Mellor **2, Supp. 3:** 1564 (1963).

Sulfur Dibromide
See POTASSIUM plus Aluminum Bromide.

Sulfur Dichloride
See POTASSIUM plus Boron Tribromide.

Tellurium
See TELLURIUM plus Potassium.

Tetrachloroethane
See SODIUM plus Tetrachloroethane.

Thallous Bromide
See POTASSIUM plus Aluminum Bromide.

Thallous Chloride
See POTASSIUM plus Ammonium Bromide.

Thiophosphoryl Fluoride
See SODIUM plus Thiophosphoryl Fluoride.

Titanium Tetrachloride
During the reduction of titanium tetrachloride to titanium metal with potassium, an explosion occurred. Prior to the explosion, the system was heated to 90°C.
Waller and Mandell (1967).

Vanadium Oxychloride
See POTASSIUM plus Boric Acid.

Vanadium Pentachloride
See POTASSIUM plus Aluminum Bromide.

Water
At 20°C the heat of reaction is adequate to ignite the hydrogen liberated.
Mellor **2:** 469 (1946-1947).
Mellor **2, Supp. 3:** 1560 (1963).

Zinc Bromide
See POTASSIUM plus Aluminum Bromide.

Zinc Chloride
See POTASSIUM plus Aluminum Bromide.

Zinc Fluoride
See POTASSIUM plus Ammonium Bromide.

Zinc Iodide
See POTASSIUM plus Aluminum Bromide.

POTASSIUM ACETYLIDE $KC{\equiv}H$

Carbon Dioxide
When potassium acetylene carbide is warmed with carbon dioxide, the mass becomes incandescent.
Mellor **5:** 849-50 (1946-1947).

Chlorine
See CHLORINE plus Potassium Acetylene Carbide.

Sulfur Dioxide
Potassium acetylene carbide reacts with sulfur dioxide at ordinary temperatures and it becomes incandescent.
Mellor **5:** 849 (1946-1947).

POTASSIUM ACI-NITROACETATE $K_2O_2N{=}CHCHO$

Water
Dipotassium nitroacetate exploded when the dry salt was moistened with a little water.
Chem. and Eng. News **27:** 1473.

POTASSIUM AMIDE KNH_2

Water
Potassium amide reacts vigorously with water and may be accompanied by ignition.
Mellor **8:** 255 (1946-1947).

POTASSIUM AZIDE KN_3

Carbon Disulfide
See CARBON DISULFIDE plus Azides.

Manganese Dioxide
See MANGANESE DIOXIDE plus Potassium Azide.

POTASSIUM AZIDODISULFATE KSO_3OSO_2NNN

Water
This reaction is an explosive one.
Mellor **8, Supp. 2:** 36 (1967).

POTASSIUM BICARBONATE $KHCO_3$

Monoammonium Phosphate
See SODIUM BICARBONATE plus Monoammonium Phosphate.

POTASSIUM BROMATE $KBrO_3$

Aluminum
See ALUMINUM plus Bromates.

Arsenic
See ARSENIC plus Bromates.

Carbon
See CARBON plus Bromates.

Copper
See COPPER plus Bromates.

Lead Acetate
During an attempt to make lead bromate, an explosion occurred that caused two deaths.
Mellor **2, Supp. 1:** 770 (1956).

Metal Sulfides
See METAL SULFIDES plus Bromates.

Organic Matter
See BROMATES plus Organic Matter.

Phosphorus
See PHOSPHORUS plus Bromates.

Selenium
See SELENIUM plus Potassium Bromate.

Sulfur
See SULFUR plus Bromates.

POTASSIUM BROMIDE KBr

Bromine Trifluoride
See BROMINE TRIFLUORIDE plus Potassium Bromide.

POTASSIUM tert.-BUTOXIDE $KOC(CH_3)_3$

Acetic Acid
See ACETONE plus Potassium Tert.-Butoxide.

Acetone
See ACETONE plus Potassium Tert.-Butoxide.

Butyl Acetate
See ACETONE plus Potassium Tert.-Butoxide.

Carbon Tetrachloride
See ACETONE plus Potassium Tert.-Butoxide.

Chloroform
See ACETONE plus Potassium Tert.-Butoxide.

Diethyl Sulfate
See ACETONE plus Potassium Tert.-Butoxide.

Dimethyl Carbonate
See ACETONE plus Potassium Tert.-Butoxide.

Epichlorohydrin
See ACETONE plus Potassium Tert.-Butoxide.

Ethyl Acetate
See ACETONE plus Potassium Tert.-Butoxide.

Ethyl Alcohol
See ACETONE plus Potassium Tert.-Butoxide.

Isopropyl Alcohol
See ACETONE plus Potassium Tert.-Butoxide.

Methyl Alcohol
See ACETONE plus Potassium Tert.-Butoxide.

Methylene Chloride
See ACETONE plus Potassium Tert.-Butoxide.

Methyl Ethyl Ketone
See ACETONE plus Potassium Tert.-Butoxide.

Methyl Isobutyl Ketone
See ACETONE plus Potassium Tert.-Butoxide.

Propyl Alcohol
See ACETONE plus Potassium Tert.-Butoxide.

Propyl Formate
See ACETONE plus Potassium Tert.-Butoxide.

Sulfuric Acid
See ACETONE plus Potassium Tert.-Butoxide.

POTASSIUM CARBIDE K_2C_2

Water
Potassium carbide may react explosively on contact with water.
Bahme, p. 27 (1961).

POTASSIUM CARBONATE K_2CO_3

Chlorine Trifluoride
See CHLORINE TRIFLUORIDE plus Nitric Acid.

POTASSIUM CARBONYL KCO

Air
See SODIUM CARBONYL plus Air.

Oxygen
See POTASSIUM plus Carbon Monoxide and Oxygen.

Water
See SODIUM CARBONYL plus Air.

POTASSIUM CHLORATE $KClO_3$

Aluminum
See ALUMINUM plus Bromates.

Ammonia
Gaseous ammonia, mixed with air reacts so vigorously with potassium chlorate that the reaction may become dangerous.
Mellor **8:** 217 (1946-1947).

Ammonium Chloride
In the manufacture of signaling smokes this combination is hazardous because of metathetical interaction to form unstable ammonium perchlorate.
Ellern, p. 155 (1968).
See POTASSIUM CHLORATE plus Ammonium Salts.

Ammonium Salts
The reaction of potassium chlorate with ammonium salts is violent.
Mellor **2, Supp. 1:** 586 (1956).

Ammonium Sulfate
The mixture of potassium chlorate and ammonium sulfate decomposes with incandescence when heated.
Mellor **2:** 702 (1946-1947).

Antimony Trisulfide
A mixture of potassium chlorate and antimony trisulfide can be exploded by an electric spark.
Mellor **9:** 523 (1946-1947).

Arsenic
See ARSENIC plus Bromates.

Barium Hypophosphite
A mixture of equal parts of these materials, previously dried at 100°C, burns in open air with great rapidity. When the mixture is confined, an explosion will result. The mixture is very sensitive to shock and friction.
Mellor **8:** 881 (1946-1947).

Barium Sulfide
See BARIUM SULFIDE plus Potassium Chlorate.

Boron
See BORON plus Potassium Chlorate.

Calcium Hypophosphite
See CALCIUM HYPOPHOSPHITE plus Potassium Chlorate.

Calcium Sulfide
See BARIUM SULFIDE plus Lead Dioxide.

Carbon
See CARBON plus Bromates.

Charcoal
See CHLORATES plus Organic Matter.

Chromium
See CHROMIUM plus Potassium Chlorate.

Copper
See COPPER plus Bromates.

Copper Phosphide
See COPPER PHOSPHIDE plus Potassium Chlorate.

Gallic Acid
Gallic acid, potassium chlorate and red gum (Formula 156) is a pyrotechnic whistle composition.
Ellern, p. 183 (1968).

Germanium
See GERMANIUM plus Potassium Nitrate.

Hydrogen Iodide
Molten potassium chlorate ignites in hydrogen iodide.
Mellor **2:** 204 (1946-1947).

Magnesium
See MAGNESIUM plus Potassium Chlorate.

Magnesium, Copper Sulfate (anhydrous), Ammonium Nitrate and Water
See MAGNESIUM plus Copper Sulfate (anhydrous), Ammonium Nitrate, Potassium Chlorate and Water.

Manganese Dioxide
See CHLORATES plus Manganese Dioxide.

Mercury Tetratriphosphide
See MERCURY TETRATRIPHOSPHIDE plus Air.

Metal Sulfides
See METAL SULFIDES plus Bromates.

Organic Acids (Dibasic)
See CHLORATES plus Organic Acids.

Organic Matter
See BROMATES plus Organic Matter. See also CHLORATES plus Organic Matter.

Phosphorus
See PHOSPHORUS plus Potassium Chlorate.
See PHOSPHORUS plus Bromates.

Silver Sulfide
A violent reaction occurs when silver sulfide is heated with potassium chlorate.
Mellor **3:** 447 (1946-1947).

Sodium Amide
A mixture of sodium amide and potassium chlorate explodes.
Mellor **8:** 258 (1946-1947).

Sulfur
See SULFUR plus Bromates. See CHLORATES plus Organic Matter.
See SULFUR plus Potassium Chlorate.

Sulfur Dioxide
If a drop of a solution of sulfur dioxide in ether or alcohol is added to powdered potassium chlorate, a reaction ensues and the mass explodes.
Mellor **2:** 311 (1946-1947).

Sulfuric Acid
These materials may react to cause fires and possible explosions.
Mellor **2:** 315 (1946-1947).

Thiocyanates
See THIOCYANATES plus Chlorates.

Titanium
See TITANIUM plus Potassium Chlorate.

Zinc
See ZINC plus Chlorates.

Zirconium
See ZIRCONIUM plus Potassium Chlorate.

POTASSIUM CHLORIDE KCl

Bromine Trifluoride
See BROMINE TRIFLUORIDE plus Potassium Bromide.

Potassium Permanganate and Sulfuric Acid
See POTASSIUM PERMANGANATE plus Sulfuric Acid and Potassium Chloride.

POTASSIUM CYANIDE KCN

Chlorates
See POTASSIUM CYANIDE plus Sodium Chlorate.

Nitrites
See NITRITES plus Potassium Cyanide.

Nitrogen Trichloride
See NITROGEN TRICHLORIDE plus Ammonia.

Sodium Chlorate
Chlorates plus potassium cyanide explode when heated.
Von Schwartz, p. 323 (1918). *Pieters,* p. 30 (1957).

POTASSIUM DICHROMATE $K_2Cr_2O_7$

Acetone and Sulfuric Acid
See ACETONE plus Sulfuric Acid and Potassium Dichromate.

Hydrazine
Potassium dichromate or sodium dichromate reacts explosively with hydrazine.
Mellor **11:** 234 (1946-1947).

Hydroxylamine
A drop of anhydrous hydroxylamine on powdered potassium dichromate produces a violent explosion.
Mellor **8:** 293 (1946-1947).

POTASSIUM FERRICYANIDE $K_3Fe(CN)_6$

Ammonia
A mixture of the two may cause an explosion.
Pieters, p. 30 (1957).

Chromic Anhydride
See CHROMIC ANHYDRIDE plus Potassium Ferricyanide.

POTASSIUM FERROCYANIDE $K_4Fe(CN)_6 \cdot 3H_2O$

Cupric Nitrate
See CUPRIC NITRATE plus Potassium Ferrocyanide.

POTASSIUM FLUORIDE KF

Platinum and Bromine Trifluoride
See PLATINUM plus Bromine Trifluoride and Potassium Fluoride.

POTASSIUM GRAPHITE KC_8; KC_{24}

Air
Potassium graphite is spontaneously flammable in air.
Brauer (1965).

POTASSIUM HEXAHYDROALUMINATE K_3AlH_6

(self-reactive)
A sample of this hydride over a period of months oxidized or hydrolized. The product of this reaction when scraped with a metal spatula exploded violently. Cesium hexahydroaluminate behaves similarly.
Chem. and Eng. News **47** (1): 9 (1969).

POTASSIUM HYDRIDE KH

Air
Potassium hydride is spontaneously flammable in air.
Coates, p. 161 (1956). *Ellern* (1961).

Chlorine
See CHLORINE plus Potassium Hydride.

Fluorine
See CHLORINE plus Potassium Hydride.

POTASSIUM HYDROXIDE KOH
(See also SODIUM HYDROXIDE)

Acetic Acid
See ACETIC ACID plus Potassium Hydroxide.

Acrolein
See SODIUM HYDROXIDE plus Acrolein.

Acrylonitrile
See SODIUM HYDROXIDE plus Acrylonitrile.

Calcium Carbide and Chlorine
See DICHLOROACETYLENE plus Air.

Chlorine Dioxide
A piece of potassium hydroxide causes liquid chlorine dioxide to explode.
Mellor **2:** 289 (1946-1947).

Chlorine and Hydrogen Peroxide
See CHLORINE plus Hydrogen Peroxide and Potassium Hydroxide.

Chloroform and Methyl Alcohol
See SODIUM HYDROXIDE plus Chloroform and Methyl Alcohol.

1,2-Dichloroethylene
The reaction produces chloroacetylene, which is explosive and spontaneously flammable in air. It is highly toxic.
Rutledge, p. 134 (1968).
See also SODIUM plus 1,2-Dichloroethylene.

Maleic Anhydride
See SODIUM HYDROXIDE plus Maleic Anhydride.

N-Methyl-N-Nitroso Urea and Methylene Chloride
See N-METHYL-N-NITROSO UREA plus Potassium Hydroxide and Methylene Chloride.

Nitroethane
See CALCIUM HYDROXIDE plus Nitroethane.

Nitrogen Trichloride
See NITROGEN TRICHLORIDE plus Ammonia.

Nitromethane
See CALCIUM HYDROXIDE plus Nitroethane.

Nitroparaffins
See CALCIUM HYDROXIDE plus Nitroethane.

o-Nitrophenol
Molten ortho nitrophenol reacts violently with potassium hydroxide (commercial 85% pellets).
Pouwels (1972).

Nitropropane
See CALCIUM HYDROXIDE plus Nitroethane.

N-Nitrosomethylurea
A reaction between n-nitrosomethylurea and potassium hydroxide in n-butyl ether resulted in an explosion due to the formation of diazomethane.
Schwab (1972).

Nitrosomethyl Urea and Methylene Chloride
See NITROSOMETHYL UREA plus Potassium Hydroxide and Methylene Chloride.

Phosphorus
See PHOSPHORUS plus Alkaline Hydroxides and PHOSPHORUS plus Potassium Hydroxide.

Potassium Persulfate and Water
See POTASSIUM PERSULFATE plus Potassium Hydroxide and Water.

Sodium Azide and Benzoyl Chloride
See SODIUM AZIDE plus Benzoyl Chloride and Potassium Hydroxide.

Tetrachloroethane
When solid potassium hydroxide and tetrachloroethane are heated, a spontaneously flammable gas, chloroacetylene, is formed.
Bahme, p. 33 (1961).

Tetrahydrofuran
See TETRAHYDROFURAN plus Potassium Hydroxide.

Trichloroethylene
See SODIUM HYDROXIDE plus Trichloroethylene.

Water
See POTASSIUM OXIDE plus Water.

POTASSIUM HYPOBORATE $K_4B_2O_4$

(self-reactive)
Potassium hypoborate is a stronger, more violent reducing agent than potassium hypophosphite.
Mellor **5:** 37 (1946-1947).

POTASSIUM HYPOPHOSPHITE KH_2PO_2

(self-reactive)
Potassium hypophosphite decomposes when heated, forming phosphine, a spontaneously flammable gas.
Mellor **8:** 881 (1946-1947).

Nitric Acid
Potassium hypophosphite explodes when evaporated with nitric acid.
Mellor **8:** 882 (1946-1947).

POTASSIUM IODATE KIO_3

Aluminum
See ALUMINUM plus Bromates.

Arsenic
See ARSENIC plus Bromates.

Carbon
See CARBON plus Bromates.

Copper
See COPPER plus Bromates.

Metal Sulfides
See METAL SULFIDES plus Bromates.

Organic Matter
See BROMATES plus Organic Matter.

Phosphorus
See PHOSPHORUS plus Potassium Iodate.

Sulfur
See SULFUR plus Bromates.

POTASSIUM IODIDE KI

Bromine Trifluoride
See BROMINE TRIFLUORIDE plus Potassium Bromide.

Chlorine Trifluoride
See CHLORINE TRIFLUORIDE plus Nitric Acid.

Fluorine Perchlorate
See FLUORINE PERCHLORATE plus Potassium Iodide.

POTASSIUM NITRATE KNO_3

Antimony
See ANTIMONY plus Potassium Nitrate.

Antimony Trisulfide
A mixture of potassium nitrate and antimony trisulfide explodes at a red heat.
Mellor **9:** 524 (1946-1947).

Arsenic
See ARSENIC plus Potassium Nitrate.

Arsenic Disulfide
Arsenic disulfide forms explosive nixtures when mixed with potassium nitrate.
Mellor **9:** 270 (1946-1947).

Barium Sulfide
See BARIUM SULFIDE plus Lead Dioxide.

Boron
See BORON plus Potassium Nitrate.

Boron Phosphide
See BORON PHOSPHIDE plus Nitric Acid.

Calcium Sulfide
See BARIUM SULFIDE plus Lead Dioxide.

Charcoal
Charcoal and potassium nitrate make a pyrotechnic mixture.
Ellern, p. 378 (1968).

Copper Phosphide
See COPPER PHOSPHIDE plus Potassium Nitrate.

Fluorine
See FLUORINE plus Potassium Nitrate.

Germanium
See GERMANIUM plus Potassium Nitrate.

Germanium Sulfide
See GERMANIUM SULFIDE plus Potassium Nitrate.

Sodium Acetate
A mixture of the two may cause an explosion.
Pieters, p. 30 (1957).

Sodium Hypophosphite
A mixture of potassium nitrate and sodium hypophosphite constitutes a powerful explosive.
Mellor **8:** 881 (1946-1947).

Sodium Peroxide and Dextrose
See SODIUM PEROXIDE plus Dextrose and Potassium Nitrate.

Sulfur and Arsenic Trisulfide
See SULFUR plus Potassium Nitrate and Arsenic Trisulfide.

Titanium
See TITANIUM plus Potassium Chlorate.

Titanium Disulfide
See TITANIUM DISULFIDE plus Potassium Nitrate.

Trichloroethylene
See TRICHLOROETHYLENE plus Potassium Nitrate.

Zinc
See ZINC plus Potassium Nitrate.

Zirconium
See ZIRCONIUM plus Potassium Nitrate.

POTASSIUM p-NITROBENZENE-DIAZOSULFONATE
$O_2N\text{-}C_6H_4\text{-}4\text{-}N=NSO_3K$

(self-reactive)
While a chemist was examining some crystals of potassium p-nitrobenzene-diazosulfonate with a loupe, the entire 10-gram batch, which was on a sheet of filter paper, exploded. The crystals were probably the "labile" form (potassium p-nitrobenzene-syn-diazosul fonate) and would have in time converted to the "stable" form.
Crucible **58** (9): 147 (1973).

POTASSIUM NITRIDE K_3N

Air
Potassium nitride generally ignites spontaneously when exposed to air.
Mellor **8:** 99 (1946-1947).

Phosphorus
See PHOSPHORUS plus Potassium Nitride.

POTASSIUM NITRITE KNO_2

Ammonium Sulfate
When a little ammonium sulfate is added to fused potassium nitrite, a vigorous reaction occurs attended by flame.
Mellor **2:** 702 (1946-1947).

Boron
See BORON plus Potassium Nitrite.

POTASSIUM OXIDE K_2O

Water
The oxides of sodium or potassium react with water vigorously and with enough evolution of heat to cause boiling and spattering of hot caustic solution.
Chem. Safety Data Sheets **SD-9, SD-10** (1947).

POTASSIUM OXIDES KxOy

Potassium
See POTASSIUM plus Air.

Sodium
See POTASSIUM plus Air.

Sodium-Potassium Alloy
See POTASSIUM plus Air.

Organic Matter
See POTASSIUM plus Air.

POTASSIUM OZONIDE KO_3

Potassium
See POTASSIUM plus Potassium Ozonide.

Sodium
See SODIUM plus Potassium Ozonide.

Water
Both potassium ozonide and potassium superoxide react explosively with water. Both are too unstable to be isolated.
Mellor **2, Supp. 3:** 1631 (1963).

POTASSIUM PERCHLORATE $KClO_4$

Aluminum and Magnesium
See ALUMINUM plus Magnesium and Potassium Perchlorate.

Charcoal
See PERCHLORATES plus Charcoal.

Fluorine
See FLUORINE plus Potassium Perchlorate.

Magnesium
See MAGNESIUM plus Potassium Perchlorate.

Nickel and Titanium
See NICKEL plus Titanium and Potassium Perchlorate.

Reducing Agents
See PERCHLORATES plus Charcoal.

Sulfur
See SULFUR plus Potassium Perchlorate.

POTASSIUM PERMANGANATE $KMnO_4$

Aluminum Carbide
See ALUMINUM CARBIDE plus Potassium Permanganate.

Antimony
See ANTIMONY plus Potassium Permanganate.

Arsenic
See ANTIMONY plus Potassium Permangnate.

Dimethyl Sulfoxide
See DIMETHYL SULFOXIDE plus Potassium Permanganate.

Glycerol
Contact between the two may produce an explosion.
Pieters, p. 30 (1957).

Hydrogen Peroxide
Potassium permanganate can produce an explosion when brought into contact with very concentrated hydrogen peroxide.
Haz. Chem. Data, p. 230 (1973).

Hydrogen Trisulfide
See HYDROGEN TRISULFIDE plus Potassium Permanganate.

Hydroxylamine
When solid hydroxylamine is brought into contact with solid potassium permanganate, there is produced immediately a white flame.
Mellor **8:** 294 (1946-1947).

Organic Matter
An explosive reaction can occur when solid, finely divided potassium permanganate comes in contact with organic substances.
Pascal 16: 1041 (1931-1934). *Pieters,* p. 28 (1957). *Haz. Chem. Data,* p. 230 (1973).

Phosphorus
See PHOSPHORUS plus Potassium Permanganate.

Polypropylene
Potassium permanganate being conveyed through a polypropylene tube ignited the tube.
MCA Case History **1842** (1972).

Sulfur
See SULFUR plus Potassium Permanganate.

Sulfuric Acid
An explosion occurred when concentrated sulfuric acid was mixed with crystalline potassium permanganate in a vessel containing moisture. Manganese heptoxide was formed, which is explosive at 70°C.
Delhez (1967).
J. R. Archer, *Chem. and Eng. News* **26:** 205 (1948).
Permanganate anhydride, Mn_2O_7, forms in the course of the reaction of concen trated sulfuric acid with crystallized potassium permanganate at low temperature (minus 20°C). An oily liquid forms under the layer of sulfuric acid that is very unstable and detonates when the temperature is increased (70°C).
Rüst and Ebert, p. 29 (1948). *Pieters,* p. 28 (1957). *Gallais,* pp. 696, 697 (1957).

Sulfuric Acid and Organic Matter
When potassium permanganate is dissolved in 95% sulfuric acid, a green solution of permanganyl sulfate is formed. This solution will oxidize most organic compounds and, if the solution is strongly concentrated, explosion may accompany the oxidation.
Waller and Mandell (1967).

Sulfuric Acid and Potassium Chloride
An attempt to prepare permanganyl chloride, MnO_3Cl, by adding cautiously, concentrated sulfuric acid to an intimate mixture of potassium permanganate and potassium chloride kept at 0°C in clean all-glass apparatus resulted in a violent explosion.
Delhez (1967).

Titanium
See TITANIUM plus Potassium Chlorate.

POTASSIUM PEROXIDE K_2O_2 (see also SODIUM PEROXIDE)

Antimony
See POTASSIUM plus Potassium Peroxide.

Arsenic
See POTASSIUM plus Potassium Peroxide.

Oxygen
See OXYGEN plus Potassium Peroxide.

Potassium
See POTASSIUM plus Potassium Peroxide and POTASSIUM plus Potassium Tetroxide.

Water
Potassium peroxide is very reactive, and can explode in air or water.
Mellor **2, Supp. 3:** 1577 (1963).

POTASSIUM PERSULFATE $K_2S_2O_3$

Potassium Hydroxide and Water
Potassium persulfate plus a little potassium hydroxide and water ignited a polythene (polyethylene) liner of a container by simultaneous release of heat and oxygen.
MCA Case History **1155** (1955).

POTASSIUM PHOSPHIDE K_3P

Water
Potassium phosphide reacts with water to form spontaneously flammable phosphine.
Van Wazer (1958).

POTASSIUM SILICIDE K_2Si_2

Acids
See POTASSIUM SILICIDE plus Water.

Air
Potassium silicide is spontaneously flammable in air and may explode.
Ellern (1961).

Water
Potassium silicide ignites spontaneously on contact with water or dilute acids.
Brauer (1965).
See also CESIUM SILICIDE plus Water.

POTASSIUM SULFATE K_2SO_4

Aluminum
See ALUMINUM plus Sulfates.

POTASSIUM SUPEROXIDE KO_2

Ethyl Alcohol
To dispose of a piece of sodium-potassium waste, it was placed in a glove box, which was then purged with argon for 10 minutes. When 10 ml of alcohol was added to the waste, an immediate pressure rise caused the glove to burst and flame issued from the port. Also, a highly oxidized sphere of potassium was cut in two and one half was dropped into a dish of alcohol; an immediate explosion shattered the dish. Potassium superoxide was considered the cause of both incidents.
Health and Safety Inf. **251** (March 31, 1967).

Graphite
Potassium superoxide forms on the surface of either solid or molten potassium metal. Attempts to extinguish burning potassium with powdered graphite have resulted in violent explosions.
Chem. Abst. **63:** 424 (1965).

Oil
Stainless steel pots containing traces of sodium-potassium alloy were immersed in oil to await cleaning. During removal of the lid from one pot, an explosion occurred that was attributed to long-term formation of potassium superoxide, which reacted with the oil when it was disturbed.
Health and Safety Inf. **251** (March 31, 1967).

Ortho-Amino Phenol
Mixture of potassium superoxide with ortho-amino phenol resulted in explosions. The explosions occurred after mixing for various periods of time from one hour to several days.
Chem. and Eng. News (August 27, 1990).

Potassium
See POTASSIUM plus Potassium Superoxide.

Selenium Monochloride
See SELENIUM MONOCHLORIDE plus Potassium Superoxide.

Sodium
See SODIUM plus Potassium Ozonide.

Sodium-Potassium Alloy
See SODIUM-POTASSIUM ALLOY plus Potassium Superoxide.

Water
See POTASSIUM OZONIDE plus Water.

POTASSIUM TETRACHLOROCUPRATE K_2CuCl_4

Potassium
See POTASSIUM plus Ammonium Bromide.

POTASSIUM TETRAETHYNYLNICKELATE $K_4[Ni(CCH)_4]$

Air
Tetraacetenyl nickel tetrapotassium is spontaneously flammable in air.
Kaufman (1961).

POTASSIUM TETRAHYDROBORATE

Air
Potassium borohydride burns quietly in air.
Lab. Govt. Chemist (1965).

POTASSIUM TETRAPEROXYCHROMATE $K_3Cr(OO)_4$

(self-reactive)
Potassium triperchromate decomposes explosively at 178°C. The impure salt is explosive.
Mellor **11:** 356 (1946-1947).

POTASSIUM TRICYANOMERCURATE $KHg(CN)_3$

Ammonia
A mixture of the two may cause an explosion.
Pieters, p. 30 (1957).

PRASEODYMIUM Pr

Air
See RARE EARTH METALS plus Air.

Halogens
See RARE EARTH METALS plus Halogens.

PROPANE $CH_3CH_2CH_3$

Chlorine Dioxide
See CHLORINE DIOXIDE plus Butadiene.

PROPANE-1,2-DIAMINE PERCHLORATE $CH_3CH(NH_2)CH_2NH_2\cdot(ClO_4)_2$

(self-reactive)
This compound is an explosive that exceeds the power and brisance of TNT.
ACS **146:** 206. *Chem. Reviews* **44:** 419-45 (1949).

PROPANE-1,3-DIAMINE PERCHLORATE $CH_2(NH_2)CH_2CH_2NH(ClO_4)_2$

(self-reactive)
This compound is an explosive that exceeds the power and brisance of TNT.
ACS **146:** 206. *Chem. Reviews* **44:** 419-45 (1949).

1-PROPANETHIOL C_3H_7SH

Calcium Hypochlorite
See CALCIUM HYPOCHLORITE plus 1-Propanethiol.
See CALCIUM HYPOCHLORITE plus Mercaptan.

PROPIOLACTONE (BETA-) $\underline{OCOCH_2CH_2}$

2-Aminoethanol
See 2-AMINOETHANOL plus Propiolactone.

Ammonium Hydroxide
Mixing propiolactone (BETA-) and 28% ammonium hydroxide in a closed container caused the temperature and pressure to increase.
Flynn and Rossow (1970). See Note under complete reference.

Aniline
See ANILINE plus Propiolactone.

Chlorosulfonic Acid
Mixing propiolactone (BETA-) and chlorosulfonic acid in a closed container caused the temperature and pressure to increase.
Flynn and Rossow (1970). See Note under complete reference.

Ethylene Diamine
See ETHYLENE DIAMINE plus Propiolactone (BETA-).

Ethyleneimine
See ETHYLENEIMINE plus Propiolactone (BETA-).

Hydrochloric Acid
Mixing propiolactone (BETA-) and 36% hydrochloric acid in a closed container caused the temperature and pressure to increase.
Flynn and Rossow (1970). See Note under complete reference.

Hydrofluoric Acid
Mixing propiolactone (BETA-) and 48.7% hydrofluoric acid in a closed container caused the temperature and pressure to increase.
Flynn and Rossow (1970). See Note under complete reference.

Nitric Acid
Mixing propiolactone (BETA-) and 70% nitric acid in a closed container caused the temperature and pressure to increase.
Flynn and Rossow (1970). See Note under complete reference.

Oleum
See OLEUM plus Propiolactone (BETA-).

Pyridine
See PYRIDINE plus Propiolactone (BETA-).

Sodium Hydroxide
See SODIUM HYDROXIDE plus Propiolactone (BETA-).

Sulfuric Acid
Mixing propiolactone (BETA-) and 96% sulfuric acid in a closed container caused the temperature and pressure to increase.
Flynn and Rossow (1970). See Note under complete reference.

PROPYL ALCOHOL $CH_3CH_2CH_2OH$

Potassium Tert.-Butoxide
See ACETONE plus Potassium Tert.-Butoxide.

PROPYLENE $H_3CCH=CH_2$

Nitrogen Dioxide
See NITROGEN TETROXIDE plus Olefins.

Nitrogen Tetroxide
See NITROGEN TETROXIDE plus Propylene.

Nitrous Oxide
See NITROUS OXIDE plus Propylene.

PROPYLENE OXIDE $CH_3\underline{CHCH_2O}$

Ammonium Hydroxide
Mixing propylene oxide and 28% ammonium hydroxide in a closed container caused the temperature and pressure to increase.
Flynn and Rossow (1970). See Note under complete reference.

Chlorosulfonic Acid
Mixing propylene oxide and chlorosulfonic acid in a closed container caused the temperature and pressure to increase.
Flynn and Rossow (1970). See Note under complete reference.

Clay Absorbents
Propylene oxide can undergo runaway self heating and ignition when certain solid spill control materials, such as clay absorbents, are used.
Haz. Chem. Data NFPA 49; (1966).

Hydrochloric Acid
Mixing propylene oxide and hydrochloric acid in a closed container caused the temperature and pressure to increase.
Flynn and Rossow (1970). See Note under complete reference.

Hydrofluoric Acid
Mixing propylene oxide and 48.7% hydrofluoric acid in a closed container caused the temperature and pressure to increase.
Flynn and Rossow (1970). See Note under complete reference.

Nitric Acid
Mixing propylene oxide and 70% nitric acid in a closed container caused the temperature and pressure to increase.
Flynn and Rossow (1970). See Note under complete reference.

Oleum
See OLEUM plus Propylene Oxide.

Sulfuric Acid
Mixing propylene oxide and 96% sulfuric acid in a closed container caused the temperature and pressure to increase.
Flynn and Rossow (1970). See Note under complete reference.

PROPYL FORMATE C_3H_7OCHO

Potassium Tert.-Butoxide
See ACETONE plus Potassium Tert.-Butoxide.

PROPYLLITHIUM C_3H_7Li

Air
Propyl lithium is spontaneously flammable in air.
Ellern (1961).

PROPYLSILANE $C_3H_7SiH_3$

Air
Propyl silane is spontaneously flammable in air.
Kaufman (1961).

PROPYNE $CH_3C=CH$

(self-reactive)
Methyl acetylene can decompose explosively at 4.5–5.6 atmospheres pressure.
Rutledge, p. 13 (1968).

2-PROPYN-1-OL $CH{\equiv}CCH_2OH$

Phosphorus Pentoxide
See PHOSPHORUS PENTOXIDE plus Propargyl Alcohol.

PYRIDINE $\underline{N=CHCH=CHCH=CH}$

Chlorosulfonic Acid
Mixing pyridine and chlorosulfonic acid in a closed container caused the temperature and pressure to increase.
Flynn and Rossow (1970). See Note under complete reference.

Chromium Trioxide
See CHROMIC ANHYDRIDE plus Pyridine.

Maleic Anhydride
See MALEIC ANHYDRIDE plus Pyridine.

Nitric Acid
Mixing pyridine and 70% nitric acid in a closed container caused the temperature and pressure to increase.
Flynn and Rossow (1970). See Note under complete reference.

Oleum
See OLEUM plus Pyridine.

Perchromates
See PERCHROMATES plus Pyridine.

Propiolactone (BETA-)
Mixing pyridine and propiolactone (BETA-) in a closed container caused the temperature and pressure to increase.
Flynn and Rossow (1970). See Note under complete reference.

Silver Perchlorate
See SILVER PERCHLORATE plus Acetic Acid.
See SILVER PERCHLORATE plus Toluene.

Sulfuric Acid
Mixing pyridine and 96% sulfuric acid in a closed container caused the temperature and pressure to increase.
Flynn and Rossow (1970). See Note under complete reference.

PYRIDINIUM PERCHLORATE $(C_5H_6N)ClO_4$

(self-reactive)
This salt may explode violently in contact with metals.
Mellor **2, Supp. 1:** 603 (1956).
Pyridine perchlorate decomposes or explodes when heated above 335°C. The kindling temperature is lowered by the addition of ammonium perchlorate.
ACS **146:** 213 (1960). *Chemiker.Ztg.* **74:** 139-40 (1950).

3-PYRIDYLDIAZONIUM FLUOROBORATE
$NC_5H_4N(\equiv)\ BF_4$

(self-reactive)
Following a procedure described in the literature for the preparation of this salt, several grams were spread on aluminum foil to dry. A small portion was removed to determine its decomposition point in a glass capillary. It exploded at 47°C. The remaining material exploded while sitting on the aluminum foil.
Chem. and Eng. News **45** (41): 44 (1967); **45** (51):**8** (1967).

QUINOLINE CHCHCHCHCCNCHCHCH

Perchromates
See PERCHROMATES plus Quinoline.

RARE EARTH HYDRIDES

Air and Water
The hydrides of the rare earths are stable in dry air, but ignite in moist air.
Hampel, pp. 407-8 (1961).

RARE EARTH METALS

Air
The rare earth metals ignite in air at 302 to 356°F., but lanthanum ignites at 824 to 860°F. With oxide impurities present, however, the rare earth metals are pyrophoric on cutting and filing.
Hampel, pp. 407-8 (1961).

Halogens (Vapor)
Rare earth metals burn vigorously in halogen vapors above 392°F.
Hampel, pp. 407-8 (1961).

RHENIUM Re

Flourine
Rhenium and fluorine react readily at 125°C.
Mellor **2, Supp. 1:** 64 (1956).

RHODIUM Rh

Chlorine Trifluoride
See ANTIMONY plus Chlorine Trifluoride.

Oxygen Difluoride
See IRIDIUM plus Oxygen Diflouride.

RHODIUM-AMMINE NITRATES

(self-reactive)
Rhodium-ammine nitrates may be impact-sensitive. $Rh(NH_3)_5I(NO_3)_2$ crystals explode when heated.
Mellor **15:** 590 (1946-1947).

RHODIUM-AMMINE PERCHLORATES

(self-reactive)
Rhodium-ammine perchlorates may be impact-sensitive.
Mellor **15:** 590 (1946-1947).

RHODIUM TETRABROMIDE $RhBr_4$

Bromine Trifluoride
See BROMINE TRIFLUORIDE plus Potassium Bromide.

RUBBER

Chlorine
See CHLORINE plus Rubber.

Chlorine Trifluoride
See CHLORINE TRIFLUORIDE plus Rubber.

Iodine Monochloride
See IODINE MONOCHLORIDE plus Organic Matter.

Lithium
See LITHIUM plus Organic Matter.

RUBBER (LS-53 and LS-63)

Fluorine
See FLUORINE plus Solid Nonmetals and Oxygen.

RUBIDIUM Rb

Air
Rubidium is spontaneously flammable in air at room temperature if the surface of the metal is clean.
Mellor **2:** 468 ff. (1946-1947).

Chlorine
See CESIUM plus Chlorine.

Oxygen
Rubidium burns spontaneously in dry oxygen.
Mellor **2:** 468 (1946-1947).

Phosphorus
See PHOSPHORUS plus Cesium.

Water
At 20°C, the heat of reaction is adequate to ignite the hydrogen liberated.
Mellor **2:** 469 (1946-1947). Bahme, p. 11 (1961).

RUBIDIUM ACETYLIDE $RbC\equiv CH$

Arsenic
See ARSENIC plus Rubidium Acetylene Carbide.

Bromine
See BROMINE plus Rubidium Acetylene Carbide.

Chlorine
See BROMINE plus Rubidium Acetylene Carbide.

Cupric Oxide
Cupric oxide is reduced vigorously and with incandescence by rubidium acetylene carbide.
Mellor **5:** 850 (1946-1947).

Fluorine
See BROMINE plus Rubidium Acetylene Carbide.

Hydrochloric Acid
Rubidium acetylene carbide burns with slightly warm hydrochloric acid or with molten sulfur.
Mellor **5:** 849 (1946-1947).

Iodine
See BROMINE plus Rubidium Acetylene Carbide.

Lead Oxide
Rubidium acetylene carbide explodes on contact with lead oxide (at 350°C).
Mellor **5:** 849 (1946-1947).

Manganese Dioxide
Manganese dioxide is reduced by rubidium acetylene carbide at elevated temperatures with incandescence and sometimes explosively.
Mellor **5:** 850 (1946-1947).

Phosphorus
See PHOSPHORUS plus Rubidium Acetylene Carbide.

Sulfur
See RUBIDIUM ACETYLENE CARBIDE plus Hydrochloric Acid.

Sulfuric Acid
Rubidium acetylene carbide burns with sulfuric acid.
Mellor **5:** 849 (1946-1947).

RUBIDIUM AZIDE RbN_3

(self-reactive)
Rubidium azide decomposes at 321°C.
Mellor **8, Supp. 2:** 43 (1967).

Carbon Disulfide
See CARBON DISULFIDE plus Azides.

RUBIDIUM CARBIDE Rb_2C_2

Arsenic
See ARSENIC plus Rubidium Carbide.

Arsenic Oxide
If warmed, rubidium carbide will burn with arsenic oxide.
Mellor **5:** 848 (1946-1947).

Boron
See SILICON plus Rubidium Carbide.

Bromine
See BROMINE plus Rubidium Carbide.

Hydrochloric Acid
Rubidium carbide ignites in contact with hydrochloric acid unless the acid is dilute.
Mellor **5:** 848 (1946-1947).

Iodine
See IODINE plus Cesium Carbide.

Lead Oxide
If warmed, rubidium carbide will burn with lead oxide.
Mellor **5:** 848 (1946-1947).

Nitric Acid
A mixture of nitric acid and rubidium carbide will explode.
Mellor **5:** 848 (1946-1947).

Nitric Oxide
See RUBIDIUM CARBIDE plus Sulfur Dioxide.

Selenium
See SELENIUM plus Rubidium Carbide.

Silicon
See SILICON plus Rubidium Carbide.

Sulfur Dioxide
Rubidium carbide ignites on warming in sulfur dioxide or nitric oxide vapor.
Mellor **5:** 848 (1946-1947).

RUBIDIUM CHLORIDE RbCl

Bromine Trifluoride
See BROMINE TRIFLUORIDE plus Barium Chloride.

RUBIDIUM HYDRIDE RbH

Acetylene
If moisture is present, rubidium hydride reacts vigorously with acetylene, even at minus 60°C.
Mellor **2:** 483 (1946-1947).

Water
Rubidium hydride ignites on contact with moist air.
Hurd, pp. 36-37 (1952).

RUBIDIUM NITRIDE Rb_3N

Air
Rubidium nitride burns in air.
Mellor **8:** 8, 99, 101 (1946-1947).

RUBIDIUM PHOSPHIDE Rb_3P

Water
Rubidium phosphide reacts instantaneously with water or moist air to yield spontaneously flammable phosphine.
Van Wazer (1958).

RUBIDIUM SILICIDE Rb_2Si_2

Water
See CESIUM SILICIDE plus Water.

RUTHENIUM Ru

Oxygen Difluoride
See IRIDIUM plus Oxygen Difluoride.

RUTHENIUM TETROXIDE RuO_4

Charcoal
Ruthenium tetroxide (gas) in contact with activated charcoal reacted violently.
Scott (1963).

Phosphorus Tribromide
Ruthenium tetroxide and phosphorus tribromide undergo a vigorous exothermic reaction.
Mellor **8, Supp. 3:** 521 (1971).

SAMARIUM Sm

Air
See RARE EARTH METALS plus Air.

Halogens
See RARE EARTH METALS plus Halogens.

1,1,2-Trichlorotrifluoroethane
A commercial mixer/mill was demolished and a technician was injured as a result of an explosion which occurred when an attempt was made to grind 20 grams of samarium in approximately 20 cc of 1,1,2-trichlorotrifluoroethane. Subsequent investigation revealed that the explosion was caused by the generation of fresh metal sur face in the presence of the chlorinated halocarbon.
Wischmeyer (1970). *NSC Newsletter, R & D Sec.* (Aug. 1970).

SELENIUM Se

Barium Carbide
A mixture of barium carbide and selenium heated to 150°C. becomes incandescent.
Mellor **5:** 862 (1946-1947).

Bromine Pentafluoride
See ARSENIC plus Bromine Pentafluoride.

Calcium Carbide
Calcium carbide and selenium vapor react with incandescence.
Mellor **5:** 862 (1946-1947).

Chlorates
A moist mixture of selenium and any chlorates but the alkali chlorates becomes incandescent.
Mellor **2, Supp. 1:** 583 (1956).

Chlorine Trifluoride
See ANTIMONY plus Chlorine Trifluoride.

Chromium Trioxide
Selenium reacts violently with chromium trioxide.
Mellor **11:** 233 (1946-1947).

Fluorine
Selenium unites directly with fluorine in the cold, giving off fumes, and finally the selenium ignites.
Mellor **10:** 747 (1946-1947).

Lithium Carbide
See SULFUR plus Lithium Carbide.

Lithium Silicide
See PHOSPHORUS plus Lithium Silicide.

Nickel
See NICKEL plus Selenium. See also SULFUR plus Nickel.

Nitric Acid
Freshly reduced selenium (from selenium dioxide) reacts vigorously with nitric acid. Trace of organic matter probably influenced the reaction.
Austin, Newman, and Riley, *J. Chem. Soc.,* p. 391 (1938).

Nitrogen Trichloride
See NITROGEN TRICHLORIDE plus Ammonia.

Oxygen
Burning selenium in oxygen has resulted in explosion, probably due to the presence of organic matter.
Austin, Newman, and Riley, *J. Chem. Soc.,* p. 391 (1938).

Potassium
A mixture of potassium and selenium ignites; sodium does likewise and is attended by vivid incandescence.
Mellor **10:** 766-7 (1946-1947).

Potassium Bromate
The reaction is violently explosive.
Mellor **2, Supp. 1:** 763 (1956).

Rubidium Carbide
The carbide burns in selenium vapor.
Mellor **5:** 848 (1946-1947).

Silver Bromate
The reaction is violently explosive.
Mellor **2, Supp. 1:** 766 (1956).

Sodium
See SELENIUM plus Potassium.

Strontium Carbide
See SULFUR plus Strontium Carbide.

Thorium Carbide
Selenium vapor attacks heated thorium carbide with incandescence.
Mellor **5:** 886 (1946-1947).

Uranium
See URANIUM plus Selenium.

Zinc
See ZINC plus Selenium.

SELENIUM CARBIDE SeC_2

Sulfur
See SULFUR plus Thorium Carbide.

SELENIUM IODOPHOSPHIDE $Se_3P_4I_2$

Nitric Acid
These compounds react explosively.
Mellor **8, Supp. 3:** 247 (1971).

SELENIUM MONOCHLORIDE Se_2Cl_2

Phosphorus
See PHOSPHORUS plus Selenium Monochloride.

Potassium
See POTASSIUM plus Selenium Monochloride.

Potassium Superoxide
Selenium monochloride and potassium superoxide react very violently.
Mellor **10:** 897 (1946-1947).

Sodium Peroxide
Sodium peroxide reacts violently with the evolution of light when it is treated with selenium monochloride.
Mellor **10:** 897 (1946-1947.)

SELENIUM OXYCHLORIDE $SeOCl_2$

Phosphorus
See PHOSPHORUS plus Selenium Oxychloride.

Potassium
See POTASSIUM plus Selenium Oxychloride.

SELENIUM OXYFLUORIDE $SeOF_2$

Phosphorus
See PHOSPHORUS plus Selenium Oxyfluoride.

SELENIUM SULFIDE SeS

Silver Oxide
See SILVER OXIDE plus Antimony Trisulfide.

SELENIUM TETRAFLUORIDE SeF_4

Phosphorus
See PHOSPHORUS plus Selenium Tetrafluoride.

SILANE SiH_4
Silane and chlorosilanes can explode when mixed with various halocarbons and ignited.
Plant Operations Progress, Britton (1990).

Air
Silicon hydride will ignite in air by slightly raising the temperature or lowering the pressure.
Mellor **6:** 220 (1946-1947).

Chlorine
See CHLORINE plus Silicon Hydride.

Nitrous Oxide
Contaminated silane cylinder exploded as it was being vented.

SILANES (SILANE, DISILANE, TRISILANE, etc.)

Air
The first seven to eight members of the series Si_nH_{2n+2} ignite spontaneously in air at room temperature or slightly higher.
Latimer and Hildebrand, p. 297 (1940). *Z. Anorg. Chemie* **117:** 209.
Mellor **1:** 376 (1946-1947).

SILICA (SILICON DIOXIDE) SiO_2

Chlorine Trifluoride
See CHLORINE TRIFLUORIDE plus Elements.

Manganese Trifluoride
See MANGANESE TRIFLUORIDE plus Glass.

Oxygen Difluoride
See OXYGEN DIFLUORIDE plus Silica.

SILICATES

Lithium
See LITHIUM plus Carbides.

SILICON Si

Alkali Carbonates
When a mixture of amorphous silicon and an alkali carbonate is heated, a vigorous reaction, attended by incandescence, occurs.
Mellor **6:** 164 (1946-1947).

Aluminum and Lead Oxide
A mixture of silicon, aluminum and lead oxide explodes when heated.
Mellor **7:** 657 (1946-1947).

Calcium
See CALCIUM plus Silicon.

Cesium Carbide
Cesium carbide reacts vigorously when heated with silicon or boron.
Mellor **5:** 848 (1946-1947).

Chlorine
Silicon burns spontaneously in gaseous chlorine.
Mellor **2:** 92, 95; **6:** 161; **9:** 626 (1946-1947).
See ANTIMONY plus Chlorine Trifluoride.

Cobaltic Fluoride
A mixture of silicon powder and cobaltic fluoride glows red on gently warming.
Mellor **2, Supp. 1:** 64 (1956).

Fluorine
See FLUORINE plus Selenium.

Iodine Pentafluoride
See ARSENIC plus Iodine Pentafluoride.

Manganese Trifluoride
See MANGANESE TRIFLUORIDE plus Glass.

Nitrosyl Fluoride
See BORON plus Nitrosyl Fluoride.

Rubidium Carbide
Rubidium carbide reacts vigorously when heated with silicon or boron.
Mellor **5:** 848 (1946-1947).

Silver Fluoride
Silicon (powdered) reacts violently with silver fluoride.
Mellor **3:** 389 (1946-1947).

Sodium-Potassium Alloy
The reaction of silicon and sodium-potassium alloy forms sodium silicide, which is spontaneously flammable in air.
Mellor **2, Supp. 2:** 564 (1961).
See also SODIUM SILICIDE plus Air.

SILICON MONOXIDE SiO

Air
Silicon monoxide is spontaneously flammable in air.
Ellern (1961).

SILICON NITRIDE $(Si_2N_2)_n$

Air
Silicocyn is spontaneously flammable in air.
Ellern (1961).

SILICON TETRAAZIDE $Si(N_3)_4$

(self-reactive)
Spontaneous explosions have been observed with this compound.
Mellor **8, Supp. 2:** 50 (1967).
See BORON TRIAZIDE (self-reactive).

SILICON TETRACHLORIDE $SiCl_4$

Potassium
See POTASSIUM plus Aluminum Bromide.

Sodium
See SODIUM plus Aluminum Bromide.

SILICON TETRAFLUORIDE SiF_4

Sodium
Mixtures form shock-sensitive explosives.
Lelei, Cahiers (1975).

SILOXANE $(OSiH_2)_3$

Air
Siloxane is spontaneously flammable in air.
Ellern (1961).

SILVER Ag

Acetylene
An insoluble, explosive acetylide is formed with silver.
Von Schwartz, p. 142 (1918); J. K. Luchs, *Phot. Sci. Eng.* **10**(6): 334-7 (1966).

Ammonia
See GOLD plus Ammonia.

Bromoazide
See ANTIMONY plus Bromoazide.

Chlorine Trifluoride
See ALUMINUM plus Chlorine Trifluoride.

Ethyl Alcohol and Nitric Acid
When silver is treated with nitric acid in the presence of ethyl alcohol, silver fulminate may be formed, which can be detonated.
P. M. Hearbjes and J. P. Howtman, *Chem. Weekblad* **38;** J. K. Luchs, *Phot. Sci. Eng.* **10**(6): 334-7 (1966).

Ethyleneimine
Ethyleneimine forms explosive compounds with silver, hence silver solder should not be used to fabricate equipment for handling ethyleneimine.
Ethyleneimine.

Hydrogen Peroxide
See IRON plus Hydrogen Peroxide. Finely divided silver and a strong hydrogen peroxide solution may explode.
Mellor **1:** 936 (1946-1947).

Oxalic Acid
Silver is said to be incompatible with oxalic acid and tartaric acid.
NavAer. 09-01-505 (November 1, 1956).

Permonosulfuric Acid
See PERMONOSULFURIC ACID plus Manganese Dioxide. See PLATINUM plus Permonosulfuric Acid.

Tartaric Acid
See SILVER plus Oxalic Acid.

SILVER AZIDE AgN_3

(self-reactive)
Silver azide decomposes at 250°C. It is explosively unstable.
Mellor **8, Supp. 2:** 43 (1967).
Silver azide is shock-sensitive when dry and has a detonation temperature of 250°C.
Photo. Sci. & Eng. **10** (6): 334-337 (1966).
See also AZIDES.

Bromine
See BROMINE plus Silver Azide.

Iodine
See IODINE plus Silver Azide.

SILVER BROMATE $AgBrO_3$

Sulfur
See SULFUR plus Silver Bromate.

Tellurium
See TELLURIUM plus Silver Bromate.

SILVER BROMIDE AgBr

Potassium
See SODIUM plus Silver Bromide.

Sodium
See SODIUM plus Silver Bromide.

SILVER CHLORATE $AgClO_3$

Sulfur
See SULFUR plus Silver Chlorate.

SILVER CHLORIDE AgCl

Aluminum
See ALUMINUM plus Silver Chloride.

Ammonia
When a solution of silver chloride in aqueous ammonia is exposed to air or to heat, a material, probably silver nitride, is formed that is detonated violently by shock.
Mellor **3:** 382 (1946-1947); J. K. Luchs, *Phot. Sci. Eng.* **10**(6): 334-7 (1966).
Kite (1973).

Bromine Trifluoride
See BROMINE TRIFLUORIDE plus Barium Chloride.

Potassium
See SODIUM plus Silver Bromide.
See POTASSIUM plus Ammonium Bromide.

Sodium
See SODIUM plus Silver Bromide.

Sodium Peroxide and Charcoal
See SODIUM PEROXIDE plus Silver Chloride and Charcoal.

SILVER CYANIDE AgCN

Fluorine
See FLUORINE plus Silver Cyanide.

SILVER DIAMIDOTRIOXYPHOSPHORANE $(AgO)_3P(NHAg)_2$

Sulfuric Acid
Pentasilver trihydroxydiamidophosphate explodes on heating, friction, or treatment with concentrated sulfuric acid.
J. Am. Chem. Soc. **17:** 275 (1895).
Tetrasilver trihydroxydiaminophosphate ignites when treated with concentrated sulfuric acid.
Mellor **8:** 705 (1946-1947).

SILVER FLUORIDE AgF

Boron
See BORON plus Silver Fluoride.

Calcium Hydride
When silver fluoride is ground with calcium hydride, the mass becomes incandescent.
Mellor **3:** 389 (1946-1947).

Dimethyl Sulfoxide
See DIMETHYL SULFOXIDE plus Silver Fluoride.

Potassium
See SODIUM plus Silver Bromide.
See POTASSIUM plus Aluminum Bromide.

Silicon
See SILICON plus Silver Fluoride.

Sodium
See SODIUM plus Silver Bromide.
See SODIUM plus Aluminum Bromide.

SILVER FULMINATE AgCNO

(self-reactive)
See SILVER CHLORIDE plus Ammonia. Silver fulminate is shock-sensitive when dry and has a detonation temperature of 175°C.
Photo. Sci. & Eng. **10** (6): 334-337 (1966).

SILVER HALIDES

Sodium-Potassium Alloy
See SODIUM-POTASSIUM ALLOY plus Silver Halides.

SILVER IODATE $AgIO_3$

Potassium
See POTASSIUM plus Boric Acid.

SILVER IODIDE AgI

Potassium
See SODIUM plus Silver Bromide.
See POTASSIUM plus Ammonium Bromide.

Sodium
See SODIUM plus Silver Bromide.

SILVER NITRATE $AgNO_3$

Acetylene
See MERCURY SALTS plus Acetylene.

Acetylene and Ammonium Hydroxide
Silver acetylide is formed on precipitation of an ammoniacal solution of silver nitrate with acetylene. Silver acetylide is highly explosive in the dry state.
Sprengstoffe, Waffen u. Munitions (1905); J. K. Luchs, *Phot. Sci. Eng.* **10** (6): 334-7 (1966).

Ammonium Hydroxide
When a mixture of 28% ammonium hydroxid and silver nitrate solution was treated with a small amount of sodium hydroxide, black material precipitated. On being stirred the mixture exploded. The cause was formation of the sensitive silver nitride.
MCA Case History **1554** (1968).

Arsenic
See ARSENIC plus Silver Nitrate.

Calcium Carbide
A highly sensitive explosive is formed by the addition of calcium carbide to a silver nitrate solution.
Mellor **5:** 881 ff. (1946-1947); J. K. Luchs, *Phot. Sci. Eng.* **10**(6): 334-7 (1966).

Charcoal
A mixture of charcoal and silver nitrate ignites under impact.
Mellor **3:** 473 (1946-1947).

Chlorine Trifluoride
See CHLORINE TRIFLUORIDE plus Nitric Acid.

Cuprous Acetylide
See CUPROUS ACETYLIDE plus Silver Nitrate.

Ethyl Alcohol
Alcohols should not be mixed with silver nitrate, an explosive fulminate may be formed.
Bahme, p. 9 (1961): J. K. Luchs, *Phot. Sci. Eng.* **10** (6): 334-7 (1966).

Magnesium
See MAGNESIUM plus Silver Nitrate.

Phosphine
An explosion occurred when purified phosphine was passed rapidly into a concentrated solution of silver nitrate.
Mellor **3:** 471 (1946-1947).

Phosphonium Iodide
See PHOSPHONIUM IODIDE plus Silver Nitrate.

Phosphorus
See PHOSPHORUS plus Silver Nitrate.

Phosphorus Isocyanate
See PHOSPHORUS ISOCYANATE plus Acetaldehyde.

Plastics
In a study to assess potential shipping and storage containers the relative flammability of various plastics in contact with silver nitrate was examined. All plastics tested were shown to undergo propellant-type burning in the presence of silver nitrate under conditions that might be encountered under fire exposure conditions.
Coffee (1969).

Sulfur
See SULFUR plus Silver Nitrate.

SILVER NITRIDE Ag_3N

(self-reactive)
Silver nitride can be detonated by shock even if wet. Detonation temperature is 100°C.
Photo. Sci. & Eng. **10** (6): 334-337 (1966).
Dried silver nitride explodes readily, even from a strong flash of light.
Mellor **8, Supp. 1:** 155 (1964).

SILVER NITRIDOOSMATE $AgOsNO_3$

(self-reactive)
Silver osmiamate detonates violently at 80°C or by percussion.
Mellor **15:** 728 (1946-1947).

SILVER OXALATE AgOCOCOOAg

(self-reactive)
Newly prepared silver oxalate, that had been oven dried for several days at 50°C maximum, was placed in a mechanical mortar-and- pestle type grinder. When the motor was turned on, an explosion occurred that seriously injured two people. Impact detonation was the probable cause of the detonation. Textbooks indicate that silver oxalate is explosive above 150°C and that the explosion hazard is moderate when exposed to heat.
BCISC **44** (175): 19 (1973).

Chlorine
See CHLORINE plus Mercuric Oxide.

SILVER OXIDE Ag_2O

Aluminum
Silver oxide is subject to thermite reactions and will also readily combust solid aluminum once the reaction is initiated. The aluminum was sub-20 micron powder held under nitrogen until mixed with silver oxide in air. The reaction was observed to occur over a wide range of mixture compositions.
L. Britton, *Union Carbide Report* (1990).

Ammonium Hydroxide
An attempt to dissolve silver oxide (prepared 24 hours previously) in ammonium hydroxide in a stainless steel can caused a muffled explosion which distorted the can; numerous subsequent small explosions occurred in the spots of slurry scattered around the room by the initial explosion. Many similar incidents are also reported.
ASESB Expl. Reports **10** (1960); **172** (1964); **190** (1965). *Health & Safety Inf.* **198** (1964); J. K. Luchs, *Phot. Sci. Eng.* **10**(6): 334-7 (1966). *MCA Case History* **976** (1964).

Antimony Trisulfide
Ignition takes place when silver oxide is ground with various metal sulfides, e.g., those of antimony, mercury, selenium.
Mellor **3:** 377 (1946-1947).

Aqueous Ammonia and Ethyl Alcohol
A mixture of silver oxide plus ethyl alcohol and aqueous ammonia forms the very sensitive silver nitride.
Mellor **8:** 101 (1946-1947); J. K. Luchs, *Phot. Sci. Eng.* **10**(6): 334-7 (1966).

Carbon Monoxide
Carbon monoxide reduces silver oxide energetically and consider able heat is generated.
Mellor **3:** 377 (1946-1947).

Magnesium
A mixture of silver oxide and magnesium heated in a sealed tube causes a reaction which proceeds with explosive violence.
Mellor **3:** 378 (1946-1947).

Mercuric Sulfide
See SILVER OXIDE plus Antimony Trisulfide.

Phosphorus
See PHOSPHORUS plus Silver Oxide.

Selenium Sulfide
See SILVER OXIDE plus Antimony Trisulfide.

Sulfur
See SULFUR plus Silver Oxide.

SILVER PERCHLORATE $AgClO_4$

(self-reactive)
Silver perchlorate filter cake exploded while being pulverized in a mortar.
ACS **146:** 209.

Acetic Acid
Silver perchlorate-acetic acid solvated salt is liable to explode when struck. Shock-sensitive solvated salts are also formed with silver perchlorate and aniline, benzene, chlorobenzene, glycerol, nitrobenzene, pyridine, and toluene.
Mellor **2, Supp. 1:** 616 (1956).

Aniline
See SILVER PERCHLORATE plus Acetic Acid.

Benzene
An explosion of silver perchlorate crystallized from benzene has been reported. A similar explosion involving ethyl alcohol was cited.
S. R. Brinkley, *J. Am. Chem. Soc.* **62:** 3524 (1940). *ACS*-**146:** 209.
See SILVER PERCHLORATE plus Acetic Acid.

Carbon Tetrachloride and Hydrochloric Acid
The reaction of silver perchlorate with carbon tetrachloride in the presence of a small amount of hydrochloric acid produces trichloromethyl perchlorate, which detonates at 40°C.
Kirk and Othmer, Second Ed. **5:** 72 (1963).
Pascal **16:** 316 (1931-1934).

Chlorobenzene
See SILVER PERCHLORATE plus Acetic Acid.

Ethyl Alcohol
See SILVER PERCHLORATE plus Benzene.

Ethylenediamine
A flask exploded while a chemist was adding ethylenediamine drop-wise to silver perchlorate.
NSC Newsletter, R & D Sec. (Jan. 1970).

Glycerol
See SILVER PERCHLORATE plus Acetic Acid.

Nitrobenzene
See SILVER PERCHLORATE plus Acetic Acid.

Pyridine
See SILVER PERCHLORATE plus Acetic Acid.

Toluene
See SILVER PERCHLORATE plus Acetic Acid.
Many "hydrocarbon-metal perchlorate" complexes are explosive, for example, the complexes of benzene, toluene, aniline, pyridine, and dioxane.
Analyst **80:** 13 (1955).

SILVER PERMANGANATE $AgMnO_4$

Ammonium Hydroxide
Silver permanganate reacts with ammonium hydroxide to form a complex of the formula $[Ag(NH_3)_2]MnO_4$ which is shock sensitive.
Pascal **16:** 1062 (1931-1934).

Sulfuric Acid (Vapor)
Moist silver permanganate stored for drying in a desiccator over sulfuric acid under vacuum produced a strong explosion.
Delhez (1967).

SILVER PEROXIDE Ag_2O_2

Polyisobutylene
An explosion occurred during filling of a container with 2 kilo grams of silver peroxide containing 1% by weight of polyisobuty lene.
Arbeitsschutz **6:** 248 (1972).

SILVER SALTS

Acetylene
See MERCURY SALTS plus Acetylene.

Nitromethane
See COPPER SALTS plus Nitromethane.

SILVER SULFIDE Ag_2S

Iodine Monochloride
See IODINE MONOCHLORIDE plus Cadmium Sulfide.

Potassium Chlorate
See POTASSIUM CHLORATE plus Silver Sulfide.

SODIUM Na

Air
The ignition temperature of sodium in air depends on size of surface exposed: vapor ignites at room temperature; droplets at about 250°F; an agitated pool at 400°F; a calm pool at 500°–800°F. In the absence of moisture and hydrogen, the reaction is insignificant below 1000°F.
Gracie and Droher (1960).
Mellor **2, Supp. 2:** 440 (1961).

Aluminum Bromide
A mixture of sodium and any of the following halide compounds produces a strong explosion on impact: aluminum bromide, aluminum chloride, aluminum fluoride, ammonium chlorocuprate, antimony tribromide, antimony trichloride, antimony triiodide, arsenic trichloride, arsenic triiodide, bismuth tribromide, bismuth trichloride, bismuth triiodide, boron tribromide, cupric chloride, ferrous chloride, iodine monobromide, manganous chloride, mercuric bromide, mercuric chloride, mercuric fluoride, mercuric iodide, mercurous chloride, silicon tetrachloride, silver fluoride, stannic chloride, stannic iodide (with sulfur), stannous chloride, sulfur dibromide, thallous bromide, vanadium pentachloride, and zinc bromide.
Mellor **2, Supp. 2:** 497 (1961).

Aluminum Chloride
See SODIUM plus Aluminum Bromide.

Aluminum Fluoride
See SODIUM plus Aluminum Bromide.

Ammonium Chlorocuprate
See SODIUM plus Aluminum Bromide.

Ammonium Nitrate
Sodium and ammonium nitrate react through a series of reductions to form a yellow explosive substance believed to be disodium nitrite.
Mellor **8: Supp. I, Part I,** p. 546 (1964).

Antimony Tribromide
See SODIUM plus Aluminum Bromide.

Antimony Trichloride
See SODIUM plus Aluminum Bromide.

Antimony Triiodide
See SODIUM plus Aluminum Bromide.

Arsenic Trichloride
See SODIUM plus Aluminum Bromide.

Arsenic Triiodide
See SODIUM plus Aluminum Bromide.

Bismuth Tribromide
See SODIUM plus Aluminum Bromide.

Bismuth Trichloride
See SODIUM plus Aluminum Bromide.

Bismuth Triiodide
See SODIUM plus Aluminum Bromide.

Bismuth Trioxide
Sodium reduces the heated trioxide to the metal and the reaction is accompanied by incandescence.
Mellor **9:** 649 (1946-1947).

Boron Tribromide Bromine
See SODIUM plus Aluminum Bromide.
Finely divided sodium reacts with bromine with luminescence. The system, solid sodium plus liquid bromine, requires a light mechanical shock to explode it.
Mellor, **Supp. II, Part I:** 714 (1956). H. Staudinger, *Z. Elektro chem.* **31:** 549-52 (1925).
See BROMINE plus Potassium.

Bromoazide
See ANTIMONY plus Bromoazide.

Carbon Dioxide
Molten sodium can be plunged into a carbon dioxide atmosphere without causing a vigorous reaction. But sodium manufacturers warn against using carbon dioxide on fires, because molten sodium burns with increasing vigor as the temperature is elevated. Small sodium fires can, however, be covered with solvent, like kerosine, and the resultant kerosine fire can be attacked with carbon dioxide.
H. N. Gilbert, *Chem. and Eng. News* **26:** 2604 (1948). *Metallic Sodium,* p. 19 (1952). "*Ethyl" Sodium,* p. 10 (1954). *Sodium, Plant Scale,* p. 38 (1956).
An explosive reaction occurs when dry ice and solid sodium are brought together by impact.
Mellor **2, Supp. 2:** 468 (1961).

Carbon Monoxide and Ammonia
The reaction of sodium and carbon monoxide in liquid ammonia forms sodium carbonyl, which explodes when heated in air.
Mellor **2, Supp. 2:** 467 (1961).
See also SODIUM CARBONYL plus Air.

Carbon Tetrachloride
Carbon tetrachloride reacts violently with hot sodium.
Bahme, p. 12 (1961). *Ellern,* p. 43 (1968).
See SODIUM plus Carbon Dioxide.
See SODIUM plus Cobaltous Bromide.

Chlorinated Hydrocarbons
Sodium forms explosive mixtures with chlorinated hydrocarbons.
H. N. Gilbert, *Chem. and Eng. News* **26:** 2604 (1948).

Chlorine
Cold sodium is spontaneously flammable in moist chlorine.
Mellor **2:** 95, 469 (1946-1947).
The vapors of sodium and chlorine react with a luminous flame.
Mellor **2, Supp. 1:** 380 (1956).

Chlorine Trifluoride
See CALCIUM plus Chlorine Trifluoride.

Chloroform
The system, sodium plus chloroform, is shock-sensitive, producing a fairly strong explosion.
H. Staudinger, *Z. Elektrochem.* **31:** 549-52 (1925).
See LITHIUM plus Chloroform.
See POTASSIUM plus Chloroform.

Chromium Tetrachloride
A mixture of sodium and chromium tetrachloride creates a very violent explosion on impact.
Mellor **2, Supp. 2:** 497 (1961).

Chromium Trioxide
Sodium or potassium reacts with chromium trioxide with incandescence.
Mellor **11:** 237 (1946-1947).

Cobaltous Bromide
A very violent explosion results when a mixture of sodium and any of the following is struck with a hammer: cobaltous bromide, carbon tetrachloride, cobaltous chloride, ferric bromide, ferric chloride, ferrous bromide, ferrous iodide, phosphorus pentachloride, phosphorus tribromide, sulfur dichloride.
Mellor **2, Supp. 2:** 497 (1961).

Cobaltous Chloride
See SODIUM plus Cobaltous Bromide.

Cupric Chloride
See SODIUM plus Aluminum Bromide.

Cupric Oxide
Cupric oxide is reduced when heated with sodium. The reaction proceeds with vivid incandescence.
Mellor **3:** 138 (1946-1947).

1,2-Dichloroethylene
The addition of sodium, caustic or caustic solutions to 1,2-dichloroethylene or to trichloroethylene may form monochloroacetylene or dichloroacetylene, respectively. The addition of sodium or caustic to tetrachloroethane may form either of the chloroacetylenes, both of which are spontaneously flammable in air. Avoid the contact of the above chlorohydrocarbons with sodium or caustic except under carefully controlled experimental conditions.
NAVWEPS OP **3237,** p. 28 (1964). *Fire and Accident Prev.* **42** (1956).

Dichloromethane
Sodium and other alkali metals form sensitive explosive mixtures with chloroform, dichloromethane, and methyl chloride.
H. Staudinger, *Z. Elektrochem.* **31:** 549 (1925).

Ferric Bromide
See SODIUM plus Cobaltous Bromide.

Ferric Chloride
See SODIUM plus Cobaltous Bromide.

Ferrous Bromide
See SODIUM plus Cobaltous Bromide.

Ferrous Chloride
See SODIUM plus Aluminum Bromide.

Ferrous Iodide
See SODIUM plus Cobaltous Bromide.

Fluorine
Sodium burns spontaneously in fluorine.
Mellor **2:** 469 (1946-1947).
Mellor **2, Supp. 2:** 450 (1961).

Hydrazine Hydrate
Hydrazine hydrate and sodium develop much heat with the liberation of hydrogen and ammonia. If hydrazine hydrate is added drop by drop to finely granulated sodium, suspended in ether, and the mixture is heated, a white substance is formed, which explodes in air.
Mellor **8:** 316 (1946-1947).

Hydrochloric Acid
Sodium explodes on contact with hydrochloric acid.
Mellor **2:** 469 (1946-1947).

Hydrofluoric Acid
An aqueous solution of hydrofluoric acid reacts with sodium with explosive violence.
Mellor **2:** 469 (1946-1947).

Hydrogen Chloride
Sodium reacts very vigorously with gaseous hydrogen chloride.
Mellor **2, Supp. 2:** 452 (1961).

Hydrogen Peroxide
See LEAD DIOXIDE plus Hydrogen Peroxide.

Hydrogen Sulfide
A very rapid reaction results when moist gaseous hydrogen sulfide contacts sodium.
Mellor **2, Supp. 2:** 456 (1961).

Hydroxylamine
Sodium and hydroxylamine (in an ether solution) form sodium hydroxylamine, which is spontaneously flammable in air.
Mellor **8:** 290 (1946-1947).

Iodine
See IODINE plus Lithium.

Iodine Monobromide
A mixture of sodium and iodine monobromide explodes when struck with a hammer.
Mellor **2, Supp. 2:** 452 (1961).
See also SODIUM plus Aluminum Bromide.

Iodine Monochloride
See POTASSIUM plus Iodine Monochloride. The reac-

tion of sodium and iodine monochloride is vigorous when both materials are molten.
Mellor **2, Supp. 2:** 451 (1961).

Iodine Pentafluoride
A mixture of iodine pentafluoride and potassium or sodium (molten) will explode.
Mellor **2:** 114 (1946-1947).

Lead Oxide
Sodium, reduced to a fine state of subdivision, when mixed with lead oxide ignites spontaneously.
Mellor **7:** 658 (1946-1947).

Maleic Anhydride
See ALKALI METALS plus Maleic Anhydride.

Manganous Chloride
See SODIUM plus Aluminum Bromide.

Mercuric Bromide
See SODIUM plus Aluminum Bromide.

Mercuric Chloride
See SODIUM plus Aluminum Bromide.

Mercuric Fluoride
See SODIUM plus Aluminum Bromide.

Mercuric Iodide
See SODIUM plus Aluminum Bromide.

Mercurous Chloride
See SODIUM plus Aluminum Bromide.

Mercurous Oxide
Molten sodium or potassium decomposes mercurous oxide with a slight explosion.
J. B. Senderens, *Bull. Soc. Chim.* (3) **6:** 802 (1891).

Methyl Chloride
Sodium and other alkali metals react explosively with methyl chloride.
H. Staudinger, *Z. Elektrochem.* **31:**549-52 (1925).

Molybdenum Trioxide
Molybdenum trioxide is reduced by either potassium or sodium with incandescence.
Z. Anorg. Chemie **190:** 270 (1930).

Monoammonium Phosphate
An explosive reaction occurred when monoammonium phosphate was used to extinguish a sodium fire. No reactions were experienced when sodium bicarbonate or potassium bicarbonate was used in a sodium fire.
Bohling (1971).

Nitric Acid
Sodium ignites spontaneously in contact with nitric acid of specific gravity exceeding 1.056.
Mellor **2:** 470 (1946-1947).
Mellor **2, Supp. 2:** 452 (1961).

Nitrogen Peroxide
Gaseous sodium reacts with the vapors of nitrogen peroxide and nitrous oxide with marked luminescence at 260°C.
Mellor **2, Supp. 2:** 463 (1961).

Nitrosyl Fluoride
The reaction between nitrosyl fluoride and sodium forms sodium fluoride with incandescence.
Z. Anorg. Chemie **47:** 190 (1905).

Nitrous Oxide
See SODIUM plus Nitrogen Peroxide.

Phosgene
Vapors of sodium and phosgene react with luminescence at about 260°C.
Mellor **2, Supp. 2:** 470 (1961).

Phosphorus
See PHOSPHORUS plus Cesium.

Phosphorus Pentachloride
Molten sodium may ignite or explode when in contact with phosphorus pentachloride.
Baudrimant.
See also SODIUM plus Cobaltous Bromide.

Phosphorus Pentoxide
See POTASSIUM plus Phosphorus Pentoxide.

Phosphorus Tribromide
Metallic sodium merely floats on liquid phosphorus tribromide, losing its metallic lustre; but, if a little water is sprinkled on the surface, there is a violent explosion.
Z. Anorg. Chemie **41:** 276 (1904).
See SODIUM plus Cobaltous Bromide.

Phosphorus Trichloride
Phosphorus trichloride explodes at the fusion temperature of sodium.
Mellor **2:** 470 (1946-1947).
See also SODIUM plus Phosphoryl Chloride.

Phosphoryl Chloride
Gaseous sodium reacts with the vapors of phosphoryl chloride and phosphorus trichloride with luminescence at 270°C.
Mellor **2, Supp. 2:** 463 (1961).

Potassium Oxides
See POTASSIUM plus Air.

Potassium Ozonide
Sodium in contact with either potassium ozonide or potassium superoxide produces an explosive reaction.
Mellor **2, Supp. 3:** 1577 (1963).

Potassium Superoxide
See SODIUM plus Potassium Ozonide.

Selenium
Potassium reacts with selenium and is attended by burning; sodium does likewise and is attended by vivid incandescence.
Mellor **10:** 766-7 (1946-1947).
The reaction of sodium and selenium is luminescent above 300°C at low pressure.
Mellor **2, Supp. 2:** 455 (1961).

Silicon Tetrachloride
See SODIUM plus Aluminum Bromide.

Silver Bromide
Silver bromide, silver chloride, silver fluoride, and silver iodide form impact-sensitive systems with sodium and other alkali metals.
H. Staudinger, *Z. Elektrochem.* **31:** 549-52 (1925).

Silver Chloride
See SODIUM plus Silver Bromide.

Silver Fluoride
See SODIUM plus Silver Bromide.
See SODIUM plus Aluminum Bromide.

Silver Iodide
See SODIUM plus Silver Bromide.

Sodium Peroxide
The reduction of sodium peroxide by molten sodium at 500°C is a very vigorous reaction.
U.S. AEC Document UCRL-**1864:** 2-23 (1954).

Stannic Chloride
See SODIUM plus Aluminum Bromide.

Stannic Iodide and Sulfur
See SODIUM plus Aluminum Bromide.

Stannic Oxide
Stannic oxide is reduced by sodium or potassium with incandescence.
Mellor **7:** 401, 418 (1946-1947).

Stannous Chloride
See SODIUM plus Aluminum Bromide.

Sulfur
When sulfur is rubbed with sodium, the reaction proceeds with explosive violence.
Mellor **2:** 469 (1946-1947).
Mellor **2, Supp. 2:** 455 (1961).

Sulfur Dibromide
See SODIUM plus Aluminum Bromide.

Sulfur Dichloride
A mixture of sodium and sulfur dichloride explodes when struck with a hammer.
Mellor **2, Supp. 2:** 460 (1961).

Sulfur Dioxide
Sulfur dioxide reacts violently with sodium near the melting point.
H. N. Gilbert, *Chem. and Eng. News* **26:** 2604 (1948).
The reaction of sodium and sulfur dioxide is almost as vigorous as that between sodium and water.
Mellor **2, Supp. 2:** 458 (1961).

Sulfuric Acid
A dilute aqueous solution of sulfuric acid reacts with sodium with explosive violence.
Mellor **2:** 470 (1946-1947).
Mellor **2, Supp. 2:** 453 (1961).

Tellurium
A vigorous reaction results when liquid tellurium is poured over solid sodium.
Mellor **2, Supp. 2:** 455 (1961).

Tetrachloroethane
Tetrachloroethane may explode with potassium or sodium. See also SODIUM plus 1,2-Dichloroethylene.
Chem. Safety Data Sheet **SD-34** (1949).

Thallous Bromide
See SODIUM plus Aluminum Bromide.

Thiophosphoryl Fluoride
When thiophosphoryl fluoride is passed over a metal such as heated sodium or potassium, the metal ignites. The residual mass, when treated with water, gives off spontaneously flammable phosphine.
Mellor **8:** 1072 (1946-1947).

Trichloroethylene
See SODIUM plus 1,2-Dichloroethylene.

Vanadium Pentachloride
See SODIUM plus Aluminum Bromide.

Vanadyl Chloride
Sodium and vanadyl chloride react violently when heated to 180°C.
Mellor **2, Supp. 2:** 496 (1961).

Water
At 40°C. the heat of reaction is adequate to ignite the hydrogen liberated.
Mellor **2:** 469 (1946-1947).
See SODIUM plus Carbon Dioxide.

Zinc Bromide
See SODIUM plus Aluminum Bromide.

SODIUM ACETATE CH_3COONa

Fluorine
See FLUORINE plus Sodium Acetate.

Potassium Nitrate
See POTASSIUM NITRATE plus Sodium Acetate.

SODIUM ACETOACETIC ESTER
$C_2H_5OCOCH=CO(Na)CH_3$

2-Iodo-3, 5-Dinitrobiphenyl
See 2-IODO-3, 5-DINITROBIPHENYL plus Ethyl Sodio-Acetoacetate.

SODIUM ACETYLIDE $NaC{\equiv}CH$

Bromine
See BROMINE plus Sodium Acetylene Carbide.

Chlorine
See BROMINE plus Sodium Acetylene Carbide.

SODIUM ACI-NITROMETHYLIDE $NaON(CH_2)O$

Water
Sodium or potassium salts of nitromethane exploded when the dry salt was moistened with a little water.
Chem. and Eng. News **28:** 1473 (1950).

SODIUM AMIDE $NaNH_2$

Chromic Anhydride
When these solids are ground together, a vigorous reaction results.
Mellor **11:** 234 (1946-1947).

1,1-Diethoxy-2-chloroethane
The reaction in the presence of ammonia produces sodiumethoxy acetylide, which is extremely pyrophoric.
Rutledge, p. 35 (1968).

Potassium Chlorate
See POTASSIUM CHLORATE plus Sodium Amide.

Water
Sodium amide reacts violently with water and frequently bursts into flame.
F. W. Bergstrom and W. C. Fernelius, *Chem. Reviews* **12:** 61 (1933).

SODIUM AZIDE NaN_3

(self-reactive)
Sodium azide decomposes at 275°C.
Mellor **8, Supp. 2:** 43 (1967).

Benzoyl Chloride and Potassium Hydroxide
The mixture of sodium azide and benzoyl chloride reacts spontane ously with evolution of heat in a potassium hydroxide solution.
Mellor **8, Supp. 2:** 55 (1967).

Bromine
See BROMINE plus Silver Azide.

Carbon Disulfide
See CARBON DISULFIDE plus Azides.

Chromyl Chloride
The reaction of sodium azide and chromyl chloride is an explosive one.
Mellor **8, Supp. 2:** 36 (1967).

Copper
A solution of sodium azide in copper pipe with lead joints formed copper azide and lead azide, both detonating compounds.
Klotz (1973).

Dibromomalononitrile
These materials react to produce a product that is extremely sensitive to light shock.
MCA Case History **820** (1962). *ASESB Expl. Report* **89** (1962).

Dimethyl Sulfate
During preparation of methyl azide from reaction of these two chemicals, a violent explosion occurred. Apparently the pH was allowed to fall below 5. At this acidity hydrazoic acid, a powerful explosive, readily forms.
MCA Case History **887** (1963).

Lead
See SODIUM AZIDE plus Copper.

Methylene Chloride
Explosive reaction can occur with methylene chloride and other halogenated solvents.
Chem. and Eng. News (Dec. 13, 1993).

Nitric Acid
The reaction of sodium azide and strong nitric acid is energetic.
Mellor **8, Supp. 2:** 315 (1967).

SODIUM BICARBONATE $NaHCO_3$

Monoammonium Phosphate
A self-propagating reaction can occur when either sodium bicarbonate- or potassium bicarbonate-based dry chemical extinguishing agent is mixed with monoammonium phosphate dry chemical extinguishing agent. Moisture will accelerate the reaction. Products are water, ammonia, carbon dioxide and various solid substances. In a fire extinguisher the pressure developed will blow out the valve.
Fire J. **60** (1):49 (1966).

Sodium-Potassium Alloy
See SODIUM-POTASSIUM ALLOY plus Water.

SODIUM BISULFIDE NaHS

m-Chloroaniline Diazonium Salt
See SODIUM SULFIDE plus Diazonium and Diazonium Chloride Salts.

4-Chloro-o-toluidine Diazonium Chloride
See SODIUM SULFIDE plus Diazonium and Diazonium Chloride Salts.

o-Nitroaniline Diazonium Salt
See SODIUM SULFIDE plus Diazonium and Diazonium Chloride Salts.

Diazonium Salts
See DIAZONIUM SALTS plus Thiophenates.

SODIUM BORINATE $NaBH_2O$

(self-reactive)
Sodium hypoborate is a stronger, more violent reducing agent than sodium hypophosphite.
Mellor **5:** 37 (1946-1947).

SODIUM BOROHYDRIDE $NaBH_4$

Hydrogen Peroxide
Sodium borohydride is oxidized by hydrogen peroxide to give sodium metaborate and water. The reaction is very exothermic with the evolution of 1776 KJ/mole.

SODIUM BROMATE $NaBrO_3$

Aluminum
See ALUMINUM plus Bromates.

Arsenic
See ARSENIC plus Bromates.

Carbon
See CARBON plus Bromates.

Copper
See COPPER plus Bromates.

Lubricant
See BROMATES plus Organic Matter.

Metal Sulfides
See METAL SULFIDES plus Bromates.

Organic Matter
See BROMATES plus Organic Matter.

Phosphorus
See PHOSPHORUS plus Bromates.

Sulfur
See SULFUR plus Bromates.

SODIUM BROMIDE NaBr

Bromine Trifluoride
See BROMINE TRIFLUORIDE plus Potassium Bromide.

SODIUM CARBIDE Na_2C_2

Aluminum
See MERCURY plus Sodium Carbide.

Bromine
See BROMINE plus Sodium Carbide.

Carbon Dioxide
Sodium carbide reacts with incandescence when placed in carbon dioxide, chlorine, or sulfur dioxide.
Von Schwartz, p. 328 (1918).
Sodium carbide ignites on warming in carbon dioxide.
Mellor **5:** 848 (1946-1947).

Chlorine
See SODIUM CARBIDE plus Carbon Dioxide.
See CHLORINE plus Sodium Carbide.

Iron
See MERCURY plus Sodium Carbide.

Lead
See MERCURY plus Sodium Carbide.

Mercury
See MERCURY plus Sodium Carbide.

Nitrogen Pentoxide
Nitrogen pentoxide attacks sodium carbide with incandescence at 150°C.
Mellor **5:** 848-50 (1946-1947).

Phosphorus
See PHOSPHORUS plus Sodium Carbide.

Sulfur Dioxide
See SODIUM CARBIDE plus Carbon Dioxide.

Water
See BROMINE plus Sodium Carbide.
An explosion of sodium carbide can occur in water if a large excess of carbide is present.
Mellor **5:** 848 (1946-1947).

SODIUM CARBONATE Na_2CO_3

Aluminum
See ALUMINUM plus Sodium Carbonate.

Fluorine
See FLUORINE plus Carbonates.

Phosphorus Pentoxide
The anhydrous reaction of sodium carbonate and phosphorus pentoxide, initiated by local heating, can generate relatively high temperatures.
Mellor **8, Supp. 3:** 406 (1971).

Sulfuric Acid
Stratified concentrated sulfuric acid in a reaction tank was suddenly contacted by alkali wash. The violent ensuing reaction caused a geyser of material, propelled by carbon dioxide and steam, to shoot from the manhole of the tank.
MCA Case History **888** (1963).

SODIUM CARBONYL NaCOCONa

Air
Sodium carbonyl or potassium carbonyl explodes on contact with air or water.
Mellor **5:** 951-54 (1946-1947).
See also SODIUM plus Carbon Monoxide and Ammonia.

Water
See SODIUM CARBONYL plus Air.

SODIUM CHLORATE $NaClO_3$
(See also CHLORATES)

Aluminum
See ALUMINUM plus Bromates.

Ammonium Thiosulfate
A bulk cargo of sodium chlorate became hot while being transported in a tank that had previously contained ammonium thiosulfate. Under controlled laboratory conditions, a small quantity of ammonium thiosulfate in sodium chlorate could be made to decompose explosively.
MCA Case History **2019** (April 1974).

Antimony Sulfide
See CHLORATES plus Antimony Sulfide.

Arsenic
See ARSENIC plus Bromates.

Arsenic Trioxide
The two chemicals form a spontaneously flammable mixture.
Ellern, p. 51 (1968).

Carbon
See CARBON plus Bromates.

Charcoal
See CHLORATES plus Organic Matter.

Copper
See COPPER plus Bromates.

Manganese Dioxide
See CHLORATES plus Manganese Dioxide.

Metal Sulfides
See METAL SULFIDES plus Bromates.

Organic Acids (Dibasic)
See CHLORATES plus Organic Acids (Dibasic).

Organic Matter
Mixtures containing more than 10 percent sodium chlorate are sufficiently combustible to be hazardous at low relative humidity. Mixtures of sodium chlorate with organic material such as charcoal, sugar, flour or shellac may be ignited by friction or shock.
Chem. Safety Data Sheet **SD-42** (1951). W. H. Cook, *Can. J. Research* **8:** 509-44 (1933).
See CHLORATES plus Organic Matter.

Phosphorus
See PHOSPHORUS plus Bromates.

Potassium Cyanide
See CHLORATES plus Antimony Sulfide. See POTASSIUM CYANIDE plus Sodium Chlorate. See CHLORATES plus Potassium Cyanide.

Sulfur
See SULFUR plus Chlorates. See SULFUR plus Bromates.

Sulfuric Acid
Chlorates when brought in contact with sulfuric acid are likely to cause fire or explosions.
Bahme, p. 29 (1961).

Thiocyanates
See CHLORATES plus Antimony Sulfide.
See THIOCYANATES plus Chlorates.

Zinc
See ZINC plus Chlorates.

SODIUM CHLORIDE NaCl

Bromine Trifluoride
See BROMINE TRIFLUORIDE plus Potassium Bromide.

Lithium
See LITHIUM plus Sodium Chloride.

SODIUM CHLORITE $NaClO_2$

(self-reactive)
An 18-month-old bottle of recrystallized sodium chlorite stored at temperatures in excess of 90°F (32.2°C) ignited as the bottle cap was turned.
Chem. and Eng. News, p. 4 (March 22, 1993).
The trihydrate crystals of sodium chlorite explode on percussion.
Mellor **2, Supp. 1:** 573 (1956).

Acids
Sodium chlorite and acids react with rapid evolution of spontane ously explosive chlorine dioxide gas. If heated above 347°F, the reaction produces adequate heat to become self-sustaining.
Diox Process (1949).

Organic Matter
A mixture of organic matter and sodium chlorite can be extremely sensitive to heat, impact, or friction.
Diox Process (1949).

Oxalic Acid
A bleach mix was prepared by placing weighed quantities of the two chemicals in a stainless steel beaker. As water was being added, the mixture fizzed a moment, then exploded. Toxic chlorine dioxide gas was evolved.
MCA Case History **839** (1962).

Phosphorus
See PHOSPHORUS plus Sodium Chlorite.

Sulfur
See SULFUR plus Sodium Chlorite.

SODIUM CYANIDE NaCN

Nitrates
See NITRATES plus Cyanides.

Nitrites
See CYANIDES plus Chlorates.

SODIUM DICHROMATE Na_2Cr_2O7

Hydrazine
See POTASSIUM DICHROMATE plus Hydrazine.

SODIUM HYDRAZIDE $NaNHNH_2$

Air
Addition of air, or alcohol, or moisture to sodium hydrazide can produce an explosion.
Mellor **8:** 336 (1946-1947).

Alcohol
See SODIUM HYDRAZIDE plus Air.

Moisture
See SODIUM HYDRAZIDE plus Air.

SODIUM HYDRIDE NaH

Acetylene
If moisture is present, the reaction between sodium hydride and acetylene is vigorous even at minus 60°C.
Mellor **2:** 483 (1946-1947).

Air
Sodium hydride is spontaneously flammable in air if moistened with water.
Von Schwartz, p. 328 (1918).

Chlorine
See CHLORINE plus Sodium Hydride.

Dimethyl Sulfoxide
See DIMETHYL SULFOXIDE plus Sodium Hydride.

Fluorine
See CHLORINE plus Sodium Hydride.

Iodine
See IODINE plus Sodium Hydride.

Oxygen
See OXYGEN plus Sodium Hydride.

Sulfur
See SULFUR plus Sodium Hydride.

Water
Sodium hydride that was accidentally spilled from a polyethylene bag ignited spontaneously on contact with moisture.
MCA Case History **1587** (1969).

SODIUM HYDROSULFITE $Na_2S_2O_4$

Aluminum Powder
An explosion occurred when 8000 pounds of sodium hydrosulfite and 1000 pounds of aluminum powder were mixed to form a precipitating agent. Water was added accidentally to the mixing vat causing a decomposition reaction in the vat, which then began to smolder.
Chemical Process Safety Report **5:** 8 (June 1995).

Water
Moist sodium hydrosulfite is likely to ignite upon drying.
Bahme, p. 95 (1961).

SODIUM HYDROXIDE NaOH

Acetaldehyde
See ACETALDEHYDE plus Sodium Hydroxide.

Acetic Acid
Mixing sodium hydroxide and glacial acetic acid in a closed container caused the temperature and pressure to increase.
Flynn and Rossow (1970). See Note under complete reference.

Acetic Anhydride
Mixing sodium hydroxide and acetic anhydride in a closed container caused the temperature and pressure to increase.
Flynn and Rossow (1970). See Note under complete reference.

Acrolein
An extremely violent polymerization reaction of acrolein results from contact with alkaline materials such as so-

dium hydroxide, potassium hydroxide, ammonia, and amines.
Chem. Safety Data Sheet **SD-85** (1961).
Mixing sodium hydroxide and acrolein in a closed container caused the temperature and pressure to increase.
Flynn and Rossow (1970). See Note under complete reference.

Acrylonitrile
Violent polymerization takes place in the presence of concentrated caustic (e.g., sodium hydroxide, potassium hydroxide).
Haz. Chem. Data (1966).

Allyl Alcohol
See ALLYL ALCOHOL plus Sodium Hydroxide.

Allyl Chloride
In contact with dry sodium hydroxide, hydrolysis may take place producing allyl alcohol.
Ventrone (1971).

Aluminum
See ALUMINUM plus Sodium Hydroxide.

Chlorine Trifluoride
See CHLORINE TRIFLUORIDE plus Nitric Acid.

Chloroform and Methyl Alcohol
When 1 gram of sodium hydroxide was added to a mixture of 1 ml methanol and 1 ml chloroform, an exothermic reaction occurred. Potassium hydroxide and other alkalies may replace sodium hydroxide as a reactant.
J. S. Snyder, *Fawcett and Wood,* p. 302 (1965).

Chlorohydrin
Mixing sodium hydroxide and chlorohydrin in a closed container caused the temperature and pressure to increase.
Flynn and Rossow (1970). See Note under complete reference.

Chloronitrotoluenes
Inadvertent contamination of mixed chloronitrotoluenes by sodium hydroxide in a feed line caused an exothermic reaction with run away pressure build-up and eventual explosion of the processing apparatus.
Queener (1966). *ASESB Expl. Report* **130** (1963).

Chlorosulfonic Acid
Mixing sodium hydroxide and chlorosulfonic acid in a closed container caused the temperature and pressure to increase.
Flynn and Rossow (1970). See Note under complete reference.

1,2-Dichloroethylene
See SODIUM plus 1,2-Dichloroethylene.

Ethylene Cyanohydrin
Mixing sodium hydroxide and ethylene cyanohydrin in a closed container caused the temperature and pressure to increase.
Flynn and Rossow (1970). See Note under complete reference.

Glyoxal
Mixing sodium hydroxide and glyoxal in a closed container caused the temperature and pressure to increase.
Flynn and Rossow (1970). See Note under complete reference.

Hydrochloric Acid
Mixing sodium hydroxide and 36% hydrochloric acid in a closed container caused the temperature and pressure to increase.
Flynn and Rossow (1970). See Note under complete reference.

Hydrofluoric Acid
Mixing sodium hydroxide and 48.7% hydrofluoric acid in a closed container caused the temperature and pressure to increase.
Flynn and Rossow (1970). See Note under complete reference.

Hydroquinone
Crude hydroquinone was pumped into a sodium hydroxide storage tank by mistake. The hydroquinone liquor at 85°C decomposed rap idly in the presence of the sodium hydroxide resulting in overflow of the tank and evolution of a considerable amount of heat.
Wischmeyer (1969).

Maleic Anhydride
The presence of a residue of weak sodium hydroxide solution in a pressure vessel caused maleic anhydride to decompose in a runaway explosive reaction.
Chem. Haz. Info. Series **C-71:** 5 (1960).
Alkali and other alkaline earth compounds such as potassium, lithium, calcium, barium and magnesium compounds, as well as amines and other nitrogen compounds will cause explosive decomposition of maleic anhydride.
MCA Case History **622** *and Suppl. to* **622** (1960).
Vogler, Cecil, and Koerner, *J. Chem. Eng. Data* **8** (4): 620-3 (1963).

Nitric Acid
Mixing sodium hydroxide and 70% nitric acid in a closed container caused the temperature and pressure to increase.
Flynn and Rossow (1970). See Note under complete reference.

Nitroethane
See CALCIUM HYDROXIDE plus Nitroethane.

Nitromethane
See CALCIUM HYDROXIDE plus Nitroethane.

Nitroparaffins
See CALCIUM HYDROXIDE plus Nitroethane.

Nitropropane
See CALCIUM HYDROXIDE plus Nitroethane.

Oleum
Mixing sodium hydroxide and oleum in a closed container caused the temperature and pressure to increase.
Flynn and Rossow (1970). See Note under complete reference.

Pentol (3-Methyl-2- Penten-4-yn-1-ol)
Pentol, being fractionated under high vacuum, was accidentally contacted by caustic cleaning solution and a violent explosion resulted.
MCA Case History **363.** *Chem. Process (Chicago)* **27:** 111 (1964).

Phosphorus
See PHOSPHORUS plus Alkaline Hydroxide.

Phosphorus Pentoxide
See CALCIUM OXIDE plus Phosphorus Pentoxide.

Propiolactone (BETA-)
Mixing sodium hydroxide and propiolactone (BETA-) in a closed container caused the temperature and pressure to increase.
Flynn and Rossow (1970). See Note under complete reference.

Sulfuric Acid
Mixing sodium hydroxide and 96% sulfuric acid in a closed container caused the temperature and pressure to increase.
Flynn and Rossow (1970). See Note under complete reference.

Tetrachlorobenzene and Methyl Alcohol
In the manufacturing of the sodium salt of trichlorophenol, sodium hydroxide, methyl alcohol and tetrachlorobenzene were heated. During the heating process, the pressure suddenly increased rapidly and an explosion occurred.
MCA Guide for Safety, Appendix 3 (1972).

Tetrahydrofuran
See TETRAHYDROFURAN plus Potassium Hydroxide.

Trichloroethylene
When heated, trichloroethylene and sodium hydroxide or potassium hydroxide form explosive mixtures of dichloroacetylene.
Chem. Safety Data Sheet **SD-14** (1956).
The presence of alkylamines as a stabilizer in commercial trichloroethylene furnishes a catalyst that accelerates this reaction.
MCA Case History **495.** *Fire and Accident Prev.* **42** (June 8, 1956).
A pail of trichloroethylene dumped into a tank of caustic caused a fireball and eruption of the contents.
MCA Case History **1065** (1965).

See SODIUM plus 1,2-Dichloroethylene.

Water
Sodium hydroxide in contact with water may generate enough heat to ignite adjacent combustible materials.
Haz. Chem. Data (1966).

SODIUM HYDROXYLAMINE NH_2ONa

Air
Sodium hydroxylamine is spontaneously flammable in air.
Mellor **8:** 290 (1946-1947).

SODIUM HYPOBROMITE NaOBr

Acetone
See ACETONE plus Sodium Hypobromite.

Cupric Salts
Solutions of sodium hypobromite are decomposed by powerful catalytic action of cupric ions, even as impurities.
Mellor **2, Supp. 1:** 751 (1956).

SODIUM HYPOCHLORITE NaOCl
(See also HYPOCHLORITES)

(self-reactive)
Anhydrous sodium hypochlorite is very explosive.
Merck Index, p. 960 (1968).

Amines
See CALCIUM HYPOCHLORITE plus Amines.

Ammonium Acetate
Decomposition of sodium hypochlorite takes place within a few seconds with the following salts: ammonium acetate, ammonium carbonate, ammonium nitrate, ammonium oxalate, and ammonium phosphate.
Mellor **2, Supp. 1:** 550 (1956).

Ammonium Carbonate
See SODIUM HYPOCHLORITE plus Ammonium Acetate.

Ammonium Nitrate
See SODIUM HYPOCHLORITE plus Ammonium Acetate.

Ammonium Oxalate
See SODIUM HYPOCHLORITE plus Ammonium Acetate.

Ammonium Phosphate
See SODIUM HYPOCHLORITE plus Ammonium Acetate.

Cellulose
See SODIUM HYPOCHLORITE plus Oxalic Acid.

Ethyleneimine
See ETHYLENEIMINE plus Sodium Hypochlorite.

SODIUM HYPOPHOSPHITE $NaPH_2O_2$

(self-reactive)
Explosions can occur when hot sodium hypophosphite solution is evaporated.
Mellor **8:** 881 (1946-1947).

Air
Sodium hypophosphite decomposes when heated, forming phosphine, a spontaneously flammable gas.
Mellor **8:** 881 (1946-1947).
Mellor **8, Supp. 3:** 623 (1971).

Chlorates
See CHLORATES plus Sodium Hypophosphite.

Nitrates
See CHLORATES plus Sodium Hypophosphite.

Potassium Nitrate
See POTASSIUM NITRATE plus Sodium Hypophosphite.

Sodium Nitrate
See SODIUM NITRATE plus Sodium Hypophosphite.

SODIUM IODATE $NaIO_3$

Aluminum
See ALUMINUM plus Bromates.

Arsenic
See ARSENIC plus Bromates.

Carbon
See CARBON plus Bromates.

Copper
See COPPER plus Bromates.

Hydrogen Peroxide
Iodates decompose hydrogen peroxide catalytically.
Mellor **1:** 940 (1946-1947).

Metal Sulfides
See METAL SULFIDES plus Bromates.

Organic Matter
See ORGANIC MATTER plus Bromates.

Phosphorus
See PHOSPHORUS plus Bromates.

Potassium
See POTASSIUM plus Boric Acid.

Sulfur
See SULFUR plus Bromates.

SODIUM IODIDE NaI

Bromine Trifluoride
See BROMINE TRIFLUORIDE plus Potassium Bromide.

Cumene Hydroperoxide
Cumene hydroperoxide catalytically decomposes with addition of small quantities of sodium iodide.
Chem. and Eng. News (February 5, 1990).

Perchloric Acid
Perchloric acid ignites in contact with sodium iodide.
J. Am. Chem. Soc. **23:** 444 (1901).

SODIUM METHOXIDE $NaOCH_3$

Chloroform
Too rapid addition of sodium methylate to a mixture of chloroform and methanol initiated an uncontrolled exothermic reaction between the chloroform and the methylate that terminated in a violent explosion.
MCA Case History **693** (1961).

Methyl Azide and Dimethyl Malonate
See METHYLAZIDE plus Dimethyl Malonate and Sodium Methylate.

Perchloryl Fluoride
See PERCHLORYL FLUORIDE plus Sodium Methylate.

Water
Sodium methylate ignites in moist air.
Wischmeyer (1966).

SODIUM MONOXIDE Na_2O

Nitric Oxide
Sodium monoxide and nitric oxide react vigorously above 100°C.
Mellor **2, Supp. 2:** 629 (1961).

SODIUM NITRATE $NaNO_3$

Antimony
See ANTIMONY plus Potassium Nitrate.

Barium Rhodanide
See BARIUM RHODANIDE plus Sodium Nitrate.

Boron Phosphide
See BORON PHOSPHIDE plus Nitric Acid.

Cyanides
See NITRATES plus Cyanides.

Sodium Hypophosphite
A mixture of sodium nitrate and sodium hypophosphite constitutes a powerful explosive.
Mellor **8:** 831 (1946-1947).

Sulfur and Charcoal
See SULFUR plus Sodium Nitrate and Charcoal.

SODIUM NITRIDE Na_3N

Air
The reactivity of sodium nitride resembles that of sodium metal.
Mellor **8, Supp. 1:** 154 (1964).

Performic Acid
See PERFORMIC ACID plus Sodium Nitride.

SODIUM NITRITE $NaNO_2$

Ammonium Salts
A violent explosion occurs if an ammonium salt is melted with a nitrite salt.
Von Schwartz, p. 299 (1918).

Cellulose
Sodium nitrite at 460°F in contact with the fiber drums in which it is shipped undergoes a vigorous decomposition reaction producing a propellant-type burning until the carton is consumed.
Wheeler (1969).

Cyanides
See CYANIDES plus Chlorates.

Lithium
See LITHIUM plus Sodium Nitrite.

Potassium and Ammonia
See POTASSIUM plus Sodium Nitrite and Ammonia.

Sodium Thiosulfate
When a sodium nitrite and thiosulfate mixture was heated to evaporate to dryness, a violent explosion occurred.
Mellor **10:** 501 (1946-1947).

SODIUM-o-NITROPHENYL SULFIDE $NaSC_6H_4NO_2$

(self-reactive)
Methanol solutions of o-nitrothiophenol and sodium methoxide were mixed and evaporated under reduced pressure, dissolved in xylene and methanol and re-evaporated. As the flask was removed from the evaporator, it exploded.
Chem. & Ind. **6:** 257 (Feb. 5, 1966).

SODIUM OXIDE Na_2O

Water
See POTASSIUM OXIDE plus Water.

SODIUM OZONIDE NaO_3

Acids
Acids initiate a fast decomposition of sodium ozonate.
Mellor **2, Supp. 2:** 641 (1961).

Water
Water initiates a fast decomposition of sodium ozonate.
Mellor **2, Supp. 2:** 641 (1961).

SODIUM PERCHLORATE $NaClO_4$

Ammonium Nitrate
A mixture of these chemicals is used as an explosive.
Mellor **2, Supp. 1:** 608 (1956).

Calcium Hydride
See BROMATES plus Calcium Hydride.

Charcoal
See PERCHLORATES plus Charcoal.

Magnesium
See MAGNESIUM plus Potassium Perchlorate.

Reducing Agents
See PERCHLORATES plus Charcoal.

Strontium Hydride
See BROMATES plus Calcium Hydride.

SODIUM PEROXIDE Na_2O_2

Acetic Acid
Acetic acid or acetic anhydride can explode with sodium peroxide if not kept cold.
Von Schwartz, p. 321 (1918).

Acetic Anhydride
See SODIUM PEROXIDE plus Acetic Acid.

Aluminum
See ALUMINUM plus Sodium Peroxide.

Aluminum and Carbon Dioxide
See ALUMINUM plus Sodium Peroxide and Carbon Dioxide.

Ammonium Persulfate
See AMMONIUM PERSULFATE plus Sodium Peroxide.

Aniline
Sodium peroxide or potassium peroxide is spontaneously flammable with aniline, benzene, organic matter such as paper and wood, and diethyl ether. Mixtures with charcoal, glycerine, certain oils, and phosphorus burn or explode.
Mellor **2:** 490-93 (1946-1947). *Von Schwartz,* p. 328 (1918).

Antimony
See ANTIMONY plus Sodium Peroxide.

Arsenic
See ARSENIC plus Sodium Peroxide.

Benzene
See SODIUM PEROXIDE plus Aniline.

Boron Nitride
See BORON NITRIDE plus Sodium Peroxide.

Calcium Carbide
When a mixture of sodium peroxide and calcium carbide (powdered) is exposed to damp air, spontaneous combustion occurs. The mixture explodes when heated.
Mellor **2:** 490 ff. (1946-1947).

Charcoal
See SODIUM PEROXIDE plus Aniline.

Copper
See COPPER plus Sodium Peroxide.

Dextrose and Potassium Nitrate
A micro Parr calorimeter exploded when the wrong proportions of these ingredients were used. The intended mixture was 4.0 g sodium peroxide, 0.2 g dextrose, and 0.2 g potassium nitrate; actual proportions were 0.35 g, 2.59 g, and 0.2 g respectively. There was insufficient sodium peroxide to dissolve decomposition gases, hence a rapid temperature and pressure build-up caused the Parr bomb to burst.
Tennessee Eastman (1967).

Diethyl Ether
See SODIUM PEROXIDE plus Aniline.

Glycerine
See SODIUM PEROXIDE plus Aniline.

Hexamethylene-tetramine
Sodium peroxide will ignite numerous organic compounds, e.g., hexamethylenetetramine, when the mixture is moistened.
Ellern, p. 46 (1968).
See also SODIUM PEROXIDE plus Aniline.
See also SODIUM PEROXIDE plus Organic Matter.

Hydrogen Sulfide
See HYDROGEN SULFIDE plus Sodium Peroxide.

Magnesium
See MAGNESIUM plus Sodium Peroxide.

Magnesium and Carbon Dioxide
See MAGNESIUM plus Sodium Peroxide and Carbon Dioxide.

Manganese Dioxide
The catalyzed decomposition of sodium peroxide with manganese dioxide may be violent.
Mellor **2, Supp. 2:** 635 (1961).

Organic Matter
When sodium peroxide is mixed with combustible materials, explosive mixtures may be formed. See also SODIUM PEROXIDE plus Aniline.
Mellor **2:** 490 (1946-1947). *Ellern,* p. 46 (1968).

Phosphorus
See PHOSPHORUS plus Sodium Peroxide.
See SODIUM PEROXIDE plus Aniline.

Potassium
See POTASSIUM plus Sodium Peroxide.

Selenium Monochloride
See SELENIUM MONOCHLORIDE plus Sodium Peroxide.

Silver Chloride and Charcoal
A mixture of sodium peroxide, silver chloride, and charcoal ignites spontaneously.
Mellor **3:** 401 (1946-1947).

Sodium
See SODIUM plus Sodium Peroxide.

Sulfur Monochloride
A violent reaction results on mixing sodium peroxide and sulfur monochloride.
Mellor **2, Supp. 2:** 634 (1961).

Tin
See TIN plus Sodium Peroxide.

Zinc
See ZINC plus Sodium Peroxide.

SODIUM PHOSPHIDE Na_3P

Water
In contact with water or damp air, sodium phosphide evolves phosphine, which is spontaneously flammable in air.
Lab. Govt. Chemist (1965). *Van Wazer* (1958).

SODIUM PHOSPHINAMIDE $NaNHPH_2$

(self-reactive)
Sodium amino phosphide is spontaneously flammable in air.
Lehman and Wilson, p. 50 (1949).

SODIUM POLYSULFIDE Na_2S_X

m-Chloroaniline Diazonium Salt
See SODIUM SULFIDE plus Diazonium and Diazonium Chloride Salts.

4-Chloro-o-toluidine Diazonium Chloride Salt
See SODIUM SULFIDE plus Diazonium and Diazonium Chloride Salts.

o-Nitroaniline Diazonium Salt
See SODIUM SULFIDE plus Diazonium and Diazonium Chloride Salts.

SODIUM-POTASSIUM ALLOY NaK
(See also the reactions listed separately under SODIUM and POTASSIUM)

Ammonium Sulfate and Ammonium Nitrate
See POTASSIUM plus Ammonium Sulfate and Ammonium Nitrate.

Bromoform
Mixtures of sodium-potassium alloy and bromoform, tetrachloroethane, or pentachloroethane can explode on standing at room temperature. They are especially sensitive to impact.
Mellor **2, Supp. 2:** 563 (1961).

Carbon Dioxide
Solid carbon dioxide with sodium-potassium alloy will explode under a slight impact.
H. Staudinger, *Z. Elektrochem.* **31:** 549-52 (1925).
Mellor **2, Supp. 2:** 563 (1961).

Carbon Tetrachloride
If carbon tetrachloride is placed on sodium-potassium alloy, a light impact will cause a violent explosion. Chloroform, dichloromethane, or methyl chloride in contact with sodium-potassium alloy is similarly impact-sensitive.
H. Staudinger, *Z. Elektrochem.* **31:** 549-52 (1925). *Ellern,* p. 43 (1968).
Addition of a small amount of carbon tetrachloride to the alloy with a trace of kerosine and carbonaceous residue resulted in a violent explosion after a few moments.
Bozich (1966).
Mellor **2, Supp. 2:** 563 (1961).
See also SODIUM-POTASSIUM ALLOY plus Water.

Chloroform
See SODIUM-POTASSIUM ALLOY plus Carbon Tetrachloride. See LITHIUM plus Chloroform.

Dichloromethane
See SODIUM-POTASSIUM ALLOY plus Carbon Tetrachloride.

Diiodomethane
Sodium-potassium alloy reacts explosively with diiodomethane.
Ellern, p. 43 (1968).

Mercuric Oxide
Red mercuric oxide causes a violent explosion with sodium-potassium alloy when struck lightly; the yellow oxide does so at a much lighter blow.
H. Staudinger, *Z. Elektrochem.* **31:** 549-52 (1925).

Methyl Chloride
See SODIUM-POTASSIUM ALLOY plus Carbon Tetrachloride.

Methyl Dichloride
The mixture of sodium-potassium alloy and methyl dichloride detonates strongly if struck.
Mellor **2, Supp. 2:** 563 (1961).

Oxalyl Bromide
A mixture of sodium-potassium alloy and either oxalyl bromide or oxalyl chloride explodes violently.
Mellor **2, Supp. 2:** 564 (1961).

Oxalyl Chloride
See SODIUM-POTASSIUM ALLOY plus Oxalyl Bromide.

Pentachloroethane
See SODIUM-POTASSIUM ALLOY plus Bromoform.

Potassium Oxides
See POTASSIUM plus Air.

Potassium Superoxide
While 100 gallons of sodium-potassium was being transferred and filtered into a receiver tank, the waste oxide accumulating on the filter was periodically scraped into drums. Drops of hot liquid NaK fell into one drum receiving the oxide waste, and a serious explosion occurred. Potassium superoxide was considered the essential ingredient of the explosive mixture.
Health and Safety Inf. **251** (March 31, 1967).

Silicon
See SILICON plus Sodium-Potassium Alloy.

Silver Halides
Sodium-potassium alloys have exploded violently on contact with silver halides.
Ellern, p. 43 (1968).

Sodium Bicarbonate
See SODIUM-POTASSIUM ALLOY plus Water.

Teflon®
Sealing tape made of Teflon® (polytetrafluoroethylene or polyhexafluoroethylene) burned vigorously in contact with sodium- potassium alloy in a helium atmosphere.
Scott (1966).

Tetrachloroethane
See SODIUM-POTASSIUM ALLOY plus Bromoform.

1,1,1-Trichloroethane
A pipe- and solenoid-valve assembly used to transfer NaK had been purged with nitrogen, then flushed with water. Trichloroethane, used subsequently to remove traces of water, contacted a hidden residue of NaK in one valve and an explosion ensued.
Inf. Exchange Bull. **1:** 2 (1961).

Trichlorotrifluoroethane
When two drops of the trichlorotrifluoroethane were added to NaK, there was a violent explosion.
Pancner (1966).

Water
Sodium-potassium alloy undergoes a violent reaction with certain extinguishing agents: water, sodium bicarbonate, carbon tetrachloride.
Mellor **2, Supp. 2:** 564 (1961).

SODIUM SILICATE $NaSiO_3$

Fluorine
See FLUORINE plus Sodium Silicate.

SODIUM SILICIDE Na_2Si_2

Air
Sodium silicide in powder form is spontaneously flammable in air.
Ellern (1968).

Water
See CESIUM SILICIDE plus Water.

SODIUM SULFATE Na_2SO_4

Aluminum
See ALUMINUM plus Sulfates.

SODIUM SULFIDE Na_2S

Carbon
See CARBON plus Sodium Sulfide.

m-Chloroaniline Diazonium Salt
See SODIUM SULFIDE plus Diazonium and Diazonium Chloride Salts.

4-Chloro-o-toluidine Diazonium Chloride Salts
See SODIUM SULFIDE plus Diazonium and Diazonium Chloride Salts.

Diazonium Salts and Diazonium Chloride Salts
In the preparation of mercaptans, the slow addition of the diazonium chloride salt of 4-chloro-o-toluidine or o- nitroaniline or m-chloroaniline to sodium sulfide, sodium bisulfide or sodium polysulfide solutions will result in explosions even at 5°C.
Chem. and Eng. News **23:** 1247 (1945).
Hodgson, *Chem. & Ind.*, p. 362 (1945).

Diazonium Salts
See DIAZONIUM SALTS plus Thiophenates.

N, N-Dichloromethyl Amine
See N, N-DICHLOROMETHYL AMINE plus Sodium Sulfide.

o-Nitroaniline Diazonium Salt
See SODIUM SULFIDE plus Diazonium and Diazonium Chloride Salts.

Water
Moist sodium sulfide is spontaneously flammable upon drying in air.
Brauer (1965).

SODIUM SUPEROXIDE NaO_2

(self-reactive)
Sodium superoxide violently evolves oxygen above 250°C.
Mellor **2, Supp. 2:** 639 (1961).

Water
The reaction of sodium superoxide and water is fast and vigorous, liberating oxygen.
Mellor **2, Supp. 2:** 639 (1961).

SODIUM TETRAHYDROALUMINATE $NaAlH_4$

Tetrahydrofuran
A violent explosion occurred during the preparation of sodium aluminum hydride from sodium and aluminum in a medium of tetrahydrofuran. Localized heating in the reaction vessel was the suspected trigger mechanism.
Chem. and Eng. News **39** (40): 57 (1961).

Water
On coming in contact with water sodium aluminum hydride ignites or explodes.
NSC Nat. Safety News **77** (2): 37-40 (1958).

SODIUM TETRAHYDROBORATE $NaBH_4$

Air
Sodium borohydride burns quietly in air.
Lab. Govt. Chemist (1965).

SODIUM TETRAPEROXYCHROMATE $Na_3Cr(OO)_4$

(self-reactive)
Sodium triperchromate decomposes explosively at 115°C.
Mellor **11:** 356 (1946-1947).

SODIUM TETRAZOLYL-5-AZIDE $NaNN{=}NN{=}CNNN$

(self-reactive)
Sodium tetrazolyl-5-azide is a shock-sensitive compound.
Chem. and Eng. News **43** (52): 29, 30 (Dec. 27, 1965).

SODIUM THIOSULFATE $Na_2S_2O_3$

Sodium Nitrite
See SODIUM NITRITE plus Sodium Thiosulfate.

STAINLESS STEEL (302)

Fluorine
See FLUORINE plus Metals.

STANNIC BROMIDE $SnBr_4$

Nitryl Chloride
See NITRYL CHLORIDE plus Stannic Bromide.

STANNIC CHLORIDE $SnCl_4$

Potassium
See POTASSIUM plus Aluminum Bromide.

Sodium
See SODIUM plus Aluminum Bromide.

Turpentine
Stannic chloride reacts with turpentine, producing heat and some times flame.
Mellor **7:** 430-46 (1946-1947).

STANNIC IODIDE SnI_4

Nitryl Chloride
See NITRYL CHLORIDE plus Stannic Bromide.

Potassium and Sulfur
See POTASSIUM plus Aluminum Bromide.

Sodium and Sulfur
See SODIUM plus Aluminum Bromide.

STANNIC OXIDE SnO_2

Chlorine Trifluoride
See CHLORINE TRIFLUORIDE plus Arsenic Trioxide.

Hydrogen Trisulfide
See HYDROGEN TRISULFIDE plus Stannic Oxide.

Magnesium
See MAGNESIUM plus Stannic Oxide.

Potassium
See POTASSIUM plus Stannic Oxide.

Sodium
See POTASSIUM plus Stannic Oxide.

STANNIC SULFIDE SnS_2

Cadmium Chlorate
Tin sulfides react with incandescence with chlorates of cadmium, magnesium, or zinc.
Mellor **Supp. II, Part I:** 584 (1956).

Chloric Acid
Tin sulfides and concentrated solutions of chloric acid react with incandescence.
Mellor **Supp. II, Part I:** 584 (1956).

Chlorine Monoxide
See CHLORINE MONOXIDE plus Calcium Phosphide.

Magnesium Chlorate
See STANNIC SULFIDE plus Cadmium Chlorate.

Zinc Chlorate
See STANNIC SULFIDE plus Cadmium Chlorate.

STANNOUS CHLORIDE $SnCl_2$

Bromine Trifluoride
See BROMINE TRIFLUORIDE plus Stannous Chloride.

Calcium Carbide
A mixture of stannous chloride and calcium carbide can be ignited with a match, and the reaction proceeds with incandescence.
Mellor **7:** 430 (1946-1947).

Ethylene Oxide
See ETHYLENE OXIDE plus Aluminum Oxide. See ETHYLENE OXIDE plus Acids and Bases.

Hydrazine Hydrate
Hydrazine hydrate reacts with stannous chloride to give a compound, stannous dihydrazinechloride. When this compound is heated, it decomposes explosively.
Mellor **7:** 430 (1946-1947).

Nitrates
See NITRATES plus Stannous Chloride.

Potassium
See POTASSIUM plus Aluminum Bromide.

Sodium
See SODIUM plus Aluminum Bromide.

STANNOUS FLUORIDE $SnFl_2$

Chlorine
See CHLORINE plus Stannous Fluoride.

STANNOUS NITRATE $Sn(NO_3)_2$

Organic Matter (flour)
In a flour-bleaching plant, dust found to contain tin nitrate was believed responsible for a violent decomposition explosion.
J. Soc. Chem. Ind. **41:** 423-24R (1922).

STANNOUS OXIDE SnO

Sulfur Dioxide
When stannous oxide is heated in an atmosphere of sulfur dioxide, the reaction is attended by incandescence.
Mellor **7:** 388 (1946-1947). Hammick, J.
Chem. Soc. **III:** 379 (1917).

STANNOUS SULFIDE SnS

Cadmium Chlorate
Tin sulfides react with incandescence with chlorates of cadmium, magnesium, or zinc.
Mellor **Supp. II, Part I:** 584 (1956).

Chloric Acid
Tin sulfides and concentrated solutions of chloric acid react with incandescence.
Mellor **Supp. II, Part I:** 584 (1956).

Chlorine Monoxide
See CHLORINE MONOXIDE plus Calcium Phosphide.

Magnesium Chlorate
See STANNOUS SULFIDE plus Cadmium Chlorate.

Zinc Chlorate
See STANNOUS SULFIDE plus Cadmium Chlorate.

STEEL

Perchloric Acid
See PERCHLORIC ACID plus Steel.

Sulfuric Acid
See IRON plus Sulfuric Acid.

STIBINE SbH_3

Ammonia
An explosion occurs if stibine is heated with ammonia or chlorine.
Mellor **9:** 397 (1946-1947).

Chlorine
See STIBINE plus Ammonia.

Nitric Acid
Stibine and concentrated nitric acid explode.
Mellor **9:** 397 (1946-1947).

Ozone
See OZONE plus Stibine.

STRONTIUM ALLOYS

Acids
Alloys containing a substantial proportion of strontium react vio lently with acids.
Lab. Govt. Chemist (1965).

Water
Alloys containing a substantial proportion of strontium rapidly decompose water. The heat of reaction is sufficient that the evolved hydrogen may ignite.
Lab. Govt. Chemist (1965).

STRONTIUM CARBIDE SrC_2

Selenium
See SULFUR plus Strontium Carbide.

Sulfur
See SULFUR plus Strontium Carbide.

STRONTIUM CHLORATE $Sr(ClO_3)_2$

Acids
See CHLORATES plus Acids. See SODIUM CHLORATE plus Sulfuric Acid.

STRONTIUM CHLORIDE $SrCl_2$

2-Furan Percarboxylic Acid
See 2-FURAN PERCARBOXYLIC ACID (self-reactive).

STRONTIUM HYDRIDE SrH_2

Bromates
See BROMATES plus Strontium Hydride.

Chlorates
See BROMATES plus Strontium Hydride.

Perchlorates
See BROMATES plus Strontium Hydride.

STRONTIUM IODIDE SrI_2

Potassium
See POTASSIUM plus Ammonium Bromide.

STRONTIUM PHOSPHIDE Sr_3P_2

Bromine
See BROMINE plus Strontium Phosphide.

Chlorine
See CHLORINE plus Strontium Phosphide.

Fluorine
See FLUORINE plus Strontium Phosphide.

STYRENE MONOMER $CH_2{=}CHC_6H_5$

Chlorosulfonic Acid
Mixing styrene monomer and chlorosulfonic acid in a closed container caused the temperature and pressure to increase.
Flynn and Rossow (1970). See Note under complete reference.

Oleum
See OLEUM plus Styrene Monomer.

Sulfuric Acid
Mixing styrene monomer and 96% sulfuric acid in a closed container caused the temperature and pressure to increase.
Flynn and Rossow (1970). See Note under complete reference.

SULFAMIC ACID HSO_3NH_2

Chlorine
See CHLORINE plus Sulfamic Acid.

Nitric Acid
Fuming nitric acid combined with sulfamic acid causes violent release of nitrous oxide.
Mellor **8, Supp. 2:** 316 (1967).

SULFATES
(See also specific sulfates as primary entries or under other reactants)

Aluminum
See ALUMINUM plus Sulfates.

Magnesium
See MAGNESIUM plus Sulfates.

SULFOLANE $O_2SCH_2CH_2CH_2CH_2$

Chrosoulfonic Acid
Mixing sulfolane and chlorosulfonic acid in a closed container caused the temperature and pressure to increase.
Flynn and Rossow (1970). See Note under complete reference.

Oleum
See OLEUM plus Sulfolane.

SULFOXIDES

Perchloric Acid
The dialkyl sulfoxides form salts with perchloric acid. The lower members of the series are unstable, hydrolyze readily, and are explosive when dry.
Chem. Abst. **44:** p. 3935d (1950).

SULFUR S

Aluminum
See ALUMINUM plus Nitrates.

Aluminum and Niobium Oxide
See ALUMINUM plus Niobium Oxide and Sulfur.

Ammonia
The reaction of ammonia with specially prepared sulfur may form explosive sulfur nitride.
Mellor **8, Supp. 1:** 330 (1964).

Ammonium Nitrate
Ammonium nitrate mixed with sulfur or with metal powders can be exploded by shock.
Kirk and Othmer **8:** 644. *Federoff* **1:** A-146.

Ammonium Perchlorate
Mixtures of ammonium perchlorate with sulfur, powdered metals, or carbonaceous materials are impact-sensitive.
Haz. Chem. Data (1966).

Barium Bromate
See SULFUR plus Bromates.

Barium Carbide
A mixture of barium carbide and sulfur heated to 150°C. becomes incandescent.
Mellor **5:** 862 (1946-1947).

Barium Chlorate
See SULFUR plus Bromates. See SULFUR plus Chlorates.
A mixture of sulfur and barium chlorate ignites at about 108–111°C.
Mellor **2, Supp. 1:** 583 (1956).

Barium Iodate
See SULFUR plus Bromates.

Boron
See BORON plus Sulfur.

Bromates
A combination of finely divided sulfur and finely divided bromates (also chlorates or iodates) of barium, calcium, magnesium, potassium, sodium, or zinc will explode with heat, percussion, and sometimes, light friction.
Mellor **2:** 310 (1946-1947).
Mellor **2, Supp. 1:** 763 (1956).

Bromine Pentafluoride
See ARSENIC plus Bromine Pentafluoride.

Bromine Trifluoride
See ANTIMONY plus Bromine Trifluoride.

Calcium
See CALCIUM plus Sulfur.

Calcium, Vanadium Oxide, and Water
See CALCIUM plus Vanadium Oxide, Sulfur, and Water.

Calcium Bromate
See SULFUR plus Bromates.

Calcium Carbide
Calcium carbide reacts incandescently with sulfur vapor at 500°C.
Mellor **5:** 862 (1946-1947).

Calcium Chlorate
See SULFUR plus Bromates. See SULFUR plus Chlorates.

Calcium Hypochlorite
A mixture of damp sulfur and calcium hypochlorite produced a brilliant crimson flash with scattering of molten sulfur. No heat is necessary. Equal parts of sulfur and bleach powder produced an explosion when heated in a closed vessel.
Halane — Prelim. Info. Sheet. Mellor **2:** 254-62 (1946-1947).
Chem. and Eng. News **46**(28):9 (1968).

Calcium Iodate
See SULFUR plus Bromates.

Calcium Phosphide
Calcium phosphide reacts with sulfur or oxygen incandescently at about 300°C.
Mellor **8:** 841 (1946-1947).

Carbon
When the metal head of a hammer struck against the inner coating material of a brick tank consisting of a carbonaceous matrix loaded with 66% sulfur (absorbed from sulfuric acid), ignition occurred producing blue flames.

Cesium Nitride
See CESIUM NITRIDE plus Air.

Charcoal
Powdered sulfur is spontaneously flammable when mixed with lampblack or freshly calcined charcoal.
Von Schwartz, p. 328 (1918).

Chlorates
A mixture of sulfur and barium chlorate, calcium chlorate, magnesium chlorate, potassium chlorate, sodium chlorate, or zinc chlorate may liberate oxygen and heat explosively.
Chem. and Eng. News **30:** 3210 (1952). *Von Schwartz,* p. 323 (1918).
A mixture of chlorates and sulfur will explode.
Von Schwartz, p. 328 (1918). *Ellern,* p. 47 (1968).
See also SULFUR plus Bromates.

Chlorates and Copper
The sulfur-plus-chlorate explosion is remarkably spontaneous in the presence of copper ion or copper, e.g., in the form of bronze screen, even at room temperature.
Ellern, p. 304 (1968).

Chlorine Dioxide
A piece of sulfur or sugar takes fire spontaneously in chlorine dioxide and may produce an explosion.
Mellor **2:** 289 (1946-1947).

Chlorine Monoxide
See POTASSIUM plus Chlorine Monoxide.

Chlorine Trifluoride
See ANTIMONY plus Chlorine Trifluoride.

Chromic Anhydride
Sulfur and chromic anhydride ignite when heated and can explode.
Mellor **10:** 102, 132-34; **11:** 232 (1946-1947).

Chromium Trioxide
See SULFUR plus Chromic Anhydride.

Chromyl Chloride
Flowers-of-sulfur moistened with chromyl chloride ignites sponta neously.
Mellor **11:** 394-96 (1946-1947).

Fluorine
See FLUORINE plus Selenium.

Hydrocarbons
Even small percentages of hydrocarbons in contact with molten sulfur generate hydrogen sulfide and carbon disulfide, which may accumulate in explosive concentrations.
NAS-USCG Advis. Com. (1966).
BM Report Invest. **6185** (1963).

Indium
See INDIUM plus Sulfur.

Iodates
See SULFUR plus Bromates.

Iodine Pentafluoride
See ARSENIC plus Iodine Pentafluoride.

Iodine Pentoxide
See CARBON plus Iodine Pentoxide.

Lead Chlorate
A mixture of sulfur and lead chlorate ignites at about 63°– 67°C.
Mellor **2, Supp. 1:** 583 (1956).
See also SULFUR plus Chlorates.

Lead Chlorite
A mixture of sulfur and lead chlorite will explode.
Von Schwartz, p. 328 (1918).

Lead Dioxide
A mixture of sulfur and lead dioxide will explode.
Von Schwartz, p. 328 (1918).

Lithium
See LITHIUM plus Sulfur.

Lithium Carbide
Lithium carbide burns in the vapor of sulfur or selenium.
Mellor **5:** 848 (1946-1947).

Magnesium Bromate
See SULFUR plus Bromates.

Magnesium Chlorate
See SULFUR plus Bromates.

Magnesium Iodate
See SULFUR plus Bromates.

Mercuric Nitrate
An explosion occurred in the use of mercuric nitrate for determining sulfur in Ball's reaction.
Chem. and Eng. News **26:** 3300 (1948).

Mercuric Oxide
When mercuric oxide is heated with sulfur in a retort, a violent explosion results.
Mellor **4:** 777 (1946-1947).

Mercurous Oxide
Mixture of the pulverized materials will ignite from light impact.
J. B. Senderens, *Bull. Soc. Chim.* (3) **6:** 802 (1891).

Nickel
Powdered nickel heated with sulfur or selenium reacts with incandescence.
Mellor **15:** 148,151 (1946-1947).

Nitrogen Dioxide
See MAGNESIUM plus Nitrogen Dioxide.

Palladium
See PALLADIUM plus Sulfur.

Perchlorates
All inorganic perchlorates can form mixtures with sulfur that will explode on impact.
ACS **146:** 211-12. *BM Report Invest.* **4169** (1948).

Phosphorus
See PHOSPHORUS plus Sulfur.

Phosphorus Trioxide
The reaction is violent; small quantities should be used to avoid an explosion.
Chem. and Eng. News **27:** 2144 (1949).
Mellor **8, Supp. 3:** 436 (1971).

Potassium
See POTASSIUM plus Aluminum Bromide.
See POTASSIUM plus Sulfur.

Potassium Bromate
See SULFUR plus Bromates.

Potassium Chlorate
See SULFUR plus Bromates.
A mixture of sulfur and potassium chlorate ignites at about 160° – 162°C.
Mellor **2, Supp. 1:** 583 (1956).
See also SULFUR plus Chlorates.

Potassium Iodate
See SULFUR plus Bromates.

Potassium Nitrate and Arsenic Trisulfide
A mixture of these ingredients is a known pyrotechnic formulation.
Ellern, p. 135 (1968).

Potassium Nitride
See PHOSPHORUS plus Potassium Nitride.

Potassium Perchlorate
This mixture, used in flashcrackers, can be exploded by a moderately strong impact.
ACS **146:** 211. *Davis. BM Report Invest.* **4169** (1948).

Potassium Permanganate
When powdered sulfur is heated with potassium permanganate, an explosion may occur.
Mellor **12:** 319 (1946-1947).

Rubidium Acetylene Carbide
See RUBIDIUM ACETYLENE CARBIDE plus Hydrochloric Acid.
See PHOSPHORUS plus Rubidium Acetylene Carbide.

Selenium Carbide
See SULFUR plus Thorium Carbide.

Silver Bromate
An explosive reaction occurs in the presence of water.
Mellor **2, Supp. 1:** 766 (1956).

Silver Chlorate
A mixture of sulfur and silver chlorate ignites at about 74°C.
Mellor **2, Supp. 1:** 583 (1956).
See also SULFUR plus Chlorates.

Silver Nitrate
A mixture of silver nitrate and sulfur explodes when struck with a hammer.
Mellor **3:** 469 (1946-1947).

Silver Oxide
When finely divided sulfur is ground with silver oxide, the mixture ignites.
Mellor **3:** 376 (1946-1947).

Sodium
See SODIUM plus Sulfur.

Sodium Bromate
See SULFUR plus Bromates.

Sodium Chlorate
See SULFUR plus Bromates.

Sodium Chlorite
Solid sulfur will ignite if mixed with solid sodium chlorite and moistened.
Mellor **2, Supp. 1:** 572 (1956).

Sodium Hydride
Sodium hydride reacts vigorously with sulfur vapor.
Mellor **2:** 483 (1946-1947).

Sodium Iodate
See SULFUR plus Bromates.

Sodium Nitrate and Charcoal
The familiar black powder explosion begins with the reaction, sulfur-plus-sodium-nitrate, which produces the energy to initiate the carbon-plus-sodium-nitrate explosion.
Trans. Faraday Soc. **55** (12):2221-8 (1959).

Sodium and Stannic Iodide
See SODIUM plus Aluminum Bromide.

Strontium Carbide
Strontium carbide mixed with selenium and heated to 500°C, or exposed to sulfur vapor at 500°C, becomes incandescent.
Mellor **5:** 852 (1946-1947).

Sulfur Dichloride
See SODIUM plus Cobaltous Bromide.

Thallic Oxide
See THALLIC OXIDE plus Antimony Sulfide.

Thorium
Thorium when heated with sulfur reacts vigorously with incandescence.
Mellor **7:** 208 (1946-1947).

Thorium Carbide
Sulfur vapor attacks heated thorium carbide or selenium carbide with incandescence.
Mellor **5:** 885-87 (1946-1947).

Tin
The reaction between tin and sulfur is vigorous and accompanied by incandescence.
Mellor **7:** 328 (1946-1947).

Uranium
See URANIUM plus Selenium.

Zinc
Powdered zinc and sulfur react explosively when warmed.
Mellor **4:** 476 (1946-1947).

Zinc Bromate
See SULFUR plus Bromates.

Zinc Chlorate
See SULFUR plus Bromates.

Zinc Iodate
See SULFUR plus Bromates.

SULFUR DIBROMIDE SBr_9

Potassium
See POTASSIUM plus Aluminum Bromide.

Sodium
See SODIUM plus Aluminum Bromide.

SULFUR DICHLORIDE SCl_2

Aluminum
See ALUMINUM plus Carbon Disulfide.

Ammonia
The reaction product of sulfur dichloride and ammonia is a powerful detonating compound, sulfur nitride.
Mellor **8:** 624 (1946-1947).

Potassium
See POTASSIUM plus Boron Tribromide.

Sodium
See SODIUM plus Cobaltous Bromide.
See SODIUM plus Sulfur Dichloride.

SULFUR DIOXIDE SO_2

Acrolein
See ACROLEIN plus Sulfur Dioxide.

Aluminum
See ALUMINUM plus Carbon Disulfide.

Cesium Acetylene Carbide
See CESIUM ACETYLENE CARBIDE plus Sulfur Dioxide.

Cesium Monoxide
See CESIUM MONOXIDE plus Sulfur Dioxide.

Chlorates
See CHLORATES plus Sulfur Dioxide.

Chlorine Trifluoride
See CHLORINE TRIFLUORIDE plus Ammonia.

Chromium
See CHROMIUM plus Sulfur Dioxide.

Ferrous Oxide
See FERROUS OXIDE plus Sulfur Dioxide.

Fluorine
See FLUORINE plus Sulfur Dioxide.

Lithium Acetylene Carbide Diammino
See LITHIUM ACETYLENE CARBIDE DIAMMINO plus Carbon Dioxide.

Manganese
See MANGANESE plus Sulfur Dioxide.

Potassium Acetylene Carbide
See POTASSIUM ACETYLENE CARBIDE plus Sulfur Dioxide.

Potassium Chlorate
See POTASSIUM CHLORATE plus Sulfur Dioxide.

Rubidium Carbide
See RUBIDIUM CARBIDE plus Sulfur Dioxide.

Sodium
See SODIUM plus Sulfur Dioxide.

Sodium Carbide
See SODIUM CARBIDE plus Carbon Dioxide.

Stannous Oxide
See STANNOUS OXIDE plus Sulfur Dioxide.

SULFUR HEXAFLUORIDE SF_6

Disilane
See DISILANE plus Sulfur Hexafluoride.

SULFURIC ACID H_2SO_4

Acetic Anhydride
See ACETIC ANHYDRIDE plus Sulfuric Acid.

Acetone Cyanhydrin
See ACETONE CYANHYDRIN plus Sulfuric Acid.

Acetone and Nitric Acid
See NITRIC ACID plus Acetone and Sulfuric Acid.

Acetone and Potassium Dichromate
See ACETONE plus Sulfuric Acid and Potassium Dichromate.

Acetonitrile
See ACETONITRILE plus Sulfuric Acid.

Acrolein
See ACROLEIN plus Sulfuric Acid.

Acrylonitrile
See ACRYLONITRILE plus Sulfuric Acid.

Acrylonitrile and Water
See ACRYLONITRILE plus Sulfuric Acid and Water.

Alcohols and Hydrogen Peroxide
See ALCOHOLS plus Hydrogen Peroxide and Sulfuric Acid.

Allyl Alcohol
See ALLYL ALCOHOL plus Sulfuric Acid.

Allyl Chloride
See ALLYL CHLORIDE plus Sulfuric Acid.
Allylchloride may polymerize violently under conditions involving an acid catalyst, such as sulfuric acid, ferric chloride, aluminum chloride, Lewis acids, and Ziegler type catalysts (initiators).
Ventrone (1971).

2-Aminoethanol
See 2-AMINOETHANOL plus Sulfuric Acid.

Ammonium Hydroxide
Mixing 96% sulfuric acid and 28% ammonia in a closed container caused the temperature and pressure to increase.
Flynn and Rossow (1970). See Note under complete reference.

Ammonium Triperchromate
See AMMONIUM TRIPERCHROMATE plus Sulfuric Acid.

Aniline
See ANILINE plus Sulfuric Acid.

Bromates and Metals
See CHLORATES plus Acids and Metals.

Bromine Pentafluoride
See BROMINE PENTAFLUORIDE plus Nitric Acid.

n-Butyraldehyde
See n-BUTYRALDEHYDE plus Sulfuric Acid.

Carbides
Sulfuric acid (concentrated) is extremely hazardous in contact with carbides, chlorates, fulminates, picrates and powdered metals.
Chem. Safety Data Sheet **SD-20** (1963).
Haz. Chem. Data (1966).

Cesium Acetylene Carbide
See CESIUM ACETYLENE CARBIDE plus Sulfuric Acid.

Chlorates
See SULFURIC ACID plus Carbides.
See CHLORATES plus Acids.
See CHLORATES plus Sulfuric Acid.

Chlorates and Metals
See CHLORATES plus Acids and Metals.

Chlorine Trifluoride
See CHLORINE TRIFLUORIDE plus Nitric Acid.

Chlorosulfonic Acid
See CHLOROSULFURIC ACID plus Sulfuric Acid.

Cuprous Nitride
See CUPROUS NITRIDE plus Sulfuric Acid.

Diisobutylene
See DIISOBUTYLENE plus Sulfuric Acid.

Dimethylbenzylcarbinol and Hydrogen Peroxide
See ALCOHOLS plus Hydrogen Peroxide and Sulfuric Acid.

Epichlorohydrin
See ETHYLENE CYANOHYDRIN plus Sulfuric Acid.
See EPICHLOROHYDRIN plus Sulfuric Acid.

Ethyl Alcohol and Hydrogen Peroxide
See ALCOHOLS plus Hydrogen Peroxide and Sulfuric Acid.

Ethylene Cyanohydrin
See ETHYLENE CYANOHYDRIN plus Sulfuric Acid.

Ethylene Diamine
See ETHYLENE DIAMINE plus Sulfuric Acid.

Ethylene Glycol
See ETHYLENE GLYCOL plus Sulfuric Acid.

Ethylenimine
See ETHYLENIMINE plus Sulfuric Acid.

Fulminates
See SULFURIC ACID plus Carbides.

Hydrochloric Acid
See HYDROCHLORIC ACID plus Sulfuric Acid.

Hydrochloric Acid and Nitric Acid
An exothermic reaction occurred when 98% sulfuric acid was added to a mixture of hydrochloric acid and nitric acid. After the container was sealed, it was agitated causing the mixture to effervesce and increase pressure until the container ruptured.

Hydrofluoric Acid
See HYDROFLUORIC ACID plus Sulfuric Acid.

Hydrogen Peroxide
See HYDROGEN PEROXIDE plus Sulfuric Acid.

Iodine Heptafluoride
See IODINE HEPTAFLUORIDE plus Sulfuric Acid.

Indane and Nitric Acid
See INDANE plus Nitric Acid and Sulfuric Acid.

Iron
See IRON plus Sulfuric Acid.

Isoprene
See ISOPRENE plus Sulfuric Acid.

Lithium Silicide
See LITHIUM SILICIDE plus Sulfuric Acid.

Mercuric Nitride
See MERCURIC NITRIDE plus Sulfuric Acid.

Mesityl Oxide
See MESITYL OXIDE plus Sulfuric Acid.

Metals (Powdered)
See SULFURIC ACID plus Carbides.

Nitric Acid and Glycerides
See NITRIC ACID plus Sulfuric Acid and Glycerides.

p-Nitrotoluene
See p-NITROTOLUENE plus Sulfuric Acid.

Pentasilver Trihydroxy- diaminophosphate
See PENTASILVER TRIHYDROXYDIAMINOPHOSPHATE plus Sulfuric Acid.

Perchlorates
See PERCHLORATES plus Sulfuric Acid.

Perchloric Acid
See PERCHLORIC ACID plus Sulfuric Acid.

Permanganates and Benzene
See PERMANGANATES plus Sulfuric Acid and Benzene.

1-Phenyl-2-methyl-propyl Alcohol and Hydrogen Peroxide
See ALCOHOLS plus Hydrogen Peroxide and Sulfuric Acid.

Phosphorus
See PHOSPHORUS plus Sulfuric Acid.

Phosphorus Isocyanate
See PHOSPHORUS ISOCYANATE plus Acetaldehyde.

Picrates
See SULFURIC ACID plus Carbides.

Potassium Tert.-Butoxide
See ACETONE plus Potassium Tert.-Butoxide.

Potassium Chlorate
See POTASSIUM CHLORATE plus Sulfuric Acid.

Potassium Permanganate
See POTASSIUM PERMANGANATE plus Sulfuric Acid.

Potassium Permanganate and Potassium Chloride
See POTASSIUM PERMANGANATE plus Sulfuric Acid and Potassium Chloride.

Potassium Permanganate and Water
See POTASSIUM PERMANGANATE plus Sulfuric Acid and Water.

Propiolactone (BETA-)
See PROPIOLACTONE (BETA-) plus Sulfuric Acid.

Propylene Oxide
See PROPYLENE OXIDE plus Sulfuric Acid.

Pyridine
See PYRIDINE plus Sulfuric Acid.

Rubidium Acetylene Carbide
See RUBIDIUM ACETYLENE CARBIDE plus Sulfuric Acid.

Silver Permanganate
See SILVER PERMANGANATE plus Sulfuric Acid.

Sodium
See SODIUM plus Sulfuric Acid.

Sodium Carbonate
See SODIUM CARBONATE plus Sulfuric Acid.

Sodium Chlorate
See SODIUM CHLORATE plus Sulfuric Acid.
See CHLORATES plus Acids.

Sodium Hydroxide
See SODIUM HYDROXIDE plus Sulfuric Acid.

Steel
See IRON plus Sulfuric Acid.

Styrene Monomer
See STYRENE MONOMER plus Sulfuric Acid.

Toluene and Nitric Acid
See NITRIC ACID plus Toluene and Sulfuric Acid.

Vinyl Acetate
See VINYL ACETATE plus Sulfuric Acid.

Water
During sulfonation of mononitrobenzene by *fuming* sulfuric acid, a leak from an internal cooling coil permitted water to enter the tank.
A violent eruption occurred due to the heat of solution.
MCA Case History **944** (1963).

Zinc Chlorate
See ZINC CHLORATE plus Sulfuric Acid.
See CHLORATES plus Acids.

SULFUR MONOCHLORIDE S_2Cl_2

Chromyl Chloride
See CHROMYL CHLORIDE plus Sulfur Monochloride.

Organic Matter
Sulfur chloride is strongly corrosive and can set fire to organic materials.
B.L. Huestis, *Safety Eng.* **54:** 95 (1927).

Phosphorus Trioxide
See PHOSPHORUS TRIOXIDE plus Sulfur Monochloride.

Sodium Peroxide
See SODIUM PEROXIDE plus Sulfur Monochloride.

Water
The mixing of sulfur chloride and water can be dangerous.
Chem. Safety Data Sheet **SD-77** (1960).

SULFUR NITRIDE S_4N_4

(self-reactive)
Sulfur nitride detonates violently on impact.
Mellor **8:** 624 (1946-1947).

Air
Disulfur dinitride explodes when above 30°C in air.
Brauer (1965).

Barium Chlorate
Nitrogen sulfide and barium chlorate form very explosive crystals.
Berichte **38:** 2659.

SULFUR TRIOXIDE SO_3

Dioxygen Difluoride
See DIOXYGEN DIFLUORIDE plus Sulfur Trioxide.

Lead Oxide
See LEAD OXIDE plus Sulfur Trioxide.

Nitryl Chloride
See NITRYL CHLORIDE plus Sulfur Trioxide.

Perchloric Acid
See PERCHLORIC ACID plus Sulfur Trioxide.

Phosphorus
See PHOSPHORUS plus Sulfur Trioxide.

Tetrafluorethylene
The reaction of sulfur trioxide in excess with tetrafluoroethylene causes explosive decomposition to carbonyl fluoride and sulfur dioxide.
Chem. and Eng. News **49** (22): 3 (1971).

SULFURYL CHLORIDE SO_2Cl_2
(See also THIONYL CHLORIDE)

Lead Dioxide
Reaction between sulfuryl chloride and lead dioxide can take place with explosive violence.
Mellor **10:** 676 (1946-1947).

TANTALUM Ta

Air
Tantalum, thorium, titanium, and zirconium (powdered and dry) ignited when a glass container of the powder was thrown at a wall with force sufficient to break the container.
Chem. and Eng. News **30:** 3210 (1952).

Bromine Trifluoride
See NIOBIUM plus Bromine Trifluoride.

Fluorine
See FLUORINE plus Tantalum.

TANTALUM PENTACHLORIDE

Reaction between tantalum pentachloride with Lithium dimethyl amido [$LiN(Me)_2$] in pentane caused two separate explosions during the preparation of pentakis-dimethylamido tantalum.
Chem. and Eng. News, p. 2 (July 30, 1990).

TANTALUM PENTOXIDE Ta_2O_5

Bromine Trifluoride
See BROMINE TRIFLUORIDE plus Bismuth Pentoxide.

Chlorine Trifluoride
See CHLORINE TRIFLUORIDE plus Aluminum Oxide.

Lithium
See LITHIUM plus Tantalum Pentoxide.

TARTARIC ACID HOOC.CHOHCHOHCO.OH

Silver
See SILVER plus Oxalic Acid.

TEFLON® (POLYTETRAFLUOROETHYLENE)
$(CF_2{=}CF_2)_X$

Fluorine
See FLUORINE plus Solid Nonmetals and Oxygen.

Oxygen
See OXYGEN plus Teflon®

Sodium-Potassium Alloy
See SODIUM-POTASSIUM ALLOY plus Teflon®

TELLURIUM Te

Cadmium
See ZINC plus Selenium.

Chlorine
See CHLORINE plus Tellurium.

Chlorine Fluoride
Tellurium is attacked by chlorine fluoride with incandescence.
Mellor **11:** 26 (1946-1947).

Chlorine Trifluoride
See ANTIMONY plus Chlorine Trifluoride.

Fluorine
See FLUORINE plus Tellurium.

Lithium Silicide
See PHOSPHORUS plus Lithium Silicide.

Potassium
When tellurium and potassium are warmed in an atmosphere of hydrogen, combination occurs with incandescence.
Mellor **11:** 40 (1946-1947).

Silver Bromate
A vigorous reaction occurs in the presence of moisture.
Mellor **2, Supp. 1:** 766 (1956).

Sodium
See SODIUM plus Tellurium.

Zinc
See ZINC plus Selenium.

TELLURIUM TETRACHLORIDE HYDROCHLORIDE
$TeCl_4{\cdot}HCl$

Ammonia
Tellurium hydropentachloride reacts with ammonia to produce a substance which detonates when heated, possibly nitrogen telluride.
Mellor **11:** 101 (1946-1947).

TERBIUM Tb

Air
See RARE EARTH METALS plus Air.

Halogens
See RARE EARTH METALS plus Halogens.

TERPENES

Nitric Acid
See NITRIC ACID plus Diborane.

TETRABORANE (6) B_4H_6

Nitric Acid
The mixture of tetraboron decahydride and nitric acid is explosive.
Mellor **5:** 36 (1946-1947).

TETRABORANE (10) B_4H_{10}

Air
See OXYGEN plus Boron Decahydride. This hydride ignites or explodes on exposure to air.
Mellor **5:** 36 (1946-1947).

Nitric Acid
A mixture of boron decahydride and concentrated nitric acid explodes.
Mellor **5:** 36 (1946-1947).

Oxygen
See OXYGEN plus Boron Decahydride.

TETRABROMOETHANE

Lithium
Mixtures of lithium shavings and several halocarbon derivatives (including carbon tetrabromide) are impact sensitive and will explode, sometimes violently.
Bretherick (1978).

Hexacyclohexyldilead
In the absence of solvent and presence of air, interaction with carbon tetrabromide is explosive.
Bretherick (1978).

TETRACHLOROBENZENE $Cl_4C_6H_2$

Sodium Hydroxide and Methyl Alcohol
See SODIUM HYDROXIDE plus Tetrachlorobenzene and Methyl Alcohol.

TETRACHLORODIBORANE B_2Cl_4

Air
Diboron tetrachloride is spontaneously flammable in air.
Douda (1966). *Chem. Abst.* **49:** 2240d (1955).

TETRACHLOROETHANE (sym-) $Cl_2CHCHCl_2$

2, 4-Dinitrophenyl Disulfide
See 2, 4-DINITROBENZENE SULFENYLCHLORIDE (self-reactive).

Nitrogen Tetroxide
See NITROGEN TETROXIDE plus 1,2-Dichloroethane.

Potassium
See SODIUM plus Tetrachloroethane.

Potassium Hydroxide
See POTASSIUM HYDROXIDE plus Tetrachloroethane.

Sodium
See SODIUM plus Tetrachloroethane.

Sodium-Potassium Alloy
See SODIUM-POTASSIUM ALLOY plus Bromoform.

TETRACHLOROETHYLENE $CCl_2=CCl_2$

Barium
See BARIUM plus Trichlorotrifluoroethane.

Beryllium
See BERYLLIUM plus Carbon Tetrachloride.

Lithium
See LITHIUM plus Trichlorotrifluoroethane.

TETRAFLUOROETHYLENE $CF_2=CF_2$

Iodine Pentafluoride and Limonene
See IODINE PENTAFLUORIDE plus Tetrafluoroethylene and Limonene

Sulfur Trioxide
See SULFUR TRIOXIDE plus Tetrafluoroethylene.

TETRAFLUOROETHYLENE POLYMER

Fluorine
See FLUORINE plus Solid Metals and Oxygen.

TETRAFLUOROHYDRAZINE F_2NNF_2

Nitrogen Trifluoride
See NITROGEN TRIFLUORIDE plus Tetrafluorohydrazine.

Oxygen
See OXYGEN plus Tetrafluorohydrazine.

TETRAFLUOROMETHANE CF_4

Aluminum
See ALUMINUM plus Dichlorodifluoromethane.

1,2,3,4-TETRAHYDROCARBAZOLE $(C_6H_4NHC_6H_8)$

Acrylonitrile
The reaction of 1,2,3,4-tetrahydrocarbazole with acrylonitrile, initiated by benzyl-tremethyl-ammonium hydroxide, is described in
J. Am. Chem. Soc. **72:** 4313 (1960). For a run, eight times the literature scale of the initiator was added at 0°C, the ice bath removed, the reaction flask placed on the steam bath and the steam turned on. After 30-60 seconds an explosion shattered the apparatus.
BCISC **39** (156): 36 (1968). *Wischmeyer* (1970).
NSC Newsletter, R & D Sec. (Feb. 1970).

TETRAHYDROFURAN $OCH_2CH_2CH_2CH_2$

Air
Purified tetrahydrofuran should not be stored for more than a few months after its container has been opened if it contains no oxidation inhibitor. In this case, it is potentially explosive because of peroxide formation.
NSC Newsletter, Chem. Sec. (Nov. 1964).

Lithium Aluminum Hydride
Fire can occur when tetrahydrofuran is used as a solvent for lithium aluminum hydride. Peroxides of tetrahydrofuran or their reaction products probably caused a vigorous reaction with lithium aluminum hydride, and subsequent fire.
MCA Guide for Safety, Appendix 3 (1972).

Potassium Hydroxide
Using potassium hydroxide to dry impure tetrahydrofuran, which can contain peroxides, is hazardous. Serious explosions can occur. This reaction will also occur with sodium hydroxide.
NSC Newsletter, Chem. Sec. (March 1967).
Wischmeyer (1967).

Sodium Aluminum Hydride
See SODIUM ALUMINUM HYDRIDE plus Tetrahydrofuran.

Sodium Hydroxide
See TETRAHYDROFURAN plus Potassium Hydroxide.

TETRAIODOETHYLENE $I_2HC=CHI_2$

Iodine Pentafluoride
See IODINE PENTAFLUORIDE plus Tetraiodoethylene.

TETRAMETHYLAMMONIUM CHLORITE $(CH_3)_4NH_4ClO_2$

(self-reactive)
Tetramethylammonium chlorite explodes on percussion.
Mellor **2, Supp. 1:** 573 (1956).

TETRAMETHYLDIALUMINUM $(CH_3)_2HAl_2H(CH_3)_2$

Air
Tetramethyl dialuminum is spontaneously flammable in air.
Hurd, p. 98 (1952).

TETRAMETHYLDIARSINE $(CH_3)_2As_2(CH_3)_2$

Air
Tetramethyldiarsine ignites spontaneously in dry air.
Brauer (1965). *Douda* (1966).

Chlorine
See CHLORINE plus Tetramethyl Diarsine.

TETRAMETHYLDIBORANE $H(CH_3)_2B_2(CH_3)_2H$

Air
Tetramethyldiborane is spontaneously flammable in air.
Lehman and Wilson, p. 50 (1949).

TETRAMETHYLDIGALLINE $(CH_3)_2Ga_2(CH_3)_2$

Air
Tetramethyldigalline is spontaneously flammable in air.
Douda (1966).

TETRAMETHYLDISTIBINE $(CH_3)_2Sb_2(CH_3)_2$

Air
Tetramethyldistibine is spontaneously flammable in air.
Coates, p. 156 (1956).

TETRAMETHYLSILICANE $Si(CH_3)_4$

Air
Tetramethylsilicane is spontaneously flammable in air.
Douda (1966).

TETRANITROMETHANE $C(NO_2)_4$

(self-reactive)
This compound is a weak, but highly sensitive explosive.
Van Dolah (1967).

Hydrocarbons
Hydrocarbons exposed to tetranitromethane form exceedingly sensitive explosives.
Van Dolah (1967).

TETRAPHENYLDIARSINE $(C_6H_5)_2As_2(C_6H_5)_2$

Air
Tetraphenyl diarsine is spontaneously flammable in air.
Ellern (1961).

TETRAPHOSPHORUS TRIIODIDE P_4I_3

Nitric Acid
Concentrated nitric acid attacks phosphorus tetratriiodide vigorously, accompanied by flame.
Comp. Rend. **141:** 257.

TETRAPHOSPHORUS TRISELENIDE P_4Se_3

Air
Phosphorus tetratriselenide ignites when warmed in air.
Z. Anorg. Chemie **30:** 258.

TETRASILANE Si_4H_{10}

Air
See TRISILANE plus Air; also SILANES plus Air.

Carbon Tetrachloride
Carbon tetrachloride reacts more vigorously on trisilane and tetrasilane than on disilane.
Mellor **6:** 224 (1946-1947).

Oxygen
See OXYGEN plus Disilane.

TETRYL $(NO_2)_3C_6H_2N(CH_3)NO_2$

Hydrazine
See HYDRAZINE plus Tetryl.

THALLIC NITRATE TRIHYDRATE $Tl(NO_3)_3{\cdot}3H_2O$

Formic Acid and Vanillin
A violent reaction occurred when a small amount of vanillin was added to thallium trinitrate trihydrate (up to 50%) in 90% formic acid.
Dean (1973).

THALLIC OXIDE Tl_2O_3

Antimony Sulfide
A mixture of thallic oxide and antimony sulfide or sulfur explodes when ground in a mortar.
Mellor **5:** 421, 434 (1946-1947).

Sulfur
See THALLIC OXIDE plus Antimony Sulfide.

THALLIUM Tl

Fluorine
See FLUORINE plus Thallium.

THALLOUS AMIDE $TlNH_2$

Acids
Thallium amide explodes with dilute acids or water.
Mellor **8:** 2, 5, 70, 261 (1946-1947).

Water
See THALLIUM AMIDE plus Acids.

THALLOUS AZIDE TlN_3

(self-reactive)
Thallous azide decomposes at 334°C. It is almost as unstable as the copper salt.
Mellor **8, Supp. 2:** 43 (1967).

THALLOUS BROMIDE $TlBr$

Potassium
See POTASSIUM plus Aluminum Bromide.

Sodium
See SODIUM plus Aluminum Bromide.

THALLOUS CHLORIDE $TlCl$

Fluorine
See FLUORINE plus Thallous Chloride.

Potassium
See POTASSIUM plus Ammonium Bromide.

THALLOUS NITRIDE Tl_3N

(self-reactive)
See THALLIUM NITRIDE plus Water.

Acids
Thallium nitride explodes with dilute acids or water.
Mellor **8:** 2, 5, 70, 271 (1946-1947).

Water
Thallium nitride explodes with great violence when subjected to shock or heat, or when treated with water or dilute acids.
Mellor **8:** 262 (1946-1947).

THALLOUS PHOSPHIDE Tl_3P

Air
This salt ignites if heated in air.
Mellor **8, Supp. 3:** 312 (1971).

THIANTHRENE PERCHLORATE $(C_6H_4S_2C_6H_4)\cdot HClO_4$

(self-reactive)
A new batch of 1–2 grams of thianthrene perchlorate exploded violently while being transferred from a sintered glass filter to a Petri dish.
BCISC **40** (158): 17 (1969).

THIOCYANATES RSCN

Chlorates
Thiocyanates and chlorates or nitrates explode when fused. If intimately mixed, the mixture explodes at a temperature of 750°F, or when touched by flame or sparks.
Von Schwartz, pp. 299-300 (1918).
See also CHLORATES plus Antimony Sulfide.

Nitrates
See THIOCYANATES plus Chlorates.

Nitric Acid
When thiocyanate solution was introduced into a pipeline containing nitric acid, an explosion ruptured the line.
MCA Case History **853** (1962).

Organic Peroxides
See THIOCYANATES plus Oxidizing Agents.

Oxidizing Agents
Caution should be exercised in treating a thiocyanate with an oxidizing agent such as a peroxide since such mixtures have been known to explode.
Kharasch Vol. 1, p. 312 (1961).

Peroxides
See THIOCYANATES plus Oxidizing Agents.

Potassium Chlorate
See THIOCYANATES plus Chlorates.

Sodium Chlorate
See THIOCYANATES plus Chlorates.

THIODIGLYCOL $(HOCH_2CH_2)_2S$

Hydrogen Peroxide and Acetone
Thiodiglycol was being oxidized with an excess of hydrogen peroxide using acetone as a solvent. At the conclusion the acetone and excess hydrogen peroxide were removed under vacuum in a steam bath. After about 15 minutes of heating on a steam bath, a violent explosion occurred.
MCA Case History 223 (1962).

THIONYL CHLORIDE $OSCl_2$

Dimethylformamide
Thionyl chloride with tetrahydrofuran and dimethylformamide demonstrate incompatibility resulting in explosions.
Chem. and Eng. News (July 4, 1988) (April 7, 1986).

Dimethyl Sulfoxide
See DIMETHYL SULFOXIDE plus Acyl Halides.

Ethyl Acetate
The mixture of thionyl chloride with ethyl acetate in the presence of zinc or iron metal results in an explosively hazardous mixture. Binary mixtures of these components seem stable, while ternary mixtures result in spontaneously violent reactions.
Chem. and Eng. News (June 1, 1992).

2, 4-Hexadiyn-1, 6-Diol
Thionyl chloride and 2, 4-hexadiyn-1, 6-diol reacting in dimethyl formamide forms 2, 4-hexadiyn-1, 6-bischlorosulfite which is shock sensitive and decomposes violently upon distillation.
P.E. Driedger and H.V. Isaacson, *Chem. and Eng. News* **50** (12): 51 (1972).

o-Nitrobenzoylacetic Acid
o-Nitrobenzoylacetic acid reacted with thionyl chloride to produce the corresponding nitrobenzoylacetyl chloride, which decomposed violently after removal of solvent by distillation. A similar reaction hazard exists for o-nitrophenylacetic acid plus thionyl chloride.
W.D. Bonner and C.O. Hurd, *J. Am. Chem. Soc.* **68:** 344 (1946).

o-Nitrophenylacetic Acid
See THIONYL CHLORIDE plus o-Nitrobenzoylacetic Acid.

Tetrahydrofuran
Thionyl chloride with tetrahydrofuran and dimethylformamide demonstrate incompatibility resulting in explosions.
Chem. and Eng. News (July 4, 1988) (April 7, 1986).

Water
VA flexible stainless hose that was being used for thionyl chloride transfer ruptured when contaminated with water. Water reacts with thionyl chloride, liberating hydrogen chloride and sulfur dioxide gases.
Wischmeyer (1972).

THIOPHENE $SCH=CHCH=CH$ (ring)

Nitric Acid
A mixture of the two may cause an explosion.
Pieters, p. 30 (1957).

THIOPHOSPHORYL FLUORIDE SPF_3

Air
Thiophosphoryl fluoride is spontaneously flammable in air; under proper conditions, it is spontaneously explosive.
Mellor **8:** 1072 (1946-1947).

Potassium
See SODIUM plus Thiophosphoryl Fluoride.

Sodium
See SODIUM plus Thiophosphoryl Fluoride.

THIOUREA $S=C(NH_2)_2$

Acrolein
See ACROLEIN plus Sulfur Dioxide.

THORIUM Th

Air
See TANTALUM plus Air.

Chlorine
Thorium, when heated with chlorine, reacts vigorously with incandescence.
Mellor **7:** 208 (1946-1947).

Phosphorus
See PHOSPHORUS plus Thorium.

Sulfur
See SULFUR plus Thorium.

THORIUM CARBIDE ThC_2

Air
When heated in air, thorium carbide readily burns with incandescence.
Mellor **5:** 885-87 (1946-1947).

Selenium
See SELENIUM plus Thorium Carbide.

Sulfur
See SULFUR plus Thorium Carbide.

THORIUM HYDRIDE ThH_4

Air
Thorium hydride explodes if heated in the presence of air.
Mellor **7:** 207-8 (1946-1947).

THORIUM NITRIDE Th_3N_4

Air
Thorium nitride burns in air with incandescence.
Mellor **8:** 121-22 (1946-1947).

Water
Thorium nitride hydrolyzes vigorously.
Mellor **8, Supp. 1:** 182 (1964).

THORIUM OXYSULFIDE ThOS

Air
Thorium oxysulfide ignites spontaneously in air.
Mellor **7:** 240 (1946-1947).

THORIUM PHOSPHIDE Th_3P_4

Acids
Thorium phosphide reacts with acids to release spontaneously flammable phosphine.
Mellor **8, Supp. 3:** 348 (1971).

THULIUM Tm

Air
See RARE EARTH METALS plus Air.

Halogens
See RARE EARTH METALS plus Halogens.

TIN Sn
(For tin compounds see STANNIC and STANNOUS compounds)

Bromine
The violent reaction between these chemicals is controlled in halocarbon solutions.
Mellor **2, Supp. 1:** 715 (1956).

Bromine Trifluoride
Tin and bromine trifluoride react violently.
Mellor **2, Supp. 1:** 164 (1956).

Chlorine
When heated in chlorine, tin reacts, producing light and much heat.
Mellor **7:** 436 (1946-1947).
Mellor **2, Supp. 1:** 380 (1956).

Chlorine Trifluoride
See ALUMINUM plus Chlorine Trifluoride.

Cupric Nitrate
In the presence of water, cupric nitrate and tin foil, on prolonged and intimate contact, will produce flaming and sparking.
Ellern, p. 46 (1968).

Potassium Peroxide
See POTASSIUM plus Potassium Peroxide.

Sodium Peroxide
Sodium peroxide oxidizes tin with incandescence.
Mellor **2:** 490-93 (1946-1947).

Sulfur
See SULFUR plus Tin.

TITANIUM Ti

Air
Most finely divided forms of titanium are flammable in air. See also TITANIUM DICHLORIDE plus Air and TANTALUM plus Air.
NSC Data Sheet **485.** *BM Report Invest.* **6516** (1964). *BM Report Invest.* **4835** (1951).

Bromine Trifluoride
See MOLYBDENUM plus Bromine Trifluoride.

Carbon Dioxide
Titanium burns in carbon dioxide above 550°C.
NSC Data Sheet **485.**

Cupric Oxide
Titanium reacts violently with cupric oxide or lead oxide when heated.
Mellor **7:** 20 (1946-1947).

Fluorine
See FLUORINE plus Titanium.

Lead Oxide
See TITANIUM plus Cupric Oxide.

Nickel and Potassium Perchlorate
See NICKEL plus Titanium and Potassium Perchlorate.

Nitric Acid
The residue from the reaction of titanium with red fuming nitric acid exploded violently when the flask was touched.
Allison (1969).

Nitrogen
Titanium burns vigorously in free nitrogen above 802°C.
NSC Data Sheet **485.**

Oxidants, strong
Metal flake plus strong oxidants, such as silver nitrate, can form extremely hazardous compositions. Mixtures can become shock sensitive upon drying.

Oxygen
Liquid oxygen gives a detonable mixture when combined with powdered titanium.
Kirschenbaum (1956).

Potassium Chlorate
When titanium is heated with potassium chlorate, potassium nitrate or potassium permanganate, an explosion occurs.
Mellor **7:** 20 (1946-1947).

Potassium Nitrate
See TITANIUM plus Potassium Chlorate.

Potassium Permanganate
See TITANIUM plus Potassium Chlorate.

Steam
Titanium at red heat, 704°C, decomposes steam. The hydrogen evolved burns or explodes.
NSC Data Sheet **485.**

Trichloroethylene
It has been determined experimentally that a mixture of titanium powder with trichloroethylene or with trichlorotrifluoroethane will flash or spark on heavy impact.
ASESB Pot. Incid. **39** (1968).

Trichlorotrifluoroethane
See TITANIUM plus Trichloroethylene.

TITANIUM ALLOY

Nitric Acid
Extreme caution is urged in handling of all titanium alloys exposed to red fuming nitric acid since the reaction may cause an explosion.
Chem. and Eng. News **31:** 3320 (1953).

Oxygen
A titanium alloy tank containing liquid oxygen exploded during a laboratory experiment. Contamination might have triggered the reaction. An explosion hazard may exist in the use of titanium with either gaseous or liquid oxygen.
MCA Case History **988** (1964). *Jolicoeur* (1966).

TITANIUM CARBIDE TiC

Air
As micron-sized titanium carbide was being removed from a ball mill, a cloud of the dust ignited.
MCA Case History **618** (1960).

TITANIUM DICHLORIDE $TiCl_2$

Air
Titanium dichloride is highly flammable in air at room temperature. In inert gases, titanium dichloride converts to titanium tetrachloride plus very finely divided titanium metal, which can ignite on subsequent exposure to air.
NSC Data Sheet **485.**

TITANIUM DIOXIDE TiO_2

Lithium
See LITHIUM plus Titanium Dioxide.

TITANIUM DISULFIDE TiS_2

Potassium Nitrate
A mixture of titanium disulfide and potassium nitrate detonated when heated.
Mellor **7:** 91 (1946-1947).

TITANIUM-MAGNESIUM ALLOY

Nitric Acid
The residue from the reaction of titanium-magnesium alloy with red-fuming nitric acid may be detonated by friction, heat, or shock.
Chem. and Eng. News **31:** 3320 (1953).

TITANIUM TETRACHLORIDE $TiCl_4$

Potassium
See POTASSIUM plus Titanium Tetrachloride.

TOLUENE $C_6H_5CH_3$

Nitric Acid and Sulfuric Acid
See NITRIC ACID plus Toluene and Sulfuric Acid.

Nitrogen Tetroxide
See NITROGEN TETROXIDE plus Toluene.

Silver Perchlorate
See SILVER PERCHLORATE plus Acetic Acid.
See SILVER PERCHLORATE plus Toluene.

TOLUENE DIISOCYANATE $CH_3C_6H_3(NCO)_2$

Acyl Chlorides and Bases
The diisocyanate can undergo exothermic polymerization in contact with bases or more than traces of acyl chlorides, sometimes used as stabilizers.

TOLUIDINE $CH_3(C_6H_4)NH_2$

Nitric Acid
See NITRIC ACID plus Aniline.

TOLYL CHLORIDE $C_6H_5CH_2Cl$

Dimethyl Sulfoxide
See DIMETHYL SULFOXIDE plus Acyl Halides.

TRIALLYL PHOSPHATE $(CH_2=CHCH_2O)_3PO$

(self-reactive)
An explosion occurred on distilling triallyl phosphate prepared from phosphorus oxychloride, allyl alcohol and pyridine. The toluene solution of the product, washed with sodium carbonate and with pyrogallol added, exploded violently while being distilled under vacuum at 135°C.
W.T. Dye, G.E. Ham, *Chem. and Eng. News* **28:** 3452 (1950).

TRIAZINE $\underline{N=CHN=CHN=C}H$

Nitric Acid
See NITRIC ACID plus Triazine.

TRI-n-BROMOMELAMINE
$\underline{N=C(NHBr)NC=(NHBr)N=C}(NHBr)$

Ally Alcohol
See ALLYL ALCOHOL plus Tri-n-Bromomelamine.

TRIBROMONEOPENANOL (Sym) $(BrCH_{2-})_3COH$

Ethyl Acetoacetate and Zinc
See ETHYL ACETOACETATE plus Tribromoneopentyl Alcohol and Zinc.

TRIBROMOTRIETHOXYDIALUMINUM
$Al_2Br_3(OC_2H_5)_3$

Air
See TRIBROMOTRIETHOXYDIALUMINUM plus Ethyl Alcohol.

Ethyl Alcohol
Aluminum sesquibromide ethylate explodes on contact with ethyl alcohol or water. It is also pyrophoric.
Chem. Eng. Progs. **62** (9): 128 (1968).

Water
See TRIBROMOTRIETHOXYDIALUMINUM plus Ethyl Alcohol.

TRIBROMOTRIMETHYLDIALUMINUM $(CH_3)_3Al_2Br_3$

Air
Trimethyl tribromo dialuminum is spontaneously flammable in air.
Douda (1966).

Water
Trimethyl tribromo dialuminum reacts violently with water.
Rose (1961).

TRIBUTYLALUMINUM $(C_4H_9)_3Al$

Air
Tri-n-butyl aluminum is spontaneously flammable in air.
Rose (1961).

TRIBUTYLBORANE $(C_4H_9)_3B$

Air
Tri-n-butyl borane, if spread over a large area, ignites spontaneously in air.
W.H. Johnson et al., *J. Res. Nat. Bur. Stand.* **62** (1): 49 (1959).

TRIBUTYLPHOSPHINE $P(C_4H_9)_3$

Air
Tributyl phosphine is spontaneously flammable in air.
A.B. Steele and J.J. Duggan, *Chem. Eng.* **66:** 160 (April 1969).

1,1,1-TRICHLOROETHANE CCl_3CH_3

Acetone
See ACETONE plus Methyl Chloroform.

Nitrogen Tetroxide
See NITROGEN TETROXIDE plus 1,2-Dichloroethane.

Oxygen
See OXYGEN plus 1,1,1-Trichloroethane.

Oxygen (Liquid)
See OXYGEN (LIQUID) plus Chlorinated Hydrocarbons.

Sodium
See SODIUM plus 1,2-Dichloroethylene.

Sodium Hydroxide
See SODIUM plus 1,2-Dichloroethylene.

Sodium-Potassium Alloy
See SODIUM-POTASSIUM ALLOY plus 1,1,1-Trichloroethane.

TRICHLOROETHYLENE $Cl_2C=CHCl$

Aluminum
See ALUMINUM plus Trichloroethylene.

Barium
See BARIUM plus Trichlorotrifluoroethane.

Nitrogen Tetroxide
See NITROGEN TETROXIDE plus 1,2-Dichloroethane.

Lithium
See LITHIUM plus Trichlorotrifluorethane.

Magnesium
See MAGNESIUM plus Trichloroethylene.

Oxygen (Liquid)
See OXYGEN (LIQUID) plus Chlorinated Hydrocarbons.

Oxygen
See OXYGEN plus Trichloroethylene.

Potassium Hydroxide
See SODIUM HYDROXIDE plus Trichloroethylene.

Potassium Nitrate
A batch of 3257 grams of boron, 9362 grams of potassium nitrate, 989 grams of laminac, and 500 grams of trichloroethylene had been mixing for 5 minutes, when an explosion occurred.
MCA Guide for Safety, Appendix 3 (1972).

Sodium
See SODIUM plus 1,2-Dichloroethylene.

Sodium Hydroxide
See SODIUM HYDROXIDE plus Trichloroethylene. See also SODIUM plus 1,2-Dichloroethylene.

Titanium
See TITANIUM plus Trichloroethylene.

TRICHLOROETHYLSILANE $C_2H_5SiCl_3$

Water
Ethyltrichlorosilane reacts violently with water.
Title 46 (1970).

1,1,1-TRICHLORO-2-FLUOROETHANE CCl_3CH_2F

Barium
See BARIUM plus Trichlorotrifluoroethane.

TRICHLOROFLUOROMETHANE $CFCl_3$

Aluminum
See ALUMINUM plus Chlorofluorohydrocarbons.
See also ALUMINUM plus Dichlorodifluoromethane.

Lithium
See LITHIUM plus Trichlorotrifluoroethane.

TRICHLOROMELAMINE $C_3N_3(NHCl)_3$

Acetone
See HEXACHLOROMELAMINE plus Organic Contaminants.

Ammonia
See HEXACHLOROMELAMINE plus Organic Contaminants.

Aniline
See HEXACHLOROMELAMINE plus Organic Contaminants.

Diphenylamine
See HEXACHLOROMELAMINE plus Organic Contaminants.

Turpentine
See HEXACHLOROMELAMINE plus Organic Contaminants.

TRICHLOROMETHYLSILANE CH_3SiCl_3

Water
Methyl trichlorosilane evolves white fumes with moist air. It reacts violently with water with the evolution of heat and white acid fumes.
Title 46 (1970).

TRICHLOROTRIETHYLDIALUMINUM $(C_2H_5)_3Al_2Cl_3$

Air
Ethyl aluminum sesquichloride is spontaneously flammable in air.
Douda (1966).

Benzene and Allyl Chloride
See ALLYL CHLORIDE plus Benzene and Ethyl Aluminum Dichloride.

Carbon Tetrachloride
See ALUMINUM TRIETHYL plus Carbon Tetrachloride.

Toluene and Allyl Chloride
See ALLYL CHLORIDE plus Benzene and Ethyl Aluminum Dichloride.

Water
Ethyl aluminum sesquichloride reacts violently with water.
Rose (1961).

1,1,2-TRICHLOROTRIFLUOROETHANE CCl_3CF_3

Aluminum
See ALUMINUM plus Chlorofluorohydrocarbons.
See also ALUMINUM plus Dichlorodifluoromethane.

Barium
See BARIUM plus Trichlorotrifluoroethane.

Lithium
See LITHIUM plus Trichlorotrifluoroethane.

Samarium
See SAMARIUM plus 1,1,2-Trichlorotrifluoroethane.

Sodium-Potassium Alloy
See SODIUM-POTASSIUM ALLOY plus Trichlorotrifluoroethane.

Titanium
See TITANIUM plus Trichloroethylene.

TRICHLOROTRIMETHYLDIALUMINUM $(CH_3)_3Al_2Cl_3$

Air
Methyl aluminum sesquichloride ignites instantly in air.
Rose (1961).

TRICHLOROVINYLSILANE $Si(CH_2{=}CH)Cl_3$

Water
Vinyl trichloro silane reacts violently with water or moist air.
Title 46 (1970).

TRIDECANAL $C_{12}H_{25}CHO$

Air
Tridecyl aldehyde is spontaneously flammable in air.
A.B. Steele and J.J. Duggan, *Chem. Eng.* **66:** 160 (April 1969).

TRIETHYLALUMINUM $Al(C_2H_5)_3$

Air
Triethyl aluminum is spontaneously flammable in air and explodes violently in water.
Von Schwartz, p. 321 (1918). *Kirk and Othmer, Second Ed.* **2:** 38 (1963). *MCA Case History* **819** (1962).

Carbon Tetrachloride
When mixtures of triethyl aluminum sesquichlorides in carbon tetrachloride that had been prepared with ice cooling were permitted to warm to room temperature, they first darkened, then exploded violently. The reaction is believed due to increased concentration of aluminum triethyl, which subsequently reacted with the carbon tet rachloride.
H. Reinheckel, *Angew. Chem. Inter. Ed. Engl.* **3:** 65 (1964).

Dimethylformamide
See DIMETHYLFORMAMIDE plus Triethyl Aluminum.

Halogenated Hydrocarbons
Violent reactions may occur when aluminum alkyls are exposed to halogenated hydrocarbons.
Kirk and Othmer, Second Ed. **2:** 38 (1963).

Triethyl Borine and Air
A mixture of 15% triethyl aluminum and 85% triethyl borine is pyrophoric.
Rocketdyne Rept., Hypergol, p. 3 (1961).

Water
See TRIETHYL ALUMINUM plus Air.

TRIETHYLALUMINUM DIETHYL ETHERATE
$4(C_2H_5)_3Al{\cdot}3(C_2H_5)_2O$

Diethyl Ether and Air
A mixture of triethyl aluminum diethyl etherate and diethyl ether is spontaneously flammable in air.
Douda (1966).

TRIETHYLARSINE $As(C_2H_5)_3$

Air
Triethyl arsine is spontaneously flammable in air.
Von Schwartz, p. 322 (1918).

TRIETHYLBISMUTHINE $(C_2H_5)_3Bi$

Air
Triethyl bismuthine is spontaneously flammable in air.
Ellern, pp. 24-25 (1968).

TRIETHYLBORANE $(C_2H_5)_3B$

Air
Triethyl borine is spontaneously flammable in air.
Douda (1966). *Ripley* (1966).

Triethyl Aluminum and Air
See TRIETHYL ALUMINUM plus Triethyl Borine and Air.

TRIETHYLDIBORANE $(C_2H_5)_3B_2H_3$

Air
Triethyl diborane is spontaneously flammable in air.
Douda (1966).

TRIETHYL ETHOXY DIPHOSPHINYL OXIDE
$(C_2H_5)_2POP(C_2H_5)(OC_2H_5)$

Air
Triethyl ethoxy diphosphinyl oxide is spontaneously flammable in air.
Kaufman (1961).

TRIETHYLGALLIUM $(C_2H_5)_3Ga$

Air
Triethyl gallium is spontaneously flammable in air.
Ellern, pp. 24-25 (1968).

TRIETHYLINDIUM $(C_2H_5)_3In$

Air
Triethyl indium is spontaneously flammable in air.
Douda (1966).

TRIETHYLSTIBINE $Sb(C_2H_5)_3$

Air
Triethyl antimony is spontaneously flammable in air.
Von Schwartz, p. 322 (1918).

TRIETHYLSTIBINE SULFATE $Sb(C_2H_5)_3SO_4$

Air
Triethyl antimony sulfate is spontaneously flammable in air.
Bahme, p. 25 (1961).

(TRIFLUOROMETHYL) PHOSPHINE F_3CPH_2

Air
Trifluoromethyl phosphine is spontaneously flammable in air.
Douda (1966).

TRIFLUORONITROANILINE $F_3C_6H(NO_2)N{=}NOH$

(self-reactive)
The recrystallized compound, which had been made from trifluoronitroaniline, hydrochloric acid and sodium nitrite, exploded violently on impact.
MCA Guide for Safety, Appendix 3 (1972).

TRIISOBUTYLALUMINUM $(CH_3CHCH_3CH_2)_3Al$

Acids
Tri-iso-butyl aluminum reacts violently with acids, alcohols, amines, halogens, and water.
Rose (1961).

Air
Tri-iso-butyl aluminum is spontaneously flammable in air.
Rose (1961).

Alcohols
See TRI-iso-BUTYL ALUMINUM plus Acids.

Amines
See TRI-iso-BUTYL ALUMINUM plus Acids.

Halogens
See TRI-iso-BUTYL ALUMINUM plus Acids.

Water
See TRI-iso-BUTYL ALUMINUM plus Acids.

TRIMANGANESE TETROXIDE Mn_3O_4

Fluorine
See FLUORINE plus Trimanganese Tetroxide.

TRIMETHYLALUMINUM $Al(CH_3)_3$

Air
Trimethyl aluminum is spontaneously flammable in air and explodes violently in water.
Von Schwartz, p. 321 (1918).

Halogenated Hydrocarbons
See TRIETHYL ALUMINUM plus Halogenated Hydrocarbons.

Water
See TRIMETHYL ALUMINUM plus Air.

TRIMETHYLALUMINUM DIETHYL ETHERATE
$(CH_3)_3Al{\cdot}(C_2H_5)_2O$

Diethyl Ether and Air
A mixture of trimethyl aluminum diethyl etherate and diethyl ether is spontaneously flammable in air.
Douda (1966).

TRIMETHYLALUMINUM DIMETHYL ETHERATE
$(CH_3)_3Al{\cdot}(CH_3)_2O$

Air
Trimethyl aluminum dimethyl etherate is spontaneously flammable in air.
Douda (1966).

TRIMETHYLAMINE OXIDE PERCHLORATE
$(CH_3)_3NO{\cdot}HClO_4$

(self-reactive)
Trimethylamine oxide perchlorate explodes when heated or struck.
ACS **146:** 213. *Berichte* **43:** 2624-30 (1910).

TRIMETHYLARSINE $As(CH_3)_3$

Air
Trimethyl arsenic is spontaneously flammable in air.
Von Schwartz, p. 322 (1918).

TRIMETHYLBISMUTHINE $(CH_3)_3Bi$

Air
Trimethyl bismuthine is spontaneously flammable in air.
Coates, p. 161 (1956).

TRIMETHYLBORANE $B(CH_3)_3$

Air
Trimethyl borine is spontaneously flammable in air.
Douda (1966).

TRIMETHYLDIALUMINUM HYDRIDE
$(CH_3)_2HAl_2H_2CH_3$

Water
Trimethyl dialuminum hydride reacts vigorously with water yielding methane and hydrogen, which ignite spontaneously.
Hurd, p. 98 (1952).

TRIMETHYLDIBORANE $(CH_3)_3B_2H_3$

Air
Trimethyl diborane is spontaneously flammable in air.
Lehman and Wilson, p. 53 (1949).

TRIMETHYLGALLIUM $(CH_3)_3Ga$

Air
Trimethyl gallium is spontaneously flammable in air.
Douda (1966).

TRIMETHYLPHOSPHINE $(CH_3)_3P$

Air
Trimethyl phosphine ignites spontaneously and burns violently in air.
R.A. Zingaro and R.E. McGlothlin, *J. Chem. Eng. Data* **8** (2): 227 (1963).

TRIMETHYL PHOSPHITE $(CH_3O)_3P$

Magnesium Perchlorate
See MAGNESIUM PERCHLORATE plus Trimethyl Phosphite.

TRIMETHYLSTIBINE $Sb(CH_3)_3$

Air
Trimethyl antimony is spontaneously flammable in air.
Von Schwartz, p. 322 (1918).

TRIMETHYLSTIBINE SULFATE $(CH_3)_3SbSO_4$

Air
Trimethyl antimony sulfate is spontaneously flammable in air.
Bahme, p. 25 (1961).

TRIMETHYLTHALLIUM $(CH_3)_3Tl$

Air
Trimethyl thallium is spontaneously flammable in air.
Douda (1966).

TRINITROETHANOL $(NO_2)_3CCH_2OH$

(self-reactive)
Explosions were encountered during the distillation of trinitroethanol.
J. Am. Chem. Soc. **72:** 5329 (1950).

TRINITROMETHANE $(NO_2)_3CH$

(self-reactive)
Explosions were encountered during the distillation of trinitromethane.
J. Am. Chem. Soc. **72:** 5329 (1950).
See also NITRIC ACID plus Acetylene.

TRIPHENYLALUMINUM $(C_6H_5)_3Al$

Water
Triphenyl aluminum reacts explosively with water.
Rose (1961).

TRIPROPYLALUMINUM $Al(C_3H_7)_3$

Air
Tripropyl aluminum is spontaneously flammable in air and explodes violently in water.
Von Schwartz, p. 321 (1918).

Halogenated Hydrocarbons
See TRIETHYL ALUMINUM plus Halogenated Hydrocarbons.

Water
See TRIPROPYL ALUMINUM plus Air.

TRIPROPYLBORANE $(C_3H_7)_3B$

Air
Tripropylborane is spontaneously flammable in air.
Douda (1966).

TRIPROPYLINDIUM $(C_3H_7)_3In$

Air
Tripropyl indium is spontaneously flammable in air.
Douda (1966).

TRIPROPYLSTIBINE $(C_3H_7)_3Sb$

Air
Tripropyl antimony is spontaneously flammable in air.
Ellern, pp. 24-25 (1968).

TRISILANE Si_3H_8

Air
In air, trisilane and tetrasilane explode. See also SILANES plus Air.
Mellor **6:** 224 (1946-1947).

Carbon Tetrachloride
Carbon tetrachloride reacts more vigorously on trisilane and tetrasilane than on disilane.
Mellor **6:** 224 (1946-1947).

Oxygen
See OXYGEN plus Disilane.

TRISILYLAMINE $(SiH_3)_3N$

Air
Trisilylamine is spontaneously flammable in air.
Mellor **8:** 262 (1946-1947).

TRISILYLARSINE $(SiH_3)_3As$

Air
Trisilyl arsine is spontaneously flammable in air.
Douda (1966).

TRISILYLPHOSPHINE $(SiH_3)_3P$

(self-reactive)
This is a spontaneously flammable liquid.
Mellor **8, Supp. 3:** 283 (1971).

Air
The liquid ignites spontaneously in air.
Ellern, p. 22 (1968). *Douda* (1966).

TRIS(TRIFLUOROMETHYL)PHOSPHINE $(CF_3)_3P$

Air
Tristrifluoromethyl phosphine is spontaneously flammable in air.
Douda (1966). *Handbook Chem. Phys.,* p. **C-428** (1970-1971).

TRIS(TRIMETHYLSILYL)PHOSPHINE $[(CH_3)_3Si]_3P$

Air
Tristrimethyl silyl phosphine is spontaneously flammable in air.
Def. Res. and Eng., p. 247 (1963).

TRITOLYLAMINE PERCHLORATE $(CH_3C_4H_6)_3NHClO_4$

(self-reactive)
Tritolylamine perchlorate explodes above 123°C.
ACS **146:** 213. *Berichte* **43:** 2624-30 (1910).

TRIVINYL ANTIMONY $(CH_2{=}CH)_3Sb$

Air
Trivinyl antimony is spontaneously flammable in air.
Zeiss, p. 92 (1960).

TRIVINYLBISMUTHINE $(CH_2{=}CH)_3Bi$

Air
Trivinyl bismuthine is spontaneously flammable in air.
Zeiss, p. 129 (1960).

TROPYLIUM PERCHLORATE $(C_7H_7)ClO_4$

(self-reactive)
An 80-gram sample of tropylium perchlorate heaped in a transfer funnel exploded violently when it was touched by a glass rod.
Angew. Chem. Intern. Ed. Engl. **1** (7): **465** (1962).

TUNGSTEN W

Bromine Trifluoride
See MOLYBDENUM plus Bromine Trifluoride.

Chlorine Trifluoride
See ANTIMONY plus Chlorine Trifluoride.

Fluorine
See FLUORINE plus Tungsten.

Iodine Pentafluoride
See ARSENIC plus Iodine Pentafluoride.

Lead Dioxide
See MOLYBDENUM plus Lead Dioxide.

TUNGSTEN CARBIDE WC

Chlorine Trifluoride
See CHLORINE TRIFLUORIDE plus Mercuric Iodide.

Fluorine
See FLUORINE plus Tungsten Carbide.

Nitrogen Dioxide
Tungsten carbide burns with incandescence if heated to dull redness in either nitrous oxide or nitrogen dioxide.
Mellor **5:** 890 (1946-1947).

Nitrous Oxide
See TUNGSTEN CARBIDE plus Nitrogen Dioxide.

TUNGSTEN DIOXIDE WO_2

Chlorine
See CHLORINE plus Tungsten Dioxide.

TUNGSTEN TRIOXIDE WO_3

Chlorine Trifluoride
The reaction between tungsten trioxide and chlorine trifluoride is accompanied by incandescence.
Mellor **11:** 730 (1946-1947).
See also CHLORINE TRIFLUORIDE plus Aluminum Oxide.

Lithium
See LITHIUM plus Tungsten Trioxide.

TURPENTINE

Calcium Hypochlorite
See CALCIUM HYPOCHLORITE plus Turpentine.

Chlorine
See CHLORINE plus Hydrocarbons.

Chromic Anhydride
See CHROMIC ANHYDRIDE plus Naphthalene.

Chromyl Chloride
See CHROMYL CHLORIDE plus Acetone.

Hexachloromelamine
See HEXACHLOROMELAMINE plus Organic Contaminants.

Stannic Chloride
See STANNIC CHLORIDE plus Turpentine.

Trichloromelamine
See HEXACHLOROMELAMINE plus Organic Contaminants.

TYGON®

Fluorine
See FLUORINE plus Solid Nonmetals and Oxygen.

URANIUM U

Air
Clean uranium turnings or chips oxidize readily in air. If confined in a container without air movement, they can ignite spontaneously. Moisture increases this reactivity.
Scott (1970).

Carbon Tetrachloride
An explosion occurred when liquid carbon tetrachloride was used in an attempt to extinguish a small fire involving about a half pound of uranium.
Allison (1969).

Chlorine
See CHLORINE plus Uranium.

Fluorine
See FLUORINE plus Uranium.

Nitric Acid
Nitric acid can react with uranium with explosive violence.
Katz and Rabinowitch (1951).
Freshly cleaned uranium turnings in a stainless steel beaker were covered with hot water and nitric acid to bring the concentration to 4 to 6 normal. When cold rinse water was turned on, an explosion accompanied by a flash, ejected the turnings from the beaker.
Serious Acc. Series **250** (1965).

Nitric Oxide
Uranium ignites in warm nitric oxide.
Mellor **12:** 31-2 (1946-1947).

Selenium
Uranium reacts with incandescence with hot selenium or sulfur (boiling).
Mellor **12:** 31-2 (1946-1947).

Sulfur
See URANIUM plus Selenium.

Water
Uranium turnings and fines stored out of doors in a closed container under water or water-soluble oil will hydride and eventually ignite during hot weather.
Scott (1970).

URANIUM DICARBIDE UC_2

Air
Uranium dicarbide ignites if powdered in a mortar.
Mellor **5:** 890 (1946-1947).

Bromine
See BROMINE plus Uranium Dicarbide.

Chlorine
See BROMINE plus Uranium Dicarbide.

Fluorine
See BROMINE plus Uranium Dicarbide.

Water
Uranium dicarbide (at dull-red heat) reacts with steam with incandescence.
Mellor **5:** 890 (1946-1947).

URANIUM DIOXIDE UO_2

Air
Uranium oxide is spontaneously flammable in air.
Brauer (1965).

URANIUM HYDRIDE UH_3

Air
Uranium hydride is spontaneously flammable in air.
J. Zehr, *Staub* **22** (11): 494-508 (1962). *Brauer* (1965).

URANIUM-NEODYMIUM ALLOY

Nitric Acid
Explosive or violent reactions have occurred during or subsequent to pickling of the alloy with nitric acid.
Allison (1969).

URANIUM-NEODYMIUM-ZIRCONIUM ALLOY

Nitric Acid
Explosive or violent reactions have occurred during or subsequent to pickling of the alloy with nitric acid.
Allison (1969).

URANIUM NITRIDE UN

Air
Uranium nitride is spontaneously flammable in air.
J. Zehr, *Staub* **22** (11): 494-508 (1962).

URANIUM OXIDES UO_2;UO_3;U_3O_8

Bromine Trifluoride
See BROMINE TRIFLUORIDE plus Uranium Oxides.

URANIUM PHOSPHIDE U_3P_4

Hydrochloric Acid
Uranium phosphide reacts with hydrochloric acid to release spontaneously flammable phosphine.
Mellor **8, Supp. 3:** 349 (1971).

URANIUM TETRAHYDROBORATE $U(BH_4)_3$

Air
Uranium borohydride is spontaneously flammable in air.
H.I. Schlesinger et al, *J. Am. Chem. Soc.* **75:** 219-223 (1953).

URANYL PERCHLORATE $UO_2(ClO_4)_2$

Ethyl Alcohol
Attempts at recrystallization from ethyl alcohol resulted in an explosion.
Mellor **2, Supp. 1:** 617 (1956).

p-URAZINE NHNHCONHNHCO

(self-reactive)
While a chemist was manipulating the material in a glass container, an explosion occurred that shattered the container. The material that exploded was probably a nitrogen-containing byproduct.
MCA Case History **144** (1966).

UREA $(NH_2)_2CO$

Gallium Perchlorate
See GALLIUM PERCHLORATE plus Urea.

Hypochlorites
See HYPOCHLORITES plus Urea.

VANADIUM V

Bromine Trifluoride
See MOLYBDENUM plus Bromine Trifluoride.

Chlorine
See CHLORINE plus Vanadium.

Lithium
See LITHIUM plus Vanadium.

VANADIUM OXYDICHLORIDE $VOCl_2$

Potassium
See POTASSIUM plus Boric Acid.

VANADIUM OXYTRICHLORIDE $VOCl_3$

Phosphorus
See PHOSPHORUS plus Vanadium Oxytrichloride.

VANADIUM PENTACHLORIDE VCl_5

Potassium
See POTASSIUM plus Aluminum Bromide.

Sodium
See SODIUM plus Aluminum Bromide.

VANADIUM PENTOXIDE V_2O_5

Calcium, Sulfur, and Water
See CALCIUM plus Vanadium Oxide, Sulfur, and Water

Chlorine Trifluoride
See CHLORINE TRIFLUORIDE plus Aluminum Oxide.

Lithium
See LITHIUM plus Vanadium Pentoxide.

VANADIUM SESQUIOXIDE V_2O_3

Air
Vanadium sesquioxide is spontaneously flammable in air.
Ellern (1961).

VANILLIN $CH_3O(HO)C_6H_3CHO$

Thallium Trinitrate Trihydrate and Formic Acid
See THALLIUM TRINITRATE TRIHYDRATE plus Formic Acid and Vanillin.

VEGETABLE GLUES

Aluminum
See ALUMINUM plus Nitrates.

VINYL ACETATE $CH_2=CHOCOCH_3$

2-Aminoethanol Chlorosulfonic Acid
See 2-AMINOETHANOL plus Vinyl Acetate. Mixing vinyl acetate and chlorosulfonic acid in a closed container caused the temperature and pressure to increase.
Flynn and Rossow (1970). See Note under complete reference.

Ethylene Diamine
See ETHYLENE DIAMINE plus Vinyl Acetate.

Ethyleneimine
Mixing vinyl acetate and ethyleneimine in a closed container caused the temperature and pressure to increase.
Flynn and Rossow (1970). See Note under complete reference.

Hydrochloric Acid
Mixing vinyl acetate and 36% hydrochloric acid in a closed container caused the temperature and pressure to increase.
Flynn and Rossow (1970). See Note under complete reference.

Hydrofluoric Acid
Mixing vinyl acetate and 48.7% hydrofluoric acid in a closed container caused the temperature and pressure to increase.
Flynn and Rossow (1970). See Note under complete reference.

Nitric Acid
Mixing vinyl acetate and 70% nitric acid in a closed container caused the temperature and pressure to increase.
Flynn and Rossow (1970). See Note under complete reference.

Oleum
See OLEUM plus Vinyl Acetate.

Peroxides
Vinyl acetate in contact with peroxides may polymerize violently.
Haz. Chem. Data (1966).

Sulfuric Acid
Mixing vinyl acetate and 96% sulfuric acid in a closed container caused the temperature and pressure to increase.
Flynn and Rossow (1970). See Note under complete reference.

VINYL ACETATE-CHLORIDE COPOLYMER

Fluorine
See FLUORINE plus Solid Nonmetals and Oxygen.

VINYL ACETYLENE C_4H_4

Vinyl acetylene is included in a list of peroxidizable monomers where the presence of peroxide can initiate exothermic polymerization of the bulk of the material.
Bretherick (1978).

VINYL AZIDE $CH_2=CHN_3$

(self-reactive)
A sample of vinyl azide in a distilling flask with a ground glass joint exploded when the joint was rotated.
R.H. Wiley and J. Moffat, *J. Org. Chem.* **22:** 995 (1957).

VINYL CHLORIDE $CH_2=CHCl$

Air
An unstable polyperoxide is apparently formed in vinyl chloride through oxidation by atmospheric oxygen in the presence of any of a variety of contaminants. Storage under these conditions for a long period increases the concentration of unstable polyperoxide to hazardous levels.
MCA Case History **1551** (1969).

VINYLIDENE CHLORIDE $CH_2=CCl_2$

(self-reactive)
A coating of vinylidene chloride polymer on the inside of a 2-inch pipe exploded when the pipe touched a fitting on a tank car.
MCA Case History **1172** (1966).

Chlorosulfonic Acid
Mixing vinylidene chloride and chlorosulfonic acid in a closed container caused the temperature and pressure to increase.
Flynn and Rossow (1970). See Note under complete reference.

Nitric Acid
Mixing vinylidene chloride and 70% nitric acid in a closed container caused the temperature and pressure to increase.
Flynn and Rossow (1970). See Note under complete reference.

Oleum
See OLEUM plus Vinylidene Chloride.

VITON A®

Fluorine
See FLUORINE plus Solid Nonmetals and Oxygen.

WAX, DRAWING

Chlorine
See CHLORINE plus Polypropylene.

XANTHATES

Diazonium Salts
See DIAZONIUM SALTS plus Thiophenates.

XENON HEXAFLUORIDE XeF_6

Water
Xenon hexafluoride reacted with water to form explosive xenon trioxide.
Health & Safety Inf. **181** (1964). *Chem. and Eng. News* **13:** 45-6 (1963). *J. Am. Chem. Soc.* **85:** 816 (1963).

2(X, Y-XYLYL)ETHANOL $(CH_3)_2C_6H_3CH_2CH_2OH$

Hydrogen Peroxide
See ALCOHOLS plus Hydrogen Peroxide and Sulfuric Acid.

YTTERBIUM Yb

Air
See RARE EARTH METALS plus Air.

Halogens
See RARE EARTH METALS plus Halogens.

YTTRIUM Yt

Air
See RARE EARTH METALS plus Air.

Halogens
See RARE EARTH METALS plus Halogens.

ZIEGLER-TYPE CATALYSTS

Allyl Chloride
See SULFURIC ACID plus Allyl Chloride.

ZINC Zn

Acids
Zinc powder or dust in contact with acids evolves hydrogen. The heat of reaction is sufficient that the hydrogen may ignite.
Lab. Govt. Chemist (1965).

Ammonium Nitrate
The two substances are mixed intimately and wetted with 3 or 4 drops of water. After a short time, a violent reaction occurs with evolution of steam and zinc oxide.
Greaves (1967).
Mellor **8, Supp. 1:** 546 (1964).
See also AMMONIUM NITRATE plus Metals (powdered).

Barium Dioxide
See MAGNESIUM plus Barium Nitrate, Barium Dioxide and Zinc.

Barium Nitrate
See MAGNESIUM plus Barium Nitrate, Barium Dioxide and Zinc.

Cadmium
See ZINC plus Selenium.

Carbon Disulfide
A mixture of zinc and carbon disulfide reacts with incandescence.
Mellor **4:** 476-90 (1946-1947).

Chlorates
A mixture of powdered zinc and an oxidizing agent such as potassium chlorate can be exploded by percussion.
Mellor **4:** 480 (1946-1947).

Chlorine
Zinc burns in moist chlorine.
Mellor **4:** 476 (1946-1947).

Chlorine Trifluoride
See ALUMINUM plus Chlorine Trifluoride.

Chromic Anhydride
A violent reaction or flaming is likely in the reaction of chromic anhydride and zinc dust.
Mellor **11:** 237 (1946-1947).

Ethyl Acetoacetate and Tribromoneopentyl Alcohol
See ETHYL ACETOACETATE plus Tribromoneopentyl and Zinc.

Fluorine
See FLUORINE plus Zinc.

Hydrazine Mononitrate
When hydrazine mononitrate is heated in contact with zinc, copper and most other metals as well as oxides, sulfides, nitrides and carbides, a flaming decomposition occurs at temperatures a little above its melting point.
Mellor **8:** 327 (1946-1947).

Hydroxylamine
Hydroxylamine is reduced when heated with zinc dust; sometimes the mixture merely ignites; other times, it explodes.
Mellor **8:** 290 (1946-1947).

Lead Azide
See COPPER plus Lead Azide.

Magnesium, Barium Nitrate, and Barium Dioxide
See MAGNESIUM plus Barium Nitrate, Barium Dioxide and Zinc.

Manganese Chloride
Zinc powder reacts explosively when heated with manganese chloride.
Mellor **4:** 479 (1946-1947).

Nitric Acid
When concentrated nitric acid is poured on molten zinc, the reaction proceeds with incandescence.
Mellor **4:** 476-90 (1946-1947).

Performic Acid
Powdered zinc can decompose performic acid violently, causing an explosion.
Berichte **48:** 1139 (1915).

Potassium Chlorate
See ZINC plus Chlorates.

Potassium Nitrate
Powdered zinc and potassium nitrate explode if heated.
Mellor **7:** 116 (1946-1947).

Potassium Peroxide
See POTASSIUM plus Potassium Peroxide.

Selenium
The reaction between zinc and selenium or tellurium is accompanied by incandescence (cadmium less so).
Mellor **4:** 480 (1946-1947).

Sodium Chlorate
See ZINC plus Chlorates.

Sodium Peroxide
Sodium peroxide oxidizes zinc with incandescence.
Mellor **2:** 490-93 (1946-1947).

Sulfur
See SULFUR plus Zinc.

Tellurium
See ZINC plus Selenium.

Water
Zinc powder or dust in contact with water or damp air evolves hydrogen. The heat of reaction is sufficient that the hydrogen may ignite.
Haz. Chem. Data p. 171 (1966).
Lab. Govt. Chemist (1965).

Zinc Peroxide
See ALUMINUM plus Zinc Peroxide.

ZINC AMIDE $Zn(NH_2)_2$

Hydrazine
The action of an ethereal solution of hydrazine on zinc diamide or diethyl zinc, gives a product, zinc hydrazine, which explodes at 70°C.
Mellor **8:** 315 (1946-1947).

ZINC BENZENEDIAZONIUM CHLORIDE
$C_6H_5\text{-}N=NClZnCl_2$

(self-reactive)
Zinc benzenediazonium chloride had been washed in dry acetone and had been stored in a vacuum desiccator 15 hours when it exploded.
Chem. & Ind. p. 58-9 (1956).

ZINC BROMATE $Zn(BrO_3)_2$

Aluminum
See ALUMINUM plus Bromates.

Arsenic
See ARSENIC plus Bromates.

Carbon
See CARBON plus Bromates.

Copper
See COPPER plus Bromates.

Metal Sulfides
See METAL SULFIDES plus Bromates.

Organic Matter
See BROMATES plus Organic Matter.

Phosphorus
See PHOSPHORUS plus Bromates.

Sulfur
See SULFUR plus Bromates.

ZINC BROMIDE $ZnBr_2$

Potassium
See POTASSIUM plus Aluminum Bromide.

Sodium
See SODIUM plus Aluminum Bromide.

ZINC CHLORATE $Zn(ClO_3)_2$

Aluminum
See ALUMINUM plus Bromates.

Antimony Sulfide
See CHLORATES plus Antimony Sulfide. See also METAL SULFIDES plus Bromates.

Arsenic
See ARSENIC plus Bromates.

Arsenic Sulfide
See CHLORATES plus Arsenic Sulfide. See also METAL SULFIDES plus Bromates.

Carbon
See CARBON plus Bromates.

Charcoal
Zinc chlorate and charcoal (or finely divided organic matter) form mixtures which may ignite or explode. Such ignition or explosion may be caused by friction, percussion, or shock.
U.S. Army Ord. Safety Man. (1951).
See also CHLORATES plus Organic Matter.

Copper
See COPPER plus Bromates.

Copper Sulfide
See COPPER SULFIDE plus Cadmium Chlorate.

Manganese Dioxide
See CHLORATES plus Manganese Dioxide.

Metal Sulfides
See METAL SULFIDES plus Bromates.

Organic Acids (Dibasic)
See CHLORATES plus Organic Acids.

Organic Matter
See ZINC CHLORATE plus Charcoal. See ALUMINUM plus Bromates.
See CHLORATES plus Organic Matter.

Phosphorus
See PHOSPHORUS plus Bromates.

Stannic Sulfide
See STANNIC SULFIDE plus Cadmium Chlorate. See METAL SULFIDES plus Bromates.

Stannous Sulfide
See STANNOUS SULFIDE plus Cadmium Chlorate. See METAL SULFIDES plus Bromates.

Sulfur
See SULFUR plus Bromates. See CHLORATES plus Organic Matter.

Sulfuric Acid
Zinc chlorate in contact with concentrated sulfuric acid is likely to cause fires and explosions.
Bahme, p. 29 (1961).
See CHLORATES plus Acids.

ZINC CHLORIDE $ZnCl_2$

Potassium
See POTASSIUM plus Aluminum Bromide.

ZINC CYANIDE $Zn(CN)_2$

Magnesium
See MAGNESIUM plus Cadmium Cyanide.

ZINC DIALKYLS

Air
These compounds are spontaneously flammable in air.
Von Schwartz, p. 329 (1918).

ZINC FLUORIDE ZnF_2

Potassium
See POTASSIUM plus Ammonium Bromide.

ZINC-HYDRAZINE CHLORATE

(self-reactive)
This compound detonates when struck but is less sensitive than tetramminiozinc chlorate.
Mellor **2, Supp. 1:** 592 (1956).

ZINC IODATE $Zn(IO_3)_2$

Aluminum
See ALUMINUM plus Bromates.

Arsenic
See ARSENIC plus Bromates.

Carbon
See CARBON plus Bromates.

ZINC IODIDE ZI_2

Potassium
See POTASSIUM plus Alumium Bromide.

ZINC NITRATE $Zn(NO_3)_2$

Carbon
See CARBON plus Zinc Nitrate.

Copper
See COPPER plus Bromates.

Metal Sulfides
See METAL SULFIDES plus Bromates.

Organic Matter
See BROMATES plus Organic Matter.

Phosphorus
See PHOSPHORUS plus Bromates.

Sulfur
See SULFUR plus Bromates.

ZINC OXIDE ZnO

Chlorinated Rubber
Reaction between zinc oxide and chlorinated rubber in a large batch resulted in a violent explosion that wrecked a manufacturing building.
Chem. and Eng. News **40** (36): 79 (1962).

Magnesium
See MAGNESIUM plus Beryllium Oxide.

ZINC PEROXIDE ZnO_2

Aluminum
See ALUMINUM plus Zinc Peroxide.

Zinc
See ALUMINUM plus Zinc Peroxide.

ZINC PHOSPHIDE Zn_3P_2

Water
Moisture reacts with zinc phosphide with production of phosphine, a spontaneously flammable gas.
Oldbury Chemicals.

ZINC SULFIDE ZnS

Iodine Monochloride
See IODINE MONOCHLORIDE plus Cadmium Sulfide.

ZINC-TETRAMMINE CHLORATE $Zn(NH_3)_4(ClO_3)_2$

(self-reactive)
This compound detonates when struck.
Mellor **2, Supp. 1:** 592 (1956).

ZINC-TETRAMMINE PERCHLORATE $Zn(NH_3)_4(ClO_4)_2$

(self-reactive)
This compound detonates when struck but is less sensitive than tetramminiozine chlorate.
Mellor **2, Supp. 1:** 592 (1956).

ZIRCONIUM Zr

Air
See TANTALUM plus Air.

Alkali Hydroxides
When a mixture of alkali hydroxide and zirconium is heated, the liberated oxygen reacts explosively with the zirconium.
Mellor **7:** 116 (1946-1947).

Alkali Metal Chromates
See ZIRCONIUM plus Alkali Metal Salts.

Alkali Metal Dichromates
See ZIRCONIUM plus Alkali Metal Salts.

Alkali Metal Molybdates
See ZIRCONIUM plus Alkali Metal Salts.

Alkali Metal Salts
Chromates, dichromates, sulfates, molybdates and tungstates of lithium, sodium, potassium, rubidium and cesium will react violently, even explosively, with an excess of zirconium powder and yield the impure metal.
Ellern, p. 249 (1968). *Mellor* **2: Supp. II and III.**

Alkali Metal Sulfates
See ZIRCONIUM plus Alkali Metal Salts

Alkali Metal Tungstates
See ZIRCONIUM plus Alkali Metal Salts.

Borax
A mixture of hydrated borax and zirconium explodes when heated.
Mellor **7:** 116 (1946-1947).

Carbon Tetrachloride
An explosion occurred when zirconium sponge was placed in a beaker of carbon tetrachloride.
Allison (1969).

Cupric Oxide
Zirconium explodes violently with cupric oxide or lead oxide.
Mellor **7:** 116 (1946-1947).

Lead
See LEAD plus Zirconium.

Lead Oxide
See ZIRCONIUM plus Cupric Oxide.

Phosphorus
See PHOSPHORUS plus Zirconium.

Potassium Chlorate
When heated, potassium chlorate reacts with zirconium with slight explosions.
Mellor **7:** 116 (1946-1947).

Potassium Nitrate
A mixture of powdered zirconium and potassium nitrate explodes when heated above the melting temperature.
Mellor **7:** 116 (1946-1947).

ZIRCONIUM CARBIDE ZrC

Air
Zirconium carbide in the form of a fine powder is spontaneously flammable in air.
Rose (1961).

ZIRCONIUM DIBROMIDE $ZrBr_2$

Air
Zirconium dibromide is spontaneously flammable in air.
Douda (1966).

ZIRCONIUM DICARBIDE ZrC_2

Bromine
See BROMINE plus Zirconium Dicarbide.

Chlorine
See BROMINE plus Zirconium Dicarbide.

Fluorine
See BROMINE plus Zirconium Dicarbide.

Iodine
See BROMINE plus Zirconium Dicarbide.

ZIRCONIUM DIHYDRIDE ZrH_2

Air

When heated in air, zirconium dihydride burns with incandescence.
Mellor **7:** 116 (1946-1947).

ZIRCONIUM TETRACHLORIDE $ZrCl_4$

Lithium

See LITHIUM plus Chromium Trichloride.

ZIRCONIUM TETRAHYDROBORATE $Zr(BH_4)_4$

Air

Zirconium borohydride is spontaneously flammable in air.
Gaylord, p. 58 (1956).

ZIRCONIUM-URANIUM ALLOY

Nitric Acid

Contact of etched or cleaned zirconium-uranium alloy with nitric acid results in a mild explosion.
Allison (1969).

REFERENCES

Abbey
Communication, D.R. Abbey, Don Mills, Ontario

ABCM Quarterly Safety Summary
ABCM Quarterly Safety Summary (1956)

Acad. Handl.
K. Krigs Vetenskaps Akadamien, Stockholm, Handlingar

Acc. Chem. Res.
Accounts of Chemical Research, American Chemical Society, Washington, D.C.

Acc. & Fire Prev. Inf.
Accident and Fire Prevention Information, U.S. Atomic Energy Commission, Washington, D.C.

Accidental Explosions
Accidental Explosions, Louis A. Medard (1989)

ACS 15 (1923)
ACS Monograph 15, "Organic Arsenical Compounds," G.W. Raizisc and J.L. Gavron, The Chemical Catalog Co., New York (1923)

ACS 146
ACS Monograph 146, "Perchlorates, Their Properties, Manufacture and Uses," J.C. Schumacher, Reinhold, New York (1960)

Acta Crystallogr.
Acta Crystallographica, Copenhagen

AEC Research & Devel. Report
Research and Development Reports, U.S. Atomic Energy Commission, Oak Ridge, Tennessee

Aero. and Astro.
Aeronautics and Astronautics, American Institute of Aeronautics and Astronautics, Inc., New York

Aero. Tech. Note
Aeronautics Technical Note, National Advisory Committee, Washington, D.C.

AIChE Loss Prevention, 1967
Loss Prevention, 1967, F. Lorentz, American Institute of Chemical Engineers, New York (1967)

AIChE Loss Prevention, 1996
Loss Prevention, Feb. 1996, L. G. Britton, "Decomposition Flame Propagation Limits of Ethylene and Mixtures with Other Gases, Paper 8e, American Institute of Chemical Engineers, New Orleans

Albrecht
Communication, A.R. Albrecht, The Dow Chemical Company, Midland, Mich.

Allison
Communication, W.W. Allison, Sandia Corp., Albuquerque, N.M.

Aluminum Alkyls
Aluminum Alkyls, Ethyl Corporation, New York

Am. Chem. J.
American Chemical Journal, American Chemical Society, Washington, D.C.

Analyst
The Analyst, Journal of the Society for Analytical Chemistry, Cambridge, England

Angew. Chem.
Angewandte Chemie, Weinheim, West Germany

Angew. Chem. Intern. Ed. Engl.
Angewandte Chemie, International Edition in English, Academic Press, New York

Aniline
Aniline, National Aniline Division, Allied Chemical Corp., New York (1964)

Ann. Chem.
Annalen der Chemie, Justus Liebigs, Weinheim

Ann. Chim. et Phys.
Annales de Chimie et de Physique, Paris

Ann. Phys.
Annalen der Physik, Barth, Leipzig

Arbeitsschutz
Arbeitsschutz, Bundesministen Fuer Arbeit and Sozialordnung, Cologne

ASESB Expl. Report
ASESB Explosives Incident Report, Armed Services Explosives Safety Board, Washington, D.C.

ASESB Pot. Incid.
ASESB Potential Incident Report, Armed Services Explosives Safety Board, Washington, D.C.

ASHRAE Journal
ASHRAE Journal, American Society of Heating, Refrigeration and Air Conditioning Engineers, New York.

Bahme
Fire Protection for Chemicals, C.W. Bahme, National Fire Protection Assn., Boston (1961)

Barrett
Communication, R.E. Barrett, Chevron Oil Field Research Company, La Holra, Calif.

Baudrimant
Recherches sur les Clorures et les Bromures de Phosphore, E. Baudrimant

BCISC
Quarterly Safety Summary of the British Chemical Industry Safety Council, Society of the Chemical Industry, London

Becker
Communication, E.I. Becker, American Chemical Society, Committee on Chemical Safety

Beilstein
Handbuch der Organischen Chemie, F. Beilstein, J. Springer Pub. (1929)

Benson
Communication, C. Benson, Federal Correctional Institution, La Tuna, Texas

Berichte
Berichte der Deutschen Chemischen Gesellschaft, Verlag Chemie, Weinheim, Germany

Bernthsen
Textbook of Organic Chemistry, A. Bernthsen, D. van Nostrand, New York (1912)

Berzelius
Lehrbuch der Chemie, J.J. Berzelius, Dresden (1825)

Bibl. Univ. Genève
Bibliothèque Universelle de Genève

Biul. Wojskowej Akad. Tech.
Biuletyn Wojskowski Akademii Techniczenj Imeni Jaroslawa Dab rowskiego, Warsaw, Poland

BM Bull.
Bulletin, Bureau of Mines, U.S. Department of the Interior, Washington

BM Explos. Div. Rep.
Report of Bureau of Mines, Explosives Division, U.S. Department of Interior, Pittsburgh, Pa.

BM Info. Circ.
Information Circular, Bureau of Mines, U.S. Department of Interior, Pittsburgh, Pa.

BM Report Invest.
Report of Investigations, Bureau of Mines, U.S. Department of the Interior, Pittsburgh, Pa.

Bozich
Communication, T.A. Bozich, Case Institute of Technology, Cleveland, Pittsburgh, Pa.

Brauer
Handbook of Preparative Inorganic Chemistry, Ed. by G. Brauer. Academic Press, New York (1965)

Brennstoff-Chem.
Brennstoff-Chemie, Zeitschrift fuer Chemie und Tecknik von Kohle, Oel und Gas, W. Girardet, Essen.

Bretherick
(1979)

Bull. Acad. Belg.
Bulletin de l'Acadée;mie de Belgique

Bull. Acad. St. Petersbourg
Académie Impériale des Sciences de St. Petersbourg, St. Peters bourg

Bull. Soc. Chim.
Bulletin de la SociétéChimique de France, Masson & Cie., Paris

Buls, Bimonthly Rept. 5
Potential CW Agents, Task 5, Boron Compounds as Toxicants, V.W. Buls. Bimonthly Rept. 5, AD 46023, Shell Development Co., Emeryville, Calif. (Apr-May, 1953)

Buls, Bimonthly Rept. 6
Potential CW Agents, Task 5, Boron Compounds as Toxicants, V.W. Buls. Bimonthly Rept. 6, AD 46101, Shell Development Co., Emeryville, Calif. (June-July, 1953)

Buls, Bimonthly Rept. 8
Potential CW Agents, Task 5, Boron Compounds as Toxicants, V.W. Buls. Bimonthly Rept. 8, AD 38431, Shell Development Co., Emeryville, Calif. (Oct-Nov., 1953)

Bureau of Mines
U.S. Bureau of Mines, Pittsburgh, Private communication

Cady
Communication, E. Cady, University of Washington, Seattle, Wash.

Can. J. Chem.
Canadian Journal of Chemistry, National Research Council, Ottawa

Can. J. Research
Canadian Journal of Research, National Research Council, Ottawa

Chaney
Communication, L.E. Chaney, Battelle Memorial Institute, Colum bus, Ohio

Chapman
Communication, F.F. Chapman, E.I. du Pont de Nemours & Co

F.F. Chapman
Communication, F.F. Chapman, Beckman Instruments, Inc., Fullerton, Calif.

Chem. Abst.
Chemical Abstracts, American Chemical Society, Columbus, Ohio

Chem. Age
Chemical Age, Benn Brothers, Ltd., London

Chem. Ber.
Chemische Berichte, Weinheim-Bergstr., West Germany

Chem. in Brit.
Chemistry in Britain, The Royal Institute of Chemistry and the Chemical Society, London

Chem. and Eng. News
Chemical and Engineering News, American Chemical Society, Washington

Chem. Eng. Progr. Tech. Man.
Chemical Engineering Progress Technical Manual, "Loss Prevention", Vol. 1, American Institute of Chemical Engineers, New York

Chem. Eng. Progs.
Chemical Engineering Progress, American Institute of Chemical Engineers, New York

Chem. Gaz.
Chemical Gazette

Chem. Haz. Info. Series
Chemical Hazards Information Series, American Insurance Assn. (Assn. of Casualty and Surety Companies prior to January 1965), New York.

Chem. & Ind.
Chemistry & Industry, Society of the Chemical Industry, London

Chem. & Met. Eng.
Chemical & Metallurgical Engineering, New York

Chem. News
The Chemical News and Journal of Physical Science

Chem. Phar. Bull.
Chemical and Pharmaceutical Bulletin, Japan Publications Trading Co., Ltd., Tokyo

Chem. Process (Chicago)
Chemical Processing, Putnam Publishing Co., Chicago

Chem. Reviews
Chemical Reviews, American Chemical Society, Washington, D.C.

Chem. Safety Data Sheet
Chemical Safety Data Sheet, Manufacturing Chemistsõ association, Inc., Washington

Chem. Weekblad
Chemisch Weekblad, Royal Netherlands Chemical Society, The Hague

Chem. Zentr.
Chemisches Zentralblatt, Akadamie-Verlag, Berlin

Chemiker Z.
Chemiker Zeitung, Alfred Huethig, Heidelberg

Chim. Ind. (Paris)
Chimie & Industrie (Paris), Paris. English Translation: AERE Trans. 1064, R.A. Slingo, Atomic Energy Research Establishment, Harwell, England

Coates
Organo-Metallic Compounds, G.E. Coates, John Wiley and Sons, Inc., New York (1956)

Coffee
Communication, R.D. Coffee, Eastman Kodak Co., Rochester, New York

Comb. & Flame
Combustion and Flame, American Elsevier Publishing Co., Inc., New York

Comp. Gas Bull.
Compressed Gas Bulletin, Compressed Gas Assn., New York

Comp. Rend.
Comptes Rendus Hebdomadaires des Séances de l'Académie des Sciences, Gauthier-Villars, Paris

Cond. Chem. Dict.
The Condensed Chemical Dictionary, Eighth Edition, Van Nostrand Reinhold Co., New York, N.Y., 1971

Corrosion
Corrosion, National Association of Corrosion Engineers, Houston

Coventry
Communication, C. C. Coventry, International Latex and Chemical Corp., Dover, Delaware

Crucible
Crucible, Pittsburgh Section, American Chemical Society

Damon
Communication, G. H. Damon, Bureau of Mines, U. S. Department of the Interior, Washington, D. C.

Dangerous Chem. Code
Dangerous Chemicals Code, Bureau of Fire Prevention, City of Los Angeles, Parker and Co., Los Angeles (1951)

Davis
Chemistry of Powder and Explosives, T. L. Davis, Wiley & Sons, Inc., New York (1943)

R. Davis
Communication, R. Davis, Essex Chemical

Dean
Communication, F. H. Dean, Ontario Research Department, Sheridan Park, Ontario

Def. Res. and Eng.
The Handling and Storage of Liquid Propellants, AD 442849, *Office of the Director of Defense Research and Engineering,* Washington, D. C. (Jan. 1963)

Delhez
Communication, R. Delhez, University of Liege, Liege, Belgium

Dept. of Commerce PB Report
Publication Board Report, Office of Technical Services, U.S. Department of Commerce, Washington, D.C.

Diox Process
The Diox Process, Wallace and Tiernan Co., Newark (1949)

Douda
Air Reactive Compounds: Listing and Properties, B. E. Douda. RDTR No. 71, AD 632686, U. S. Naval Ammunition Depot, Crane, Ind. (Feb. 24, 1966)

Douglas and Thompson
Some Studies in Chemical Fire Hazards, Douglas and Thompson, Oklahoma Engineering Experiment Station (1949)

Dowicil
Dowicil, Technical Bulletin, Dow Chemical Co., Midland, Mich.

Doyle
Communication, W. H. Doyle, Factory Insurance Association, Hartford, Conn.

Dupont Prod. Inf. Bull.
Product Information Bulletins, E. I. duPont de Nemours, Inc., Wilmington, Dela.

Durrant
Introduction to Advanced Inorganic Chemistry, P. J. Durrant and B. Durrant, John Wiley & Sons, Inc., New York (1962)

Edin. Roy. Soc.
Edinburgh Royal Society, Edinburgh

Ellern (1961)
Modern Pyrotechnics, H. Ellern, Chemical Publishing Co., Inc., New York (1961)

Ellern (1968)
Military and Civilian Pyrotechnics, H. Ellern, Chemical Publishing Co., Inc., New York (1968)

"Ethyl" Sodium
Handling "Ethyl" Sodium, Ethyl Corp., New York (1954)

Ethyleneimine
Ethyleneimine, Dow Chemical Co., Midland, Mich.

Fatt and Tashima
Alkali Metal Dispersions, I. Fatt and M. Tashima, Van Nostrand, New York

Fawcett
Communication, H. H. Fawcett, National Academy of Sciences, Washington, D. C.

Fawcett and Wood
Safety and Accident Prevention in Chemical Operations, H. H. Fawcett and W. S. Wood, John Wiley & Sons, Inc., New York (1965).

Federoff
Encyclopedia of Explosives and Related Items, B. T. Federoff, et al., Picatinny Arsenal, Dover, New Jersey (1960).

Fire and Accident Prev.
Fire and Accident Prevention, Information Bulletin Series, U.S. Atomic Energy Commission, Washington, D. C.

Fire Haz. Prop.
Fire Hazard Properties of Flammable Liquids, Gases and Volatile Solids, NFPA No. 325M (1969 Edition), National Fire Protection Assn., Boston

Fire J.
Fire Journal, National Fire Protection Association, Boston

Fire Tech.
Fire Technology, National Fire Protection Association, Boston

Flynn and Rossow
Classification of Chemical Reactivity Hazards for the Advisory Committee to the U.S. Coast Guard, National Academy of Sciences. J. P. Flynn and H. E. Rossow, The Dow Chemical Company, Mid land, Michigan (1970)

NOTE: The authors observed temperature and pressure effects when equimolar quantities of two chemicals were mixed in a closed container. In some cases the changes were solely vapor pressure effects due to heat of solution.

Gallais
Chimie Minérale Théorique et Expérimentale (Chimie Electron ique), F. Gallais, Masson, Paris (1957)

Gaylord
Reduction with Complex Metal Hydrides, N. G. Gaylord, Inter science Publishers, Inc., New York (1956)

Gazz. Chim. Ital.
Gazzetta Chimica Italiana, Rome, Italy

Gen. Inorg. Chem.
General Inorganic Chemistry, P. J. Durrant, Longmans, Green & Co., Ltd., London, (1953)

German Pat.
German Patent

Gilbert's Ann.
Gilbert's Annalen der Physik

Gracie and Droher
A Study of Sodium Fires, J. D. Gracie and J. J. Droher, Atomics International NAA SR 4383, Conoga Park, California (1960)

Greaves
Communication, G. A. Greaves, Explosives Branch, Mines Department, Perth, Western Australia

Grignard
Traite de Chimie Organique, Grignard, Dupont and Locquin, Masson, Paris (1935-1954)

Halane—Prelim. Info. Sheet
Halane—Preliminary Information Sheet, Wyandotte Chemicals, Wyandotte, Mich. (1953)

Hampel
Rare Metals Handbook, 2nd ed., C. A. Hampel, editor, Reinhold, New York (1961)

Handbook Chem. Phys.
Handbook of Chemistry and Physics, Chemical Rubber Publishing Co., Cleveland

Haz. Chem. Data
Hazardous Chemicals Data, NFPA No. 49 (1966 Edition), National Fire Protection Assn., Boston

Hazards Home Chem.
"Hazards of Home Chemistry," H. H. Fawcett, *Transactions,* National Safety Congress, National Safety Council, Chicago (1963)

Health & Safety Inf.
Health and Safety Information, U.S. Atomic Energy Commission, Washington, D.C.

Helv. Chim. Acta
Edenda Curat Societas Chimica Helvetica, Verlag Helvetica Chimica Acta, Basel, Switzerland

Helv. Chim. Acta
Helvetica Chimica Acta, Basel, Switzerland

Hexagon Alpha Chi Sigma
The Hexagon of Alpha Chi Sigma, Indianapolis

Himiceskaja Promyslennost
Himiceskaja Promyslennost. Ministry of Chemical Industry, Moscow (U.S.S.R.)

Houghton
Communication, J. A. Houghton, Liberty Mutual Fire Insurance Company, Boston

Hurd
An Introduction to the Chemistry of the Hydrides, D. T. Hurd, John Wiley and Sons, Inc., New York, (1952)

IIT Progs. Rept.
Inhibition of Flashing of Aerosols, R. Kamo, Quarterly Progress Report 7, AD 272972, Illinois Institute of Technology (Feb. 21, 1962)

Ind. Eng. Chem.
Industrial and Engineering Chemistry, American Chemical Society, Washington, D.C.

Ind. & Eng. Chem. News
Industrial and Engineering Chemistry, News Edition, American Chem. Society, Washington, D.C.

Ind. Eng. Chem. Proc. Dev.
Industrial and Engineering Chemistry, Process Development, American Chemical Society, Washington, D.C.

Ind. Eng. Chem. Prod. Res. Dev.
Industrial and Engineering Chemistry, Product Research and Development, American Chemical Society, Washington, D.C.

Ind. Saf. Equip.
Industrial Safety Equipment

Inf. Exchange Bull.
Information Exchange Bulletin, Lawrence Radiation Laboratory, University of California, Livermore

Inorg. Chem.
Inorganic Chemistry, American Chemical Society, Washington, D.C.

J. Agri. Food Chem.
Journal of Agriculture and Food Chemistry, American Chemical Society, Washington, D.C.

J. Am. Chem. Soc.
Journal of the American Chemical Society, Washington

J. Am. Rocket Soc.
Journal of the American Rocket Society, New York

J. Chem. Edu.
Journal of Chemical Education, American Chemical Society, Division of Chemical Education, N.Y.

J. Chem. Eng. Data
Journal of Chemical and Engineering Data, American Chemical Society, Washington, D.C.

J. Chem. Phys.
Journal of Chemical Physics, American Institute of Physics, New York

J. Chem. Soc.
Journal of the Chemical Society, London

J. Chem. Soc. Japan Ind. Chem. Sect.
Journal of the Chemical Society of Japan, Industrial Chemistry Section, Chemical Society of Japan, Tokyo

J. Chim. Phys.
Journal de Chimie Physique et de Physicochimie Biologique, Société de Chimie Physique, Paris

J. Indian Chem. Soc.
Journal of the Indian Chemical Society, Calcutta

J. Inst. Pet.
Journal of the Institute of Petroleum, London

J. Loss Prevention
Journal of Loss Prevention and Safety Promotion in the Process Industries, H. P. Schildberg, M. Heider, B. Maurer, and W. Berthold (1995)

J. Org. Chem.
The Journal of Organic Chemistry, American Chemical Society, Washington, D.C.

J. Phys. Chem.
The Journal of Physical Chemistry, American Chemical Society, Washington, D.C.

J. Prakt. Chem.
Journal für Praktische Chemie, Barth, Leipzig

J. Res. Nat. Bur. Stand. Sect. A.
Journal of Research, Section A: Physics and Chemistry (National Bureau of Standards), Sup't of Documents, Gov't Printing Office, Washington, D.C.

J. Sci. Instr.
Journal of Scientific Instruments, Inst. of Physics and the Physical Society, London

J. Soc. Chem. Ind.
Journal of the Society of Chemical Industry, Burlington House, London

Jolicoeur
Communication, D. J. Jolicoeur, North American Aviation, Inc., El Segundo, California

Karasch
Organic Sulfur Compounds, N. Karasch, Pergamon Press, New York (1961)

Kastner's Arch.
Kastner's Archives

Katz and Rabinowitch
Chemistry of Uranium, J. J. Katz and E. Rabinowitch, McGraw-Hill Co., New York (1951)

Kaufman
Handbook of Organometallic Compounds, H. C. Kaufman, D. Van Nostrand Co., Inc., New York (1961)

Kharasch
Organic Sulfuric Compounds, W. Kharasch, Editor, Pergamon Press, Elmsford, N.Y. (1961)

Khim. Prom. USSR
Khimicheskaya Promyshlennost USSR, Leningrad

Kirk and Othmer
Encyclopedia of Chemical Technology, Kirk and Othmer, Inter science Publishers, New York (1947)

Kirk and Othmer, Second Ed.
Encyclopedia of Chemical Technology, Second Edition, Kirk and Othmer, Interscience Publishers, New York (1963).

Kirschenbaum
Fundamental Studies of New Reactions, Final Report, A. O. Kirschenbaum, Office of Ordnance Research Institute, Temple University, Philadelphia (1956).

Kit and Evered
Rocket Propellant Handbook, B. Kit and D. S. Evered, The Macmillan Co., New York (1960).

Kite
Communication, G. F. Kite, Phillip Morris Research Center, Richmond, Va.

Kittila
Dimethylformamide Chemical Uses, R. S. Kittila, E. I. duPont de Nemours, Wilmington, Del. (1967).

Klotz
Communication, M. O. Klotz, Ottawa Civic Hospital, Ottawa, Ontario.

Kruk-Schuster
A. Kruk-Schuster, Laboratory Chemical

Lab. Govt. Chemist
Laboratory of the Government Chemist, "Rules for the Pack-

ing, Storage, and Labelling of Explosives for Carriage by Sea," Board of Trade, London (1965)

Laccabue
Report No. 7E 1500, Fluorolube-Aluminum Detonation Point, J. R. Laccabue, Convair (Astronautic Division), General Dynamics Corp., San Diego (1958)

Latimer and Hildebrand
Reference Book of Inorganic Chemistry, Latimer & Hildebrand, Macmillan Co., New York (1940)

Lawless and Smith
High Energy Oxidizers, E. W. Lawless and I. C. Smith, Marcel Dekker, Inc., New York (1968)

Lehman and Wilson
The Inflammable Properties of Combustible Materials, Part I, A. S. Lehman and W. B. Wilson. Final Rept. AD 455079, Shell Development Co., Emeryville, Calif. (June 30, 1949)

Lelei
(1975)

Lockheed
Aluminum Hydride, A Literature Review, Lockheed Aircraft Corp., Tech. note, AD 244583, p. 3. Sunnyvale, Calif. (Aug. 1960)

Lowig
Das Brom und seine chemische Vorhaltnisse, C. Lowig, Heidelberg (1829)

Magnesium Standard
Standard for the Storage, Handling and Processing of Magnesium, No. 48, National Fire Protection Association, Boston

Matheson Gas Data
Matheson Gas Data Book, Matheson Chemical Company, Inc., New York (1961)

Mathieson Chlorine
Mathieson Chlorine, Mathieson Chemical Co., New York (1948)

Matsuguma
Communication, H. J. Matsuguma, Picatinny Arsenal, Dover, N. J.

MCA Case History
Case Histories of Accidents in the Chemical Industry, Manufacturing Chemists' Assn., Inc., Washington, D. C.

MCA Guide for Safety
Guide for Safety in the Chemical Laboratory (Second Edition), Van Nostrand Publishing Company, New York (1972)

MCA Task Group, POCl
Safety and Fire Protection Committee, Task Group on Hazards of POCl, Manufacturing Chemists' Association, Washington, D. C.

Mellor
A Comprehensive Treatise on Inorganic and Theoretical Chemistry, J. W. Mellor, Longmans, Green & Co., London (1946-1947)

Mem. Poudres
Mémorial des Poudres, Paris

Mem. Proc. Manchester Lit. Phil. Soc.
Memoirs and Proceedings of the Manchester Literary Philosophical Society, Manchester, England

Merck Index
The Merck Index of Chemicals and Drugs, Merck & Co., Inc., Rahway, N. J.

Merck Safety Report
Merck & Co., Inc., Rahway, N. J.

Metallic Sodium
Handling Metallic Sodium, National Distillers Chemical Corp., New York (1951)

Mich. Occ. Health
Michigan's Occupational Health, Div. of Occupational Health, Mich. Dept. of Health, Lansing, Mich.

Military Explosives
Military Explosives, TM 9-2900, War Department, U.S. Government.

Miller
Acetylene, Its Properties, Manufacture and Uses, Vol. 1, S. A. Miller, Academic Press, Inc., New York (1965)

Moissan
Le Fluor et ses Composés, H. Moissan, Paris (1900)

Monroe
Communication, R. F. Monroe, Dow Chemical Company, Midland, Michigan

Morse
Communication, A. R. Morse, National Research Council, Ottawa.

Mosher
(1996)

Muir
(1977)

Mukerjee
Communication, N. C. Mukerjee. Chemplast, P. O. Raman Nagar, Tamilnadu, India

Mustaparta
Communication, G. R. Mustaparta, Hercules Incorporated, Cumberland, Maryland.

N. A. Aviation
Comparative Flammability Testing of Insulated Wire, North American Aviation, Inc., El Segundo, California

NAS-USCG Advis. Com.
NAS-USCG Advisory Committee on Hazardous Materials, "A Study of the Hazards Created by Gas Evolution in the Transportation of Liquid Sulfur," Washington, D.C. (1966)

NASA SP-3037
NASA SP-3037, H. W. Schmidt and J. T. Harper, "Handling and Use of Fluorine and Fluorine-Oxygen Mixtures in Rocket Systems," National Aeronautics and Space Administration, Washington, D.C. (1967)

Naturwissenschaften
Naturwissenschaften, Springer, Berlin

NavAer
NavAer, Bureau of Aeronautics, U.S. Navy, Washington, D.C.

NAVWEPS OP 3237
NAVWEPS OP 3237, Bureau of Naval Weapons, Department of the Navy, Washington, D.C.

NBFU Research Report
Research Report, National Board of Fire Underwriters, New York

NFPA Fire News
Fire News, National Fire Protection Assn., Boston

NFPA Quarterly
Quarterly, National Fire Protection Assn., Boston

NSC Data Sheet
Data Sheet, National Safety Council, Chicago

NSC Nat. Saf. News
National Safety News, National Safety Council, Chicago

NSC Newsletter, Aero. Sec.
Newsletter, Aerospace Section, National Safety Council, Chicago

NSC Newsletter, Campus Safety
Newsletter, Campus Safety Association, National Safety Council, Chicago

NSC Newsletter, Chem. Sec.
Newsletter, Chemical Section, National Safety Council, Chicago

NSC Newsletter, R & D Sec.
Newsletter, Research and Development Section, National Safety Council, Chicago

Occ. Haz.
Occupational Hazards, Industrial Publishing Co., Cleveland, Ohio

Occupancy Fire Record
Occupancy Fire Record, National Fire Protection Assn., Boston

Oldbury Chemicals
Oldbury Chemicals, Oldbury Electro-Chemical Co., Niagara Falls, N. Y.

Organic Synthesis
Organic Synthesis, Collective Volume III, E. C. Horning, ed., John Wiley & Sons, New York (1955)

Pancner
Communication, F. O. Pancner, Argonne National Laboratory, Argonne, Illinois

Pascal
Traite de chimie minérale, Paul Pascal, Paris, Masson (1931-1934)

Pease
Project Squid, R. N. Pease. Quarterly Rept. TIP U12580, Princeton Univ., N.J. (March 31, 1950)

Phar. Weekblad
Pharmaceutisch Weekblad, Centen Pub. Co., Hilversum, Netherlands

Phil. Trans. Roy. Soc. London
Philosophical Transactions of the Royal Society of London, London

Phot. Sci. Eng.
Photographic Science and Engineering, Society of Photographic Scientists and Engineers, Washington, D.C.

Pieters
Safety in the Chemical Laboratory, 2nd. Edition, H.A.J. Pieters and J. W. Creyghton, Academic Press, Inc., New York (1957)

Plant Operations Progress
Britton (1990)

Poole
Communication, H. G. Poole, Bureau of Mines, Albany, Ore.

Pouwels
Communication, H. Pouwels, ACF Chemiefarma N.V., Maarssen, Netherlands

Proc. Roy. Soc.
Proceedings of the Royal Society of London

Reactor Fuel Process.
Reactor Fuel Processing, U.S. Government Printing Office, Washington, D.C.

Remy
Treatise on Inorganic Chemistry, H. Remy (translated by J. S. Anderson), Elsevier Publishing Co., New York (1956)

Répert. Pharm.
Répertoire de Pharmacie, Paris

Report, Amer. Potash and Chemical Co.
Report of Accident, Dinsmore and DeRopp, American Potash and Chemical Co., Trona, Calif.

Report Anal. Chem.
Analytical Chemistry, Washington

Report, L. A. Fire Dept.
Report, Los Angeles Fire Department

Rev. Met.
Revue de Métallurgie, Paris

Ripley
A Background Survey of Air and Water Reactive Materials and Their Uses, W. Ripley. RDTN No. 32, U.S. Naval Ammunition Depot, Crane, Ind. (Oct. 28, 1966)

Roblee
Communication, C. L. Roblee, University of Illinois, Champaign-Urbana, Ill.

Rocketdyne Rept., Hypergol
Hypergol Cartridge Maintenance and Storage, Rocketdyne (North American Aviation, Inc.), R-3066; AD 445908, Canoga Park, Calif. (July 13, 1961)

Rolston
Communication, C. H. Rolston, duPont Research and Development Center, Wilmington, Del.

Rose
The Condensed Chemical Dictionary, A. Rose, E. Rose and F. M. Turner, Reinhold Publishing Corp., New York (1961)

Rüst and Ebert
Unfälle Beim Chemischen Arbeiten, E. Rüst and A. Ebert, Rascher Verlag, Zürich (1948)

Rutledge
Acetylenic Compounds, T. F. Rutledge, Reinhold, New York (1968)

Safety Eng.
Safety Engineering, New York

Safety Eng. Reports
Safety Engineering Reports, California Division of Industrial Safety, Sacramento

Scaros and Serauskas
Communication, M. G. Scaros and J. A. Serauskas, Searle Laboratories, Chicago

Schwab
Communication, R. F. Schwab, Allied Chemical Corporation, Morristown, N.J.

Schweigger's Jour.
Schweigger's Journal

Science
Science, American Assn. for The Advancement of Science, Washington, D.C.

Scott
Communication, R. H. Scott, Batelle-Northwest, Richland, Wash ington

Serious Acc. Series
Serious Accident Series, U.S. Atomic Energy Commission, Washington, D.C.

Short
Communication, J. F. Short, The Distillers Company, Ltd., Great Burgh, Epsom, Surrey, England

Sidgwick
The Chemical Elements and Their Compounds, N. V. Sidgwick, Oxford University Press, New York (1950)

Smart
The Technology of Industrial Fire & Explosion Hazards, R. C. Smart, Chapman & Hall, London (1947)

Sodium, Plant Scale
Handling Metallic Sodium on a Plant Scale, U.S. Industrial Chemicals, Inc., New York (1956)

Spence
Communication, S. F. Spence, American Cyanamid Co., Wayne, N.J.

Sprengstoffe, Waffen u. Munitions
Sprengstoffe, Waffen und Munitions, Charlotteburg, Germany (1905)

Staub
Staub (Dust) VDI-Verlag GmbH Duesseldorf, Germany

Stecher
Fire Prevention and Protection Fundamentals, G. E. Stecher and H. N. Lendall, Chilton Co., Philadelphia (1953)

Stephenson
Communication, F. G. Stephenson, Manufacturing Chemists' Association, Washington, D.C.

1965 Sum. Serious Acc.
1965 Summary of Serious Accidents, U.S. Atomic Energy Commission, Washington, D.C. (1966)

Svenska Akad.
Svenska Akademien, Stockholm, Handlingar, Series 2

Swanson
Communication, J. L. Swanson, Battelle-Northwest, Richland, Washington

Symposium Comb. (Fourth)
Symposium on Combustion (Fourth), Williams & Wilkins, Baltimore, Md. (1953)

Symposium Comb. (Fifth)
Symposium on Combustion (Fifth), Reinhold, New York (1955)

Taylor
Taylor's Scientific Memoirs, A. J. Taylor (1831)

Tenn. Eastman
Safety Memorandum, Tennessee Eastman, Co., Kingsport, Tenn.

Title 46
Code of Federal Regulations: Title 46—Shipping [Parts 146 to 149], Washington, D.C.

Trans. Faraday Soc.
Transactions of the Faraday Society, Aberdeen

Trans. Roy. Soc., Can. Sect. III
Transactions of the Royal Society of Canada, Section III, Ottawa

Tricon
Communication, A. J. Tricon, Houston, Texas

Tr. po Khim. i Khim. Tekhnol.
Trudy po Khimii i Khimicheskoi Tekhnologii, Gorki, U.S.S.R.

Turley
Safety Study of Halogenated Hydrocarbon-Nitrogen Tetroxide Det onations, M64-171, R. E. Turley, Martin Co., Denver (1964)

UL Technical Report
Technical Report, Underwriters Laboratories Inc., Chicago

Union Carbide Report
(1990)

Urbanski
Chemistry and Technology of Explosions, T. Urbanski, Pergamon Press, New York (1964)

USAEC Document
Research and Development Report, U.S. Atomic Energy Commission, Washington, D.C.

U.S. Army Ord. Safety Man.
U.S. Army Ordnance Safety Manual, Rev. 4, Washington (1951)

USDA Tech. Bull.
U.S. Department of Agriculture Technical Bulletin, Washington, D.C.

U.S. Pat.
U.S. Patent

U.S. Pat. Gaz.
Official Gazette, U.S. Patent Office, Washington, D.C.

U. Wash. Occ. Health Newsletter
University of Washington Occupational Health Newsletter, Environmental Health Division, Seattle, Wash.

Van Dolah
Communication, R. W. Van Dolah, Bureau of Mines, Pittsburgh, Pa.

Van Slyke
Communication, W. J. Van Slyke, Battelle-Northwest, Richland, Wash.

Van Wazer
Phosphorus and Its Compounds. Vol. 1, J. R. Van Wazer, Inter science Publishers Inc., New York (1958)

Veiligheid
Veiligheid, de Amsterdam, Veiligheidsinstituut, Amsterdam

Ventrone
Communication, T. A. Ventrone, American Cyanamid Co., Bound Brook, N. J.

Vervalin
Fire Protection Manual for Hydrocarbon Processing Plants, C. H. Vervalin, Gulf Publishing Co., Houston (1964)

Von Schwartz
Fire and Explosion Risks, E. Von Schwartz, Griffin & Co., London (1918)

Von Schwartz and Salter
Fire and Explosions Risks, E. Von Schwartz; Translated from the revised German edition by Charles T. C. Salter, Griffen & Co., London (1940)

Wallace
Communication, E. R. Wallace, Eastman Kodak Co., Rochester, N. Y.

Waller and Mandell
Communication, D. K. Waller and D. Mandell, Los Angeles

WAPD-TM
Westinghouse Atomic Power Division Technical Memorandum, Clearinghouse for Federal Scientific and Technical Information, U. S. Department of Commerce, Springfield, Virginia

Weed
Communication, R. D. Weed, Battelle-Northwest, Richland, Wash ington

Wheeler
Communication, J. J. Wheeler, Eastman Kodak Co., Rochester, New York

Whitmore
Organic Chemistry, F. C. Whitmore, D. Van Nostrand, New York (1937)

Wick
Plutonium Handbook, Vol. 1, O. J. Wick et al, Gordon and Breach, Science Publishers, Inc., New York (1967)

Wischmeyer
Communication, F. W. Wischmeyer, Eastman Kodak Co., Rochester, N. Y.

Wood
Communication, W. S. Wood, Sun Oil Company, Philadelphia (1966).

Woodcock
Communication, S. H. Woodcock, Battelle-Northwest, Richland, Wash.

Yunker
Communication, W. Yunker, Battelle-Northwest, Richland, Wash.

Z. Angew. Chem.
Zeitschrift für angewandte Chemie, Verlag Chemie, Weinheim, Germany

Z. Anorg. Chemie
Zeitschrift für anorganische und allgemeine Chemie, Barth, Leipzig

Zeiss
Organometallic Chemistry, H. Zeiss, Reinhold Publishing Corp., New York (1960)

Z. Elektrochem
Zeitschrift für Elektrochemie und angewandte physikalische Che mie, Verlag Chemie, Weinheim, Germany

Zh. Obshch. Khim.
Zhurnol Obshchei Khimii, U.S.S.R.

Z. Naturforsch
Zeitschrift fuer Naturforschung, Tuebinger, West Germany

REPORT OF HAZARDOUS REACTION

MAIL TO: Amy B. Spencer, Chemical Engineer
National Fire Protection Association
1 Batterymarch Park, P.O. Box 9101
Quincy, MA 02269-9101

REACTANTS: ____________________

____

____

DESCRIPTION OF REACTION: ____________________

____

____

____

____

____

____

SOURCE OF INFORMATION (If possible, please include a copy of the documentation): ____________________

____

____

____

____

SUBMITTED BY:

NAME ____________________

ADDRESS ____________________

____

____

phone/fax/e-mail ____________________

NFPA 497

1997 Edition

Classification of Flammable Liquids, Gases, or Vapors and of Hazardous (Classified) Locations for Electrical Installations in Chemical Process Areas

NFPA 497

Recommended Practice for the

Classification of Flammable Liquids, Gases, or Vapors and of Hazardous (Classified) Locations for Electrical Installations in Chemical Process Areas

1997 Edition

This edition of NFPA 497, *Recommended Practice for the Classification of Flammable Liquids, Gases, or Vapors and of Hazardous (Classified) Locations for Electrical Installations in Chemical Process Areas,* was prepared by the Technical Committee on Electrical Equipment in Chemical Atmospheres and acted on by the National Fire Protection Association, Inc., at its Annual Meeting held May 19–22, 1997, in Los Angeles, CA. It was issued by the Standards Council on July 24, 1997, with an effective date of August 15, 1997, and supersedes all previous editions.

This edition of NFPA 497 was approved as an American National Standard on August 15, 1997.

Origin and Development of NFPA 497

The Committee on Electrical Equipment in Chemical Atmospheres began the development of this recommended practice in 1973. The Committee based the diagrams in this document on various codes and standards of the National Fire Protection Association and on the accepted practices of the chemical process industries and the petroleum refining industry. The first edition of this recommended practice was adopted by the Association at the 1975 Annual Meeting.

The Committee began a thorough review of this document in 1980 and completed its work in 1985. The designation was changed to NFPA 497A in anticipation of a similar recommended practice for Class II hazardous (classified) locations.

In 1989, the Technical Committee on Electrical Equipment in Chemical Atmospheres recognized a need for editorial revisions to the drawings referenced in Section 3-4. There were also new drawings included for flammable liquid tank truck loading and unloading and for marine terminal handling of flammable liquids.

In 1993, the Electrical Equipment in Chemical Atmospheres Committee decided to combine the information on group classifications of flammable liquids, gases, and vapors located in NFPA 497M, *Classification of Gases, Vapors, and Dusts for Electrical Equipment in Hazardous (Classified) Locations,* with the information in NFPA 497. The expanded version of 497 was renamed *Recommended Practice for the Classification of Flammable Liquids, Gases, or Vapors and of Hazardous (Classified) Locations for Electrical Installations in Chemical Process Areas.* Table information was expanded, examples were provided in the appendix, and Class I, Zone 0, 1, and 2 information was incorporated into the text for this edition.

Technical Committee on Electrical Equipment in Chemical Atmospheres

R. F. Schwab, *Chair*
Allied-Signal Inc., NJ [U]

Mark C. Ode, *Nonvoting Secretary*
Nat'l. Fire Protection Assn., MA

Alonza W. Ballard, Crouse-Hinds, NY [M]
Rep. Nat'l Electrical Mfgs. Assoc.
Michael K. Baucom, BEBCO Industries, Inc., TX [M]
Francis X. Bender, Hazards Research Corp., NJ [SE]
Edward M. Briesch, Underwriters Laboratories Inc., IL [RT]
Joseph A. Cannatelli, Arco Chemical Co., PA [U]
James DeLuca, Bechtel Corp., CA [SE]
William T. Fiske, Inchcape Testing Services NA Inc., NY [RT]
William G. Lawrence, Jr., Factory Mutual Research Corp., MA [I]
Richard C. Masek, Bailey Controls, OH [M]
Robert E. McKenney, City of Tacoma, WA [E]
John M. Mesina, U.S. Dept. of Labor, WV [E]
George W. Moore, Industrial Risk Insurers, CT [I]
Richard E. Munson, The DuPont Co., DE [U]
Milton H. Ramsey, Chevron U.S.A. Inc., TX [U]
Rep. Inst. of Electrical & Electronics Engr, Inc.
Joseph V. Saverino, Air Products and Chemicals, Inc., PA [U]
Sukanta Sengupta, FMC Corp., NJ [U]
George H. St. Onge, Bernardsville, NJ [SE]
James G. Stallcup, GRAYBOY & Assoc., TX [SE]
Ronald J. Strancar, BP Oil Co., OH [U]
Rep. American Petroleum Inst.
Dann M. Strube, Lanesville, IN [SE]
David Wechsler, Union Carbide Corp., WV [U]
Rep. Chemical Mfrs. Assoc.
Charles J. Wolf, Teledyne Brown Engr - Energy Systems, MD [SE]
Jack H. Zewe, Electrical Consultants Inc., LA [SE]

Alternates

Jane I. Lataille, Industrial Risk Insurers, CT [I]
(Alt. to G. W. Moore)
Kerry L. McManama, Underwriters Laboratories Inc., IL [RT]
(Alt. to E. M. Briesch)
Robert S. Pellizze, Inchcape Testing Services NA Inc., NY [RT]
(Alt. to W. T. Fiske)
James A. Robertson, Dow Chemical Co., TX [U]
(Alt. to M. H. Ramsey)
Samuel A. Rodgers, Allied-Signal Inc., VA [U]
(Alt. to R. F. Schwab)
James W. Stallcup, GRAYBOY & Assoc., TX [SE]
(Alt. to J. G. Stallcup)

Nonvoting

Richard Y. LeVine, Stamford, CT
(Member Emeritus)
Mark C. Ode, NFPA Staff Liaison
John E. Rogerson, Cedar Lane Farm, OH
(Member Emeritus)

This list represents the membership at the time the Committee was balloted on the text of this edition. Since that time, changes in membership may have occurred. A key to classifications is found at the back of this document.

NOTE: Membership on a committee shall not in and of itself constitute an endorsement of the Association or any document developed by the committee on which the member serves.

Committee Scope: This Committee shall have primary responsibility for documents on (1) developing data on the properties of chemicals enabling proper selection of electrical equipment for use in atmospheres containing flammable gases, vapors, or dusts; (2) making recommendations for the prevention of fires and explosions through the use of continuously purged, pressurized, explosion-proof, or dust-ignition-proof electrical equipment where installed in such chemical atmospheres.

Contents

NFPA 497

Recommended Practice for the

Classification of Flammable Liquids, Gases, or Vapors and of Hazardous (Classified) Locations for Electrical Installations in Chemical Process Areas

1997 Edition

NOTICE: An asterisk (*) following the number or letter designating a paragraph indicates that explanatory material on the paragraph can be found in Appendix A.

Information on referenced publications can be found in Chapter 4 and Appendix C.

Chapter 1 General

1-1 Scope.

1-1.1 This recommended practice applies to those locations where flammable gases or vapors, flammable liquids, or combustible liquids are processed or handled; and where their release into the atmosphere may result in their ignition by electrical systems or equipment.

1-1.2 This recommended practice provides information on specific flammable gases and vapors, flammable liquids, and combustible liquids, whose relevant combustion properties have been sufficiently identified to allow their classification into the groups established by NFPA 70, *National Electrical Code® (NEC®)* for proper selection of electrical equipment in hazardous (classified) locations. The tables in this document are not intended to be all-inclusive.

1-1.3 This recommended practice applies to chemical process areas. As used in this document, a chemical process area may be a large, integrated chemical process plant or it may be a part of such a plant. It may be a part of a manufacturing facility where flammable gases or vapors, flammable liquids, or combustible liquids are produced or used in chemical reactions, or are handled or used in certain unit operations such as mixing, filtration, coating, spraying, and distillation.

1-1.4 This recommended practice does not apply to situations that may involve catastrophic failure of or catastrophic discharge from process vessels, pipelines, tanks, or systems.

1-1.5 This recommended practice does not apply to oxygen-enriched atmospheres or pyrophoric materials.

1-1.6 This recommended practice is not intended to supersede or conflict with the NFPA standards listed in Appendix D.

NOTE: It is not the intent of this edition to fully address issues associated with Article 505 in the *NEC.*

1-2 Purpose.

1-2.1 The purpose of this recommended practice is to provide the user with a basic understanding of the parameters that determine the degree and the extent of the hazardous (classified) location. This recommended practice also provides the user with examples of the applications of these parameters.

1-2.2 Information is provided on specific flammable gases and vapors, flammable liquids, and combustible liquids, whose relevant properties determine their classification into groups. This will assist in the selection of special electrical equipment for hazardous (classified) locations where such electrical equipment is required.

1-2.3 This recommended practice is intended as a guide and should be applied with sound engineering judgment. Where all factors are properly evaluated, a consistent area classification scheme can be developed.

1-3 Definitions. For the purpose of this recommended practice, the following terms shall have the meanings given below.

Adequate Ventilation. A ventilation rate that affords either 6 air changes per hour, or 1 cfm per square foot of floor area, or other similar criteria that prevent the accumulation of significant quantities of vapor-air concentrations from exceeding 25 percent of the lower flammable limit.

Autoignition Temperature (AIT). The minimum temperature required to initiate or cause self-sustained combustion of a solid, liquid, or gas independently of the heating or heated element. *(See NFPA 325, Guide to Fire Hazard Properties of Flammable Liquids, Gases, and Volatile Solids.)*

CAS. Chemical Abstract Service.

Class I, Division 1. A location where (1) ignitable concentrations of flammable gases or vapors exist under normal operating conditions; or (2) ignitable concentrations of such gases or vapors may exist frequently because of repair or maintenance operations or because of leakage; or (3) breakdown or faulty operation of equipment or processes might release ignitable concentrations of flammable gases or vapors and might also cause simultaneous failure of electrical equipment. *[See Section 500-5(a) of the NEC.]*

Class I, Division 2. A location (1) in which volatile flammable liquids or flammable gases are handled, processed, or used, but in which the liquids, vapors, or gases will normally be confined within closed containers or closed systems from which they can escape only in case of accidental rupture or breakdown of such containers or systems, or in case of abnormal operation of equipment; or (2) in which ignitable concentrations of gases or vapors are normally prevented by positive mechanical ventilation, and which might become hazardous through failure or abnormal operation of the ventilating equipment; or (3) that is adjacent to a Class I, Division 1 location, and to which ignitable concentrations of gases or vapors might occasionally be communicated unless such communication is prevented by adequate positive-pressure ventilation from a source of clean air and effective safeguards against ventilation failure are provided. *[See Section 500-5(b) of the NEC.]*

Class I, Zone 0. A Class I, Zone 0 location is a location that meets the following conditions:

(a) Ignitable concentrations of flammable gases or vapors that are present continuously

(b) Ignitable concentrations of flammable gases or vapors that are present for long periods of time

Class I, Zone 1. A Class I, Zone 1 location is a location that meets the following conditions:

(a) Ignitable concentrations of flammable gases or vapors that are likely to exist under normal operating conditions

(b) Ignitable concentrations of flammable gases or vapors

that may exist frequently because of repair or maintenance operations or because of leakage

(c) Equipment that is operated or processes that are carried on, of such a nature that equipment breakdown or faulty operations could result in the release of ignitable concentrations of flammable gases or vapors, and that also could cause simultaneous failure of electrical equipment in a mode to cause the electrical equipment to become a source of ignition

(d) Being adjacent to a Class I, Zone 0 location from which ignitable concentrations of vapors could be communicated, unless communication is prevented by adequate positive-pressure ventilation from a source of clean air and effective safeguards against ventilation failure are provided

Class I, Zone 2. A Class I, Zone 2 location is a location that meets the following conditions:

(a) Ignitable concentrations of flammable gases or vapors that are not likely to occur in normal operation, and if they do occur, they will exist only for a short period

(b) Volatile flammable liquids, flammable gases, or flammable vapors that are handled, processed, or used, but in which the liquids, gases, or vapors normally are confined within closed containers or closed systems from which they can escape only as a result of accidental rupture or breakdown of the containers or system, or as the result of the abnormal operation of the equipment with which the liquids or gases are handled, processed, or used

(c) Ignitable concentrations of flammable gases or vapors that normally are prevented by positive mechanical ventilation, but that may become hazardous as the result of failure or abnormal operation of the ventilation equipment

(d) Being adjacent to a Class I, Zone 1 location, from which ignitable concentrations of flammable gases or vapors could be communicated, unless such communication is prevented by adequate positive-pressure ventilation from a source of clean air, and effective safeguards against ventilation failure are provided

Combustible Liquid. A liquid having a flash point at or above 100°F (37.8°C).

Combustible liquids are subdivided as follows:

(a) Class II liquids are those having flash points at or above 100°F (37.8°C) and below 140°F (60°C).

(b) Class III liquids are those having flash points at or above 140°F (60°C), and are subdivided as follows:

1. Class IIIA liquids are those having flash points at or above 140°F (60°C) and below 200°F (93.4°C).
2. Class IIIB liquids are those having flash points at or above 200°F (93.4°C).

Combustible Material.* A generic term used to describe a flammable gas, flammable liquid-produced vapor, or combustible liquid-produced vapor mixed with air that may burn or explode.

Class I combustible materials are divided into four groups:

Group A. Acetylene.

Group B. Flammable gas, flammable liquid-produced vapor, or combustible liquid-produced vapor mixed with air that may burn or explode, having either a maximum experimental safe gap (MESG) value less than or equal to 0.45 mm or a minimum igniting current ratio (MIC ratio) less than or equal to 0.40.

NOTE: A typical Class I, Group B material is hydrogen.

Group C. Flammable gas, flammable liquid-produced vapor, or combustible liquid-produced vapor mixed with air that may burn or explode, having either a maximum experimental safe gap (MESG) value greater than 0.45 mm and less than or equal to 0.75 mm, or a minimum igniting current ratio (MIC ratio) greater than 0.40 and less than or equal to 0.80.

NOTE: A typical Class I, Group C material is ethylene.

Group D. Flammable gas, flammable liquid-produced vapor, or combustible liquid-produced vapor mixed with air that may burn or explode, having either a maximum experimental safe gap (MESG) value greater than 0.75 mm or a minimum igniting current ratio (MIC ratio) greater than 0.80.

NOTE: A typical Class I, Group D material is propane.

The group designation is listed in Table 2-1.

Class I, Zone combustible materials are divided into three groups:

Group IIC. Atmospheres containing acetylene, hydrogen, or flammable gas, flammable liquid-produced vapor, or combustible liquid-produced vapor mixed with air that may burn or explode, having either a maximum experimental safe gap (MESG) value less than or equal to 0.50 mm or minimum igniting current ratio (MIC ratio) less than or equal to 0.45.

Group IIB. Atmospheres containing acetaldehyde, ethylene, or flammable gas, flammable liquid-produced vapor, or combustible liquid-produced vapor mixed with air that may burn or explode, having either maximum experimental safe gap (MESG) values greater than 0.50 mm and less than or equal to 0.90 mm or minimum igniting current ratio (MIC ratio) greater than 0.45 and less than or equal to 0.80.

Group IIA. Atmospheres containing acetone, ammonia, ethyl alcohol, gasoline, methane, propane, or flammable gas, flammable liquid-produced vapor, or combustible liquid produced vapor mixed with air that may burn or explode, having either a maximum experimental safe gap (MESG) value greater than 0.90 mm or minimum igniting current ratio (MIC ratio) greater than 0.80.

These groups are also reflected in Table 2-1, as Class I, Zone Groups.

Flammable Liquid. A liquid designated as Class I, having a flash point below 100°F (37.8°C) and having a vapor pressure not exceeding 40 psia at 100°F (37.8°C). Class I liquids are subdivided as follows:

(a) Class IA liquids are those having flash points below 73°F (22.8°C) and having boiling points below 100°F (37.8°C).

(b) Class IB liquids are those having flash points below 73°F (22.8°C) and having boiling points at or above 100°F (37.8°C).

(c) Class IC liquids are those having flash points at or above 73°F (22.8°C) and below 100°F (37.8°C).

Flash Point. The minimum temperature at which a liquid gives off vapor in sufficient concentration to form an ignitable mixture with air near the surface of the liquid, as specified by test.

Ignitable Mixture. A combustible material that is within its flammable range.

MESG (Maximum Experimental Safe Gap). The maximum clearance between two parallel metal surfaces that has been found, under specified test conditions, to prevent an explosion in a test chamber from being propagated to a secondary chamber containing the same gas or vapor at the same concentration.

MIC (Minimum Igniting Current) Ratio. The ratio of the minimum current required from an inductive spark discharge to ignite the most easily ignitable mixture of a gas or vapor, divided by the minimum current required from an inductive spark discharge to ignite methane under the same test conditions. *(See IEC 79-3.)*

MIE (Minimum Ignition Energy). The minimum energy required from a capacitive spark discharge to ignite the most easily ignitable mixture of a gas or vapor.

Chapter 2 Classification of Combustible Materials

2-1 ***National Electrical Code*® Criteria.**

2-1.1 Article 500 of the *NEC* designates as hazardous (classified) any area in which a combustible material is or may be present in the atmosphere in sufficient concentration to produce an ignitable mixture. Article 500 designates three major categories of hazardous areas: Class I, Class II, and Class III.

In a Class I hazardous area, the material present is a flammable gas or vapor.

In a Class II hazardous area, the material present is a combustible dust.

In a Class III hazardous area, the material present is an ignitable fiber or flying.

This recommended practice is limited to Class I hazardous (classified) areas.

The Class I category is further subdivided into either Class I, Division 1 or Division 2; or Class I, Zone 0, Zone 1, or Zone 2 as follows:

(a) Class I, Division 1 in which the combustible material is present normally or frequently

(b) Class I, Division 2 in which the combustible material is present as a result of infrequent failure of equipment or containers

(c) Class I, Zone 0 in which the combustible material is present continuously or for long periods

(d) Class I, Zone 1 in which the combustible material is likely to be present normally or frequently because of repair or maintenance operations or because of leakage

(e) Class I, Zone 2 in which the combustible material is not likely to occur in normal operation, and if it does occur, it will exist only for a short period

2-1.2* The intent of Article 500 of the *NEC* is to prevent combustible material from being ignited by electrical equipment and wiring systems.

2-1.3 For the purpose of this recommended practice, areas not classified either as Class I, Division 1 or Division 2 or Class I, Zone 0, Zone 1, or Zone 2, are "unclassified" areas.

2-2 Behavior of Class I (Combustible Material) Gases, Vapors, and Liquids.

2-2.1 Lighter-than-Air (Vapor Density Less than 1.0) Gases. These gases tend to dissipate rapidly in the atmosphere. They will not affect as great an area as heavier-than-air gases or vapors. Except in enclosed spaces, such gases seldom accumulate to form an ignitable mixture near grade level, where most electrical installations are located. A lighter-than-air gas that has been cooled sufficiently may behave as a heavier-than-air gas until it absorbs heat from the surrounding atmosphere.

2-2.2 Heavier-than-Air (Vapor Density Greater than 1.0) Gases. These gases tend to fall to grade level when released. The gas may remain for a significant period of time, unless dispersed by natural or forced ventilation. A heavier-than-air gas that has been heated sufficiently to decrease its density may behave as a lighter- than-air gas until cooled by the surrounding atmosphere.

2-2.3 Applicable to All Densities. As the gas diffuses into the surrounding air, the density of the mixture approaches that of air.

2-2.4 Compressed Liquefied Gases. These gases are stored above their normal boiling point but are kept in the liquid state by pressure. When released, the liquid immediately expands and vaporizes, creating large volumes of cold gas. The cold gas behaves like a heavier-than-air gas.

2-2.5 Cryogenic Flammable Liquids and Other Cold Liquefied Combustible Materials. Cryogenic liquids are generally handled below −150°F (−101°C). These behave like flammable liquids when they are spilled. Small liquid spills will immediately vaporize, but larger spills may remain in the liquid state for an extended time. As the liquid absorbs heat, it vaporizes and may form an ignitable mixture. Some liquefied combustible materials (not cryogenic) are stored at low temperatures and at pressures close to atmospheric pressure; these include anhydrous ammonia, propane, ethane, ethylene, and propylene. These materials will behave as described above.

2-2.6 Flammable Liquids. When released in appreciable quantity, a Class I liquid will begin to evaporate at a rate that depends on its volatility: the lower the flash point, the greater the volatility; hence, the faster the evaporation. The vapors of Class I liquids form ignitable mixtures with air at ambient temperatures more or less readily. Even when evolved rapidly, the vapors tend to disperse rapidly, becoming diluted to a concentration below the lower flammable limit. Until this dispersion takes place, however, these vapors will behave like heavier-than-air gases. Class I liquids normally will produce ignitable mixtures that will travel some finite distance from the point of origin; thus, they will normally require area classification for proper electrical system design.

2-2.7 Combustible Liquids. A combustible liquid will form an ignitable mixture only when heated above its flash point.

2-2.7.1 With Class II liquids, the degree of hazard is lower because the vapor release rate is low at the normal handling and storage temperatures. In general, these liquids will not form ignitable mixtures with air at ambient temperatures unless heated above their flash points. Also, the vapors will not travel as far because they tend to condense as they are cooled by ambient air. Class II liquids should be considered capable of producing an ignitable mixture near the point of release when handled, processed, or stored under conditions where the liquid may exceed its flash point.

2-2.7.2 Class IIIA liquids have flash points at or above 140°F (60°C) but below 200°F (93.4°C). These liquids do not form ignitable mixtures with air at ambient temperatures unless heated above their flash points. Furthermore, the vapors cool rapidly in air and condense. Hence, the extent of the area requiring electrical classification will be very small or nonexistent.

2-2.7.3 Class IIIB liquids have flash points at or above 200°F (93.4°C). These liquids seldom evolve enough vapors to form ignitable mixtures even when heated, and they are seldom ignited by properly installed and maintained general purpose electrical equipment. A Class IIIB liquid will cool below its flash point very quickly when released. Therefore, area classification is seldom needed and Class IIIB liquids are not included in Table 2-1.

2-3 Conditions Necessary for Ignition. In a Class I area, the following three conditions must be satisfied for the combustible material to be ignited by the electrical installation:

(a) A combustible material must be present.

(b) It must be mixed with air in the proportions required to produce an ignitable mixture.

(c) There must be a release of sufficient energy to ignite the mixture.

2-4 Classification of Class I Combustible Materials.

2-4.1 Combustible materials are classified into four Class I, Division Groups, A, B, C, and D, or three Class I, Zone Groups, IIC, IIB, and IIA, depending upon their properties.

2-4.2* An alphabetical listing of selected combustible materials, with their group classification and relevant physical properties, is provided in Table 2-1. Table 2-2 provides a cross-

Table 2-1 Selected Chemicals

Chemical	CAS No.	*NEC* Group	Type[6]	Flash Point (°C)	AIT (°C)	%LFL	%UFL	Vapor Density (Air = 1)	Vapor Pressure[7] (mm Hg)	Class I Zone Group[3]	MIE (mJ) TR	MIC Ratio	MESG (mm)
Acetaldehyde	75-07-0	C*	I	−38	175	4.0	60.0	1.5	874.9	IIA	0.37	0.98	0.92
Acetic Acid	64-19-7	D*	II	43	464	4.0	19.9	2.1	15.6	IIA		2.67	1.76
Acetic Acid-Tert.-Butyl Ester	540-88-5	D	II			1.7	9.8	4.0	40.6				
Acetic Anhydride	108-24-7	D	II	54	316	2.7	10.3	3.5	4.9				
Acetone	67-64-1	D*	I		465	2.5	12.8	2.0	230.7	IIA	1.15	1.00	1.02
Acetone Cyanohydrin	75-86-5	D	IIIA	74	688	2.2	12.0	2.9	0.3				
Acetonitrile	75-05-8	D	I	6	524	3.0	16.0	1.4	91.1	IIA			1.50
Acetylene	74-86-2	A*	GAS		305	2.5	99.9	0.9	36600	IIC	0.017	0.28	0.25
Acrolein (Inhibited)	107-02-8	B(C)*	I		235	2.8	31.0	1.9	274.1	IIB	0.12		
Acrylic Acid	79-10-7	D	II	54	438	2.4	8.0	2.5	4.3				
Acrylonitrile	107-13-1	D*	I	−26	481	3.0	17.0	1.8	108.5	IIB	0.16	0.78	0.87
Adiponitrile	111-69-3	D	IIIA	93	550			1.0	0.002				
Allyl Alcohol	107-18-6	C*	I	22	378	2.5	18.0	2.0	25.4				0.84
Allyl Chloride	107-05-1	D	I	−32	485	2.9	11.1	2.6	366			1.33	1.17
Allyl Glycidyl Ether	106-92-3	B(C)[1]	II		57			3.9					
Alpha-Methyl Styrene	98-83-9	D	II		574	0.8	11.0	4.1	2.7				
n-Amyl Acetate	628-63-7	D	I	25	360	1.1	7.5	4.5	4.2				1.02
sec-Amyl Acetate	626-38-0	D	I	23		1.1	7.5	4.5		IIA			
Ammonia	7664-41-7	D*[2]	I		498	15.0	28.0	0.6	7498.0	IIA	.680	6.85	3.17
Aniline	62-53-3	D	IIIA	70	615	1.3	11.0	3.2	0.7	IIA			
Benzene	71-43-2	D*	I	−11	498	1.2	7.8	2.8	94.8	IIA	0.20	1.00	0.99
Benzyl Chloride	98-87-3	D	IIIA		585	1.1		4.4	0.5				
Bromopropyne	106-96-7	D	I	10	324	3.0							
n-Butane	3583-47-9	D*[5]	GAS		288	1.9	8.5	2.0			0.25	0.94	1.07
1,3-Butadiene	106-99-0	B(D)*[1]	GAS	−76	420	2	12	1.9		IIB	0.12	0.76	0.79
1-Butanol	71-36-3	D*	I	36	343	1.4	11.2	2.6	7.0	IIA			0.91
2-Butanol	71-36-5	D*	I	36	405	1.7	9.8	2.6		IIA			
Butylamine	109-73-9	D	GAS	−12	312	1.7	9.8	2.5	92.9			1.13	
Butylene	25167-67-3	D	I		385	1.6	10.0	1.9	2214.6				
n-Butyraldehyde	123-72-8	C*	I	−12	218	1.9	12.5	2.5	112.2				0.92
n-Butyl Acetate	123-86-4	D*	I	22	421	1.7	7.6	4.0	11.5	IIA		1.08	1.04
sec-Butyl Acetate	105-46-4	D	II	−8		1.7	9.8	4.0	22.2				
tert.-Butyl Acetate	540-88-5	D	II			1.7	9.8	4.0	40.6				
n-Butyl Acrylate (Inhibited)	141-32-2	D	II	49	293	1.7	9.9	4.4	5.5				
n-Butyl Glycidyl Ether	2426-08-6	B(C)[1]	II										
n-Butyl Formal	110-62-3	C	IIIA						34.3				
Butyl Mercaptan	109-79-5	C	I	2				3.1	46.4				
Butyl-2-Propenoate	141-32-2	D	II	49		1.7	9.9	4.4	5.5				
para tert.-Butyl Toluene	98-51-1	D	IIIA										
n-Butyric Acid	107-92-6	D	IIIA	72	443	2.0	10.0	3.0	0.8				
Carbon Disulfide	75-15-0	*3	I	−30	90	1.3	50.0	2.6	358.8	IIC	0.009	0.39	0.20

(continues)

Table 2-1 Selected Chemicals *(Continued)*

Chemical	CAS No.	*NEC* Group	Type[6]	Flash Point (°C)	AIT (°C)	%LFL	%UFL	Vapor Density (Air = 1)	Vapor Pressure[7] (mm Hg)	Class I Zone Group[3]	MIE (mJ) TR	MIC Ratio	MESG (mm)
Carbon Monoxide	630-08-0	C*	GAS	609	700	12.5	74.	0.97		IIA			
Chloroacetaldehyde	107-20-0	C	IIIA	88					63.1				
Chlorobenzene	108-90-7	D	I	29	593	1.3	9.6	3.9	11.9				
1-Chloro-1-Nitropropane	2425-66-3	C	IIIA										
Chloroprene	126-99-8	D	GAS	−20		4.0	20.0	3.0					
Cresol	1319-77-3	D	IIIA	81	559	1.1		3.7					
Crotonaldehyde	4170-30-3	C*	I	13	232	2.1	15.5	2.4	33.1	IIB			0.81
Cumene	98-82-8	D	I	36	424	0.9	6.5	4.1	4.6	IIA			
Cyclohexane	110-82-7	D	I	−17	245	1.3	8.0	2.9	98.8	IIA	0.22	1.0	0.94
Cyclohexanol	108-93-0	D	IIIA	68	300			3.5	0.7	IIA			
Cyclohexanone	108-94-1	D	II	44	245	1.1	9.4	3.4	4.3	IIA			0.98
Cyclohexene	110-83-8	D	I	−6	244	1.2		2.8	89.4				0.97
Cyclopropane	75-19-4	D*	I		503	2.4	10.4	1.5	5430	IIB	0.17	0.84	0.91
p-Cymene	99-87-6	D	II	47	436	0.7	5.6	4.6	1.5	IIA			
Decene	872-05-9	D	II		235			4.8	1.7				
n-Decaldehyde	112-31-2	C	IIIA						0.09				
n-Decanol	112-30-1	D	IIIA	82	288			5.3	0.008				
Decyl Alcohol	112-30-1	D	IIIA	82	288			5.3	0.008				
Diacetone Alcohol	123-42-2	D	IIIA	64	603	1.8	6.9	4.0	1.4				
Di-Isobutylene	25167-70-8	D*	I	2	391	0.8	4.8	3.8			0.96		
Di-Isobutyl Ketone	108-83-8	D	II	60	396	0.8	7.1	4.9	1.7				
o-Dichlorobenzene	955-50-1	D	IIIA	66	647	2.2	9.2	5.1		IIA			
1,4-Dichloro-2,3 Epoxybutane	3583-47-9	D*	I			1.9	8.5	2.0			0.25	0.98	1.07
1,1-Dichloroethane	1300-21-6	D	I		438	6.2	16.0	3.4	227				1.82
1,2-Dichloroethylene	156-59-2	D	I	97	460	5.6	12.8	3.4	204	IIA			
1,1-Dichloro-1-Nitroethane	594-72-9	C	IIIA	76				5.0					
1,3-Dichloropropene	10061-02-6	D	I	35		5.3	14.5	3.8					
Dicyclopentadiene	77-73-6	C	I	32	503				2.8				0.91
Diethylamine	109-87-9	C*	I	−28	312	1.8	10.1	2.5		IIA			1.15
Diethylaminoethanol	100-37-8	C	IIIA	60	320			4.0	1.6	IIA			
Diethyl Benzene	25340-17-4	D	II	57	395			4.6					
Diethyl Ether	60-29-7	C*	I	12	160	1.9	36.0	2.6	38.2	IIB	0.19	0.88	0.83
Diethylene Glycol Monobutyl Ether	112-34-5	C	IIIA	78	228	0.9	24.6	5.6	0.02				
Diethylene Glycol Monomethyl Ether	111-77-3	C	IIIA	93	241				0.2				
n-n-Dimethyl Aniline	121-69-7	C	IIIA	63	371	1.0		4.2	0.7				
Dimethyl Formamide	68-12-2	D	II	58	455	2.2	15.2	2.5	4.1				1.08
Dimethyl Sulfate	77-78-1	D	IIIA	83	188			4.4	0.7				
Dimethylamine	124-40-3	C	GAS		400	2.8	14.4	1.6		IIA			
2,2-Dimethylbutane	75-83-2	D[5]	I	−48	405				319.3				
2,3-Dimethylbutane		D[5]	I		396								
3,3-Dimethylheptane	1071-26-7	D[5]	I		325				10.8				
2,3-Dimethylhexane	31394-54-4	D[5]	I		438								
2,3-Dimethylpentane	107-83-5	D[5]	I		335				211.7				
Di-N-Propylamine	142-84-7	C	I	17	299				27.1				
1,4-Dioxane	123-91-1	C*	I	12	180	2.0	22.0	3.0	38.2	IIB	0.19		0.70
Dipentene	138-86-3	D	II	45	237	0.7	6.1	4.7					1.18
Dipropylene Glycol Methyl Ether	34590-94-8	C	IIIA	85		1.1	3.0	5.1	0.5				
Diisopropylamine	108-18-9	C	GAS	−6	316	1.1	7.1	3.5					
Dodecene	6842-15-5	D	IIIA	100	255								
Epichlorohydrin	3132-64-7	C*	I	33	411	3.8	21.0	3.2	13.0				
Ethane	74-84-0	D*	GAS	−29	472	3.0	12.5	1.0		IIA	0.24	0.82	0.91
Ethanol	64-17-5	D*	I	13	363	3.3	19.0	1.6	59.5	IIA		0.88	0.89
Ethylamine	75-04-7	D*	I	−18	385	3.5	14.0	1.6	1048		2.4		

Table 2-1 Selected Chemicals *(Continued)*

Chemical	CAS No.	*NEC* Group	Type[6]	Flash Point (°C)	AIT (°C)	%LFL	%UFL	Vapor Density (Air = 1)	Vapor Pressure[7] (mm Hg)	Class I Zone Group[3]	MIE (mJ) TR	MIC Ratio	MESG (mm)
Ethylene	74-85-1	C*	GAS	0	450	2.7	36.0	1.0		IIB	0.070	0.53	0.65
Ethylenediamine	107-15-3	D*	I	33	385	2.5	12.0	2.1	12.5				
Ethylenimine	151-56-4	C*	I	−11	320	3.3	54.8	1.5	211		0.48		
Ethylene Chlorohydrin	107-07-3	D	IIIA	59	425	4.9	15.9	2.8	7.2				
Ethylene Dichloride	107-06-2	D*	I	13	413	6.2	16.0	3.4	79.7				
Ethylene Glycol Monoethyl Ether Acetate	111-15-9	C	II	47	379	1.7		4.7	2.3			0.53	0.97
Ethylene Glycol Monobutyl Ether Acetate	112-07-2	C	IIIA		340	0.9	8.5		0.9				
Ethylene Glycol Monobutyl Ether	111-76-2	C	IIIA		238	1.1	12.7	4.1	1.0				
Ethylene Glycol Monoethyl Ether	110-80-5	C	II		235	1.7	15.6	3.0	5.4				
Ethylene Glycol Monomethyl Ether	109-86-4	D	II		285	1.8	14.0	2.6	9.2				
Ethylene Oxide	75-21-8	B(C)*[1]	I	−20	429	3.0	99.9	1.5	1314	IIB	0.065		0.47
2-Ethylhexaldehyde	123-05-7	C	II	52	191	0.8	7.2	4.4	1.9				
2-Ethylhexanol	104-76-7	D	IIIA	81		0.9	9.7	4.5	0.2				
2-Ethylhexyl Acrylate	103-09-3	D	IIIA	88	252				0.3				
Ethyl Acetate	141-78-6	D*	I	−4	427	2.0	11.5	3.0	93.2		0.46		
Ethyl Acrylate (Inhibited)	140-88-5	D*	I	9	372	1.4	14.0	3.5	37.5	IIA			
Ethyl Alcohol	64-17-5	D*	I	13	363	3.3	19.0	1.6	59.5				0.89
Ethyl Sec-Amyl Ketone	541-85-5	D	II	59									
Ethyl Benzene	100-41-4	D	I	21	432	0.8	6.7	3.7	9.6				
Ethyl Butanol	97-95-0	D	II	57		1.2	7.7	3.5	1.5				
Ethyl Butyl Ketone	106-35-4	D	II	46				4.0	3.6				
Ethyl Chloride	75-00-3	D	GAS	−50	519	3.8	15.4	2.2					
Ethyl Ether	60-29-7	C*	I	−45	160	1.9	36.0	2.6	538		0.19	0.88	0.84
Ethyl Formate	109-94-4	D	GAS	−20	455	2.8	16.0	2.6		IIA			0.94
Ethyl Mercaptan	75-08-1	C*	I	−18	300	2.8	18.0	2.1	527.4				0.90
n-Ethyl Morpholine	100-74-3	C	I	32				4.0					
2-Ethyl-3-Propyl Acrolein	645-62-5	C	IIIA	68				4.4					
Ethyl Silicate	78-10-4	D	II					7.2					
Formaldehyde (Gas)	50-00-0	B	GAS	60	429	7.0	73.0	1.0					
Formic Acid	64-18-6	D	II	50	434	18.0	57.0	1.6	42.7				
Fuel Oil 1	8008-20-6	D	II	72	210	0.7	5.0						
Furfural	98-01-1	C	IIIA	60	316	2.1	19.3	3.3	2.3				
Furfuryl Alcohol	98-00-0	C	IIIA	75	490	1.8	16.3	3.4	0.6				
Gasoline	8006-61-9	D*	I	−46	280	1.4	7.6	3.0					
n-Heptane	142-82-5	D*	I	−4	204	1.0	6.7	3.5	45.5	IIA	0.24	0.88	0.91
n-Heptene	81624-04-6	D[5]	I	−1	204			3.4					
n-Hexane	110-54-3	D*[5]	I	−23	225	1.1	7.5	3.0	152	IIA	0.24	0.88	0.93
Hexanol	111-27-3	D	IIIA	63				3.5	0.8	IIA			0.98
2-Hexanone	591-78-6	D	I	35	424	1.2	8.0	3.5	10.6				
Hexene	592-41-6	D	I	−26	245	1.2	6.9		186				
sec-Hexyl Acetate	108-84-9	D	II	45				5.0					
Hydrazine	302-01-2	C	II	38	23		98.0	1.1	14.4				
Hydrogen	1333-74-0	B*	GAS		520	4.0	75.0	0.1		IIC	0.019	0.25	0.28
Hydrogen Cyanide	74-90-8	C*	GAS	−18	538	5.6	40.0	0.9		IIB			0.80
Hydrogen Selenide	7783-07-5	C	I						7793				
Hydrogen Sulfide	7783-06-4	C*	GAS		260	4.0	44.0	1.2			0.068		0.90
Isoamyl Acetate	123-92-2	D	I	25	360	1.0	7.5	4.5	6.1				
Isoamyl Alcohol	123-51-3	D	II	43	350	1.2	9.0	3.0	3.2				1.02
Isobutane	75-28-5	D[5]	GAS		460	1.8	8.4	2.0					
Isobutyl Acetate	110-19-0	D*	I	18	421	2.4	10.5	4.0	17.8				
Isobutyl Acrylate	106-63-8	D	I		427			4.4	7.1				

(continues)

Table 2-1 Selected Chemicals *(Continued)*

Chemical	CAS No.	*NEC* Group	Type[6]	Flash Point (°C)	AIT (°C)	%LFL	%UFL	Vapor Density (Air = 1)	Vapor Pressure[7] (mm Hg)	Class I Zone Group[3]	MIE (mJ) TR	MIC Ratio	MESG (mm)
Isobutyl Alcohol	78-83-1	D*	I	−40	416	1.2	10.9	2.5	10.5			0.92	0.98
Isobutyraldehyde	78-84-2	C	GAS	−40	196	1.6	10.6	2.5					
Isodecaldehyde	112-31-2	C	IIIA					5.4	0.09				
Isohexane	107-83-5	D[5]			264				211.7			1.00	
Isopentane	78-78-4	D[5]			420				688.6				
Isooctyl Aldehyde	123-05-7	C	II		197				1.9				
Isophorone	78-59-1	D		84	460	0.8	3.8	4.8	0.4				
Isoprene	78-79-5	D*	I	−54	220	1.5	8.9	2.4	550.6				
Isopropyl Acetate	108-21-4	D	I		460	1.8	8.0	3.5	60.4				
Isopropyl Ether	108-20-3	D*	I	−28	443	1.4	7.9	3.5	148.7		1.14		0.94
Isopropyl Glycidyl Ether	4016-14-2	C	I										
Isopropylamine	75-31-0	D	GAS	−26	402	2.3	10.4	2.0			2.0		
Kerosene	8008-20-6	D	II	72	210	0.7	5.0			IIA			
Liquified Petroleum Gas	68476-85-7	D	I		405								
Mesityl Oxide	141-97-9	D*	I	31	344	1.4	7.2	3.4	47.6				
Methane	74-82-8	D*	GAS	−223	630	5.0	15.0	0.6		IIA	0.28	1.00	1.12
Methanol	67-56-1	D*	I	12	385	6.0	36.0	1.1	126.3	IIA	0.14	0.82	0.92
Methyl Acetate	79-20-9	D	GAS	−10	454	3.1	16.0	2.6		IIB		1.08	0.99
Methyl Acrylate	96-33-3	D	GAS	−3	468	2.8	25.0	3.0				0.98	0.85
Methyl Alcohol	67-56-1	D*	I		385	6.0	36.0	1.1	126.3				0.91
Methyl Amyl Alcohol	108-11-2	D	II	41		1.0	5.5	3.5	5.3				1.01
Methyl Chloride	74-87-3	D	GAS	−46	632	8.1	17.4	1.7					1.00
Methyl Ether	115-10-6	C*	GAS	−41	350	3.4	27.0	1.6				0.85	0.84
Methyl Ethyl Ketone	78-93-3	D*	I	−6	404	1.4	11.4	2.5	92.4		0.53	0.92	0.84
Methyl Formal	534-15-6	C*	I	1	238			3.1					
Methyl Formate	107-31-3	D	GAS	−19	449	4.5	23.0	2.1					0.94
2-Methylhexane	31394-54-4	D[5]	I		280								
Methyl Isobutyl Ketone	141-79-7	D*	I	31	440	1.2	8.0	3.5	11				
Methyl Isocyanate	624-83-9	D	GAS	−15	534	5.3	26.0	2.0					
Methyl Mercapatan	74-93-1	C	GAS	−18		3.9	21.8	1.7					
Methyl Methacrylate	80-62-6	D	I	10	422	1.7	8.2	3.6	37.2	IIA			0.95
Methyl N-Amyl Ketone	110-43-0	D	II	49	393	1.1	7.9	3.9	3.8				
Methyl Tertiary Butyl Ether	1634-04-4	D	I	−80	435	1.6	8.4	0.2	250.1				
2-Methyloctane	3221-61-2				220				6.3				
2-Methylpropane	75-28-5	D[5]	I		460				2639				
Methyl-1-Propanol	78-83-1	D*	I	−40	416	1.2	10.9	2.5	10.1				0.98
Methyl-2-Propanol	75-65-0	D*	I	10	360	2.4	8.0	2.6	42.2				
2-Methyl-5-Ethyl Pyridine	104-90-5	D		74		1.1	6.6	4.2					
Methylacetylene	74-99-7	C*	I			1.7		1.4	4306		0.11		
Methylacetylene-Propadiene	27846-30-6	C	I										0.74
Methylal	109-87-5	C	I	−18	237	1.6	17.6	2.6	398				
Methylamine	74-89-5	D	GAS		430	4.9	20.7	1.0		IIA			1.10
2-Methylbutane	78-78-4	D[5]		−56	420	1.4	8.3	2.6	688.6				
Methylcyclohexane	208-87-2	D	I	−4	250	1.2	6.7	3.4			0.27		
Methylcyclohexanol	25630-42-3	D		68	296			3.9					
2-Methycyclohexanone	583-60-8	D	II					3.9					
2-Methylheptane		D[5]			420								
3-Methylhexane	589-34-4	D[5]			280				61.5				
3-Methylpentane	94-14-0	D[5]			278								
2-Methylpropane	75-28-5	D[5]	I		460				2639				
2-Methyl-1-Propanol	78-83-1	D*	I	−40	223	1.2	10.9	2.5	10.5				
2-Methyl-2-Propanol	75-65-0	D*	I		478	2.4	8.0	2.6	42.2				
2-Methyloctane	2216-32-2	D[5]			220								
3-Methyloctane	2216-33-3	D[5]			220				6.3				
4-Methyloctane	2216-34-4	D[5]			225				6.8				
Monoethanolamine	141-43-5	D		85	410			2.1	0.4	IIA			

Table 2-1 Selected Chemicals *(Continued)*

Chemical	CAS No.	*NEC* Group	Type[6]	Flash Point (°C)	AIT (°C)	%LFL	%UFL	Vapor Density (Air = 1)	Vapor Pressure[7] (mm Hg)	Class I Zone Group[3]	MIE (mJ) TR	MIC Ratio	MESG (mm)
Monoisopropanolamine	78-96-6	D		77	374			2.6	1.1				
Monomethyl Aniline	100-61-8	C			482				0.5				
Monomethyl Hydrazine	60-34-4	C	I	23	194	2.5	92.0	1.6					
Morpholine	110-91-8	C*	II	35	310	1.4	11.2	3.0	10.1				0.95
Naphtha (Coal Tar)	8030-30-6	D	II	42	277					IIA			
Naphtha (Petroleum)	8030-30-6	D*[4]	I	42	288	1.1	5.9	2.5		IIA			
Neopentane	463-82-1	D[5]		−65	450	1.4	8.3	2.6	1286				
Nitrobenzene	98-95-3	D		88	482	1.8		4.3	0.3				0.94
Nitroethane	79-24-3	C	I	28	414	3.4		2.6	20.7	IIA			0.87
Nitromethane	75-52-5	C	I	35	418	7.3		2.1	36.1	IIA		0.92	1.17
1-Nitropropane	108-03-2	C	I	34	421	2.2		3.1	10.1				0.84
2-Nitropropane	79-46-9	C*	I	28	428	2.6	11.0	3.1	17.1				
n-Nonane	111-84-2	D[5]	I	31	205	0.8	2.9	4.4	4.4	IIA			
Nonene	27214-95-8	D	I			0.8		4.4					
Nonyl Alcohol	143-08-8	D				0.8	6.1	5.0	0.02	IIA			
n-Octane	111-65-9	D*[5]	I	13	206	1.0	6.5	3.9	14.0	IIA			0.94
Octene	25377-83-7	D	I	8	230	0.9		3.9					
n-Octyl Alcohol	111-87-5	D						4.5	0.08	IIA			1.05
n-Pentane	109-66-0	D*[5]	I	−40	243	1.5	7.8	2.5	513		0.28	0.97	0.93
1-Pentanol	71-41-0	D*	I	33	300	1.2	10.0	3.0	2.5	IIA			
2-Pentanone	107-87-9	D	I	7	452	1.5	8.2	3.0	35.6				0.99
1-Pentene	109-67-1	D	I	−18	275	1.5	8.7	2.4	639.7				
2-Pentene	109-68-2	D	I	−18				2.4					
2-Pentyl Acetate	626-38-0	D	I	23		1.1	7.5	4.5					
Phenylhydrazine	100-63-0	D		89				3.7	0.03				
Process Gas > 30% H2	1333-74-0	B**	GAS		520	4.0	75.0	0.1			0.019	0.45	
Propane	74-98-6	D*	GAS	−104	450	2.1	9.5	1.6		IIA	0.25	0.82	0.97
1-Propanol	71-23-8	D*	I	15	413	2.2	13.7	2.1	20.7	IIA			0.89
2-Propanol	67-63-0	D*	I	12	399	2.0	12.7	2.1	45.4		0.65		1.00
Propiolactone	57-57-8	D				2.9		2.5	2.2				
Propionaldehyde	123-38-6	C	I	−9	207	2.6	17.0	2.0	318.5				
Propionic Acid	79-09-4	D	II	54	466	2.9	12.1	2.5	3.7				
Propionic Anhydride	123-62-6	D		74	285	1.3	9.5	4.5	1.4				
n-Propyl Acetate	109-60-4	D	I	14	450	1.7	8.0	3.5	33.4				1.05
n-Propyl Ether	111-43-3	C*	I	21	215	1.3	7.0	3.5	62.3				
Propyl Nitrate	627-13-4	B*	I	20	175	2.0	100.0						
Propylene	115-07-1	D*	GAS	−108	455	2.0	11.1	1.5			0.28		0.91
Propylene Dichloride	78-87-5	D	I	16	557	3.4	14.5	3.9	51.7				1.32
Propylene Oxide	75-56-9	B(C)*[1]	I	−37	449	2.3	36.0	2.0	534.4		0.13		0.70
Pyridine	110-86-1	D*	I	20	482	1.8	12.4	2.7	20.8	IIA			
Styrene	100-42-5	D*	I	31	490	0.9	6.8	3.6	6.1	IIA		1.21	
Tetrahydrofuran	109-99-9	C*	I	−14	321	2.0	11.8	2.5	161.6	IIB	0.54		0.87
Tetrahydronaphthalene	119-64-2	D	IIIA		385	0.8	5.0	4.6	0.4				
Tetramethyl Lead	75-74-1	C	II	38				9.2					
Toluene	108-88-3	D*	I	4	480	1.1	7.1	3.1	28.53	IIA	0.24		
n-Tridecene	2437-56-1	D	IIIA			0.6		6.4	593.4				
Triethylamine	121-44-8	C*	I	−9	249	1.2	8.0	3.5	68.5	IIA	0.75		
Triethylbenzene	25340-18-5	D		83			56.0	5.6					
2,2,3-Trimethylbutane		D[5]			442								
2,2,4-Trimethylbutane		D[5]			407								
2,2,3-Trimethylpentane		D[5]			396								
2,2,4-Trimethylpentane		D[5]			415								
2,3,3-Trimethylpentane		D[5]			425								
Tripropylamine	102-69-2	D	II	41				4.9	1.5				1.13
Turpentine	8006-64-2	D	I	35	253	0.8			4.8				
n-Undecene	28761-27-5	D	IIIA			0.7		5.5					
Unsymmetrical Dimethyl Hydrazine	57-14-7	C*	I	−15	249	2.0	95.0	1.9					0.85
Valeraldehyde	110-62-3	C	I	280	222			3.0	34.3				
Vinyl Acetate	108-05-4	D*	I	−6	402	2.6	13.4	3.0	113.4	IIA	0.70		0.94

(continues)

Table 2-1 Selected Chemicals *(Continued)*

Chemical	CAS No.	*NEC* Group	Type[6]	Flash Point (°C)	AIT (°C)	%LFL	%UFL	Vapor Density (Air = 1)	Vapor Pressure[7] (mm Hg)	Class I Zone Group[3]	MIE (mJ) TR	MIC Ratio	MESG (mm)
Vinyl Chloride	75-01-4	D*	GAS	−78	472	3.6	33.0	2.2					0.96
Vinyl Toluene	25013-15-4	D		52	494	0.8	11.0	4.1					
Vinylidene Chloride	75-35-4	D	I		570	6.5	15.5	3.4	599.4				3.91
Xylene	1330-20-7	D*	I	25	464	0.9	7.0	3.7		IIA	0.2		
Xylidine	121-69-7	C	IIIA	63	371	1.0		4.2	0.7				

*Material has been classified by test.

**Fuel and process gas mixtures found by test not to present hazards similar to those of hydrogen, may be grouped based on the test results.

NOTES:

[1]If explosionproof equipment is isolated by sealing all conduits 1/2 in. or larger, in accordance with Section 501-5(a) of NFPA 70, *National Electrical Code,* equipment for the group classification shown in parentheses is permitted.

[2]For classification of areas involving ammonia, see *Safety Code for Mechanical Refrigeration,* ANSI/ASHRAE 15, and *Safety Requirements for the Storage and Handling of Anhydrous Ammonia,* ANSI/CGA G2.1.

[3]Certain chemicals may have characteristics that require safeguards beyond those required for any of the above groups. Carbon disulfide is one of these chemicals because of its low autoignition temperature and the small joint clearance necessary to arrest its flame propagation.

[4]Petroleum naphtha is a saturated hydrocarbon mixture whose boiling range is 68°F to 275°F (20°C to 135°C). It is also known as benzine, ligroin, petroleum ether, and naphtha.

[5]Commercial grades of aliphatic hydrocarbon solvents are mixtures of several isomers of the same chemical formula (or molecular weight). The autoignition temperatures of the individual isomers are significantly different. The electrical equipment should be suitable for the AIT of the solvent mixture. *(See A-2-1, Table Note 5.)*

[6]Type is used to designate if the material is a gas, flammable liquid, or combustible liquid. *(See 2-2.6 and 2-2.7.)*

[7]Vapor pressure reflected in units of mm Hg at 77°F (25°C) unless stated otherwise.

[8]Class I, Zone Groups are based upon "Electrical apparatus for explosive gas atmospheres—Part 20: Data for flammable gases and vapors, relating to the use of electrical apparatus, IEC 79-20 (1996)."

Table 2-2 Cross-Reference of Chemical CAS Numbers to Chemical Names

CAS Number	Chemical Name
50-00-0	Formaldehyde (Gas)
57-14-7	Unsymmetrical Dimethyl Hydrazine
57-57-8	Propiolactone
60-29-7	Ethyl Ether
60-34-4	Monomethyl Hydrazine
62-53-3	Aniline
64-17-5	Ethanol
64-17-5	Ethyl Alcohol
64-18-6	Formic Acid
64-19-7	Acetic Acid
67-56-1	Methanol
67-56-1	Methyl Alcohol
67-63-0	2-Propanol
67-64-1	Acetone
68-12-2	Dimethyl Formamide
71-23-8	1-Propanol
71-36-3	1-Butanol
71-36-5	2-Butanol
71-41-0	1-Pentanol
71-43-2	Benzene
74-82-8	Methane
74-84-0	Ethane
74-85-1	Ethylene

Table 2-2 Cross-Reference of Chemical CAS Numbers to Chemical Names *(Continued)*

CAS Number	Chemical Name
74-86-2	Acetylene
74-87-3	Methyl Chloride
74-89-5	Methylamine
74-90-8	Hydrogen Cyanide
74-93-1	Methyl Mercapatan
74-98-6	Propane
74-99-7	Methylacetylene
75-00-3	Ethyl Chloride
75-01-4	Vinyl Chloride
75-04-7	Ethylamine
75-05-8	Acetonitrile
75-07-0	Acetaldehyde
75-08-1	Ethyl Mercaptan
75-15-0	Carbon Disulfide
75-19-4	Cyclopropane
75-21-8	Ethylene Oxide
75-28-5	Isobutane
75-28-5	2-Methylpropane
75-28-5	3-Methylpropane
75-31-0	Isopropylamine
75-35-4	Vinylidene Chloride
75-52-5	Nitromethane
75-56-9	Propylene Oxide
75-65-0	2-Methyl-2-Propanol

Table 2-2 Cross-Reference of Chemical CAS Numbers to Chemical Names *(Continued)*

CAS Number	Chemical Name
75-74-1	Tetramethyl Lead
75-83-2	Dimethylbutane
75-83-2	Neohexane
75-86-5	Acetone Cyanohydrin
77-78-1	Dimethyl Sulfate
78-10-4	Ethyl Silicate
78-59-1	Isophorone
78-78-4	Isopentane
78-78-4	Methylbutane
78-79-5	Isoprene
78-83-1	Isobutyl Alcohol
78-83-1	Methyl-1-Propanol
78-84-2	Isobutyraldehyde
78-87-5	Propylene Dichloride
78-93-3	Methyl Ethyl Ketone
78-96-6	Monoisopropanolamine
79-09-4	Propionic Acid
79-10-7	Acrylic Acid
79-20-9	Methyl Acetate
79-24-3	Nitroethane
79-46-9	2-Nitropropane
80-62-6	Methyl Methacrylate
96-14-0	3-Methylpentane
96-33-3	Methyl Acrylate
97-95-0	Ethyl Butanol
98-00-0	Furfuryl Alcohol
98-01-1	Furfural
98-51-1	tert.-Butyl Toluene
98-82-8	Cumene
98-83-9	Alpha-Methyl Styrene
98-87-3	Benzyl Chloride
98-95-3	Nitrobenzene
99-87-6	p-Cymene
100-41-4	Ethyl Benzene
100-42-5	Styrene
100-61-8	Monomethyl Aniline
100-63-0	Phenylhydrazine
100-74-3	n-Ethyl Morpholine
102-69-2	Tripropylamine
103-09-3	Ethyl Hexyl Acrylate
104-76-7	Ethylhexanol
104-90-5	2-Methyl-5-Ethyl Pyridine
105-46-4	sec-Butyl Acetate
106-35-4	Ethyl Butyl Ketone
106-63-8	Isobutyl Acrylate
106-88-7	Butylene Oxide
106-92-3	Allyl Glycidyl Ether
106-96-7	Bromopropyne
106-99-0	1,3-Butadiene
107-02-8	Acrolein (Inhibited)
107-05-1	Allyl Chloride
107-06-2	Ethylene Dichloride
107-07-3	Ethylene Chlorohydrin
107-13-1	Acrylonitrile
107-15-3	Ethylenediamine
107-18-6	Allyl Alcohol
107-20-0	Chloroacetaldehyde
107-31-3	Methyl Formate
107-83-5	Dimethylpentane
107-83-5	Isohexane
107-83-5	2-Methylpentane
107-87-9	2-Pentanone
107-92-6	n-Butyric Acid
108-03-2	1-Nitropropane
108-05-4	Vinyl Acetate
108-11-2	Methyl Amyl Alcohol
108-18-9	Diisopropylamine
108-20-3	Isopropyl Ether
108-21-4	Isopropyl Acetate
108-24-7	Acetic Anhydride
108-84-9	sec-Hexyl Acetate
108-88-3	Toluene
108-90-7	Chlorobenzene
108-93-0	Cyclohexanol
108-94-1	Cyclohexanone
109-60-4	n-Propyl Acetate
109-66-0	n-Pentane
109-67-1	1-Pentene
109-68-2	2-Pentene
109-73-9	Butylamine
109-79-5	Butyl Mercaptan
109-86-4	Ethylene Glycol Monomethyl Ether
109-87-5	Methylal
109-94-4	Ethyl Formate
109-99-9	Tetrahydrofuran
110-19-0	Isobutyl Acetate
110-43-0	Methyl n-Amyl Ketone
110-54-3	n-Hexane
110-62-3	n-Butyl Formal
110-62-3	Valeraldehyde
110-80-5	Ethylene Glycol Monoethyl Ether
110-82-7	Cyclohexane
110-83-8	Cyclohexene

(continues)

Table 2-2 Cross-Reference of Chemical CAS Numbers to Chemical Names *(Continued)*

CAS Number	Chemical Name
110-86-1	Pyridine
110-91-8	Morpholine
111-15-9	Ethylene Glycol Monoethyl Ether Acetate
111-27-3	Hexanol
111-43-3	n-Propyl Ether
111-65-9	n-Octane
111-69-3	Adiponitrile
111-76-2	Ethylene Glycol Monobutyl Ether
111-84-2	n-Nonane
111-87-5	n-Octyl Alcohol
112-07-2	Ethylene Glycol Monobutyl E' Ace
112-30-1	n-Decanol
112-31-2	Isodecaldehyde
112-31-2	n-Decaldehyde
115-07-1	Propylene
115-10-6	Methyl Ether
119-64-2	Tetrahydronaphthalene
121-44-8	Triethylamine
123-05-7	Ethylhexaldehyde
123-05-7	Isooctyl Aldehyde
123-38-6	Propionaldehyde
123-51-3	Isoamyl Alcohol
123-62-6	Propionic Anhydride
123-72-8	n-Butyraldehyde
123-86-4	n-Butyl Acetate
123-91-1	1,4-Dioxane
123-92-2	Isoamyl Acetate
124-40-3	Dimethylamine
126-99-8	Chloroprene
138-86-3	Dipentene
140-88-5	Ethyl Acrylate (Inhibited)
141-32-2	n-Butyl Acrylate (Inhibited)
141-43-5	Monoethanolamine
141-78-6	Ethyl Acetate
141-79-7	Methyl Isobutyl Ketone
141-97-9	Mesityl Oxide
142-82-5	n-Heptane
143-08-8	Nonyl Alcohol
151-56-4	Ethylenimine
208-87-2	Methylcyclohexane
302-01-2	Hydrazine
463-82-1	Dimethylpropane
463-82-1	Neopentane
534-15-6	Methyl Formal
540-88-5	tert. Butyl Acetate

Table 2-2 Cross-Reference of Chemical CAS Numbers to Chemical Names *(Continued)*

CAS Number	Chemical Name
541-85-5	Ethyl Sec-Amyl Ketone
589-34-4	3-Methylhexane
591-78-6	Hexanone
592-41-6	Hexenes
624-83-9	Methyl Isocyanate
626-38-0	sec-Amyl Acetate
627-13-4	Propyl Nitrate
628-63-7	n-Amyl Acetate
630-08-0	Carbon Monoxide
645-62-5	Ethyl-3-Propyl Acrolein
1068-19-5	Methylheptane
1071-26-7	Dimethylheptane
1319-77-3	Cresol
1330-20-7	Xylene
1333-74-0	Hydrogen
1333-74-0	Process Gas > 30% H2
1634-04-4	Methyl Tertiary Butyl Ether
2216-32-2	2-Methyloctane
2216-33-3	3-Methyloctane
2216-34-4	4-Methyloctane
2425-66-3	1-Chloro-1-Nitropropane
2426-08-6	n-Butyl Glycidyl Ether
2437-56-1	Tridecene
3132-64-7	Epichlorohydrin
3221-61-2	2-Methyloctane
3583-47-9	Butane
4016-14-2	Isopropyl Glycidyl Ether
4170-30-3	Crotonaldehyde
6842-15-5	Dodecene
7664-41-7	Ammonia
7783-06-4	Hydrogen Sulfide
7783-07-5	Hydrogen Selenide
8006-61-9	Gasoline
8006-64-2	Turpentine
8008-20-6	Fuel Oil 1
8008-20-6	Kerosene
8030-30-6	Naphtha (Coal Tar)
8030-30-6	Naphtha (Petroleum)
25013-15-4	Vinyl Toluene
25167-67-3	Butylene
25340-18-5	Triethylbenzene
25377-83-7	Octene
25630-42-3	Methylcyclohexanol
26952-21-6	Isooctyl Alcohol

Table 2-2 Cross-Reference of Chemical CAS Numbers to Chemical Names *(Continued)*

CAS Number	Chemical Name
27214-95-8	Nonene
27846-30-6	Methylacetylene-Propadiene
28761-27-5	Undecene
31394-54-4	Dimethylhexane
31394-54-4	2-Methylhexane
34590-94-8	Dipropylene Glycol Methyl Ether
68476-85-7	Liquified Petroleum Gas
81624-04-6	Heptene

reference of these chemicals sorted by their Chemical Abstracts Service or CAS number.

2-4.3 Appendix C lists references that deal with the testing of various characteristics of combustible materials.

Chapter 3 Classification of Class I (Combustible Material) Areas

The decision to classify an area as hazardous is based upon the possibility that an ignitable mixture may occur. Having decided that an area should be classified, the next step is to determine which classification methodology should be utilized; the U.S. traditional *NEC* Articles 500-501, Class, Division, Group; or the *NEC* Article 505, Class, Zone, Group.

Refer to Sections 3-1 and 3-3 for use with the U.S. traditional Class, Division criteria to determine the degree of hazard: Is the area Division 1 or Division 2?

Refer to Sections 3-2 and 3-3 for using *NEC* Article 505 Class, Zone criteria to determine the degree of hazard: Is the area Zone 0, Zone 1, or Zone 2?

3-1 Class, Division Classified Locations.

3-1.1 Division 1 Classified Areas. A condition for Division 1 is whether the area is likely to have an ignitable mixture present under normal conditions. For instance, the presence of a combustible material in the immediate vicinity of an open dip tank is normal and requires a Division 1 classification.

Normal does not necessarily mean the situation that prevails when everything is working properly. For instance, there may be cases in which frequent maintenance and repair are necessary. These are viewed as normal and, if quantities of a flammable liquid or a combustible material are released as a result of the maintenance, the area is Division 1. However, if repairs are not usually required between turnarounds, the need for repair work is considered abnormal. In any event, the classification of the area, as related to equipment maintenance, is influenced by the maintenance procedures and frequency of maintenance.

3-1.2 Division 2 Classified Areas. The criterion for a Division 2 area is whether the area is likely to have ignitable mixtures present only under abnormal conditions. The term "abnormal" is used here in a limited sense and does not include a major catastrophe.

As an example, consider a vessel containing liquid hydrocarbons (the source) that releases combustible material only under abnormal conditions. In this case, there is no Division 1 area because the vessel is normally tight. To release vapor, the vessel would have to leak, and that would not be normal. Thus, the vessel is surrounded by a Division 2 area.

Chemical process equipment does not often fail. Furthermore, the electrical installation requirement of NFPA 70 for Division 2 areas is such that an ignition-capable spark or hot surface will occur only in the event of abnormal operation or failure of electrical equipment. Otherwise, sparks and hot surfaces are not present or are contained in enclosures. On a realistic basis, the possibility of process equipment and electrical equipment failing simultaneously is remote.

The Division 2 classification is also applicable to conditions not involving equipment failure. For example, consider an area classified as Division 1 because of normal presence of an ignitable mixture. Obviously, one side of the Division 1 boundary cannot be normally hazardous and the opposite side never hazardous. When there is no wall, a surrounding transition Division 2 area separates a Division 1 area from an unclassified area.

In cases in which an unpierced barrier, such as a blank wall, completely prevents the spread of the combustible material, area classification does not extend beyond the barrier.

3-2 Class I, Zone Classified Locations.

3-2.1 Zone 0 Classified Areas. A condition for Zone 0 is whether the area has an ignitable mixture present continuously or for long periods of time.

This classification includes the following locations:

(a) Inside vented tanks or vessels containing volatile flammable liquids

(b) Inside inadequately vented spraying or coating enclosures where volatile flammable solvents are used

(c) Between the inner and outer roof sections of a floating roof tank containing volatile flammable liquids

(d) Inside open vessels, tanks, and pits containing volatile flammable liquids

(e) The interior of an exhaust duct that is used to vent ignitable concentrations of gases or vapors

(f) Inside inadequately ventilated enclosures containing normally venting instruments utilizing or analyzing flammable fluids and venting to the inside of the enclosures.

It is not good practice to install electrical equipment in Zone 0 locations except when the equipment is essential to the process or when other locations are not feasible.

3-2.2 Zone 1 Classified Areas. The criteria for a Zone 1 area include the following:

(a) Is the area likely to have ignitable mixtures present under normal conditions?

(b) Is the area likely to have ignitable mixtures exist frequently because of repair or maintenance operations or because of leakage?

(c) Does the area have conditions in which equipment is operated or processes are carried on, where equipment breakdown or faulty operations could result in the release of ignitable concentrations of flammable gases or vapors, and also could cause simultaneous failure of electrical equipment in a mode to cause the electrical equipment to become a source of ignition?

(d) Is the area located adjacent to a Class I, Zone 0 location from which ignitable concentrations of vapors could be communicated, unless communication is prevented by adequate positive-pressure ventilation from a source of clean air and effective safeguards against ventilation failure are provided?

This classification usually includes the following locations:

(a) Where volatile flammable liquids or liquefied flammable gases are transferred from one container to another, in areas in the vicinity of spraying and painting operations where flammable solvents are used

(b) Adequately ventilated drying rooms or compartments for the evaporation of flammable solvents

(c) Adequately ventilated locations containing fat and oil extraction equipment using volatile flammable solvents

(d) Portions of cleaning and dyeing plants where volatile flammable liquids are used

(e) Adequately ventilated gas generator rooms and other portions of gas manufacturing plants where flammable gas may escape

(f) Inadequately ventilated pump rooms for flammable gas or for volatile flammable liquids

(g) The interiors of refrigerators and freezers in which volatile flammable materials are stored in the open, lightly stoppered, or easily ruptured containers

(h) Other locations where ignitable concentrations of flammable vapors or gases are likely to occur in the course of normal operation, but not classified Zone 0.

3-2.3 Zone 2 Classified Areas. The criteria for a Zone 2 area include the following:

(a) Ignitable mixtures are not likely to occur in normal operation, and if they do occur, will exist only for a short period.

(b) Ignitable mixtures are handled, processed, or used in the area, but liquids, gases, or vapors normally are confined within closed containers or closed systems from which they can escape only as a result of accidental rupture or breakdown of the containers or system, or as the result of the abnormal operation of the equipment with which the liquids or gases are handled, processed, or used.

(c) Ignitable mixtures normally are prevented by positive mechanical ventilation, but may become hazardous as the result of failure or abnormal operation of the ventilation equipment.

(d) The area is adjacent to a Class I, Zone 1 location, from which ignitable concentrations of flammable gases or vapors could be communicated, unless such communication is prevented by adequate positive-pressure ventilation from a source of clean air, and effective safeguards against ventilation failure are provided.

The Zone 2 classification usually includes locations where volatile flammable liquids or flammable gases or vapors are used, but which would become hazardous only in case of an accident or of some unusual operating condition.

3-3 Unclassified Areas.

3-3.1 Experience has shown that the release of ignitable mixtures from some operations and apparatus is so infrequent that area classification is not necessary. For example, it is not usually necessary to classify the following areas where combustible materials are processed, stored, or handled:

(a) Areas that have adequate ventilation, where combustible materials are contained within suitable, well-maintained, closed piping systems

(b) Areas that lack adequate ventilation, but where piping systems are without valves, fittings, flanges, and similar accessories that may be prone to leaks

(c) Areas where combustible materials are stored in suitable containers

3-3.2 Areas considered to have adequate ventilation include the following:

(a) An outside area

(b) A building, room, or space that is substantially open and free of obstruction to the natural passage of air, either vertically or horizontally (Such areas may be roofed over with no walls, may be roofed over and closed on one side, or may be provided with suitably designed windbreaks.)

(c) An enclosed or partly enclosed space provided with ventilation equivalent to natural ventilation (The ventilation system must have adequate safeguards against failure.)

3-3.3 Open flames and hot surfaces associated with the operation of certain equipment, such as boilers and fired heaters, provide inherent thermal ignition sources. Electrical classification is not appropriate in the immediate vicinity of these facilities. However, it is prudent to avoid installing electrical equipment that could be a primary ignition source for potential leak sources in pumps, valves, and so forth, or in waste product and fuel feed lines.

3-3.4 Experience indicates that Class IIIB liquids seldom evolve enough vapors to form ignitable mixtures even when heated, and are seldom ignited by properly installed and maintained general purpose electrical equipment.

3-3.5 Experience has shown that some halogenated liquid hydrocarbons, such as trichloroethylene; 1,1,1-trichloroethane; methylene chloride; and 1,1-dichloro-1-fluoroethane (HCFC-141b), which do not have flash points, but do have a flammable range, are for practical purposes nonflammable and do not require special electrical equipment for hazardous (classified) locations.

3-4 Extent of Classified Areas.

3-4.1 The extent of a Division 1 or Division 2; or Zone 0, Zone 1, or Zone 2 area requires careful consideration of the following factors:

(a) The combustible material

(b) The vapor density of the material

(c) The temperature of the material

(d) The process or storage pressure

(e) The size of release

(f) The ventilation

3-4.2* The first step is to identify the materials being handled and their vapor densities. Hydrocarbon vapors and gases are generally heavier than air, while hydrogen and methane are lighter than air. The following guidelines apply:

(a) In the absence of walls, enclosures, or other barriers, and in the absence of air currents or similar disturbing forces, the combustible material will disperse. Heavier- than-air vapors will travel primarily downward and outward; lighter-than-air vapors will travel upward and outward. If the source of the vapors is a single point, the horizontal area covered by the vapor will be a circle.

(b) For heavier-than-air vapors released at or near grade level, ignitable mixtures are most likely to be found below grade level; next most likely at grade level; with decreasing likelihood of presence as height above grade increases. For lighter-than-air gases, the opposite is true: there is little or no hazard at and below grade but greater hazard above grade.

(c) In cases where the source of the combustible material is above grade or below grade or in cases where the combustible material is released under pressure, the limits of the classified area are altered substantially. Also, a very mild breeze may extend these limits. However, a stronger breeze may accelerate dispersion of the combustible material so that the extent of the classified area is greatly reduced. Thus, dimensional limits recommended for either Class I, Division 1 or Division 2; or Class I, Zone 0, Zone 1, or Zone 2 classified areas must be based on experience rather than relying solely on the theoretical diffusion of vapors.

3-4.3 The size of a building and its design may influence considerably the classification of the enclosed volume. In the case of a small, inadequately ventilated room, it may be appropriate to classify the entire room as Class I, Division 1 or Class I, Zone 1.

3-4.4 When classifying buildings, careful evaluation of prior experience with the same or similar installations should be made. It is not enough to merely identify a potential source of the combustible material within the building and proceed immediately to defining the extent of either the Class I, Division 1 or Division 2; or Class I, Zone 1 or Zone 2 classified areas. Where experience indicates that a particular design concept is sound, a more hazardous classification for similar installations may not be justified. Furthermore, it is conceivable that an area might be reclassified from either Class I, Division 1 to Division 2, or from Class I, Division 2 to unclassified or from Class I, Zone 1 to Zone 2, or from Class I, Zone 2 to unclassified based on experience.

3-4.5 Correctly evaluated, an installation will be found to be a multiplicity of Class I, Division 1 areas of very limited extent. The same will be true for Class I, Zone 1 areas. Probably the most numerous of offenders are packing glands. A packing gland leaking a quart per minute (0.95 L/min), or 360 gallons per day, would certainly not be commonplace. Yet, if a quart bottle were emptied each minute outdoors, the zone made hazardous would be difficult to locate with a combustible gas detector.

3-4.6 The volume of combustible material released is of extreme importance in determining the extent of a hazardous area, and it is this consideration that necessitates the greatest application of sound engineering judgment. However, one cannot lose sight of the purpose of this judgment; the area is classified solely for the installation of electrical equipment.

3-5 Discussion of Diagrams and Recommendations.

3-5.1 This chapter contains a series of diagrams that illustrate how typical sources of combustible material should be classified and the recommended extent of the various classifications. Some of the diagrams are for single-point sources; others apply to multiple sources in an enclosed space or in an operating area. The basis for the diagrams is explained in Section 3-6.

3-5.2 The intended use of the diagrams is to aid in developing electrical classification maps of operating units, process plants, and buildings. Most of the maps will be plan views. Elevations or sectional views may be required where different classifications apply at different levels.

3-5.3 An operating unit may have many interconnected sources of combustible material, including pumps, compressors, vessels, tanks, and heat exchangers. These in turn present sources of leaks such as flanged and screwed connections, fittings, valves, meters, and so forth. Thus, considerable judgment will be required to establish the boundaries of Division 1 and Division 2, or Zone 0, Zone 1, and Zone 2 areas.

3-5.4 In some cases, individual classification of a multitude of point sources within an operating unit is neither feasible nor economical. In such cases, the entire unit may be classified as a single-source entity. However, this should be considered only after a thorough evaluation of the extent and interaction of the various sources, both within the unit and adjacent to it.

3-5.5 In developing these diagrams, vapor density is generally assumed to be greater than that of air. Lighter-than-air gases, such as hydrogen and methane, will quite readily disperse, and the diagrams for lighter-than-air gases should be used. However, if such gases are being evolved from the cryogenic state (i.e., liquefied hydrogen or LNG), caution must be exercised, because for some finite period of time, these gases will be heavier than air due to their low temperature when first released.

3-6 Basis for Recommendations.

3-6.1 The practices of the petroleum refining industry are published in the American Petroleum Institute's RP 500, *Recommended Practice for Classification of Locations for Electrical Installations at Petroleum Facilities.* These practices are based on an analysis of the practices of a large segment of the industry, experimental data, and careful weighing of pertinent factors. Petroleum facility operations are characterized by the handling, processing, and storage of large quantities of materials, often at elevated temperatures. The recommended limits of classified areas for petroleum facility installations may therefore be stricter than are warranted for more traditional chemical processing facilities that handle smaller quantities.

3-6.2 Various codes, standards, and recommended practices of the National Fire Protection Association include recommendations for classifying hazardous areas. These recommendations are based on many years of experience. NFPA 30, *Flammable and Combustible Liquids Code,* and NFPA 58, *Standard for the Storage and Handling of Liquefied Petroleum Gases,* are two of these documents.

3-6.3 Continuous process plants and large batch chemical plants may be almost as large as refineries and should therefore follow the practices of the refining industry. Leakage from pump and agitator shaft packing glands, piping flanges, and valves generally increases with process equipment size, pressure, and flow rate, as does the travel distance and area of dispersion from the discharge source.

3-6.4 In deciding whether to use an overall plant classification scheme or individual equipment classification, process equipment size, flow rate, and pressure should be taken into consideration. Generally speaking, point-source diagrams can be used for small or batch chemical plants; for large, high-pressure plants, the API recommendations are more suitable. Table 3-6 gives ranges of process equipment size, pressure, and flow rate for equipment and piping handling combustible material.

3-6.5 The great majority of chemical plants fall in the moderate range of size, pressure, and flow rate for equipment and

Table 3-6 Relative Magnitudes of Process Equipment and Piping Handling Combustible Materials

Process Equipment	Units	Small (Low)	Moderate	Large (High)
Size	gal	< 5000	5000 to 25,000	> 25,000
Pressure	psi	< 100	100 to 500	> 500
Flow Rate	gpm	< 100	100 to 500	> 500

piping handling combustible materials. However, since all cases are not the same, sound engineering judgment is required.

3-7 Procedure for Classifying Areas. The following procedure should be used for each room, section, or area being classified.

3-7.1 Step One—Determining Need for Classification. The area should be classified if a combustible material is processed, handled, or stored there.

3-7.2 Step Two—Gathering Information.

3-7.2.1 Proposed Facility Information. For a proposed facility that exists only in drawings, a preliminary area classification can be done so that suitable electrical equipment and instrumentation can be purchased. Plants are rarely built exactly as the drawings portray them, so the area classification should be modified later based upon the actual facility.

3-7.2.2 Existing Facility History. For an existing facility, the individual plant experience is extremely important in classifying areas within the plant. Both operation and maintenance personnel in the actual plant should be asked the following questions:

(a) Have there been instances of leaks?

(b) Do leaks occur frequently?

(c) Do leaks occur during normal or abnormal operation?

(d) Is the equipment in good condition, questionable condition, or in need of repair?

(e) Do maintenance practices result in the formation of ignitable mixtures?

(f) Does routine flushing of process lines, changing of filters, opening of equipment, and so forth, result in the formation of ignitable mixtures?

3-7.2.3 Process Flow Diagram. A process flow diagram showing the pressure, temperature, flow rates, composition and quantities of various materials (i.e., mass flow balance sheets) passing through the process is needed.

3-7.2.4 Plot Plan. A plot plan (or similar drawing) is needed showing all vessels, tanks, trenches, lagoons, sumps, building structures, dikes, partitions, levees, ditches, and similar items that would affect dispersion of any liquid, gas, or vapor. The plot plan should include the prevailing wind direction.

3-7.2.5* Fire Hazard Properties of Combustible Material. The properties needed for determining area classification for many materials are shown in Table 2-1.

NOTE: A material could be listed in Table 2-1 under a chemical name different from the chemical name used at a facility. Table 2-2 is provided to cross-reference the CAS number of the material to the chemical name used in Table-2-1.

If materials being used are not listed in Table 2-1 or in other reputable chemical references, the needed information may be obtained by the following:

(a) Contact the material supplier to determine if the material has been tested or group-classified. If tested, estimate the group classification using the criteria shown in Appendix A.

(b) Have the material tested and estimate the group classification using the criteria shown in Appendix A.

(c) Refer to Appendix B for a method for determining the group classification for some mixed combustible material streams.

3-7.3 Step Three—Selecting the Appropriate Classification Diagram. Correlate the list of combustible materials from the process flow diagram and the material mass balance data with the quantities, pressures, flow rates *(see Table 3-6)*, and temperatures to determine the following:

(a) Whether the process equipment size is low, moderate, or high

(b) Whether the pressure is low, moderate, or high

(c) Whether the flow rate is low, moderate, or high

(d) Whether the combustible material is lighter than air (vapor density < 1) or heavier than air (vapor density > 1)

(e) Whether the source of leaks is above or below grade

(f) Whether the process is a loading/unloading station, product dryer, filter press, compressor shelter, hydrogen storage, or marine terminal

Use Table 3-8 and the above information to select the appropriate classification diagram(s).

3-7.4 Step Four—Determining the Extent of the Classified Area. The extent of the classified area may be determined by using sound engineering judgment to apply the methods discussed in 3-4.2 and the diagrams contained in this chapter.

3-7.4.1 Locate the potential sources of leaks on the plan drawing or at the actual location. These sources may include rotating or reciprocating shafts (e.g., pumps, compressors, and control valves) and atmospheric discharges from pressure relief devices.

3-7.4.2 For each leakage source, find an equivalent example on the selected classification diagram to determine the minimum extent of classification around the leakage source. The extent may be modified by considering the following:

(a) Whether an ignitable mixture is likely to occur frequently due to repair, maintenance, or leakage

(b) Where conditions of maintenance and supervision are such that leaks are likely to occur in process equipment, storage vessels, and piping systems containing combustible material

(c) Whether the combustible material could be transmitted by trenches, pipes, conduits, or ducts

(d) Ventilation or prevailing wind in the specific area, and the dispersion rates of the combustible materials

3-7.4.3 Once the minimum extent is determined, utilize distinct landmarks (e.g., curbs, dikes, walls, structural supports, edges of roads, etc.) for the actual boundaries of the area classification. These landmarks permit easy identification of the boundaries of the hazardous areas for electricians, instrument technicians, operators, and other personnel.

3-8 Classification Diagrams for Divisions. Most diagrams in Sections 3-8 and 3-9 include tables of "suggested applicability" and use check marks to show the ranges of process equipment size, pressure, and flow rates. *(See Table 3-6.)* Unless otherwise stated, these diagrams assume that the material being handled is a flammable liquid. Table 3-8 provides a summary of where each diagram is intended to apply. Class I, Division diagrams include Figures 3-8.1 through 3-8.34.

Figure 3-8.1 shows a source of leakage located outdoors, at grade. The material being handled is a flammable liquid.

Figure 3-8.2 shows a source of leakage located outdoors, above grade. The material being handled is a flammable liquid.

Figure 3-8.3 shows a source of leakage located indoors, at floor level. Adequate ventilation is provided. The material being handled is a flammable liquid.

Figure 3-8.4 shows a source of leakage located indoors, above floor level. Adequate ventilation is provided. The material being handled is a flammable liquid.

Figure 3-8.5 shows a source of leakage located indoors, at floor level, adjacent to an opening in an exterior wall. Adequate ventilation is provided. The material being handled is a flammable liquid.

Figure 3-8.6 shows a source of leakage located indoors, at floor level, adjacent to an opening in an exterior wall. Ventilation is not adequate. The material being handled is a flammable liquid.

Figure 3-8.7 shows a source of leakage located outdoors, at grade. The material being handled may be a flammable liquid, a liquefied or compressed flammable gas, or a flammable cryogenic liquid.

Figure 3-8.8 shows a source of leakage located outdoors, above grade. The material being handled may be a flammable liquid, a liquefied or compressed flammable gas, or a flammable cryogenic liquid.

Figure 3-8.9 shows a source of leakage located outdoors, at grade. The material being handled is a flammable liquid.

Figure 3-8.10 shows a source of leakage located outdoors, above grade. The material being handled is a flammable liquid.

Figure 3-8.11 shows a source of leakage located indoors, adjacent to an opening in an exterior wall. Ventilation is not adequate. The material being handled is a flammable liquid.

Figure 3-8.12 shows a source of leakage located indoors, adjacent to an opening in an exterior wall. Adequate ventilation is provided. The material being handled is a flammable liquid.

Figure 3-8.13 shows multiple sources of leakage, located both at grade and above grade, in an outdoor process area. The material being handled is a flammable liquid.

Figure 3-8.14 shows multiple sources of leakage, located both at grade and above grade, in an outdoor process area. The material being handled is a flammable liquid.

Figure 3-8.15 shows multiple sources of leakage, located both at and above grade, in an outdoor process area. The material being handled is a flammable liquid.

Figure 3-8.16 shows multiple sources of leakage, located both at and above floor level, in an adequately ventilated building. The material being handled is a flammable liquid.

Figure 3-8.17 shows a product dryer located in an adequately ventilated building. The product dryer system is totally enclosed. The material being handled is a solid wet with a flammable liquid.

Figure 3-8.18 shows a plate and frame filter press. Adequate ventilation is provided. The material being handled is a solid wet with a flammable liquid.

Figure 3-8.19 shows a product storage tank located outdoors, at grade. The material that is being stored is a flammable liquid.

Figure 3-8.20 shows tank car loading and unloading via a closed transfer system. Material is transferred only through the dome. The material being transferred is a flammable liquid.

Figures 3-8.21(a) and 3-8.21(b) show tank car and tank truck loading and unloading via a closed transfer system. Material is transferred through the bottom fittings. The material being transferred is a flammable liquid.

Figure 3-8.22 shows tank car (or tank truck) loading and unloading via an open transfer system. Material is transferred either through the dome or the bottom fittings. The material being transferred is a flammable liquid.

Figure 3-8.23 shows tank car (or tank truck) loading and unloading via a closed transfer system. Material is transferred only through the dome. The material being transferred may be a liquefied or compressed flammable gas or a flammable cryogenic liquid.

Figure 3-8.24 shows a drum filling station located either outdoors or indoors in an adequately ventilated building. The material being handled is a flammable liquid.

Figure 3-8.25 shows an emergency impounding basin or oil/water separator and an emergency or temporary drainage ditch or oil/water separator. The material being handled is a flammable liquid.

Figure 3-8.26 shows liquid hydrogen storage located outdoors or indoors in an adequately ventilated building. This diagram applies to liquid hydrogen only.

Figure 3-8.27 shows gaseous hydrogen storage located outdoors, or indoors in an adequately ventilated building. This diagram applies to gaseous hydrogen only.

Figure 3-8.28 shows an adequately ventilated compressor shelter. The material being handled is a lighter-than-air gas.

Figure 3-8.29 shows an inadequately ventilated compressor shelter. The material being handled is a lighter-than-air gas.

Figure 3-8.30 shows tanks for the storage of cryogenic and other cold liquefied flammable gases. [From NFPA 59A, *Standard for the Production, Storage, and Handling of Liquefied Natural Gas (LNG)*.]

Figure 3-8.31 shows a source of leakage from equipment handling liquefied natural gas or other cold liquefied flammable gas, and located outdoors, at or above grade. (From NFPA 59A.)

Figure 3-8.32 shows a source of leakage from equipment handling liquefied natural gas or other cold liquefied flammable gas and located indoors in an adequately ventilated building. (From NFPA 59A.)

Figure 3-8.33 shows the classified zones around liquefied natural gas routinely operating bleeds, drips, vents, and drains both outdoors, at or above grade, and indoors, in an adequately ventilated building. This diagram also applies to other cold liquefied flammable gases. (From NFPA 59A.)

Figure 3-8.34 shows the classified zones at a marine terminal handling flammable liquids and includes the area around the stored position of loading arms and hoses.

Table 3-8 Matrix of Diagrams Versus Material/Property/Application

Diagram Class I Division (Zone)	Special Condition	VD > 1	VD < 1	Cryogenic	Indoor	Indoor, Poor Ventilation	Outdoor	Above Grade	At Grade	Size	Pressure	Flow
3-8.1 (3-9.1)		X					X		X	S/M	S/M	S/M
3-8.2 (3-9.2)		X					X	X		S/M	S/M	S/M
3-8.3 (3-9.3)		X			X				X	S/M	S/M	S/M
3-8.4 (3-9.4)		X			X			X		S/M	S/M	S/M
3-8.5 (3-9.5)		X			X				X	S/M	S/M	S/M
3-8.6 (3-9.6)		X				X			X	S/M	S/M	S/M
3-8.7 (3-9.7)		X		X			X		X	S/M	M/H	S/M
3-8.8 (3-9.8)		X		X			X	X		S/M	M/H	S/M
3-8.9 (3-9.9)		X					X		X	L	M/L	L
3-8.10 (3-9.10)		X					X	X		L	M/L	L
3-8.11 (3-9.11)		X				X		X		M/L	L	M/L
3-8.12 (3-9.12)		X			X			X		M/L	L	M/L
3-8.13 (3-9.13)		X					X	X	X	S/M	S/M	S/M
3-8.14 (3-9.14)		X					X	X	X	M/L	M/L	M/L
3-8.15 (3-9.15)		X					X	X	X	S/M	S/M	S/M
3-8.16 (3-9.16)		X			X			X	X	S/M	S/M	S/M
3-8.17 (3-9.17)	Product dryer	FL			X		X	X				
3-8.18 (3-9.18)	Filter press	FL			X			X				
3-8.19 (3-9.19)	Storage tank	FL					X		X	M/L	L	M/L
3-8.20 (3-9.20)	Tank car loading	FL					X	X				
3-8.21 (3-9.21)	Tank car loading Tank truck loading	FL					X	X	X			
3-8.22 (3-9.22)	Tank car loading Tank truck loading	FL					X	X	X			
3-8.23 (3-9.23)	Tank car loading Tank truck loading	FL		X			X	X				
3-8.24 (3-9.24)	Drum filling station	FL			X		X	X				
3-8.25 (3-9.25)	Emergency basin	FL					X	X	X			
3-8.26 (3-9.26)	Liquid H_2 storage		X	X	X		X	X	X			
3-8.27 (3-9.27)	Gaseous H_2 storage		X		X		X	X	X			
3-8.28 (3-9.28)	Compressor shelter		X		X			X	X			
3-8.29 (3-9.29)	Compressor shelter		X			X		X	X			
3-8.30 (3-9.30)	Cryogenic storage			X			X	X	X			
3-8.31 (3-9.31)		LNG					X	X	X			
3-8.32 (3-9.32)		LNG			X			X	X			
3-8.33 (3-9.33)		LNG						X				
3-8.34 (3-9.34)	Marine terminal	FL			X		X	X				

NOTES: FL = Flammable Liquid LNG = Liquefied Natural Gas X = Diagram Applies
L = Large M = Moderate S = Small H = High

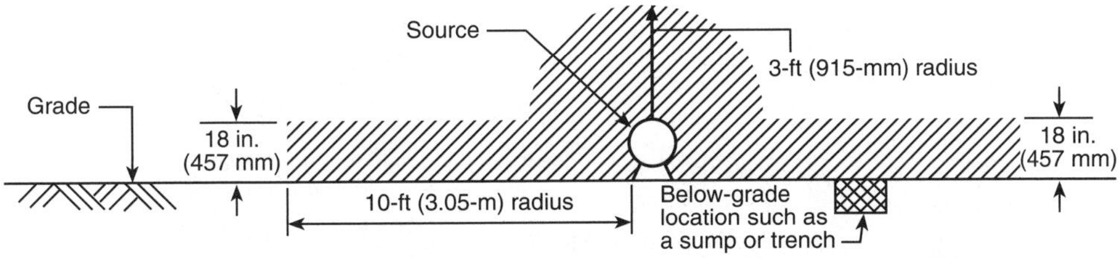

Material: Flammable liquid

	Small/low	Moderate	Large/high
Process equipment size	X	X	
Pressure	X	X	
Flow rate	X	X	

Division 1

Division 2

Figure 3-8.1 Leakage source located outdoors, at grade.

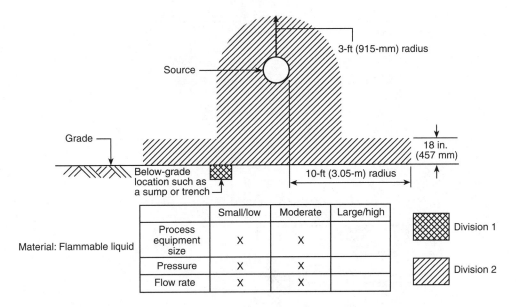

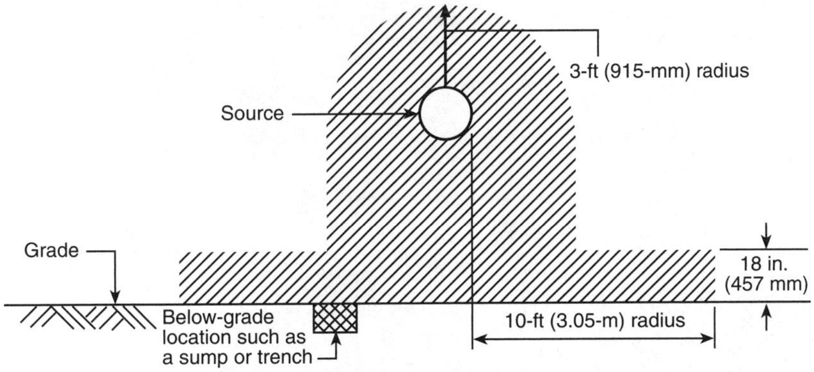

Material: Flammable liquid

	Small/low	Moderate	Large/high
Process equipment size	X	X	
Pressure	X	X	
Flow rate	X	X	

Division 1

Division 2

Figure 3-8.2 Leakage source located outdoors, above grade.

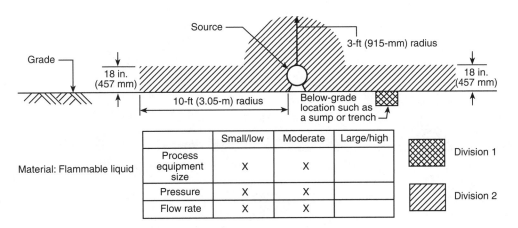

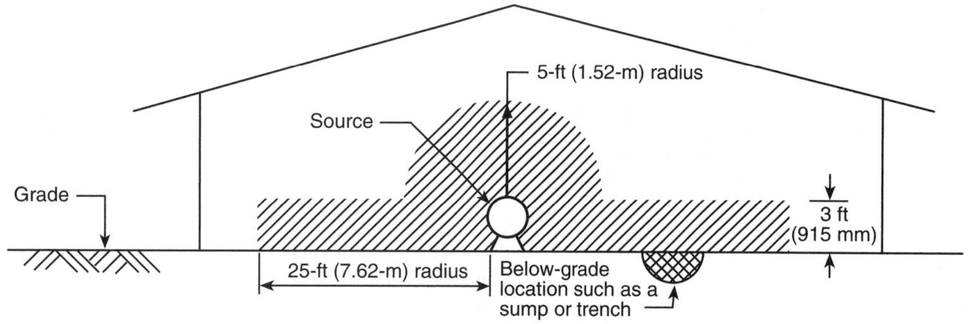

Material: Flammable liquid

	Small/low	Moderate	Large/high
Process equipment size	X	X	
Pressure	X	X	
Flow rate	X	X	

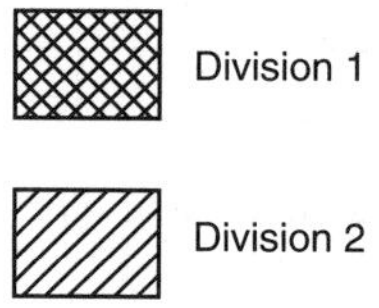

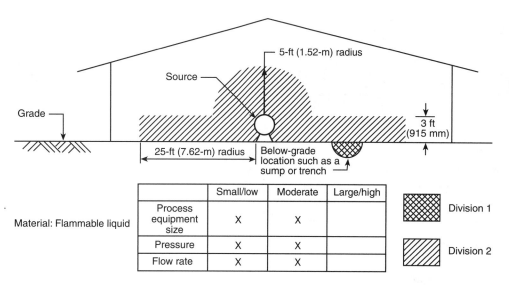

Figure 3-8.3 Leakage source located indoors, at floor level. Adequate ventilation is provided.

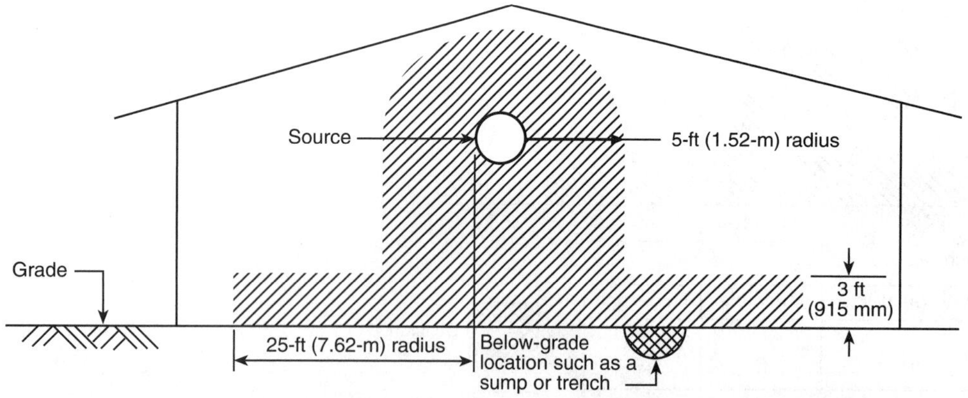

Material: Flammable liquid

	Small/low	Moderate	Large/high
Process equipment size	X	X	
Pressure	X	X	
Flow rate	X	X	

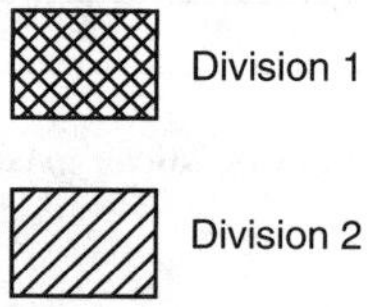

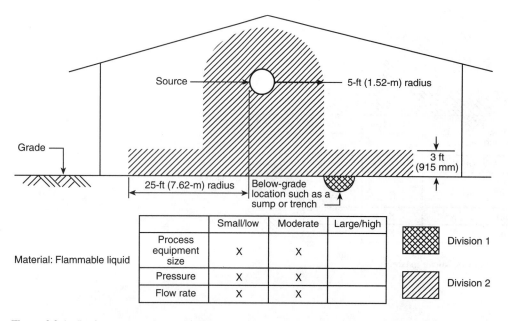

Figure 3-8.4 Leakage source located indoors, above floor level. Adequate ventilation is provided.

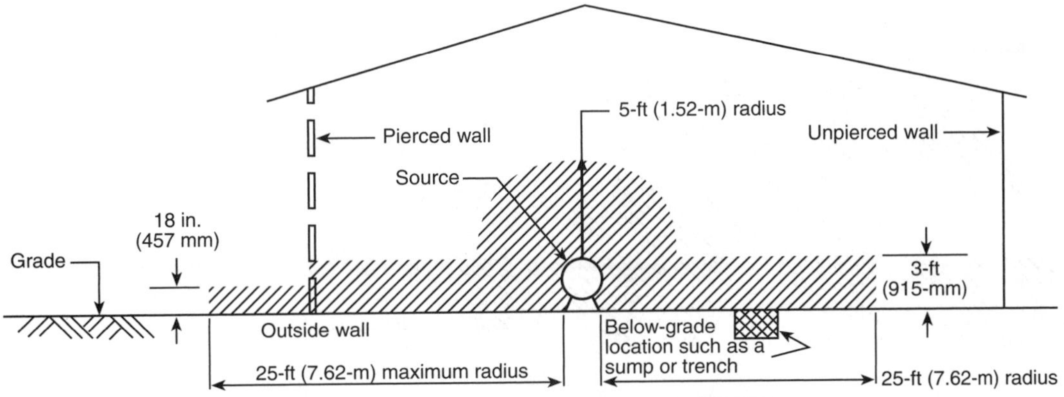

Material: Flammable liquid

	Small/low	Moderate	Large/high
Process equipment size	X	X	
Pressure	X	X	
Flow rate	X	X	

Division 1

Division 2

Figure 3-8.5 Leakage source located indoors, at floor level, adjacent to opening in exterior wall. Adequate ventilation is provided.

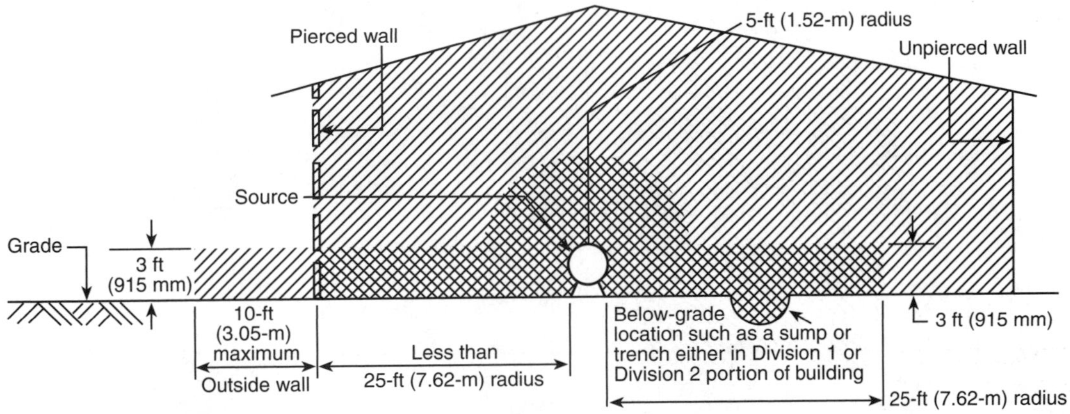

Note: If building is small compared to size of equipment, and leakage can fill the building, the entire building interior is classified Division 1.

Material: Flammable liquid

	Small/low	Moderate	Large/high
Process equipment size	X	X	
Pressure	X	X	
Flow rate	X	X	

Division 1

Division 2

Figure 3-8.6 Leakage source located indoors, at floor level, adjacent to opening in exterior wall. Adequate ventilation is not provided.

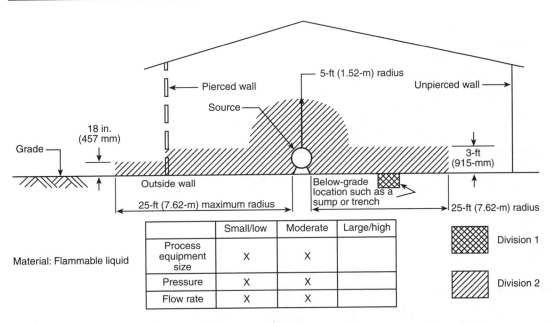

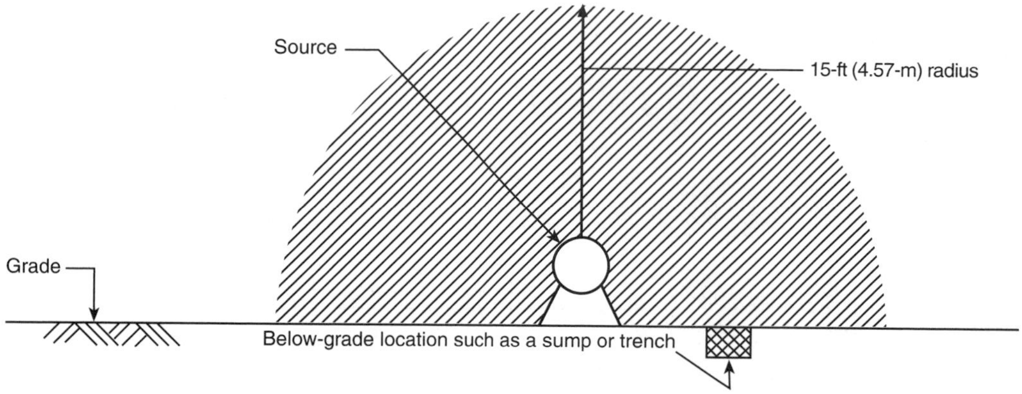

Material: Flammable liquid, liquefied flammable gas, compressed flammable gas, and cryogenic liquid

	Small/low	Moderate	Large/high
Process equipment size	X	X	
Pressure		X	X
Flow rate	X	X	

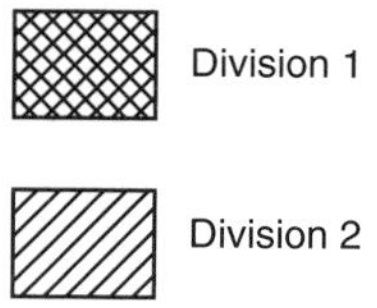

Figure 3-8.7 Leakage source located outdoors, at grade.

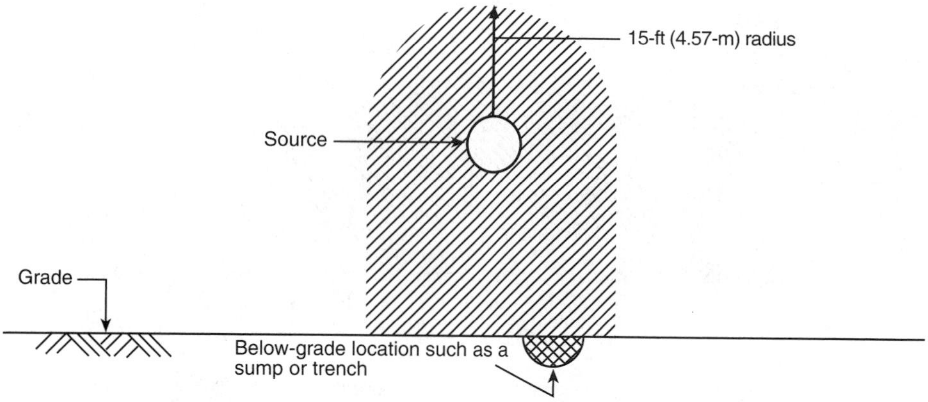

Material: Flammable liquid, liquefied flammable gas, compressed flammable gas, and cryogenic liquid

	Small/low	Moderate	Large/high
Process equipment size	X	X	
Pressure		X	X
Flow rate	X	X	

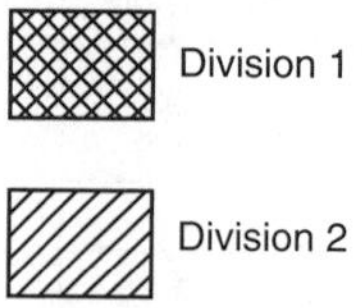

Figure 3-8.8 Leakage source located outdoors, above grade.

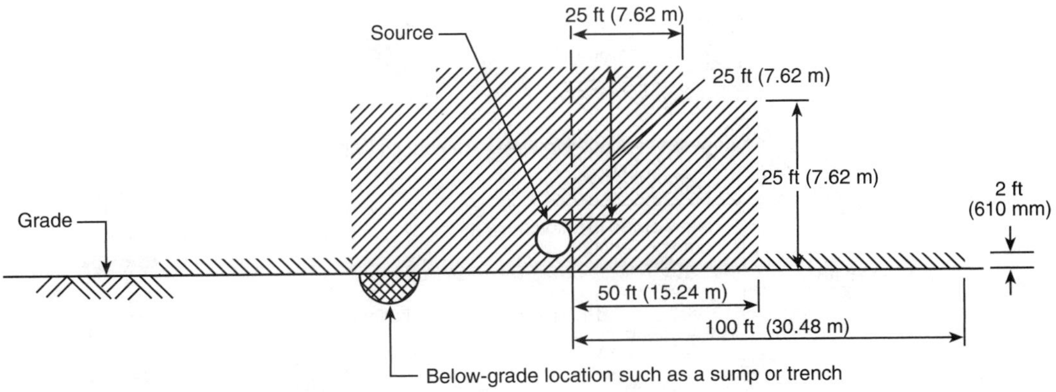

Material: Flammable liquid

	Small/low	Moderate	Large/high
Process equipment size			X
Pressure		X	X
Flow rate			X

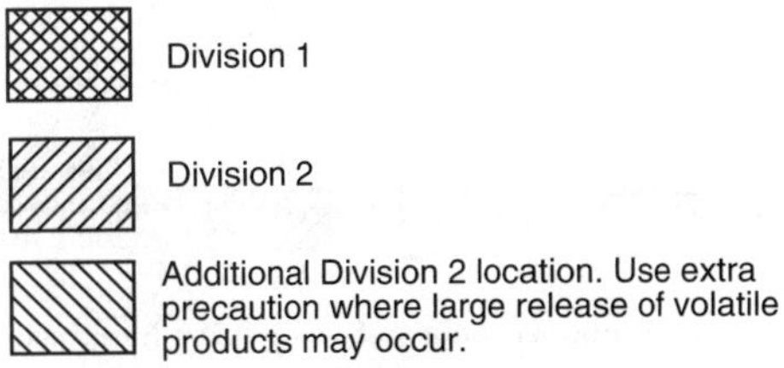

Figure 3-8.9 Leakage source located outdoors, at grade.

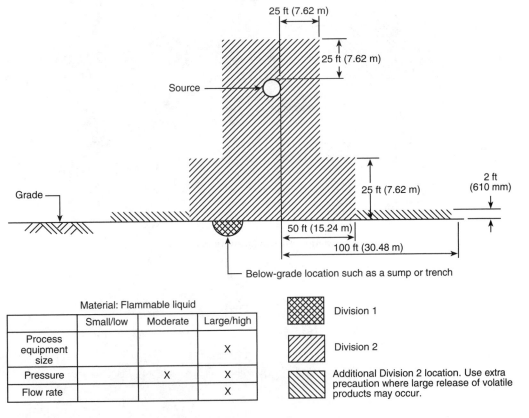

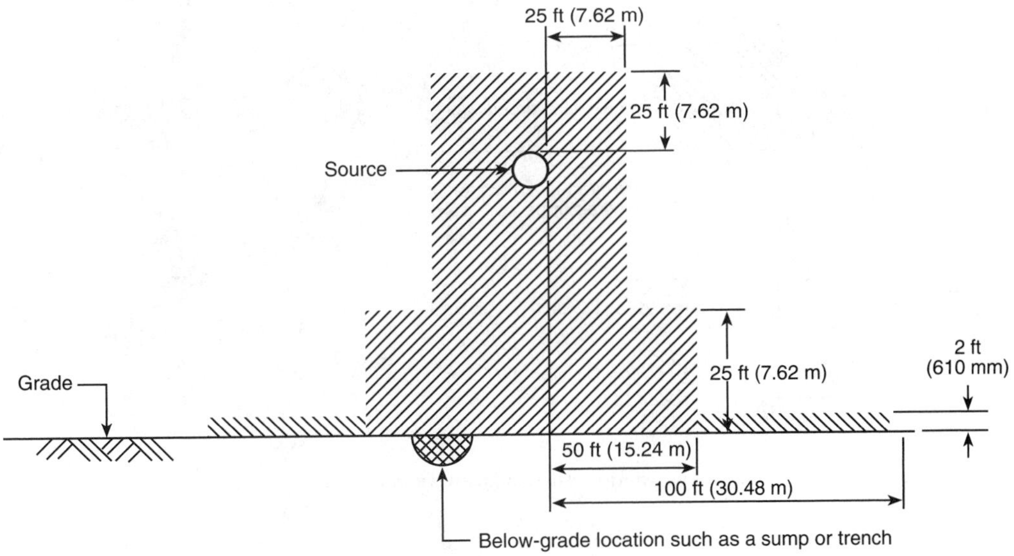

Material: Flammable liquid

	Small/low	Moderate	Large/high
Process equipment size			X
Pressure		X	X
Flow rate			X

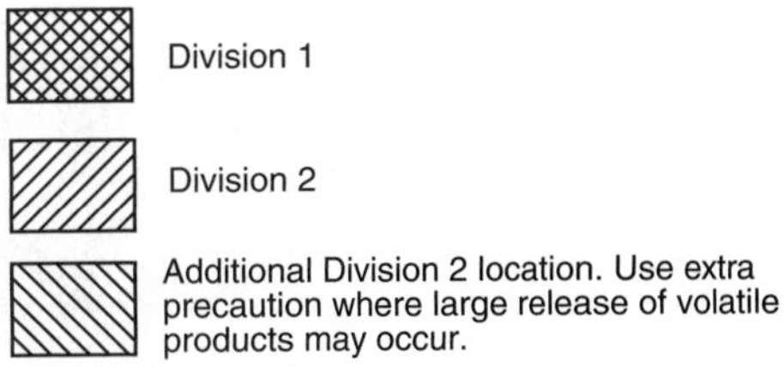

Figure 3-8.10 Leakage source located outdoors, above grade.

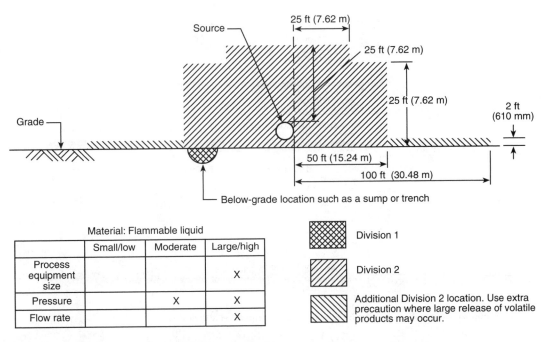

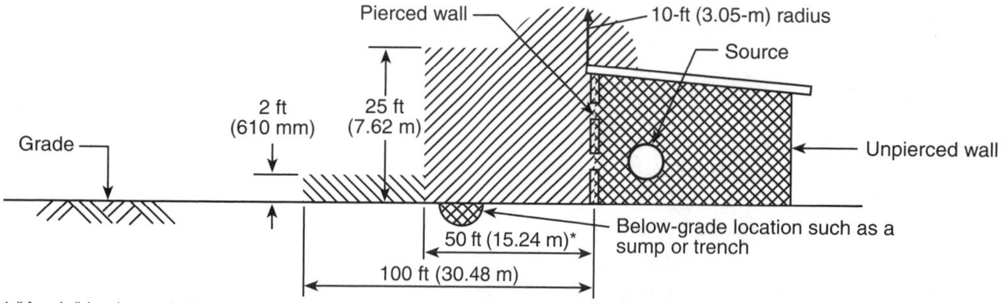

* "Apply" horizontal distances of 50 feet from the source of vapor or 10 feet beyond the perimeter of the building, whichever is greater, except that beyond unpierced vaportight walls the area is nonclassified.

Material: Flammable liquid

	Small/low	Moderate	Large/high
Process equipment size		X	X
Pressure			X
Flow rate		X	X

Division 1

Division 2

Additional Division 2 location. Use extra precaution where large release of volatile products may occur.

Figure 3-8.11 Leakage source located indoors, adjacent to opening in exterior wall. Adequate ventilation is not provided.

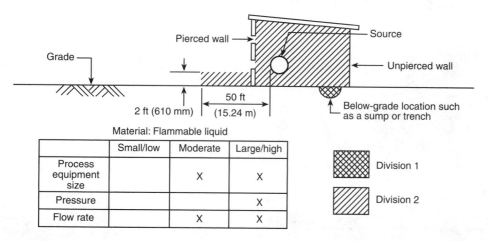

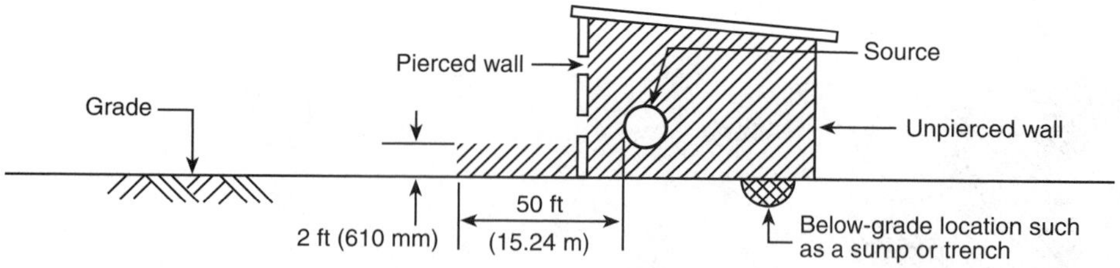

Material: Flammable liquid

	Small/low	Moderate	Large/high
Process equipment size		X	X
Pressure			X
Flow rate		X	X

Division 1

Division 2

Figure 3-8.12 Leakage source located indoors, adjacent to opening in exterior wall. Adequate ventilation is provided.

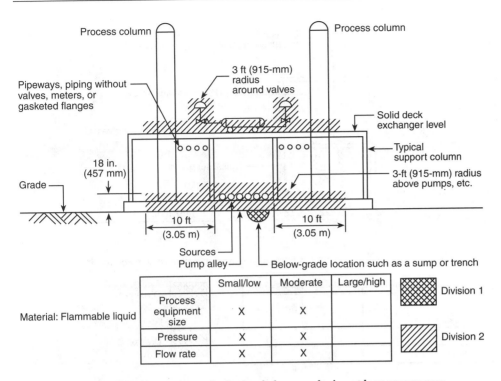

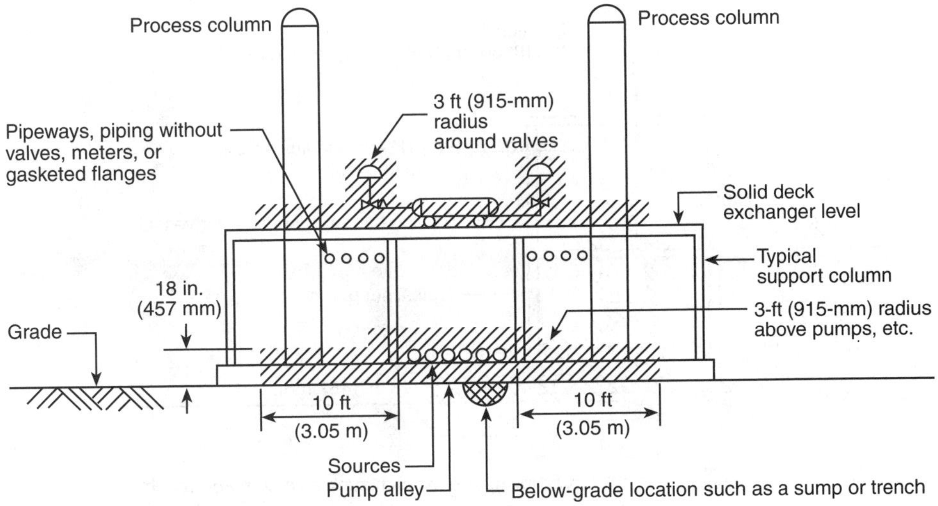

Material: Flammable liquid

	Small/low	Moderate	Large/high
Process equipment size	X	X	
Pressure	X	X	
Flow rate	X	X	

Division 1

Division 2

Figure 3-8.13 Multiple leakage sources, both at and above grade, in outdoor process area.

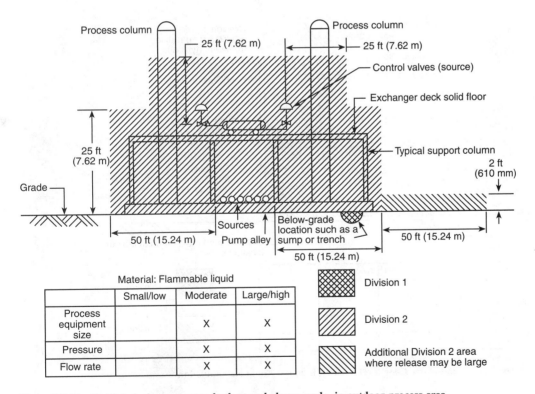

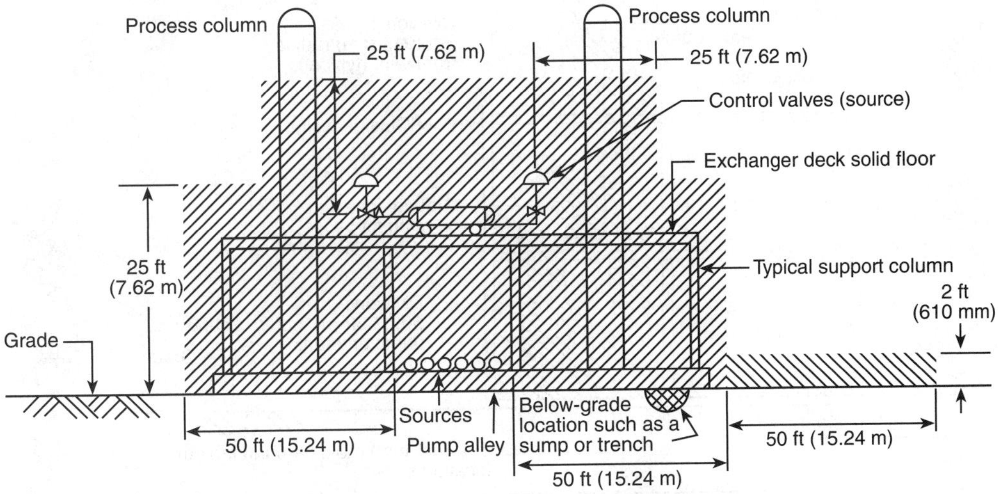

Material: Flammable liquid

	Small/low	Moderate	Large/high
Process equipment size		X	X
Pressure		X	X
Flow rate		X	X

Division 1

Division 2

Additional Division 2 area where release may be large

Figure 3-8.14 Multiple leakage sources, both at and above grade, in outdoor process area.

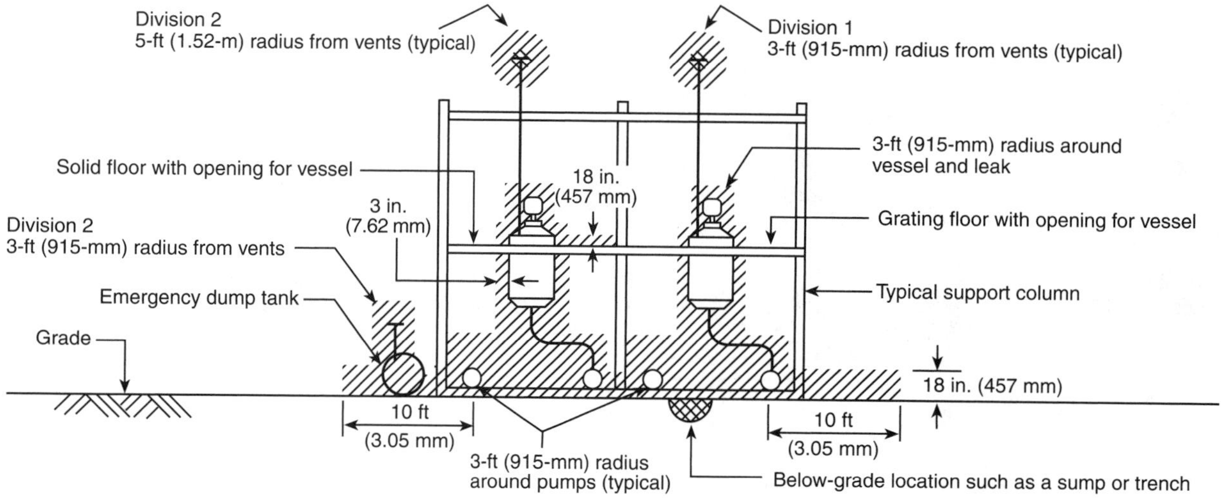

Material: Flammable liquid

	Small/low	Moderate	Large/high
Process equipment size	X	X	
Pressure	X	X	
Flow rate	X	X	

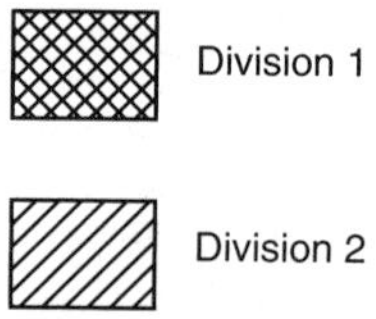

Figure 3-8.15 Multiple leakage sources, both at and above grade, in outdoor process area.

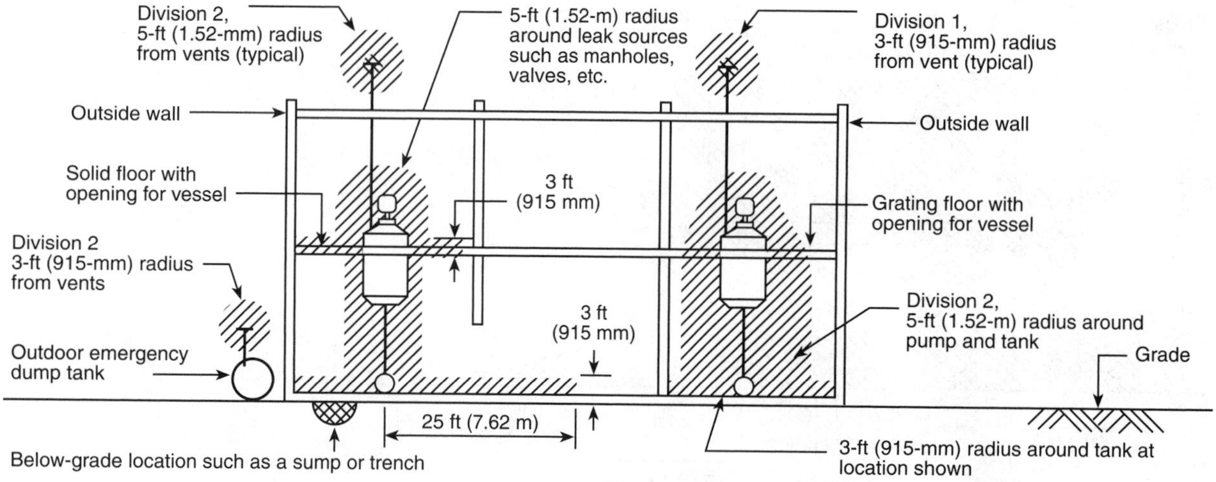

Material: Flammable liquid

	Small/low	Moderate	Large/high
Process equipment size	X	X	
Pressure	X	X	
Flow rate	X	X	

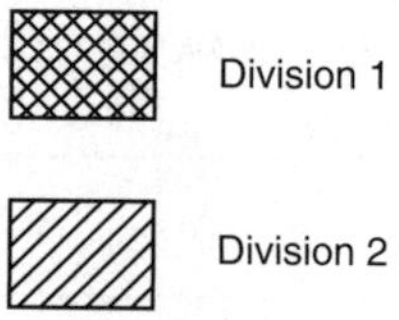

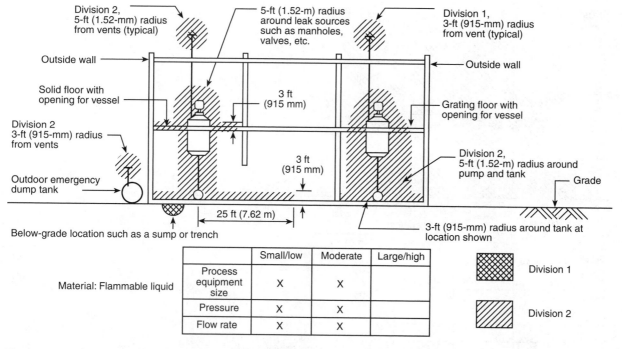

Figure 3-8.16 Multiple leakage sources, both at and above floor level, located indoors. Adequate ventilation is provided.

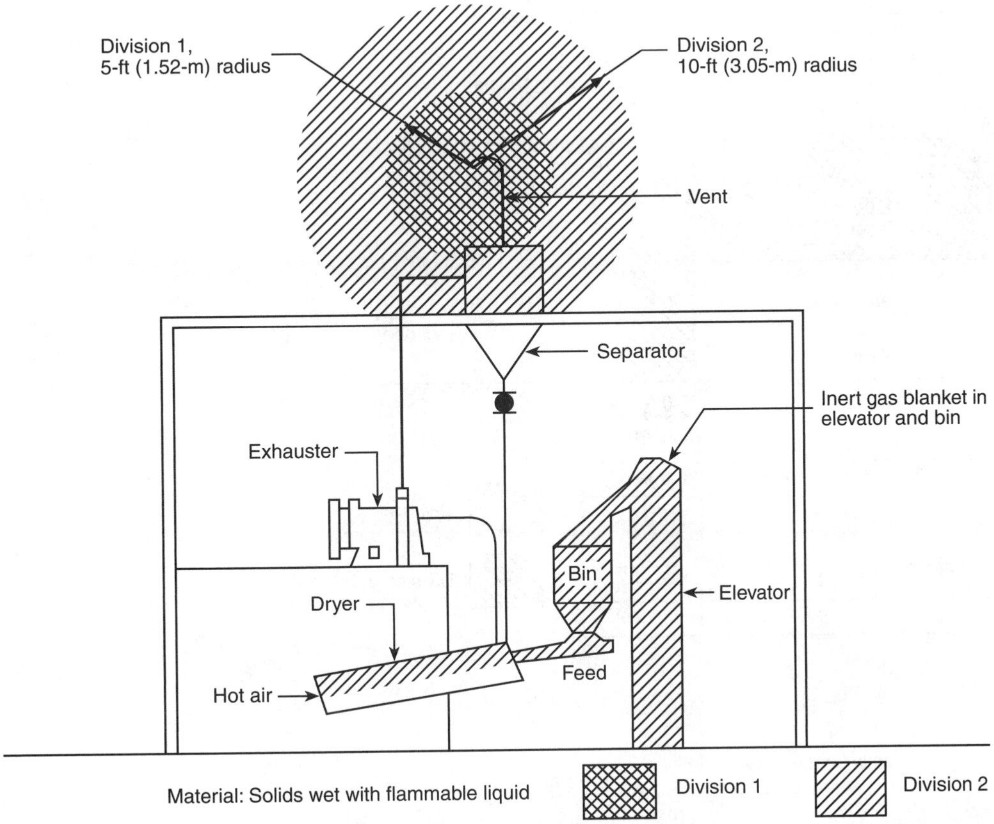

Figure 3-8.17 Totally enclosed product dryer located in adequately ventilated building.

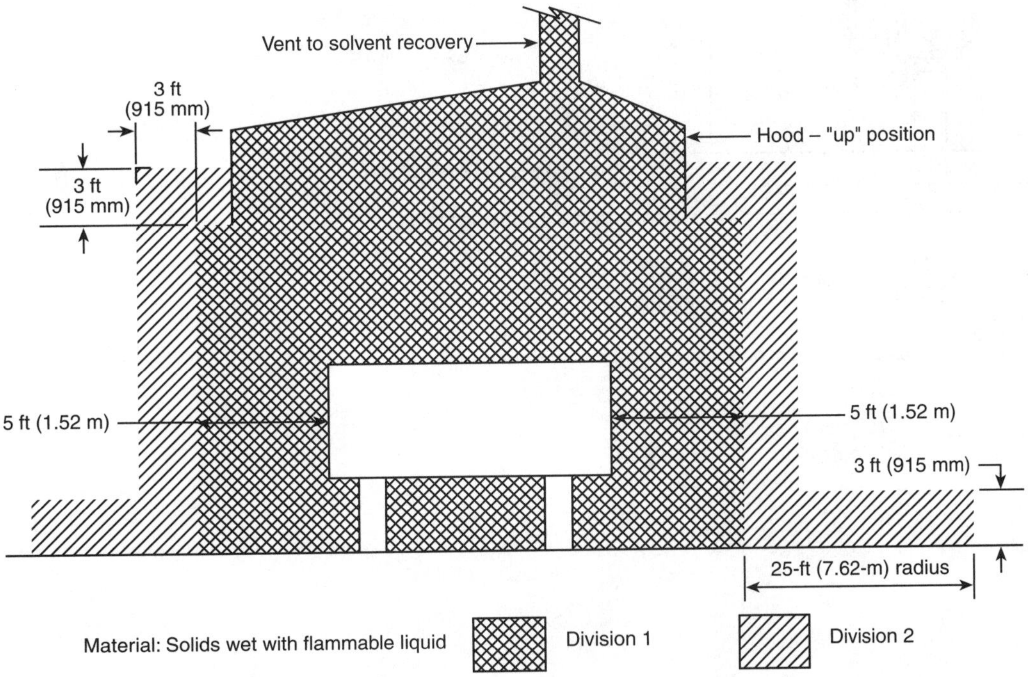

Figure 3-8.18 Plate and frame filter press provided with adequate ventilation.

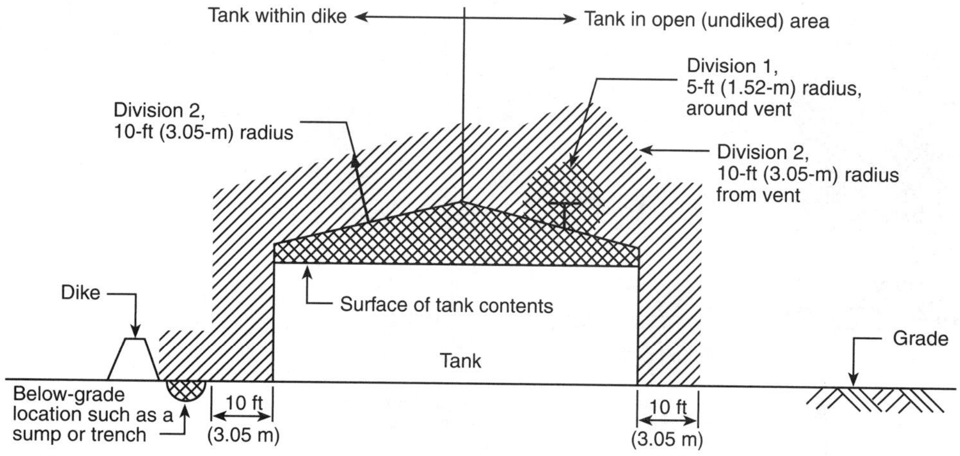

Material: Flammable liquid

	Small/low	Moderate	Large/high
Process equipment size		X	X
Pressure			X
Flow rate		X	X

Division 1

Division 2

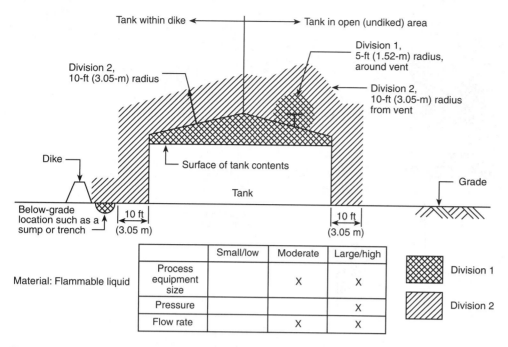

Figure 3-8.19 Storage tanks outdoors, at grade.

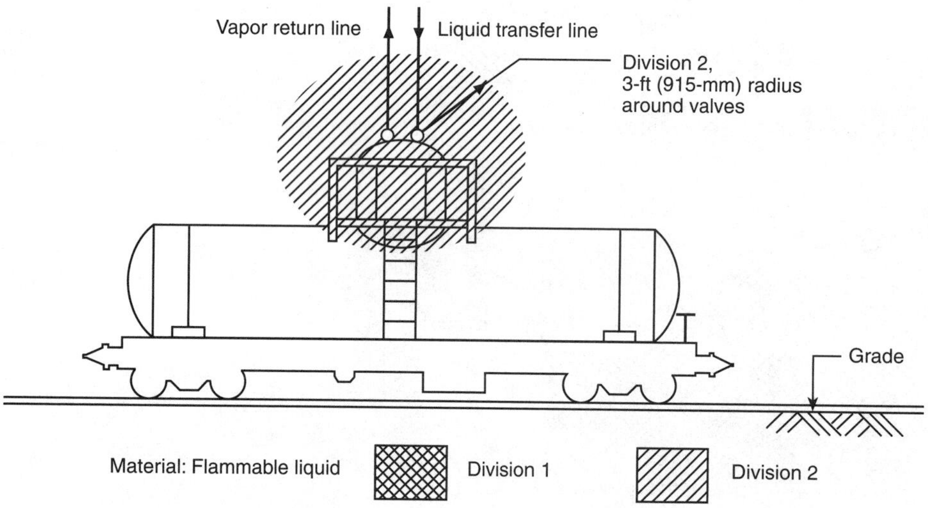

Figure 3-8.20 Tank car loading and unloading via closed system. Transfer through dome only.

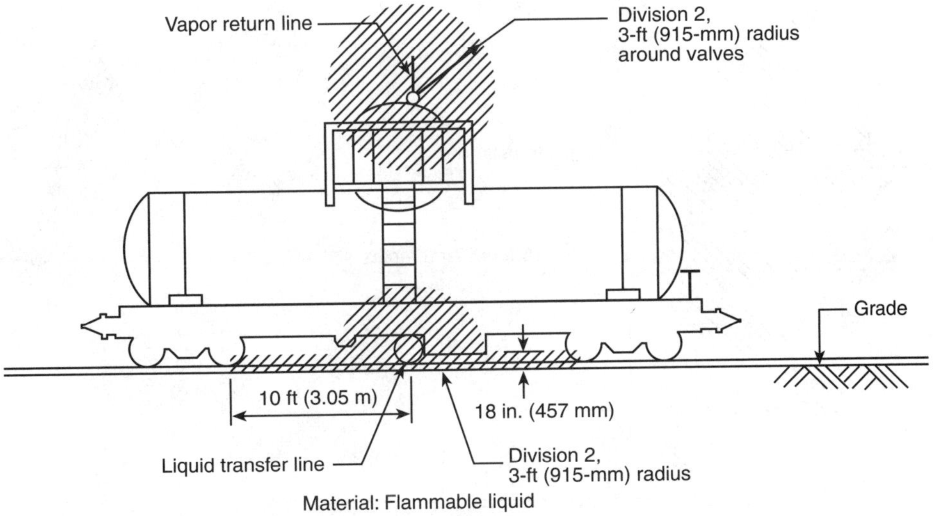

Figure 3-8.21(a) **Tank car loading and unloading via closed system. Bottom product transfer only.**

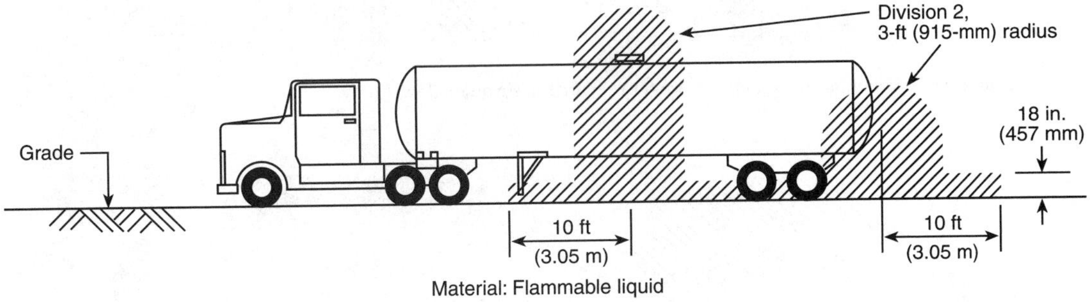

Figure 3-8.21(b) **Tank truck loading and unloading via closed system.**

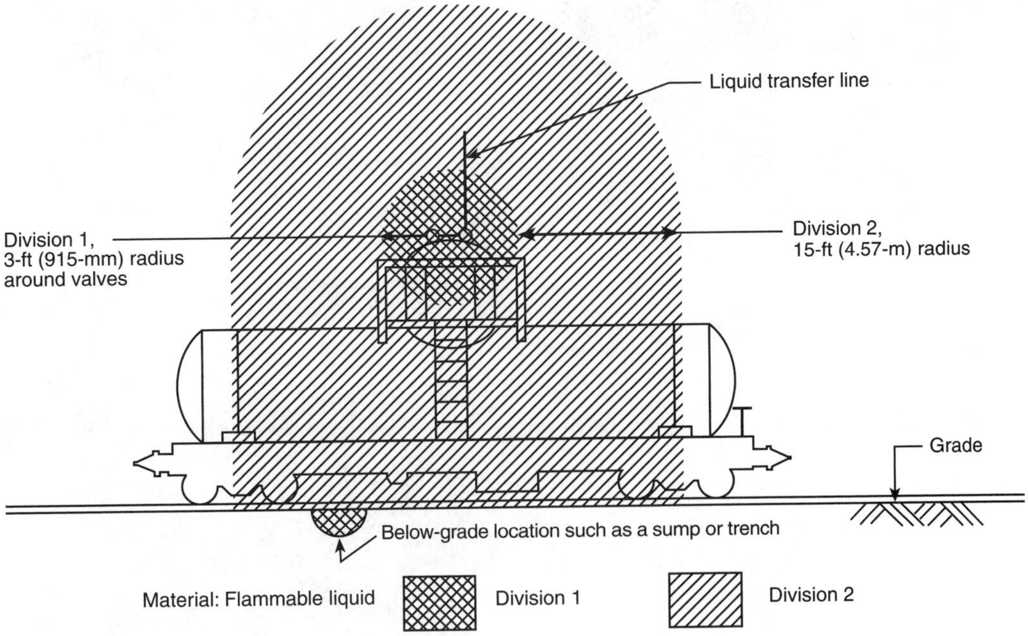

Figure 3-8.22 **Tank car/tank truck loading and unloading via open system. Top or bottom product transfer.**

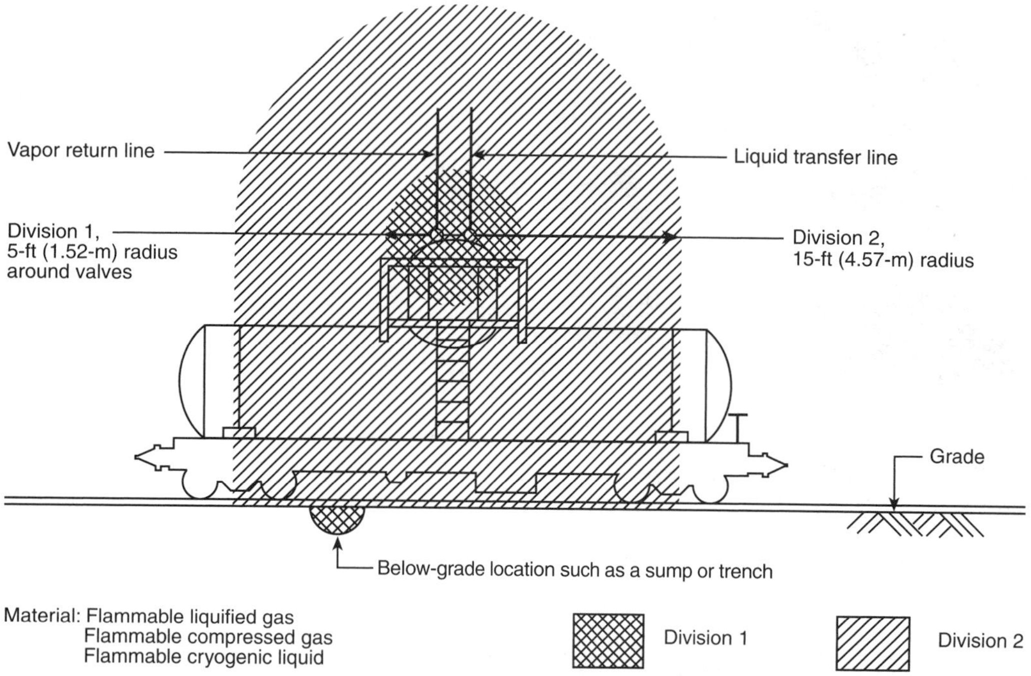

Figure 3-8.23 Tank car/tank truck loading and unloading via closed system. Transfer through dome only.

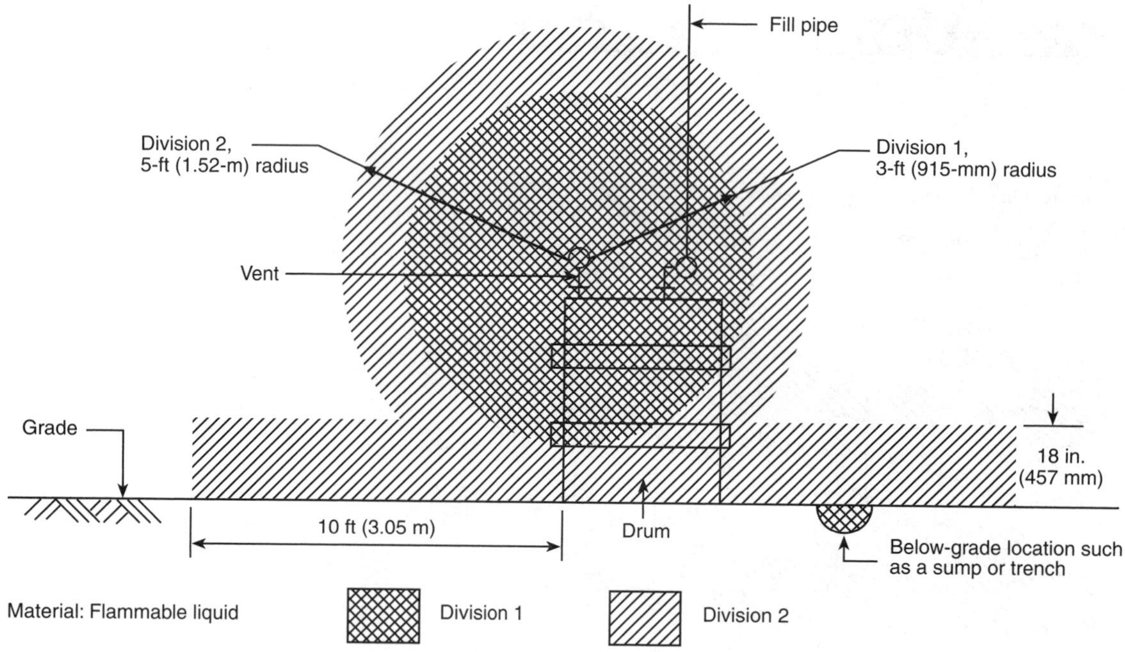

Figure 3-8.24 Drum filling station, outdoors or indoors with adequate ventilation.

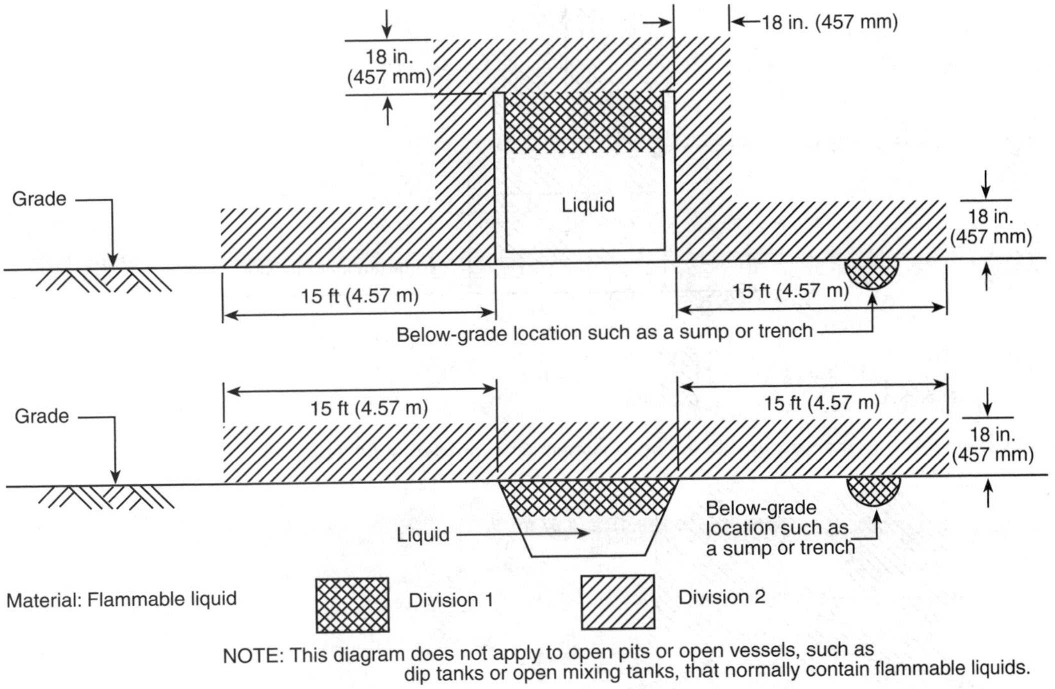

Figure 3-8.25 Emergency impounding basin or oil/water separator (top) and emergency or temporary drainage ditch or oil/water separator (bottom).

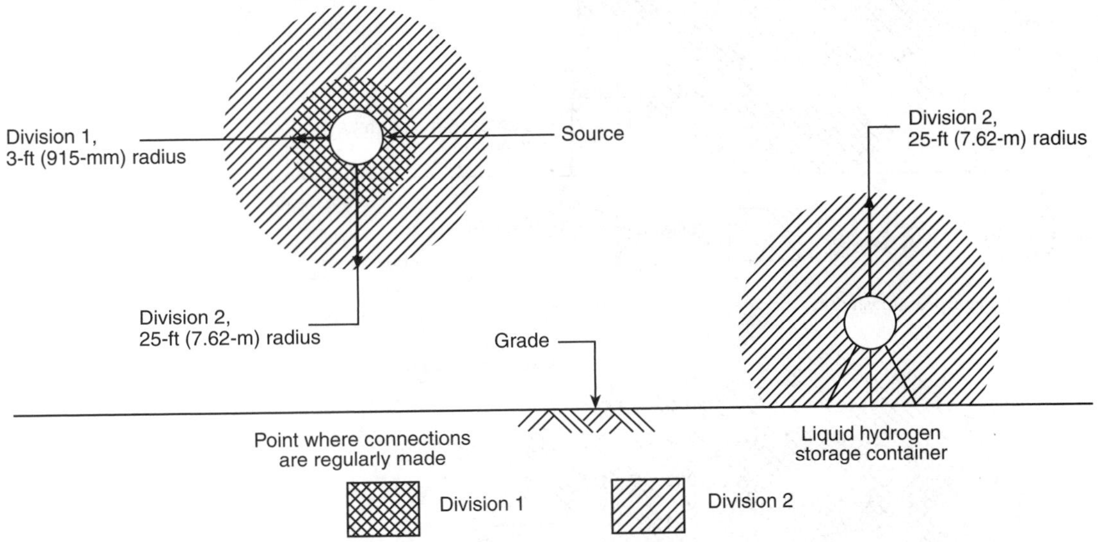

Figure 3-8.26 Liquid hydrogen storage located outdoors or in an adequately ventilated building.

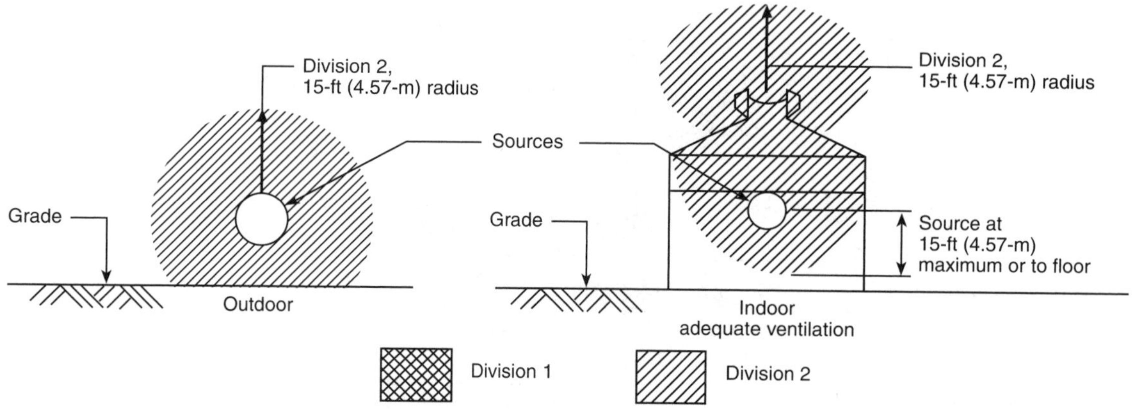

Figure 3-8.27 Gaseous hydrogen storage located outdoors, or indoors in an adequately ventilated building.

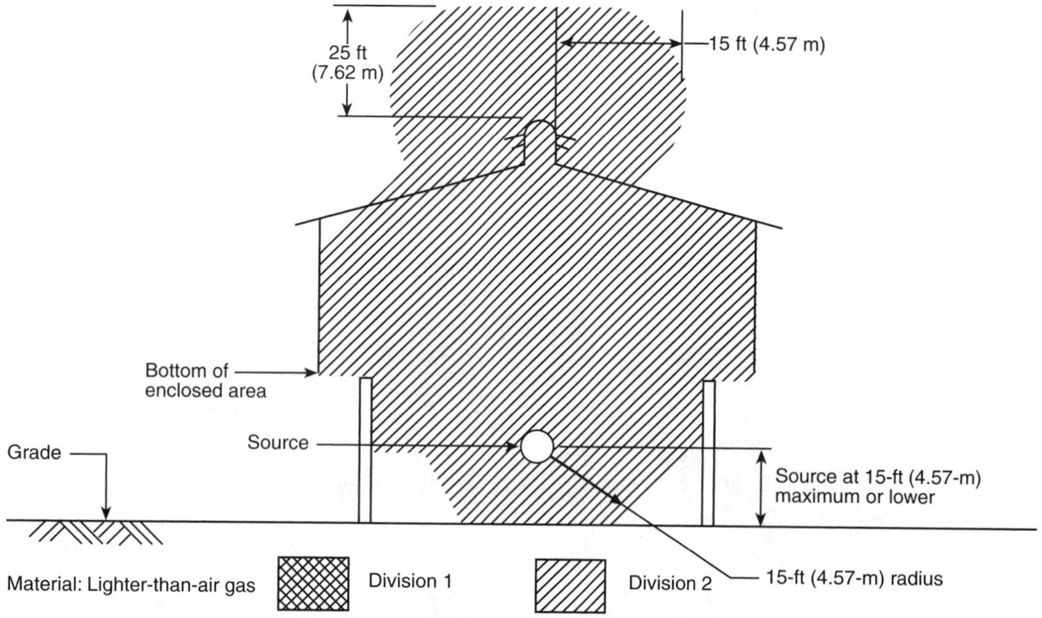

Figure 3-8.28 Adequately ventilated compressor shelter.

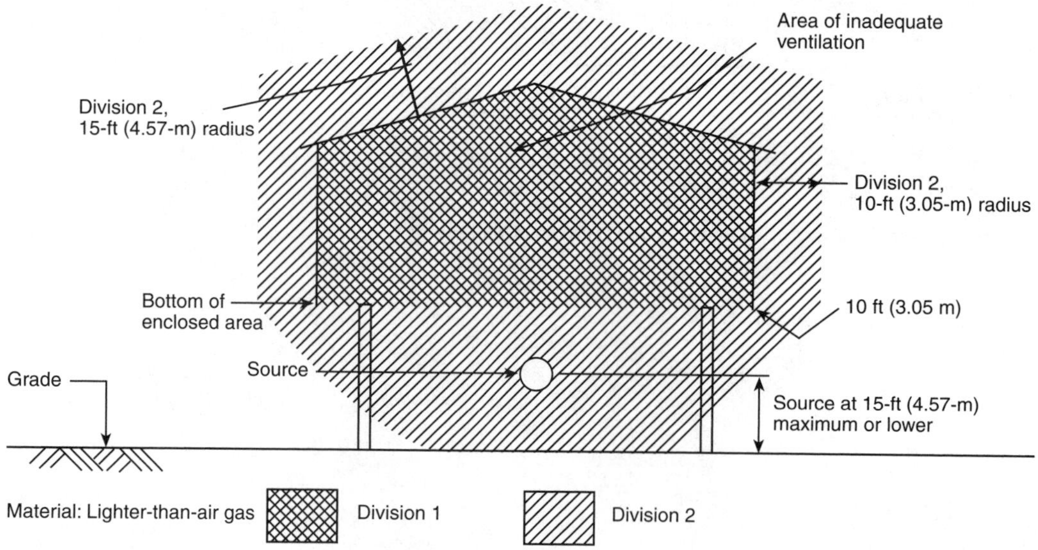

Figure 3-8.29 Inadequately ventilated compressor shelter.

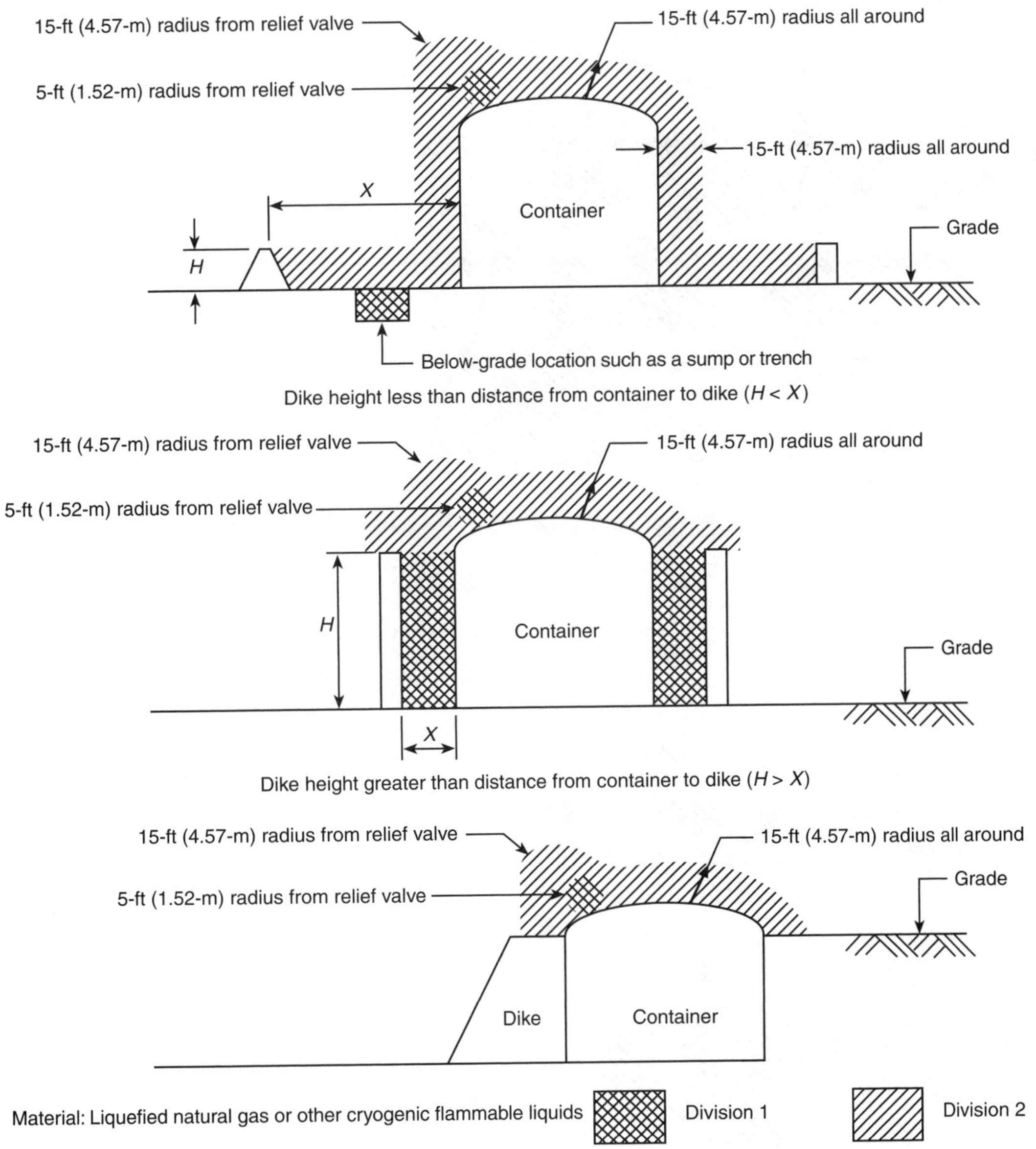
15-ft (4.57-m) radius from relief valve
15-ft (4.57-m) radius all around
5-ft (1.52-m) radius from relief valve
15-ft (4.57-m) radius all around
X
Container
Grade
H
Below-grade location such as a sump or trench
Dike height less than distance from container to dike (H < X)
15-ft (4.57-m) radius from relief valve
15-ft (4.57-m) radius all around
5-ft (1.52-m) radius from relief valve
H
Container
Grade
X
Dike height greater than distance from container to dike (H > X)
15-ft (4.57-m) radius from relief valve
15-ft (4.57-m) radius all around
Grade
5-ft (1.52-m) radius from relief valve
Dike
Container
Material: Liquefied natural gas or other cryogenic flammable liquids
Division 1
Division 2

Figure 3-8.30 Storage tanks for cryogenic liquids.

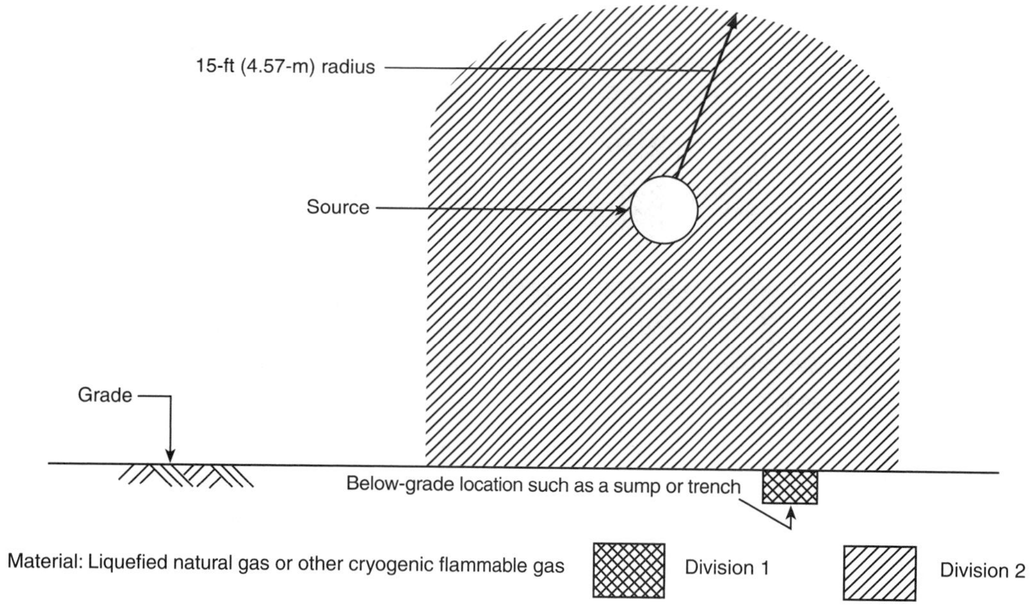

Figure 3-8.31 Leakage source from equipment handling liquefied natural gas. Source is located outdoors, at or above grade.

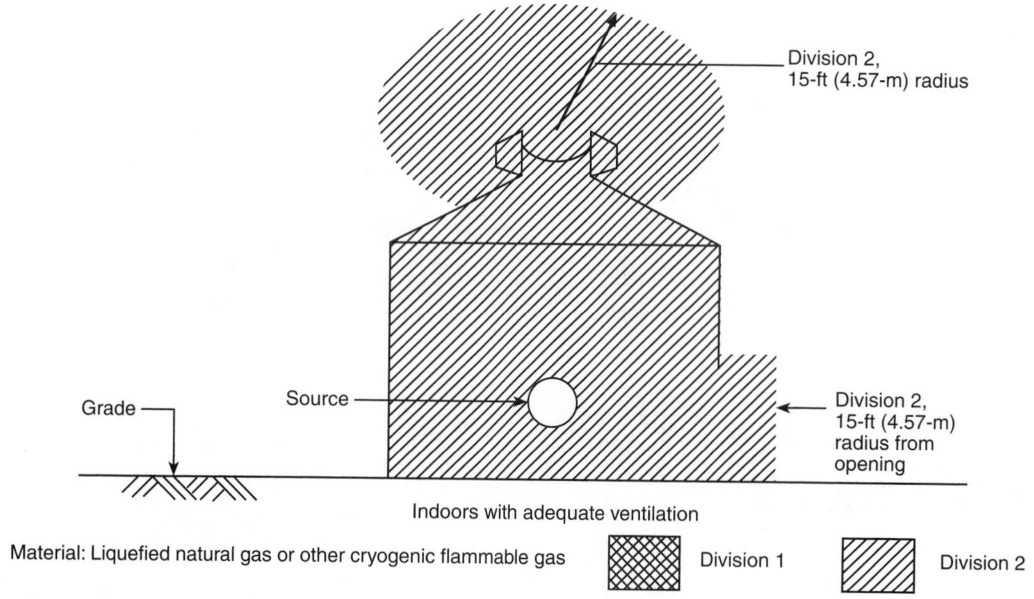

Figure 3-8.32 Leakage source from equipment handling liquefied natural gas in an adequately ventilated building.

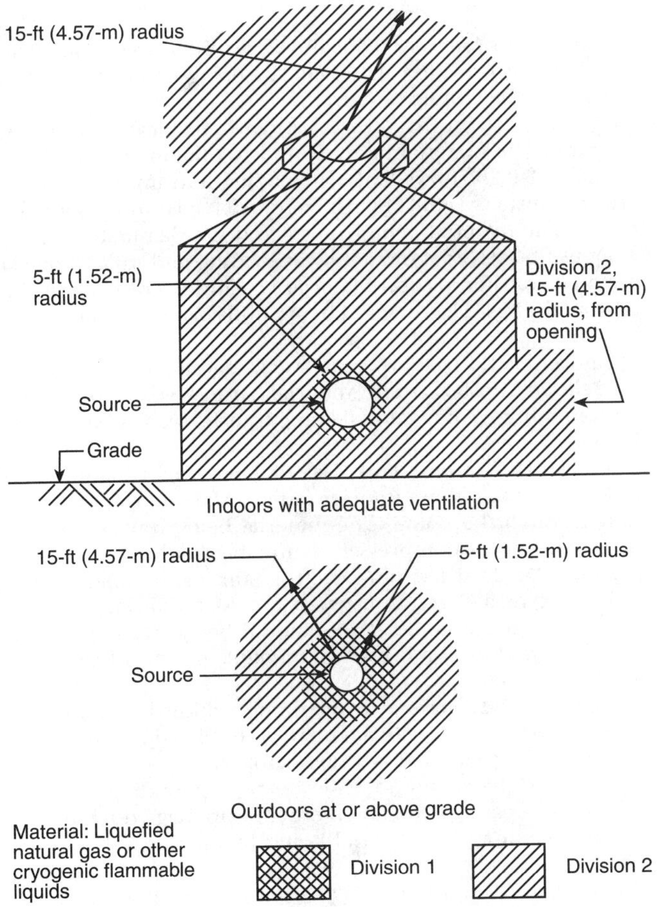

Figure 3-8.33 Leakage source from routinely operating bleeds, equipment handling liquefied natural gas in an adequately ventilated building.

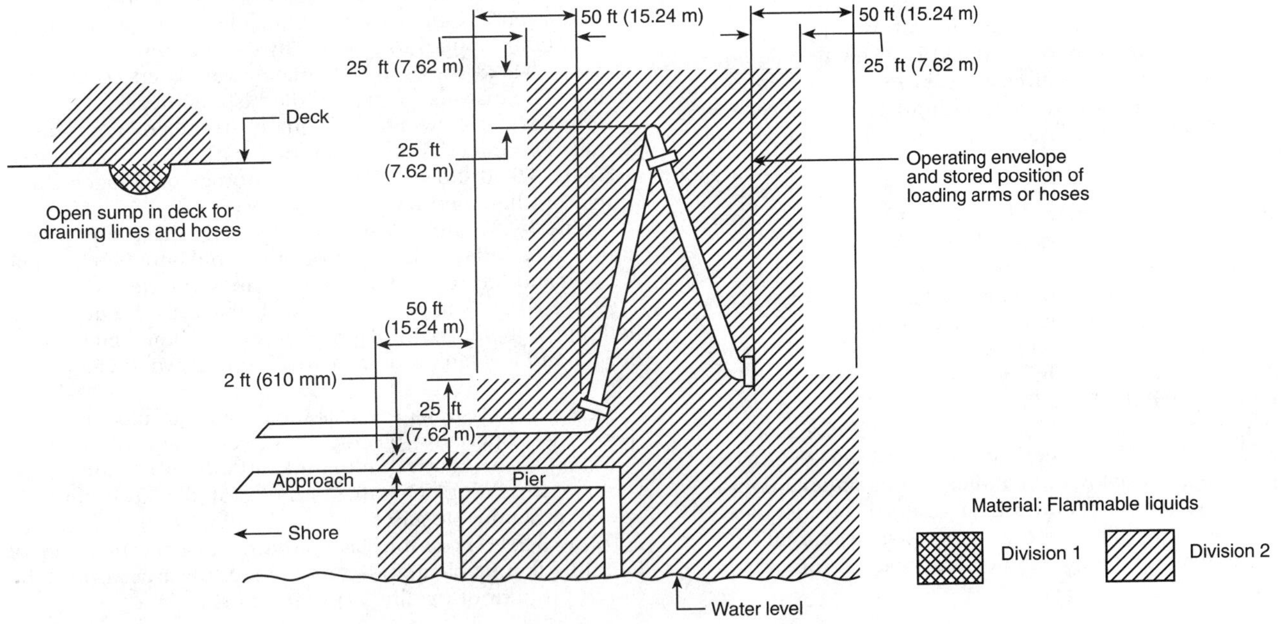

NOTES:
1. The "source of vapor" shall be the operating envelope and stored position of the outboard flange connection of the loading arm (or hose).
2. The berth area adjacent to tanker and barge cargo tanks is to be Division 2 to the following extent:
   (a) 25 ft (7.62 m) horizontally in all directions on the pier side from that portion of the hull containing cargo tanks.
   (b) From the water level to 25 ft (7.62 m) above the cargo tanks at their highest position.
3. Additional locations may have to be classified as required by the presence of other sources of flammable liquids or by Coast Guard or other regulations.

Figure 3-8.34 Marine terminal handling flammable liquids.

3-9 Classification Diagrams for Zones. Class I, Zone diagrams include Figures 3-9.1 through 3-9.34. Table 3-8 provides a summary of where each diagram is intended to apply.

Figure 3-9.1 shows a source of leakage located outdoors, at grade. The material being handled is a flammable liquid.

Figure 3-9.2 shows a source of leakage located outdoors, above grade. The material being handled is a flammable liquid.

Figure 3-9.3 shows a source of leakage located indoors, at floor level. Adequate ventilation is provided. The material being handled is a flammable liquid.

Figure 3-9.4 shows a source of leakage located indoors, above floor level. Adequate ventilation is provided. The material being handled is a flammable liquid.

Figure 3-9.5 shows a source of leakage located indoors, at floor level, adjacent to an opening in an exterior wall. Adequate ventilation is provided. The material being handled is a flammable liquid.

Figure 3-9.6 shows a source of leakage located indoors, at floor level, adjacent to an opening in an exterior wall. Ventilation is not adequate. The material being handled is a flammable liquid.

Figure 3-9.7 shows a source of leakage located outdoors, at grade. The material being handled may be a flammable liquid or a liquefied or compressed flammable gas, or a flammable cryogenic liquid.

Figure 3-9.8 shows a source of leakage located outdoors, above grade. The material being handled may be a flammable liquid or liquefied or compressed flammable gas, or a flammable cryogenic liquid.

Figure 3-9.9 shows a source of leakage located outdoors, at grade. The material being handled is a flammable liquid

Figure 3-9.10 shows a source of leakage located outdoors, above grade. The material being handled is a flammable liquid.

Figure 3-9.11 shows a source of leakage located indoors, adjacent to an opening in an exterior wall. Ventilation is not adequate. The material being handled is flammable liquid.

Figure 3-9.12 shows a source of leakage located indoors, adjacent to an opening in an exterior wall. Adequate ventilation is provided. The material being handled is a flammable liquid.

Figure 3-9.13 shows multiple sources of leakage, located both at grade and above grade, in an outdoor process area. The material being handled is a flammable liquid.

Figure 3-9.14 shows multiple sources of leakage, located both at grade and above grade, in an outdoor process area. The material being handled is a flammable liquid.

Figure 3-9.15 shows multiple sources of leakage, located both at and above grade, in an outdoor process area. The material being handled is a flammable liquid.

Figure 3-9.16 shows multiple sources of leakage, located both at and above floor level, in an adequately ventilated building. The material being handled is a flammable liquid.

Figure 3-9.17 shows a product dryer located in an adequately ventilated building. The product dryer system is totally enclosed. The material being handled is a solid wet with a flammable liquid.

Figure 3-9.18 shows a plate and frame filter press. Adequate ventilation is provided. The material being handled is a solid wet with a flammable liquid.

Figure 3-9.19 shows a product storage tank located outdoors, at grade. The material being stored is a flammable liquid.

Figure 3-9.20 shows tank car loading and unloading via a closed transfer system. Material is transferred only through the dome. The material being transferred is a flammable liquid.

Figure 3-9.21(a) shows tank car loading and unloading via a closed transfer system. Material is transferred through the bottom fittings. The material being transferred is a flammable liquid.

Figure 3-9.21(b) shows tank truck loading and unloading via a closed transfer system. Material is transferred through the bottom fittings. The material being transferred is a flammable liquid.

Figure 3-9.22 shows tank car (or tank truck) loading and unloading via an open transfer system. Material is transferred only through the dome. The material being transferred can be a liquefied or compressed flammable liquid.

Figure 3-9.23 shows tank car (or tank truck) loading and unloading via a closed transfer system. Material is transferred only through the dome. The material being transferred can be a liquefied or compressed flammable gas or a flammable cryogenic liquid.

Figure 3-9.24 shows a drum filling station located either outdoors or indoors in an adequately ventilated building. The material being handled is a flammable liquid.

Figure 3-9.25 shows an emergency impounding basin or oil/ water separator and an emergency drainage ditch or oil/ water separator. The material being handled is a flammable liquid.

Figure 3-9.26 shows a liquid hydrogen storage located outdoors or indoors in an adequately ventilated building. This diagram applies to liquid hydrogen only.

Figure 3-9.27 shows a gaseous hydrogen storage located outdoors, or indoors in an adequately ventilated building. This diagram applies to gaseous hydrogen only.

Figure 3-9.28 shows an adequately ventilated compressor shelter. The material being handled is a lighter-than-air gas.

Figure 3-9.29 shows an inadequately ventilated compressor shelter. The material being handled is a lighter-than-air gas.

Figure 3-9.30 shows tanks for the storage of cryogenic and other cold liquefied flammable gases.

Figure 3-9.31 shows a source of leakage from equipment handling liquefied natural gas or other cold liquefied flammable gas, and located outdoors, at or above grade.

Figure 3-9.32 shows a source of leakage from equipment handling liquefied natural gas or other cold liquefied flammable gas and located indoors in an adequately ventilated building.

Figure 3-9.33 shows the classified zones around liquefied natural gas operating bleeds, drips, vents, and drains both outdoors, at or above grade, and indoors in an adequately ventilated building. This diagram also applies to other cold liquefied flammable gases.

Figure 3-9.34 shows the classified zones at a marine terminal handling flammable liquids and includes the area around the stored position of loading arms and hoses.

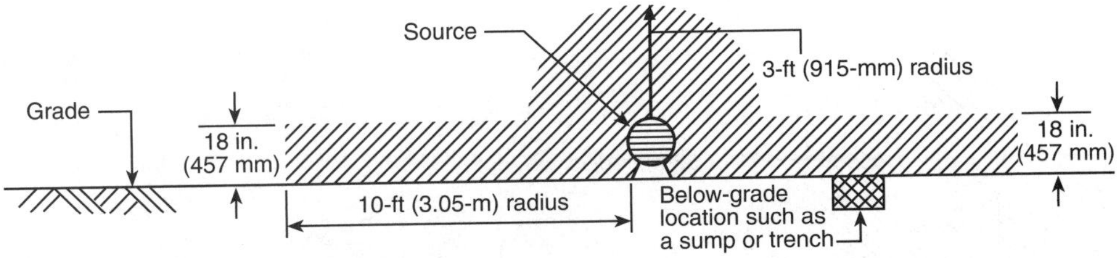

Material: Flammable liquid

	Small/low	Moderate	Large/high
Process equipment size	X	X	
Pressure	X	X	
Flow rate	X	X	

Zone 1

Zone 2

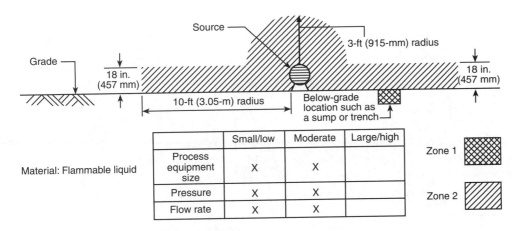

Figure 3-9.1 Leakage source located outdoors, at grade.

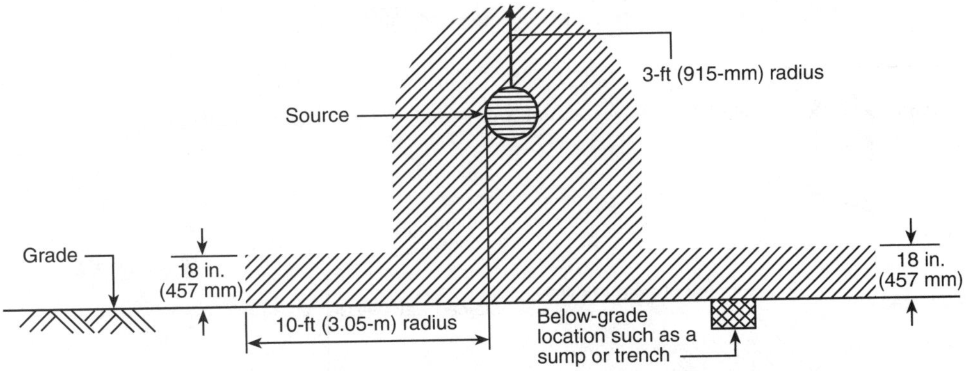

Material: Flammable liquid

	Small/low	Moderate	Large/high
Process equipment size	X	X	
Pressure	X	X	
Flow rate	X	X	

Zone 1

Zone 2

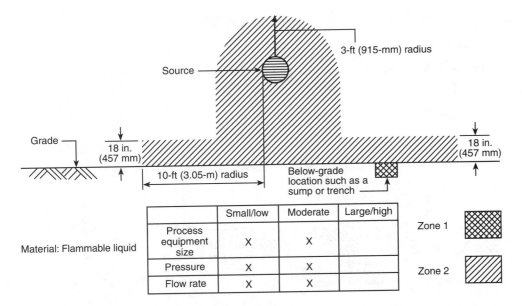

Figure 3-9.2 Leakage source located outdoors, above grade.

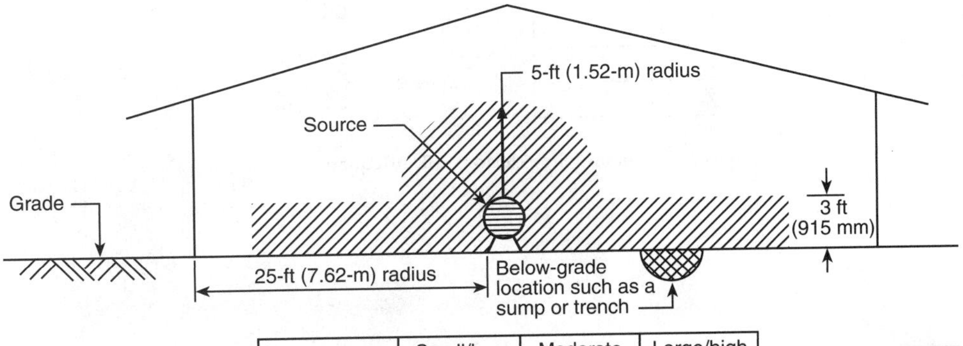

Material: Flammable liquid

	Small/low	Moderate	Large/high
Process equipment size	X	X	
Pressure	X	X	
Flow rate	X	X	

Zone 1

Zone 2

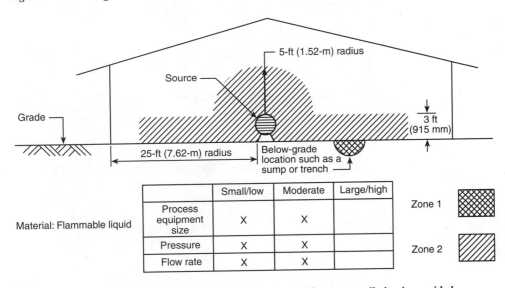

Figure 3-9.3 Leakage source located indoors, at floor level. Adequate ventilation is provided.

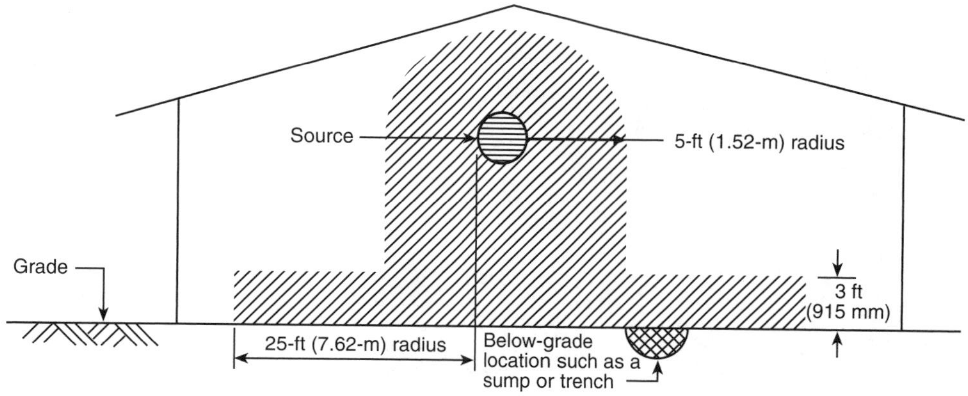

Material: Flammable liquid

	Small/low	Moderate	Large/high
Process equipment size	X	X	
Pressure	X	X	
Flow rate	X	X	

Zone 1

Zone 2

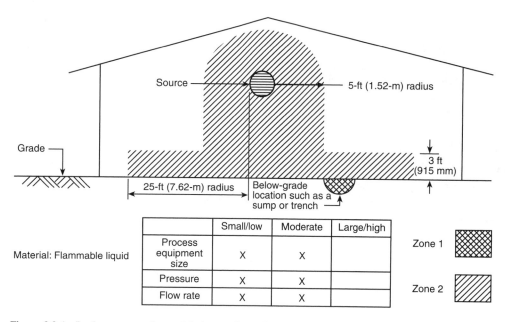

Figure 3-9.4 Leakage source located indoors, above floor level. Adequate ventilation is provided.

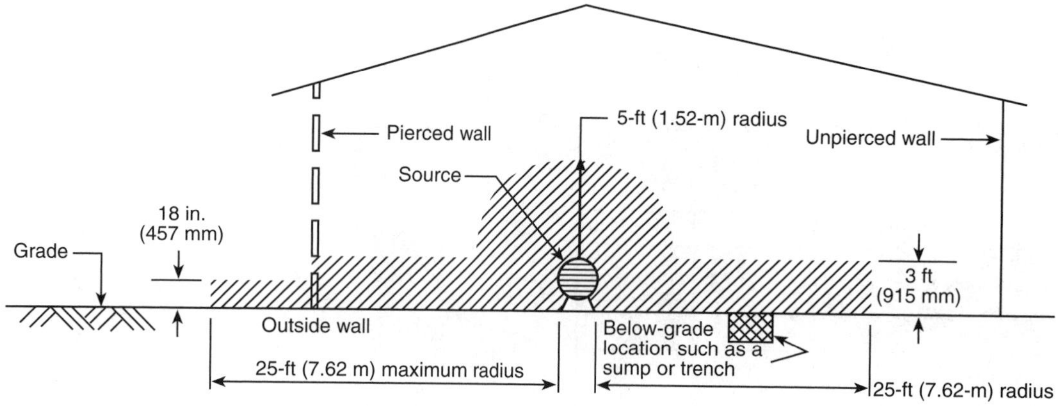

Material: Flammable liquid

	Small/low	Moderate	Large/high
Process equipment size	X	X	
Pressure	X	X	
Flow rate	X	X	

Zone 1

Zone 2

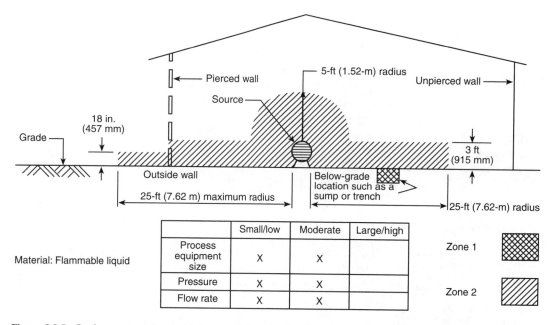

Figure 3-9.5 Leakage source located indoors, at floor level, adjacent to opening in exterior wall. Adequate ventilation is provided.

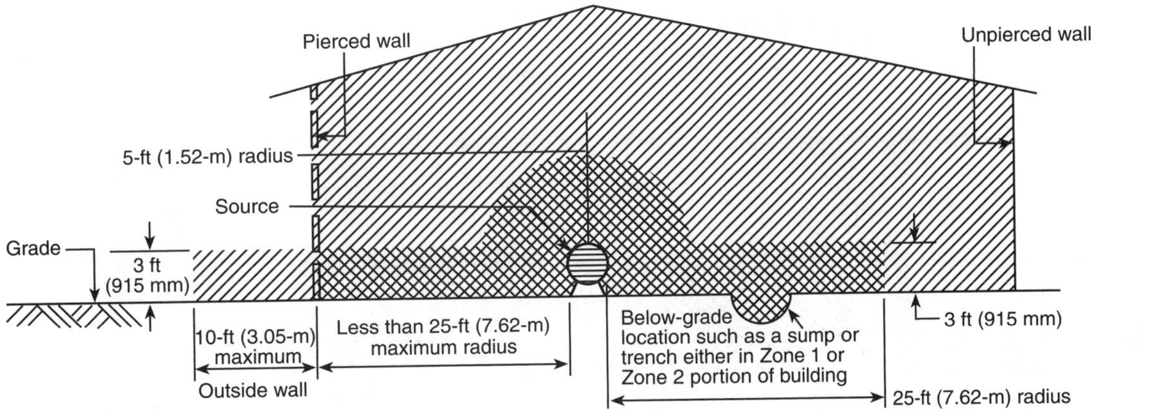

NOTE: If building is small compared to size of equipment and leakage can fill the building, the entire building interior is classified Zone 1.

Material: Flammable liquid

	Small/low	Moderate	Large/high
Process equipment size	X	X	
Pressure	X	X	
Flow rate	X	X	

Zone 1 (cross-hatched); Zone 2 (hatched)

Figure 3-9.6 Leakage source located indoors, at floor level, adjacent to opening in exterior wall. Adequate ventilation is not provided.

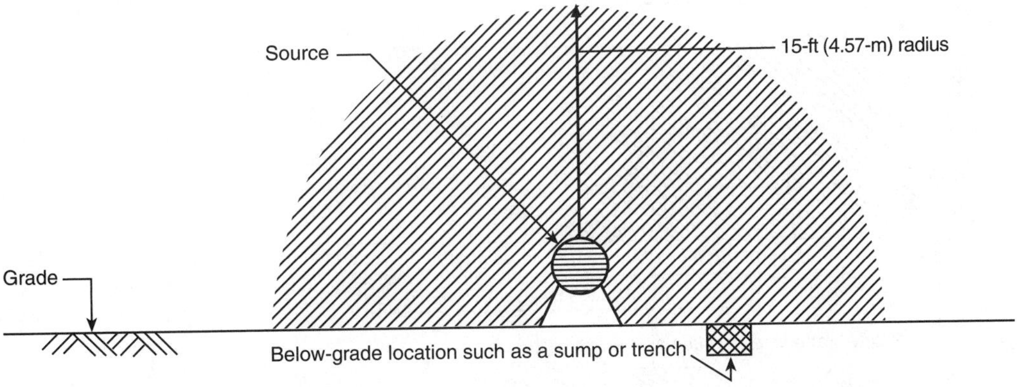

Material: Flammable liquid, liquefied flammable gas, compressed flammable gas and cryogenic liquid

	Small/low	Moderate	Large/high
Process equipment size	X	X	
Pressure		X	X
Flow rate	X	X	

Zone 1 (cross-hatched); Zone 2 (hatched)

Figure 3-9.7 Leakage source located outdoors, at grade.

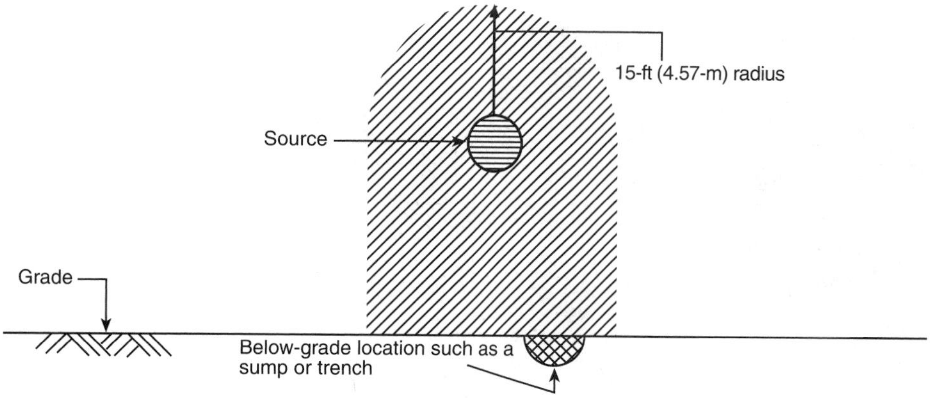

Material: Flammable liquid, liquefied flammable gas, compressed flammable gas, and cryogenic liquid

	Small/low	Moderate	Large/high
Process equipment size	X	X	
Pressure		X	X
Flow rate	X	X	

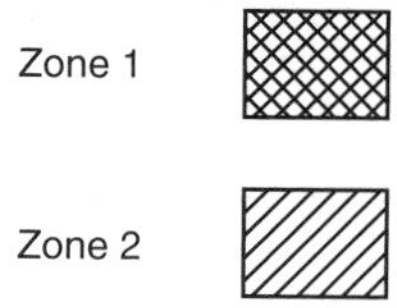

Figure 3-9.8 Leakage source located outdoors, above grade.

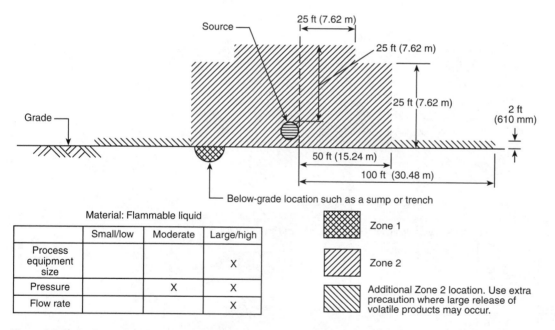

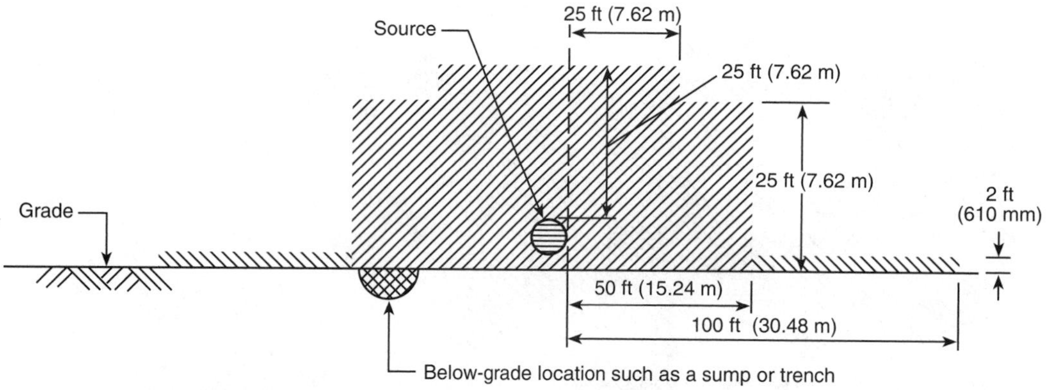

Material: Flammable liquid

	Small/low	Moderate	Large/high
Process equipment size			X
Pressure		X	X
Flow rate			X

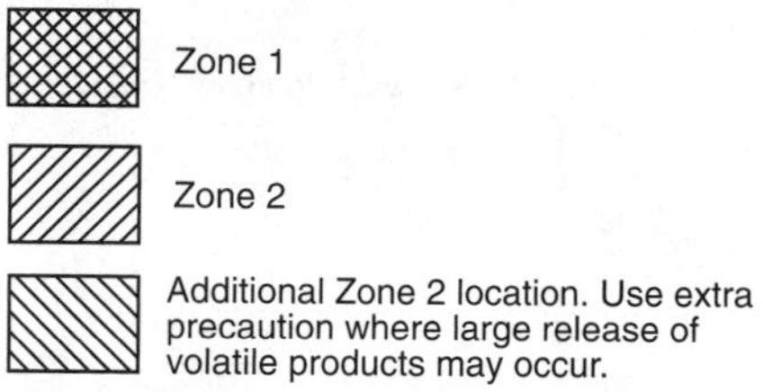

Figure 3-9.9 Leakage source located outdoors, at grade.

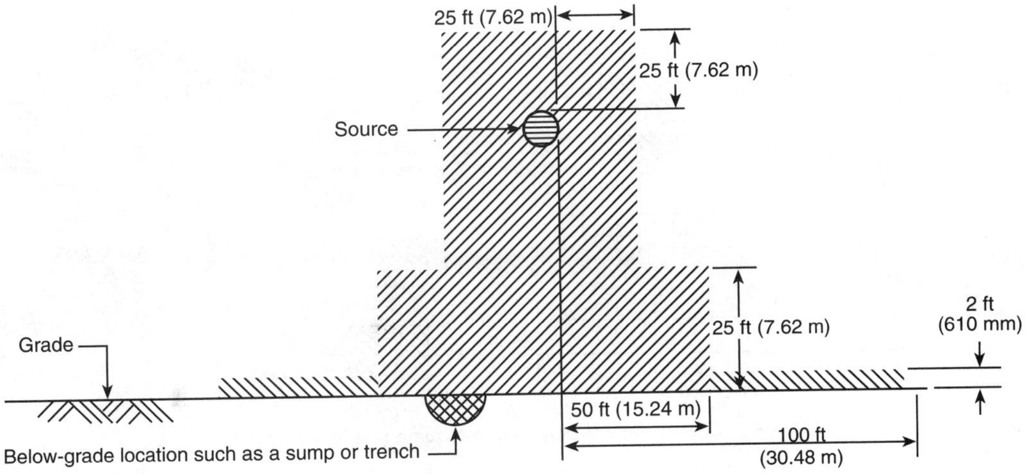

Material: Flammable liquid

	Small/low	Moderate	Large/high
Process equipment size			X
Pressure		X	X
Flow rate			X

Figure 3-9.10 Leakage source located outdoors, above grade.

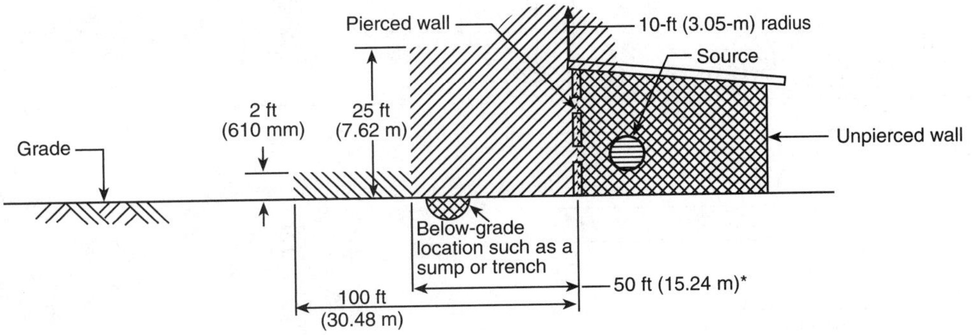

* "Apply" horizontal distances of 50 feet from the source of vapor or 10 feet beyond the perimeter of the building, whichever is greater, except that beyond unpierced vaportight walls the area in unclassified.

Material: Flammable liquid

	Small/low	Moderate	Large/high
Process equipment size		X	X
Pressure			X
Flow rate		X	X

Figure 3-9.11 Leakage source located indoors, adjacent to opening in exterior wall. Adequate ventilation is not provided.

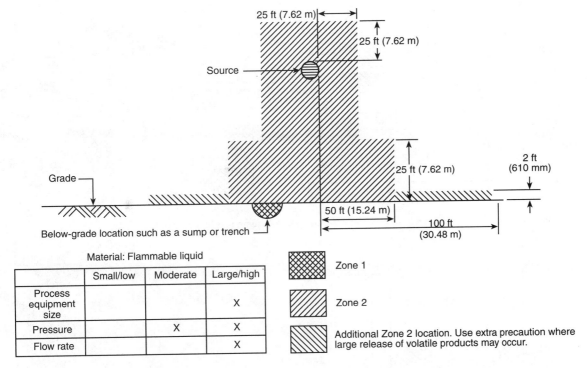

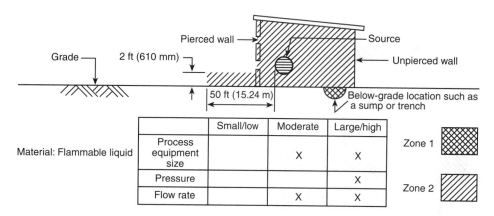

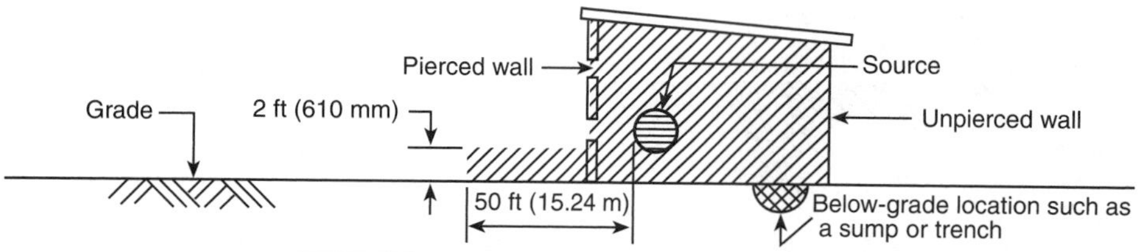

Material: Flammable liquid

	Small/low	Moderate	Large/high
Process equipment size		X	X
Pressure			X
Flow rate		X	X

Zone 1 (cross-hatched) · Zone 2 (hatched)

Figure 3-9.12 Leakage source located indoors, adjacent to opening in exterior wall. Adequate ventilation is provided.

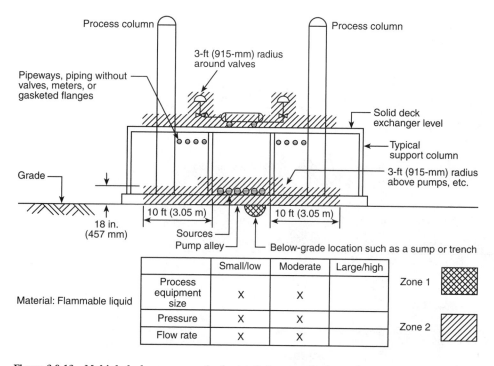

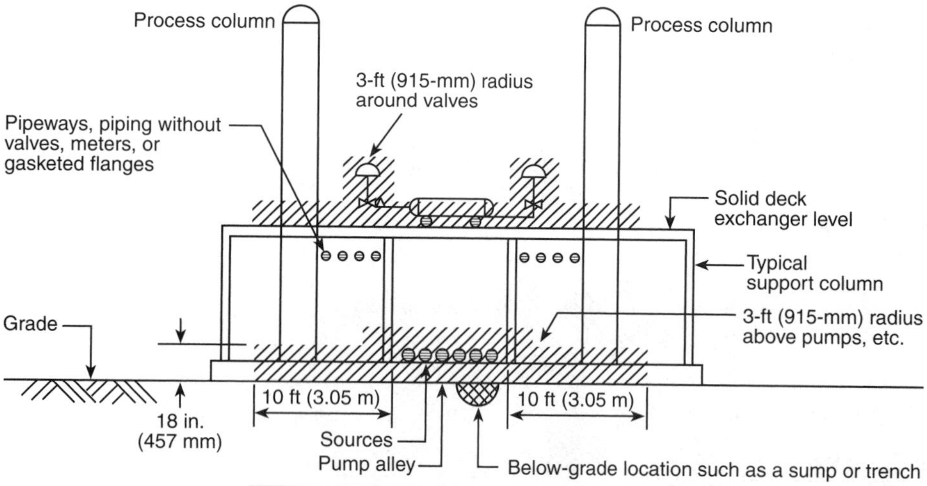

Material: Flammable liquid

	Small/low	Moderate	Large/high
Process equipment size	X	X	
Pressure	X	X	
Flow rate	X	X	

Zone 1 (cross-hatched) · Zone 2 (hatched)

Figure 3-9.13 Multiple leakage sources, both at and above grade, in outdoor process area.

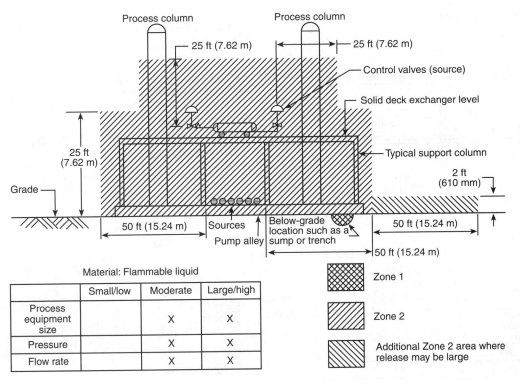

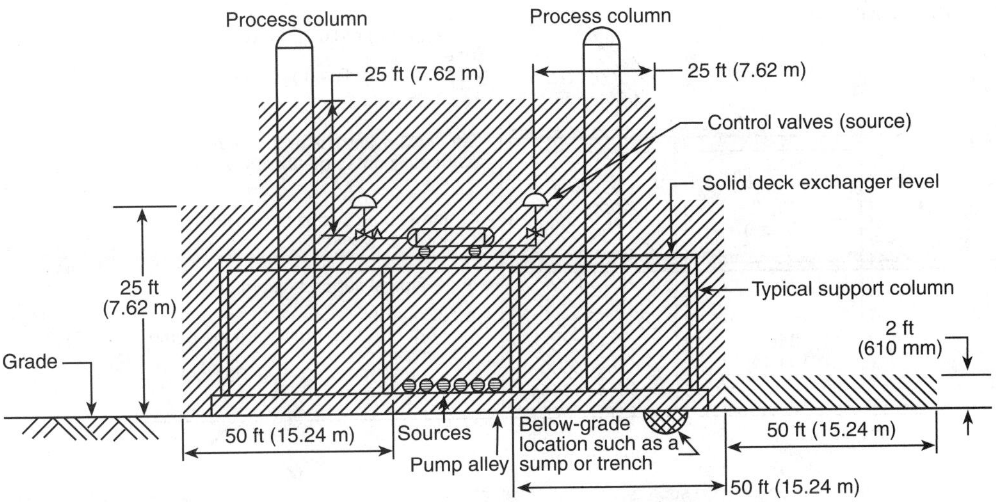

Material: Flammable liquid

	Small/low	Moderate	Large/high
Process equipment size		X	X
Pressure		X	X
Flow rate		X	X

Figure 3-9.14 Multiple leakage sources, both at and above grade, in outdoor process area.

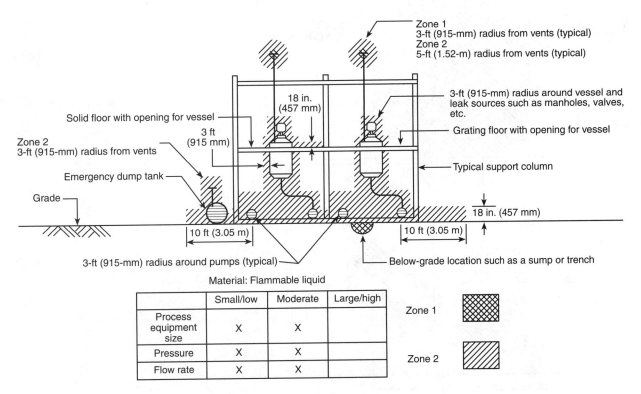

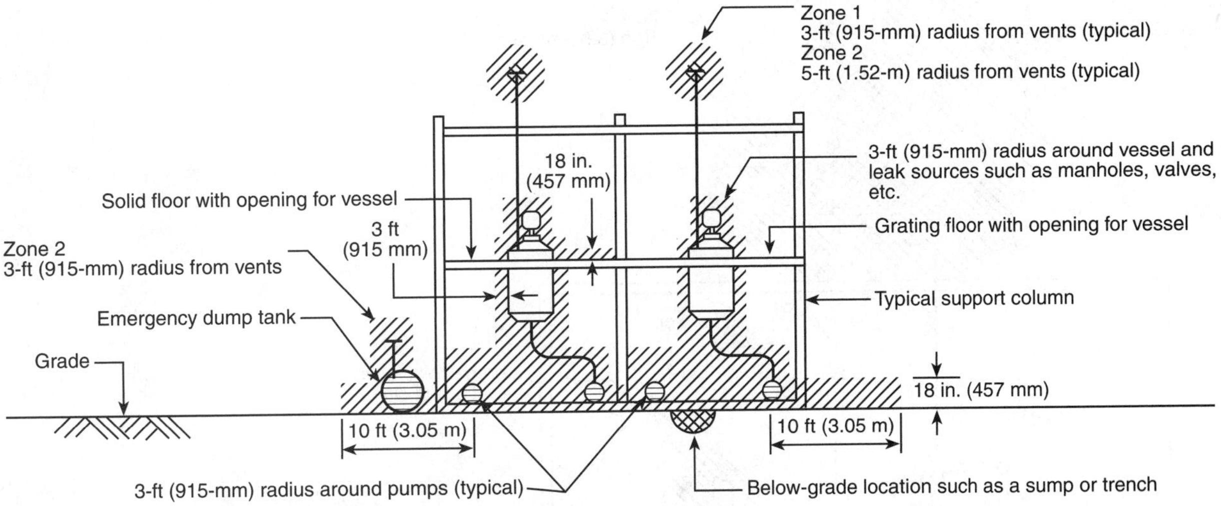

Material: Flammable liquid

	Small/low	Moderate	Large/high
Process equipment size	X	X	
Pressure	X	X	
Flow rate	X	X	

Figure 3-9.15 Multiple leakage sources, both at and above grade, in outdoor process area.

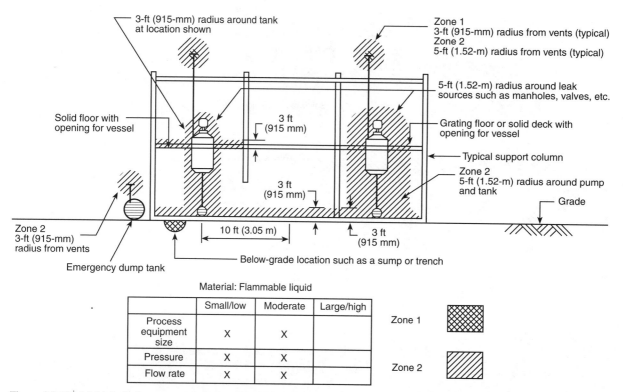

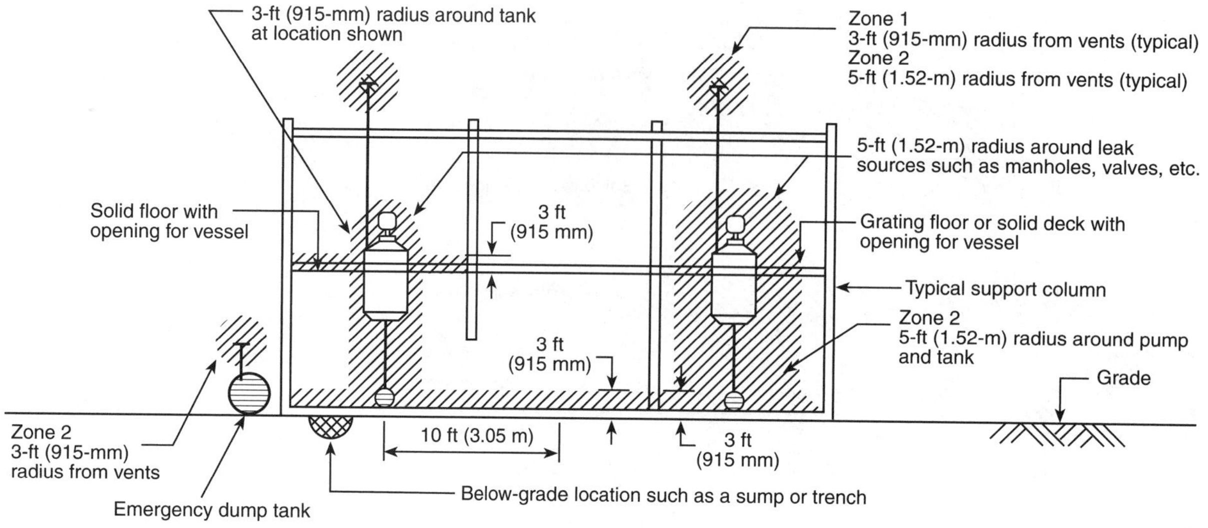

Material: Flammable liquid

	Small/low	Moderate	Large/high
Process equipment size	X	X	
Pressure	X	X	
Flow rate	X	X	

Zone 1 Zone 2

Figure 3-9.16 Multiple leakage sources, both at and above floor level, located indoors. Adequate ventilation is provided.

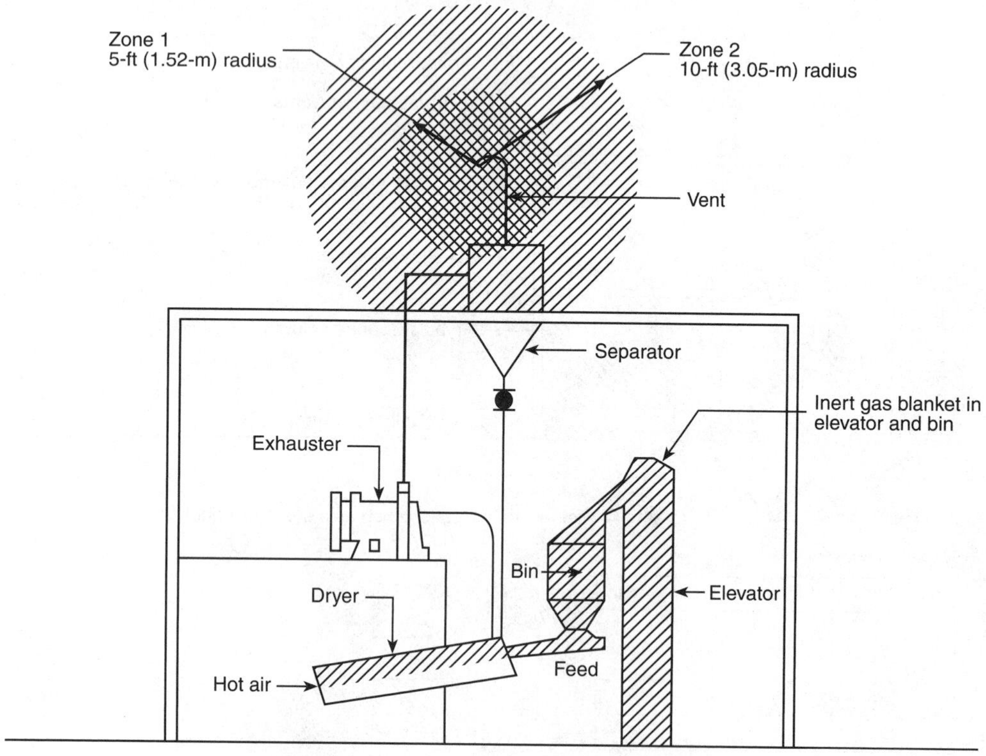

Figure 3-9.17 Totally enclosed product dryer located in adequately ventilated building.

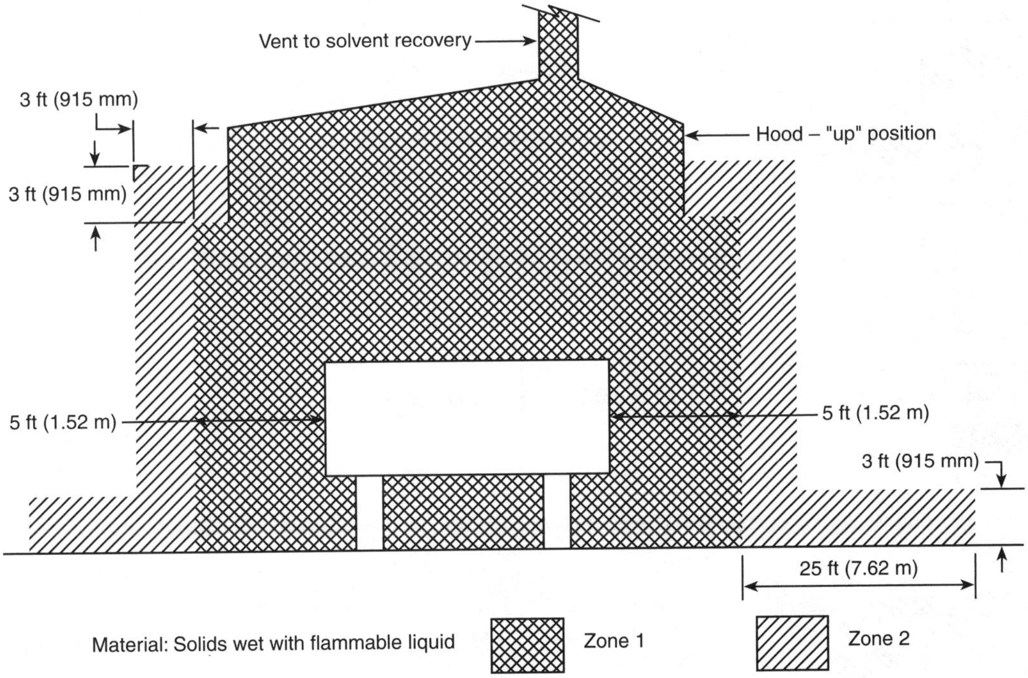

Figure 3-9.18 Plate and frame filter press provided with adequate ventilation.

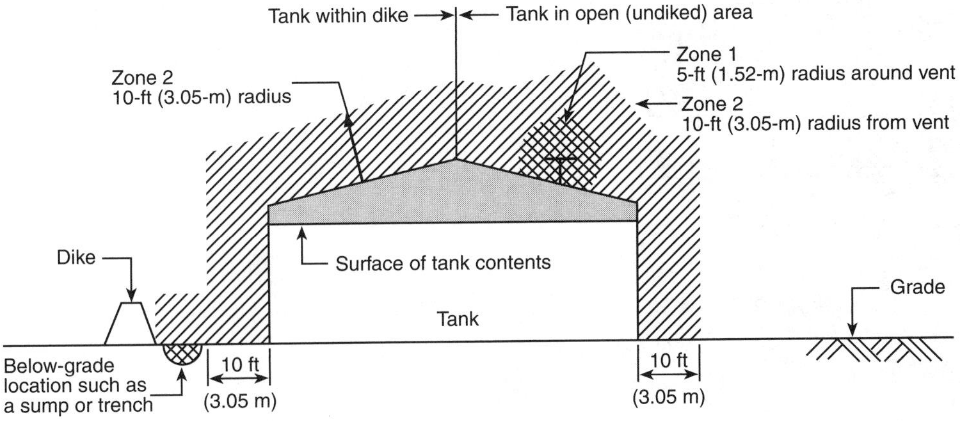

Material: Flammable liquid

	Small/low	Moderate	Large/high
Process equipment size		X	X
Pressure			X
Flow rate		X	X

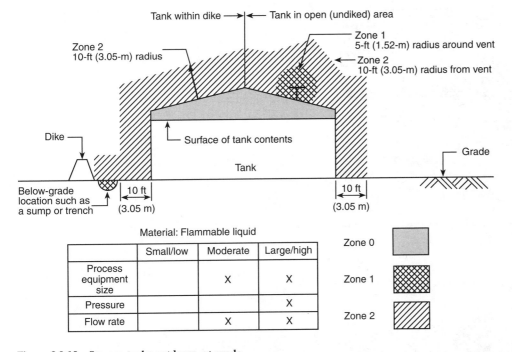

Figure 3-9.19 Storage tanks outdoors, at grade.

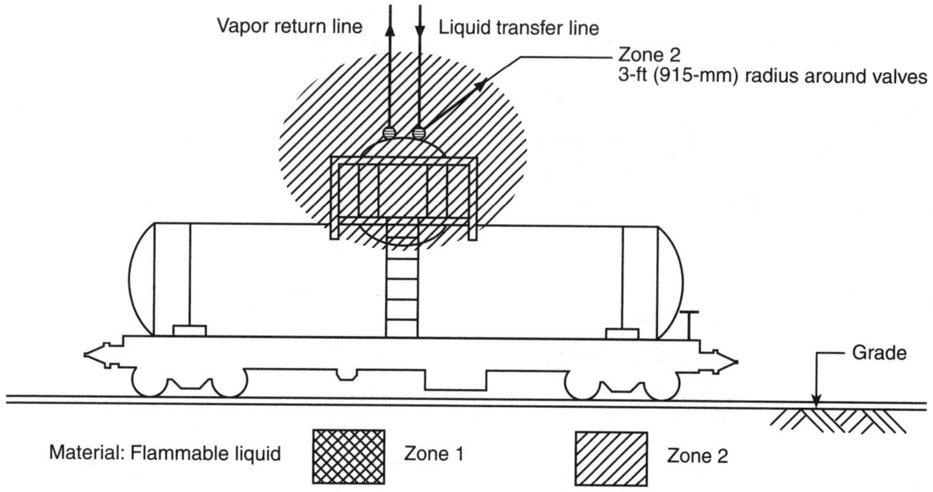

Figure 3-9.20 Tank car loading and unloading via closed system. Transfer through dome only.

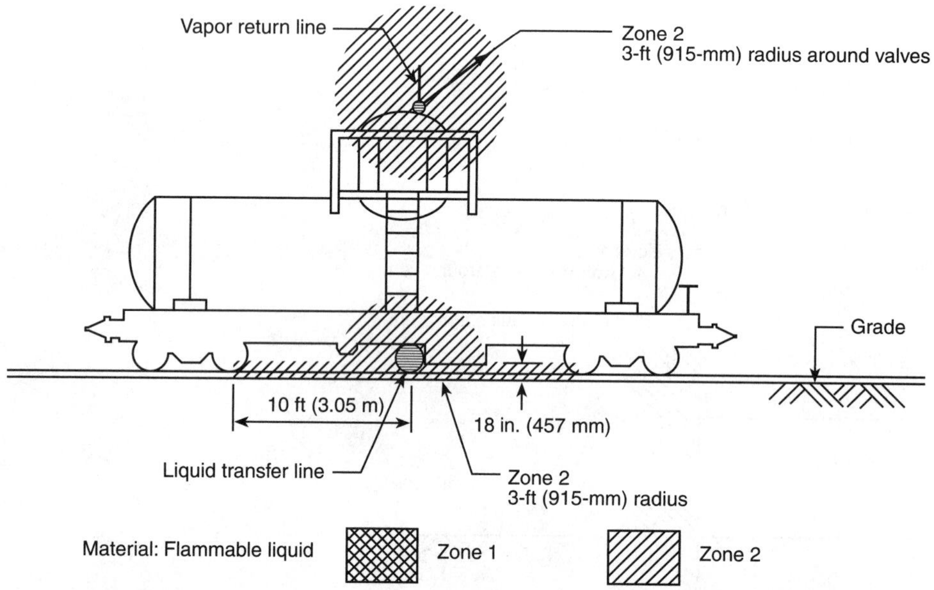

Figure 3-9.21(a) Tank car loading and unloading via closed system. Bottom product transfer only.

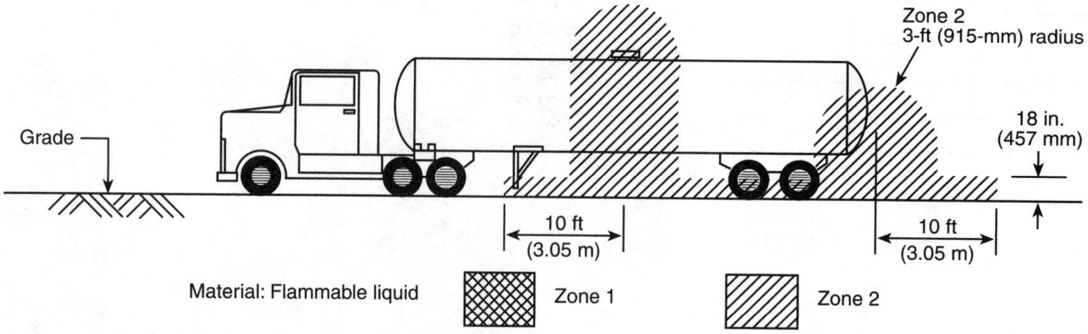

Figure 3-9.21(b) Tank truck loading and unloading via closed system.

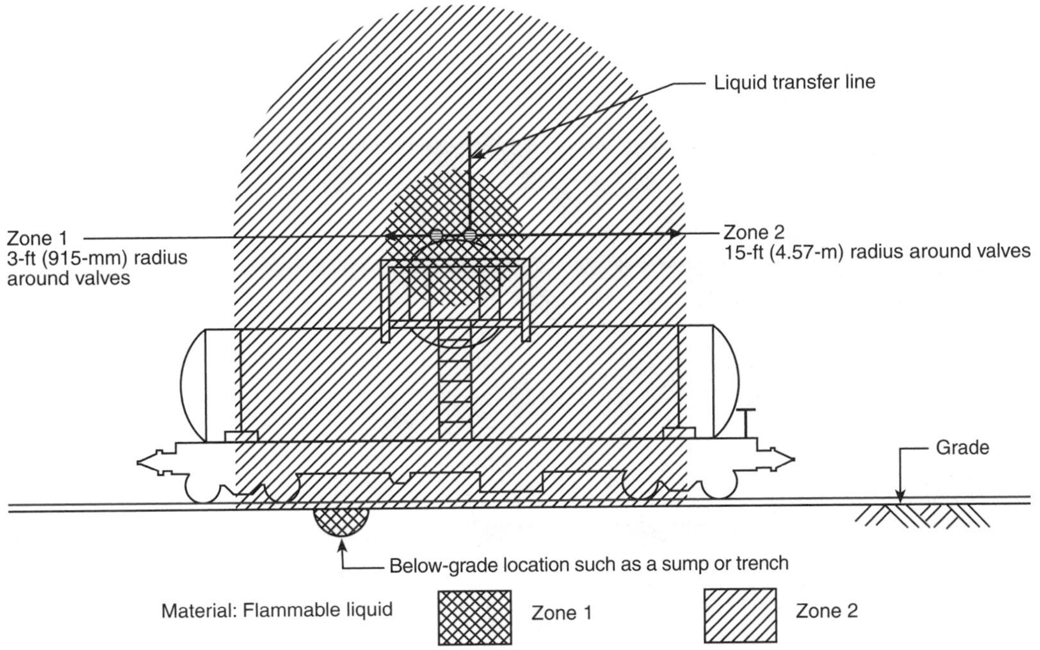

Figure 3-9.22 Tank car/tank truck loading and unloading via open system. Top or bottom product transfer.

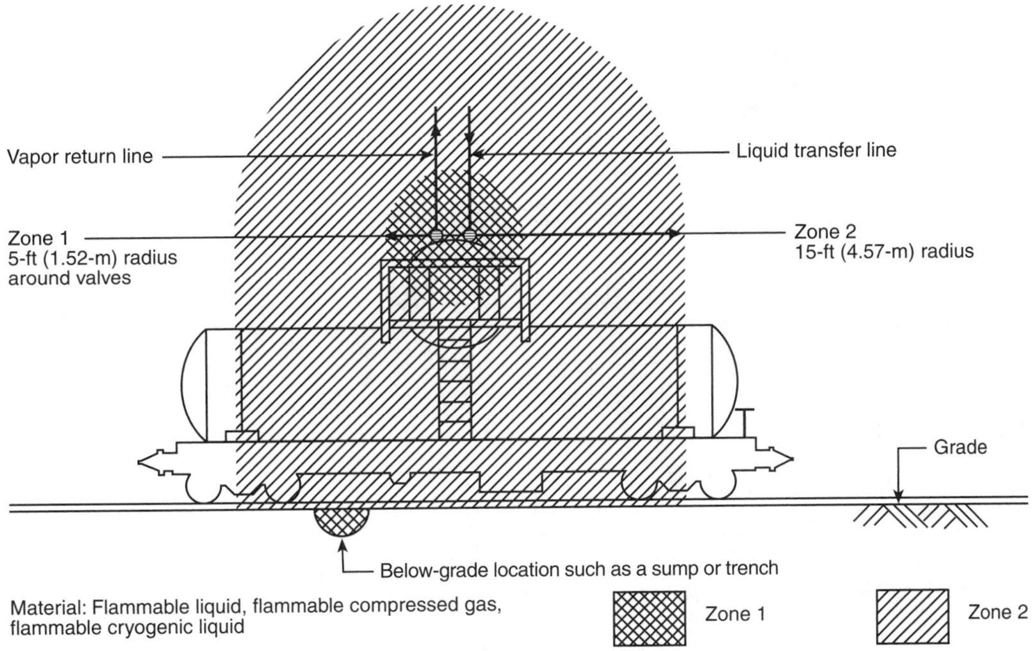

Figure 3-9.23 Tank car/tank truck loading and unloading via closed system. Transfer through dome only.

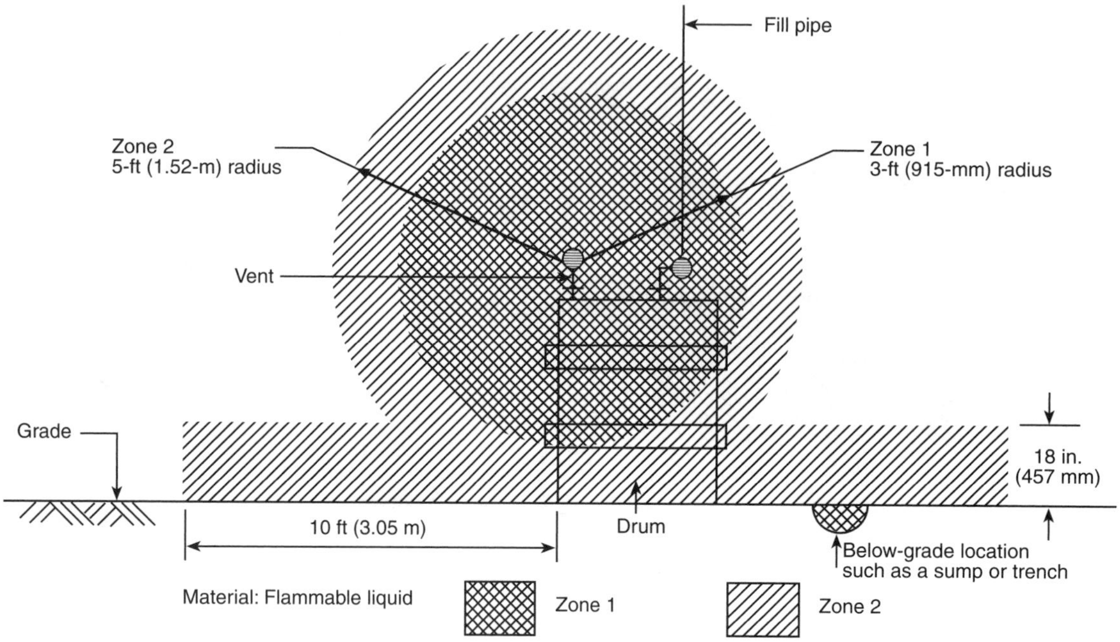

Figure 3-9.24 Drum filling station, outdoors, or indoors with adequate ventilation.

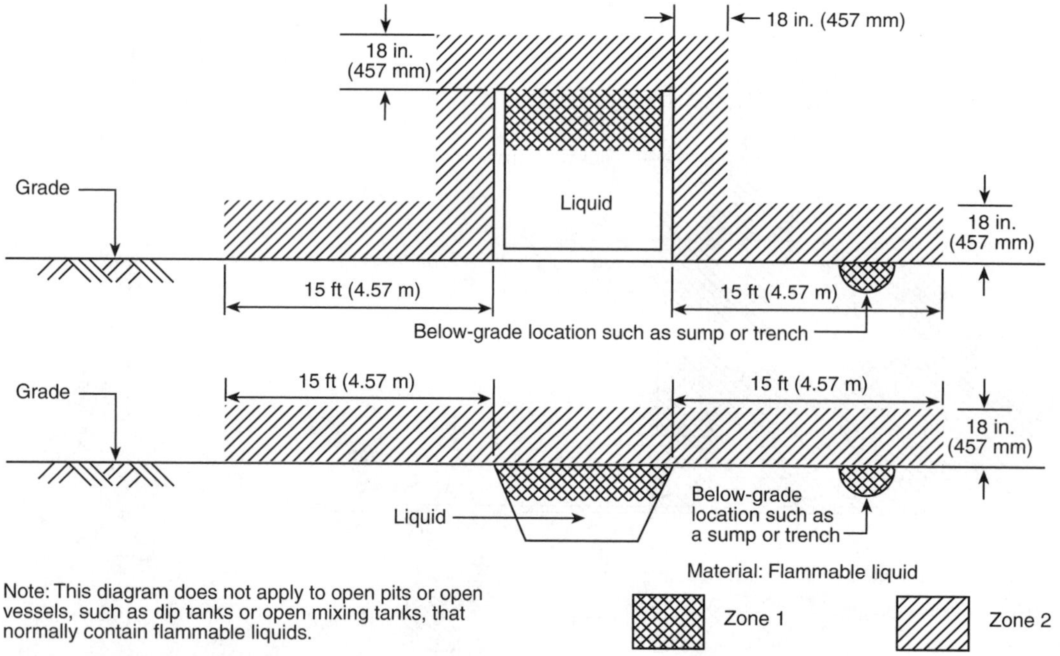

Figure 3-9.25 Emergency impounding basin or oil/water separator (top) and emergency drainage ditch or oil/water separator (bottom).

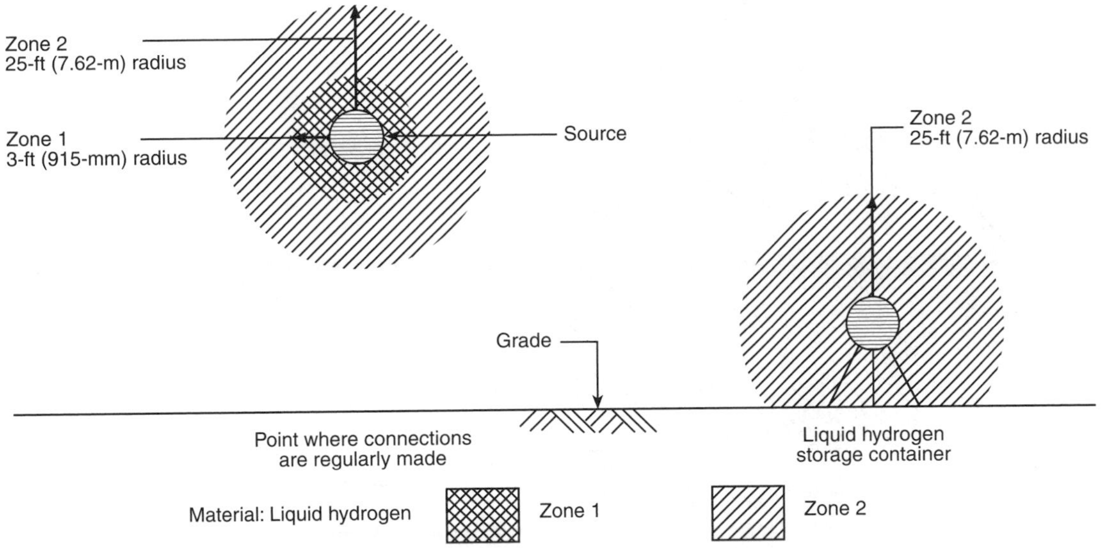

Figure 3-9.26 Liquid hydrogen storage located outdoors or in an adequately ventilated building.

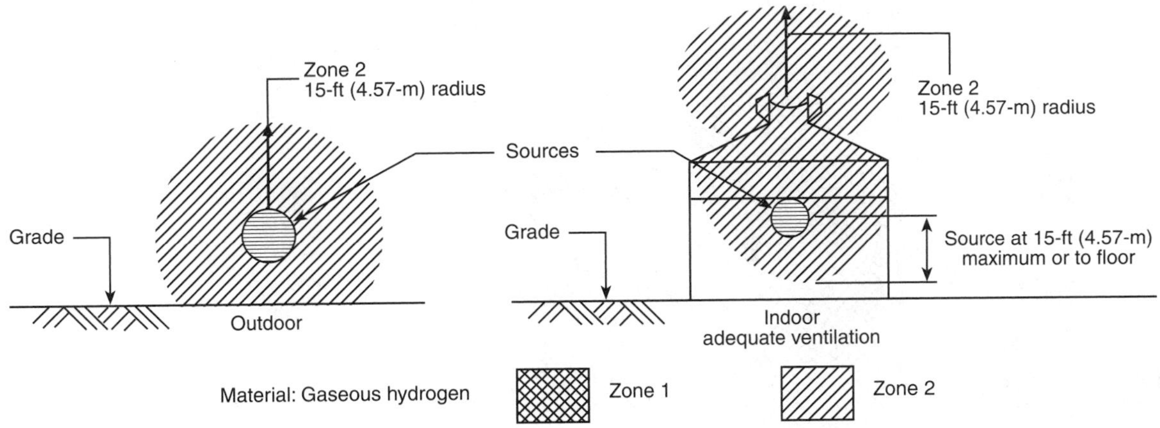

Figure 3-9.27 Gaseous hydrogen storage located outdoors, or indoors in an adequately ventilated building.

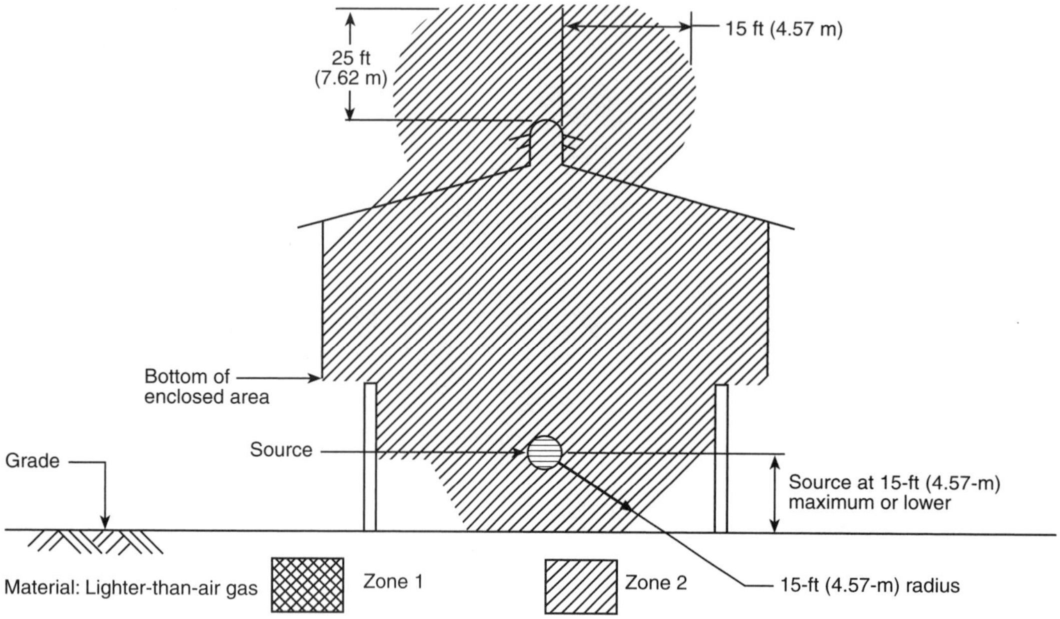

Figure 3-9.28 Adequately ventilated compressor shelter.

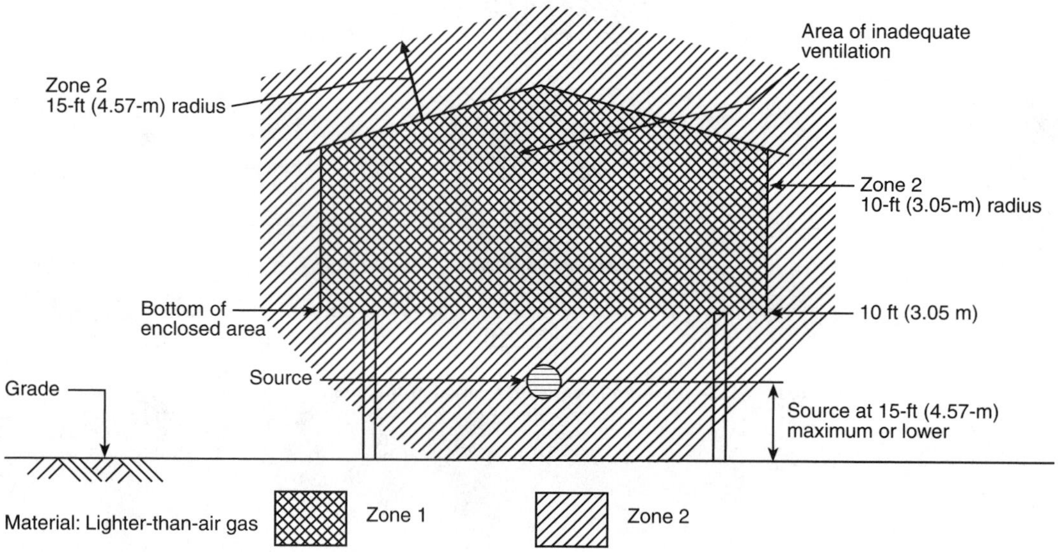

Figure 3-9.29 Inadequately ventilated compressor shelter.

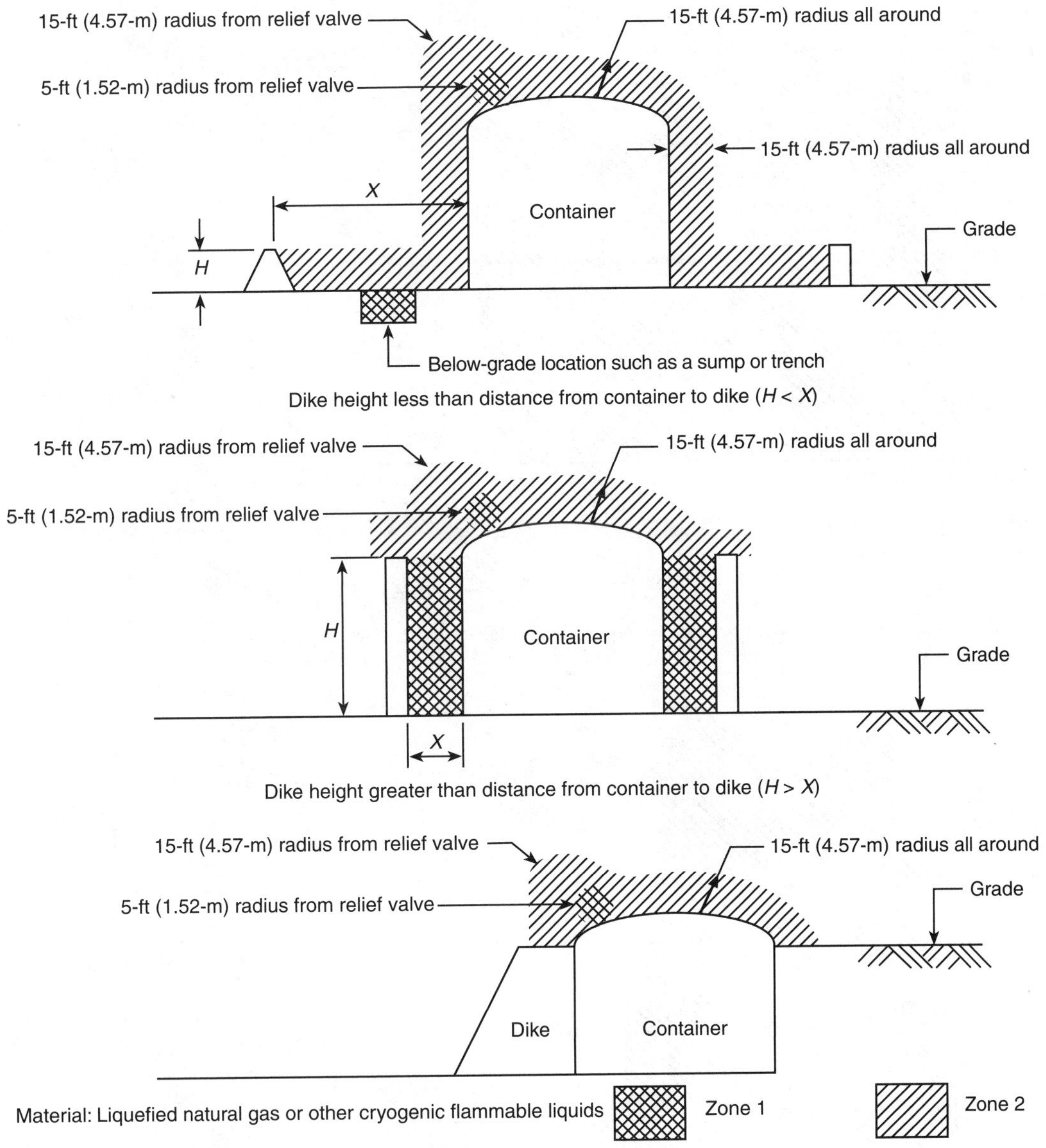

Figure 3-9.30 Storage tanks for cryogenic liquids.

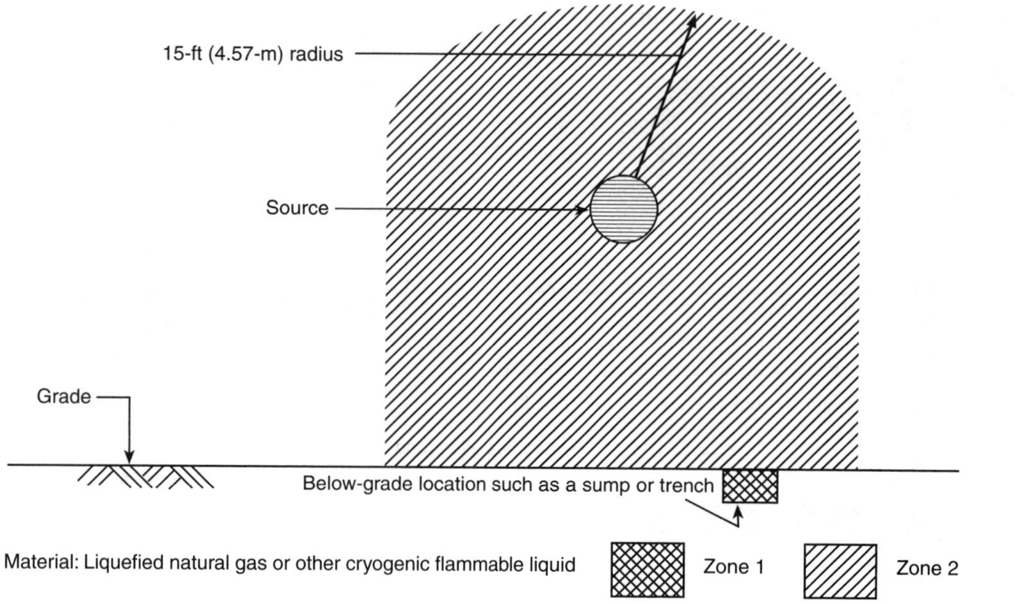

Figure 3-9.31 Leakage source from equipment handling liquefied natural gas. Source is located outdoors, at or above grade.

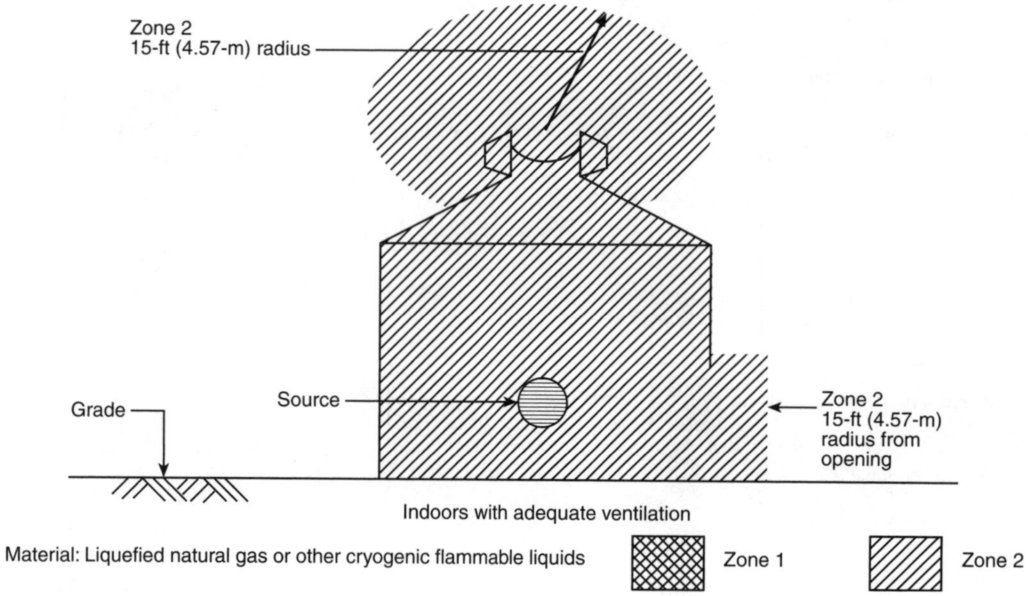

Figure 3-9.32 Leakage source from equipment handling liquefied natural gas in an adequately ventilated building.

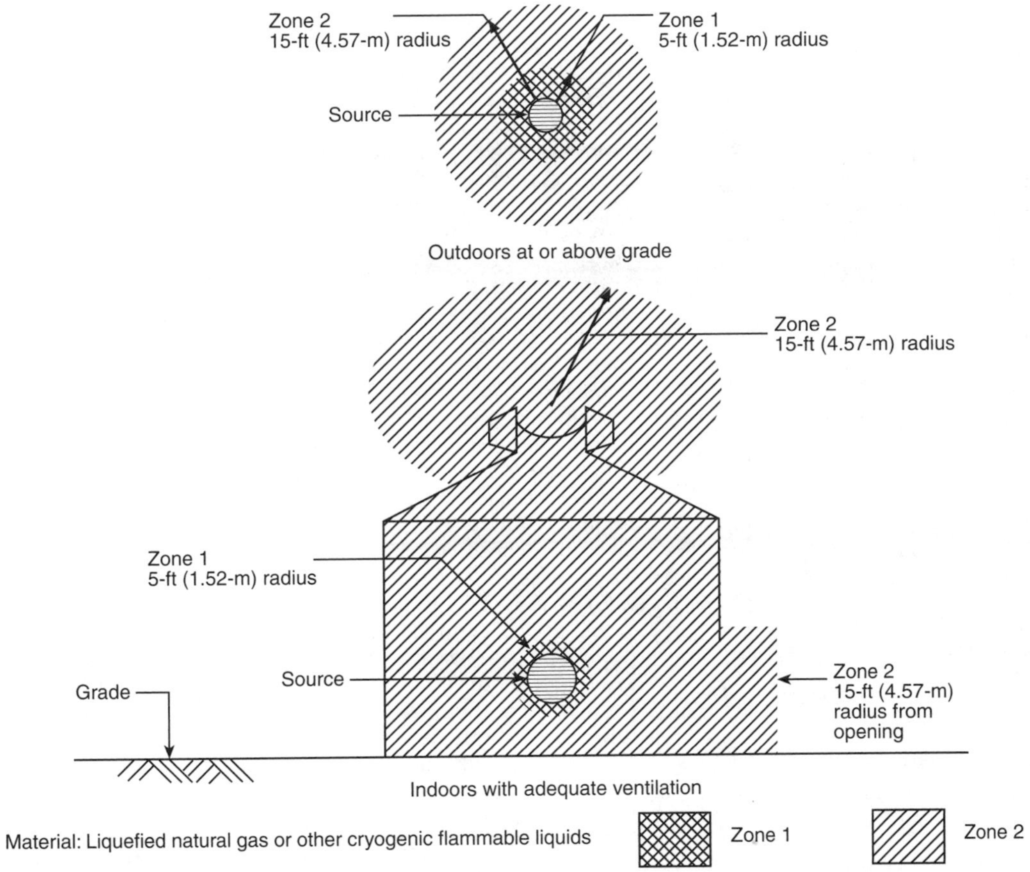

Figure 3-9.33 Leakage source from routinely operating bleeds, equipment handling liquefied natural gas in an adequately ventilated building.

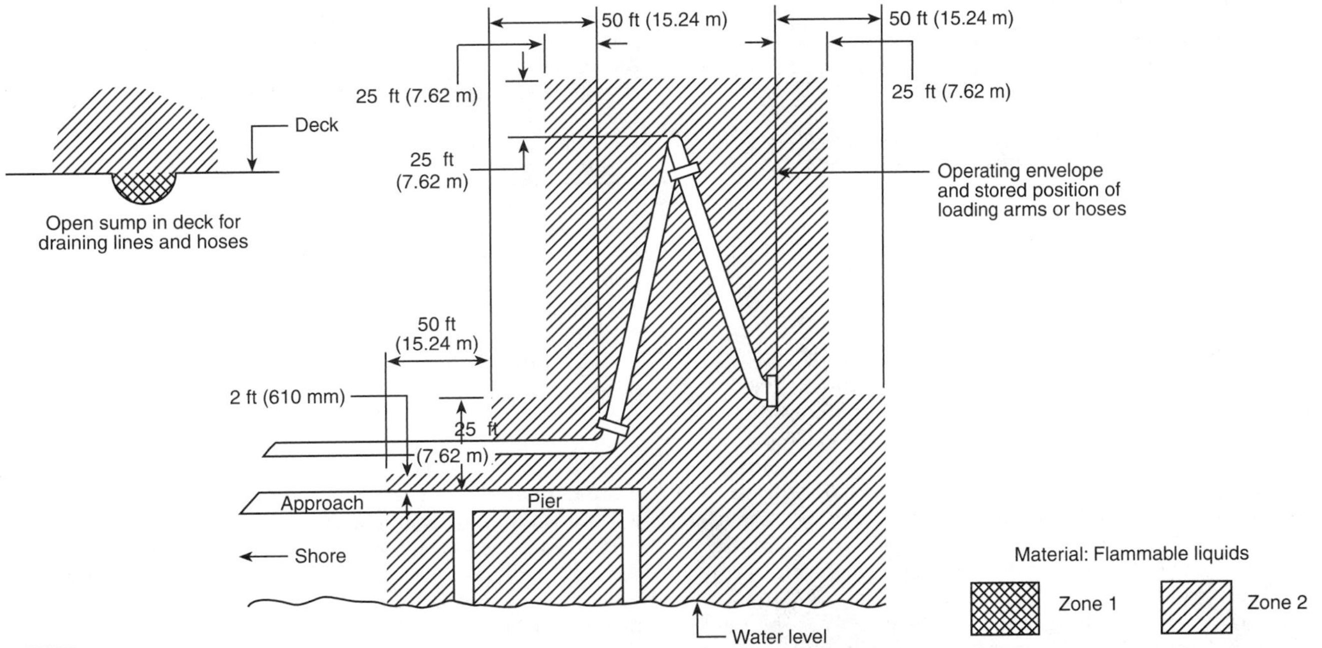

Figure 3-9.34 Marine terminal handling flammable liquids.

Chapter 4 Referenced Publications

4-1 The following documents or portions thereof are referenced within this recommended practice and should be considered as part of its recommendations. The edition indicated for each referenced document is the current edition as of the date of the NFPA issuance of this recommended practice. Some of these documents might also be referenced in this recommended practice for specific informational purposes and, therefore, are also listed in Appendix C.

4-1.1 NFPA Publications. National Fire Protection Association, 1 Batterymarch Park, P.O. Box 9101, Quincy, MA 02269-9101.

NFPA 30, *Flammable and Combustible Liquids Code,* 1996 edition.

NFPA 58, *Standard for the Storage and Handling of Liquefied Petroleum Gases,* 1995 edition.

NFPA 59A, *Standard for the Production, Storage, and Handling of Liquefied Natural Gas (LNG),* 1996 edition.

NFPA 70, *National Electrical Code®,* 1996 edition.

NFPA 325, *Guide to Fire Hazard Properties of Flammable Liquids, Gases, and Volatile Solids,* 1994 edition.

4-1.2 ANSI Publications. American National Standards Institute, 11 West 42nd Street, New York, NY 10036.

ANSI/ASHRAE 15, *Safety Code for Mechanical Refrigeration,* 1989.

ANSI/CGA G2.1, *Safety Requirements for the Storage and Handling of Anhydrous Ammonia,* 1989.

4-1.3 API Publication. American Petroleum Institute, 1220 L Street, NW, Washington, DC 20005.

ANSI/RP 500, *Recommended Practice for Classification of Locations for Electrical Installations at Petroleum Facilities,* 1992.

4-1.4 IEC Publication. International Electrotechnical Commission Central Office, 3 Rue de Varembe, P.O. Box 131, 1211 Geneva 20, Switzerland.

ELECTRIC CODE
GROUP A, B, C, D
CLASSIFICATION

…s *for explosive gas atmospheres,* Part … intrinsically-safe circuits.

…Explanatory Material

…*f the recommendations of this NFPA … nformational purposes only.*

…**, Groups A, B, C, and D.** Histori…us (classified) locations first ap…*rical Code (NEC)* in 1923, when a …-Hazardous Locations" was ac…sed rooms or compartments in which highly flammable gases, liquids, mixtures, or other substances were manufactured, used, or stored. In 1931, "classifications" consisting of Class I, Class II, and so on, for the hazardous locations were defined. However, it was not until 1935 that "groups" were introduced into the *NEC.* (Note: "Divisions" were introduced into the *NEC* in 1947.) The four gas groups, Groups A, B, C, and D, complemented the design of electrical equipment used in hazardous (classified) locations and were defined based on the level of hazard associated with explosion pressures of specific atmospheres and the likelihood that the effects of that explosion could be transmitted outside the enclosure. Group A was defined as atmospheres containing acetylene. Group B was defined as atmospheres containing hydrogen or gas or vapors of equivalent hazard. Group C was defined as atmospheres containing ethyl ether vapor, and Group D was defined as atmospheres containing gasoline, petroleum, naphtha, alcohols, acetone, lacquers, solvent vapors, and natural gas. Despite the fact that the introduction of these groups was done without standardized testing and without the advantage of today's technological advances or equipment, these definitions have changed little since that time. The first major testing, in fact, was only conducted in the late 1950s, when engineers at Underwriters Laboratories Inc. developed a test apparatus that provided a means to determine how various materials behaved with respect to explosion pressures and transmission when the specific combustible material was ignited in the test vessel. This apparatus, called the Westerberg Explosion Test Vessel, provided standardized documentation of a factor called the "Maximum Experimental Safe Gap" (MESG) and permitted other materials to be "classified by test" into one of the four gas groups. The results of these tests are contained in Underwriters Laboratories Inc. (UL) Bulletin Nos. 58 and 58A (reissued in July 1993, as UL Technical Report No. 58). In 1971, the International Electrotechnical Commission (IEC) published IEC 79-1A defining a different type of apparatus for obtaining MESG results. While the two "MESG" test apparatuses are physically different in both size and shape, the results are statistically comparative, although in some cases differences have been observed. A sample of values is shown in the following table.

Material	Westerberg apparatus, MESG, mm	IEC apparatus, MESG, mm
Propane	.92	.94
Ethylene	.69	.65
Butadiene	.79	.79
Diethyl ether	.30	.87
Hydrogen	.08	.29

Papers have been written to attempt to explain the reasons for these differences in the test data. One by H. Phillips, entitled "Differences between Determinations of Maximum Experimental Safe Gaps in Europe and U.S.A.," appeared in a 1981 edition of the *Journal of Hazardous Materials.* The paper cites a condition of spontaneous combustion in one portion of the Westerberg Apparatus, which was reflected in materials (such as diethyl ether) having low ignition temperatures. Additionally, testing on the Westerberg Apparatus has demonstrated that this theory was true, and the MESG value for diethyl ether more than doubled. Further Westerberg apparatus testing has also shown that hydrogen MESG value is .23 mm.

While acetylene remains segregated in Group A because of the high explosion pressure that results from its very fast flame speed, newer test methodologies have defined other types of protection methods that now consider acetylene and hydrogen to be of equivalent hazard. One such method examines the "minimum igniting current" required to ignite a specific combustible material. This testing produced more variability when the results of specific combustible materials were compared. However, it was found that the minimum igniting currents of one test could be favorably compared with those of other tests if a ratio value based on methane was applied. This testing has resulted in the generation of MIC ratio data.

Other testing has been performed when it was incorrectly assumed that a factor called "Minimum Ignition Energy" (MIE) and "Autoignition Temperature" (AIT) were related and could be used to place materials into groups. The fact that these were independent factors resulted in deletion of AITs as a basis for group determination in the 1971 NEC.

MIEs have been found to exhibit theoretical results that do not translate into practical designs that can be applied to actual electrical devices with their associated energy levels.

Since the primary concern is to have electrical devices that can safely operate when used in locations classified by class, group, and division, the definitions for the four gas groups have been defined on the basis of the parameters providing the most significant basis for that design, which are MESG and MIC ratio. Lacking these values, experience-based data indicating equivalency to atmospheres providing similar hazards may be used.

A-2-1, Table Note 5. Selecting electrical equipment based on the lowest AIT shown in Table 2-1 may be unnecessarily restrictive. As an example, in an area handling a commercial grade of hexane, Table 2-1 tabulates five different isomers of hexane solvent (C_6H_{14}) with the AIT ranging from a low of 225°C to a high of 405°C. The AIT of the solvent mixtures should be determined either experimentally or from the supplier. It would be expected that the commercial grade of hexane would have an AIT ranging from 265°C to 290°C.

A-2-1.2 Electrical installations for classified areas may be designed in various manners. No single manner is best in all respects for all types of equipment used in a chemical plant. Explosionproof enclosures, pressurized equipment, and intrinsically safe circuits are applicable to both Division 1 and Division 2 areas. Nonincendive equipment is permitted in Division 2 areas. Nonsparking electrical equipment and other less restrictive equipment, as specified in NFPA 70, *National Electrical Code,* are permitted in Division 2 areas.

Factors such as corrosion, weather, maintenance, equipment standardization and interchangeability, and possible process changes or expansion frequently dictate the use of special enclosures or installations for electrical systems. However, such factors are outside the scope of this recommended practice, which is concerned entirely with the proper application of electrical equipment to avoid ignition of combustible materials.

A-2-4.2 Combustible materials shown in Table 2-1 have been classified in groups. Some of these combustible materials are indicated in groups that may not seem to agree with defined MESG or MIC ratio values, but have been continued within groups due to historical experiences and specific properties that are not reflected in MESG or MIC ratio testing. For example, one source for group classifications was *Matrix of Combustion-Relevant Properties and Classification of Gases, Vapors, and Selected Solids,* NMAB 353- 1, published by the National Academy of Sciences. Those materials whose group classifications are marked with asterisks were previously assigned group classifications based on tests conducted in the Westerberg Apparatus at Underwriters Laboratories Inc. *(See An Investigation of Flammable Gases or Vapors with Respect to Explosion-Proof Electrical Equipment, UL Bulletin of Research No. 58, and subsequent Bulletins Nos. 58A and 58B, reissued July 23, 1993, as UL Technical Report No. 58.)* All other materials were assigned group classifications based on analogy with tested materials and on chemical structure, or on reputable published data reflecting MESG or MIC ratio values. *(See, for example, IEC 79- 20.)* While the classifications of these latter materials represent the best judgment of three groups of experts, it is conceivable that the group classification of any particular untested material may be incorrect. Users of these data should be aware that the data are the result of experimental determination, and as such are influenced by variation in experimental apparatus and procedures and in the accuracy of the instrumentation. Additionally, some of the data have been determined at an above-ambient temperature in order that the vapor is within the flammable region. Variation in the temperature for the determination would be expected to influence the result of the determination. Also, values shown generally represent the lowest reported in reputable, documented studies. In certain instances, therefore, it may be advisable to submit an untested material to a qualified testing laboratory for verification of the assigned group classification. Autoignition temperatures listed in Table 2-1 are the lowest value for each material as listed in NFPA 325, *Guide to Fire Hazard Properties of Flammable Liquids, Gases, and Volatile Solids,* or as reported in an article by C. J. Hilado and S. W. Clark in *Chemical Engineering,* September 4, 1972.

A-3-4.2 The degree to which air movement and material volatility combine to affect the extent of the classified area can be illustrated by two experiences monitored by combustible gas detectors. Gasoline spilled in a sizable open manifold pit gave no indication of ignitable mixtures beyond 3 ft to 4 ft (0.9 m to 1.2 m) from the pit when the breeze was 8 to 10 mph (13 to 16 km/hr). A slightly smaller pool of a more volatile material, blocked on one side, was monitored during a gentle breeze. At grade, vapors could be detected for approximately 100 ft (30 m) downwind; however, at 18 in. (46 cm) above grade there was no indication of vapor as close as 30 ft (9 m) from the pool.

These examples show the great variability that may be present in situations of this type, and point out again that careful consideration must be given to a large number of factors when classifying areas.

A-3-7.2.5 When fire hazard properties of a combustible material are not available, the appropriate group may be estimated using the following information:

(a) Minimum igniting current (MIC) ratio

(b) Ratio of upper flammable limit to lower flammable limit

(c) Molar heat of combustion multiplied by the lower flammable limit

(d) Ratio of the lower flammable limit to the stoichiometric concentration

(e) Maximum experimental safe gap (MESG)

(f) Minimum ignition energy (MIE)

(g) Stoichiometric flame temperature

(h) Knowledge of the chemical structure

Appendix B Example

This appendix is not a part of the recommendations of this NFPA document but is included for informational purposes only.

This example is provided to show how the information in this document can help determine an *NEC* group classifica-

Properties of Selected Materials

Material	Mol. wt.	%LFL	%UFL	AIT °C	Vapor pressure, mm Hg at 25°C	BP°C	*NEC* Group	MESG mm	MIC ratio
Ethylene	28.05	2.7	36	450	52,320	−104	C	0.65	.53
Propane	44.09	2.1	9.5	450	7150	−42	D	0.97	.82
Nitrogen	14.0							∞	
Methane	16.04	5.0	15	600	463,800	−162	D	1.12	1.0
Isopropyl ether	102.17	1.4	21	443	148.7	69	D	0.94	
Diethyl ether	74.12	1.9	36	160	38.2	34.5	C	0.83	.88

tion. It should not be applied with mixtures and/or streams that have acetylene or its equivalent hazard.

The following materials are used in a tank having a total capacity of 100,000 kg as a single mixed stream and having the following composition:

Material	% by vol
Ethylene	45
Propane	12
Nitrogen	20
Methane	3
Isopropyl ether	17.5
Diethyl ether	2.5

Question:

What is the appropriate *NEC* group to use for the mixed stream?

The above is a list of the properties of selected materials taken from NFPA 497 Table 2-1 and other references.

One method to estimate the *NEC* group is to determine the MESG of the mixture by applying a form of Le Chatielier relationship shown below:

$$MESG_{mix} = \frac{1}{\sum_i \left(\frac{X_i}{MESG_i}\right)}$$

Applying the volume percent and property information above results in the following equation:

$$\frac{1}{\frac{0.45}{0.65} + \frac{0.12}{0.97} + \frac{0.20}{\infty} + \frac{0.03}{1.12} + \frac{0.175}{0.94} + \frac{0.025}{0.83}} = 0.9442$$

Solving the equation above results in an MESG mixture value of 0.9442. From the definitions in Section 1-3 for Groups A, B, C and D, this calculated MESG value would fall under Group D. Thus this mixture may be considered a Group D material.

Appendix C Referenced Publications

C-1 The following documents or portions thereof are referenced within this recommended practice for informational purposes only and are thus not considered part of its recommendations. The edition indicated for each reference is the current edition as of the date of the NFPA issuance of this recommended practice.

C-1.1 NFPA Publications. National Fire Protection Association, 1 Batterymarch Park, P.O. Box 9101, Quincy, MA 02269-9101.

NFPA 30, *Flammable and Combustible Liquids Code,* 1996 edition.

NFPA 36, *Standard for Solvent Extraction Plants,* 1993 edition.

NFPA 70, *National Electrical Code,* 1996 edition.

NFPA 325, *Guide to Fire Hazard Properties of Flammable Liquids, Gases, and Volatile Solids,* 1994 edition.

C-1.2 Other Publications.

A-1.2.1 ANSI Publications. American National Standards Institute, 11 West 42nd Street, New York, NY 10036.

ANSI/ASHRAE 15, *Safety Code for Mechanical Refrigeration,* 1989.

ANSI/CGA G2.1, *Safety Requirements for the Storage and Handling of Anhydrous Ammonia,* 1989.

C-1.2.2 ASTM Publications. American Society for Testing and Materials, 100 Barr Harbor Drive, West Conshohocken, PA 19428- 2959.

ASTM D 56, *Standard Method of Test for Flash Point by the Tag Closed Tester,* 1987.

ASTM D 93, *Standard Method of Test for Flash Point by the Pensky-Martens Closed Tester,* 1985.

ASTM E 659, *Test for Autoignition Temperature of Liquid Chemicals,* 1978.

ASTM E 681, *Test for Limits of Flammability of Chemicals,* 1985.

ASTM D 3278, *Standard Method of Tests for Flash Point of Liquids by Setaflash Closed Tester,* 1982.

C-1.2.3 Bureau of Mines Publication. U.S. Government Printing Office, Washington, DC 20402.

RI 7009, *Minimum Ignition Energy and Quenching Distance in Gaseous Mixture.*

C-1.2.4 IEC Publications. International Electrotechnical Commission, Central Office, 3 Rue de Varembe, P.O. Box 131, 1211 Geneva 20 Switzerland.

IEC 79-1A, First supplement to publication 79-1(1971), *Electrical apparatus for explosive gas atmospheres,* Part 1: Construction and test of flameproof enclosures of electrical apparatus, and Appendix D: Method of test for ascertainment of maximum experimental safe gap.

IEC 79-3, *Electrical apparatus for explosive gas atmospheres,* Part 3: Spark-test apparatus for intrinsically-safe circuits.

IEC 79-12, *Electrical apparatus for explosive gas atmospheres,* Part 12: Classification of mixtures of gases or vapors with air according to their maximum experimental safe gaps and minimum igniting currents.

IEC 79-20, *Electrical apparatus for explosive atmospheres,* Part 20: Data for flammable gases and vapors, relating to the use of electrical apparatus.

C-1.2.5 National Academy of Sciences Publication. National Materials Advisory Board of the National Academy of Sciences, 2101 Constitution Avenue, NW, Washington, DC 20418.

NMAB 353-1, *Matrix of Combustion-Relevant Properties and Classification of Gases, Vapors and Selected Solids.*

C-1.2.6 UL Publication. Underwriters Laboratories Inc., 333 Pfingsten Road, Northbrook, IL 60062.

Technical Report No. 58, *An Investigation of Flammable Gases or Vapors With Respect to Explosion-Proof Electrical Equipment,* 1993.

C-1.2.7 Additional Publications.

Hilado, C. J. and S. W. Clark. 1972. "Autoignition Temperatures of Organic Chemicals." *Chemical Engineering* September 4.

Institute of Petroleum. 1990. *Area Classification Code for Petroleum Installations,* Part 15. John Wiley and Sons. March.

Phillips, H. 1981. "Differences between Determinations of Maximum Experimental Safe Gaps in Europe and U.S.A." *Journal of Hazardous Materials.*

Appendix D Additional References

This recommended practice is not intended to supersede or conflict with applicable requirements of the following NFPA standards:

NFPA 30, *Flammable and Combustible Liquids Code,* 1996 edition.

NFPA 33, *Standard for Spray Application Using Flammable or Combustible Materials,* 1995 edition.

NFPA 34, *Standard for Dipping and Coating Processes Using Flammable or Combustible Liquids,* 1995 edition.

NFPA 35, *Standard for the Manufacture of Organic Coatings,* 1995 edition.

NFPA 36, *Standard for Solvent Extraction Plants,* 1997 edition.

NFPA 45, *Standard on Fire Protection for Laboratories Using Chemicals,* 1996 edition.

NFPA 50A, *Standard for Gaseous Hydrogen Systems at Consumer Sites,* 1994 edition.

NFPA 50B, *Standard for Liquefied Hydrogen Systems at Consumer Sites,* 1994 edition.

NFPA 58, *Standard for the Storage and Handling of Liquefied Petroleum Gases,* 1995 edition.

NFPA 59A, *Standard for the Production, Storage, and Handling of Liquefied Natural Gas (LNG),* 1996 edition.

Index

NFPA 704

2001 Edition

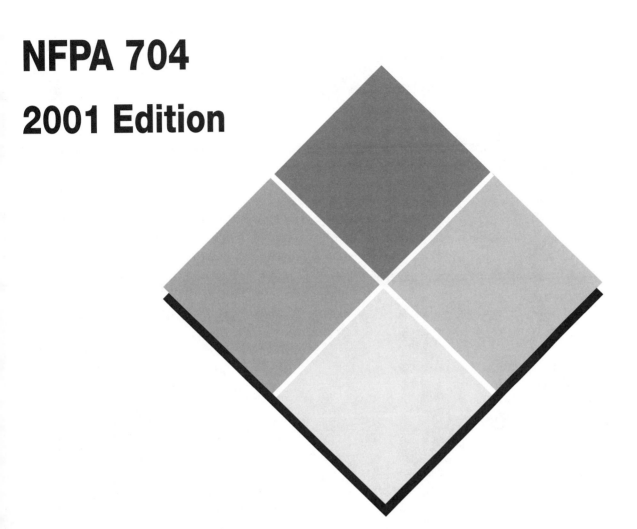

Identification of the Hazards of Materials for Emergency Response

NFPA 704

Standard System for the

Identification of the Hazards of Materials for Emergency Response

2001 Edition

This edition of NFPA 704, *Standard System for the Identification of the Hazards of Materials for Emergency Response,* was prepared by the Technical Committee on Classification and Properties of Hazardous Chemical Data and acted on by NFPA at its May Association Technical Meeting held May 13–17, 2001, in Anaheim, CA. It was issued by the Standards Council on July 13, 2001, with an effective date of August 2, 2001, and supersedes all previous editions.

This edition of NFPA 704 was approved as an American National Standard on August 2, 2001.

Origin and Development of NFPA 704

Work on this standard originated in 1957; a great deal of the development work had been done by the NFPA Sectional Committee on Classification, Labeling, and Properties of Flammable Liquids starting in 1952. Background data was published by the Association in its quarterly magazine in July 1954, 1956, and 1958. The material in its present form was first tentatively adopted in 1960. Official adoption was secured in 1961, and revisions were adopted in 1964, 1966, 1969, 1975, 1980, and 1985. In the 1987 and 1990 editions, the Committee on Fire Hazards of Materials introduced quantitative guidelines for assigning the Health Hazard and Reactivity Hazard Ratings. The 1996 edition introduced additional quantitative guidelines and an amended definition for the Instability Hazard Rating, formerly the Reactivity Hazard Rating.

This 2001 edition clarifies numerous topics, including the following: rating of mixtures; three options of how to rate areas with multiple chemical storage and use; location of signs; more quantitative criteria for flammability ratings for solids; and quantitative criteria for a flammability rating of zero, including introduction of a new test method. Guidance material has been added for quantifying the degree of water reactivity. An entire annex covers water reactivity, identification criteria, as well as additional information on flash point test methods. The document has also been modified to comply with the updated NFPA *Manual of Style.*

Technical Committee on Classification and Properties of Hazardous Chemical Data

Gary Robinson, *Chair*
LMG Property Engineering, IL [I]
Rep. The Alliance of American Insurers

Robert A. Michaels, *Secretary*
RAM TRAC Corporation, NY [SE]

Laurence G. Britton, Union Carbide Corporation, WV [M]
Lance "Skip" Edwards, National Paint & Coatings Association, DC [M]
Richard Gowland, Dow Chemical, Great Britain [M]
Ron A. Kirsch, OHS Associates, Inc., TN [SE]
Arthur A. Krawetz, Phoenix Chemical Laboratory, Inc., IL [RT]
F. Owen Kubias, Rocky River, OH [SE]
Roland J. Land, Risk Control Consultants, LLC, NJ [SE]
Jennifer L. Nelson, AT&T — EH&S, NY [U]
Rep. NFPA Industrial Fire Protection Section
Curtis G. Payne, U.S. Coast Guard, DC [U]
Thomas A. Salamone, Health Care & Life Safety Concepts, NY [I]
William J. Satterfield, III, RODE & Associates, LLC, RI [I]

Nonvoting

Whitney Fay Long, c/o CDR Long SACLANTCEN, APO AE
Ira Wainless, U.S. Department of Labor/OSHA, DC

Amy B. Spencer, NFPA Staff Liaison

Committee Scope: This Committee shall have primary responsibility for documents on the classification of the relative hazards of all chemical solids, liquids and gases and to compile data on the hazard properties of these hazardous chemicals.

This list represents the membership at the time the Committee was balloted on the final text of this edition. Since that time, changes in the membership may have occurred. A key to classifications is found at the back of the document.

NOTE: Membership on a committee shall not in and of itself constitute an endorsement of the Association or any document developed by the committee on which the member serves.

Contents

NFPA 704

Standard System for the

Identification of the Hazards of Materials for Emergency Response

2001 Edition

NOTICE: An asterisk (*) following the number or letter designating a paragraph indicates that explanatory material on the paragraph can be found in Annex A.

A reference in brackets [ ] following a section or paragraph indicates material that has been extracted from another NFPA document. The complete title and edition of the document the material is extracted from is found in Annex G. Editorial changes to extracted material consist of revising references to an appropriate division in this document or the inclusion of the document number with the division number when the reference is to the original document. Requests for interpretations or revisions of extracted text shall be sent to the appropriate technical committee.

Information on referenced publications can be found in Chapter 2 and Annex G.

Chapter 1 Administration

1.1 Scope. This standard shall address the health, flammability, instability, and related hazards that are presented by short-term, acute exposure to a material under conditions of fire, spill, or similar emergencies.

1.2 Purpose.

1.2.1 This standard shall provide a simple, readily recognized and easily understood system of markings that provides a general idea of the hazards of a material and the severity of these hazards as they relate to emergency response.

1.2.2 The objectives of the system shall be as follows:

(1) Provide an appropriate signal or alert and on-the-spot information to safeguard the lives of both public and private emergency response personnel
(2) Assist in planning for effective fire and emergency control operations, including cleanup
(3) Assist all designated personnel, engineers, and plant and safety personnel in evaluating hazards

1.2.3 This system shall provide basic information to fire-fighting, emergency, and other personnel, enabling them to easily decide whether to evacuate the area or to commence emergency control procedures.

1.2.4 This system also shall provide them with information to assist in selecting fire-fighting tactics and emergency procedures.

1.2.5 Local conditions can have a bearing on evaluation of hazards; therefore, discussion shall be kept in general terms.

1.3 Application.

1.3.1 This standard shall apply to industrial, commercial, and institutional facilities that manufacture, process, use, or store hazardous materials.

1.3.2* This standard shall not apply to transportation or use by the general public and is not intended to address the following:

(1) Occupational exposure
(2) Explosive and blasting agents, including commercial explosive material as defined in NFPA 495, *Explosive Materials Code*
(3) Chemicals whose only hazard is one of chronic health hazards
(4) Teratogens, mutagens, oncogens, etiologic agents, and other similar hazards

1.4 Retroactivity. The provisions of this standard reflect a consensus of what is necessary to provide an acceptable degree of protection from the hazards addressed in this standard at the time the standard was issued.

1.4.1 Unless otherwise specified, the provisions of this standard shall not apply to facilities, equipment, structures, or installations that existed or were approved for construction or installation prior to the effective date of the standard. Where specified, the provisions of this standard shall be retroactive.

1.4.2 In those cases where the authority having jurisdiction determines that the existing situation presents an unacceptable degree of risk, the authority having jurisdiction shall be permitted to apply retroactively any portions of this standard deemed appropriate.

1.4.3 The retroactive requirements of this standard shall be permitted to be modified if their application clearly would be impractical in the judgment of the authority having jurisdiction, and only where it is clearly evident that a reasonable degree of safety is provided.

1.5 Equivalency. Nothing in this standard is intended to prevent the use of systems, methods, or devices of equivalent or superior quality, strength, fire resistance, effectiveness, durability, and safety over those prescribed by this standard. Technical documentation shall be submitted to the authority having jurisdiction to demonstrate equivalency. The system, method, or device shall be approved for the intended purpose by the authority having jurisdiction.

Chapter 2 Referenced Publications

2.1 General. The documents or portions thereof listed in this chapter are referenced within this standard and shall be considered part of the requirements of this document.

2.1.1 NFPA Publications. National Fire Protection Association, 1 Batterymarch Park, P.O. Box 9101, Quincy, MA 02269-9101.

NFPA 495, *Explosive Materials Code,* 2001 edition.

Fire Protection Guide to Hazardous Materials, 1997 edition.

2.1.2 Other Publications.

2.1.2.1 ASTM Publications. American Society for Testing and Materials, 100 Barr Harbor Drive, West Conshohocken, PA 19428-2959.

ASTM D 86, *Standard Test Method for Distillation of Petroleum Products at Atmospheric Pressure,* 2001.

ASTM D 92, *Standard Test Method for Flash and Fire Points by Cleveland Open Cup,* 1998.

2.1.2.2 Other Publication. Britton, L. G., "Survey of Fire Hazard Classification Systems for Liquids," *Process Safety Progress*, Vol. 18, No. 4, Winter, 1999.

2.1.2.3 UN Publications. United Nations, UN Plaza, New York, NY 10017.

Manual of Tests Criteria, 3rd revised edition.

Recommendations on the Transport of Dangerous Goods, Model Regulations, 11th revised edition.

2.1.2.4 U.S. Government Publication. U.S. Government Printing Office, Washington, DC 20402.

Title 49, *Code of Federal Regulations*, "Method of Testing for Sustained Combustibility," Part 173, Appendix H.

Chapter 3 Definitions

3.1 General. The definitions contained in this chapter shall apply to the terms used in this standard. Where terms are not included, common usage of the terms shall apply.

3.2 NFPA Official Definitions.

3.2.1* Approved. Acceptable to the authority having jurisdiction.

3.2.2* Authority Having Jurisdiction. The organization, office, or individual responsible for approving equipment, materials, an installation, or a procedure.

3.2.3 Shall. Indicates a mandatory requirement.

3.3 General Definitions.

3.3.1* Boiling Point. The temperature at which the vapor pressure of a liquid equals the surrounding atmospheric pressure. For purposes of defining the boiling point, atmospheric pressure shall be considered to be 14.7 psia (760 mm Hg). For mixtures that do not have a constant boiling point, the 20 percent evaporated point of a distillation performed in accordance with ASTM D 86, *Standard Test Method for Distillation of Petroleum Products at Atmospheric Pressure*, shall be considered to be the boiling point. [**30:**1.7]

3.3.2 Fire Point. The lowest temperature at which a liquid will ignite and achieve sustained burning when exposed to a test flame in accordance with ASTM D 92, *Standard Test Method for Flash and Fire Points by Cleveland Open Cup.*

3.3.3* Flash Point. The minimum temperature at which a liquid or a solid emits vapor sufficient to form an ignitable mixture with air near the surface of the liquid or the solid.

3.3.4* Frostbite. Frostbite is a localized condition that occurs when the layers of the skin and deeper tissue freeze.

3.3.5 Materials.

3.3.5.1 Stable Materials. Those materials that normally have the capacity to resist changes in their chemical composition, despite exposure to air, water, and heat as encountered in fire emergencies.

3.3.5.2 Unstable Materials. A material that, in the pure state or as commercially produced, will vigorously polymerize, decompose or condense, become self-reactive, or otherwise undergo a violent chemical change under conditions of shock, pressure, or temperature.

Chapter 4 General

4.1 Description.

4.1.1 This system shall identify the hazards of a material in terms of the following three principal categories:

(1) Health
(2) Flammability
(3) Instability

4.1.2 The system shall indicate the degree of severity by a numerical rating that ranges from four, indicating severe hazard, to zero, indicating minimal hazard.

4.1.3 The information shall be presented by a spatial arrangement of numerical ratings, with the health rating always at the nine o'clock position, the flammability rating always at the twelve o'clock position, and the instability rating always at the three o'clock position.

4.1.4* Each rating shall be located in a square-on-point field (commonly referred to as a diamond), each of which is assigned a color: (1) Blue for health hazard; (2) Red for flammability hazard; and (3) Yellow for instability hazard. Alternately, the square-on-point field shall be permitted to be any convenient contrasting color and the numbers themselves shall be permitted to be colored. *(See Figure 9.1(a) through Figure 9.1(c) for examples of the spatial arrangements.)*

4.1.5 The fourth quadrant, at the six o'clock position, shall be reserved for indicating special hazards and shall be in accordance with Chapter 8. No special color is associated with this quadrant.

4.2 Assignment of Ratings.

4.2.1 The hazard evaluation required to determine the correct numerical ratings for a specific material shall be performed by persons who are technically competent and experienced in the interpretation of the hazard criteria set forth in this standard.

4.2.2* Assignment of ratings shall be based on factors that encompass a knowledge of the inherent hazards of the material, including the extent of change in behavior to be anticipated under conditions of exposure to fire or fire control procedures.

4.2.3 The system shall be based on relative rather than absolute values, requiring considerable judgment be exercised.

4.2.3.1 Based upon professional judgment, the hazard rating shall be permitted to be either increased or decreased to more accurately assess the likely degree of hazard that will be encountered.

4.2.3.2* It shall be anticipated that different physical forms of the material or conditions of storage and use could result in different ratings being assigned to the same material.

4.2.3.3* Where more than one chemical is present in a building or specific area, professional judgment shall be exercised to indicate ratings using the following methods:

(1) *Composite Method.* Where many chemicals are present, a single sign shall summarize the maximum ratings contributed by the material(s) in each category and the special hazard category for the building and/or the area.

(2) *Individual Method.* Where only a few chemicals are present or where only a few chemicals are of concern to emergency responders (taking into account factors including physical form, hazard rating, and quantity), individual signs shall be displayed. The chemical name shall be displayed below each sign.
(3) *Composite–Individual Combined Method.* A single sign shall be used to summarize the ratings via the Composite Method for buildings or other areas containing numerous chemicals. Signs based on the Individual Method shall be used for rooms or smaller areas within the building containing small numbers of chemicals.

4.2.3.4* When rating mixtures of chemicals, actual data on the mixture itself shall be used to obtain the ratings for health, flammability, and instability.

4.3* Location of Signs. Signs shall be in locations approved by the authority having jurisdiction and as a minimum shall be posted at the following locations:

(1) Two exterior walls or enclosures containing a means of access to a building or facility
(2) Each access to a room or area
(3) Each principal means of access to an exterior storage area

Chapter 5 Health Hazards

5.1 General.

5.1.1* This chapter shall address the capability of a material to cause personal injury due to contact with or entry into the body via inhalation, ingestion, skin contact, or eye contact.

5.1.2 Injury resulting from the heat of a fire or from the force of an explosion shall not be considered.

5.1.3* Health hazards that can result from chronic or repeated long-term exposure to low concentrations of a hazardous material shall not be considered.

5.1.4* If the oral toxicity values indicate a significantly different health hazard rating than from other more likely routes of exposure, or where the oral toxicity values would tend to either exaggerate or minimize the hazards likely to be encountered, then professional judgment shall be exercised in assigning the health hazard rating.

5.1.5* For purposes of assigning the health hazard rating, only the inherent physical and toxic properties of the material shall be considered. However, if the combustion or decomposition products are known, generated in significant quantities, and present a significantly greater degree of risk, they shall be rated accordingly.

5.1.6 The degree of hazard shall indicate to fire-fighting and emergency response personnel one of the following:

(1) They can work safely only with specialized protective equipment.
(2) They can work safely with suitable respiratory protective equipment.
(3) They can work safely in the area with ordinary clothing.

5.2* Degrees of Hazard. The degrees of health hazard shall be ranked according to the probable severity of the effects of exposure to emergency response personnel detailed in Table 5.2.

5.2.1 Data from all routes of exposure shall be considered when applying professional judgment to assign a health hazard rating.

Table 5.2 Degrees of Health Hazards

Degree of Hazard*	Criteria
4 — Materials that, under emergency conditions, can be lethal.	Gases whose LC_{50} for acute inhalation toxicity is less than or equal to 1000 parts per million (ppm).
	Any liquid whose saturated vapor concentration at 20°C (68°F) is equal to or greater than ten times its LC_{50} for acute inhalation toxicity, if its LC_{50} is less than or equal to 1000 ppm.
	Dusts and mists whose LC_{50} for acute inhalation toxicity is less than or equal to 0.5 milligrams per liter (mg/L).
	Materials whose LD_{50} for acute dermal toxicity is less than or equal to 40 milligrams per kilogram (mg/kg).
	Materials whose LD_{50} for acute oral toxicity is less than or equal to 5 mg/kg.
3 — Materials that, under emergency conditions, can cause serious or permanent injury.	Gases whose LC_{50} for acute inhalation toxicity is greater than 1000 ppm but less than or equal to 3000 ppm.
	Any liquid whose saturated vapor concentration at 20°C (68°F) is equal to or greater than its LC_{50} for acute inhalation toxicity, if its LC_{50} is less than or equal to 3000 ppm and that does not meet the criteria for degree of hazard 4.
	Dusts and mists whose LC_{50} for acute inhalation toxicity is greater than 0.5 mg/L but less than or equal to 2 mg/L.
	Materials whose LD_{50} for acute dermal toxicity is greater than 40 mg/kg but less than or equal to 200 mg/kg.
	Materials that are corrosive to the respiratory tract.

Table 5.2 *Continued*

Degree of Hazard*	Criteria
3 — Materials that, under emergency conditions, can cause serious or permanent injury.	Materials that are corrosive to the eye or cause irreversible corneal opacity. Materials that are corrosive to skin. Cryogenic gases that cause frostbite and irreversible tissue damage. Compressed liquefied gases with boiling points at or below −55°C (−66.5°F) that cause frostbite and irreversible tissue damage. Materials whose LD_{50} for acute oral toxicity is greater than 5 mg/kg but less than or equal to 50 mg/kg.
2 — Materials that, under emergency conditions, can cause temporary incapacitation or residual injury.	Gases whose LC_{50} for acute inhalation toxicity is greater than 3000 ppm but less than or equal to 5000 ppm Any liquid whose saturated vapor concentration at 20°C (68°F) is equal to or greater than one-fifth its LC_{50} for acute inhalation toxicity, if its LC_{50} is less than or equal to 5000 ppm and that does not meet the criteria for either degree of hazard 3 or degree of hazard 4. Dusts and mists whose LC_{50} for acute inhalation toxicity is greater than 2 mg/L but less than or equal to 10 mg/L. Materials whose LD_{50} for acute dermal toxicity is greater than 200 mg/kg but less than or equal to 1000 mg/kg. Compressed liquefied gases with boiling points between −30°C (−22°F) and −55°C (−66.5°F) that can cause severe tissue damage, depending on duration of exposure. Materials that are respiratory irritants. Materials that cause severe but reversible irritation to the eyes or lacrimators. Materials that are primary skin irritants or sensitizers. Materials whose LD_{50} for acute oral toxicity is greater than 50 mg/kg but less than or equal to 500 mg/kg.
1 — Materials that, under emergency conditions, can cause significant irritation.	Gases and vapors whose LC_{50} for acute inhalation toxicity is greater than 5000 ppm but less than or equal to 10,000 ppm. Dusts and mists whose LC_{50} for acute inhalation toxicity is greater than 10 mg/L but less than or equal to 200 mg/L. Materials whose LD_{50} for acute dermal toxicity is greater than 1000 mg/kg but less than or equal to 2000 mg/kg. Materials that cause slight to moderate irritation to the respiratory tract, eyes, and skin. Materials whose LD_{50} for acute oral toxicity is greater than 500 mg/kg but less than or equal to 2000 mg/kg.
0 — Materials that, under emergency conditions, would offer no hazard beyond that of ordinary combustible materials.	Gases and vapors whose LC_{50} for acute inhalation toxicity is greater than 10,000 ppm. Dusts and mists whose LC_{50} for acute inhalation toxicity is greater than 200 mg/L. Materials whose LD_{50} for acute dermal toxicity is greater than 2000 mg/kg. Materials whose LD_{50} for acute oral toxicity is greater than 2000 mg/kg. Materials that are essentially nonirritating to the respiratory tract, eyes, and skin.

*For each degree of hazard, the criteria are listed in a priority order based upon the likelihood of exposure.

Chapter 6 Flammability Hazards

6.1 General.

6.1.1 This chapter shall address the degree of susceptibility of materials to burning.

6.1.2* Because many materials will burn under one set of conditions but will not burn under others, the form or condition of the material shall be considered, along with its inherent properties.

6.2* Degrees of Hazard. The degrees of flammability hazard shall be ranked according to the susceptibility of materials to burning detailed in Table 6.2.

Table 6.2 Degrees of Flammability Hazards

Degree of Hazard	Criteria
4 — Materials that will rapidly or completely vaporize at atmospheric pressure and normal ambient temperature or that are readily dispersed in air and will burn readily.	Flammable gases. Flammable cryogenic materials. Any liquid or gaseous material that is liquid while under pressure and has a flash point below 22.8°C (73°F) and a boiling point below 37.8°C (100°F) (i.e., Class IA liquids). Materials that ignite spontaneously when exposed to air. Solids containing greater than 0.5 percent by weight of a flammable or combustible solvent are rated by the closed cup flash point of the solvent.
3 — Liquids and solids that can be ignited under almost all ambient temperature conditions. Materials in this degree produce hazardous atmospheres with air under almost all ambient temperatures or, though unaffected by ambient temperatures, are readily ignited under almost all conditions.	Liquids having a flash point below 22.8°C (73°F) and having a boiling point at or above 37.8°C (100°F) and those liquids having a flash point at or above 22.8°C (73°F) and below 37.8°C (100°F) (i.e., Class IB and Class IC liquids). Materials that on account of their physical form or environmental conditions can form explosive mixtures with air and that are readily dispersed in air. Flammable or combustible dusts with representative diameter less than 420 microns (40 mesh). Materials that burn with extreme rapidity, usually by reason of self-contained oxygen (e.g., dry nitrocellulose and many organic peroxides). Solids containing greater than 0.5 percent by weight of a flammable or combustible solvent are rated by the closed cup flash point of the solvent.
2 — Materials that must be moderately heated or exposed to relatively high ambient temperatures before ignition can occur. Materials in this degree would not under normal conditions form hazardous atmospheres with air, but under high ambient temperatures or under moderate heating could release vapor in sufficient quantities to produce hazardous atmospheres with air.	Liquids having a flash point at or above 37.8°C (100°F) and below 93.4°C (200°F) (i.e., Class II and Class IIIA liquids). Solid materials in the form of powders or coarse dusts of representative diameter between 420 microns (40 mesh) and 2 mm (10 mesh) that burn rapidly but that generally do not form explosive mixtures with air. Solid materials in a fibrous or shredded form that burn rapidly and create flash fire hazards, such as cotton, sisal, and hemp. Solids and semisolids that readily give off flammable vapors. Solids containing greater than 0.5 percent by weight of a flammable or combustible solvent are rated by the closed cup flash point of the solvent.

Table 6.2 *Continued*

Degree of Hazard	Criteria
1 — Materials that must be preheated before ignition can occur. Materials in this degree require considerable preheating, under all ambient temperature conditions, before ignition and combustion can occur.	Materials that will burn in air when exposed to a temperature of 815.5°C (1500°F) for a period of 5 minutes in accordance with Annex D. Liquids, solids, and semisolids having a flash point at or above 93.4°C (200°F) (i.e., Class IIIB liquids). Liquids with a flash point greater than 35°C (95°F) that do not sustain combustion when tested using the *Method of Testing for Sustained Combustibility*, per 49 CFR 173, Appendix H or the UN *Recommendations on the Transport of Dangerous Goods, Model Regulations*, 11th revised edition, and the related *Manual of Tests and Criteria*, 3rd revised edition. Liquids with a flash point greater than 35°C (95°F) in a water-miscible solution or dispersion with a water noncombustible liquid/solid content of more than 85 percent by weight. Liquids that have no fire point when tested by ASTM D 92, *Standard Test Method for Flash and Fire Points by Cleveland Open Cup*, up to the boiling point of the liquid or up to a temperature at which the sample being tested shows an obvious physical change. Combustible pellets with a representative diameter greater than 2 mm (10 mesh). Most ordinary combustible materials. Solids containing greater than 0.5 percent by weight of a flammable or combustible solvent are rated by the closed cup flash point of the solvent.
0 — Materials that will not burn under typical fire conditions, including intrinsically noncombustible materials such as concrete, stone, and sand.	Materials that will not burn in air when exposed to a temperature of 816°C (1500°F) for a period of 5 minutes in accordance with Annex D.

Chapter 7 Instability Hazards

7.1 General.

7.1.1* This chapter shall address the degree of intrinsic susceptibility of materials to release energy.

7.1.1.1 This chapter shall apply to those materials capable of rapidly releasing energy by themselves, through self-reaction or polymerization.

7.1.1.2 Water reactivity shall be assessed in accordance with Chapter 8.

7.1.1.3* When evaluating the hazards of organic peroxides, additional factors shall be taken into account.

7.1.2* Because of the wide variations of unintentional combinations possible in fire or other emergencies, these extraneous hazard factors (except for the effect of water) shall not be applied to a general numerical rating of hazards. Where large quantities of materials are stored together, inadvertent mixing shall be considered in order to establish appropriate separation or isolation.

7.1.3 The degree of instability hazard shall indicate to fire-fighting and emergency personnel whether the area shall be evacuated, whether a fire shall be fought from a protected location, whether caution shall be used in approaching a spill or fire to apply extinguishing agents, or whether a fire can be fought using normal procedures.

7.2 Degrees of Hazard. The degrees of hazard shall be ranked according to ease, rate, and quantity of energy release of the material in pure or commercial form detailed in Table 7.2.

Table 7.2 Degrees of Instability Hazards

Degree of Hazard	Criteria
4 — Materials that in themselves are readily capable of detonation or explosive decomposition or explosive reaction at normal temperatures and pressures.	Materials that are sensitive to localized thermal or mechanical shock at normal temperatures and pressures. Materials that have an instantaneous power density (product of heat of reaction and reaction rate) at 250°C (482°F) of 1000 W/mL or greater.
3 — Materials that in themselves are capable of detonation or explosive decomposition or explosive reaction, but that require a strong initiating source or that must be heated under confinement before initiation.	Materials that have an instantaneous power density (product of heat of reaction and reaction rate) at 250°C (482°F) at or above 100 W/mL and below 1000 W/mL. Materials that are sensitive to thermal or mechanical shock at elevated temperatures and pressures.
2 — Materials that readily undergo violent chemical change at elevated temperatures and pressures.	Materials that have an instantaneous power density (product of heat of reaction and reaction rate) at 250°C (482°F) at or above 10 W/mL and below 100 W/mL.
1 — Materials that in themselves are normally stable, but that can become unstable at elevated temperatures and pressures.	Materials that have an instantaneous power density (product of heat of reaction and reaction rate) at 250°C (482°F) at or above 0.01 W/mL and below 10 W/mL.
0 — Materials that in themselves are normally stable, even under fire conditions.	Materials that have an instantaneous power density (product of heat of reaction and reaction rate) at 250°C (482°F) below 0.01 W/mL. Materials that do not exhibit an exotherm at temperatures less than or equal to 500°C (932°F) when tested by differential scanning calorimetry.

Chapter 8 Special Hazards

8.1 General.

8.1.1* This chapter shall address water reactivity and oxidizing properties of the materials that cause special problems or require special fire-fighting techniques.

8.1.2 Special hazards symbols shall be shown in the fourth space of the sign or immediately above or below the entire sign.

8.2 Symbols. Special hazards shall be represented by a spatial arrangement denoted by symbols always at the six o'clock position.

8.2.1* Materials that react violently or explosively with water (i.e., water reactivity rating 2 or 3) shall be identified by the letter "W" with a horizontal line through the center (₩).

8.2.2* Materials that possess oxidizing properties shall be identified by the letters "OX."

Chapter 9 Identification of Materials by Hazard Rating System

9.1 Symbol Arrangement. One of the systems delineated in Figure 9.1(a), Figure 9.1(b), or Figure 9.1(c) shall be used for the implementation of this standard.

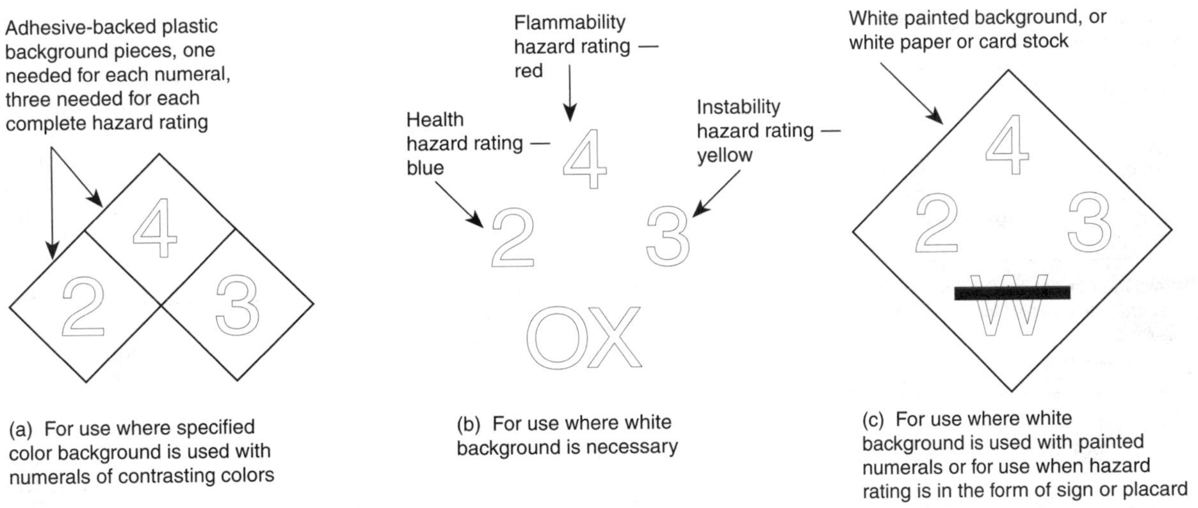

FIGURE 9.1(a) Alternate arrangements for display of NFPA 704 hazard identification system.

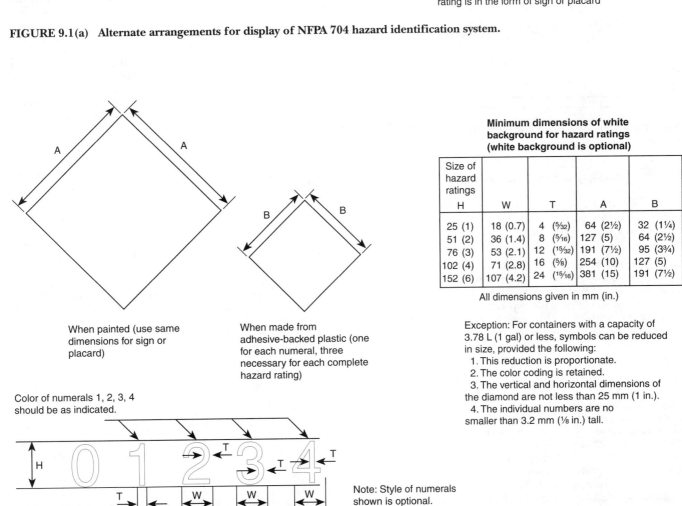

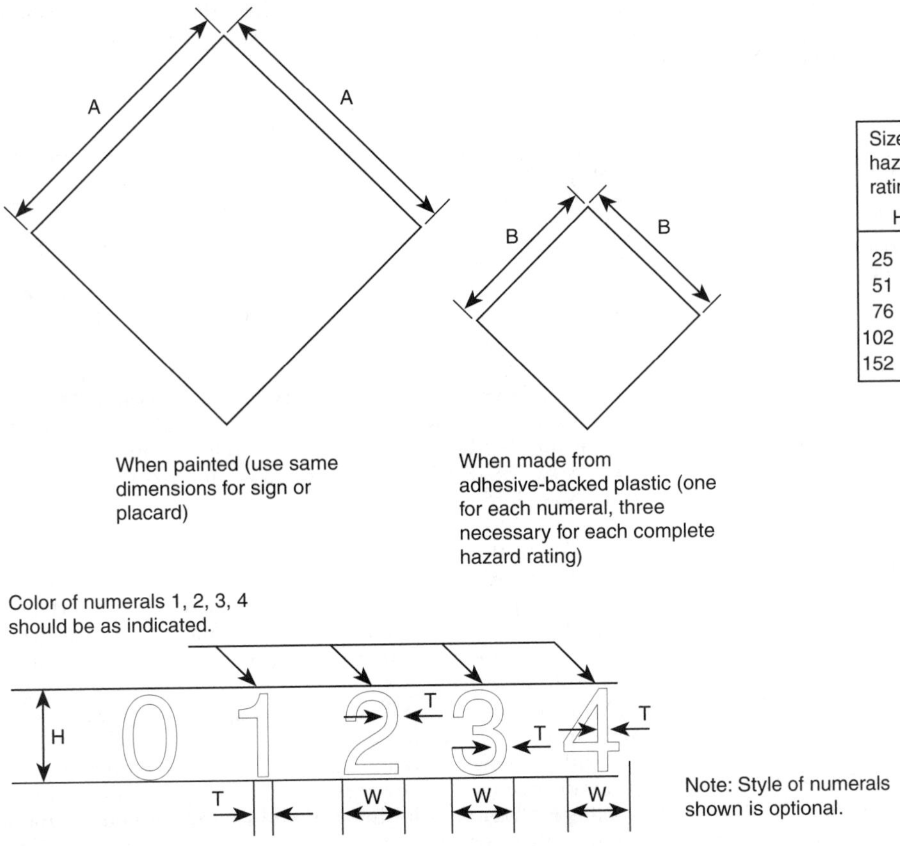

Minimum dimensions of white background for hazard ratings (white background is optional)

Size of hazard ratings H	W	T	A	B
25 (1)	18 (0.7)	4 (5⁄32)	64 (2½)	32 (1¼)
51 (2)	36 (1.4)	8 (5⁄16)	127 (5)	64 (2½)
76 (3)	53 (2.1)	12 (15⁄32)	191 (7½)	95 (3¾)
102 (4)	71 (2.8)	16 (5⁄8)	254 (10)	127 (5)
152 (6)	107 (4.2)	24 (15⁄16)	381 (15)	191 (7½)

All dimensions given in mm (in.)

Exception: For containers with a capacity of 3.78 L (1 gal) or less, symbols can be reduced in size, provided the following:

1. This reduction is proportionate.
2. The color coding is retained.
3. The vertical and horizontal dimensions of the diamond are not less than 25 mm (1 in.).
4. The individual numbers are no smaller than 3.2 mm (⅛ in.) tall.

FIGURE 9.1(b) Dimensions of NFPA 704 placard and numerals.

Arrangement and order of hazard ratings—optional form of application

Distance at which hazard ratings are legible	Minimum size of hazard ratings required
15.24 m (50 ft)	25 mm (1 in.)
22.86 m (75 ft)	51 mm (2 in.)
30.48 m (100 ft)	76 mm (3 in.)
60.96 m (200 ft)	102 mm (4 in.)
91.44 m (300 ft)	152 mm (6 in.)

Note: This shows the correct spatial arrangement and order of hazard ratings used for identification of materials by hazard.

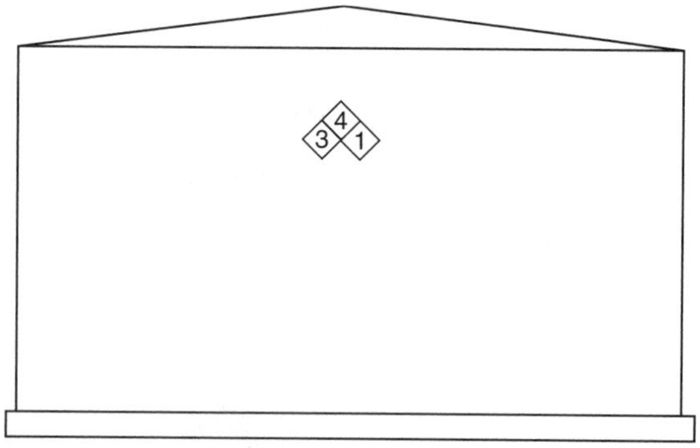

FIGURE 9.1(c) Minimum size of numerals for legibility at distance.

Annex A Explanatory Material

Annex A is not a part of the requirements of this NFPA document but is included for informational purposes only. This annex contains explanatory material, numbered to correspond with the applicable text paragraphs.

A.1.3.2 The Technical Committee on Classification and Properties of Hazardous Chemical Data recognizes that the potential exists for certain materials to cause a carcinogenic or teratogenic effect from acute exposure(s). However, sufficient data are not available to this committee to allow for the development of numerical ratings based upon carcinogenic or teratogenic potential.

A.3.2.1 Approved. The National Fire Protection Association does not approve, inspect, or certify any installations, procedures, equipment, or materials; nor does it approve or evaluate testing laboratories. In determining the acceptability of installations, procedures, equipment, or materials, the authority having jurisdiction may base acceptance on compliance with NFPA or other appropriate standards. In the absence of such standards, said authority may require evidence of proper installation, procedure, or use. The authority having jurisdiction may also refer to the listings or labeling practices of an organization that is concerned with product evaluations and is thus in a position to determine compliance with appropriate standards for the current production of listed items.

A.3.2.2 Authority Having Jurisdiction. The phrase "authority having jurisdiction" is used in NFPA documents in a broad manner, since jurisdictions and approval agencies vary, as do their responsibilities. Where public safety is primary, the authority having jurisdiction may be a federal, state, local, or other regional department or individual such as a fire chief; fire marshal; chief of a fire prevention bureau, labor department, or health department; building official; electrical inspector; or others having statutory authority. For insurance purposes, an insurance inspection department, rating bureau, or other insurance company representative may be the authority having jurisdiction. In many circumstances, the property owner or his or her designated agent assumes the role of the authority having jurisdiction; at government installations, the commanding officer or departmental official may be the authority having jurisdiction.

A.3.3.1 Boiling Point. For single component liquids at the boiling point, the surrounding atmospheric pressure can no longer hold the liquid in the liquid state and the liquid boils. A low boiling point is indicative of a high vapor pressure and a high rate of evaporation.

Where an accurate boiling point is unavailable for the material in question, or for mixtures that do not have a constant boiling point, for purposes of this standard the 20 percent point of a distillation performed in accordance with ASTM D 86, *Standard Test Method for Distillation of Petroleum Products at Atmospheric Pressure*, can be used as the boiling point of the liquid. The user is warned that this definition of boiling point is inconsistent with that given in other flammability classification systems that generally use the initial boiling point of the distillation curve. Therefore, boiling points assigned for mixtures by these different classification systems are not interchangeable. For more information, see Britton (1999).

A.3.3.3 Flash Point. Flash point is a direct measure of a liquid's volatility, its tendency to vaporize. The lower the flash point, the greater the volatility and the greater the risk of fire. Flash point is determined using one of several different test procedures and apparatus that are specified.

A.3.3.4 Frostbite. Frostbite causes the skin to have a pale waxy-white appearance, and the tissue becomes numb and hard. The blood vessels in the affected area constrict and decrease circulation. Ice crystals then form in the tissue and cause structural damage with death of the affected cells.

In mild cases where ice crystal formation has not yet occurred or is very limited, recovery is usually complete, and circulation and tissue will revert to their normal state. Depending on the depth at which the tissue freezes, four degrees of severity can be distinguished. The first and second degrees of severity are limited to the top layers of skin where circulation is impaired. The second degree of severity results in blistering of the skin. Both the first- and second-degree levels do not extend beyond the top layers of the skin, and tissue death is limited. The third degree of severity involves tissue death below the skin layers. The fourth and most severe degree results in deep-tissue death that involves the muscle, tendon, and bone.

When exposure to cold is prolonged or extremely low temperatures are encountered as in the case of unprotected contact with liquefied cryogenic gases, irreversible tissue damage generally occurs. In the more severe cases of frostbite, tissue viability is affected, resulting in tissue death. Depending upon the severity of tissue damage and the location affected, surgical removal or amputation of affected tissue or extremity can be necessary.

A.4.1.4 No specific color shade is recommended, but the blue, red, and yellow used must provide an adequate contrast so that the rating numbers are easily identified. There are many environmental conditions that can affect the stability of the colors.

A.4.2.2 The NFPA 704 ratings are applied to numerous chemicals in the NFPA *Fire Protection Guide to Hazardous Materials*, which contains withdrawn standards NFPA 49, *Hazardous Chemicals Data*, and NFPA 325, *Guide to Fire Hazard Properties of Flammable Liquids, Gases, and Volatile Solids*. These were withdrawn as NFPA standards (and are therefore no longer published in the *National Fire Codes*®). However, they are maintained by NFPA staff in a database that will be available to the public electronically in the future and in updates of the NFPA *Fire Protection Guide to Hazardous Materials*. The Committee wished to note that the documents were withdrawn solely for expediency in updating the data, which was not possible in a 3- to 5-year revision cycle.

A.4.2.3.2 Due to the large number of variables, the guidance presented in the following chapters is general in nature and is limited to the most important and common factors. For example, although flash point is the primary criterion for assigning the flammability rating, other criteria could be of equal importance. For example, autoignition temperature, flammability limits, and susceptibility of a container to failure due to fire exposure also should be considered. For instability, emphasis has been placed on the ease by which an energy-releasing reaction is triggered. These factors should all be considered when calling on one's judgment during the assignment of ratings.

A.4.2.3.3 The purpose of the "Composite Method" is to characterize the hazards as simply as possible where many chemicals are present. The sign reflects the rating for the area, not for individual chemicals. For example, a building contains materials with individual chemical ratings of 1-2-1 OX, 1-2-2 ~~W~~, 3-1-2, and 2-3-4. A specific area of the building contains individual chemicals with ratings of 1-2-1 OX and 2-3-4. This would result in the following:

(1) The building would be placarded as 3-3-4 OX ~~W~~.
(2) This specific area would be placarded as 2-3-4 OX.

Using the Individual Method for the same building containing the same chemicals, there would be four signs with the following ratings: 1-2-1 OX, 1-2-2 ~~W~~, 3-1-2, and 2-3-4. Each sign would include the chemical name below the sign.

The specific area of the building would have two signs with the ratings of 1-2-1 OX and 2-3-4, each of which would include the chemical name below the sign. It should be recognized that the purpose of the standard is for recognition of hazards in an emergency; therefore, the number of signs displayed in a single place should generally not exceed five.

The Composite–Individual Combined Method allows users to utilize the best features of the other two methods. The outside of the building, enclosure, or area is posted with a single Composite sign for quick recognition of the overall hazards. Areas or rooms within the building would be posted using either the Individual Method or the Composite Method, depending on the number of chemicals they contain.

A.4.2.3.4 In the absence of data on the specific mixture, the most conservative rating (numerically highest) for each component of the mixture for health and instability should be used, with adjustment for professional judgment in accordance with 4.2.3. The synergistic effects or reactions of the components of the mixture should also be considered when assigning the ratings.

When different materials are mixed together, the instability hazard of the mixture can be entirely different from those of the individual components. An example discussed by Stull (1977) is the unrecognized mixing of a reducing agent with an oxidizing agent. This compares directly to mixing a fuel with an oxidizer. In this example, a green pigment was manufactured by mixing the yellow pigment lead chromate with the blue pigment ferric ferrocyanide. During fine grinding in a hammer mill, the mixture ignited and deflagrated, resulting in a severe fire. The chemist recognizes lead chromate as an oxidizing agent and ferric ferrocyanide as a reducing agent. In the NFPA rating system, although lead chromate should be labeled an oxidizer (OX) in the Special Hazards quadrant, there is no corresponding provision for labeling reducing agents, such as ferric ferrocyanide. While the individual components involved both have NFPA instability ratings of 0 or 1, the mixture could have a higher instability rating up to a 3, depending on the ratio of the components and intimacy of mixing.

Flammability ratings should be based on measured flash point rather than an estimated value, since the mixture's flash point and boiling point can be readily tested and quantified. In advance of testing, the flash point for a mixture can be predicted using the method described in Hanley (1998). The flammability rating is determined per Annex C.

A.4.3 The quantity and location of NFPA 704 placards are based on factors such as fire department response and access; fire department operations; location, configuration, size, and arrangement of storage areas; location, configuration, and construction of the buildings; and other factors. The authority having jurisdiction should be consulted regarding the placement of identification to assist in responding to incidents at the location.

A.5.1.1 See Annex B for additional health hazard rating background information.

A.5.1.3 In general, the health hazard that results from a fire or other emergency condition is one of acute (single) short-term exposure to a concentration of a hazardous material. This exposure can vary from a few seconds to as long as 1 hour. The physical exertion demanded by fire fighting or other emergency activity can be expected to intensify the effects of any exposure. In addition, the hazard under ambient conditions will likely be exaggerated at elevated temperatures.

A.5.1.4 The oral route of exposure (i.e., ingestion) is highly unlikely under the conditions anticipated by this standard. In such cases, other routes of entry should be considered to be more appropriate in assessing the hazard. Similarly, inhalation of dusts and mists is unlikely under the conditions anticipated by this standard. In such cases, the health hazard ratings should also be based on data for the more likely routes of exposure.

A.5.1.5 Some materials have products of combustion or decomposition that present a significantly greater degree of hazard than the inherent physical and toxic properties of the original material. The degree of hazard is dependent on the conditions at the time of the incident. In limited cases, NFPA 49, *Hazardous Chemicals Data*, provides information on the hazardous products of combustion or decomposition. (Note: Although NFPA 49 has been officially withdrawn from the *National Fire Codes*, the information is still available in NFPA's *Fire Protection Guide to Hazardous Materials*.)

In general, the Technical Committee on Classification and Properties of Hazardous Chemical Data does not consider elevating ratings based on decomposition or combustion products except for unusual circumstances. An example where the health rating could conceivably be increased is vinylidene chloride. Vinylidene chloride can emit a significant amount of phosgene under fire conditions, and under certain storage and use conditions, the rating of a 2 could be increased to a 4 for health. Another example is polyvinyl chloride, which emits hydrogen chloride and possibly chlorine under fire conditions. The rating of 0 or 1 could be increased to a 3 or 4 for health. The conditions play a large part in any rating, as noted in Section 4.2, and professional judgment should be exercised. Some materials have combustion or decomposition products that present a significantly greater degree of hazard than the inherent physical and toxic properties of the original material. The degree of hazard is dependent on the conditions at the time of the incident.

A.5.2 Certain materials upon release can cause frostbite. Frostbite, as a health hazard, should be related to the skin/eye component of the health hazard rating criteria.

A.6.1.2 The definitions for liquid classification are found in NFPA 30, *Flammable and Combustible Liquids Code.*

Solids should normally be rated as pellets unless the form and handling conditions of the solid require otherwise.

A.6.2 For water-miscible solutions and liquids that do not sustain combustion in accordance with the hazard rating 1 criteria, the individual performing the hazard evaluation should recognize that in large vapor spaces, evaporation of volatile components of the mixture can create a flammable mixture, which could increase the fire or explosion hazard. This could occur even though the bulk material meets the aforementioned criteria.

In the case of mixtures stored in non-inerted tanks where the vapor space can contain ignitable vapor, the flammability rating should be based exclusively on a closed cup flash point test. In some cases, even solutions containing less than 1 percent volatile flammable materials could produce ignitable atmospheres (Britton 1999).

A.7.1.1 The violence of a reaction or decomposition can be increased by heat or pressure. The violence of a reaction or decomposition can also be increased by mixing with other materials to form fuel–oxidizer combinations, or by contact with incompatible substances, sensitizing contaminants, or catalysts.

A.7.1.1.3 Refer to NFPA 432, *Code for the Storage of Organic Peroxide Formulations,* for more specific information regarding the classification of organic peroxides.

A.7.1.2 The hazards of inadvertent mixing can be addressed by developing a chemical compatibility chart. Information to develop such a chart can be found in NFPA 491. (Note: Although NFPA 491 has been officially withdrawn from the *National Fire Codes,* the information is still available in NFPA's *Fire Protection Guide to Hazardous Materials.*) Information can also be found in Bretherick (1999).

A.8.1.1 Other special hazard symbols (beyond OX and ₩) should not be considered to be part of the NFPA 704 hazard rating system. In many cases, the hazards represented by these symbols are already considered in either the health, flammability, or instability rating categories. For example, a polymerization hazard is covered by the numerical instability rating and does not require a separate symbol. Also, corrosive properties are considered in the health rating and again, do not require a separate symbol. In addition, since these additional symbols are not defined by the standard, emergency responders might not recognize their significance.

A.8.2.1 Numerical ratings indicating degrees of water reactivity hazards are detailed in Table A.8.2.1. This number, alongside the water reactivity symbol, can be used when the information is available to provide information about the degree of water reactivity for emergency responders.

Table A.8.2.1 Degrees of Water Reactivity Hazards

Degree of Hazard	Criteria
4	Not applicable.
3	Materials that react explosively with water without requiring heat or confinement (This qualitative description is most applicable when assigning water reactivity ratings to solids since the heat of mixing is determined by physical characteristics and the degree to which the material has dissolved). Materials whose heat of mixing is greater or equal to 600 cal/g.
2	Materials that react violently with water, including the ability to boil water, or that evolve flammable or toxic gas at a sufficient rate to create hazards under emergency response conditions (This qualitative description is most applicable when assigning water reactivity ratings to solids since the heat of mixing is determined by physical characteristics and the degree to which the material has dissolved). Materials whose heat of mixing is at or above 100 cal/g and less than 600 cal/g.
1	Materials that react vigorously with water, but not violently. This criterion is most applicable when assigning water reactivity rating to solids since the heat of mixing is determined by physical characteristics and the degree to which the material has dissolved. Materials whose heat of mixing is at or above 30 cal/g and less than 100 cal/g. Materials that react with water, producing either heat or gas leading to pressurization or toxic or flammable gas hazards. The ₩ symbol is not used on the sign.
0	Nonreactive below 30 cal/g. The ₩ symbol is not used on the sign.

It should be emphasized that the water reactivity rating is not shown in the instability hazard space in the sign, which refers specifically to the intrinsic instability of the material.

Materials that have ratings of 0 or 1 for water reactivity should not be given the ₩ symbol in the special hazards space on the placard.

The special hazard ₩ rating of 3 is the highest rating for water reactivity; there is no special hazard rating of 4 for water reactivity. The purpose of water reactivity is to warn of cases where the use of water (in nonflooding quantities) during emergency response may increase the hazard or change the perceived hazard due to a chemical. Heat of mixing tests between a chemical and water can provide a measure of how vigorous the reaction with water will be in a fire-fighting scenario. The following two scenarios are to be considered: a material that rapidly releases heat on contact with water, and a material that rapidly releases heat and gas on contact with water. These guidelines apply only to the first scenario, that is, a chemical that reacts exothermically to release heat on contact with water but does not produce gaseous or low boiling [<100°C (<212°F)] by-products or azeotropes. The heat of mixing shall be determined using a Two Drop Mixing Calorimeter (Hofelich, 1994) or equivalent technique using a 1:1 wt/wt ratio of chemical to water. Alternatively, the heat of mixing data can be found in handbooks or calculated.

A.8.2.2 For further information on oxidizers, including oxidizer classes, see NFPA 430, *Code for the Storage of Liquid and Solid Oxidizers.*

The severity of the hazard posed by an oxidizer can be ranked according to the classification system presented in NFPA 430. This numerical class can be included in the special hazards quadrant of the NFPA 704 placard. For example, since ammonium permanganate is a Class 4 oxidizer (per NFPA 430), the special hazards quadrant would be marked OX 4 to better define the hazard.

The adding of the quantification of the oxidation helps to better define the hazard. For example, manganese dioxide (NFPA 430, Class 1) and ammonium permanganate (NFPA 430, Class 4) would both be listed under the current system as OX in the NFPA 704 system, with no information on the degree of hazard.

Annex B Health Hazard Rating

This annex is not a part of the requirements of this NFPA document but is included for informational purposes only.

B.1 Development of Quantitative Guidelines for Health. In developing this edition of NFPA 704, the Technical Committee on Classification and Properties of Hazardous Chemical Data determined that the standard should provide quantitative guidelines for determining the numerical health hazard rating of a material *(see Table B.1)*.

B.1.1 Inhalation Hazard Considerations Using DOT Criteria. In addition, the committee agreed that a 4 or a 3 health hazard rating should be assigned to any material classified as a "Poison-Inhalation Hazard" by the U.S. Department of Transportation (DOT). The poison-inhalation hazard classification was adopted by DOT from the United Nations (UN) criteria detailed in the UN publication, *Recommendations on the Transport of Dangerous Goods. (See also "Notice of Proposed Rulemaking," Federal Register, Vol. 50, p. 5270 et seq., February 7, 1985, and "Notice of Final Rule," Federal Register, Vol. 50, p. 41092 et seq., October 8, 1985.)*

B.1.2 Inhalation Hazard Considerations Using UN Criteria. The UN criteria for inhalation toxicity are based upon the LC_{50} and saturated vapor concentration of the material.

B.1.3 Oral and Dermal Hazard Considerations Using UN Criteria. Furthermore, in addition to inhalation toxicity, the UN has established criteria for oral and dermal toxicity, as well as corrosivity. Based upon these criteria, the UN assigns a given material to categories called Packing Groups I, II, or III. Packing Group I materials represent a severe hazard in transport, Group II materials represent a serious hazard, and Group III materials represent a low hazard.

The committee decided to adopt the UN criteria for toxicity and corrosivity, and correlate Packing Groups I, II, and III with the health hazard ratings 4, 3, and 2, respectively.

B.1.4 Adoption of UN Criteria. Adoption of the UN system has several advantages.

B.1.4.1 First, it addresses hazards in transportation that are similar to the type of emergencies likely to be encountered by fire-fighting personnel and emergency responders. Most other hazard ranking systems have been developed for occupational exposures.

B.1.4.2 Secondly, the UN system is well established, and it is presumed that a large number of chemical manufacturers have already classified (or can easily classify) materials into the appropriate packing groups.

B.1.4.3 Finally, users of chemicals can assign a 4, 3, or 2 health hazard rating by establishing whether chemicals have been assigned to UN packing groups due to toxicity or corrosivity.

B.1.5 Hazard Considerations Using HMIS Criteria. In order to establish 1 and 0 health hazard rankings, the committee utilized criteria for the 1 and 0 ratings contained in the Hazardous Materials Identification System (HMIS) developed by the National Paint & Coatings Association (NPCA) *(see Hazardous Materials Identification System Revised, Implementation Manual).* Although the NPCA criteria were developed for occupational exposure, the 1 and 0 criteria are on the low end of the hazard spectrum and are fairly consistent with, and complementary to, the 4, 3, and 2 ratings based upon the UN criteria. No UN criteria were established for eye irritation, and the committee adopted NPCA 3, 2, 1, and 0 criteria as health hazard ratings for eye irritation.

B.2 Additional Revisions to Health Hazard Rating. The committee made a number of revisions to the proposed hazard rating system to provide conformity with existing industrial practice and to recognize the limitations and availability of corrosivity and eye irritation in a single "skin/eye contact" category and to utilize descriptive terms for the health hazard ratings. Minor changes were made to the 2, 1, and 0 criteria for oral toxicity and to the 1 and 0 criteria for dermal toxicity. Specifically, the distinction between solids and liquids in the oral toxicity criteria was eliminated, and the cutoff between 1 and 0 rankings for oral and dermal toxicity was lowered from 5000 to 2000 mg/kg.

In summary, the 4, 3, and 2 health hazard rankings for oral, dermal, and inhalation toxicity are based primarily on UN criteria. The 1 and 0 health hazard rankings for oral, dermal, inhalation toxicity, and all of the "skin/eye contact" rankings are based primarily on NPCA criteria.

Table B.1 Health Hazard Rating Chart

	Gas/Vapor					
Degree of Hazard	**Inhalation LC_{50} (ppm-v)**	**Saturated Vapor Concentration (× LC_{50} in ppm-v)**	**Dust/Mist Inhalation LC_{50} (mg/L)**	**Oral LD_{50} (mg/kg)**	**Dermal LD_{50} (mg/kg)**	**Skin/Eye**
4	0 to 1,000	10 to >10	0.00 to 0.5	0.00 to 5	0 to 40	
3	1,001 to 3,000	1 to <10	0.51 to 2	5.01 to 50	40.1 to 200	Corrosive, irreversible eye injury Corrosive if pH ≤2 or ≥11.5
2	3,001 to 5,000	0.2 to <1	2.01 to 10	50.1 to 500	201 to 1,000	Severe irritation, reversible injury Sensitizers Lacrimators Frostbite from compressed liquefied gases
1	5,001 to 10,000	0 to <0.2	10.1 to 200	501 to 2,000	1,001 to 2,000	Slight to moderate eye irritation Mild irritation is borderline 0/1
0	>10,000	0 to <0.2	>200	>2,000	>2,000	Essentially nonirritating

Notes:

1. $$\text{ppm} = \frac{\text{mg/m}^3 \times 24.45}{\text{molecular weight}}$$

2. SVC = saturated vapor concentration (ppm) at 20°C @ standard atmospheric pressure

$$\text{SVC} = \frac{\text{Vapor pressure (mmHg)} \times 106}{760}$$

B.3 UN Definitions. For the user's assistance in utilizing this standard, the following definitions are extracted from Section 6.5 of *Recommendations on the Transport of Dangerous Goods.* In the absence of data for the species defined as follows, the committee currently considers other mammalian species, including human data and professional judgment to assign health ratings. In addition, Table B.1 can be used for guidance.

B.3.1 LD_{50} for acute oral toxicity: That dose of the substance administered which is most likely to cause death within 14 days in one half of both male and female young adult albino rats. The number of animals tested shall be sufficient to give a statistically significant result and be in conformity with good pharmacological practice. The result is expressed in milligrams per kilogram of body weight.

B.3.2 LD_{50} for acute dermal toxicity: That dose of the substance which, administered by continuous contact for 24 hours with the bare skin of albino rabbits, is most likely to cause death within 14 days in one half of the animals tested. The number of animals tested shall be sufficient to give a statistically significant result and be in conformity with good pharmacological practice. The result is expressed in milligrams per kilogram of body weight.

B.3.3 LC_{50} for acute toxicity on inhalation: That concentration of vapor, mist or dust which, administered by continuous inhalation to both male and female young adult albino rats for one hour, is most likely to cause death within 14 days in one half of the animals tested. If the substance is administered to the animals as dust or mist, more than 90 percent of the particles available for inhalation in the test must have a diameter of 10 microns or less, provided that it is reasonably foreseeable that such concentrations could be encountered by man during transport. The result is expressed in milligrams per liter of air for dusts and mists or in milliliters per cubic meter of air (parts per million) for vapors.

B.4 The following information extracted from Section 6.4 of *Recommendations on the Transport of Dangerous Goods* also applies:

The criteria for inhalation toxicity of dusts and mists are based on LC_{50} data relating to 1 hour exposures and where such information is available it should be used. However, where only LC_{50} data relating to 4 hour exposures to dusts and mists are available, such figures can be multiplied by four and the product substituted in the above criteria, i.e., LC_{50} (4 hour) × 4 is considered equivalent of LC_{50} (1 hour).

The criteria for inhalation toxicity of vapors are based on LC_{50} data relating to 1 hour exposures, and where such information is available it should be used. However, where only LC_{50} data relating to 4 hour exposures to dusts and mists are available, such figures can be multiplied by two and the product substituted in the above criteria, i.e., LC_{50} (4 hour) × 2 is considered equivalent of LC_{50} (1 hour).

Annex C Flammability

This annex is not a part of the requirements of this NFPA document but is included for informational purposes only.

C.1 Development of Flammability Ratings. The selection of the flash point breaks for the assigning of ratings within the flammability category has been based upon the recommendations of the Technical Committee on Classification and Properties of Flammable Liquids of the NFPA Committee on Flammable Liquids. This Technical Committee initiated the study that led to the development of this standard. Close cooperation between the Technical Committee and the Committee on Fire Hazards of Materials has continued.

C.2 Significance of Flash Point. Flash point indicates several things. One, if the liquid has no flash point, it is not a flammable liquid. Two, if the liquid has a flash point, it has to be considered flammable or combustible. Three, the flash point is normally an indication of susceptibility to ignition.

The flash point test can give results that would indicate if a liquid is nonflammable or if it should be rated 1 or 2 as a mixture containing, for example, carbon tetrachloride. As a specific example, sufficient carbon tetrachloride can be added to gasoline so that the mixture has no flash point. However, on standing in an open container, the carbon tetrachloride will evaporate more rapidly than the gasoline. Over a period of time, the residual liquid will first show a high flash point, then a progressively lower one until the flash point of the final 10 percent of the original sample will approximate that of the heavier fractions of the gasoline. In order to evaluate the fire hazard of such liquid mixtures, fractional evaporation tests can be conducted at room temperature in open vessels. After evaporation of appropriate fractions, such as 10, 20, 40, 60, and 90 percent of the original sample, flash point tests can be conducted on the residue. The results of such tests indicate the grouping into which the liquid should be placed if the conditions of use are such as to make it likely that appreciable evaporation will take place. For open system conditions, such as in open dip tanks, the open-cup test method will give a more reliable indication of the flammability hazard.

C.3 Flash Point Test Methods. In the interest of reproducible results, the following procedures are recommended for determining flash point:

(1) The flash point of liquids having a viscosity less than 5.5 mm^2/s (5.5 cSt) at 40°C (104°F) or less than 9.5 mm^2/s (9.5 cSt) at 25°C (77°F) and a flash point below 93.4°C (200°F) may be determined in accordance with ASTM D 56, *Standard Method of Test for Flash Point by the Tag Closed Tester.* (In those countries that use the Abel or Abel-Pensky closed cup tests as an official standard, these tests will be equally acceptable to the Tag Closed Cup Method.)
(2) For liquids having flash points in the range of 0°C (32°F) to 110°C (230°F) the determination may be made in accordance with ASTM D 3278, *Flash Point of Liquids by Setaflash Closed Tester,* or ASTM D 3828, *Standard Test Method for Flash Point by Small Scale Closed Tester.*
(3) For viscous and solid chemicals, the determination may be made in accordance with ASTM E 502, *Flash Point of Chemicals by Closed Cup Methods.*
(4) The flash point of liquids having a viscosity of 5.5 mm^2/s (5.5 cSt) or greater at 40°C (100°F) or 9.5 mm^2/s (9.5 cSt) or greater at 25°C (77°F) can be determined in accordance with ASTM D 93, *Test Methods for Flash Point by the Pensky-Martens Closed Tester.*

Annex D ASTM D 6668, *Standard Test Method for the Discrimination Between Flammability Ratings of F = 0 and F = 1*

This annex is not a part of the requirements of this NFPA document but is included for informational purposes only.

D.1 Description of Test Procedure.

D.1.1 Flammability Hazard Degree Zero. Materials that will not burn in air when exposed to a temperature of 816°C (1500°F) for 5 minutes under the conditions of this test, provided that they do not exhibit properties including flash point, fire point, autoignition temperature, or sustained combustibility, which could cause them to be rated or classified as a more hazardous material (i.e., F = 1 or higher) would be rated as flammability hazard degree zero.

D.1.2 Flammability Hazard Degree One. Materials that will burn in air when exposed to a temperature of 816°C (1500°F) for 5 minutes under the conditions of this test or, by reason of their flash point, fire point, autoignition temperature, or sustained combustibility, would be rated as Hazard Degree One regardless of their performance in this test procedure.

D.1.3 Burning. For the purposes of this procedure, burning is defined to include the presence of any visible flame, sparks, or glowing embers when the sample is exposed to 816°C (1500°F) for 5 minutes under the conditions of the test. Charring without visible evidence of flame, sparks, or glowing embers is not considered to constitute burning.

D.2 Summary of the Test Method. Small, measured amounts of the sample are placed on a stainless steel surface heated to 816°C (1500°F). Reactions that occur during the 5-minute interval thereafter are observed and recorded.

D.3 Significance and Use. A material that does not exhibit any evidence of burning as defined herein under the conditions of the test procedure can be classified as Flammability Degree of Hazard Zero material, provided other properties of the material are not such as to require a higher degree of classification.

D.4 Test Specimen.

D.4.1 For a liquid sample, 30 mL are sufficient for the performance of this test procedure.

D.4.2 For a solid specimen, 30 g are sufficient for the performance of this test procedure.

D.5 Apparatus. The following test materials are necessary to perform the procedure:

(1) Heater, Precision Scientific Co., flask heater, model no. 61600, 750W, 120 VAC, with transformer heat control
(2) Temperature readout device — any potentiometric or electronic device capable of reading the temperature of a chromel alumel thermocouple within ±0.6°C (±1°F)
(3) Precision grade chromel alumel thermocouple, 24 gauge, welded to center of stainless steel planchet
(4) Stainless steel planchet, 26 gauge, 50 mm diameter × 12.7 mm deep
(5) Pyrex® chimney, 70 mm O.D. × 230 mm high mounted over planchet with 2.5 mm air gap between bottom of chimney and top of planchet holder surface
(6) Planchet holder, ceramic composite capable of withstanding 816°C (1500°F), 127 mm × 127 mm thick with 54-mm centrally located hole to hold planchet
(7) Ceramic cord, 0.8 mm diameter to be wrapped around planchet, if needed to hold it firmly in place in the planchet holder
(8) Hypodermic syringe, 0.5 mL with 450 mm 26 gauge needle; Teflon®-tipped plunger is preferred
(9) Assembled test apparatus, see Figure D.5

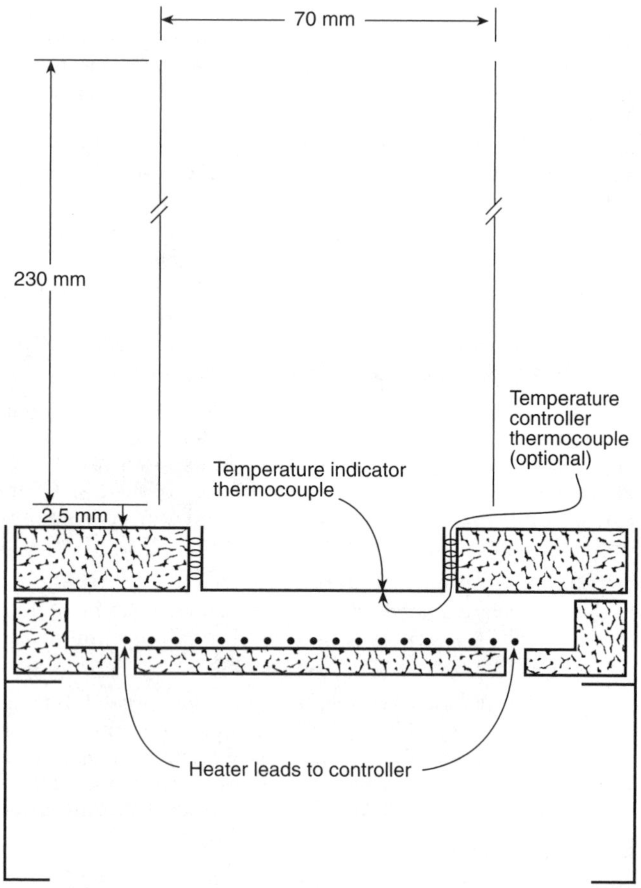

FIGURE D.5 Assembled test apparatus.

D.6 Materials. The following materials are necessary to perform the procedure:

(1) Mineral spirits, ASTM D 235, Type 1
(2) Steel wool
(3) Absorbent tissue

D.7 Procedure. The test procedures are as follows:

(1) Rinse interior of planchet with mineral spirits and wipe dry with absorbent tissue.
(2) Set the control transformer to bring the interior surface of the planchet to 816°C (1500°F) and adjust the transformer setting until the surface temperature remains at ±816°C (±1500°F).
(3) For liquid samples, introduce a 0.1-mL specimen onto the heated planchet surface and observe for evidence of burning as defined in D.1.3. If no burning is observed, repeat for 0.2-mL, 0.5-mL, and 1.0-mL specimens as required to establish whether burning occurs. If burning is observed for any specimen size, further investigation with larger specimens is not required.
(4) For solid specimens, introduce a 0.1-g specimen onto the heated planchet surface and observe for evidence of burning as defined by D.1.3. If no burning is observed, repeat for 0.2-g, 0.5-g, and 1.0-g specimens as required to establish whether burning occurs. If burning is observed for any specimen size, further investigation with larger specimens is not required.

D.7.1 A complete test for either liquid or solid specimens should include duplication of Sections D.7(1), D.7(2), D.7(3) and/or D.7(4), as can be required to confirm initial findings.

D.7.2 This procedure can be conducted at individual temperatures lower than 816°C (1500°F) or at a series of lower temperatures to determine the threshold for burning. Any such variations in test procedure should be reported.

D.8 Report.

D.8.1 Report whether or not burning as defined in D.1.3 occurs at the test temperature.

D.8.2 If no burning occurs, report that the Flammability Hazard Rating of the sample is zero, provided that no conflicting properties of the sample require a higher rating.

D.8.3 If burning occurs, report that the Flammability Hazard Rating of the sample is one, provided that no conflicting properties of the sample require a higher rating.

Annex E Instability, Thermal Hazard Evaluation Techniques

This annex is not a part of the requirements of this NFPA document but is included for informational purposes only.

E.1 Intrinsic Thermal Stability. Thermal stability for hazard evaluation purposes can be done by a number of methods. Frequently used techniques include differential scanning calorimetry (DSC) and accelerating rate calorimetry (ARC). These tests should be performed in a manner meeting or exceeding the requirements outlined in ASTM E 537, *Standard Test Method for Assessing the Thermal Stability of Chemicals by Methods of Differential Thermal Analysis*, or ASTM E 1981, *Guide for Assessing the Thermal Stability of Materials by Methods of Accelerating Rate Calorimetry.*

Obtaining the instability rating through testing and Instantaneous Power Density data (IPD) is preferred. This method is discussed in Annex E.2, and IPD takes precedence over other small-scale calorimetric methods. When data are unavailable to apply the IPD method, the following two alternatives are available: Data from DSC or ARC (or their equivalent) may be used to determine the adiabatic exotherm initiation temperature. This can be used to define ratings of 0, 1, or 2.

Materials that exhibit adiabatic exotherm initiation temperatures below 200°C should be rated as at least 2; materials that polymerize vigorously with evolution of heat should also be rated at least 2.

Materials that exhibit adiabatic exotherm initiation temperatures between 200°C and 500°C should be rated 1; materials that may polymerize when heated should also be rated 1.

Materials that do not exhibit an exotherm at temperatures less than or equal to 500°C should be rated zero.

Professional judgment should be applied to a chemical being rated using this method that might have an instability rating of 2 or greater.

Reactive materials are far more likely to suffer catalytic or surface effects in small test containers, hence biasing the adiabatic exotherm initiation temperature.

This judgment should include comparisons with the qualitative criteria described in Table 7.2, Degrees of Instability Hazards, analogy with chemicals of similar chemical structure and historical incidents, plus data obtained using the following methods.

Information to assist this professional judgment includes, but is not limited to, data obtained via DSC or ARC. ASTM D 2879, *Standard Test Method for Vapor Pressure-Temperature Relationship and Initial Decomposition Temperature of Liquids by Isoteniscope*, may be used as an indication of thermal stability when data meeting the requirements of ASTM E 537 are not available. Self-Accelerating Decomposition Temperature (SADT) test results may also be used. Alternatively, calculations based on the "CHETAH" program could be carried out.

It should be noted that tests that are performed in small volume analytical apparatus are not predictive of the explosive behavior of large masses of material, and therefore cannot distinguish instability ratings of 3 and 4.

Appropriate testing should be conducted for mixtures because the mixtures may react differently than indicated by the individual components.

E.2 Instantaneous Power Density. IPD is calculated as the product of the enthalpy of decomposition/reaction and the initial rate of reaction, determined at 250°C (482°F). This quantity represents the amount of heat energy per unit time per unit volume (W/mL) that a material will initially give at 250°C (482°F). The values that make up the power density can be obtained from thermodynamic tables, calculations, and experimental measurements. The values are obtained from appropriate measurements using DSC *(see ASTM E 698, Standard Test Method for Arrhenius Kinetic Constants for Thermally Unstable Materials)*, or ARC *(see ASTM E 1981, Guide for Assessing the Thermal Stability of Materials by Methods of Accelerating Rate Calorimetry)*. In a typical calculation, the rates of reaction as a function of temperature are obtained and expressed in terms of an Arrhenius expression and an overall, initial-rate expression (Laidler, 1965). This rate expression represents the initial rate of decomposition where the decrease in concentration of the material as a result of the decomposition/reaction has not progressed to a significant (<5%) level. This allows one to use the initial concentration of the material in the simplified rate expression. *(See Table E.2.)*

In order to clarify the calculation of instantaneous power density, a sample calculation is provided.

Table E.2 Instability Rating as a Result of Thermal Instability

Instability Rating	Instantaneous Power Density at 250°C
4	1000 W/mL or greater
3	At or above 100 W/mL and below 1000 W/mL
2	At or above 10 W/mL and below 100 W/mL
1	At or above 0.01 W/mL and below 10 W/mL
0	Below 0.01 W/mL

Differential scanning calorimetry was carried out, and the following parameters were obtained for a material of interest:

Enthalpy of decomposition (ΔH):	–80.5 cal/g
Arrhenius Activation Energy (E_a):	36.4 kcal/mol
Arrhenius Pre-exponential (A_{PRE}):	1.60×10^{15} s^{-1}
Reaction Order (n)	1
Initial concentration of material or density of pure material (conc.):	0.80 g/mL

The initial rate of decomposition of the material at 250°C (482°F) can be calculated using the following Arrhenius expression, where *R* is the universal gas constant whose value is taken as 1.987 cal/(mol°C):

$$\text{Rate} = \text{Conc}^{\text{Order}} \times A_{\text{PRE}} \times e^{-E_{a}/RT}$$

The units used are as follows:

$$\frac{g}{mL \times s} = \left(\frac{g}{mL}\right)^{\text{order}} \times \left(\frac{g}{mL \times s}\right)^{1-\text{order}} \times e^{-\frac{cal/mol}{cal/(mol \times K)^{K}}}$$

$$\text{Rate} = 0.80^{+1} \times 1.60 \times 10^{+15} \times e^{-\frac{36400}{1.987 \times (273+250)}}$$

$$\text{Rate} = 0.79 \frac{g}{mL \times s}$$

$$\text{Rate} = 0.80^{+1} \times 1.60 \times 10^{+15} \times e^{-\frac{36400}{1039}}$$

The power density is given as the product of this decomposition and the enthalpy of decomposition (the value of 4.184 W/cal/sec allows the use of units W/mL):

$$\text{IPD} = -\Delta H \times \text{Rate}$$

$$\text{UNITS: } \frac{W}{mL} = \frac{cal}{g} \times \frac{g}{mL \times s} \times 4.184 \frac{W}{cal/s}$$

$$\text{IPD} = -(80.5) \times 0.79 \times 4.184 \frac{W}{cal/s}$$

$$\text{IPD} = 63 \frac{cal}{s \times mL} \times 4.184 \frac{W}{cal/s}$$

$$\text{IPD} = 270 \frac{W}{mL}$$

The instantaneous power density (IPD) is used as a positive value: the greater the power density, the greater the rate of energy release per volume. Therefore, the exothermic enthalpy of reaction, thermodynamically taken with a negative sign to show release of heat to the surroundings, is taken as a negative so as to rectify the sign of IPD.

This material, having an IPD of 270 W/mL, would be rated a 3 per Table E.2.

Annex F Water Reactivity Identification Criteria

This annex is not a part of the requirements of this NFPA document but is included for informational purposes only.

F.1 General. It is again noted that with the assignment of water reactivity ratings, a considerable degree of judgment can be needed, as noted in Section 4.2, combined with the guidance below.

F.2 Water Reactivity Hazard Degree Zero. Indicates the chemical is essentially non-reactive with water, therefore the ₩ symbol is not used. Using the Two Drop Mixing Calorimeter (Hofelich 1994) or equivalent technique, the heat of reaction is less than 30 calories per gram of total mixture (cal/g), using a 1:1 wt/wt ratio of chemical to water. Gas is not generated, although the evaporation rate of a volatile liquid chemical can be increased during water application. The heat of reaction can also be capable of generating sufficient water vapor pressure to damage some closed containers. An example of a water reactivity rating of zero is diethanolamine with a –6.5 cal/g Two Drop Mixing Calorimeter Test result, with no gas release.

F.3 Water Reactivity Hazard Degree One. The heat of reaction is too small to preclude the use of water during emergency response. Since water is an acceptable agent for dilution of spills and for fire control, chemicals with this rating are not assigned the ₩ symbol. Using the Two Drop Mixing Calorimeter (Hofelich 1994) or equivalent technique, the heat of reaction is greater than or equal to 30 calories per gram of total mixture (cal/g), but less than 100 cal/g, using a 1:1 wt/wt ratio of chemical to water. The heat of reaction may be capable of causing the water to boil at atmospheric pressure. The ₩ 1 rating should be used if any gas is generated via reaction with water, even if the heat of reaction is below 30 cal/g. The following are three examples:

(1) *50 percent sodium hydroxide.* The exothermic heat of solution measured using the Two Drop Mixing Calorimeter is –35.3 cal/g with no gas release, therefore a ₩ 1 rating is assigned. It should be noted that the heat of solution of a solid material such as sodium hydroxide is not constant, but decreases as the solid goes into solution. The first water that is added to sodium hydroxide could in fact boil, even though the Two Drop Calorimeter indicates a heat release of much less than 100 cal/g. Where large quantities of such solids are wetted by small quantities of water, the instability hazard might be better represented by a water reactivity rating of ₩ 2.
(2) *Sodium hydrosulfite.* The exothermic reaction with water releases heat which can lead to spontaneous combustion of solid. The rating assigned to this chemical is ₩ 1.
(3) *Acetic anhydride.* The exothermic 1:1 molar reaction with water produces 2 moles of acetic acid and no gas release. Since the reactants are not completely miscible at ambient temperature, the reaction tends to be slow unless a solubilizing agent is present. The rating assigned to this chemical is ₩ 1.

F.4 Water Reactivity Hazard Degree Two. Indicates that the reaction with water is rapid and should be used only where it can be applied in flooding quantities (which can be impractical for large piles of solids). Using the Two Drop Mixing Calorimeter test, the heat of reaction is greater than or equal to 100 cal/g, but less than 600 cal/g using a 1:1 wt/wt ratio of chemical to water. The heat of reaction is likely to boil the water at 1:1 wt/wt ratios and may be sufficient to boil both the water and vaporize the chemical. Other than carbon dioxide or steam (or other nonhazardous gases), if flammable or toxic gases are generated in hazardous quantities via reaction with water, the rating determined on the basis of heat of reaction should be increased by 1. The following are four examples of ₩ 2 ratings:

(1) *Calcium carbide.* Although the dry solid does not burn, a nonviolent but vigorous exothermic reaction with water produces calcium hydroxide plus flammable acetylene gas. Trapped pockets of acetylene in a pile of solid may ignite and explode.
(2) *Dichlorosilane.* In contact with water, exothermic hydrolysis is accompanied by evaporation of the volatile liquid phase. Toxic dichlorosilane plus hydrogen chloride gases are released and spontaneous ignition of the dichlorosilane can occur.
(3) *Thionyl chloride.* The heat release using the Two Drop Mixing Calorimeter test is –61.1 cal/g with release of gas.
(4) *Titanium tetrachloride.* The heat release using the Two Drop Mixing Calorimeter test is –350 cal/g with release of hydrogen chloride gas.

F.5 Water Reactivity Hazard Degree Three. Using the Two Drop Mixing Calorimeter test, the heat of reaction is greater than or equal to 600 cal/g. This is often sufficient to cause ignition of flammable components.

The ₩ 3 rating is not increased to a ₩ 4 rating if gas is generated, since "explosive reaction" already implies gas generation. An example of a ₩ 3 rating is triethyl aluminum. The heat release using the Two Drop Mixing Calorimeter test is –1008 cal/g with release of gas.

The Two Drop Mixing Calorimeter test data presented in this annex were published by Hofelich (1997).

Annex G Informational References

G.1 Referenced Publications. The following documents or portions thereof are referenced within this standard for informational purposes only and are thus not part of the requirements of this document unless also listed in Chapter 2.

G.1.1 NFPA Publications. National Fire Protection Association, 1 Batterymarch Park, P.O. Box 9101, Quincy, MA 02269-9101.

NFPA 30, *Flammable and Combustible Liquids Code*, 2000 edition.

NFPA 430, *Code for the Storage of Liquid and Solid Oxidizers*, 2000 edition.

NFPA 432, *Code for the Storage of Organic Peroxide Formulations*, 1997 edition.

Fire Protection Guide to Hazardous Materials, 1997 edition.

G.1.2 Other Publications.

G.1.2.1 ASTM Publications. American Society for Testing and Materials, 100 Barr Harbor Drive, West Conshohocken, PA 19428-2959.

ASTM D 56, *Standard Method of Test for Flash Point by the Tag Closed Tester,* 1993.

ASTM D 86, *Standard Test Method for Distillation of Petroleum Products at Atmospheric Pressure,* 2000.

ASTM D 92, *Standard Test Method for Flash Point and Fire Point by Cleveland Open Cup,* 1990.

ASTM D 93, *Test Methods for Flash Point by the Pensky-Martens Closed Tester,* 1994.

ASTM D 235, *Standard Specification for Mineral Spirits (Petroleum Spirits) (Hydrocarbon Dry Cleaning Solvent),* 1999.

ASTM D 2879, *Standard Test Method for Vapor Pressure–Temperature Relationship and Initial Decomposition Temperature of Liquids by Isoteniscope,* 1997.

ASTM D 3278, *Flash Point of Liquids by Setaflash Closed Tester,* 1989.

ASTM D 3828, *Standard Test Method for Flash Point by Small Scale Closed Tester,* 1993.

ASTM D 6668, *Standard Test Method for the Discrimination Between Flammability Ratings of F = 0 and F = 1,* 2001.

ASTM E 502, *Flash Point of Chemicals by Closed Cup Methods,* 1984.

ASTM E 537, *Standard Test Method for Assessing the Thermal Stability of Chemicals by Methods of Differential Thermal Analysis,* 1986.

ASTM E 698, *Standard Test Method for Arrhenius Kinetic Constants for Thermally Unstable Materials,* 1979.

ASTM E 1981, *Guide for Assessing the Thermal Stability of Materials by Methods of Accelerating Rate Calorimetry,* 1998.

G.1.2.2 UN Publication. United Nations, UN Plaza, New York, NY 10017.

Recommendations on the Transport of Dangerous Goods, 4th revised edition.

G.1.2.3 U.S. Government Publications. U.S. Government Printing Office, Washington, DC 20402.

Federal Register, "Notice of Final Rule," Vol. 50, p. 41092 et seq., October 8, 1985.

Federal Register, "Notice of Proposed Rulemaking," Vol. 50, p. 5270 et seq., February 7, 1985.

G.2 Informational References. The following documents or portions thereof are listed here as informational resources only. They are not a part of the requirements of this document.

Britton, L. G., "Survey of Fire Hazard Classification Systems for Liquids," *Process Safety Progress,* Vol. 18, No. 4, Winter, 1999.

Bretherick, *Handbook of Reactive Chemicals,* Butterworths, Boston, sixth ed., 1999.

Hanley, B., "A Model for the Calculation and the Verification of Closed Cup Flash Points for Multicomponent Mixtures," *Process Safety Progress,* Summer 1998, pp. 86–97.

Hofelich, T. C., D. J. Frurip, and J. B. Powers, "The Determination of Compatibility via Thermal Analysis and Mathematical Modeling," *Process Safety Progress,* Vol. 13, No 4. pp. 227–233, 1994.

Hofelich, T. C., "A Quantitative Approach to Determination of NFPA Reactivity Hazard Rating Parameters," *Process Safety Progress,* Vol. 16, No. 3, p. 121, 1997.

Laidler, K. L., *Chemical Kinetics,* Chapter 3, McGraw Hill, New York, 1965.

National Paint & Coatings Association, *Hazardous Materials Identification System Revised, Implementation Manual,* 1981.

Stull, D. R., "Fundamentals of Fire and Explosion," AIChE Monograph Series, No. 10, Vol. 73, 1977.

G.3 References for Extracts. The following documents are listed here to provide reference information, including title and edition, for extracts given throughout this standard as indicated by a reference in brackets [ ] following a section or paragraph. These documents are not a part of the requirements of this document unless also listed in Chapter 2 for other reasons.

G.3.1 NFPA Publication. National Fire Protection Association, 1 Batterymarch Park, P.O. Box 9101, Quincy, MA 02269–9101.

NFPA 30, *Flammable and Combustible Liquids Code,* 2000.

G.3.2 UN Publication. United Nations, UN Plaza, New York, NY 10017.

Recommendations on the Transport of Dangerous Goods, 4th revised edition.

Index

Annex

Extracts of

NFPA 77, Recommended Practice on Static Electricity, 2000 Edition

NFPA 430, Code for the Storage of Liquid and Solid Oxidizers, 2000 Edition

NFPA 499, Classification of Combustible Dusts and of Hazardous (Classified) Locations for Electrical Installations in Chemical Process Areas, 1997 Edition

Extract Annex A

from

NFPA 77
Recommended Practice on Static Electricity

2000 edition

In an effort to make the NFPA *Fire Protection Guide to Hazardous Materials* more useful, data were extracted and introduced from three documents and incorporated into three extract annexes. These data are presented in the *Guide* for convenience of reference and should be used in conjunction with the associated document to fully understand the associated applicable requirements.

In this Extract Annex A, data were extracted from NFPA 77 for numerous commercially significant materials. The data are relevant to static electricity, including combustibility parameters for approximately 75 gases and vapors, and static electric characteristics for approximately 155 conductive liquids, 21 semiconductive liquids, and 33 nonconductive liquids.

Table B.1 Combustibility Parameters of Gases and Vapors

Gas or Vapor (in air at standard temperature and pressure, unless otherwise noted)	Lowest Minimum Ignition Energy (mJ)	Stoichiometric Mixture (% by volume)	Flammable Limits (% by volume)
acetaldehyde	0.37	7.73	4.05–7.0
acetone	1.15 @ 4.5%	4.97	2.61–2.8
acetylene	0.017 @ 8.5%	7.72	2.5–100
acetylene in oxygen	0.0002 @ 40%	—	—
acrolein	0.13	5.64	2.8–31
acrylonitrile	0.16 @ 9.0%	5.29	3.0–17.0
allyl chloride	0.77	—	2.9–11.1
ammonia	680	21.8	15–28
benzene	0.2 @ 4.7%	2.72	1.3–8.0
1,3-butadiene	0.13 @ 5.2%	3.67	2.0–12
butane	0.25 @ 4.7%	3.12	1.6–8.4
n-butyl chloride	1.24	3.37	1.8–10.1
carbon disulfide	0.009 @ 7.8%	6.53	1.0–50.0
cyclohexane	0.22 @ 3.8%	2.27	1.3–7.8
cyclopentadiene	0.67	—	—
cyclopentane	0.54	2.71	1.5–nd
cyclopropane	0.17 @ 6.3%	4.44	2.4–10.4
dichlorosilane	0.015	17.36	4.7–96
diethyl ether	0.19 @ 5.1%	3.37	1.85–36.5
diethyl ether in oxygen	0.0012	—	2.0–82
diisobutylene	0.96	—	1.1–6.0
diisopropyl ether	1.14	—	1.4–7.9
dimethoxymethane	0.42	—	2.2–13.8
2,2-dimethylbutane	0.25 @ 3.4%	2.16	1.2–7.0
dimethyl ether	0.29	—	3.4–27.0
2,2-dimethyl propane	1.57	—	1.4–7.5
dimethyl sulfide	0.48	—	2.2–19.7
di-t-butyl peroxide	0.41	—	—
ethane	0.24 @ 6.5%	5.64	3.0–12.5
ethane in oxygen	0.0019	—	3.0–66
ethyl acetate	0.46 @ 5.2%	4.02	2.0–11.5
ethylamine	2.4	5.28	3.5–14.0
ethylene	0.07	—	2.7–36.0
ethylene in oxygen	0.0009	—	3.0–80
ethyleneimine	0.48	—	3.6–46
ethylene oxide	0.065 @ 10.8%	7.72	3.0–100
furan	0.22	4.44	2.3–14.3

(continues)

Table B.1 Combustibility Parameters of Gases and Vapors *(Continued)*

Gas or Vapor (in air at standard temperature and pressure, unless otherwise noted)	Lowest Minimum Ignition Energy (mJ)	Stoichiometric Mixture (% by volume)	Flammable Limits (% by volume)
heptane	0.24 @ 3.4%	1.87	1.05–6.7
hexane	0.24 @ 3.8%	2.16	1.1–7.5
hydrogen	0.016 @ 28%	29.5	4.0–75
hydrogen in oxygen	0.0012	—	4.0–94
hydrogen sulfide	0.068	—	4.0–44
isooctane	1.35	—	0.95–6.0
isopentane	0.21 @ 3.8%	—	1.4–7.6
isopropyl alcohol	0.65	4.44	2.0–12.7
isopropyl chloride	1.08	—	2.8–10.7
isopropylamine	2.0	—	—
isopropyl mercaptan	0.53	—	—
methane	0.21 @ 8.5%	9.47	5.0–15.0
methane in oxygen	0.0027	—	5.1–61
methanol	0.14 @ 14.7%	12.24	6.0–36.0
methylacetylene	0.11 @ 6.5%	—	1.7–nd
methylene chloride	>1000	—	14–22
methyl butane	<0.25	—	1.4–7.6
methyl cyclohexane	0.27 @ 3.5%	—	1.2–6.7
methyl ethyl ketone	0.53 @ 5.3%	3.66	2.0–12.0
methyl formate	0.4	—	4.5–23
n-pentane	0.28 @ 3.3%	2.55	1.5–7.8
2-pentane	0.18 @ 4.4%	—	—
propane	0.25 @ 5.2%	4.02	2.1–9.5
propane in oxygen	0.0021	—	—
propionaldehyde	0.32	—	2.6–17
n-propyl chloride	1.08	—	2.6–11.1
propylene	0.28	—	2.0–11.0
propylene oxide	0.13 @ 7.5%	—	2.3–36.0
tetrahydrofuran	0.54	—	2.0–11.8
tetrahydropyran	0.22 @ 4.7%	—	—
thiophene	0.39	—	—
toluene	0.24 @ 4.1%	2.27	1.2–77.0
trichlorosilane	0.017	—	7.083
triethylamine	0.75	2.10	—
2,2,3-trimethyl butane	1.0	—	—
vinyl acetate	0.7	4.45	2.6–13.4
vinyl acetylene	0.082	—	1.7–100
xylene	0.2	1.96	1.0–7.0

nd = not determined.

Source: L. G. Britton, "Using Material Data in Static Hazard Assessment," *Plant/Operations Progress,* American Institute of Chemical Engineers, New York, NY, Vol. 11, No. 2, April 1992, pp. 56–70.

Table B.2 Static Electric Characteristics of Liquids

Liquid	Conductivity (pS/m)	Dielectric Constant	Relaxation Time Constant (sec)
	Conductive Liquids: Conductivity >10^4 pS/m		
acetaldehyde (15°C)	1.7×10^8	21.1	1.1×10^{-6}
acetamide	8.8×10^7	59	5.9×10^{-6}
acetic acid (0°C)	5×10^5	6.15	1.1×10^{-4}
acetic acid (25°C)	1.12×10^6	6.15	4.9×10^{-5}
acetic anhydride (25°C)	4.8×10^7	n/a	n/a
acetone (25°C)	6×10^6	20.7	3×10^{-5}
acetonitrile (20°C)	7×10^8	37.5	5×10^{-7}
acetophenone (25°C)	3.1×10^5	17.39	5.0×10^{-4}
acetyl bromide (25°C)	2.4×10^8	n/a	n/a
acetyl chloride (25°C)	4×10^7	n/a	n/a
acrolein	1.55×10^7	n/a	n/a
acrylonitrile	7×10^5	38	4.8×10^{-4}
allyl alcohol (25°C)	7×10^8	n/a	n/a

Table B.2 Static Electric Characteristics of Liquids *(Continued)*

Liquid	Conductivity (pS/m)	Dielectric Constant	Relaxation Time Constant (sec)
aminoethyl-ethanolamine	$> 1 \times 10^6$	n/a	n/a
n-aminoethyl piperazine	2.4×10^5	n/a	n/a
ammonia (−79°C)	1.3×10^7	n/a	n/a
iso-amyl alcohol	1.4×10^5	14.7	9.3×10^{-4}
aniline (25°C)	2.4×10^6	6.89	2.5×10^{-5}
anthracene (25°C)	3×10^4	n/a	n/a
arsenic tribromide (25°C)	$.5 \times 10^8$	n/a	n/a
arsenic trichloride (25°C)	1.2×10^8	n/a	n/a
benzaldehyde (25°C)	1.5×10^7	n/a	n/a
benzoic acid (125°C)	3×10^5	n/a	n/a
benzonitrile (25°C)	5×10^6	25.2	4.5×10^{-5}
benzyl alcohol (25°C)	1.8×10^8	n/a	n/a
benzylamine (25°C)	$< 1.7 \times 10^6$	n/a	n/a
benzyl benzoate (25°C)	$< 1 \times 10^5$	n/a	n/a
benzyl cyanide	$< 5 \times 10^6$	18.7	$> 3.3 \times 10^{-5}$
biphenyl (liquid above 120°C)	$> 1 \times 10^4$	n/a	n/a
bromoform (25°C)	$< 2 \times 10^6$	4.39	$> 1.9 \times 10^{-5}$
iso-butyl alcohol	9.12×10^5	17.51	1.7×10^{-4}
sec-butyl alcohol	$< 1 \times 10^7$	16.56	$> 1.5 \times 10^{-5}$
t-butyl alcohol	2.66×10^6	12.47	4.2×10^{-5}
iso-butyl chloride	1×10^4	6.49	5.7×10^{-3}
sec-butyl chloride	1×10^4	7.09	6.3×10^{-3}
capronitrile (25°C)	3.7×10^8	n/a	n/a
m-chloroaniline (25°C)	5×10^6	n/a	n/a
chlorohydrin (25°C)	5×10^7	n/a	n/a
m-cresol	1.397×10^6	11.8	7.5×10^{-5}
o-cresol	1.27×10^5	11.5	8.0×10^{-4}
p-cresol	1.378×10^6	9.91	6.4×10^{-5}
cyanogen	$<7 \times 10^5$	n/a	n/a
cyclohexanone	5×10^5	n/a	n/a
cymene (25°C)	$<2 \times 10^6$	n/a	n/a
dibutyl-o-phthalate	$.8 \times 10^5$	6.436	3.2×10^{-4}
dichloroacetic acid (25°C)	7×10^6	n/a	n/a
cis-dichloroethylene	8.5×10^5	9.20	9.6×10^{-5}
dichlorohydrin (25°C)	1.2×10^9	n/a	n/a
diethylamine (−33.5°C)	2.2×10^5	n/a	n/a
diethyl carbonate (25°C)	1.7×10^6	2.82	1.5×10^{-5}
diethylene glycol	5.86×10^7	31.69	4.8×10^{-6}
diethylenetriamine	$> 1 \times 10^6$	n/a	n/a
diethyl oxalate (25°C)	7.6×10^7	n/a	n/a
diethyl sulfate (25°C)	2.6×10^7	n/a	n/a
dimethyl acetamide	$.1 \times 10^7$	n/a	n/a
dimethyl formamide	6×10^6	36.71	5.4×10^{-5}
dimethyl sulfate (0°C)	1.6×10^7	n/a	n/a
dimethyl sulfoxide	2×10^5	46.68	2.1×10^{-3}
diphenyl oxide	$< 1.7 \times 10^6$	4.22	$> 2.2 \times 10^{-5}$
epichlorohydrin (25°C)	3.4×10^6	22.6	5.9×10^{-5}
ethanolamine	1.1×10^9	37.72	3.0×10^{-7}
ethylacetate (25°C)	4.6×10^4	6.02	1.2×10^{-3}
ethyl acetoacetate (25°C)	4×10^6	15.7	3.5×10^{-5}
ethyl acrylate	3.35×10^5	n/a	n/a
ethyl alcohol (25°C)	1.35×10^5	24.55	1.6×10^{-3}
ethylamine (0°C)	4×10^7	n/a	n/a
ethyl benzoate (25°C)	$< 1 \times 10^5$	6.02	$> 5.3 \times 10^{-4}$
ethyl bromide (25°C)	$< 2 \times 10^6$	9.39	$> 4.2 \times 10^{-5}$
ethyl chloride	$< 3 \times 10^5$	9.45	$> 2.8 \times 10^{-4}$
ethyl cyanoacetate	6.9×10^7	26.7	3.4×10^{-6}
ethylene carbonate	$< 1 \times 10^7$	89.6	$> 7.9 \times 10^{-5}$
ethylenediamine	9×10^6	12.9	1.3×10^{-5}
ethylene dibromide (25°C)	$< 2 \times 10^4$	4.78	$> 2.1 \times 10^{-3}$
ethylene glycol	1.16×10^8	37.7	2.9×10^{-6}
ethylene glycol monobutyl ether	4.32×10^7	9.30	1.9×10^{-6}
ethylene glycol monoethyl ether	9.3×10^6	29.6	2.8×10^{-5}
ethylene glycol monomethyl ether	1.09×10^8	16.93	1.4×10^{-6}
ethyleneimene	8×10^8	18.3	2.0×10^{-7}
ethylene oxide	4×10^6	12.7	2.8×10^{-5}

(continues)

Table B.2 Static Electric Characteristics of Liquids *(Continued)*

Liquid	Conductivity (pS/m)	Dielectric Constant	Relaxation Time Constant (sec)
ethyl formate	1.45×10^5	7.16	4.4×10^{-4}
ethylidene chloride	2.0×10^5	10.0	4.4×10^{-4}
ethyl isothiocyanate (25°C)	1.26×10^7	n/a	n/a
ethyl lactate	1.0×10^8	13.1	1.2×10^{-6}
ethyl nitrate (25°C)	5.3×10^7	n/a	n/a
ethyl oxalate	7.12×10^7	n/a	n/a
ethyl propionate	8.33×10^{10}	5.65	6×10^{-10}
ethyl thiocyanate (25°C)	1.2×10^8	n/a	n/a
eugenol (25°C)	$< 1.7 \times 10^6$	n/a	n/a
formamide (25°C)	4×10^8	111.0	2×10^{-6}
formic acid (25°C)	6.4×10^9	58.5	8.1×10^{-8}
furfural (25°C)	1.5×10^8	n/a	n/a
glycerol (25°C)	6.4×10^6	42.5	5.9×10^{-5}
guaiacol (25°C)	2.8×10^7	n/a	n/a
hydrogen bromide (−80°C)	8×10^5	n/a	n/a
hydrogen chloride (−96°C)	1×10^6	n/a	n/a
hydrogen cyanide (0°C)	3.3×10^8	n/a	n/a
hydrogen iodide (at boiling point)	2×10^7	n/a	n/a
iodine (110°C)	1.3×10^4	n/a	n/a
mercury (0°C)	1.063×10^{18}	n/a	n/a
methoxy triglycol	$> 1 \times 10^6$	n/a	n/a
methyl acetamide	2×10^7	191.3	8.5×10^{-5}
methyl acetate (25°C)	3.4×10^8	6.68	1.7×10^{-7}
methyl alcohol (18°C)	4.4×10^7	32.70	6.6×10^{-6}
methyl cyanoacetate	4.49×10^7	29.30	5.8×10^{-6}
methyl ethyl ketone (25°C)	1×10^7	18.51	1.6×10^{-5}
methyl formamide	8×10^7	182.4	2.0×10^{-5}
methyl formate	1.92×10^8	8.5	3.9×10^{-7}
methyl iodide (25°C)	$< 2 \times 10^6$	n/a	n/a
methyl isobutyl ketone	$< 5.2 \times 10^6$	13.11	$> 2.2 \times 10^{-5}$
methyl nitrate (25°C)	4.5×10^8	n/a	n/a
n-methyl-2-pyrolidone	2×10^6	32.0	1.4×10^{-4}
methyl thiocyanate (25°C)	1.5×10^8	n/a	n/a
naphthalene (82°C)	4×10^4	n/a	n/a
nitrobenzene (0°C)	5×10^5	34.82	6.2×10^{-4}
nitroethane	5×10^7	28.06	5.0×10^{-6}
nitromethane (18°C)	6×10^7	35.87	5.3×10^{-6}
1-nitropropane	3.3×10^7	23.24	6.2×10^{-6}
2-nitropropane	5×10^7	25.52	4.5×10^{-6}
nitrotoluene (25°C) (ortho or meta)	$< 2 \times 10^7$	n/a	n/a
octyl alcohol	1.39×10^7	10.34	6.9×10^{-6}
phenetole (25°C)	$< 1.7 \times 10^6$	n/a	n/a
phenol	1×10^6	9.78	8.7×10^{-5}
phenyl isothiocyante (25°C)	1.4×10^8	n/a	n/a
phosgene (25°C)	7×10^5	n/a	n/a
phosphorus (25°C)	4×10^8	n/a	n/a
phosphorus oxychloride (25°C)	2.2×10^8	n/a	n/a
pinene (23°C)	$< 2 \times 10^4$	n/a	n/a
piperidine (25°C)	$< 2 \times 10^7$	n/a	n/a
propionaldehyde (25°C)	8.5×10^7	18.5	1.9×10^{-6}
propionic acid (25°C)	$< 1 \times 10^5$	3.44	$> 3.0 \times 10^{-4}$
propionitrile	8.51×10^6	27.2	2.8×10^{-5}
propyl acetate (i- or n-)	$1-6 \times 10^4$	6.002	n/a
n-propyl alcohol (25°C)	2×10^6	20.33	9×10^{-5}
iso-propyl alcohol (25°C)	3.5×10^8	19.92	5×10^{-7}
propyl formate	5.5×10^9	7.72	1.2×10^{-8}
pyridine (18°C)	5.3×10^6	12.4	2.1×10^{-5}
quinoline (25°C)	2.2×10^6	9.0	3.6×10^{-5}
salicylaldehyde (25°C)	1.6×10^7	13.9	7.5×10^{-6}
succinonitrile	5.64×10^{10}	56.5	8.9×10^{-9}
sulfolane	$< 2 \times 10^6$	43.3	$> 1.9 \times 10^{-4}$
sulfonyl chloride (25°C)	2×10^8	n/a	n/a
sulfuric acid (25°C)	1×10^{12}	n/a	n/a
tetraethylene-pentamine	$> 1 \times 10^6$	n/a	n/a
tetramethylurea	$< 6 \times 10^6$	23.06	$> 3.4 \times 10^{-5}$
m-toluidine	5.5×10^4	9.91	1.6×10^{-3}
o-toluidine	3.79×10^7	6.34	1.5×10^{-6}
p-toluidine (100°C)	6.2×10^6	4.98	7.1×10^{-6}

Table B.2 Static Electric Characteristics of Liquids *(Continued)*

Liquid	Conductivity (pS/m)	Dielectric Constant	Relaxation Time Constant (sec)
trichloroacetic acid (25°C)	3×10^5	n/a	n/a
1,1,1-trichloroethane	7.3×10^5	7.53	9.1×10^{-5}
triethylene glycol	8.4×10^6	23.69	2.5×10^{-5}
triethylenetetramine	$> 1 \times 10^6$	n/a	n/a
trimethylamine (−35°C)	2.2×10^4	n/a	n/a
vinyl acetate	2.6×10^4	n/a	n/a
water (extremely pure)	4.3×10^6	80.4	1.7×10^{-4}
water (air distilled)	$\sim 1 \times 10^9$	80.4	7.1×10^{-4}
Semiconductive Liquids: Conductivity from 50 pS/m to 10^4 pS/m			
amyl acetate	2160	4.75	1.9×10^{-2}
armeen	470	n/a	n/a
biphenyl (liquid at 69°C−120°C)	2500–10,000	n/a	n/a
bromobenzene	1200	5.40	4×10^{-2}
1-bromonaphthalene	3660	4.83	1.1×10^{-2}
butyl acetate (i- or n-)	4300	n/a	n/a
butyl acrylate	3580	n/a	n/a
chlorobenzene	7000	5.621	7.1×10^{-3}
chloroform	< 10,000	4.806	$> 4.3 \times 10^{-3}$
dibutyl sebacate	1700	4.54	2.4×10^{-2}
dichlorobenzene	3000	9.93	2.9×10^{-3}
ethylene dichloride	4000	10.36	2.2×10^{-2}
2-ethylhexyl acrylate	610	n/a	n/a
gasoline (leaded)	> 50	2.3	<0.41
hydrogen sulfide (at boiling point)	1000	n/a	n/a
methylene chloride	4300	8.93	1.8×10^{-2}
pentachloroethane	100	3.83	0.3
sulfur (130°C)	5000	n/a	n/a
1,2,4-trichlorobenzene	200	4.08	0.18
trichloroethylene	800	3.42	3.7×10^{-2}
vinyltrimethoxysilane (<2% methanol)	5900	n/a	n/a
Nonconductive Liquids: Conductivity <50 pS/m			
anisole	0	4.33	3.8
benzene (pure)	5×10^{-3}	2.3	~100 (dissipation)
biphenyl (solid <69°C)	0.17	n/a	n/a
bromine (17.2°C)	13	n/a	n/a
butyl stearate	21	3.111	1.3
caprylic acid	< 37	2.45	> 0.58
carbon disulfide (1°C)	7.8×10^{-4}	2.6	~100 (dissipation)
carbon tetrachloride	4×10^{-4}	2.238	~100 (dissipation)
chlorine (−70°C)	< 0.01	n/a	n/a
cyclohexane	< 2	2.0	> 8.8
decalin	6	2.18	3.2
dichlorosilane	n/a	n/a	n/a
diesel oil (purified)	~0.1	~2	~100 (dissipation)
diethyl ether	30	4.6	1.4
1,4-dioxane	0.1	2.2	~100 (dissipation)
ethyl benzene	30	2.3	0.68
gasoline (straight run)	~0.1	~2	~100 (dissipation)
gasoline (unleaded)	< 50 (varies)		
heptane (pure)	3×10^{-2}	2.0	~100 (dissipation)
hexane (pure)	1×10^{-5}	1.90	~100 (dissipation)
hexamethyldisilazane	29	n/a	n/a
isovaleric acid	40	2.64	> 0.58
jet fuel	0.01−50	2.2	0.39–100
kerosene	1−50	2.2	0.39–19
pentachlorodiphenyl	0.8	5.06	~100
silicon tetrachloride	n/a	n/a	n/a
stearic acid (80°C)	< 40	n/a	n/a
styrene monomer	0	2.43	2.2
sulfur (115°C)	100	n/a	n/a
toluene	< 1	2.38	21
trichlorosilane	n/a	n/a	n/a
turpentine	22	n/a	n/a
xylene	0.1	2.38	~100

Source: L. G. Britton, "Using Material Data in Static Hazard Assessment," *Plant/Operations Progress*, American Institute of Chemical Engineers, New York, NY, Vol. 11, No. 2, April 1992, pp. 56–70.

Extract Annex B

from

NFPA 430
Code for the Storage of Liquid and Solid Oxidizers

2000 edition

In an effort to make the NFPA *Fire Protection Guide to Hazardous Materials* more useful, data were extracted and introduced from three documents and incorporated into three extract annexes. These data are presented in the *Guide* for convenience of reference and should be used in conjunction with the associated document to fully understand the associated applicable requirements.

In this Extract Annex B, data were extracted from NFPA 430 for classification of 90 typical liquid and solid oxidizers to assist with safe handling, fire prevention, and storage provisions.

1.6 Classification of Oxidizers. For the purpose of this code, oxidizers are classified according to the system listed in (a) through (d) of Section 1-6. The classification is based on the technical committee's evaluation of available scientific and technical data, actual experience, and its considered opinion. Classification refers to the pure oxidizer. Gross contamination can cause oxidizers of all classes to undergo exothermic or explosive reaction, particularly if they also are subjected to confinement and heating. *(See definition 1-5.13, Oxidizer. See Sections B-2 through B-5 for oxidizer classifications.)*

(a) *Class 1.* An oxidizer that meets the definition of an oxidizer in 1-5.13 and does not moderately increase the burning rate of combustible materials with which it comes into contact.

(b) *Class 2.* An oxidizer that will cause a moderate increase in the burning rate of combustible materials with which it comes into contact.

(c) **Class 3.* An oxidizer that will cause a severe increase in the burning rate of combustible materials with which it comes into contact or that will undergo vigorous self-sustained decomposition due to contamination or exposure to heat.

(d) **Class 4.* An oxidizer that can undergo an explosive reaction due to contamination or exposure to thermal or physical shock. In addition, the oxidizer will cause a severe increase in the burning rate of combustible materials with which it comes into contact.

Appendix B Typical Oxidizers

This appendix is not a part of the requirements of this NFPA document but is included for informational purposes only.

B.1 Unless concentration is specified, undiluted material is referenced. The following lists of oxidizers are provided to clarify how the committee has classified typical oxidizers. The lists are not all-inclusive and are amended to reflect typical oxidizers used.

B.2 Typical Class 1 Oxidizers.

All inorganic nitrites (unless otherwise classified)

Ammonium persulfate

Barium peroxide

Calcium peroxide

Hydrogen peroxide solutions (greater than 8 percent up to 27.5 percent)

Lead dioxide

Lithium hypochlorite (39 percent or less available chlorine)

Lithium peroxide

Magnesium peroxide

Manganese dioxide

Nitric acid (40 percent concentration or less)

Perchloric acid solutions (less than 50 percent by weight)

Potassium dichromate

Potassium percarbonate

Potassium persulfate

Sodium carbonate peroxide

Sodium dichloro-*s*-triazinetrione dihydrate

Sodium dichromate

Sodium perborate (anhydrous)

Sodium perborate monohydrate

Sodium perborate tetrahydrate

Sodium percarbonate

Sodium persulfate

Strontium peroxide

Trichloro-*s*-triazinetrione (trichloroisocyanuric) (acid all forms)

Zinc peroxide

B.3 Typical Class 2 Oxidizers.

Barium bromate

Barium chlorate

Barium hypochlorite

Barium perchlorate

Barium permanganate

1-Bromo-3-chloro-5,5-dimethylhydantoin (BCDMH)

Calcium chlorate

Calcium chlorite

Calcium hypochlorite (50 percent or less by weight)

Calcium perchlorate

Calcium permanganate

Chromium trioxide (chromic acid)

Copper chlorate

Halane (1,3-dichloro-5,5-dimethylhydantoin)

Hydrogen peroxide (greater than 27.5 percent up to 52 percent)

Lead perchlorate

Lithium chlorate

Lithium hypochlorite (more than 39 percent available chlorine)

Lithium perchlorate

Magnesium bromate

Magnesium chlorate

Magnesium perchlorate

Mercurous chlorate

Nitric acid (more than 40 percent but less than 86 percent)

Nitrogen tetroxide

Perchloric acid solutions (more than 50 percent but less than 60 percent)

Potassium perchlorate

Potassium permanganate

Potassium peroxide

Potassium superoxide

Silver peroxide

Sodium chlorite (40 percent or less by weight)

Sodium perchlorate

Sodium perchlorate monohydrate

Sodium permanganate

Sodium peroxide

Strontium chlorate

Strontium perchlorate

Thallium chlorate

Urea hydrogen peroxide

Zinc bromate

Zinc chlorate

Zinc permanganate

B.4 Typical Class 3 Oxidizers.

Ammonium dichromate

Calcium hypochlorite (over 50 percent by weight)

Chloric acid (10 percent maximum concentration)

Hydrogen peroxide solutions (greater than 52 percent up to 91 percent)

Mono-(trichloro)-tetra-(monopotassium dichloro)-penta-*s*-triazinetrione

Nitric acid, fuming (more than 86 percent concentration)

Perchloric acid solutions (60 percent to 72 percent by weight)

Potassium bromate

Potassium chlorate

Potassium dichloro-*s*-triazinetrione (potassium dichloroisocyanurate)

Sodium bromate

Sodium chlorate

Sodium chlorite (over 40 percent by weight)

Sodium dichloro-*s*-triazinetrione (sodium dichloroisocyanurate)

B.5 Typical Class 4 Oxidizers.

Ammonium perchlorate (particle size greater than 15 microns)

Ammonium permanganate

Guanidine nitrate

Hydrogen peroxide solutions (greater than 91 percent)

Tetranitromethane

Ammonium perchlorate less than 15 microns is classified as an explosive and, as such, is not covered by this code. *(See NFPA 495, Explosive Materials Code.)*

Extract Annex C

from

NFPA 499

Recommended Practice for the Classification of Combustible Dusts and of Hazardous (Classified) Locations for Electrical Installations in Chemical Process Areas

1997 edition

In an effort to make the NFPA *Fire Protection Guide to Hazardous Materials* more useful, data were extracted and introduced from three documents and incorporated into three extract annexes. These data are presented in the *Guide* for convenience of reference and should be used in conjunction with the associated document to fully understand the associated applicable requirements.

In this Extract Annex C, data from NFPA 499 relating to the parameters to determine the degree and extent of hazardous locations for dusts, including CAS number, NEC group, and layer or cloud ignition temperature are provided for approximately 220 combustible materials.

Table 2-5 Selected Combustible Materials

Chemical Name	CAS #	NEC Group	Code	Layer or Cloud Ignition Temp °C
Acetal, Linear		G	NL	440
Acetoacet-p-phenetidide	122-82-7	G	NL	560
Acetoacetanilide	102-01-2	G	M	440
Acetylamino-t-nitrothiazole		G		450
Acrylamide Polymer		G		240
Acrylonitrile Polymer		G		460
Acrylonitrile-Vinyl Chloride-Vinylidenechloride copolymer (70-20-10)		G		210
Acrylonitrile-Vinyl Pyridine Copolymer		G		240
Adipic Acid	124-04-9	G	M	550
Alfalfa Meal		G		200
Alkyl Ketone Dimer Sizing Compound		G		160
Allyl Alcohol Derivative (CR-39)		G	NL	500
Almond Shell		G		200
Aluminum, A422 Flake	7429-90-5	E		320
Aluminum, Atomized Collector Fines		E	CL	550
Aluminum—cobalt alloy (60-40)		E		570
Aluminum—copper alloy (50-50)		E		830
Aluminum—lithium alloy (15% Li)		E		400
Aluminum—magnesium alloy (Dowmetal)		E	CL	430
Aluminum—nickel alloy (58-42)		E		540
Aluminum—silicon alloy (12% Si)		E	NL	670
Amino-5-nitrothiazole	121-66-4	G		460
Anthranilic Acid	118-92-3	G	M	580
Apricot Pit		G		230
Aryl-nitrosomethylamide		G	NL	490
Asphalt	8052-42-4	F		510
Aspirin [acetol (2)]	50-78-2	G	M	660
Azelaic Acid	109-31-9	G	M	610
Azo-bis-butyronitrile	78-67-1	G		350
Benzethonium Chloride		G	CL	380
Benzoic Acid	65-85-0	G	M	440
Benzotriazole	95-14-7	G	M	440
Beta-naphthalene-axo-dimethylaniline		G		175

(continues)

Table 2-5 Selected Combustible Materials *(Continued)*

Chemical Name	CAS #	NEC Group	Code	Layer or Cloud Ignition Temp °C
Bis(2-hydroxy-5-chlorophenyl) Methane	97-23-4	G	NL	570
Bisphenol-A	80-05-7	G	M	570
Boron, Commercial Amorphous (85% B)	7440-42-8	E		400
Calcium Silicide		E		540
Carbon Black (More Than 8% Total Entrapped Volatiles)		F		
Carboxymethyl Cellulose	9000-11-7	G		290
Carboxypolymethylene		G	NL	520
Cashew Oil, Phenolic, Hard		G		180
Cellulose		G		260
Cellulose Acetate		G		340
Cellulose Acetate Butyrate		G	NL	370
Cellulose Triacetate		G	NL	430
Charcoal (Activated)	64365-11-3	F		180
Charcoal (More Than 8% Total Entrapped Volatiles)		F		
Cherry Pit		G		220
Chlorinated Phenol		G	NL	570
Chlorinated Polyether Alcohol		G		460
Chloroacetoacetanilide	101-92-8	G	M	640
Chromium (97%) Electrolytic, Milled	7440-47-3	E		400
Cinnamon		G		230
Citrus Peel		G		270
Coal, Kentucky Bituminous		F		180
Coal, Pittsburgh Experimental		F		170
Coal, Wyoming		F		
Cocoa Bean Shell		G		370
Cocoa, Natural, 19% Fat		G		240
Coconut Shell		G		220
Coke (More Than 8% Total Entrapped Volatiles)		F		
Cork		G		210
Corn		G		250
Corn Dextrine		G		370
Corncob Grit		G		240
Cornstarch, Commercial		G		330
Cornstarch, Modified		G		200
Cottonseed Meal		G		200
Coumarone-Indene, Hard		G	NL	520
Crag No. 974	533-74-4	G	CL	310
Cube Root, South America	83-79-4	G		230
Di-alphacumyl Peroxide, 40-60 on CA	80-43-3	G		180
Diallyl Phthalate	131-17-9	G	M	480
Dicyclopentadiene Dioxide		G	NL	420
Dieldrin (20%)	60-57-1	G	NL	550
Dihydroacetic Acid		G	NL	430
Dimethyl Isophthalate	1459-93-4	G	M	580
Dimethyl Terephthalate	120-61-6	G	M	570
Dinitro-o-toluamide	148-01-6	G	NL	500
Dinitrobenzoic Acid		G	NL	460
Diphenyl	92-52-4	G	M	630
Ditertiary-butyl-paracresol	128-37-0	G	NL	420
Dithane m-45	8018-01-7	G		180
Epoxy		G	NL	540
Epoxy-bisphenol A		G	NL	510
Ethyl Cellulose		G	CL	320
Ethyl Hydroxyethyl Cellulose		G	NL	390
Ethylene Oxide Polymer		G	NL	350
Ethylene-maleic Anhydride Copolymer		G	NL	540
Ferbam™	14484-64-1	G		150
Ferromanganese, Medium Carbon	12604-53-4	E		290
Ferrosilicon (88% Si, 9% Fe)	8049-17-0	E		800

Table 2-5 Selected Combustible Materials *(Continued)*

Chemical Name	CAS #	NEC Group	Code	Layer or Cloud Ignition Temp °C
Ferrotitanium (19% Ti, 74.1% Fe, 0.06% C)		E	CL	380
Flax Shive		G		230
Fumaric Acid	110-17-8	G	M	520
Garlic, Dehydrated		G	NL	360
Gilsonite	12002-43-6	F		500
Green Base Harmon Dye		G		175
Guar Seed		G	NL	500
Gulasonic Acid, Diacetone		G	NL	420
Gum, Arabic		G		260
Gum, Karaya		G		240
Gum, Manila		G	CL	360
Gum, Tragacanth	9000-65-1	G		260
Hemp Hurd		G		220
Hexamethylene Tetramine	100-97-0	G	S	410
Hydroxyethyl Cellulose		G	NL	410
Iron, 98% H_2 Reduced		E		290
Iron, 99% Carbonyl	13463-40-6	E		310
Isotoic Anhydride		G	NL	700
L-sorbose		G	M	370
Lignin, Hydrolized, Wood-type, Fine		G	NL	450
Lignite, California		F		180
Lycopodium		G		190
Malt Barley		G		250
Manganese	7439-96-5	E		240
Magnesium, Grade B, Milled		E		430
Manganese Vancide		G		120
Mannitol	69-65-8	G	M	460
Methacrylic Acid Polymer		G		290
Methionine (l-methionine)	63-68-3	G		360
Methyl Cellulose		G		340
Methyl Methacrylate Polymer	9011-14-7	G	NL	440
Methyl Methacrylate-ethyl Acrylate		G	NL	440
Methyl Methacrylate-styrene-butadiene		G	NL	480
Milk, Skimmed		G		200
N,N-Dimethylthio-formamide		G		230
Nitropyridone	100703-82-0	G	M	430
Nitrosamine		G	NL	270
Nylon Polymer	63428-84-2	G		430
Para-oxy-benzaldehyde	123-08-0	G	CL	380
Paraphenylene Diamine	106-50-3	G	M	620
Paratertiary Butyl Benzoic Acid	98-73-7	G	M	560
Pea Flour		G		260
Peach Pit Shell		G		210
Peanut Hull		G		210
Peat, Sphagnum	94114-14-4	G		240
Pecan Nut Shell	8002-03-7	G		210
Pectin	5328-37-0	G		200
Pentaerythritol	115-77-5	G	M	400
Petrin Acrylate Monomer	7659-34-9	G	NL	220
Petroleum Coke (More Than 8% Total Entrapped Volatiles)		F		
Petroleum Resin	64742-16-1	G		500
Phenol Formaldehyde	9003-35-4	G	NL	580
Phenol Formaldehyde, Polyalkylene-p	9003-35-4	G		290
Phenol Furfural	26338-61-4	G		310
Phenylbetanaphthylamine	135-88-6	G	NL	680
Phthalic Anydride	85-44-9	G	M	650
Phthalimide	85-41-6	G	M	630
Pitch, Coal Tar	65996-93-2	F	NL	710

(continues)

Table 2-5 Selected Combustible Materials *(Continued)*

Chemical Name	CAS #	NEC Group	Code	Layer or Cloud Ignition Temp °C
Pitch, Petroleum	68187-58-6	F	NL	630
Polycarbonate		G	NL	710
Polyethylene, High Pressure Process	9002-88-4	G		380
Polyethylene, Low Pressure Process	9002-88-4	G	NL	420
Polyethylene Terephthalate	25038-59-9	G	NL	500
Polyethylene Wax	68441-04-8	G	NL	400
Polypropylene (no antioxidant)	9003-07-0	G	NL	420
Polystyrene Latex	9003-53-6	G		500
Polystyrene Molding Compound	9003-53-6	G	NL	560
Polyurethane Foam, Fire Retardant	9009-54-5	G		390
Polyurethane Foam, No Fire Retardant	9009-54-5	G		440
Polyvinyl Acetate	9003-20-7	G	NL	550
Polyvinyl Acetate/Alcohol	9002-89-5	G		440
Polyvinyl Butyral	63148-65-2	G		390
Polyvinyl Chloride-dioctyl Phthalate		G	NL	320
Potato Starch, Dextrinated	9005-25-8	G	NL	440
Pyrethrum	8003-34-7	G		210
Rayon (Viscose) Flock	61788-77-0	G		250
Red Dye Intermediate		G		175
Rice		G		220
Rice Bran		G	NL	490
Rice Hull		G		220
Rosin, DK	8050-09-7	G	NL	390
Rubber, Crude, Hard	9006-04-6	G	NL	350
Rubber, Synthetic, Hard (33% S)	64706-29-2	G	NL	320
Safflower Meal		G		210
Salicylanilide	87-17-2	G	M	610
Sevin	63-25-2	G		140
Shale, Oil	68308-34-9	F		
Shellac	9000-59-3	G	NL	400
Sodium Resinate	61790-51-0	G		220
Sorbic Acid (Copper Sorbate or Potash)	110-44-1	G		460
Soy Flour	68513-95-1	G		190
Soy Protein	9010-10-0	G		260
Stearic Acid, Aluminum Salt	637-12-7	G		300
Stearic Acid, Zinc Salt	557-05-1	G	M	510
Styrene Modified Polyester-Glass Fiber	100-42-5	G		360
Styrene-acrylonitrile (70-30)	9003-54-7	G	NL	500
Styrene-butadiene Latex (>75% styrene)	903-55-8	G	NL	440
Styrene-maleic Anhydride Copolymer	9011-13-6	G	CL	470
Sucrose	57-50-1	G	CL	350
Sugar, Powdered	57-50-1	G	CL	370
Sulfur	7704-34-9	G		220
Tantalum	7440-25-7	E		300
Terephthalic Acid	100-21-0	G	NL	680
Thorium, 1.2% O_2	7440-29-1	E	CL	280
Tin, 96%, Atomized, (2% Pb)	7440-31-5	E		430
Titanium, 99% Ti	7440-32-6	E	CL	330
Titanium Hydride (95% Ti, 3.8% H_2)	7704-98-5	E	CL	480
Trithiobisdimethylthio-formamide		G		230
Tung, Kernels, Oil-free	8001-20-5	G		240
Urea Formaldehyde Molding Compound	9011-05-6	G	NL	460
Urea Formaldehyde-phenol Formaldehyde	25104-55-6	G		240
Vanadium, 86.4%	7440-62-2	E		490
Vinyl Chloride-acrylonitrile Copolymer	9003-00-3	G		470
Vinyl Toluene-acrylonitrile Butadiene	76404-69-8	G	NL	530
Violet 200 Dye		G		175
Vitamin B1, Mononitrate	59-43-8	G	NL	360
Vitamin C	50-81-7	G		280
Walnut Shell, Black		G		220

Table 2-5 Selected Combustible Materials *(Continued)*

Chemical Name	CAS #	NEC Group	Code	Layer or Cloud Ignition Temp °C
Wheat		G		220
Wheat Flour	130498-22-5	G		360
Wheat Gluten, Gum	100684-25-1	G	NL	520
Wheat Starch		G	NL	380
Wheat Straw		G		220
Wood Flour		G		260
Woodbark, Ground		G		250
Yeast, Torula	68602-94-8	G		260
Zirconium Hydride	7704-99-6	E		270
Zirconium		E	CL	330

Notes:
1. Normally, the minimum ignition temperature of a layer of a specific dust is lower then the minimum ignition temperature of a cloud of that dust. Since this is not universally true, the lower of the two minimum ignition temperatures is listed. If no symbol appears between the two temperature columns, then the layer ignition temperature is shown. "CL" means the cloud ignition temperature is shown. "NL" means that no layer ignition temperature is available, and the cloud ignition temperature is shown. "M" signifies that the dust layer melts before it ignites; the cloud ignition temperature is shown. "S" signifies that the dust layer sublimes before it ignites; the cloud ignition temperature is shown.
2. Certain metal dusts may have characteristics that require safeguards beyond those required for atmospheres containing the dusts of aluminum, magnesium, and their commercial alloys. For example, zirconium, thorium, and uranium dusts have extremely low ignition temperatures [as low as 68°F (20°C)] and minimum ignition energies lower than any material classified in any of the Class I or Class II groups.